Contents

1001418202

CHAPTER THREE
Some Basic Concepts of Engineering Analysis and an Introduction to the Finite Element Method

77

CHAPTER FOUR
Formulation of the Finite Element Method—Linear Analysis in Solid and Structural Mechanics

148

CHAPTER SEVEN _____
Finite Element Analysis of Heat Transfer, Field Problems, and Incompressible Fluid Flows   **642**

CHAPTER TEN _____
Preliminaries to the Solution of Eigenproblems   **838**

Preface

Finite element procedures are now an important and frequently indispensable part of engineering analysis and design. Finite element computer programs are now widely used in practically all branches of engineering for the analysis of structures, solids, and fluids.

My objective in writing this book was to provide a text for upper-level undergraduate and graduate courses on finite element analysis and to provide a book for self-study by engineers and scientists.

With this objective in mind, I have developed this book from my earlier publication *Finite Element Procedures in Engineering Analysis* (Prentice-Hall, 1982). I have kept the same mode of presentation but have consolidated, updated, and strengthened the earlier writing to the current state of finite element developments. Also, I have added new sections, both to cover some important additional topics for completeness of the presentation and to facilitate (through exercises) the teaching of the material discussed in the book.

This text does not present a survey of finite element methods. For such an endeavor, a number of volumes would be needed. Instead, this book concentrates only on certain finite element procedures, namely, on techniques that I consider very useful in engineering practice and that will probably be employed for many years to come. Also, these methods are introduced in such a way that they can be taught effectively—and in an exciting manner—to students.

An important aspect of a finite element procedure is its reliability, so that the method can be used in a confident manner in computer-aided design. This book emphasizes this point throughout the presentations and concentrates on finite element procedures that are general and reliable for engineering analysis.

Hence, this book is clearly biased in that it presents only certain finite element procedures and in that it presents these procedures in a certain manner. In this regard, the book reflects my philosophy toward the teaching and the use of finite element methods.

While the basic topics of this book focus on mathematical methods, an exciting and thorough understanding of finite element procedures for engineering applications is achieved only if sufficient attention is given to both the physical and mathematical characteristics of the procedures. The combined physical and mathematical understanding greatly enriches our confident use and further development of finite element methods and is therefore emphasized in this text.

These thoughts also indicate that a collaboration between engineers and mathematicians to deepen our understanding of finite element methods and to further advance in the fields of research can be of great benefit. Indeed, I am thankful to the mathematician Franco Brezzi for our research collaboration in this spirit, and for his valuable suggestions regarding this book.

I consider it one of the greatest achievements for an educator to write a valuable book. In these times, all fields of engineering are rapidly changing, and new books for students are needed in practically all areas of engineering. I am therefore grateful that the Mechanical Engineering Department of M.I.T. has provided me with an excellent environment in which to pursue my interests in teaching, research, and scholarly writing. While it required an immense effort on my part to write this book, I wanted to accomplish this task as a commitment to my past and future students, to any educators and researchers who might have an interest in the work, and, of course, to improve upon my teaching at M.I.T.

I have been truly fortunate to work with many outstanding students at M.I.T., for which I am very thankful. It has been a great privilege to be their teacher and work with them. Of much value has also been that I have been intimately involved, at my company ADINA R & D, Inc., in the development of finite element methods for industry. This involvement has been very beneficial in my teaching and research, and in my writing of this book.

A text of significant depth and breadth on a subject that came to life only a few decades ago and that has experienced tremendous advances, can be written only by an author who has had the benefit of interacting with many people in the field. I would like to thank all my students and friends who contributed—and will continue to contribute—to my knowledge and understanding of finite element methods. My interaction with them has given me great joy and satisfaction.

I also would like to thank my secretary, Kristan Raymond, for her special efforts in typing the manuscript of this text.

Finally, truly unbounded thanks are due to my wife, Zorka, and children, Ingrid and Mark, who, with their love and their understanding of my efforts, supported me in writing this book.

K. J. Bathe

CHAPTER ONE

An Introduction to the Use of Finite Element Procedures

1.1 INTRODUCTION

Finite element procedures are at present very widely used in engineering analysis, and we can expect this use to increase significantly in the years to come. The procedures are employed extensively in the analysis of solids and structures and of heat transfer and fluids, and indeed, finite element methods are useful in virtually every field of engineering analysis.

The development of finite element methods for the solution of practical engineering problems began with the advent of the digital computer. That is, the essence of a finite element solution of an engineering problem is that a set of governing algebraic equations is established and solved, and it was only through the use of the digital computer that this process could be rendered effective and given general applicability. These two properties—effectiveness and general applicability in engineering analysis—are inherent in the theory used and have been developed to a high degree for practical computations, so that finite element methods have found wide appeal in engineering practice.

As is often the case with original developments, it is rather difficult to quote an exact "date of invention," but the roots of the finite element method can be traced back to three separate research groups: applied mathematicians—see R. Courant [A]; physicists—see J. L. Synge [A]; and engineers—see J. H. Argyris and S. Kelsey [A]. Although in principle published already, the finite element method obtained its real impetus from the developments of engineers. The original contributions appeared in the papers by J. H. Argyris and S. Kelsey [A]; M. J. Turner, R. W. Clough, H. C. Martin, and L. J. Topp [A]; and R. W. Clough [A]. The name "finite element" was coined in the paper by R. W. Clough [A]. Important early contributions were those of J. H. Argyris [A] and O. C. Zienkiewicz and Y. K. Cheung [A]. Since the early 1960s, a large amount of research has been devoted to the technique, and a very large number of publications on the finite element method is available (see, for example, the compilation of references by A. K. Noor [A] and the *Finite Element Handbook* edited by H. Kardestuncer and D. H. Norrie [A]).

The finite element method in engineering was initially developed on a physical basis for the analysis of problems in structural mechanics. However, it was soon recognized that the technique could be applied equally well to the solution of many other classes of problems. The objective of this book is to present finite element procedures comprehensively and in a broad context for solids and structures, field problems (specifically heat transfer), and fluid flows.

To introduce the topics of this book we consider three important items in the following sections of this chapter. First, we discuss the important point that in any analysis we always select a *mathematical model* of a physical problem, and then we solve *that* model. The finite element method is employed to solve very complex mathematical models, but it is important to realize that the finite element solution can never give more information than that contained in the mathematical model.

Then we discuss the importance of finite element analysis in the complete process of computer-aided design (CAD). This is where finite element analysis procedures have their greatest utility and where an engineer is most likely to encounter the use of finite element methods.

In the last section of this chapter we address the question of how to study finite element methods. Since a voluminous amount of information has been published on these techniques, it can be rather difficult for an engineer to identify and concentrate on the most important principles and procedures. Our aim in this section is to give the reader some guidance in studying finite element analysis procedures and of course also in studying the various topics discussed in this book.

1.2 PHYSICAL PROBLEMS, MATHEMATICAL MODELS, AND THE FINITE ELEMENT SOLUTION

The finite element method is used to solve physical problems in engineering analysis and design. Figure 1.1 summarizes the process of finite element analysis. The physical problem typically involves an actual structure or structural component subjected to certain loads. The idealization of the physical problem to a mathematical model requires certain assumptions that together lead to differential equations governing the mathematical model (see Chapter 3). *The finite element analysis solves this mathematical model.* Since the finite element solution technique is a numerical procedure, it is necessary to assess the solution accuracy. If the accuracy criteria are not met, the numerical (i.e., finite element) solution has to be repeated with refined solution parameters (such as finer meshes) until a sufficient accuracy is reached.

It is clear that the finite element solution will solve only the selected mathematical model and that all assumptions in this model will be reflected in the predicted response. We cannot expect any more information in the prediction of physical phenomena than the information contained in the mathematical model. Hence the choice of an appropriate mathematical model is crucial and completely determines the insight into the actual physical problem that we can obtain by the analysis.

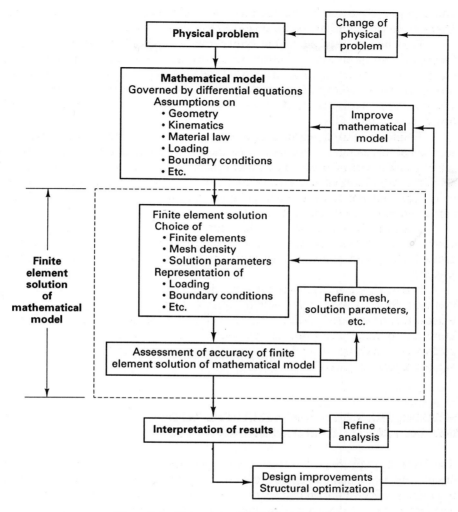

Figure 1.1   The process of finite element analysis

Let us emphasize that, by our analysis, we can of course only obtain *insight* into the physical problem considered: we cannot predict the response of the physical problem *exactly* because it is impossible to reproduce even in the most refined mathematical model all the information that is present in nature and therefore contained in the physical problem.

Once a mathematical model has been solved accurately and the results have been interpreted, we may well decide to consider next a refined mathematical model in order to increase our insight into the response of the physical problem. Furthermore, a change in the physical problem may be necessary, and this in turn will also lead to additional mathematical models and finite element solutions (see Fig. 1.1).

The key step in engineering analysis is therefore choosing appropriate mathematical models. These models will clearly be selected depending on what phenomena are to be predicted, and it is most important to select mathematical models that are *reliable* and *effective* in predicting the quantities sought.

To define the reliability and effectiveness of a chosen model we think of a *very-comprehensive* mathematical model of the physical problem and measure the response of our chosen model against the response of the comprehensive model. In general, the very-comprehensive mathematical model is a fully three-dimensional description that also includes nonlinear effects.

Effectiveness of a mathematical model
The most effective mathematical model for the analysis is surely that one which yields the required response to a sufficient accuracy and at least cost.

Reliability of a mathematical model
The chosen mathematical model is reliable if the required response is known to be predicted within a selected level of accuracy measured on the response of the very-comprehensive mathematical model.

Hence to assess the results obtained by the solution of a chosen mathematical model, it may be necessary to also solve higher-order mathematical models, and we may well think of (but of course not necessarily solve) a sequence of mathematical models that include increasingly more complex effects. For example, a beam structure (using engineering terminology) may first be analyzed using Bernoulli beam theory, then Timoshenko beam theory, then two-dimensional plane stress theory, and finally using a fully three-dimensional continuum model, and in each case nonlinear effects may be included. Such a sequence of models is referred to as a hierarchy of models (see K. J. Bathe, N. S. Lee, and M. L. Bucalem [A]). Clearly, with these hierarchical models the analysis will include ever more complex response effects but will also lead to increasingly more costly solutions. As is well known, a fully three-dimensional analysis is about an order of magnitude more expensive (in computer resources and engineering time used) than a two-dimensional solution.

Let us consider a simple example to illustrate these ideas.

Figure 1.2(a) shows a bracket used to support a vertical load. For the analysis, we need to choose a mathematical model. This choice must clearly depend on what phenomena are to be predicted and on the geometry, material properties, loading, and support conditions of the bracket.

We have indicated in Fig. 1.2(a) that the bracket is fastened to a very thick steel column. The description "very thick" is of course relative to the thickness t and the height h of the bracket. We translate this statement into the assumption that the bracket is fastened to a (practically) rigid column. Hence we can focus our attention on the bracket by applying a "rigid column boundary condition" to it. (Of course, at a later time, an analysis of the column may be required, and then the loads carried by the two bolts, as a consequence of the load W, will need to be applied to the column.)

We also assume that the load W is applied very slowly. The condition of time "very slowly" is relative to the largest natural period of the bracket; that is, the time span over which the load W is increased from zero to its full value is much longer than the fundamental period of the bracket. We translate this statement into requiring a static analysis (and not a dynamic analysis).

With these preliminary considerations we can now establish an appropriate mathematical model for the analysis of the bracket—depending on what phenomena are to be predicted. Let us assume, in the first instance, that only the total bending moment at section AA in the bracket and the deflection at the load application are sought. To predict these quantities, we consider a beam mathematical model including shear deformations [see Fig. 1.2(b)] and obtain

$$M = WL$$
$$= 27,500 \text{ N cm} \tag{1.1}$$

$$\delta \big|_{\text{at load } W} = \frac{1}{3} \frac{W(L + r_N)^3}{EI} + \frac{W(L + r_N)}{\frac{5}{6}AG}$$
$$= 0.053 \text{ cm} \tag{1.2}$$

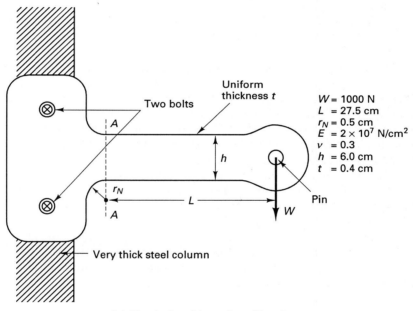

W = 1000 N
L = 27.5 cm
r_N = 0.5 cm
E = 2×10^7 N/cm²
v = 0.3
h = 6.0 cm
t = 0.4 cm

(a) Physical problem of steel bracket

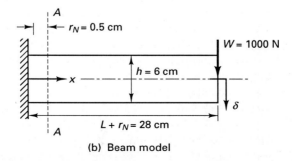

(b) Beam model

Figure 1.2 Bracket to be analyzed and two mathematical models

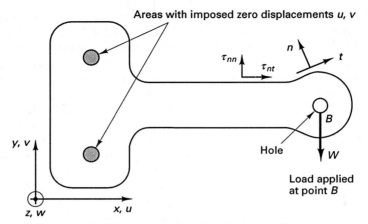

Equilibrium equations (see Example 4.2)

$$\left. \begin{aligned} \frac{\partial \tau_{xx}}{\partial x} + \frac{\partial \tau_{xy}}{\partial y} = 0 \\ \frac{\partial \tau_{yx}}{\partial x} + \frac{\partial \tau_{yy}}{\partial y} = 0 \end{aligned} \right\} \text{ in domain of bracket}$$

$\tau_{nn} = 0$, $\tau_{nt} = 0$ on surfaces except at point B
and at imposed zero displacements

Stress-strain relation (see Table 4.3):

$$\begin{bmatrix} \tau_{xx} \\ \tau_{yy} \\ \tau_{xy} \end{bmatrix} = \frac{E}{1 - \nu^2} \begin{bmatrix} 1 & \nu & 0 \\ \nu & 1 & 0 \\ 0 & 0 & (1 - \nu)/2 \end{bmatrix} \begin{bmatrix} \epsilon_{xx} \\ \epsilon_{yy} \\ \gamma_{xy} \end{bmatrix}$$

$E = $ Young's modulus, $\nu = $ Poisson's ratio

Strain-displacement relations (see Section 4.2):

$$\epsilon_{xx} = \frac{\partial u}{\partial x}; \qquad \epsilon_{yy} = \frac{\partial v}{\partial y}; \qquad \gamma_{xy} = \frac{\partial u}{\partial y} + \frac{\partial v}{\partial x}$$

(c) Plane stress model

Figure 1.2 *(continued)*

where L and r_N are given in Fig. 1.2(a), E is the Young's modulus of the steel used, G is the shear modulus, I is the moment of inertia of the bracket arm ($I = \frac{1}{12} h^3 t$), A is the cross-sectional area ($A = ht$), and the factor $\frac{5}{6}$ is a shear correction factor (see Section 5.4.1).

Of course, the relations in (1.1) and (1.2) assume linear elastic infinitesimal displacement conditions, and hence the load must not be so large as to cause yielding of the material and/or large displacements.

Let us now ask whether the mathematical model used in Fig. 1.2(b) was *reliable* and *effective*. To answer this question, strictly, we should consider a very-comprehensive mathematical model, which in this case would be a fully three-dimensional representation of the full bracket. This model should include the two bolts fastening the bracket to the (assumed rigid) column as well as the pin through which the load W is applied. The three-dimensional solution of this model using the appropriate geometry and material data would give the numbers against which we would compare the answers given in (1.1) and (1.2). Note that this three-dimensional mathematical model contains contact conditions (the contact is between the bolts, the bracket, and the column, and between the pin carrying the load and the bracket) and stress concentrations in the fillets and at the holes. Also, if the stresses are high, nonlinear material conditions should be included in the model. Of course, an analytical solution of this mathematical model is not available, and all we can obtain is a numerical solution. We describe in this book how such solutions can be calculated using finite element procedures, but we may note here already that the solution would be relatively expensive in terms of computer resources and engineering time used.

Since the three-dimensional comprehensive mathematical model is very likely too comprehensive a model (for the analysis questions we have posed), we instead may consider a linear elastic two-dimensional plane stress model as shown in Fig. 1.2(c). This mathematical model represents the geometry of the bracket more accurately than the beam model and assumes a two-dimensional stress situation in the bracket (see Section 4.2). The bending moment at section AA and deflection under the load calculated with this model can be expected to be quite close to those calculated with the very-comprehensive three-dimensional model, and certainly this two-dimensional model represents a higher-order model against which we can measure the adequacy of the results given in (1.1) and (1.2). Of course, an analytical solution of the model is not available, and a numerical solution must be sought.

Figures 1.3(a) to (e) show the geometry and the finite element discretization used in the solution of the plane stress mathematical model and some stress and displacement results obtained with this discretization. Let us note the various assumptions of this mathematical model when compared to the more comprehensive three-dimensional model discussed earlier. Since a plane stress condition is assumed, the only nonzero stresses are τ_{xx}, τ_{yy}, and τ_{xy}. Hence we assume that the stresses τ_{zz}, τ_{yz}, and τ_{zx} are zero. Also, the actual bolt fastening and contact conditions between the steel column and the bracket are not included

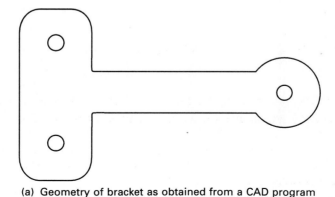

(a) Geometry of bracket as obtained from a CAD program

Figure 1.3   Plane stress analysis of bracket in Fig. 1.2. AutoCAD was used to create the geometry, and ADINA was used for the finite element analysis.

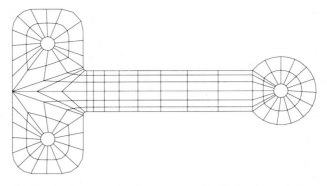

(b) Mesh of nine-node elements used in finite element discretization

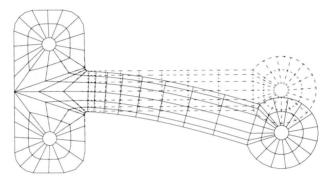

(c) Deflected shape. Deflections are drawn with a magnification factor of 100 together with the original configuration

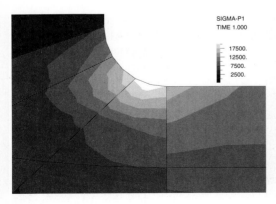

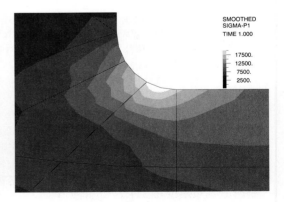

(d) Maximum principal stress near notch. Unsmoothed stress results are shown. The small breaks in the bands indicate that a reasonably accurate solution of the mathematical model has been obtained (see Section 4.3.6)

(e) Maximum principal stress near notch. Smoothed stress results. (The averages of nodal point stresses are taken and interpolated over the elements.)

Figure 1.3 *(continued)*

in the model, and the pin carrying the load into the bracket is not modeled. However, since our objective is only to predict the bending moment at section AA and the deflection at point B, these assumptions are deemed reasonable and of relatively little influence.

Let us assume that the results obtained in the finite element solution of the mathematical model are sufficiently accurate that we can refer to the solution given in Fig. 1.3. as *the* solution of the plane stress mathematical model.

Figure 1.3(c) shows the calculated deformed configuration. The deflection at the point of load application B as predicted in the plane stress solution is

$$\delta\big|_{\text{at load }W} = 0.064 \text{ cm} \tag{1.3}$$

Also, the total bending moment predicted at section AA is

$$M\big|_{x=0} = 27,500 \text{ N cm} \tag{1.4}$$

Whereas the same magnitude of bending moment at section AA is predicted by the beam model and the plane stress model,[1] the deflection of the beam model is considerably less than that predicted by the plane stress model [because of the assumption that the beam in Fig. 1.2(b) is supported rigidly at its left end, which neglects any deformation between the beam end and the bolts].

Considering these results, we can say that the beam mathematical model in Fig. 1.2(b) is *reliable* if the required bending moment is to be predicted within 1 percent and the deflection is to be predicted only within 20 precent accuracy. The beam model is of course also *effective* because the calculations are performed with very little effort.

On the other hand, if we next ask for the maximum stress in the bracket, then the simple mathematical beam model in Fig. 1.2(b) will not yield a sufficiently accurate answer. Specifically, the beam model totally neglects the stress increase due to the fillets.[2] Hence a plane stress solution including the fillets is necessary.

The important points to note here are the following.

1. The selection of the mathematical model must depend on the response to be predicted (i.e., on the questions asked of nature).

2. The most effective mathematical model is that one which delivers the answers to the questions in a reliable manner (i.e., within an acceptable error) with the least amount of effort.

3. A finite element solution can solve accurately only the chosen mathematical model (e.g., the beam model or the plane stress model in Fig. 1.2) and cannot predict any more information than that contained in the model.

4. The notion of reliability of the mathematical model hinges upon an accuracy assessment of the results obtained with the chosen mathematical model (in response to the questions asked) against the results obtained with the very-comprehensive mathematical model. However, in practice the very-comprehensive mathematical model is

---

[1] The bending moment at section AA in the plane stress model is calculated here from the finite element nodal point forces, and for this statically determinate analysis problem the internal resisting moment must be equal to the externally applied moment (see Example 4.9).

[2] Of course, the effect of the fillets could be estimated by the use of stress concentration factors that have been established from plane stress solutions.

usually not solved, and instead engineering experience is used, or a more refined mathematical model is solved, to judge whether the mathematical model used was adequate (i.e., reliable) for the response to be predicted.

Finally, there is one further important general point. The chosen mathematical model may contain extremely high stresses because of sharp corners, concentrated loads, or other effects. These high stresses may be due solely to the simplifications used in the model when compared with the very-comprehensive mathematical model (or with nature). For example, the concentrated load in the plane stress model in Fig. 1.2(c) is an idealization of a pressure load over a small area. (This pressure would in nature be transmitted by the pin carrying the load into the bracket.) The exact solution of the mathematical model in Fig. 1.2(c) gives an infinite stress at the point of load application, and we must therefore expect a very large stress at point *B* as the finite element mesh is refined. Of course, this very large stress is an artifice of the chosen model, and the concentrated load should be replaced by a pressure load over a small area when a very fine discretization is used (see further discussion). Furthermore, if the model then still predicts a very high stress, a nonlinear mathematical model would be appropriate.

Note that the concentrated load in the beam model in Fig. 1.2(b) does not introduce any solution difficulties. Also, the right-angled sharp corners at the support of the beam model, of course, do not introduce any solution difficulties, whereas such corners in a plane stress model would introduce infinite stresses. Hence, for the plane stress model, the corners have to be rounded to more accurately represent the geometry of the actual physical bracket.

We thus realize that the solution of a mathematical model may result in artificial difficulties that are easily removed by an *appropriate* change in the mathematical model to more closely represent the actual physical situation. Furthermore, the choice of a more encompassing mathematical model may result, in such cases, in a decrease in the required solution effort.

While these observations are of a general nature, let us consider once again, specifically, the use of concentrated loads. This idealization of load application is extensively used in engineering practice. We now realize that in many mathematical models (and therefore also in the finite element solutions of these models), such loads create stresses of infinite value. Hence, we may ask under what conditions in engineering practice solution difficulties may arise. We find that in practice solution difficulties usually arise only when the finite element discretization is very fine, and for this reason the matter of infinite stresses under concentrated loads is frequently ignored. As an example, Fig. 1.4 gives finite element results obtained in the analysis of a cantilever, modeled as a plane stress problem. The cantilever is subjected to a concentrated tip load. In practice, the 6×1 mesh is usually considered sufficiently fine, and clearly, a much finer discretization would have to be used to accurately show the effects of the stress singularities at the point of load application and at the support. As already pointed out, if such a solution is pursued, it is necessary to change the mathematical model to more accurately represent the actual physical situation of the structure. This change in the mathematical model may be important in self-adaptive finite element analyses because in such analyses new meshes are generated automatically and artificial stress singularities cause—artificially—extremely fine discretizations.

We refer to these considerations in Section 4.3.4 when we state the general elasticity problem considered for finite element solution.

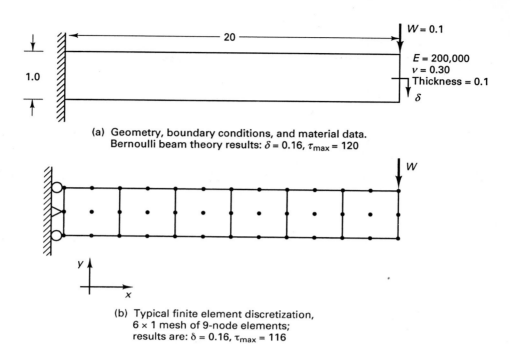

(a) Geometry, boundary conditions, and material data.
Bernoulli beam theory results: $\delta = 0.16$, $\tau_{max} = 120$

(b) Typical finite element discretization,
6 × 1 mesh of 9-node elements;
results are: $\delta = 0.16$, $\tau_{max} = 116$

Figure 1.4   Analysis of a cantilever as a plane stress problem

In summary, we should keep firmly in mind that the crucial step in any finite element analysis is always choosing an appropriate mathematical model since a finite element solution solves only this model. Furthermore, the mathematical model must depend on the analysis questions asked and should be reliable and effective (as defined earlier). In the process of analysis, the engineer has to judge whether the chosen mathematical model has been solved to a sufficient accuracy and whether the chosen mathematical model was appropriate (i.e., reliable) for the questions asked. Choosing the mathematical model, solving the model by appropriate finite element procedures, and judging the results are the fundamental ingredients of an engineering analysis using finite element methods.

1.3 FINITE ELEMENT ANALYSIS AS AN INTEGRAL PART OF COMPUTER-AIDED DESIGN

Although a most exciting field of activity, engineering analysis is clearly only a support activity in the larger field of engineering design. The analysis process helps to identify good new designs and can be used to improve a design with respect to performance and cost.

In the early use of finite element methods, only specific structures were analyzed, mainly in the aerospace and civil engineering industries. However, once the full potential of finite element methods was realized and the use of computers increased in engineering design environments, emphasis in research and development was placed upon making the use of finite element methods an integral part of the design process in mechanical, civil, and aeronautical engineering.

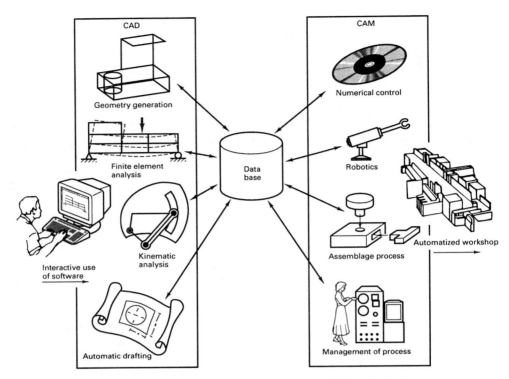

Figure 1.5   The field of CAD/CAM viewed schematically

Figure 1.5 gives an overview of the steps in a typical computer-aided design process. Finite element analysis is only a small part of the complete process, but it is an important part.

We note that the first step in Figure 1.5 is the creation of a geometric representation of the design part. Many different computer programs can be employed (e.g., a typical and popular program is AutoCAD). In this step, the material properties, the applied loading and boundary conditions on the geometry also need to be defined. Given this information, a finite element analysis may proceed. Since the geometry and other data of the actual physical part may be quite complex, it is usually necessary to simplify the geometry and loading in order to reach a tractable mathematical model. Of course, the mathematical model should be reliable and effective for the analysis questions posed, as discussed in the preceding section. The finite element analysis solves the chosen mathematical model, which may be changed and evolve depending on the purpose of the analysis (see Fig. 1.1).

Considering this process—which generally is and should be performed by engineering designers and not only specialists in analysis—we recognize that the finite element methods must be very reliable and robust. By *reliability of the finite element methods* we now[3] mean that in the solution of a well-posed mathematical model, the finite element procedures should *always* for a reasonable finite element mesh give a reasonable solution,

---

[3] Note that this meaning of "reliability of finite element methods" is different from that of "reliability of a mathematical model" defined in the previous section.

and if the mesh is reasonably fine, an accurate solution should *always* be obtained. By *robustness of the finite element methods* we mean that the performance of the finite element procedures should not be unduly sensitive to the material data, the boundary conditions, and the loading conditions used. Therefore, finite element procedures that are not robust will also not be reliable.

For example, assume that in the plane stress solution of the mathematical model in Fig. 1.2(c), any reasonable finite element discretization using a certain element type is employed. Then the solution obtained from any such analysis should not be hugely in error, that is, an order of magnitude larger (or smaller) than the exact solution. Using an unreliable finite element for the discretization would typically lead to good solutions for some mesh topologies, whereas with other mesh topologies it would lead to bad solutions. Elements based on reduced integration with spurious zero energy modes can show this unreliable behavior (see Section 5.5.6).

Similarly, assume that a certain finite element discretization of a mathematical model gives accurate results for one set of material parameters and that a small change in the parameters corresponds to a small change in the exact solution of the mathematical model. Then the same finite element discretization should also give accurate results for the mathematical model with the small change in material parameters and not yield results that are very much in error.

These considerations regarding effective finite element discretizations are very important and are discussed in the presentation of finite element discretizations and their stability and convergence properties (see Chapters 4 to 7). For use in engineering design, it is of utmost importance that the finite element methods be reliable, robust, and of course efficient. Reliability and robustness are important because a designer has relatively little time for the process of analysis and must be able to obtain an accurate solution of the chosen mathematical model quickly and without "trial and error." The use of unreliable finite element methods is simply unacceptable in engineering practice.

An important ingredient of a finite element analysis is the calculation of error estimates, that is, estimates of how closely the finite element solution approximates the exact solution of the mathematical model (see Section 4.3.6). These estimates indicate whether a specific finite element discretization has indeed yielded an accurate response prediction, and a designer can then rationally decide whether the given results should be used. In the case that unacceptable results have been obtained using unreliable finite element methods, the difficulty is of course *how* to obtain accurate results.

Finally, we venture to comment on the future of finite element methods in computer-aided design. Surely, many engineering designers do not have time to study finite element methods in depth or finite element procedures in general. Their sole objective is to use these techniques to enhance the design product. Hence the integrated use of finite element methods in CAD in the future will probably involve to an increasingly smaller degree the scrutiny of finite element meshes during the analysis process. Instead, we expect that in linear elastic static analysis the finite element solution process will be automatized such that, given a mathematical model to be solved, the finite element meshes will be automatically created, the solution will be calculated with error estimates, and depending on the estimated errors and the desired solution accuracy, the finite element discretization will be automatically refined (without the analyst or the designer ever seeing a finite element mesh) until the required solution accuracy has been attained. In this automatic analysis process—in which of course the engineer must still choose the appropriate mathematical model for analysis—the engineer can concentrate on the design aspects while using analysis tools with great efficiency and benefit. While this design and analysis environment will be commonly available for linear elastic static analysis, the dynamic or nonlinear analysis of structures and fluids will probably still require from the engineer a greater degree of involvement and expertise in finite element methods for many years to come.

With these remarks we do not wish to suggest overconfidence but to express a realistic outlook with respect to the valuable and exciting future use of finite element procedures. For some remarks on overconfidence in regard to finite element methods (which are still pertinent after almost two decades), see the article "A Commentary on Computational Mechanics" by J. T. Oden and K. J. Bathe [A].

1.4 A PROPOSAL ON HOW TO STUDY FINITE ELEMENT METHODS

With a voluminous number of publications available on the use and development of finite element procedures, it may be rather difficult for a student or teacher to identify an effective plan of study. Of course, such a plan must depend on the objectives of the study and the time available.

In very general terms, there are two different objectives:

1. To learn the proper *use* of finite element methods for the solution of complex problems, and
2. To understand finite element methods in depth so as to be able to pursue *research* on finite element methods.

This book has been written to serve students with either objective, recognizing that the population of students with objective 1 is the much larger one and that frequently a student may first study finite element methods with objective 1 and then develop an increasing interest in the methods and also pursue objective 2. While a student with objective 2 will need to delve still much deeper into the subject matter than we do in this book, it is hoped that this book will provide a strong basis for such further study and that the "philosophy" of this text (see Section 1.3) with respect to the use of and research into finite element methods will be valued.

Since this book has not been written to provide a broad survey of finite element methods—indeed, for a survey, a much more comprehensive volume would be necessary—it is clearly biased toward a particular way of introducing finite element procedures and toward only certain finite element procedures.

The finite element methods that we concentrate on in this text are deemed to be effective techniques that can be used (and indeed are abundantly used) in engineering practice. The methods are also considered basic and important and will probably be employed for a long time to come.

The issue of what methods should be used, and can be best used in engineering practice, is important in that only reliable techniques should be employed (see Section 1.3), and this book concentrates on the discussion of only such methods.

In introducing finite element procedures we endeavor to explain the basic concepts and equations with emphasis on physical explanations. Also, short examples are given to demonstrate the basic concepts used, and exercises are provided for hand calculations and the use of a finite element computer program.

The preceding thoughts lead to our proposal for the study of finite element procedures. If objective 1 is being pursued, the reader will be mostly interested in the basic formulations, the properties of the finite elements and solution algorithms, and issues of convergence and efficiency.

An important point to keep in mind is that numerical finite element procedures are used to solve a mathematical model (with some reasonably small solution errors) (see Section 1.2). Hence, it is important for the user of a finite element computer program to always be able to judge the quality of the finite element results obtained in a solution. We demonstrate in this book how such judging is properly performed.

However, if objective 2 is being pursued, much more depth in the formulations and numerical algorithms must be acquired. This text provides a broad basis for such study (but of course does not give all details of derivations and implementations).

In either case, we believe that for a study of finite element methods, it is effective to use a finite element computer program while learning about the theory and numerical procedures. Then, at the same time as the theoretical concepts are being studied on paper, it will be possible to test and demonstrate these concepts on a computer.

Based on this book, various courses can be taught depending on the aim of the instruction. A first course would be "Introduction to Finite Element Analysis," which could be based on Sections 1.1 to 1.4, 2.1 to 2.3, 3.1 to 3.4, 4.1 to 4.3, 5.1 to 5.3, and 8.1 to 8.2.2.

A more advanced course would be "Finite Element Procedures," based on Sections 1.1. to 1.4, 3.1, 3.3, 4.1 to 4.4, 5.1 to 5.6, and 8.1 to 8.3.

A course on finite element methods for dynamic analysis would be "Computer Methods in Dynamics" and could be based on Sections 1.1 to 1.4, 2.1 to 2.7, 3.1, 3.3, 4.1, 4.2, 5.1 to 5.3, 8.1 to 8.2.2, 9.1 to 9.4, 10.1, 10.2, 11.1, 11.2.1, 11.3.1, and 11.6.

A course emphasizing the continuum mechanics principles for linear and nonlinear finite element analysis would be "Theory and Practice of Continuum Mechanics," which could be based on Sections 1.1 to 1.4, 3.1, 3.3, 4.1, 4.2.1, 4.2.2, 5.1, 5.2, 5.3.1, 5.3.3, 5.3.5, 6.1, 6.2, 6.3.1, 6.3.2, 6.4.1, 6.6, 7.1, and 7.4.

A course on the analysis of field problems and fluid flows would be "Finite Element Analysis of Heat Transfer, Field Problems, and Fluid Flows," based on Sections 1.1 to 1.4, 3.1, 3.3, 7.1 to 7.4, 5.3, 5.5, and 4.5.1 to 4.5.6. Note that the presentation in this course would first provide the finite element formulations (Sections 7.1 to 7.4) and then numerical procedures and mathematical results.

A course on nonlinear finite element analysis of solids and structures would be "Nonlinear Analysis of Solids and Structures" and could be based on Sections 1.1 to 1.4, 6.1 to 6.8, 8.1, and 8.4.

A course on the numerical methods used in finite element analysis would be "Numerical Methods in Finite Element Analysis," which could be based on Sections 1.1 to 1.4, 2.1 to 2.7, 4.1, 4.2.1, 5.1, 5.3, 5.5, 8.1 to 8.4, 9.1 to 9.6, 10.1 to 10.3, and 11.1 to 11.6.

And, finally, a course on more theoretical aspects of finite element analysis could be offered, entitled "Theoretical Concepts of Finite Element Analysis," based on Sections 1.1 to 1.4, 4.1 to 4.5, and 5.1 to 5.5.

In addition, in most of these courses, the material in Chapter 12 would be useful.

In general, such courses are best taught with homework that includes problem solutions, as suggested in the exercise sections of this book, as well as the completion of a project in which a finite element computer program is used.

Various projects are proposed in the exercise sections of this book. One type of project requires the student to use the program STAP and to modify this program for certain new capabilities as suggested in Section 12.5. Such a project would be of value to students interested in learning about the actual detailed implementation of finite element methods.

The other type of project is based on the use of a standard (commercial) finite element program—as it might be employed in engineering practice—to analyze an interesting physical problem. A valuable way to then proceed is to first solve a mathematical model for which an analytical exact solution is known and then introduce complicating features in the mathematical model that require a numerical solution. In this way, studies using different finite element discretizations and solution procedures in which the results are evaluated against a known exact solution can first be performed, which establishes confidence in the use of the methods. The required expertise and confidence then become valuable assets in the finite element solution of more complicated mathematical models.

It is of particular importance during the study of finite element procedures that good judgment be developed and exercised concerning the quality of any finite element solution and of any mathematical model considered. Of course, exercising such judgments requires that the analyst be sufficiently familiar with possible mathematical models and available finite element procedures, and this aspect stimulates learning about mathematical models and methods of solution. The value of using a finite element computer code—the program STAP or a commercial finite element program as previously mentioned—is clearly in stimulating the process of learning and in reinforcing the understanding of what has been learned in class and from homework problem solutions. Using a powerful analysis program, in particular, also adds to the excitement of actually solving complicated analysis problems that heretofore could not be tackled.

Vectors, Matrices, and Tensors

2.1 INTRODUCTION

The use of vectors, matrices, and tensors is of fundamental importance in engineering analysis because it is only with the use of these quantities that the complete solution process can be expressed in a compact and elegant manner. The objective of this chapter is to present the fundamentals of matrices and tensors, with emphasis on those aspects that are important in finite element analysis.

From a simplistic point of view, matrices can simply be taken as ordered arrays of numbers that are subjected to specific rules of addition, multiplication, and so on. It is of course important to be thoroughly familiar with these rules, and we review them in this chapter.

However, by far more interesting aspects of matrices and matrix algebra are recognized when we study how the elements of matrices are derived in the analysis of a physical problem and why the rules of matrix algebra are actually applicable. In this context, the use of tensors and their matrix representations are important and provide a most interesting subject of study.

Of course, only a rather limited discussion of matrices and tensors is given here, but we hope that the focused practical treatment will provide a strong basis for understanding the finite element formulations given later.

2.2 INTRODUCTION TO MATRICES

The effectiveness of using matrices in practical calculations is readily realized by considering the solution of a set of linear simultaneous equations such as

$$
\begin{aligned}
5x_1 - 4x_2 + x_3 \qquad\qquad &= 0 \\
-4x_1 + 6x_2 - 4x_3 + x_4 &= 1 \\
x_1 - 4x_2 + 6x_3 - 4x_4 &= 0 \\
x_2 - 4x_3 + 5x_4 &= 0
\end{aligned}
\tag{2.1}
$$

where the unknowns are x_1, x_2, x_3, and x_4. Using matrix notation, this set of equations is written as

$$
\begin{bmatrix}
5 & -4 & 1 & 0 \\
-4 & 6 & -4 & 1 \\
1 & -4 & 6 & -4 \\
0 & 1 & -4 & 5
\end{bmatrix}
\begin{bmatrix}
x_1 \\ x_2 \\ x_3 \\ x_4
\end{bmatrix}
=
\begin{bmatrix}
0 \\ 1 \\ 0 \\ 0
\end{bmatrix}
\tag{2.2}
$$

where it is noted that, rather logically, the coefficients of the unknowns $(5, -4, 1, \text{etc.})$ are grouped together in one array; the left-hand-side unknowns $(x_1, x_2, x_3, \text{and } x_4)$ and the right-hand-side known quantities are each grouped together in additional arrays. Although written differently, the relation (2.2) still reads the same way as (2.1). However, using matrix symbols to represent the arrays in (2.2), we can now write the set of simultaneous equations as

$$
\mathbf{Ax} = \mathbf{b}
\tag{2.3}
$$

where $\mathbf{A}$ is the matrix of the coefficients in the set of linear equations, $\mathbf{x}$ is the matrix of unknowns, and $\mathbf{b}$ is the matrix of known quantities; i.e.,

$$
\mathbf{A} =
\begin{bmatrix}
5 & -4 & 1 & 0 \\
-4 & 6 & -4 & 1 \\
1 & -4 & 6 & -4 \\
0 & 1 & -4 & 5
\end{bmatrix};
\qquad
\mathbf{x} =
\begin{bmatrix}
x_1 \\ x_2 \\ x_3 \\ x_4
\end{bmatrix};
\qquad
\mathbf{b} =
\begin{bmatrix}
0 \\ 1 \\ 0 \\ 0
\end{bmatrix}
\tag{2.4}
$$

The following formal definition of a matrix now seems apparent.

Definition: A matrix is an array of ordered numbers. A general matrix consists of mn numbers arranged in m rows and n columns, giving the following array:

$$
\mathbf{A} =
\begin{bmatrix}
a_{11} & a_{12} & \cdots & a_{1n} \\
a_{21} & a_{22} & \cdots & a_{2n} \\
\vdots & \vdots & & \vdots \\
a_{m1} & a_{m2} & \cdots & a_{mn}
\end{bmatrix}
\tag{2.5}
$$

We say that this matrix has order $m \times n$ (m by n). When we have only one row ($m = 1$) or one column ($n = 1$), we also call $\mathbf{A}$ a vector. Matrices are represented in this book by boldface letters, usually uppercase letters when they are not vectors. On the other hand, vectors can be uppercase or lowercase boldface.

We therefore see that the following are matrices:

$$\begin{bmatrix} 1 \\ 2 \end{bmatrix}; \qquad \begin{bmatrix} 1 & 4 & -5.3 \\ 3 & 2.1 & 6 \end{bmatrix}; \qquad [6.1 \quad 2.2 \quad 3] \qquad (2.6)$$

where the first and the last matrices are also column and row vectors, respectively.

A typical element in the ith row and jth column of $\mathbf{A}$ is identified as a_{ij}; e.g., in the first matrix in (2.4), $a_{11} = 5$ and $a_{12} = -4$. Considering the elements a_{ij} in (2.5), we note that the subscript i runs from 1 to m and the subscript j runs from 1 to n. A comma between subscripts will be used when there is any risk of confusion, e.g., $a_{1+r,\,j+s}$, or to denote differentiation (see Chapter 6).

In general, the utility of matrices in practice arises from the fact that we can identify and manipulate an array of many numbers by use of a single symbol. We shall use matrices in this way extensively in this book.

Symmetric, Diagonal, and Banded Matrices; A Storage Scheme

Whenever the elements of a matrix obey a certain law, we can consider the matrix to be of special form. A *real matrix* is a matrix whose elements are all real. A *complex matrix* has elements that may be complex. We shall deal only with real matrices. In addition, the matrix will often be symmetric.

> *Definition:*   The transpose *of the* $m \times n$ *matrix* $\mathbf{A}$, *written as* $\mathbf{A}^T$, *is obtained by interchanging the rows and columns in* $\mathbf{A}$. *If* $\mathbf{A} = \mathbf{A}^T$, *it follows that the number of rows and columns in* $\mathbf{A}$ *are equal and that* $a_{ij} = a_{ji}$. *Because* $m = n$, *we say that* $\mathbf{A}$ *is a* square matrix *of order* n, *and because* $a_{ij} = a_{ji}$, *we say that* $\mathbf{A}$ *is a* symmetric matrix. *Note that symmetry implies that* $\mathbf{A}$ *is square, but not vice versa; i.e., a square matrix need not be symmetric.*

For example, the coefficient matrix $\mathbf{A}$ in (2.2) is a symmetric matrix of order 4. We can verify that $\mathbf{A}^T = \mathbf{A}$ by simply checking that $a_{ji} = a_{ij}$ for $i, j = 1, \ldots, 4$.

Another special matrix is the *identity* (or *unit*) *matrix* $\mathbf{I}_n$, which is a square matrix of order n with only zero elements except for its diagonal entries, which are unity. For example, the identity matrix of order 3 is

$$\mathbf{I}_3 = \begin{bmatrix} 1 & 0 & 0 \\ 0 & 1 & 0 \\ 0 & 0 & 1 \end{bmatrix} \qquad (2.7)$$

In practical calculations the order of an identity matrix is often implied and the subscript is not written. In analogy with the identity matrix, we also use *identity* (or *unit*) *vectors* of order n, defined as $\mathbf{e}_i$, where the subscript i indicates that the vector is the ith column of an identity matrix.

We shall work abundantly with symmetric banded matrices. Bandedness means that all elements beyond the bandwidth of the matrix are zero. Because $\mathbf{A}$ is symmetric, we can state this condition as

$$a_{ij} = 0 \qquad \text{for } j > i + m_{\mathbf{A}} \qquad (2.8)$$

where $2m_A + 1$ *is the bandwidth of* **A**. As an example, the following matrix is a symmetric banded matrix of order 5. The half-bandwidth m_A is 2:

$$\mathbf{A} = \begin{bmatrix} 3 & 2 & 1 & 0 & 0 \\ 2 & 3 & 4 & 1 & 0 \\ 1 & 4 & 5 & 6 & 1 \\ 0 & 1 & 6 & 7 & 4 \\ 0 & 0 & 1 & 4 & 3 \end{bmatrix} \tag{2.9}$$

If the half-bandwidth of a matrix is zero, we have nonzero elements only on the diagonal of the matrix and denote it as a *diagonal matrix*. For example, the identity matrix is a diagonal matrix.

In computer calculations with matrices, we need to use a scheme of storing the elements of the matrices in high-speed storage. An obvious way of storing the elements of a matrix **A** of order $m \times n$ is simply to dimension in the FORTRAN program an array A(M, N), where M = m and N = n, and store each matrix element a_{ij} in the storage location A(I, J). However, in many calculations we store in this way unnecessarily many zero elements of **A**, which are never needed in the calculations. Also, if **A** is symmetric, we should probably take advantage of it and store only the upper half of the matrix, including the diagonal elements. In general, only a restricted number of high-speed storage locations are available, and it is necessary to use an effective storage scheme in order to be able to take into high-speed core the maximum matrix size possible. If the matrix is too large to be contained in high-speed storage, the solution process will involve reading and writing on secondary storage, which can add significantly to the solution cost. Fortunately, in finite element analysis, the system matrices are symmetric and banded. Therefore, with an effective storage scheme, rather large-order matrices can be kept in high-speed core.

Let us denote by A(I) the Ith element in the one-dimensional storage array A. A diagonal matrix of order n would simply be stored as shown in Fig. 2.1(a):

$$\text{A(I)} = a_{ii}; \qquad \text{I} = i = 1, \ldots, n \tag{2.10}$$

Consider a banded matrix as shown in Fig. 2.1(b). We will see later that zero elements within the "skyline" of the matrix may be changed to nonzero elements in the solution process; for example, a_{35} may be a zero element but becomes nonzero during the solution process (see Section 8.2.3). Therefore we allocate storage locations to zero elements within the skyline but do not need to store zero elements that are outside the skyline. The storage scheme that will be used in the finite element solution process is indicated in Fig. 2.1 and is explained further in Chapter 12.

Matrix Equality, Addition, and Multiplication by a Scalar

We have defined matrices to be ordered arrays of numbers and identified them by single symbols. In order to be able to deal with them as we deal with ordinary numbers, it is necessary to define rules corresponding to those which govern equality, addition, subtraction, multiplication, and division of ordinary numbers. We shall simply state the matrix rules and not provide motivation for them. The rationale for these rules will appear later, as it will turn out that these are precisely the rules that are needed to use matrices in the

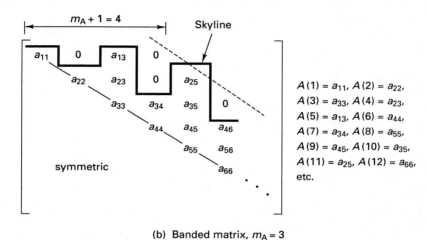

(a) Diagonal matrix

$A(1) = a_{11}, A(2) = a_{22}, A(3) = a_{33}$
$A(4) = a_{44}, ..., A(N) = a_{nn}$

$A(1) = a_{11}, A(2) = a_{22},$
$A(3) = a_{33}, A(4) = a_{23},$
$A(5) = a_{13}, A(6) = a_{44},$
$A(7) = a_{34}, A(8) = a_{55},$
$A(9) = a_{45}, A(10) = a_{35},$
$A(11) = a_{25}, A(12) = a_{66},$
etc.

(b) Banded matrix, $m_A = 3$

Figure 2.1   Storage of matrix A in a one-dimensional array

solution of practical problems. For matrix equality, matrix addition, and matrix multiplication by a scalar, we provide the following definitions.

Definition: The matrices **A** *and* **B** *are equal if and only if*

1. **A** *and* **B** *have the same number of rows and columns.*
2. *All corresponding elements are equal; i.e.* $a_{ij} = b_{ij}$ *for all i and j.*

Definition: Two matrices **A** *and* **B** *can be* added *if and only if they have the same number of rows and columns. The addition of the matrices is performed by adding all corresponding elements; i.e., if* a_{ij} *and* b_{ij} *denote general elements of* **A** *and* **B***, respectively, then* $c_{ij} = a_{ij} + b_{ij}$ *denotes a general element of* **C***, where* **C** = **A** + **B**. *It follows that* **C** *has the same number of rows and columns as* **A** *and* **B**.

EXAMPLE 2.1:   Calculate **C** = **A** + **B**, where

$$\mathbf{A} = \begin{bmatrix} 2 & 1 & 1 \\ 0.5 & 3 & 0 \end{bmatrix}; \qquad \mathbf{B} = \begin{bmatrix} 3 & 1 & 2 \\ 2 & 4 & 1 \end{bmatrix}$$

Here we have

$$\mathbf{C} = \mathbf{A} + \mathbf{B} = \begin{bmatrix} 5 & 2 & 3 \\ 2.5 & 7 & 1 \end{bmatrix}$$

It should be noted that the order in which the matrices are added is not important. The subtraction of matrices is defined in an analogous way.

EXAMPLE 2.2:   Calculate $\mathbf{C} = \mathbf{A} - \mathbf{B}$, where $\mathbf{A}$ and $\mathbf{B}$ are given in Example 2.1. Here we have

$$\mathbf{C} = \mathbf{A} - \mathbf{B} = \begin{bmatrix} -1 & 0 & -1 \\ -1.5 & -1 & -1 \end{bmatrix}$$

From the definition of the subtraction of matrices, it follows that the subtraction of a matrix from itself results in a matrix with zero elements only. Such a matrix is defined to be a *null matrix* **0**. We turn now to the multiplication of a matrix by a scalar.

Definition: A matrix is multiplied *by a scalar by multiplying each matrix element by the scalar; i.e.,* $\mathbf{C} = k\mathbf{A}$ *means that* $c_{ij} = ka_{ij}$.

The following example demonstrates this definition.

EXAMPLE 2.3:   Calculate $\mathbf{C} = k\mathbf{A}$, where

$$\mathbf{A} = \begin{bmatrix} 2 & 1 & 1 \\ 0.5 & 3 & 0 \end{bmatrix}; \qquad k = 2$$

We have
$$\mathbf{C} = k\mathbf{A} = \begin{bmatrix} 4 & 2 & 2 \\ 1 & 6 & 0 \end{bmatrix}$$

It should be noted that so far all definitions are completely analogous to those used in the calculation with ordinary numbers. Furthermore, to add (or subtract) two general matrices of order $n \times m$ requires nm addition (subtraction) operations, and to multiply a general matrix of order $n \times m$ by a scalar requires nm multiplications. Therefore, when the matrices are of special form, such as symmetric and banded, we should take advantage of the situation by evaluating only the elements below the skyline of the matrix $\mathbf{C}$ because all other elements are zero.

Multiplication of Matrices

We consider two matrices $\mathbf{A}$ and $\mathbf{B}$ and want to find the matrix product $\mathbf{C} = \mathbf{AB}$.

Definition: Two matrices $\mathbf{A}$ *and* $\mathbf{B}$ *can be* multiplied *to obtain* $\mathbf{C} = \mathbf{AB}$ *if and only if the number of columns in* $\mathbf{A}$ *is equal to the number of rows in* $\mathbf{B}$. *Assume that* $\mathbf{A}$ *is of order* $p \times m$ *and* $\mathbf{B}$ *is of order* $m \times q$. *Then for each element in* $\mathbf{C}$ *we have*

$$c_{ij} = \sum_{r=1}^{m} a_{ir}b_{rj} \tag{2.11}$$

where $\mathbf{C}$ *is of order* $p \times q$; *i.e., the indices i and j in (2.11) vary from 1 to p and 1 to q, respectively.*

Therefore, to calculate the (i, j)th element in $\mathbf{C}$, we multiply the elements in the ith row of $\mathbf{A}$ by the elements in the jth column of $\mathbf{B}$ and add all individual products. By taking the product of each row in $\mathbf{A}$ and each column in $\mathbf{B}$, it follows that $\mathbf{C}$ must be of order $p \times q$.

EXAMPLE 2.4: Calculate the matrix product $\mathbf{C} = \mathbf{AB}$, where

$$\mathbf{A} = \begin{bmatrix} 5 & 3 & 1 \\ 4 & 6 & 2 \\ 10 & 3 & 4 \end{bmatrix}; \qquad \mathbf{B} = \begin{bmatrix} 1 & 5 \\ 2 & 4 \\ 3 & 2 \end{bmatrix}$$

We have

$$c_{11} = (5)(1) + (3)(2) + (1)(3) = 14$$

$$c_{21} = (4)(1) + (6)(2) + (2)(3) = 22$$

$$c_{31} = (10)(1) + (3)(2) + (4)(3) = 28 \quad \text{etc.}$$

Hence we obtain

$$\mathbf{C} = \begin{bmatrix} 14 & 39 \\ 22 & 48 \\ 28 & 70 \end{bmatrix}$$

As can readily be verified, the number of multiplications required in this matrix multiplication is $p \times q \times m$. When we deal with matrices in practice, however, we can often reduce the number of operations by taking advantage of zero elements within the matrices.

EXAMPLE 2.5: Calculate the matrix product $\mathbf{c} = \mathbf{Ab}$, where

$$\mathbf{A} = \begin{bmatrix} 2 & -1 & 0 & 0 \\ & 2 & -1 & 0 \\ & & 2 & -1 \\ \text{symmetric} & & & 1 \end{bmatrix}; \qquad \mathbf{b} = \begin{bmatrix} 4 \\ 1 \\ 2 \\ 3 \end{bmatrix}$$

Here we can take advantage of the fact that the bandwidth of $\mathbf{A}$ is 3; i.e., $m_{\mathbf{A}} = 1$. Thus, taking into account only the elements within the band of $\mathbf{A}$, we have

$$c_1 = (2)(4) + (-1)(1) = 7$$

$$c_2 = (-1)(4) + (2)(1) + (-1)(2) = -4$$

$$c_3 = (-1)(1) + (2)(2) + (-1)(3) = 0$$

$$c_4 = (-1)(2) + (1)(3) = 1$$

Hence

$$\mathbf{c} = \begin{bmatrix} 7 \\ -4 \\ 0 \\ 1 \end{bmatrix}$$

As is well known, the multiplication of ordinary numbers is commutative; i.e., $ab = ba$. We need to investigate if the same holds for matrix multiplication. If we consider the matrices

$$\mathbf{A} = \begin{bmatrix} 1 \\ 2 \end{bmatrix}; \qquad \mathbf{B} = \begin{bmatrix} 3 & 4 \end{bmatrix} \tag{2.12}$$

we have

$$\mathbf{AB} = \begin{bmatrix} 3 & 4 \\ 6 & 8 \end{bmatrix}; \qquad \mathbf{BA} = \begin{bmatrix} 11 \end{bmatrix} \tag{2.13}$$

Therefore, the products **AB** and **BA** are not the same, and it follows that matrix multiplication is not commutative. Indeed, depending on the orders of **A** and **B**, the orders of the two product matrices **AB** and **BA** can be different, and the product **AB** may be defined, whereas the product **BA** may not be calculable.

To distinguish the order of multiplication of matrices, we say that in the product **AB**, the matrix **A** premultiplies **B**, or the matrix **B** postmultiplies **A**. Although **AB** ≠ **BA** in general, it may happen that **AB** = **BA** for special **A** and **B**, in which case we say that **A** and **B** commute.

Although the commutative law does not hold in matrix multiplication, the distributive law and associative law are both valid. The distributive law states that

$$\mathbf{E} = (\mathbf{A} + \mathbf{B})\mathbf{C} = \mathbf{AC} + \mathbf{BC} \tag{2.14}$$

In other words, we may first add **A** and **B** and then multiply by **C**, or we may first multiply **A** and **B** by **C** and then do the addition. Note that considering the number of operations, the evaluation of **E** by adding **A** and **B** first is much more economical, which is important to remember in the design of an analysis program.

The distributive law is proved using (2.11); that is, using

$$e_{ij} = \sum_{r=1}^{m} (a_{ir} + b_{ir})c_{rj} \tag{2.15}$$

we obtain

$$e_{ij} = \sum_{r=1}^{m} a_{ir}c_{rj} + \sum_{r=1}^{m} b_{ir}c_{rj} \tag{2.16}$$

The associative law states that

$$\mathbf{G} = (\mathbf{AB})\mathbf{C} = \mathbf{A}(\mathbf{BC}) = \mathbf{ABC} \tag{2.17}$$

in other words, that the order of multiplication is immaterial. The proof is carried out by using the definition of matrix multiplication in (2.11) and calculating in either way a general element of **G**.

Since the associative law holds, in practice, a string of matrix multiplications can be carried out in an arbitrary sequence, and by a clever choice of the sequence, many operations can frequently be saved. The only point that must be remembered when manipulating the matrices is that brackets can be removed or inserted and that powers can be combined, but that the order of multiplication must be preserved.

Consider the following examples to demonstrate the use of the associative and distributive laws in order to simplify a string of matrix multiplications.

> **EXAMPLE 2.6:**   Calculate $\mathbf{A}^4$, where
>
> $$\mathbf{A} = \begin{bmatrix} 2 & 1 \\ 1 & 3 \end{bmatrix}$$
>
> One way of evaluating $\mathbf{A}^4$ is to simply calculate
>
> $$\mathbf{A}^2 = \begin{bmatrix} 2 & 1 \\ 1 & 3 \end{bmatrix}\begin{bmatrix} 2 & 1 \\ 1 & 3 \end{bmatrix} = \begin{bmatrix} 5 & 5 \\ 5 & 10 \end{bmatrix}$$
>
> Hence $\mathbf{A}^3 = \mathbf{A}^2\mathbf{A} = \begin{bmatrix} 5 & 5 \\ 5 & 10 \end{bmatrix}\begin{bmatrix} 2 & 1 \\ 1 & 3 \end{bmatrix} = \begin{bmatrix} 15 & 20 \\ 20 & 35 \end{bmatrix}$

and
$$\mathbf{A}^4 = \mathbf{A}^3\mathbf{A} = \begin{bmatrix} 15 & 20 \\ 20 & 35 \end{bmatrix}\begin{bmatrix} 2 & 1 \\ 1 & 3 \end{bmatrix} = \begin{bmatrix} 50 & 75 \\ 75 & 125 \end{bmatrix}$$

Alternatively, we may use
$$\mathbf{A}^4 = \mathbf{A}^2\mathbf{A}^2 = \begin{bmatrix} 5 & 5 \\ 5 & 10 \end{bmatrix}\begin{bmatrix} 5 & 5 \\ 5 & 10 \end{bmatrix} = \begin{bmatrix} 50 & 75 \\ 75 & 125 \end{bmatrix}$$

and save one matrix multiplication.

EXAMPLE 2.7:   Evaluate the product $\mathbf{v}^T\mathbf{A}\mathbf{v}$, where

$$\mathbf{A} = \begin{bmatrix} 3 & 2 & 1 \\ 2 & 4 & 2 \\ 1 & 2 & 6 \end{bmatrix}; \qquad \mathbf{v} = \begin{bmatrix} 1 \\ 2 \\ -1 \end{bmatrix}$$

The formal procedure would be to calculate $\mathbf{x} = \mathbf{A}\mathbf{v}$; i.e.,

$$\mathbf{x} = \mathbf{A}\mathbf{v} = \begin{bmatrix} 3 & 2 & 1 \\ 2 & 4 & 2 \\ 1 & 2 & 6 \end{bmatrix}\begin{bmatrix} 1 \\ 2 \\ -1 \end{bmatrix} = \begin{bmatrix} 6 \\ 8 \\ -1 \end{bmatrix}$$

and then calculate $\mathbf{v}^T\mathbf{x}$ to obtain

$$\mathbf{v}^T\mathbf{A}\mathbf{v} = \begin{bmatrix} 1 & 2 & -1 \end{bmatrix}\begin{bmatrix} 6 \\ 8 \\ -1 \end{bmatrix} = 23$$

However, it is more effective to calculate the required product in the following way. First, we write

$$\mathbf{A} = \mathbf{U} + \mathbf{D} + \mathbf{U}^T$$

where $\mathbf{U}$ is a lower triangular matrix and $\mathbf{D}$ is a diagonal matrix,

$$\mathbf{U} = \begin{bmatrix} 0 & 0 & 0 \\ 2 & 0 & 0 \\ 1 & 2 & 0 \end{bmatrix}; \qquad \mathbf{D} = \begin{bmatrix} 3 & 0 & 0 \\ 0 & 4 & 0 \\ 0 & 0 & 6 \end{bmatrix}$$

Hence we have
$$\mathbf{v}^T\mathbf{A}\mathbf{v} = \mathbf{v}^T(\mathbf{U} + \mathbf{D} + \mathbf{U}^T)\mathbf{v}$$

$$\mathbf{v}^T\mathbf{A}\mathbf{v} = \mathbf{v}^T\mathbf{U}\mathbf{v} + \mathbf{v}^T\mathbf{D}\mathbf{v} + \mathbf{v}^T\mathbf{U}^T\mathbf{v}$$

However, $\mathbf{v}^T\mathbf{U}\mathbf{v}$ is a single number and hence $\mathbf{v}^T\mathbf{U}^T\mathbf{v} = \mathbf{v}^T\mathbf{U}\mathbf{v}$, and it follows that

$$\mathbf{v}^T\mathbf{A}\mathbf{v} = 2\mathbf{v}^T\mathbf{U}\mathbf{v} + \mathbf{v}^T\mathbf{D}\mathbf{v} \tag{a}$$

The higher efficiency in the matrix multiplication is obtained by taking advantage of the fact that $\mathbf{U}$ is a lower triangular and $\mathbf{D}$ is a diagonal matrix. Let $\mathbf{x} = \mathbf{U}\mathbf{v}$; then we have

$$x_1 = 0$$
$$x_2 = (2)(1) = 2$$
$$x_3 = (1)(1) + (2)(2) = 5$$

Hence
$$\mathbf{x} = \begin{bmatrix} 0 \\ 2 \\ 5 \end{bmatrix}$$

Next, we obtain

$$\mathbf{v}^T\mathbf{U}\mathbf{v} = \mathbf{v}^T\mathbf{x} = (2)(2) + (-1)(5) = -1$$

Also
$$\mathbf{v}^T\mathbf{D}\mathbf{v} = (1)(1)(3) + (2)(2)(4) + (-1)(-1)(6)$$
$$= 25$$

Hence using (a) we have $\mathbf{v}^T\mathbf{A}\mathbf{v} = 23$, as before.

Apart from the commutative law, which in general does not hold in matrix multiplications, the cancellation of matrices in matrix equations also cannot be performed, in general, as the cancellation of ordinary numbers. In particular, if $\mathbf{AB} = \mathbf{CB}$, it does not necessarily follow that $\mathbf{A} = \mathbf{C}$. This is easily demonstrated considering a specific case:

$$\begin{bmatrix} 2 & 1 \\ 4 & 0 \end{bmatrix}\begin{bmatrix} 1 \\ 2 \end{bmatrix} = \begin{bmatrix} 4 & 0 \\ 0 & 2 \end{bmatrix}\begin{bmatrix} 1 \\ 2 \end{bmatrix} \tag{2.18}$$

but
$$\begin{bmatrix} 2 & 1 \\ 4 & 0 \end{bmatrix} \neq \begin{bmatrix} 4 & 0 \\ 0 & 2 \end{bmatrix} \tag{2.19}$$

However, it must be noted that $\mathbf{A} = \mathbf{C}$ if the equation $\mathbf{AB} = \mathbf{CB}$ holds for all possible $\mathbf{B}$. Namely, in that case, we simply select $\mathbf{B}$ to be the identity matrix $\mathbf{I}$, and hence $\mathbf{A} = \mathbf{C}$.

It should also be noted that included in this observation is the fact that if $\mathbf{AB} = \mathbf{0}$, it does not follow that either $\mathbf{A}$ or $\mathbf{B}$ is a null matrix. A specific case demonstrates this observation:

$$\mathbf{A} = \begin{bmatrix} 1 & 0 \\ 2 & 0 \end{bmatrix}; \qquad \mathbf{B} = \begin{bmatrix} 0 & 0 \\ 3 & 4 \end{bmatrix}; \qquad \mathbf{AB} = \begin{bmatrix} 0 & 0 \\ 0 & 0 \end{bmatrix} \tag{2.20}$$

Some special rules concerning the use of transposed matrices in matrix multiplications need to be pointed out. It is noted that the transpose of the product of two matrices $\mathbf{A}$ and $\mathbf{B}$ is equal to the product of the transposed matrices in reverse order; i.e.,

$$(\mathbf{AB})^T = \mathbf{B}^T\mathbf{A}^T \tag{2.21}$$

The proof that (2.21) does hold is obtained using the definition for the evaluation of a matrix product given in (2.11).

Considering the matrix products in (2.21), it should be noted that although $\mathbf{A}$ and $\mathbf{B}$ may be symmetric, $\mathbf{AB}$ is, in general, not symmetric. However, if $\mathbf{A}$ is symmetric, the matrix $\mathbf{B}^T\mathbf{AB}$ is always symmetric. The proof follows using (2.21):

$$(\mathbf{B}^T\mathbf{AB})^T = (\mathbf{AB})^T(\mathbf{B}^T)^T \tag{2.22}$$

$$= \mathbf{B}^T\mathbf{A}^T\mathbf{B} \tag{2.23}$$

But, because $\mathbf{A}^T = \mathbf{A}$, we have

$$(\mathbf{B}^T\mathbf{AB})^T = \mathbf{B}^T\mathbf{AB} \tag{2.24}$$

and hence $\mathbf{B}^T\mathbf{AB}$ is symmetric.

The Inverse Matrix

We have seen that matrix addition and subtraction are carried out using essentially the same laws as those used in the manipulation of ordinary numbers. However, matrix multiplication is quite different, and we have to get used to special rules. With regard to matrix division, it strictly does not exist. Instead, an inverse matrix is defined. We shall define and use the inverse of square matrices only.

Definition: *The* inverse *of a matrix* $\mathbf{A}$ *is denoted by* $\mathbf{A}^{-1}$. *Assume that the inverse exists; then the elements of* $\mathbf{A}^{-1}$ *are such that* $\mathbf{A}^{-1}\mathbf{A} = \mathbf{I}$ *and* $\mathbf{A}\mathbf{A}^{-1} = \mathbf{I}$. *A matrix that possesses an inverse is said to be* nonsingular. *A matrix without an inverse is a* singular *matrix.*

As mentioned previously, the inverse of a matrix does not need to exist. A trivial example is the null matrix. Assume that the inverse of $\mathbf{A}$ exists. Then we still want to show that either of the conditions $\mathbf{A}^{-1}\mathbf{A} = \mathbf{I}$ or $\mathbf{A}\mathbf{A}^{-1} = \mathbf{I}$ implies the other. Assume that we have evaluated the elements of the matrices $\mathbf{A}_l^{-1}$ and $\mathbf{A}_r^{-1}$ such that $\mathbf{A}_l^{-1}\mathbf{A} = \mathbf{I}$ and $\mathbf{A}\mathbf{A}_r^{-1} = \mathbf{I}$. Then we have

$$\mathbf{A}_l^{-1} = \mathbf{A}_l^{-1}(\mathbf{A}\mathbf{A}_r^{-1}) = (\mathbf{A}_l^{-1}\mathbf{A})\mathbf{A}_r^{-1} = \mathbf{A}_r^{-1} \tag{2.25}$$

and hence $\mathbf{A}_l^{-1} = \mathbf{A}_r^{-1}$.

EXAMPLE 2.8:   Evaluate the inverse of the matrix $\mathbf{A}$, where

$$\mathbf{A} = \begin{bmatrix} 2 & -1 \\ -1 & 3 \end{bmatrix}$$

For the inverse of $\mathbf{A}$ we need $\mathbf{A}\mathbf{A}^{-1} = \mathbf{I}$. By trial and error (or otherwise) we find that

$$\mathbf{A}^{-1} = \begin{bmatrix} \frac{3}{5} & \frac{1}{5} \\ \frac{1}{5} & \frac{2}{5} \end{bmatrix}$$

We check that $\mathbf{A}\mathbf{A}^{-1} = \mathbf{I}$ and $\mathbf{A}^{-1}\mathbf{A} = \mathbf{I}$:

$$\mathbf{A}\mathbf{A}^{-1} = \begin{bmatrix} 2 & -1 \\ -1 & 3 \end{bmatrix}\begin{bmatrix} \frac{3}{5} & \frac{1}{5} \\ \frac{1}{5} & \frac{2}{5} \end{bmatrix} = \begin{bmatrix} 1 & 0 \\ 0 & 1 \end{bmatrix}$$

$$\mathbf{A}^{-1}\mathbf{A} = \begin{bmatrix} \frac{3}{5} & \frac{1}{5} \\ \frac{1}{5} & \frac{2}{5} \end{bmatrix}\begin{bmatrix} 2 & -1 \\ -1 & 3 \end{bmatrix} = \begin{bmatrix} 1 & 0 \\ 0 & 1 \end{bmatrix}$$

To calculate the inverse of a product $\mathbf{AB}$, we proceed as follows. Let $\mathbf{G} = (\mathbf{AB})^{-1}$, where $\mathbf{A}$ and $\mathbf{B}$ are both square matrices. Then

$$\mathbf{GAB} = \mathbf{I} \tag{2.26}$$

and postmultiplying by $\mathbf{B}^{-1}$ and $\mathbf{A}^{-1}$, we obtain

$$\mathbf{GA} = \mathbf{B}^{-1} \tag{2.27}$$

$$\mathbf{G} = \mathbf{B}^{-1}\mathbf{A}^{-1} \tag{2.28}$$

Therefore, $$(\mathbf{AB})^{-1} = \mathbf{B}^{-1}\mathbf{A}^{-1} \tag{2.29}$$

We note that the same law of matrix reversal was shown to apply when the transpose of a matrix product is calculated.

EXAMPLE 2.9:   For the matrices $\mathbf{A}$ and $\mathbf{B}$ given, check that $(\mathbf{AB})^{-1} = \mathbf{B}^{-1}\mathbf{A}^{-1}$.

$$\mathbf{A} = \begin{bmatrix} 2 & -1 \\ -1 & 3 \end{bmatrix}; \qquad \mathbf{B} = \begin{bmatrix} 3 & 0 \\ 0 & 4 \end{bmatrix}$$

The inverse of $\mathbf{A}$ was used in Example 2.8. The inverse of $\mathbf{B}$ is easy to obtain:

$$\mathbf{B}^{-1} = \begin{bmatrix} \frac{1}{3} & 0 \\ 0 & \frac{1}{4} \end{bmatrix}$$

To check that $(\mathbf{AB})^{-1} = \mathbf{B}^{-1}\mathbf{A}^{-1}$, we need to evaluate $\mathbf{C} = \mathbf{AB}$:

$$\mathbf{C} = \begin{bmatrix} 2 & -1 \\ -1 & 3 \end{bmatrix}\begin{bmatrix} 3 & 0 \\ 0 & 4 \end{bmatrix} = \begin{bmatrix} 6 & -4 \\ -3 & 12 \end{bmatrix}$$

Assume that $\mathbf{C}^{-1} = \mathbf{B}^{-1}\mathbf{A}^{-1}$. Then we would have

$$\mathbf{C}^{-1} = \begin{bmatrix} \frac{1}{3} & 0 \\ 0 & \frac{1}{4} \end{bmatrix}\begin{bmatrix} \frac{3}{5} & \frac{1}{5} \\ \frac{1}{5} & \frac{2}{5} \end{bmatrix} = \begin{bmatrix} \frac{1}{5} & \frac{1}{15} \\ \frac{1}{20} & \frac{1}{10} \end{bmatrix} \qquad\qquad\text{(a)}$$

To check that the matrix given in (a) is indeed the inverse of $\mathbf{C}$, we evaluate $\mathbf{C}^{-1}\mathbf{C}$ and find that

$$\mathbf{C}^{-1}\mathbf{C} = \begin{bmatrix} \frac{1}{5} & \frac{1}{15} \\ \frac{1}{20} & \frac{1}{10} \end{bmatrix}\begin{bmatrix} 6 & -4 \\ -3 & 12 \end{bmatrix} = \mathbf{I}$$

But since $\mathbf{C}^{-1}$ is unique and only the correct $\mathbf{C}^{-1}$ satisfies the relation $\mathbf{C}^{-1}\mathbf{C} = \mathbf{I}$, we indeed have found in (a) the inverse of $\mathbf{C}$, and the relation $(\mathbf{AB})^{-1} = \mathbf{B}^{-1}\mathbf{A}^{-1}$ is satisfied.

In Examples 2.8 and 2.9, the inverse of $\mathbf{A}$ and $\mathbf{B}$ could be found by trial and error. However, to obtain the inverse of a general matrix, we need to have a general algorithm. One way of calculating the inverse of a matrix $\mathbf{A}$ of order n is to solve the n systems of equations

$$\mathbf{AX} = \mathbf{I} \qquad\qquad\qquad\qquad (2.30)$$

where $\mathbf{I}$ is the identity matrix of order n and we have $\mathbf{X} = \mathbf{A}^{-1}$. For the solution of each system of equations in (2.30), we can use the algorithms presented in Section 8.2.

These considerations show that a system of equations could be solved by calculating the inverse of the coefficient matrix; i.e., if we have

$$\mathbf{Ay} = \mathbf{c} \qquad\qquad\qquad\qquad (2.31)$$

where $\mathbf{A}$ is of order $n \times n$ and $\mathbf{y}$ and $\mathbf{c}$ are of order $n \times 1$, then

$$\mathbf{y} = \mathbf{A}^{-1}\mathbf{c} \qquad\qquad\qquad\qquad (2.32)$$

However, the inversion of $\mathbf{A}$ is very costly, and it is much more effective to only solve the equations in (2.31) without inverting $\mathbf{A}$ (see Chapter 8). *Indeed, although we may write symbolically that* $\mathbf{y} = \mathbf{A}^{-1}\mathbf{c}$, *to evaluate* $\mathbf{y}$ *we actually only solve the equations.*

Partitioning of Matrices

To facilitate matrix manipulations and to take advantage of the special form of matrices, it may be useful to partition a matrix into submatrices. A submatrix is a matrix that is obtained from the original matrix by including only the elements of certain rows and columns. The idea is demonstrated using a specific case in which the dashed lines are the lines of partitioning:

$$A = \begin{bmatrix} a_{11} & \vdots & a_{12} & a_{13} & a_{14} & \vdots & a_{15} & a_{16} \\ a_{21} & \vdots & a_{22} & a_{23} & a_{24} & \vdots & a_{25} & a_{26} \\ \hdashline a_{31} & \vdots & a_{32} & a_{33} & a_{34} & \vdots & a_{35} & a_{36} \end{bmatrix} \tag{2.33}$$

It should be noted that each of the partitioning lines must run completely across the original matrix. Using the partitioning, matrix $\mathbf{A}$ is written as

$$\mathbf{A} = \begin{bmatrix} \mathbf{A}_{11} & \mathbf{A}_{12} & \mathbf{A}_{13} \\ \mathbf{A}_{21} & \mathbf{A}_{22} & \mathbf{A}_{23} \end{bmatrix} \tag{2.34}$$

where

$$\mathbf{A}_{11} = \begin{bmatrix} a_{11} \\ a_{21} \end{bmatrix}; \qquad \mathbf{A}_{12} = \begin{bmatrix} a_{12} & a_{13} & a_{14} \\ a_{22} & a_{23} & a_{24} \end{bmatrix}; \qquad \text{etc.} \tag{2.35}$$

The right-hand side of (2.34) could again be partitioned, such as

$$\mathbf{A} = \begin{bmatrix} \mathbf{A}_{11} & \vdots & \mathbf{A}_{12} & \mathbf{A}_{13} \\ \mathbf{A}_{21} & \vdots & \mathbf{A}_{22} & \mathbf{A}_{23} \end{bmatrix} \tag{2.36}$$

and we may write $\mathbf{A}$ as

$$\mathbf{A} = [\bar{\mathbf{A}}_1 \quad \bar{\mathbf{A}}_2]; \qquad \bar{\mathbf{A}}_1 = \begin{bmatrix} \mathbf{A}_{11} \\ \mathbf{A}_{21} \end{bmatrix}; \qquad \bar{\mathbf{A}}_2 = \begin{bmatrix} \mathbf{A}_{12} & \mathbf{A}_{13} \\ \mathbf{A}_{22} & \mathbf{A}_{23} \end{bmatrix} \tag{2.37}$$

The partitioning of matrices can be of advantage in saving computer storage; namely, if submatrices repeat, it is necessary to store the submatrix only once. The same applies in arithmetic. Using submatrices, we may identify a typical operation that is repeated many times. We then carry out this operation only once and use the result whenever it is needed.

The rules to be used in calculations with partitioned matrices follow from the definition of matrix addition, subtraction, and multiplication. Using partitioned matrices we can add, subtract, or multiply as if the submatrices were ordinary matrix elements, provided the original matrices have been partitioned in such a way that it is permissible to perform the individual submatrix additions, subtractions, or multiplications.

These rules are easily justified and remembered if we keep in mind that *the partitioning of the original matrices is only a device to facilitate matrix manipulations and does not change any results.*

EXAMPLE 2.10:   Evaluate the matrix product $\mathbf{C} = \mathbf{AB}$ in Example 2.4 by using the following partitioning:

$$\mathbf{A} = \begin{bmatrix} 5 & 3 & \vdots & 1 \\ 4 & 6 & \vdots & 2 \\ \hdashline 10 & 3 & \vdots & 4 \end{bmatrix}; \qquad \mathbf{B} = \begin{bmatrix} 1 & 5 \\ 2 & 4 \\ 3 & 2 \end{bmatrix}$$

Here we have

$$\mathbf{A} = \begin{bmatrix} \mathbf{A}_{11} & \mathbf{A}_{12} \\ \mathbf{A}_{21} & \mathbf{A}_{22} \end{bmatrix}; \qquad \mathbf{B} = \begin{bmatrix} \mathbf{B}_1 \\ \mathbf{B}_2 \end{bmatrix}$$

Therefore,

$$\mathbf{AB} = \begin{bmatrix} \mathbf{A}_{11}\mathbf{B}_1 + \mathbf{A}_{12}\mathbf{B}_2 \\ \mathbf{A}_{21}\mathbf{B}_1 + \mathbf{A}_{22}\mathbf{B}_2 \end{bmatrix} \tag{a}$$

But
$$\mathbf{A}_{11}\mathbf{B}_1 = \begin{bmatrix} 5 & 3 \\ 4 & 6 \end{bmatrix}\begin{bmatrix} 1 & 5 \\ 2 & 4 \end{bmatrix} = \begin{bmatrix} 11 & 37 \\ 16 & 44 \end{bmatrix}$$

$$\mathbf{A}_{12}\mathbf{B}_2 = \begin{bmatrix} 1 \\ 2 \end{bmatrix}[3 \quad 2] = \begin{bmatrix} 3 & 2 \\ 6 & 4 \end{bmatrix}$$

$$\mathbf{A}_{21}\mathbf{B}_1 = [10 \quad 3]\begin{bmatrix} 1 & 5 \\ 2 & 4 \end{bmatrix} = [16 \quad 62]$$

$$\mathbf{A}_{22}\mathbf{B}_2 = [4][3 \quad 2] = [12 \quad 8]$$

Then substituting into (a) we have

$$\mathbf{AB} = \begin{bmatrix} 14 & 39 \\ 22 & 48 \\ 28 & 70 \end{bmatrix}$$

EXAMPLE 2.11:   Taking advantage of partitioning, evaluate $\mathbf{c} = \mathbf{Ab}$, where

$$\mathbf{A} = \begin{bmatrix} 4 & 3 & \vdots & 1 & 2 \\ 3 & 6 & \vdots & 2 & 1 \\ \hdashline 1 & 2 & \vdots & 8 & 6 \\ 2 & 1 & \vdots & 6 & 12 \end{bmatrix}; \qquad \mathbf{b} = \begin{bmatrix} 2 \\ 2 \\ 1 \\ 1 \end{bmatrix}$$

The only products that we need to evaluate are

$$\mathbf{w}_1 = \begin{bmatrix} 4 & 3 \\ 3 & 6 \end{bmatrix}\begin{bmatrix} 1 \\ 1 \end{bmatrix} = \begin{bmatrix} 7 \\ 9 \end{bmatrix}$$

and
$$\mathbf{w}_2 = \begin{bmatrix} 1 & 2 \\ 2 & 1 \end{bmatrix}\begin{bmatrix} 1 \\ 1 \end{bmatrix} = \begin{bmatrix} 3 \\ 3 \end{bmatrix}$$

We can now construct $\mathbf{c}$:

$$\mathbf{c} = \begin{bmatrix} 2\mathbf{w}_1 + \mathbf{w}_2 \\ 2\mathbf{w}_1 + 2\mathbf{w}_2 \end{bmatrix}$$

or, substituting,
$$\mathbf{c} = \begin{bmatrix} 17 \\ 21 \\ 20 \\ 24 \end{bmatrix}$$

The Trace and Determinant of a Matrix

The trace and determinant of a matrix are defined only if the matrix is square. Both quantities are single numbers, which are evaluated from the elements of the matrix and are therefore functions of the matrix elements.

Definition: The trace *of the matrix* $\mathbf{A}$ *is denoted as* $tr(\mathbf{A})$ *and is equal to* $\Sigma_{i=1}^{n} a_{ii,}$ *where* n *is the order of* $\mathbf{A}$.

EXAMPLE 2.12:   Calculate the trace of the matrix **A** given in Example 2.11.
Here we have

$$\text{tr}(\mathbf{A}) = 4 + 6 + 8 + 12 = 30$$

The determinant of a matrix **A** can be defined in terms of the determinants of submatrices of **A** and by noting that the determinant of a matrix of order 1 is simply the element
of the matrix; i.e., if $\mathbf{A} = [a_{11}]$, then $\det \mathbf{A} = a_{11}$.

Definition: *The determinant of an n × n matrix* **A** *is denoted as det* **A** *and is defined by the*
recurrence relation

$$\det \mathbf{A} = \sum_{j=1}^{n} (-1)^{1+j} a_{1j} \det \mathbf{A}_{1j} \tag{2.38}$$

where $\mathbf{A}_{1j}$ is the (n − 1) × (n − 1) matrix obtained by eliminating the 1st row and jth column
from the matrix **A**.

EXAMPLE 2.13:   Evaluate the determinant of **A**, where

$$\mathbf{A} = \begin{bmatrix} a_{11} & a_{12} \\ a_{21} & a_{22} \end{bmatrix}$$

Using the relation in (2.38), we obtain

$$\det \mathbf{A} = (-1)^2 a_{11} \det \mathbf{A}_{11} + (-1)^3 a_{12} \det \mathbf{A}_{12}$$

But $\qquad\qquad\qquad \det \mathbf{A}_{11} = a_{22}; \qquad \det \mathbf{A}_{12} = a_{21}$

Hence $\qquad\qquad\qquad \det \mathbf{A} = a_{11}a_{22} - a_{12}a_{21}$

This relation is the general formula for the determinant of a 2 × 2 matrix.

It can be shown that to evaluate the determinant of a matrix we may use the recurrence
relation given in (2.38) along any row or column, as indicated in Example 2.14.

EXAMPLE 2.14:   Evaluate the determinant of the matrix **A**, where

$$\mathbf{A} = \begin{bmatrix} 2 & 1 & 0 \\ 1 & 3 & 1 \\ 0 & 1 & 2 \end{bmatrix}$$

Using the recurrence relation in (2.38), we obtain

$$\det \mathbf{A} = (-1)^2 (2) \det \begin{bmatrix} 3 & 1 \\ 1 & 2 \end{bmatrix}$$
$$+ (-1)^3 (1) \det \begin{bmatrix} 1 & 1 \\ 0 & 2 \end{bmatrix}$$
$$+ (-1)^4 (0) \det \begin{bmatrix} 1 & 3 \\ 0 & 1 \end{bmatrix}$$

We now employ the formula for the determinant of a 2×2 matrix given in Example 2.13 and have

$$\det \mathbf{A} = (2)\{(3)(2) - (1)(1)\} - \{(1)(2) - (0)(1)\} + 0$$

Hence
$$\det \mathbf{A} = 8$$

Let us check that the same result is obtained by using (2.38) along the second row instead of the first row. In this case we have, changing the 1 to 2 in (2.38),

$$\det \mathbf{A} = (-1)^3(1) \det \begin{bmatrix} 1 & 0 \\ 1 & 2 \end{bmatrix}$$

$$+ (-1)^4(3) \det \begin{bmatrix} 2 & 0 \\ 0 & 2 \end{bmatrix}$$

$$+ (-1)^5(1) \det \begin{bmatrix} 2 & 1 \\ 0 & 1 \end{bmatrix}$$

Again using the formula given in Example 2.13, we have

$$\det \mathbf{A} = -\{(1)(2) - (0)(1)\} + (3)\{(2)(2) - (0)(0)\} - \{(2)(1) - (1)(0)\}$$

or, as before,

$$\det \mathbf{A} = 8$$

Finally, using (2.38) along the third column, we have

$$\det \mathbf{A} = (-1)^4(0) \det \begin{bmatrix} 1 & 3 \\ 0 & 1 \end{bmatrix}$$

$$+ (-1)^5(1) \det \begin{bmatrix} 2 & 1 \\ 0 & 1 \end{bmatrix}$$

$$+ (-1)^6(2) \det \begin{bmatrix} 2 & 1 \\ 1 & 3 \end{bmatrix}$$

and, as before, obtain $\det \mathbf{A} = 8$.

Many theorems are associated with the use of determinants. Typically, the solution of a set of simultaneous equations can be obtained by a series of determinant evaluations (see, for example, B. Noble [A]). However, from a modern viewpoint, most of the results that are obtained using determinants can be obtained much more effectively. For example, the solution of simultaneous equations using determinants is very inefficient. As we shall see later, a primary value of using determinants lies in the convenient shorthand notation we can use in the discussion of certain questions, such as the existence of an inverse of a matrix. We shall use determinants in particular in the solution of eigenvalue problems.

In evaluating the determinant of a matrix, it may be effective to first factorize the matrix into a product of matrices and then use the following result:

$$\det (\mathbf{BC} \cdots \mathbf{F}) = (\det \mathbf{B})(\det \mathbf{C}) \cdots (\det \mathbf{F}) \tag{2.39}$$

Relation (2.39) states that the determinant of the product of a number of matrices is equal to the product of the determinants of each matrix. The proof of this result is rather lengthy and clumsy [it is obtained using the determinant definition in (2.38)], and therefore we shall not include it here. We shall use the result in (2.39) often in eigenvalue calculations when the determinant of a matrix, say matrix **A**, is required. The specific decomposition used is **A** = **LDL**^{T}, where **L** is a lower unit triangular matrix and **D** is a diagonal matrix (see Section 8.2.2). In that case,

$$\det \mathbf{A} = \det \mathbf{L} \det \mathbf{D} \det \mathbf{L}^T \qquad (2.40)$$

and because det **L** = 1, we have

$$\det \mathbf{A} = \prod_{i=1}^{n} d_{ii} \qquad (2.41)$$

EXAMPLE 2.15:   Using the **LDL**^{T} decomposition, evaluate the determinant of **A**, where **A** is given in Example 2.14.

The procedure to obtain the **LDL**^{T} decomposition of **A** is presented in Section 8.2. Here we simply give **L** and **D**, and it can be verified that **LDL**^{T} = **A**:

$$\mathbf{L} = \begin{bmatrix} 1 & 0 & 0 \\ \frac{1}{2} & 1 & 0 \\ 0 & \frac{2}{5} & 1 \end{bmatrix}; \qquad \mathbf{D} = \begin{bmatrix} 2 & 0 & 0 \\ 0 & \frac{5}{2} & 0 \\ 0 & 0 & \frac{8}{5} \end{bmatrix}$$

Using (2.41), we obtain

$$\det \mathbf{A} = (2)(\tfrac{5}{2})(\tfrac{8}{5}) = 8$$

This is also the value obtained in Example 2.14.

The determinant and the trace of a matrix are functions of the matrix elements. However, it is important to observe that the off-diagonal elements do not affect the trace of a matrix, whereas the determinant is a function of all the elements in the matrix. Although we can conclude that a large determinant or a large trace means that some matrix elements are large, we cannot conclude that a small determinant or a small trace means that all matrix elements are small.

EXAMPLE 2.16:   Calculate the trace and determinant of **A**, where

$$\mathbf{A} = \begin{bmatrix} 1 & 10{,}000 \\ 10^{-4} & 2 \end{bmatrix}$$

Here we have

$$\text{tr } (\mathbf{A}) = 3$$

and

$$\det \mathbf{A} = (1)(2) - (10^{-4})(10{,}000)$$

i.e.,

$$\det \mathbf{A} = 1$$

Hence both the trace and the determinant of **A** are small in relation to the off-diagonal element a_{12}.

2.3 VECTOR SPACES

In the previous section we defined a vector of order n to be an array of n numbers written in matrix form. We now want to associate a geometric interpretation with the elements of a vector. Consider as an example a column vector of order 3 such as

$$\mathbf{x} = \begin{bmatrix} x_1 \\ x_2 \\ x_3 \end{bmatrix} = \begin{bmatrix} 2 \\ 4 \\ 3 \end{bmatrix} \tag{2.42}$$

We know from elementary geometry that $\mathbf{x}$ represents a geometric vector in a chosen coordinate system in three-dimensional space. Figure 2.2 shows assumed coordinate axes and the vector corresponding to (2.42) in this system. We should note that the geometric representation of $\mathbf{x}$ depends completely on the coordinate system chosen; in other words, if (2.42) would give the components of a vector in a different coordinate system, then the geometric representation of $\mathbf{x}$ would be different from the one in Fig. 2.2. Therefore, the coordinates (or components of a vector) alone do not define the actual geometric quantity, but they need to be given together with the specific coordinate system in which they are measured.

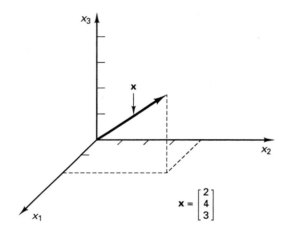

$$\mathbf{x} = \begin{bmatrix} 2 \\ 4 \\ 3 \end{bmatrix}$$

Figure 2.2   Geometric representation of vector $\mathbf{x}$

The concepts of three-dimensional geometry generalize to a vector of any finite order n. If $n > 3$, we can no longer obtain a plot of the vector; however, we shall see that mathematically all concepts that pertain to vectors are independent of n. As before, when we considered the specific case $n = 3$, the vector of order n represents a quantity in a specific coordinate system of an n-dimensional space.

Assume that we are dealing with a number of vectors all of order n, which are defined in a fixed coordinate system. Some fundamental concepts that we shall find extremely powerful in the later chapters are summarized in the following definitions and facts.

Definition: *A collection of vectors* $\mathbf{x}_1, \mathbf{x}_2, \ldots, \mathbf{x}_s$ *is said to be* linearly dependent *if there exist numbers* $\alpha_1, \alpha_2, \ldots, \alpha_s$, *which are not all zero, such that*

$$\alpha_1 \mathbf{x}_1 + \alpha_2 \mathbf{x}_2 + \cdots + \alpha_s \mathbf{x}_s = \mathbf{0} \tag{2.43}$$

If the vectors are not linearly dependent, they are called linearly independent *vectors.*

We consider the following examples to clarify the meaning of this definition.

EXAMPLE 2.17:   Let $n = 3$ and determine if the vectors $\mathbf{e}_i$, $i = 1, 2, 3$, are linearly dependent or independent.

According to the definition of linear dependency, we need to check if there are constants α_1, α_2, and α_3, not all zero, that satisfy the equation

$$\alpha_1 \begin{bmatrix} 1 \\ 0 \\ 0 \end{bmatrix} + \alpha_2 \begin{bmatrix} 0 \\ 1 \\ 0 \end{bmatrix} + \alpha_3 \begin{bmatrix} 0 \\ 0 \\ 1 \end{bmatrix} = \begin{bmatrix} 0 \\ 0 \\ 0 \end{bmatrix} \tag{a}$$

But the equations in (a) read

$$\begin{bmatrix} \alpha_1 \\ \alpha_2 \\ \alpha_3 \end{bmatrix} = \begin{bmatrix} 0 \\ 0 \\ 0 \end{bmatrix}$$

which is satisfied only if $\alpha_i = 0$, $i = 1, 2, 3$; therefore, the vectors $\mathbf{e}_i$ are linearly independent.

EXAMPLE 2.18:   With $n = 4$, investigate whether the following vectors are linearly dependent or independent.

$$\mathbf{x}_1 = \begin{bmatrix} 1 \\ 1 \\ 0 \\ 0.5 \end{bmatrix}; \qquad \mathbf{x}_2 = \begin{bmatrix} -1 \\ 0 \\ 1 \\ 0 \end{bmatrix}; \qquad \mathbf{x}_3 = \begin{bmatrix} 0 \\ -0.5 \\ -0.5 \\ -0.25 \end{bmatrix}$$

We need to consider the system of equations

$$\alpha_1 \begin{bmatrix} 1 \\ 1 \\ 0 \\ 0.5 \end{bmatrix} + \alpha_2 \begin{bmatrix} -1 \\ 0 \\ 1 \\ 0 \end{bmatrix} + \alpha_3 \begin{bmatrix} 0 \\ -0.5 \\ -0.5 \\ -0.25 \end{bmatrix} = \begin{bmatrix} 0 \\ 0 \\ 0 \\ 0 \end{bmatrix}$$

or, considering each row,

$$\begin{aligned} \alpha_1 - \alpha_2 \qquad\qquad &= 0 \\ \alpha_1 \qquad - 0.5\,\alpha_3 &= 0 \\ \alpha_2 - 0.5\,\alpha_3 &= 0 \\ 0.5\alpha_1 \qquad - 0.25\alpha_3 &= 0 \end{aligned}$$

where we note that the equations are satisfied for $\alpha_1 = 1$, $\alpha_2 = 1$, and $\alpha_3 = 2$. Therefore, the vectors are linearly dependent.

In the preceding examples, the solution for α_1, α_2, and α_3 could be obtained by inspection. We shall later develop a systematic procedure of checking whether a number of vectors are linearly dependent or independent.

Another way of looking at the problem, which may be more appealing, is to say that the vectors are *linearly dependent* if any one of them can be expressed in terms of the others. That is, if not all of the α_i in (2.43) are zero, say $\alpha_j \neq 0$, then we can write

$$\mathbf{x}_j = -\sum_{\substack{k=1 \\ k \neq j}}^{s} \frac{\alpha_k}{\alpha_j} \mathbf{x}_k \tag{2.44}$$

Geometrically, when $n \leq 3$, we could plot the vectors and if they are linearly dependent, we would be able to plot one vector in terms of multiples of the other vectors. For example, plotting the vectors used in Example 2.17, we immediately observe that none of them can be expressed in terms of multiples of the remaining ones; hence the vectors are linearly independent.

Assume that we are given q vectors of order n, $n \geq q$, which are linearly dependent, but that we only consider any $(q - 1)$ of them. These $(q - 1)$ vectors may still be linearly dependent. However, by continuing to decrease the number of vectors under consideration, we would arrive at p vectors, which are linearly independent, where, in general, $p \leq q$. The other $(q - p)$ vectors can be expressed in terms of the p vectors. We are thus led to the following definition.

> *Definition: Assume that we have p linearly independent vectors of order n, where $n \geq p$. These p vectors form a basis for a p-dimensional vector space.*

We talk about a vector space of dimension p because any vector in the space can be expressed as a linear combination of the p base vectors. We should note that the base vectors for the specific space considered are not unique; linear combinations of them can give another basis for the same space. Specifically, if $p = n$, then a basis for the space considered is $\mathbf{e}_i$, $i = 1, \ldots, n$, from which it also follows that p cannot be larger than n.

> *Definition: q vectors, of which p vectors are linearly independent, are said to span a p-dimensional vector space.*

We therefore realize that all the importance lies in the base vectors since they are the smallest number of vectors that span the space considered. All q vectors can be expressed in terms of the base vectors, however large q may be (and indeed q could be larger than n).

> **EXAMPLE 2.19:**   Establish a basis for the space spanned by the three vectors in Example 2.18.
> In this case $q = 3$ and $n = 4$. We find by inspection that the two vectors $\mathbf{x}_1$ and $\mathbf{x}_2$ are linearly independent. Hence $\mathbf{x}_1$ and $\mathbf{x}_2$ can be taken as base vectors of the two-dimensional space spanned by $\mathbf{x}_1$, $\mathbf{x}_2$, and $\mathbf{x}_3$. Also, using the result of Example 2.18, we have $\mathbf{x}_3 = -\frac{1}{2}\mathbf{x}_2 - \frac{1}{2}\mathbf{x}_1$.

Assume that we are given a p-dimensional vector space which we denote as E_p, for which $\mathbf{x}_1, \mathbf{x}_2, \ldots, \mathbf{x}_p$ are chosen base vectors, $p > 1$. Then we might like to consider only all those vectors that can be expressed in terms of x_1 and x_2. But the vectors x_1 and x_2 also form the basis of a vector space that we call E_2. If $p = 2$, we note that E_p and E_2 coincide. We call E_2 a subspace of E_p, the concise meaning of which is defined next.

> *Definition:*   A subspace *of a vector space is a vector space such that any vector in the subspace is also in the original space. If* x_1, x_2, . . . , x_p *are the base vectors of the original space, any subset of these vectors forms the basis of a subspace; the* dimension *of the subspace is equal to the number of base vectors selected.*

> **EXAMPLE 2.20:**   The three vectors x_1, x_2, and x_3 are linearly independent and therefore form the basis of a three-dimensional vector space E_3:
>
> $$ x_1 = \begin{bmatrix} 1 \\ 2 \\ 1 \\ 0 \end{bmatrix}; \qquad x_2 = \begin{bmatrix} 1 \\ 0 \\ 0 \\ 0 \end{bmatrix}; \qquad x_3 = \begin{bmatrix} 0 \\ -1 \\ 0 \\ 1 \end{bmatrix} \tag{a} $$
>
> Identify some possible two-dimensional subspaces of E_3.
>
> Using the base vectors in (a), a two-dimensional subspace is formed by any two of the three vectors; e.g., x_1 and x_2 represent a basis for a two-dimensional subspace; x_1 and x_3 are the basis for another two-dimensional subspace; and so on. Indeed, any two linearly independent vectors in E_3 from the basis of a two-dimensional subspace, and it follows that there are an infinite number of two-dimensional subspaces in E_3.

Having considered the concepts of a vector space, we may now recognize that the columns of any rectangular matrix A also span a vector space. We call this space the column space of A. Similarly, the rows of a matrix span a vector space, which we call the row space of A. Conversely, we may assemble any q vectors of order n into a matrix A of order $n \times q$. The number of linearly independent vectors used is equal to the dimension of the column space of A. For example, the three vectors in Example 2.20 form the matrix

$$ A = \begin{bmatrix} 1 & 1 & 0 \\ 2 & 0 & -1 \\ 1 & 0 & 0 \\ 0 & 0 & 1 \end{bmatrix} \tag{2.45} $$

Assume that we are given a matrix A and that we need to calculate the dimension of the column space of A. In other words, we want to evaluate how many columns in A are linearly independent. The number of linearly independent columns in A is neither increased nor decreased by taking any linear combinations of them. Therefore, in order to identify the column space of A, we may try to transform the matrix, by linearly combining its columns, to obtain unit vectors e_i. Because unit vectors e_i with distinct i are linearly independent, the dimension of the column space of A is equal to the number of unit vectors that can be obtained. While frequently we are not able to actually obtain unit vectors e_i (see Example 2.21), the process followed in the transformation of A will always lead to a form that displays the dimension of the column space.

EXAMPLE 2.21: Calculate the dimension of the column space of the matrix **A** formed by the vectors x_1, x_2, and x_3 considered in Example 2.20.

The matrix considered is

$$
A = \begin{bmatrix} 1 & 1 & 0 \\ 2 & 0 & -1 \\ 1 & 0 & 0 \\ 0 & 0 & 1 \end{bmatrix}
$$

Writing the second and third columns as the first and second columns, respectively, we obtain

$$
A_1 = \begin{bmatrix} 1 & 0 & 1 \\ 0 & -1 & 2 \\ 0 & 0 & 1 \\ 0 & 1 & 0 \end{bmatrix}
$$

Subtracting the first column from the third column, adding twice the second column to the third column, and finally multiplying the second column by (-1), we obtain

$$
A_2 = \begin{bmatrix} 1 & 0 & 0 \\ 0 & 1 & 0 \\ 0 & 0 & 1 \\ 0 & -1 & 2 \end{bmatrix}
$$

But we have now reduced the matrix to a form where we can identify that the three columns are linearly independent; i.e., the columns are linearly independent because the first three elements in the vectors are the columns of the identity matrix of order 3. However, since we obtained A_2 from **A** by interchanging and linearly combining the original columns of **A** and thus in the solution process have not increased the space spanned by the columns of the matrix, we find that the dimension of the column space of **A** is 3.

In the above presentation we linearly combined the vectors $x_1, \ldots, x_q$, which were the columns of **A**, in order to identify whether they were linearly independent. Alternatively, to find the dimension of the space spanned by a set of vectors $x_1, x_2, \ldots, x_q$, we could use the definition of vector linear independence in (2.43) and consider the set of simultaneous homogeneous equations

$$
\alpha_1 x_1 + \alpha_2 x_2 + \cdots \alpha_q x_q = 0 \tag{2.46}
$$

which is, in matrix form,

$$
A\alpha = 0 \tag{2.47}
$$

where α is a vector with elements $\alpha_1, \ldots \alpha_q$, and the columns of **A** are the vectors x_1, $x_2, \ldots, x_q$. The solution for the unknowns $\alpha_1, \ldots, \alpha_q$ is not changed by linearly combining or multiplying any of the rows in the matrix **A**. Therefore, we may try to reduce **A** by multiplying and combining its rows into a matrix in which the columns consist only of unit vectors. This reduced matrix is called the *row-echelon form* of **A**. The number of unit column vectors in the row-echelon form of **A** is equal to the dimension of the column space of **A** and, from the preceding discussion, is also equal to the dimension of the row space of **A**. It follows that the dimension of the column space of **A** is equal to the dimension of the row space of **A**. In other words, the number of linearly independent columns in **A** is equal to the number of linearly independent rows in **A**. This result is summarized in the definition of the rank of **A** and the definition of the null space (or kernel) of **A**.

Definition: *The* rank *of a matrix* **A** *is equal to the dimension of the column space and equal to the dimension of the row space of* **A**.

Definition: *The space of vectors* $\boldsymbol{\alpha}$ *such that* $\mathbf{A}\boldsymbol{\alpha} = \mathbf{0}$ *is the* null space *(or* kernel*) of* **A**.

EXAMPLE 2.22:   Consider the following three vectors:

$$
\mathbf{x}_1 = \begin{bmatrix} 1 \\ 2 \\ 1 \\ 3 \\ 4 \\ 3 \end{bmatrix}; \quad
\mathbf{x}_2 = \begin{bmatrix} 3 \\ 1 \\ -2 \\ 4 \\ 2 \\ -1 \end{bmatrix}; \quad
\mathbf{x}_3 = \begin{bmatrix} 2 \\ 3 \\ 1 \\ 5 \\ 6 \\ 4 \end{bmatrix}
$$

Use these vectors as the columns of a matrix **A** and reduce the matrix to row-echelon form. We have

$$
\mathbf{A} = \begin{bmatrix} 1 & 3 & 2 \\ 2 & 1 & 3 \\ 1 & -2 & 1 \\ 3 & 4 & 5 \\ 4 & 2 & 6 \\ 3 & -1 & 4 \end{bmatrix}
$$

Subtracting multiples of the first row from the rows below it in order to obtain the unit vector $\mathbf{e}_1$ in the first column, we obtain

$$
\mathbf{A}_1 = \begin{bmatrix} 1 & 3 & 2 \\ 0 & -5 & -1 \\ 0 & -5 & -1 \\ 0 & -5 & -1 \\ 0 & -10 & -2 \\ 0 & -10 & -2 \end{bmatrix}
$$

Dividing the second row by (-5) and then subtracting multiples of it from the other rows in order to reduce the second column to the unit vector $\mathbf{e}_2$, we obtain

$$
\mathbf{A}_2 = \begin{bmatrix} 1 & 0 & \frac{7}{5} \\ 0 & 1 & \frac{1}{5} \\ 0 & 0 & 0 \\ 0 & 0 & 0 \\ 0 & 0 & 0 \\ 0 & 0 & 0 \end{bmatrix}
$$

Hence we can give the following equivalent statements:

1. The solution to $\mathbf{A}\boldsymbol{\alpha} = \mathbf{0}$ is

$$\alpha_1 = -\tfrac{7}{5}\,\alpha_3$$
$$\alpha_2 = -\tfrac{1}{5}\,\alpha_3$$

2. The three vectors $\mathbf{x}_1$, $\mathbf{x}_2$, and $\mathbf{x}_3$ are linearly dependent. They form a two-dimensional vector space. The vectors $\mathbf{x}_1$ and $\mathbf{x}_2$ are linearly independent, and they form a basis of the two-dimensional space in which $\mathbf{x}_1$, $\mathbf{x}_2$, and $\mathbf{x}_3$ lie.
3. The rank of $\mathbf{A}$ is 2.
4. The dimension of the column space of $\mathbf{A}$ is 2.
5. The dimension of the row space of $\mathbf{A}$ is 2.
6. The null space (kernel) of $\mathbf{A}$ has dimension 1 and a basis is the vector

$$\begin{bmatrix} -\tfrac{7}{5} \\ -\tfrac{1}{5} \\ 1 \end{bmatrix}$$

Note that the rank of $\mathbf{A}^T$ is also 2, but that the kernel of $\mathbf{A}^T$ has dimension 4.

2.4 DEFINITION OF TENSORS

In engineering analysis, the concept of tensors and their matrix representations can be important. We shall limit our discussion to tensors in three-dimensional space and primarily be concerned with the representation of tensors in rectangular Cartesian coordinate frames.

Let the Cartesian coordinate frame be defined by the unit base vectors $\mathbf{e}_i$ (see Fig. 2.3). A vector $\mathbf{u}$ in this frame is given by

$$\mathbf{u} = \sum_{i=1}^{3} u_i \mathbf{e}_i \tag{2.48}$$

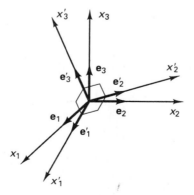

Figure 2.3 Cartesian coordinate systems for definition of tensors

where the u_i are the components of the vector. In tensor algebra it is convenient for the purpose of a compact notation to omit the summation sign in (2.48); i.e., instead of (2.48) we simply write

$$\mathbf{u} = u_i\mathbf{e}_i \tag{2.49}$$

where the summation on the repeated index i is implied (here $i = 1, 2, 3$). Since i could be replaced by any other subscript without changing the result (e.g., k or j), it is also called a *dummy index* or a *free index*. This convention is referred to as the summation convention of indicial notation (or the Einstein convention) and is used with efficiency to express in a compact manner relations involving tensor quantities (see Chapter 6 where we use this notation extensively).

Considering vectors in three-dimensional space, vector algebra is employed effectively.

The scalar (or *dot*) *product* of the vectors $\mathbf{u}$ and $\mathbf{v}$, denoted by $\mathbf{u} \cdot \mathbf{v}$ is given by

$$\mathbf{u} \cdot \mathbf{v} = |\mathbf{u}|\,|\mathbf{v}|\cos\theta \tag{2.50}$$

where $|\mathbf{u}|$ is equal to the length of the vector $\mathbf{u}$, $|\mathbf{u}| = \sqrt{u_iu_i}$. The dot product can be evaluated using the components of the vectors,

$$\mathbf{u} \cdot \mathbf{v} = u_iv_i \tag{2.51}$$

The *vector* (or *cross*) *product* of the vectors $\mathbf{u}$ and $\mathbf{v}$ produces a new vector $\mathbf{w} = \mathbf{u} \times \mathbf{v}$

$$\mathbf{w} = \det \begin{bmatrix} \mathbf{e}_1 & \mathbf{e}_2 & \mathbf{e}_3 \\ u_1 & u_2 & u_3 \\ v_1 & v_2 & v_3 \end{bmatrix} \tag{2.52}$$

Figure 2.4 illustrates the vector operations performed in (2.50) and (2.52). We should note that the direction of the vector $\mathbf{w}$ is obtained by the right-hand rule; i.e., the right-hand thumb points in the direction of $\mathbf{w}$ when the fingers curl from $\mathbf{u}$ to $\mathbf{v}$.

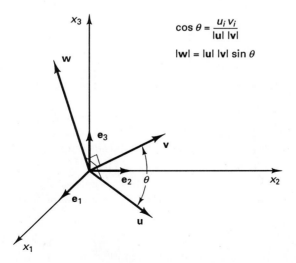

$$\cos\theta = \frac{u_i v_i}{|u|\,|v|}$$

$$|w| = |u|\,|v|\sin\theta$$

Figure 2.4   Vectors used in products

These vector algebra procedures are frequently employed in finite element analysis to evaluate angles between two given directions and to establish the direction perpendicular to a given plane.

EXAMPLE 2.23: Assume that the vectors **u** and **v** in Fig. 2.4 are

$$\mathbf{u} = \begin{bmatrix} 3 \\ 3 \\ 0 \end{bmatrix}; \qquad \mathbf{v} = \begin{bmatrix} 0 \\ 2 \\ 2 \end{bmatrix}$$

Calculate the angle between these vectors and establish a vector perpendicular to the plane that is defined by these vectors.

Here we have

$$|\mathbf{u}| = 3\sqrt{2}$$
$$|\mathbf{v}| = 2\sqrt{2}$$

Hence
$$\cos \theta = \tfrac{1}{2}$$

and $\theta = 60°$.

A vector perpendicular to the plane defined by **u** and **v** is given by

$$\mathbf{w} = \det \begin{bmatrix} \mathbf{e}_1 & \mathbf{e}_2 & \mathbf{e}_3 \\ 3 & 3 & 0 \\ 0 & 2 & 2 \end{bmatrix}$$

hence
$$\mathbf{w} = \begin{bmatrix} 6 \\ -6 \\ 6 \end{bmatrix}$$

Using $|\mathbf{w}| = \sqrt{w_i w_i}$, we obtain

$$|\mathbf{w}| = 6\sqrt{3}$$

which is also equal to the value obtained using the formula given in Fig. 2.4.

Although not specifically stated, the typical vector considered in (2.48) is a tensor. Let us now formally define what we mean by a tensor.

For this purpose, we consider in addition to the *unprimed Cartesian coordinate frame* a *primed Cartesian coordinate frame* with base vectors $\mathbf{e}_j'$ which spans the same space as the unprimed frame (see Fig. 2.3).

An entity is called a scalar, a vector (i.e., a tensor of first order or rank 1), or a tensor (i.e., a tensor of higher order or rank) depending on how the components of the entity are defined in the unprimed frame (coordinate system) and how these components transform to the primed frame.

Definition: An entity is called a scalar *if it has only a single component ϕ in the coordinates x_i measured along $\mathbf{e}_i$ and this component does not change when expressed in the coordinates x_i' measured along $\mathbf{e}_i'$:*

$$\phi(x_1, x_2, x_3) = \phi'(x_1', x_2', x_3') \tag{2.53}$$

A scalar is also a tensor of order 0. As an example, temperature at a point is a scalar.

Definition: *An entity is called a* vector *or tensor of first order if it has three components ξ_i in the unprimed frame and three components ξ_i' in the primed frame, and if these components are related by the characteristic law (using the summation convention)*

$$\xi_i' = p_{ik}\xi_k \tag{2.54}$$

where $$p_{ik} = \cos(\mathbf{e}_i', \mathbf{e}_k) \tag{2.55}$$

The relation (2.54) can also be written in matrix form as

$$\boldsymbol{\xi}' = \mathbf{P}\boldsymbol{\xi} \tag{2.56}$$

where $\boldsymbol{\xi}'$, $\mathbf{P}$, and $\boldsymbol{\xi}$ contain the elements of (2.54).

The transformation in (2.54) corresponds to a change of basis in the representation of the vector. To arrive at (2.54) we recognize that the same vector is considered in the two different bases; hence we have

$$\xi_j'\mathbf{e}_j' = \xi_k\mathbf{e}_k \tag{2.57}$$

Using the fact that the base vectors in each coordinate frame are orthogonal to each other and are of unit length, we can take the dot products [see (2.50)] on both sides of (2.57) with $\mathbf{e}_i'$ and obtain (2.54). Of course, analogously we could also take the dot product on both sides with $\mathbf{e}_m$ to obtain the inverse transformation

$$\xi_m = \cos(\mathbf{e}_m, \mathbf{e}_j')\xi_j' \tag{2.58}$$

or in matrix form, $$\boldsymbol{\xi} = \mathbf{P}^T\boldsymbol{\xi}' \tag{2.59}$$

Hence we note that $\mathbf{P}^{-1} = \mathbf{P}^T$, and this leads us to the following definition.

Definition: *A matrix* $\mathbf{Q}$ *is an* orthogonal matrix *if* $\mathbf{Q}^T\mathbf{Q} = \mathbf{Q}\mathbf{Q}^T = \mathbf{I}$. *Therefore, for an orthogonal matrix, we have* $\mathbf{Q}^{-1} = \mathbf{Q}^T$.

Hence the matrix $\mathbf{P}$ defined in (2.55) and (2.56) is an orthogonal matrix, and because the elements of $\mathbf{P}$ produce a rotation, we also refer to $\mathbf{P}$ as a rotation matrix.

We demonstrate the preceding discussion in the following example.

EXAMPLE 2.24:   The components of a force expressed in the unprimed coordinate system shown in Fig. E2.24 are

$$\mathbf{R} = \begin{bmatrix} 0 \\ 1 \\ \sqrt{3} \end{bmatrix}$$

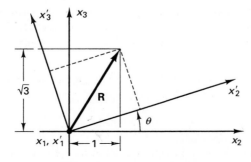

Figure E2.24   Representation of a force in different coordinate systems

Evaluate the components of the force in the primed coordinate system in Fig. E2.24.

Here we have, using (2.56),

$$\mathbf{P} = \begin{bmatrix} 1 & 0 & 0 \\ 0 & \cos\theta & \sin\theta \\ 0 & -\sin\theta & \cos\theta \end{bmatrix}$$

and then

$$\mathbf{R'} = \mathbf{PR} \tag{a}$$

where $\mathbf{R'}$ gives the components of the force in the primed coordinate system. As a check, if we use $\theta = -30°$ we obtain, using (a),

$$\mathbf{R'} = \begin{bmatrix} 0 \\ 0 \\ 2 \end{bmatrix}$$

which is correct because the $\mathbf{e'_3}$-vector is now aligned with the force vector.

To define a second-order tensor we build on the definition given in (2.54) for a tensor of rank 1.

Definition: An entity is called a second-order tensor *if it has nine components t_{ij}, $i = 1, 2, 3$, and $j = 1, 2, 3$, in the unprimed frame and nine components t'_{ij} in the primed frame and if these components are related by the characteristic law*

$$t'_{ij} = p_{ik}p_{jl}t_{kl} \tag{2.60}$$

As in the case of the definition of a first-order tensor, the relation in (2.60) represents a change of basis in the representation of the entity (see Example 2.25) and we can formally derive (2.60) in essentially the same way as we derived (2.54). That is, if we write the same tensor of rank 2 in the two different bases, we obtain

$$t'_{mn}\mathbf{e'_m}\mathbf{e'_n} = t_{kl}\mathbf{e_k}\mathbf{e_l} \tag{2.61}$$

where clearly in the tensor representation the first base vector goes with the first subscript (the row in the matrix representation) and the second base vector goes with the second subscript (the column in the matrix representation). The open product[1] or tensor product $\mathbf{e_k}\mathbf{e_l}$ is called a *dyad* and a linear combination of dyads as used in (2.61) is called a *dyadic*, (see, for example, L. E. Malvern [A]).

Taking the dot product from the right in (2.61), first with $\mathbf{e'_j}$ and then with $\mathbf{e'_i}$, we obtain

$$t'_{mn}\mathbf{e'_m}\delta_{nj} = t_{kl}\mathbf{e_k}(\mathbf{e_l} \cdot \mathbf{e'_j})$$

$$t'_{mn}\delta_{mi}\delta_{nj} = t_{kl}(\mathbf{e_k} \cdot \mathbf{e'_i})(\mathbf{e_l} \cdot \mathbf{e'_j}) \tag{2.62}$$

or

$$t'_{ij} = t_{kl}p_{ik}p_{jl}$$

---

[1] The open product or tensor product of two vectors denoted as $\mathbf{ab}$ is defined by the requirement that

$$(\mathbf{ab}) \cdot \mathbf{v} = \mathbf{a}(\mathbf{b} \cdot \mathbf{v})$$

for all vectors $\mathbf{v}$. Some writers use the notation $\mathbf{a} \otimes \mathbf{b}$ instead of $\mathbf{ab}$.

Here δ_{ij} is the Kronecker delta ($\delta_{ij} = 1$ for $i = j$, and $\delta_{ij} = 0$ for $i \neq j$). This transformation may also be written in matrix form as

$$\mathbf{t}' = \mathbf{P t P}^T \tag{2.63}$$

where the (i, k)th element in $\mathbf{P}$ is given by p_{ik}. Of course, the inverse transformation also holds:

$$\mathbf{t} = \mathbf{P}^T \mathbf{t}' \mathbf{P} \tag{2.64}$$

This relation can be derived using (2.61) and [similar to the operation in (2.62)] taking the dot product from the right with $\mathbf{e}_j$ and then $\mathbf{e}_i$, or simply using (2.63) and the fact that $\mathbf{P}$ is an orthogonal matrix.

In the preceding definitions we assumed that all indices vary from 1 to 3; special cases are when the indices vary from 1 to n, with $n < 3$. In engineering analysis we frequently deal only with two-dimensional conditions, in which case $n = 2$.

EXAMPLE 2.25:   Stress is a tensor of rank 2. Assume that the stress at a point measured in an unprimed coordinate frame in a plane stress analysis is (not including the third row and column of zeros)

$$\tau = \begin{bmatrix} 1 & -1 \\ -1 & 1 \end{bmatrix}$$

Establish the components of the tensor in the primed coordinate system shown in Fig. E2.25.

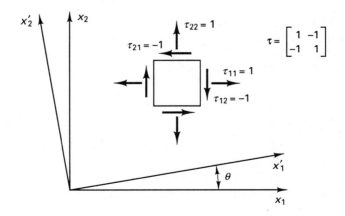

Figure E2.25   Representation of a stress tensor in different coordinate systems

Here we use the rotation matrix $\mathbf{P}$ as in Example 2.24, and the transformation in (2.63) is

$$\tau' = \mathbf{P} \tau \mathbf{P}^T; \qquad \mathbf{P} = \begin{bmatrix} \cos\theta & \sin\theta \\ -\sin\theta & \cos\theta \end{bmatrix}$$

Assume that we are interested in the specific case when $\theta = 45°$. In this case we have

$$\tau' = \frac{1}{2} \begin{bmatrix} 1 & 1 \\ -1 & 1 \end{bmatrix} \begin{bmatrix} 1 & -1 \\ -1 & 1 \end{bmatrix} \begin{bmatrix} 1 & -1 \\ 1 & 1 \end{bmatrix} = \begin{bmatrix} 0 & 0 \\ 0 & 2 \end{bmatrix}$$

and we recognize that in this coordinate system the off-diagonal elements of the tensor (shear components) are zero. The primed axes are called the principal coordinate axes, and the diagonal elements $\tau'_{11} = 0$ and $\tau'_{22} = 2$ are the principal values of the tensor. We will see in Section 2.5 that the principal tensor values are the eigenvalues of the tensor and that the primed axes define the corresponding eigenvectors.

The previous discussion can be directly expanded to also define tensors of higher order than 2. In engineering analysis we are, in particular, interested in the constitutive tensors that relate the components of a stress tensor to the components of a strain tensor (see, for example, Sections 4.2.3 and 6.6)

$$\tau_{ij} = C_{ijkl} \epsilon_{kl} \tag{2.65}$$

The stress and strain tensors are both of rank 2, and the constitutive tensor with components C_{ijkl} is of rank 4 because its components transform in the following way:

$$C'_{ijkl} = p_{im}p_{jn}p_{kr}p_{ls}C_{mnrs} \tag{2.66}$$

In the above discussion we used the orthogonal base vectors $\mathbf{e}_i$ and $\mathbf{e}'_j$ of two Cartesian systems. However, we can also express the tensor in components of a basis of nonorthogonal base vectors. It is particularly important in shell analysis to be able to use such base vectors (see Sections 5.4.2 and 6.5.2).

In continuum mechanics it is common practice to use what is called a covariant basis with the covariant base vectors $\mathbf{g}_i$, $i = 1, 2, 3$, and what is called a contravariant basis with the contravariant base vectors, $\mathbf{g}^j$, $j = 1, 2, 3$; see Fig. 2.5 for an example. The covariant and contravariant base vectors are in general not of unit length and satisfy the relationships

$$\mathbf{g}_i \cdot \mathbf{g}^j = \delta_i^j \tag{2.67}$$

where δ_i^j is the (mixed) Kronecker delta ($\delta_i^j = 1$ for $i = j$, and $\delta_i^j = 0$ for $i \neq j$).

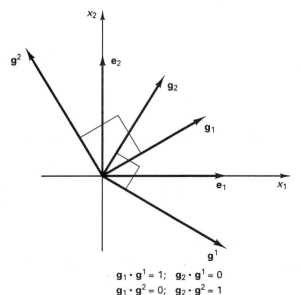

$$\mathbf{g}_1 \cdot \mathbf{g}^1 = 1; \quad \mathbf{g}_2 \cdot \mathbf{g}^1 = 0$$
$$\mathbf{g}_1 \cdot \mathbf{g}^2 = 0; \quad \mathbf{g}_2 \cdot \mathbf{g}^2 = 1$$

Figure 2.5 Example of covariant and contravariant base vectors, $n = 2$ (plotted in Cartesian reference frame)

Hence the contravariant base vectors are orthogonal to the covariant base vectors. Furthermore, we have

$$\mathbf{g}_i = g_{ij}\mathbf{g}^j \tag{2.68}$$

with

$$g_{ij} = \mathbf{g}_i \cdot \mathbf{g}_j \tag{2.69}$$

and

$$\mathbf{g}^i = g^{ij}\mathbf{g}_j \tag{2.70}$$

with

$$g^{ij} = \mathbf{g}^i \cdot \mathbf{g}^j \tag{2.71}$$

where g_{ij} and g^{ij} are, respectively, the covariant and contravariant components of the metric tensor.

To prove that (2.68) holds, we tentatively let

$$\mathbf{g}_i = a_{ik}\mathbf{g}^k \tag{2.72}$$

with the a_{ik} unknown elements. Taking the dot product on both sides with $\mathbf{g}_j$, we obtain

$$\begin{aligned} \mathbf{g}_i \cdot \mathbf{g}_j &= a_{ik}\mathbf{g}^k \cdot \mathbf{g}_j \\ &= a_{ik}\delta_j^k \\ &= a_{ij} \end{aligned} \tag{2.73}$$

Of course, (2.70) can be proven in a similar way (see Exercise 2.11).

Frequently, in practice, the covariant basis is conveniently selected and then the contravariant basis is given by the above relationships.

Assume that we need to use a basis with nonorthogonal base vectors. The elegance of then using both the covariant and contravariant base vectors is seen if we simply consider the work done by a force $\mathbf{R}$ going through a displacement $\mathbf{u}$, given by $\mathbf{R} \cdot \mathbf{u}$. If we express both $\mathbf{R}$ and $\mathbf{u}$ in the covariant basis given by the base vectors $\mathbf{g}_i$, we have

$$\begin{aligned} \mathbf{R} \cdot \mathbf{u} &= (R^1\mathbf{g}_1 + R^2\mathbf{g}_2 + R^3\mathbf{g}_3) \cdot (u^1\mathbf{g}_1 + u^2\mathbf{g}_2 + u^3\mathbf{g}_3) \\ &= R^i u^j g_{ij} \end{aligned} \tag{2.74}$$

On the other hand, if we express only $\mathbf{R}$ in the covariant basis, but $\mathbf{u}$ in the contravariant basis, given by the base vectors $\mathbf{g}^j$, we have

$$\begin{aligned} \mathbf{R} \cdot \mathbf{u} &= (R^1\mathbf{g}_1 + R^2\mathbf{g}_2 + R^3\mathbf{g}_3) \cdot (u_1\mathbf{g}^1 + u_2\mathbf{g}^2 + u_3\mathbf{g}^3) = R^i u_j \delta_i^j \\ &= R^i u_i \end{aligned} \tag{2.75}$$

which is a much simpler expression. Fig. 2.6 gives a geometrical representation of this evaluation in a two-dimensional case.

We shall use covariant and contravariant bases in the formulation of plate and shell elements. Since we are concerned with the product of stress and strain (e.g., in the principle of virtual work), we express the stress tensor in contravariant components [as for the force $\mathbf{R}$ in (2.75)],

$$\boldsymbol{\tau} = \tilde{\tau}^{mn}\mathbf{g}_m\mathbf{g}_n \tag{2.76}$$

and the strain tensor in covariant components [as for the displacement in (2.75)],

$$\boldsymbol{\epsilon} = \tilde{\epsilon}_{ij}\mathbf{g}^i\mathbf{g}^j \tag{2.77}$$

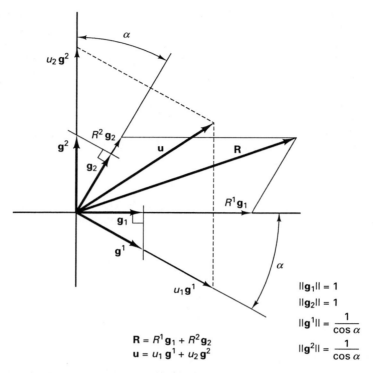

$$\mathbf{R} = R^1\mathbf{g}_1 + R^2\mathbf{g}_2$$
$$\mathbf{u} = u_1\,\mathbf{g}^1 + u_2\,\mathbf{g}^2$$

$$\|\mathbf{g}_1\| = 1$$
$$\|\mathbf{g}_2\| = 1$$
$$\|\mathbf{g}^1\| = \frac{1}{\cos\alpha}$$
$$\|\mathbf{g}^2\| = \frac{1}{\cos\alpha}$$

Figure 2.6   Geometrical representation of **R** and **u** using covariant and contravariant bases

Using these dyadics we obtain for the product of stress and strain

$$
\begin{aligned}
W &= (\tilde{\tau}^{mn}\mathbf{g}_m\mathbf{g}_n)\cdot(\tilde{\epsilon}_{ij}\mathbf{g}^i\mathbf{g}^j) \\
&= \tilde{\tau}^{mn}\tilde{\epsilon}_{ij}\delta_m^i\,\delta_n^j \\
&= \tilde{\tau}^{ij}\tilde{\epsilon}_{ij}
\end{aligned}
\tag{2.78}
$$

This expression for W is as simple as the result in (2.75). Note that here we used the convention—designed such that its use leads to correct results[2]—that in the evaluation of the dot product the first base vector of the first tensor multiplies the first base vector of the second tensor, and so on.

Instead of writing the product in summation form of products of components, we shall also simply use the notation

$$W = \boldsymbol{\tau}\cdot\boldsymbol{\epsilon} \tag{2.79}$$

and simply imply the result in (2.78), in whichever coordinate system it may be obtained. The notation in (2.79) is, in essence, a simple extension of the notation of a dot product between two vectors. Of course, when considering $\mathbf{u}\cdot\mathbf{v}$, a unique result is implied, but this result can be obtained in different ways, as given in (2.74) and (2.75). Similarly, when

---

[2] Namely, consider $(\mathbf{ab})\cdot(\mathbf{cd})$. Let $\mathbf{A} = \mathbf{ab}$, $\mathbf{B} = \mathbf{cd}$; then $\mathbf{A}\cdot\mathbf{B} = A_{ij}B_{ij} = a_ib_jc_id_j = (a_ic_i)(b_jd_j) = (\mathbf{a}\cdot\mathbf{c})(\mathbf{b}\cdot\mathbf{d})$.

writing (2.79), the unique result of W is implied, and this result may also be obtained in different ways, but the use of $\tilde{\tau}^{ij}$ and $\tilde{\epsilon}_{ij}$ can be effective (see Example 2.26).

Hence we note that the covariant and contravariant bases are used in the same way as Cartesian bases but provide much more generality in the representation and use of tensors. Consider the following examples.

EXAMPLE 2.26:   Assume that the stress and strain tensor components at a point in a continuum corresponding to a Cartesian basis are τ_{ij} and ϵ_{ij} and that the strain energy, per unit volume, is given by $U = \frac{1}{2} \tau_{ij} \epsilon_{ij}$. Assume also that a basis of covariant base vectors $\mathbf{g}_i, i = 1, 2, 3$, is given. Show explicitly that the value of U is then also given by $\frac{1}{2} \tilde{\tau}^{mn} \tilde{\epsilon}_{mn}$.

Here we use

$$\tilde{\tau}^{mn} \mathbf{g}_m \mathbf{g}_n = \tau_{ij} \mathbf{e}_i \mathbf{e}_j \tag{a}$$

and

$$\tilde{\epsilon}_{mn} \mathbf{g}^m \mathbf{g}^n = \epsilon_{ij} \mathbf{e}_i \mathbf{e}_j \tag{b}$$

But from (a) and (b) we obtain

$$\tau_{kl} = \tilde{\tau}^{mn} (\mathbf{g}_m \cdot \mathbf{e}_k)(\mathbf{g}_n \cdot \mathbf{e}_l) \qquad \text{sum on } m \text{ and } n$$

and

$$\epsilon_{kl} = \tilde{\epsilon}_{mn} (\mathbf{g}^m \cdot \mathbf{e}_k)(\mathbf{g}^n \cdot \mathbf{e}_l) \qquad \text{sum on } m \text{ and } n$$

Now since

$$(\mathbf{g}_i \cdot \mathbf{e}_j)(\mathbf{g}^i \cdot \mathbf{e}_j) = 1 \qquad \text{sum on } j$$

we also have

$$U = \frac{1}{2} \tilde{\tau}^{mn} \tilde{\epsilon}_{mn}$$

EXAMPLE 2.27:   The Cartesian components τ_{ij} of the stress tensor $\tau_{ij} \mathbf{e}_i \mathbf{e}_j$ are $\tau_{11} = 100$, $\tau_{12} = 60$, $\tau_{22} = 200$, and the components ϵ_{ij} of the strain tensor $\epsilon_{ij} \mathbf{e}_i \mathbf{e}_j$ are $\epsilon_{11} = 0.001$, $\epsilon_{12} = 0.002$, $\epsilon_{22} = 0.003$.

Assume that the stress and strain tensors are to be expressed in terms of covariant strain components and contravariant stress components with

$$\mathbf{g}_1 = \begin{bmatrix} 1 \\ 0 \end{bmatrix}; \qquad \mathbf{g}_2 = \begin{bmatrix} \dfrac{1}{\sqrt{2}} \\ \dfrac{1}{\sqrt{2}} \end{bmatrix}$$

Calculate these components and, using these components, evaluate the product $\frac{1}{2} \tau_{ij} \epsilon_{ij}$.

Here we have, using (2.67),

$$\mathbf{g}^1 = \begin{bmatrix} 1 \\ -1 \end{bmatrix}; \qquad \mathbf{g}^2 = \begin{bmatrix} 0 \\ \sqrt{2} \end{bmatrix}$$

To evaluate $\tilde{\tau}^{ij}$ we use

$$\tilde{\tau}^{ij} \mathbf{g}_i \mathbf{g}_j = \tau_{mn} \mathbf{e}_m \mathbf{e}_n$$

so that

$$\tilde{\tau}^{ij} = \tau_{mn} (\mathbf{e}_m \cdot \mathbf{g}^i)(\mathbf{e}_n \cdot \mathbf{g}^j)$$

Therefore, the contravariant stress components are

$$\tilde{\tau}^{11} = 180; \qquad \tilde{\tau}^{12} = \tilde{\tau}^{21} = -140\sqrt{2}; \qquad \tilde{\tau}^{22} = 400$$

Similarly,

$$\tilde{\epsilon}_{ij} \mathbf{g}^i \mathbf{g}^j = \epsilon_{mn} \mathbf{e}_m \mathbf{e}_n$$

$$\tilde{\epsilon}_{ij} = \epsilon_{mn} (\mathbf{e}_m \cdot \mathbf{g}_i)(\mathbf{e}_n \cdot \mathbf{g}_j)$$

and the covariant strain components are

$$\tilde{\epsilon}_{11} = \frac{1}{1000}; \qquad \tilde{\epsilon}_{12} = \tilde{\epsilon}_{21} = \frac{3}{1000\sqrt{2}}; \qquad \tilde{\epsilon}_{22} = \frac{4}{1000}$$

Then we have

$$\tfrac{1}{2}\tilde{\tau}^{ij}\tilde{\epsilon}_{ij} = \tfrac{1}{2000}(180 + 1600 - 840) = 0.47$$

This value is of course also equal to $\tfrac{1}{2}\tau_{ij}\epsilon_{ij}$.

EXAMPLE 2.28:   The Green-Lagrange strain tensor can be defined as

$$\epsilon = \tilde{\epsilon}_{ij}\mathbf{g}^i\mathbf{g}^j$$

with the components

$$\tilde{\epsilon}_{ij} = \tfrac{1}{2}(^1\mathbf{g}_i \cdot {}^1\mathbf{g}_j - {}^0\mathbf{g}_i \cdot {}^0\mathbf{g}_j) \tag{a}$$

where

$$^0\mathbf{g}_i = \frac{\partial \mathbf{x}}{\partial r_i}; \qquad {}^1\mathbf{g}_i = \frac{\partial(\mathbf{x} + \mathbf{u})}{\partial r_i} \tag{b}$$

and $\mathbf{x}$ denotes the vector of Cartesian coordinates of the material point considered, $\mathbf{u}$ denotes the vector of displacements into the Cartesian directions, and the r_i are convected coordinates (in finite element analysis the r_i are the isoparametric coordinates; see Sections 5.3 and 5.4.2).

1. Establish the linear and nonlinear components (in displacements) of the strain tensor.
2. Assume that the convected coordinates are identical to the Cartesian coordinates. Show that the components in the Cartesian system can be written as

$$\epsilon_{ij} = \frac{1}{2}\left(\frac{\partial u_i}{\partial x_j} + \frac{\partial u_j}{\partial x_i} + \frac{\partial u_k}{\partial x_i}\frac{\partial u_k}{\partial x_j}\right) \tag{c}$$

To establish the linear and nonlinear components, we substitute from (b) into (a). Hence

$$\tilde{\epsilon}_{ij} = \frac{1}{2}\left[\left(\frac{\partial \mathbf{x}}{\partial r_i} + \frac{\partial \mathbf{u}}{\partial r_i}\right) \cdot \left(\frac{\partial \mathbf{x}}{\partial r_j} + \frac{\partial \mathbf{u}}{\partial r_j}\right) - \frac{\partial \mathbf{x}}{\partial r_i} \cdot \frac{\partial \mathbf{x}}{\partial r_j}\right]$$

The terms linear in displacements are therefore

$$\tilde{\epsilon}_{ij}|_{\text{linear}} = \frac{1}{2}\left(\frac{\partial \mathbf{u}}{\partial r_i} \cdot \frac{\partial \mathbf{x}}{\partial r_j} + \frac{\partial \mathbf{x}}{\partial r_i} \cdot \frac{\partial \mathbf{u}}{\partial r_j}\right) \tag{d}$$

and the terms nonlinear in displacements are

$$\tilde{\epsilon}_{ij}|_{\text{nonlinear}} = \frac{1}{2}\left(\frac{\partial \mathbf{u}}{\partial r_i} \cdot \frac{\partial \mathbf{u}}{\partial r_j}\right) \tag{e}$$

If the convected coordinates are identical to the Cartesian coordinates, we have $r_i \equiv x_i$, $i = 1, 2, 3$, and $\partial x_i/\partial x_j = \delta_{ij}$. Therefore, (d) becomes

$$\epsilon_{ij}|_{\text{linear}} = \frac{1}{2}\left(\frac{\partial u_i}{\partial x_j} + \frac{\partial u_j}{\partial x_i}\right) \tag{f}$$

and (e) becomes

$$\epsilon_{ij}|_{\text{nonlinear}} = \frac{1}{2}\left(\frac{\partial u_k}{\partial x_i}\frac{\partial u_k}{\partial x_j}\right) \tag{g}$$

Adding the linear and nonlinear terms (f) and (g), we obtain (c).

The preceding discussion was only a very brief introduction to the definition and use of tensors. Our objective was merely to introduce the basic concepts of tensors so that we can work with them later (see Chapter 6). The most important point about tensors is that the components of a tensor are always represented in a chosen coordinate system and that these components differ when different coordinate systems are employed. It follows from the definition of tensors that if all components of a tensor vanish in one coordinate system, they vanish likewise in any other (admissible) coordinate system. Since the sum and difference of tensors of a given type are tensors of the same type, it also follows that if a tensor equation can be established in one coordinate system, then it must also hold in any other (admissible) coordinate system. This property detaches the fundamental physical relationships between tensors under consideration from the specific reference frame chosen and is the most important characteristic of tensors: *in the analysis of an engineering problem we are concerned with the physics of the problem, and the fundamental physical relationships between the variables involved must be independent of the specific coordinate system chosen;* otherwise, a simple change of the reference system would destroy these relationships, and they would have been merely fortuitous. As an example, consider a body subjected to a set of forces. If we can show using one coordinate system that the body is in equilibrium, then we have proven the physical fact that the body is in equilibrium, and this force equilibrium will hold in any other (admissible) coordinate system.

The preceding discussion also hinted at another important consideration in engineering analysis, namely, that for an effective analysis suitable coordinate systems should be chosen because the effort required to express and work with a physical relationship in one coordinate system can be a great deal less than when using another coordinate system. We will see in the discussion of the finite element method (see, for example, Section 4.2) that indeed one important ingredient for the effectiveness of a finite element analysis is the flexibility to choose different coordinate systems for different finite elements (domains) that together idealize the complete structure or continuum.

2.5 THE SYMMETRIC EIGENPROBLEM $\mathbf{A}v = \lambda v$

In the previous section we discussed how a change of basis can be performed. In finite element analysis we are frequently interested in a change of basis as applied to symmetric matrices that have been obtained from a variational formulation, and we shall assume in the discussion to follow that $\mathbf{A}$ is symmetric. For example, the matrix $\mathbf{A}$ may represent the stiffness matrix, mass matrix, or heat capacity matrix of an element assemblage.

There are various important applications (see Examples 2.34 to 2.36 and Chapter 9) in which for overall solution effectiveness a change of basis is performed using in the transformation matrix the eigenvectors of the eigenproblem

$$\mathbf{A}\mathbf{v} = \lambda\mathbf{v} \tag{2.80}$$

The problem in (2.80) is a *standard eigenproblem*. If the solution of (2.80) is considered in order to obtain eigenvalues and eigenvectors, the problem $\mathbf{A}\mathbf{v} = \lambda\mathbf{v}$ is referred to as an *eigenproblem*, whereas if only eigenvalues are to be calculated, $\mathbf{A}\mathbf{v} = \lambda\mathbf{v}$ is called an *eigenvalue problem*. The objective in this section is to discuss the various properties that pertain to the solutions of (2.80).

Let n be the order of the matrix $\mathbf{A}$. The first important point is that there exist n nontrivial solutions to (2.80). Here the word "nontrivial" means that $\mathbf{v}$ must not be a null vector for which (2.80) is always satisfied. The ith nontrivial solution is given by the *eigenvalue* λ_i and the corresponding *eigenvector* $\mathbf{v}_i$, for which we have

$$\mathbf{A}\mathbf{v}_i = \lambda_i\mathbf{v}_i \tag{2.81}$$

Therefore, each solution consists of an eigenpair, and we write the n solutions as $(\lambda_1, \mathbf{v}_1)$, $(\lambda_2, \mathbf{v}_2), \ldots, (\lambda_n, \mathbf{v}_n)$, where

$$\lambda_1 \leq \lambda_2 \leq \cdots \leq \lambda_n \tag{2.82}$$

We also call all n eigenvalues and eigenvectors the *eigensystem* of $\mathbf{A}$.

The proof that there must be n eigenvalues and corresponding eigenvectors can conveniently be obtained by writing (2.80) in the form

$$(\mathbf{A} - \lambda\mathbf{I})\mathbf{v} = \mathbf{0} \tag{2.83}$$

But these equations have a solution only if

$$\det (\mathbf{A} - \lambda\mathbf{I}) = 0 \tag{2.84}$$

Unfortunately, the necessity for (2.84) to hold can be explained only after the solution of simultaneous equations has been presented. For this reason we postpone until Section 10.2.2 a discussion of why (2.84) is indeed required.

Using (2.84), the eigenvalues of $\mathbf{A}$ are thus the roots of the polynomial

$$p(\lambda) = \det (\mathbf{A} - \lambda\mathbf{I}) \tag{2.85}$$

This polynomial is called the *characteristic polynomial* of $\mathbf{A}$. However, since the order of the polynomial is equal to the order of $\mathbf{A}$, we have n eigenvalues, and using (2.83) we obtain n corresponding eigenvectors. It may be noted that the vectors obtained from the solution of (2.83) are defined only within a scalar multiple.

EXAMPLE 2.29: Consider the matrix

$$\mathbf{A} = \begin{bmatrix} -1 & 2 \\ 2 & 2 \end{bmatrix}$$

Show that the matrix has two eigenvalues. Calculate the eigenvalues and eigenvectors.

The characteristic polynomial of $\mathbf{A}$ is

$$p(\lambda) = \det \begin{bmatrix} -1 - \lambda & 2 \\ 2 & 2 - \lambda \end{bmatrix}$$

Using the procedure given in Section 2.2 to calculate the determinant of a matrix (see Example 2.13), we obtain

$$p(\lambda) = (-1 - \lambda)(2 - \lambda) - (2)(2)$$

$$= \lambda^2 - \lambda - 6$$

$$= (\lambda + 2)(\lambda - 3)$$

The order of the polynomial is 2, and hence there are two eigenvalues. In fact, we have

$$\lambda_1 = -2; \quad \lambda_2 = 3$$

The corresponding eigenvectors are obtained by applying (2.83) at the eigenvalues. Thus we have for λ_1,

$$\begin{bmatrix} -1 - (-2) & 2 \\ 2 & 2 - (-2) \end{bmatrix}\begin{bmatrix} v_1 \\ v_2 \end{bmatrix} = \begin{bmatrix} 0 \\ 0 \end{bmatrix} \tag{a}$$

with the solution (within a scalar multiple)

$$\mathbf{v}_1 = \begin{bmatrix} 2 \\ -1 \end{bmatrix}$$

For λ_2, we have

$$\begin{bmatrix} -1 - 3 & 2 \\ 2 & 2 - 3 \end{bmatrix}\begin{bmatrix} v_1 \\ v_2 \end{bmatrix} = \begin{bmatrix} 0 \\ 0 \end{bmatrix} \tag{b}$$

with the solution (within a scalar multiple)

$$\mathbf{v}_2 = \begin{bmatrix} \frac{1}{2} \\ 1 \end{bmatrix}$$

A change of basis on the matrix $\mathbf{A}$ is performed by using

$$\mathbf{v} = \mathbf{P}\tilde{\mathbf{v}} \tag{2.86}$$

where $\mathbf{P}$ is an orthogonal matrix and $\tilde{\mathbf{v}}$ represents the solution vector in the new basis. Substituting into (2.80), we obtain

$$\tilde{\mathbf{A}}\tilde{\mathbf{v}} = \lambda\tilde{\mathbf{v}} \tag{2.87}$$

where

$$\tilde{\mathbf{A}} = \mathbf{P}^T\mathbf{AP} \tag{2.88}$$

and since $\mathbf{A}$ is a symmetric matrix, $\tilde{\mathbf{A}}$ is a symmetric matrix also. This transformation is called a *similarity transformation,* and because $\mathbf{P}$ is an orthogonal matrix, the transformation is called an *orthogonal similarity transformation.*

If $\mathbf{P}$ were not an orthogonal matrix, the result of the transformation would be

$$\tilde{\mathbf{A}}\tilde{\mathbf{v}} = \lambda\mathbf{B}\tilde{\mathbf{v}} \tag{2.89}$$

where

$$\tilde{\mathbf{A}} = \mathbf{P}^T\mathbf{AP}; \qquad \mathbf{B} = \mathbf{P}^T\mathbf{P} \tag{2.90}$$

The eigenproblem in (2.89) is called a *generalized eigenproblem.* However, since a generalized eigenproblem is more difficult to solve than a standard problem, the transformation to a generalized problem should be avoided. This is achieved by using an orthogonal matrix $\mathbf{P}$, which yields $\mathbf{B} = \mathbf{I}$.

In considering a change of basis, it should be noted that the problem $\tilde{\mathbf{A}}\tilde{\mathbf{v}} = \lambda\mathbf{B}\tilde{\mathbf{v}}$ in (2.89) has the same eigenvalues as the problem $\mathbf{Av} = \lambda\mathbf{v}$, whereas the eigenvectors are related as given in (2.86). To show that the eigenvalues are identical, we consider the characteristic polynomials.

For the problem in (2.89), we have

$$\tilde{p}(\lambda) = \det(\mathbf{P}^T\mathbf{AP} - \lambda\mathbf{P}^T\mathbf{P}) \tag{2.91}$$

which can be written as

$$\tilde{p}(\lambda) = \det\mathbf{P}^T \det(\mathbf{A} - \lambda\mathbf{I}) \det\mathbf{P} \tag{2.92}$$

and therefore,

$$\tilde{p}(\lambda) = \det\mathbf{P}^T \det\mathbf{P}\, p(\lambda) \tag{2.93}$$

where $p(\lambda)$ is given in (2.85). Hence the characteristic polynomials of the problems $\mathbf{A}\mathbf{v} = \lambda\mathbf{v}$ and $\tilde{\mathbf{A}}\tilde{\mathbf{v}} = \lambda\mathbf{B}\tilde{\mathbf{v}}$ are the same within a multiplier. This means that the eigenvalues of the two problems are identical.

So far we have shown that there are n eigenvalues and corresponding eigenvectors, but we have not yet discussed the properties of the eigenvalues and vectors.

A first observation is that the eigenvalues are real. Consider the ith eigenpair $(\lambda_i, \mathbf{v}_i)$, for which we have

$$\mathbf{A}\mathbf{v}_i = \lambda_i\mathbf{v}_i \tag{2.94}$$

Assume that $\mathbf{v}_i$ and λ_i are complex, which includes the case of real eigenvalues, and let the elements of $\bar{\mathbf{v}}_i$ and $\bar{\lambda}_i$ be the complex conjugates of the elements of $\mathbf{v}_i$ and λ_i. Then premultiplying (2.94) by $\bar{\mathbf{v}}_i^T$, we obtain

$$\bar{\mathbf{v}}_i^T\mathbf{A}\mathbf{v}_i = \lambda_i\bar{\mathbf{v}}_i^T\mathbf{v}_i \tag{2.95}$$

On the other hand, we also obtain from (2.94),

$$\bar{\mathbf{v}}_i^T\mathbf{A} = \bar{\mathbf{v}}_i^T\bar{\lambda}_i \tag{2.96}$$

and postmultiplying by $\mathbf{v}_i$, we have

$$\bar{\mathbf{v}}_i^T\mathbf{A}\mathbf{v}_i = \bar{\lambda}_i\bar{\mathbf{v}}_i^T\mathbf{v}_i \tag{2.97}$$

But the left-hand sides of (2.95) and (2.97) are the same, and thus we have

$$(\lambda_i - \bar{\lambda}_i)\bar{\mathbf{v}}_i^T\mathbf{v}_i = 0 \tag{2.98}$$

Since $\mathbf{v}_i$ is nontrivial, it follows that $\lambda_i = \bar{\lambda}_i$, and hence the eigenvalue must be real. However, it then also follows from (2.83) that the eigenvectors can be made real because the coefficient matrix $\mathbf{A} - \lambda\mathbf{I}$ is real.

Another important point is that the eigenvectors that correspond to distinct eigenvalues are unique (within scalar multipliers) and *orthogonal,* whereas the eigenvectors corresponding to multiple eigenvalues are not unique, but we can always choose an orthogonal set.

Assume first that the eigenvalues are distinct. In this case we have for two eigenpairs,

$$\mathbf{A}\mathbf{v}_i = \lambda_i\mathbf{v}_i \tag{2.99}$$

and
$$\mathbf{A}\mathbf{v}_j = \lambda_j\mathbf{v}_j \tag{2.100}$$

Premultiplying (2.99) by $\mathbf{v}_j^T$ and (2.100) by $\mathbf{v}_i^T$, we obtain

$$\mathbf{v}_j^T\mathbf{A}\mathbf{v}_i = \lambda_i\mathbf{v}_j^T\mathbf{v}_i \tag{2.101}$$

$$\mathbf{v}_i^T\mathbf{A}\mathbf{v}_j = \lambda_j\mathbf{v}_i^T\mathbf{v}_j \tag{2.102}$$

Taking the transpose in (2.102), we have

$$\mathbf{v}_j^T\mathbf{A}\mathbf{v}_i = \lambda_j\mathbf{v}_j^T\mathbf{v}_i \tag{2.103}$$

and thus from (2.103) and (2.101) we obtain

$$(\lambda_i - \lambda_j)\mathbf{v}_j^T\mathbf{v}_i = 0 \tag{2.104}$$

Since we assumed that $\lambda_i \neq \lambda_j$, it follows that $\mathbf{v}_j^T\mathbf{v}_i = 0$, i.e., that $\mathbf{v}_j$ and $\mathbf{v}_i$ are orthogonal.

Furthermore, we can scale the elements of the vector $\mathbf{v}_i$ to obtain

$$\mathbf{v}_i^T\mathbf{v}_j = \delta_{ij} \qquad\qquad (2.105)$$

where δ_{ij} = the Kronecker delta; i.e., $\delta_{ij} = 1$ when $i = j$, and $\delta_{ij} = 0$ when $i \neq j$. If (2.105) is satisfied, we say that the eigenvectors are *orthonormal*.

It should be noted that the solution of (2.83) yields a vector in which only the relative magnitudes of the elements are defined. If all elements are scaled by the same amount, the new vector would still satisfy (2.83). In effect, the solution of (2.83) yields the direction of the eigenvector, and we use the orthonormality condition in (2.105) to fix the magnitudes of the elements in the vector. Therefore, *when we refer to eigenvectors from now on it is implied that the vectors are orthonormal.*

EXAMPLE 2.30:   Check that the vectors calculated in Example 2.29 are orthogonal and then orthonormalize them.

The orthogonality is checked by forming $\mathbf{v}_1^T\mathbf{v}_2$, which gives

$$\mathbf{v}_1^T\mathbf{v}_2 = (2)(\tfrac{1}{2}) + (-1)(1) = 0$$

Hence the vectors are orthogonal. To orthonormalize the vectors, we need to make the lengths of the vectors equal to 1. Then we have

$$\mathbf{v}_1 = \frac{1}{\sqrt{5}}\begin{bmatrix} 2 \\ -1 \end{bmatrix} \quad\text{or}\quad \mathbf{v}_1 = \frac{1}{\sqrt{5}}\begin{bmatrix} -2 \\ 1 \end{bmatrix}; \qquad \mathbf{v}_2 = \frac{1}{\sqrt{5}}\begin{bmatrix} 1 \\ 2 \end{bmatrix} \quad\text{or}\quad \mathbf{v}_2 = \frac{1}{\sqrt{5}}\begin{bmatrix} -1 \\ -2 \end{bmatrix}$$

We now turn to the case in which multiple eigenvalues are also present. The proof of eigenvector orthonormality given in (2.99) to (2.105) is not possible because for a multiple eigenvalue, λ_i is equal to λ_j in (2.104). Assume that $\lambda_i = \lambda_{i+1} = \cdots = \lambda_{i+m-1}$; i.e., λ_i is an m-times multiple root. Then we can show that it is still always possible to choose m orthonormal eigenvectors that correspond to $\lambda_i, \lambda_{i+1}, \ldots, \lambda_{i+m-1}$. This follows because for a symmetric matrix of order n, we can always establish a complete set of n orthonormal eigenvectors. Corresponding to each distinct eigenvalue we have an *eigenspace* with dimension equal to the multiplicity of the eigenvalue. All eigenspaces are unique and are orthogonal to the eigenspaces that correspond to other distinct eigenvalues. The eigenvectors associated with an eigenvalue provide a basis for the eigenspace, and since the basis is not unique if $m > 1$, the eigenvectors corresponding to a multiple eigenvalue are not unique. The formal proofs of these statements are an application of the principles discussed earlier and are given in the following examples.

EXAMPLE 2.31:   Show that for a symmetric matrix $\mathbf{A}$ of order n, there are always n orthonormal eigenvectors.

Assume that we have calculated an eigenvalue λ_i and corresponding eigenvector $\mathbf{v}_i$. Let us construct an orthonormal matrix $\mathbf{Q}$ whose first column is $\mathbf{v}_i$,

$$\mathbf{Q} = [\mathbf{v}_i \quad \hat{\mathbf{Q}}]; \qquad \mathbf{Q}^T\mathbf{Q} = \mathbf{I}$$

This matrix can always be constructed because the vectors in $\mathbf{Q}$ provide an orthonormal basis for the n-dimensional space in which $\mathbf{A}$ is defined. However, we can now calculate

$$\mathbf{Q}^T\mathbf{AQ} = \begin{bmatrix} \lambda_i & \mathbf{0} \\ \mathbf{0} & \mathbf{A}_1 \end{bmatrix} \qquad\qquad \text{(a)}$$

where
$$\mathbf{A}_1 = \hat{\mathbf{Q}}^T \mathbf{A} \hat{\mathbf{Q}}$$

and $\mathbf{A}_1$ is a full matrix of order $(n - 1)$. If $n = 2$, we note that $\mathbf{Q}^T \mathbf{A} \mathbf{Q}$ is diagonal. In that case, if we premultiply (a) by $\mathbf{Q}$ and let $a \equiv \mathbf{A}_1$ we obtain

$$\mathbf{A}\mathbf{Q} = \mathbf{Q} \begin{bmatrix} \lambda_i & 0 \\ 0 & a \end{bmatrix}$$

and hence the vector in $\hat{\mathbf{Q}}$ is the other eigenvector and a is the other eigenvalue regardless of whether λ_i is a multiple eigenvalue or not.

The complete proof is now obtained by induction. Assume that the statement is true for a matrix of order $(n - 1)$; then we will show that it is also true for a matrix of order n. But since we demonstrated that the statement is true for $n = 2$, it follows that it is true for any n.

The assumption that there are $(n - 1)$ orthonormal eigenvectors for a matrix of order $(n - 1)$ gives

$$\mathbf{Q}_1^T \mathbf{A}_1 \mathbf{Q}_1 = \mathbf{\Lambda} \tag{b}$$

where $\mathbf{Q}_1$ is a matrix of the eigenvectors of $\mathbf{A}_1$ and $\mathbf{\Lambda}$ is a digonal matrix listing the eigenvalues of $\mathbf{A}_1$. However, if we now define

$$\mathbf{S} = \begin{bmatrix} 1 & \mathbf{0} \\ \mathbf{0} & \mathbf{Q}_1 \end{bmatrix}$$

we have
$$\mathbf{S}^T \mathbf{Q}^T \mathbf{A} \mathbf{Q} \mathbf{S} = \begin{bmatrix} \lambda_i & \mathbf{0} \\ \mathbf{0} & \mathbf{\Lambda} \end{bmatrix} \tag{c}$$

Let
$$\mathbf{P} = \mathbf{Q}\mathbf{S}; \qquad \mathbf{P}^T \mathbf{P} = \mathbf{I}$$

Then premultiplying (c) by $\mathbf{P}$, we obtain

$$\mathbf{A}\mathbf{P} = \mathbf{P} \begin{bmatrix} \lambda_i & \mathbf{0} \\ \mathbf{0} & \mathbf{\Lambda} \end{bmatrix}$$

Therefore, under the assumption in (b), the statement is also true for a matrix of order n, which completes the proof.

EXAMPLE 2.32:   Show that the eigenvectors corresponding to a multiple eigenvalue of multiplicity m define an m-dimensional space in which each vector is also an eigenvector. This space is called the *eigenspace* corresponding to the eigenvalue considered.

Let λ_i be the eigenvalue of multiplicity m; i.e., we have

$$\lambda_i = \lambda_{i+1} = \cdots = \lambda_{i+m-1}$$

We showed in Example 2.31 that there are m orthonormal eigenvectors $\mathbf{v}_i, \mathbf{v}_{i+1}, \ldots, \mathbf{v}_{i+m-1}$ corresponding to λ_i. These vectors provide the basis of an m-dimensional space. Consider any vector $\mathbf{w}$ in this space, such as

$$\mathbf{w} = \alpha_i \mathbf{v}_i + \alpha_{i+1} \mathbf{v}_{i+1} + \cdots + \alpha_{i+m-1} \mathbf{v}_{i+m-1}$$

where the $\alpha_i, \alpha_{i+1}, \ldots,$ are constants. The vector $\mathbf{w}$ is also an eigenvector because we have

$$\mathbf{A}\mathbf{w} = \alpha_i \mathbf{A}\mathbf{v}_i + \alpha_{i+1} \mathbf{A}\mathbf{v}_{i+1} + \cdots + \alpha_{i+m-1} \mathbf{A}\mathbf{v}_{i+m-1}$$

which gives
$$\mathbf{A}\mathbf{w} = \alpha_i \lambda_i \mathbf{v}_i + \alpha_{i+1} \lambda_i \mathbf{v}_{i+1} + \cdots + \alpha_{i+m-1} \lambda_i \mathbf{v}_{i+m-1} = \lambda_i \mathbf{w}$$

Therefore, any vector $\mathbf{w}$ in the space spanned by the m eigenvectors $\mathbf{v}_i, \mathbf{v}_{i+1}, \ldots, \mathbf{v}_{i+m-1}$ is also an eigenvector. It should be noted that the vector $\mathbf{w}$ will be orthogonal to the eigenvectors that correspond to eigenvalues not equal to λ_i. Hence there is one eigenspace that corresponds to each, distinct or multiple, eigenvalue. The dimension of the eigenspace is equal to the multiplicity of the eigenvalue.

Now that the main properties of the eigenvalues and eigenvectors of A have been presented, we can write the n solutions to $Av = \lambda v$ in various forms. First, we have

$$AV = V\Lambda \tag{2.106}$$

where V is a matrix storing the eigenvectors, $V = [v_1, \ldots, v_n]$, and Λ is a diagonal matrix with the corresponding eigenvalues on its diagonal, $\Lambda = \text{diag} (\lambda_i)$. Using the orthonormality property of the eigenvectors (i.e., $V^T V = I$), we obtain from (2.106),

$$V^T A V = \Lambda \tag{2.107}$$

Furthermore, we obtain the *spectral decomposition* of A,

$$A = V\Lambda V^T \tag{2.108}$$

where it may be convenient to write the spectral decomposition of A as

$$A = \sum_{i=1}^{n} \lambda_i v_i v_i^T \tag{2.109}$$

It should be noted that each of these equations represents the solution to the eigenproblem $Av = \lambda v$. Consider the following example.

EXAMPLE 2.33:   Establish the relations given in (2.106) to (2.109) for the matrix A used in Example 2.29.

The eigenvalues and eigenvectors of A have been calculated in Examples 2.29 and 2.30. Using the information given in these examples, we have for (2.106),

$$
\begin{bmatrix} -1 & 2 \\ 2 & 2 \end{bmatrix}
\begin{bmatrix} -\dfrac{2}{\sqrt{5}} & \dfrac{1}{\sqrt{5}} \\ \dfrac{1}{\sqrt{5}} & \dfrac{2}{\sqrt{5}} \end{bmatrix}
=
\begin{bmatrix} -\dfrac{2}{\sqrt{5}} & \dfrac{1}{\sqrt{5}} \\ \dfrac{1}{\sqrt{5}} & \dfrac{2}{\sqrt{5}} \end{bmatrix}
\begin{bmatrix} -2 & 0 \\ 0 & 3 \end{bmatrix}
$$

for (2.107),

$$
\begin{bmatrix} -\dfrac{2}{\sqrt{5}} & \dfrac{1}{\sqrt{5}} \\ \dfrac{1}{\sqrt{5}} & \dfrac{2}{\sqrt{5}} \end{bmatrix}
\begin{bmatrix} -1 & 2 \\ 2 & 2 \end{bmatrix}
\begin{bmatrix} -\dfrac{2}{\sqrt{5}} & \dfrac{1}{\sqrt{5}} \\ \dfrac{1}{\sqrt{5}} & \dfrac{2}{\sqrt{5}} \end{bmatrix}
=
\begin{bmatrix} -2 & 0 \\ 0 & 3 \end{bmatrix}
$$

for (2.108),

$$
\begin{bmatrix} -1 & 2 \\ 2 & 2 \end{bmatrix}
=
\begin{bmatrix} -\dfrac{2}{\sqrt{5}} & \dfrac{1}{\sqrt{5}} \\ \dfrac{1}{\sqrt{5}} & \dfrac{2}{\sqrt{5}} \end{bmatrix}
\begin{bmatrix} -2 & 0 \\ 0 & 3 \end{bmatrix}
\begin{bmatrix} -\dfrac{2}{\sqrt{5}} & \dfrac{1}{\sqrt{5}} \\ \dfrac{1}{\sqrt{5}} & \dfrac{2}{\sqrt{5}} \end{bmatrix}
$$

and for (2.109),

$$
A = (-2)
\begin{bmatrix} -\dfrac{2}{\sqrt{5}} \\ \dfrac{1}{\sqrt{5}} \end{bmatrix}
\begin{bmatrix} -\dfrac{2}{\sqrt{5}} & \dfrac{1}{\sqrt{5}} \end{bmatrix}
+ (3)
\begin{bmatrix} \dfrac{1}{\sqrt{5}} \\ \dfrac{2}{\sqrt{5}} \end{bmatrix}
\begin{bmatrix} \dfrac{1}{\sqrt{5}} & \dfrac{2}{\sqrt{5}} \end{bmatrix}
$$

The relations in (2.107) and (2.108) can be employed effectively in various important applications. The objective in the following examples is to present some solution procedures in which they are used.

EXAMPLE 2.34:   Calculate the kth power of a given matrix $\mathbf{A}$; i.e., evaluate $\mathbf{A}^k$. Demonstrate the result using $\mathbf{A}$ in Example 2.29.

One way of evaluating $\mathbf{A}^k$ is to simply calculate $\mathbf{A}^2 = \mathbf{AA}$, $\mathbf{A}^4 = \mathbf{A}^2\mathbf{A}^2$, etc. However, if k is large, it may be more effective to employ the spectral decomposition of $\mathbf{A}$. Assume that we have calculated the eigenvalues and eigenvectors of $\mathbf{A}$; i.e., we have

$$\mathbf{A} = \mathbf{V}\boldsymbol{\Lambda}\mathbf{V}^T$$

To calculate $\mathbf{A}^2$, we use

$$\mathbf{A}^2 = \mathbf{V}\boldsymbol{\Lambda}\mathbf{V}^T\mathbf{V}\boldsymbol{\Lambda}\mathbf{V}^T$$

but because $\mathbf{V}^T\mathbf{V} = \mathbf{I}$, we have

$$\mathbf{A}^2 = \mathbf{V}\boldsymbol{\Lambda}^2\mathbf{V}^T$$

Proceeding in the same manner, we thus obtain

$$\mathbf{A}^k = \mathbf{V}\boldsymbol{\Lambda}^k\mathbf{V}^T$$

As an example, let $\mathbf{A}$ be the matrix considered in Example 2.29. Then we have

$$\mathbf{A}^k = \frac{1}{\sqrt{5}}\begin{bmatrix} -2 & 1 \\ 1 & 2 \end{bmatrix}\begin{bmatrix} (-2)^k & 0 \\ 0 & (3)^k \end{bmatrix}\frac{1}{\sqrt{5}}\begin{bmatrix} -2 & 1 \\ 1 & 2 \end{bmatrix}$$

or

$$\mathbf{A}^k = \frac{1}{5}\left[\begin{array}{c:c} (-2)^{k+2} + (3)^k & (-2)^{k+1} + (2)(3)^k \\ \hdashline (-2)^{k+1} + (2)(3)^k & (-2)^k + (4)(3)^k \end{array}\right]$$

It is interesting to note that if the largest absolute value of all the eigenvalues of $\mathbf{A}$ is smaller than 1, we have $\mathbf{A}^k \to \mathbf{0}$ as $k \to \infty$. Thus, defining the spectral radius of $\mathbf{A}$,

$$\rho(\mathbf{A}) = \max_{\text{all } i} |\lambda_i|$$

we have $\lim_{k \to \infty} \mathbf{A}^k = \mathbf{0}$, provided that $\rho(\mathbf{A}) < 1$.

EXAMPLE 2.35:   Consider the system of differential equations

$$\dot{\mathbf{x}} + \mathbf{A}\mathbf{x} = \mathbf{f}(t) \tag{a}$$

and obtain the solution using the spectral decomposition of $\mathbf{A}$. Demonstrate the result using the matrix $\mathbf{A}$ in Example 2.29 and

$$\mathbf{f}(t) = \begin{bmatrix} e^{-t} \\ 0 \end{bmatrix}; \qquad {}^0\mathbf{x} = \begin{bmatrix} 1 \\ 1 \end{bmatrix}$$

where ${}^0\mathbf{x}$ are the initial conditions.

Substituting $\mathbf{A} = \mathbf{V}\boldsymbol{\Lambda}\mathbf{V}^T$ and premultiplying by $\mathbf{V}^T$, we obtain

$$\mathbf{V}^T\dot{\mathbf{x}} + \boldsymbol{\Lambda}(\mathbf{V}^T\mathbf{x}) = \mathbf{V}^T\mathbf{f}(t)$$

Thus if we define $\mathbf{y} = \mathbf{V}^T\mathbf{x}$, we need to solve the equations

$$\dot{\mathbf{y}} + \boldsymbol{\Lambda}\mathbf{y} = \mathbf{V}^T\mathbf{f}(t)$$

But this is a set of n decoupled differential equations. Consider the rth equation, which is typical:

$$\dot{y}_r + \lambda_r y_r = \mathbf{v}_r^T \mathbf{f}(t)$$

The solution is
$$y_r(t) = {}^0 y_r\, e^{-\lambda_r t} + e^{-\lambda_r t} \int_0^t e^{\lambda_r \tau}\, \mathbf{v}_r^T \mathbf{f}(\tau)\, d\tau$$

where ${}^0 y_r$ is the value of y_r at time $t = 0$. The complete solution to the system of equations in (a) is

$$\mathbf{x} = \sum_{r=1}^{n} \mathbf{v}_r y_r \tag{b}$$

As an example, we consider the system of differential equations

$$\begin{bmatrix} \dot{x}_1 \\ \dot{x}_2 \end{bmatrix} + \begin{bmatrix} -1 & 2 \\ 2 & 2 \end{bmatrix} \begin{bmatrix} x_1 \\ x_2 \end{bmatrix} = \begin{bmatrix} e^{-t} \\ 0 \end{bmatrix}$$

In this case we have to solve the two decoupled differential equations

$$\dot{y}_1 + (-2) y_1 = 2 e^{-t}$$
$$\dot{y}_2 + 3 y_2 = e^{-t}$$

with initial conditions

$$^0\mathbf{y} = \mathbf{V}^{T0}\mathbf{x} = \frac{1}{\sqrt{5}} \begin{bmatrix} 2 & -1 \\ 1 & 2 \end{bmatrix} \begin{bmatrix} 1 \\ 1 \end{bmatrix} = \frac{1}{\sqrt{5}} \begin{bmatrix} 1 \\ 3 \end{bmatrix}$$

We obtain
$$y_1 = \frac{1}{\sqrt{5}} e^{2t} - \frac{2}{3} e^{-t}$$

$$y_2 = \frac{3}{\sqrt{5}} e^{-3t} + \frac{1}{2} e^{-t}$$

Thus, using (b), we have

$$\begin{bmatrix} x_1 \\ x_2 \end{bmatrix} = \frac{1}{\sqrt{5}} \left(\begin{bmatrix} 2 \\ -1 \end{bmatrix} y_1 + \begin{bmatrix} 1 \\ 2 \end{bmatrix} y_2 \right)$$

$$= \begin{bmatrix} -\dfrac{\sqrt{5}}{6} e^{-t} + \dfrac{3}{5} e^{-3t} + \dfrac{2}{5} e^{2t} \\[2mm] \dfrac{\sqrt{5}}{3} e^{-t} + \dfrac{6}{5} e^{-3t} - \dfrac{1}{5} e^{2t} \end{bmatrix}$$

To conclude the presentation, we may note that by introducing auxiliary variables, higher-order differential equations can be reduced to a system of first-order differential equations. However, the coefficient matrix $\mathbf{A}$ is in that case nonsymmetric.

EXAMPLE 2.36:   Using the spectral decomposition of an $n \times n$ symmertric matrix $\mathbf{A}$, evaluate the inverse of the matrix. Demonstrate the result using the matrix $\mathbf{A}$ in Example 2.29.

Assume that we have evaluated the eigenvalues λ_i and corresponding eigenvectors $\mathbf{v}_i$, $i = 1, \ldots, n$, of the matrix $\mathbf{A}$; i.e., we have solved the eigenproblem

$$\mathbf{Av} = \lambda \mathbf{v} \tag{a}$$

Premultiplying both sides of (a) by $\lambda^{-1}\mathbf{A}^{-1}$, we obtain the eigenproblem

$$\mathbf{A}^{-1}\mathbf{v} = \lambda^{-1}\mathbf{v}$$

But this relation shows that the eigenvalues of $\mathbf{A}^{-1}$ are $1/\lambda_i$ and the eigenvectors are $\mathbf{v}_i$, $i = 1, \ldots, n$. Thus using (2.109) for $\mathbf{A}^{-1}$, we have

$$\mathbf{A}^{-1} = \mathbf{V}\boldsymbol{\Lambda}^{-1}\mathbf{V}^T$$

or

$$\mathbf{A}^{-1} = \sum_{i=1}^{n} \left(\frac{1}{\lambda_i}\right)\mathbf{v}_i\mathbf{v}_i^T$$

These equations show that we cannot find the inverse of $\mathbf{A}$ if the matrix has a zero eigenvalue.

As an example, we evaluate the inverse of the matrix $\mathbf{A}$ considered in Example 2.29. In this case we have

$$\mathbf{A}^{-1} = \frac{1}{5}\begin{bmatrix} 2 & 1 \\ -1 & 2 \end{bmatrix}\begin{bmatrix} -\frac{1}{2} & 0 \\ 0 & \frac{1}{3} \end{bmatrix}\begin{bmatrix} 2 & -1 \\ 1 & 2 \end{bmatrix} = \frac{1}{6}\begin{bmatrix} -2 & 2 \\ 2 & 1 \end{bmatrix}$$

The key point of the tranformation (2.107) is that in (2.107) we perform a change of basis [see (2.86) and (2.88)]. Since the vectors in $\mathbf{V}$ correspond to a new basis, they span the n-dimensional space in which $\mathbf{A}$ and $\boldsymbol{\Lambda}$ are defined, and any vector $\mathbf{w}$ can be expressed as a linear combination of the eigenvectors $\mathbf{v}_i$; i.e., we have

$$\mathbf{w} = \sum_{i=1}^{n} \alpha_i\mathbf{v}_i \tag{2.110}$$

An important observation is that $\boldsymbol{\Lambda}$ shows directly whether the matrices $\mathbf{A}$ and $\boldsymbol{\Lambda}$ are singular. Using the definition given in Section 2.2, we find that $\boldsymbol{\Lambda}$ and hence $\mathbf{A}$ are singular if and only if an eigenvalue is equal to zero, because in that case $\boldsymbol{\Lambda}^{-1}$ cannot be calculated. In this context it is useful to define some additional terminology. If all eigenvalues are positive, we say that the matrix is *positive definite*. If all eigenvalues are greater than or equal to zero, the matrix is *positive semidefinite;* with negative, zero, or positive eigenvalues, the matrix is *indefinite*.

2.6 THE RAYLEIGH QUOTIENT AND THE MINIMAX CHARACTERIZATION OF EIGENVALUES

In the previous section we defined the eigenproblem $\mathbf{A}\mathbf{v} = \lambda\mathbf{v}$ and discussed the basic properties that pertain to the solutions of the problem. The objective in this section is to complement the information given with some very powerful principles.

A number of important principles are derived using the Rayleigh quotient $\rho(\mathbf{v})$, which is defined as

$$\rho(\mathbf{v}) = \frac{\mathbf{v}^T\mathbf{A}\mathbf{v}}{\mathbf{v}^T\mathbf{v}} \tag{2.111}$$

The first observation is that

$$\lambda_1 \leq \rho(\mathbf{v}) \leq \lambda_n \tag{2.112}$$

and it follows that using the definitions given in Section 2.5, we have for any vector $\mathbf{v}$, if $\mathbf{A}$ is positive definite $\rho(\mathbf{v}) > 0$, if $\mathbf{A}$ is positive semidefinite $\rho(\mathbf{v}) \geq 0$, and for $\mathbf{A}$ indefinite $\rho(\mathbf{v})$

can be negative, zero, or positive. For the proof of (2.112) we use

$$\mathbf{v} = \sum_{i=1}^{n} \alpha_i \mathbf{v}_i \tag{2.113}$$

where $\mathbf{v}_i$ are the eigenvectors of $\mathbf{A}$. Substituting for $\mathbf{v}$ into (2.111) and using that $\mathbf{A}\mathbf{v}_i = \lambda_i \mathbf{v}_i$, $\mathbf{v}_i^T \mathbf{v}_j = \delta_{ij}$, we obtain

$$\rho(\mathbf{v}) = \frac{\lambda_1 \alpha_1^2 + \lambda_2 \alpha_2^2 + \cdots + \lambda_n \alpha_n^2}{\alpha_1^2 + \cdots + \alpha_n^2} \tag{2.114}$$

Hence, if $\lambda_1 \neq 0$,

$$\rho(\mathbf{v}) = \lambda_1 \frac{\alpha_1^2 + (\lambda_2/\lambda_1)\alpha_2^2 + \cdots + (\lambda_n/\lambda_1)\alpha_n^2}{\alpha_1^2 + \cdots + \alpha_n^2} \tag{2.115}$$

and if $\lambda_n \neq 0$, $\qquad \rho(\mathbf{v}) = \lambda_n \dfrac{(\lambda_1/\lambda_n)\alpha_1^2 + (\lambda_2/\lambda_n)\alpha_2^2 + \cdots + \alpha_n^2}{\alpha_1^2 + \cdots + \alpha_n^2}$ $\tag{2.116}$

But since $\lambda_1 \leq \lambda_2 \leq \cdots \leq \lambda_n$, the relations in (2.114) to (2.116) show that (2.112) holds. Furthermore, it is seen that if $\mathbf{v} = \mathbf{v}_i$, we have $\rho(\mathbf{v}) = \lambda_i$.

Considering the practical use of the Rayleigh quotient, the following property is of particular value. Assume that $\mathbf{v}$ is an approximation to the eigenvector $\mathbf{v}_i$; i.e., say with ϵ small, we have

$$\mathbf{v} = \mathbf{v}_i + \epsilon \mathbf{x} \tag{2.117}$$

Then the Rayleigh quotient of $\mathbf{v}$ will give an approximation to λ_i of order ϵ^2; i.e.,

$$\rho(\mathbf{v}) = \lambda_i + o(\epsilon^2) \tag{2.118}$$

The notation $o(\epsilon^2)$ means "of order ϵ^2" and indicates that if $\delta = o(\epsilon^2)$, then $|\delta| \leq b\epsilon^2$, where b is a constant.

To prove this property of the Rayleigh quotient, we substitute for $\mathbf{v}$ from (2.113) into the Rayleigh quotient expression to obtain

$$\rho(\mathbf{v}_i + \epsilon \mathbf{x}) = \frac{(\mathbf{v}_i^T + \epsilon \mathbf{x}^T)\mathbf{A}(\mathbf{v}_i + \epsilon \mathbf{x})}{(\mathbf{v}_i^T + \epsilon \mathbf{x}^T)(\mathbf{v}_i + \epsilon \mathbf{x})} \tag{2.119}$$

or $\qquad\qquad \rho(\mathbf{v}_i + \epsilon \mathbf{x}) = \dfrac{\mathbf{v}_i^T \mathbf{A} \mathbf{v}_i + 2\epsilon \mathbf{v}_i^T \mathbf{A} \mathbf{x} + \epsilon^2 \mathbf{x}^T \mathbf{A} \mathbf{x}}{\mathbf{v}_i^T \mathbf{v}_i + 2\epsilon \mathbf{x}^T \mathbf{v}_i + \epsilon^2 \mathbf{x}^T \mathbf{x}}$ $\tag{2.120}$

However, since $\mathbf{x}$ is an error in $\mathbf{v}_i$, we can write

$$\mathbf{x} = \sum_{\substack{j=1 \\ j \neq i}}^{n} \alpha_j \mathbf{v}_j \tag{2.121}$$

But then using $\mathbf{v}_i^T \mathbf{v}_j = \delta_{ij}$ and $\mathbf{A}\mathbf{v}_j = \lambda_j \mathbf{v}_j$, we have $\mathbf{v}_i^T \mathbf{A} \mathbf{x} = 0$ and $\mathbf{x}^T \mathbf{v}_i = 0$, and hence

$$\rho(\mathbf{v}_i + \epsilon \mathbf{x}) = \frac{\lambda_i + \epsilon^2 \sum_{\substack{j=1 \\ j \neq i}}^{n} \alpha_j^2 \lambda_j}{1 + \epsilon^2 \sum_{\substack{j=1 \\ j \neq i}}^{n} \alpha_j^2} \tag{2.122}$$

However, using the binomial theorem to expand the denominator in (2.122), we have

$$\rho(\mathbf{v}_i + \epsilon\mathbf{x}) = \left(\lambda_i + \epsilon^2 \sum_{\substack{j=1 \\ j\neq i}}^{n} \alpha_j^2 \lambda_j\right)\left[1 - \epsilon^2\left(\sum_{\substack{j=1 \\ j\neq i}}^{n} \alpha_j^2\right) + \epsilon^4\left(\sum_{\substack{j=1 \\ j\neq i}}^{n} \alpha_j^2\right)^2 + \cdots\right] \quad (2.123)$$

or

$$\rho(\mathbf{v}_i + \epsilon\mathbf{x}) = \lambda_i + \epsilon^2\left(\sum_{\substack{j=1 \\ j\neq i}}^{n} \alpha_j^2 \lambda_j - \lambda_i \sum_{\substack{j=1 \\ j\neq i}}^{n} \alpha_j^2\right) + \text{higher-order terms} \quad (2.124)$$

The relation in (2.118) thus follows. We demonstrate the preceding results in a brief example.

EXAMPLE 2.37: Evaluate the Rayleigh quotients $\rho(\mathbf{v})$ for the matrix $\mathbf{A}$ used in Example 2.29. Using $\mathbf{v}_1$ and $\mathbf{v}_2$ in Example 2.29, consider the following cases:

1. $\mathbf{v} = \mathbf{v}_1 + 2\mathbf{v}_2$;   2. $\mathbf{v} = \mathbf{v}_1$;   3. $\mathbf{v} = \mathbf{v}_1 + 0.02\mathbf{v}_2$.

In case **1**, we have

$$\mathbf{v} = \begin{bmatrix} 2 \\ -1 \end{bmatrix} + \begin{bmatrix} 1 \\ 2 \end{bmatrix} = \begin{bmatrix} 3 \\ 1 \end{bmatrix}$$

and thus

$$\rho(\mathbf{v}) = \frac{[3 \quad 1]\begin{bmatrix} -1 & 2 \\ 2 & 2 \end{bmatrix}\begin{bmatrix} 3 \\ 1 \end{bmatrix}}{[3 \quad 1]\begin{bmatrix} 3 \\ 1 \end{bmatrix}} = \frac{1}{2}$$

Recalling that $\lambda_1 = -2$ and $\lambda_2 = 3$, we have, as expected,

$$\lambda_1 \leq \rho(\mathbf{v}) \leq \lambda_2$$

In case **2**, we have

$$\mathbf{v} = \begin{bmatrix} 2 \\ -1 \end{bmatrix}$$

and hence

$$\rho(\mathbf{v}) = \frac{[2 \quad -1]\begin{bmatrix} -1 & 2 \\ 2 & 2 \end{bmatrix}\begin{bmatrix} 2 \\ -1 \end{bmatrix}}{[2 \quad -1]\begin{bmatrix} 2 \\ -1 \end{bmatrix}} = -2$$

and so, as expected, $\rho(\mathbf{v}) = \lambda_1$.

Finally, in case **3**, we use

$$\mathbf{v} = \begin{bmatrix} 2 \\ -1 \end{bmatrix} + \begin{bmatrix} 0.01 \\ 0.02 \end{bmatrix} = \begin{bmatrix} 2.01 \\ -0.98 \end{bmatrix}$$

and hence

$$\rho(\mathbf{v}) = \frac{[2.01 \quad -0.98]\begin{bmatrix} -1 & 2 \\ 2 & 2 \end{bmatrix}\begin{bmatrix} 2.01 \\ -0.98 \end{bmatrix}}{[2.01 \quad -0.98]\begin{bmatrix} 2.01 \\ -0.98 \end{bmatrix}}$$

$$= -1.99950005$$

Here we note that $\rho(\mathbf{v}) > \lambda_1$ and that $\rho(\mathbf{v})$ approximates λ_1 more closely than $\mathbf{v}$ approximates $\mathbf{v}_1$.

Having introduced the Rayleigh quotient, we can now proceed to a very important principle, the minimax characterization of eigenvalues. We know from Rayleigh's principle that

$$\rho(\mathbf{v}) \geq \lambda_1 \tag{2.125}$$

where $\mathbf{v}$ is any vector. In other words, if we consider the problem of varying $\mathbf{v}$, we will always have $\rho(\mathbf{v}) \geq \lambda_1$, and the minimum will be reached when $\mathbf{v} = \mathbf{v}_1$, in which case $\rho(\mathbf{v}_1) = \lambda_1$. Suppose that we now impose a restriction on $\mathbf{v}$, namely that $\mathbf{v}$ be orthogonal to a specific vector $\mathbf{w}$, and that we consider the problem of minimizing $\rho(\mathbf{v})$ subject to this restriction. After calculating the minimum of $\rho(\mathbf{v})$ with the condition $\mathbf{v}^T\mathbf{w} = 0$, we could start varying $\mathbf{w}$ and for each new $\mathbf{w}$ evaluate a new minimum of $\rho(\mathbf{v})$. We would then find that the maximum value of all the minimum values evaluated is λ_2. This result can be generalized to the following principle, called the *minimax characterization of eigenvalues,*

$$\lambda_r = \max \left\{ \min \frac{\mathbf{v}^T\mathbf{A}\mathbf{v}}{\mathbf{v}^T\mathbf{v}} \right\} \qquad r = 1, \ldots, n \tag{2.126}$$

with $\mathbf{v}$ satisfying $\mathbf{v}^T\mathbf{w}_i = 0$ for $i = 1, \ldots, r - 1, r \geq 2$. In (2.126) we choose vectors $\mathbf{w}_i$, $i = 1, \ldots, r - 1$, and then evaluate the minimum of $\rho(\mathbf{v})$ with $\mathbf{v}$ subject to the condition $\mathbf{v}^T\mathbf{w}_i = 0$, $i = 1, \ldots, r - 1$. After calculating this minimum we vary the vectors $\mathbf{w}_i$ and always evaluate a new minimum. The maximum value that the minima reach is λ_r.

The proof of (2.126) is as follows. Let

$$\mathbf{v} = \sum_{i=1}^{n} \alpha_i \mathbf{v}_i \tag{2.127}$$

and evaluate the right-hand side of (2.126), which we call R,

$$R = \max \left\{ \min \frac{\alpha_1^2 \lambda_1 + \cdots + \alpha_r^2 \lambda_r + \alpha_{r+1}^2 \lambda_{r+1} + \cdots + \alpha_n^2 \lambda_n}{\alpha_1^2 + \cdots + \alpha_r^2 + \alpha_{r+1}^2 + \cdots + \alpha_n^2} \right\} \tag{2.128}$$

The coefficients α_i must satisfy the conditions

$$\mathbf{w}_j^T \sum_{i=1}^{n} \alpha_i \mathbf{v}_i = 0 \qquad j = 1, \ldots, r - 1 \tag{2.129}$$

Rewriting (2.128), we obtain

$$R = \max \left\{ \min \left[\lambda_r - \frac{\begin{array}{c} \alpha_1^2(\lambda_r - \lambda_1) + \cdots + \alpha_{r-1}^2(\lambda_r - \lambda_{r-1}) \\ + \alpha_{r+1}^2(\lambda_r - \lambda_{r+1}) + \cdots + \alpha_n^2(\lambda_r - \lambda_n) \end{array}}{\alpha_1^2 + \cdots + \alpha_r^2 + \alpha_{r+1}^2 + \cdots + \alpha_n^2} \right] \right\} \tag{2.130}$$

But we can now see that for the condition $\alpha_{r+1} = \alpha_{r+2} = \cdots = \alpha_n = 0$, we have

$$R \leq \lambda_r \tag{2.131}$$

and the condition in (2.129) can still be satisfied by a judicious choice for α_r. On the other hand, suppose that we now choose $\mathbf{w}_j = \mathbf{v}_j$ for $j = 1, \ldots, r - 1$. This would require that $\alpha_j = 0$ for $j = 1, \ldots, r - 1$, and consequently we would have $R = \lambda_r$, which completes the proof.

A most important property that can be established using the minimax characterization of eigenvalues is the *eigenvalue separation property.* Suppose that in addition to the problem $\mathbf{A}\mathbf{v} = \lambda\mathbf{v}$, we consider the problems

$$\mathbf{A}^{(m)}\mathbf{v}^{(m)} = \lambda^{(m)}\mathbf{v}^{(m)} \tag{2.132}$$

where $\mathbf{A}^{(m)}$ is obtained by omitting the last m rows and columns of $\mathbf{A}$. Hence $\mathbf{A}^{(m)}$ is a square-symmetric matrix of order $(n - m)$. Using also the notation $\mathbf{A}^{(0)} = \mathbf{A}$, $\lambda^{(0)} = \lambda$, $\mathbf{v}^{(0)} = \mathbf{v}$, the eigenvalue separation property states that the eigenvalues of the problem $\mathbf{A}^{(m+1)}\mathbf{v}^{(m+1)} = \lambda^{(m+1)}\mathbf{v}^{(m+1)}$ separate the eigenvalues of the problem in (2.132); i.e., we have

$$\lambda_1^{(m)} \leq \lambda_1^{(m+1)} \leq \lambda_2^{(m)} \leq \lambda_2^{(m+1)} \leq \cdots \leq \lambda_{n-m-1}^{(m)} \leq \lambda_{n-m-1}^{(m+1)} \leq \lambda_{n-m}^{(m)}$$
$$\text{for } m = 0, \ldots, n - 2 \tag{2.133}$$

For the proof of (2.133) we consider the problems $\mathbf{A}\mathbf{v} = \lambda\mathbf{v}$ and $\mathbf{A}^{(1)}\mathbf{v}^{(1)} = \lambda^{(1)}\mathbf{v}^{(1)}$. If we can show that the eigenvalue separation property holds for these two problems, it will hold also for $m = 1, 2, \ldots, n - 2$. Specifically, we therefore want to prove that

$$\lambda_r \leq \lambda_r^{(1)} \leq \lambda_{r+1} \qquad r = 1, \ldots, n - 1 \tag{2.134}$$

Using the minimax characterization, we have

$$\left.\begin{array}{c} \lambda_{r+1} = \max\left\{\min \dfrac{\mathbf{v}^T\mathbf{A}\mathbf{v}}{\mathbf{v}^T\mathbf{v}}\right\} \\ \mathbf{v}^T\mathbf{w}_i = 0; \qquad i = 1, \ldots, r; \text{ all } \mathbf{w}_i \text{ arbitrary} \end{array}\right\} \tag{2.135}$$

Similarly, we have

$$\left.\begin{array}{l} \lambda_r^{(1)} = \max\left\{\min \dfrac{\mathbf{v}^T\mathbf{A}\mathbf{v}}{\mathbf{v}^T\mathbf{v}}\right\} \\ \mathbf{v}^T\mathbf{w}_i = 0; \qquad i = 1, \ldots, r \\ \mathbf{w}_i \text{ arbitrary for } i = 1, \ldots, r - 1 \\ \mathbf{w}_r = \mathbf{e}_n \end{array}\right\} \tag{2.136}$$

where $\mathbf{w}_r$ is constrained to be equal to $\mathbf{e}_n$ to ensure that the last element in $\mathbf{v}$ is zero because $\mathbf{e}_n$ is the last column of the $n \times n$ identity matrix $\mathbf{I}$. However, since the constraint for λ_{r+1} can be more severe and includes that for $\lambda_r^{(1)}$, we have

$$\lambda_r^{(1)} \leq \lambda_{r+1} \tag{2.137}$$

To determine λ_r we use

$$\left.\begin{array}{l} \lambda_r = \max\left\{\min \dfrac{\mathbf{v}^T\mathbf{A}\mathbf{v}}{\mathbf{v}^T\mathbf{v}}\right\} \\ \mathbf{v}^T\mathbf{w}_i = 0; \qquad i = 1, \ldots, r - 1 \\ \text{all } \mathbf{w}_i \text{ arbitrary} \end{array}\right\} \tag{2.138}$$

Comparing the characterizations of $\lambda_r^{(1)}$ and λ_r, i.e., (2.136) with (2.138), we observe that to calculate $\lambda_r^{(1)}$ we have the same constraints as in the calculation of λ_r plus one more (namely, $\mathbf{v}^T\mathbf{e}_n = 0$), and hence

$$\lambda_r \leq \lambda_r^{(1)} \tag{2.139}$$

But (2.137) and (2.139) together establish the required result given in (2.134).

The eigenvalue separation property now yields the following result. If we write the eigenvalue problems in (2.132) including the problem $\mathbf{Av} = \lambda\mathbf{v}$ in the form

$$p^{(m)}(\lambda^{(m)}) = \det(\mathbf{A}^{(m)} - \lambda^{(m)}\mathbf{I}); \qquad m = 0, \ldots, n-1 \qquad (2.140)$$

where $p^{(0)} = p$, we see that the roots of the polynomial $p(\lambda^{(m+1)})$ separate the roots of the polynomial $p(\lambda^{(m)})$. However, a sequence of polynomials $p_i(x)$, $i = 1, \ldots, q$, form a Sturm sequence if the roots of the polynomial $p_{j+1}(x)$ separate the roots of the polynomial $p_j(x)$. *Hence the eigenvalue separation property states that the characteristic polynomials of the problems* $\mathbf{A}^{(m)}\mathbf{v}^{(m)} = \lambda^{(m)}\mathbf{v}^{(m)}$, $n = 0, 1, \ldots, n-1$, *form a Sturm sequence.* It should be noted that in the presentation we considered all symmetric matrices; i.e., the minimax characterization of eigenvalues and the Sturm sequence property are applicable to positive definite and indefinite matrices. We shall use the Sturm sequence property extensively in later chapters (see Sections 8.2.5, 10.2.2, 11.4.3, and 11.6.4). Consider the following example.

EXAMPLE 2.38:   Consider the eigenvalue problem $\mathbf{Av} = \lambda\mathbf{v}$, where

$$\mathbf{A} = \begin{bmatrix} 5 & -4 & -7 \\ -4 & 2 & -4 \\ -7 & -4 & 5 \end{bmatrix}$$

Evaluate the eigenvalues of $\mathbf{A}$ and of the matrices $\mathbf{A}^{(m)}$, $m = 1, 2$. Show that the separation property given in (2.133) holds and sketch the characteristic polynomials $p(\lambda)$, $p^{(1)}(\lambda^{(1)})$, and $p^{(2)}(\lambda^{(2)})$.

We have

$$p(\lambda) = \det(\mathbf{A} - \lambda\mathbf{I}) = (5 - \lambda)[(2 - \lambda)(5 - \lambda) - 16]$$
$$+ 4[-4(5 - \lambda) - 28] - 7[16 + 7(2 - \lambda)]$$

Hence

$$p(\lambda) = (-6 - \lambda)(6 - \lambda)(12 - \lambda)$$

and the eigenvalues are

$$\lambda_1 = -6; \qquad \lambda_2 = 6; \qquad \lambda_3 = 12$$

Also,

$$p^{(1)}(\lambda^{(1)}) = \det(\mathbf{A}^{(1)} - \lambda^{(1)}\mathbf{I})$$
$$= (5 - \lambda^{(1)})(2 - \lambda^{(1)}) - 16$$

or

$$p^{(1)}(\lambda^{(1)}) = \lambda^{(1)2} - 7\lambda^{(1)} - 6$$

Hence

$$\lambda_1^{(1)} = \tfrac{7}{2} - \tfrac{1}{2}\sqrt{73} = -0.7720$$
$$\lambda_2^{(1)} = \tfrac{7}{2} + \tfrac{1}{2}\sqrt{73} = 7.772$$

Finally,

$$p^{(2)}(\lambda^{(2)}) = \det(A^{(2)} - \lambda^{(2)}\mathbf{I})$$
$$= 5 - \lambda^{(2)}$$

Hence

$$\lambda_1^{(2)} = 5$$

The separation property holds because

$$\lambda_1 \leq \lambda_1^{(1)} \leq \lambda_2 \leq \lambda_2^{(1)} \leq \lambda_3$$

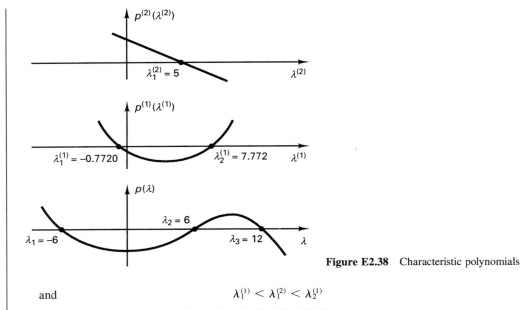

Figure E2.38   Characteristic polynomials

and

$$\lambda_1^{(1)} < \lambda_1^{(2)} < \lambda_2^{(1)}$$

The characteristic polynomials are sketched in Fig. E2.38.

2.7 VECTOR AND MATRIX NORMS

We have discussed vectors, matrices, eigenvalues, and eigenvectors of symmetric matrices and have investigated the deeper significance of the elements in these entities. However, one important aspect has not been discussed so far. If we deal with single numbers, we can identify a number as being large or small. Vectors and matrices are functions of many elements, but we also need to measure their "size." Specifically, if single numbers are used in iterative processes, the convergence of a series of numbers, say $x_1, x_2, \ldots, x_k$, to a number x is simply measured by

$$\lim_{k \to \infty} |x_k - x| = 0 \tag{2.141}$$

or, in words, convergence is obtained if the residual $y_k = |x_k - x|$ approaches zero as $k \to \infty$. Furthermore, if we can find constants $p \geq 1$ and $c > 0$ such that

$$\lim_{k \to \infty} \frac{|x_{k+1} - x|}{|x_k - x|^p} = c \tag{2.142}$$

we say that convergence is of order p. If $p = 1$, convergence is linear and the rate of convergence is c, in which case c must be smaller than 1.

In iterative solution processes using vectors and matrices we also need a measure of convergence. Realizing that the size of a vector or matrix should depend on the magnitude of all elements in the arrays, we arrive at the definition of vector and matrix norms. A norm is a single number that depends on the magnitude of all elements in the vector or matrix.

Definition: A norm of a vector $\mathbf{v}$ of order n written as $\|\mathbf{v}\|$ is a single number. The norm is a function of the elements of $\mathbf{v}$, and the following conditions are satisfied:

1. $\|\mathbf{v}\| \geq 0$ *and* $\|\mathbf{v}\| = 0$ *if and only if* $\mathbf{v} = \mathbf{0}$. $\hspace{2cm}$ (2.143)
2. $\|c\mathbf{v}\| = |c|\|\mathbf{v}\|$ *for any scalar c.* $\hspace{2cm}$ (2.144)
3. $\|\mathbf{v} + \mathbf{w}\| \leq \|\mathbf{v}\| + \|\mathbf{w}\|$ *for vectors* $\mathbf{v}$ *and* $\mathbf{w}$. $\hspace{1cm}$ (2.145)

The relation (2.145) is the triangle inequality. The following three vector norms are commonly used and are called the infinity, one, and two vector norms:

$$\|\mathbf{v}\|_\infty = \max_i |v_i| \tag{2.146}$$

$$\|\mathbf{v}\|_1 = \sum_{i=1}^n |v_i| \tag{2.147}$$

$$\|\mathbf{v}\|_2 = \left(\sum_{i=1}^n |v_i|^2\right)^{1/2} \tag{2.148}$$

$\|\mathbf{v}\|_2$ is also known as the *Euclidean vector norm*. Geometrically, this norm is equal to the length of the vector $\mathbf{v}$. All three norms are special cases of the vector norm $\sqrt[p]{\Sigma_i |v_i|^p}$, where for (2.146), (2.147), and (2.148), $p = \infty$, 1, and 2, respectively. It should be noted that each of the norms in (2.146) to (2.148) satisfies the conditions in (2.143) to (2.145).

We can now measure convergence of a sequence of vectors $\mathbf{x}_1, \mathbf{x}_2, \mathbf{x}_3, \ldots, \mathbf{x}_k$ to a vector $\mathbf{x}$. That is, for the sequence to converge to $\mathbf{x}$ it is sufficient and necessary that

$$\lim_{k \to \infty} \|\mathbf{x}_k - \mathbf{x}\| = 0 \tag{2.149}$$

for any one of the vector norms. The order of convergence p, and in case $p = 1$, the rate of convergence c, are calculated in an analogous manner as in (2.142) but using norms; i.e., we have

$$\lim_{k \to \infty} \frac{\|\mathbf{x}_{k+1} - \mathbf{x}\|}{\|\mathbf{x}_k - \mathbf{x}\|^p} = c \tag{2.150}$$

Looking at the relationship between the vector norms, we note that they are equivalent in the sense that for any two norms $\|\cdot\|_{s_1}$ and $\|\cdot\|_{s_2}$ there exist two positive constants α_1 and α_2 such that

$$\|\mathbf{v}\|_{s_1} \leq \alpha_1 \|\mathbf{v}\|_{s_2} \tag{2.151}$$

and
$$\|\mathbf{v}\|_{s_2} \leq \alpha_2 \|\mathbf{v}\|_{s_1} \tag{2.152}$$

where s_1 and s_2 denote the ∞-, 1-, or 2-norms. Hence it follows that

$$c_1 \|\mathbf{v}\|_{s_1} \leq \|\mathbf{v}\|_{s_2} \leq c_2 \|\mathbf{v}\|_{s_1} \tag{2.153}$$

where c_1 and c_2 are two positive constants that may depend on n, and of course also

$$\frac{1}{c_2}\|\mathbf{v}\|_{s_2} \leq \|\mathbf{v}\|_{s_1} \leq \frac{1}{c_1}\|\mathbf{v}\|_{s_2}$$

EXAMPLE 2.39: Give the constants c_1 and c_2 in (2.153) if, first, the norms s_1 and s_2 are the ∞- and 1-norms, and then, second, the ∞- and 2-norms. Then show that in each case (2.153) is satisfied using the vector

$$\mathbf{v} = \begin{bmatrix} 1 \\ -3 \\ 2 \end{bmatrix}$$

In the first case we have

$$\|\mathbf{v}\|_\infty \le \|\mathbf{v}\|_1 \le n\|\mathbf{v}\|_\infty \tag{a}$$

with $c_1 = 1$, $c_2 = n$, and in the second case we have

$$\|\mathbf{v}\|_\infty \le \|\mathbf{v}\|_2 \le \sqrt{n}\|\mathbf{v}\|_\infty \tag{b}$$

with $c_1 = 1$ and $c_2 = \sqrt{n}$. These relations show that the 1- and 2-norms are equivalent to the ∞- norm. We can easily show that lower and upper bounds on $\|\mathbf{v}\|_1$ in (a) and $\|\mathbf{v}\|_2$ in (b) cannot be closer because the equal signs are reached for the vectors $\mathbf{v}^T = [1\ 1\ldots 1]$ and $\mathbf{v}^T = \mathbf{e}_i$ (and any scalar multiples thereof).

If we apply (a) and (b) to the given vector $\mathbf{v}$, we have

$$\|\mathbf{v}\|_\infty = 3$$
$$\|\mathbf{v}\|_1 = 1 + 3 + 2 = 6$$
$$\|\mathbf{v}\|_2 = \sqrt{1 + 9 + 4} = \sqrt{14}$$

and the relations in (a) and (b) read

$$3 \le 6 \le (3)(3); \qquad 3 < \sqrt{14} \le (\sqrt{3})(3)$$

In analogy with the definition of a vector norm, we also define a matrix norm.

Definition: A norm of a matrix $\mathbf{A}$ of order $n \times n$, written as $\|\mathbf{A}\|$, is a single number. The norm is a function of the elements of $\mathbf{A}$, and the following relations hold:

1. $\|\mathbf{A}\| \ge 0$ *and* $\|\mathbf{A}\| = 0$ *if and only if* $\mathbf{A} = \mathbf{0}$. $\hfill$ (2.154)
2. $\|c\mathbf{A}\| = |c|\|\mathbf{A}\|$ *for any scalar c.* $\hfill$ (2.155)
3. $\|\mathbf{A} + \mathbf{B}\| \le \|\mathbf{A}\| + \|\mathbf{B}\|$ *for matrices $\mathbf{A}$ and $\mathbf{B}$.* $\hfill$ (2.156)
4. $\|\mathbf{A}\mathbf{B}\| \le \|\mathbf{A}\|\|\mathbf{B}\|$ *for matrices $\mathbf{A}$ and $\mathbf{B}$.* $\hfill$ (2.157)

The relation in (2.156) is the triangle inequality equivalent to (2.145). The additional condition in (2.157), which was not postulated in the definition of a vector norm, must be satisfied in order to be able to use matrix norms when matrix products occur.

The following are frequently used matrix norms:

$$\|\mathbf{A}\|_\infty = \max_i \sum_{j=1}^n |a_{ij}| \tag{2.158}$$

$$\|\mathbf{A}\|_1 = \max_j \sum_{i=1}^n |a_{ij}| \tag{2.159}$$

$$\|\mathbf{A}\|_2 = \sqrt{\tilde{\lambda}_n}; \qquad \tilde{\lambda}_n = \text{maximum eigenvalue of } \mathbf{A}^T\mathbf{A} \tag{2.160}$$

where for a symmetric matrix $\mathbf{A}$ we have $\|\mathbf{A}\|_\infty = \|\mathbf{A}\|_1$ and $\|\mathbf{A}\|_2 = \max_i |\lambda_i|$ (see Exercise 2.21). The norm $\|\mathbf{A}\|_2$ is called the *spectral norm* of $\mathbf{A}$. Each of these norms satisfies the relations in (2.154) to (2.157). The proof that the relation in (2.157) is satisfied for the infinity norm is given in Example 2.41.

> **EXAMPLE 2.40:**   Calculate the ∞-, 1-, and 2-norms of the matrix $\mathbf{A}$, where $\mathbf{A}$ was given in Example 2.38.
>
> The matrix $\mathbf{A}$ considered is
>
> $$\mathbf{A} = \begin{bmatrix} 5 & -4 & -7 \\ -4 & 2 & -4 \\ -7 & -4 & 5 \end{bmatrix}$$
>
> Using the definitions given in (2.158) to (2.160), we have
>
> $$\|\mathbf{A}\|_\infty = 5 + 4 + 7 = 16$$
>
> $$\|\mathbf{A}\|_1 = 5 + 4 + 7 = 16$$
>
> The 2-norm is equal to $|\lambda_3|$, and hence (see Example 2.38) $\|\mathbf{A}\|_2 = 12$.

> **EXAMPLE 2.41:**   Show that for two matrices $\mathbf{A}$ and $\mathbf{B}$, we have
>
> $$\|\mathbf{A}\mathbf{B}\|_\infty \le \|\mathbf{A}\|_\infty \|\mathbf{B}\|_\infty$$
>
> Using the definition of the infinity matrix norm in (2.158), we have
>
> $$\|\mathbf{A}\mathbf{B}\|_\infty = \max_i \sum_{j=1}^{n} \left| \sum_{k=1}^{n} a_{ik} b_{kj} \right|$$
>
> but then
>
> $$\|\mathbf{A}\mathbf{B}\|_\infty \le \max_i \sum_{j=1}^{n} \sum_{k=1}^{n} |a_{ik}| \, |b_{kj}|$$
>
> $$= \max_i \sum_{k=1}^{n} \left\{ |a_{ik}| \sum_{j=1}^{n} |b_{kj}| \right\}$$
>
> $$\le \left\{ \max_i \sum_{k=1}^{n} |a_{ik}| \right\} \left\{ \max_k \sum_{j=1}^{n} |b_{kj}| \right\}$$
>
> This proves the desired result.

As in the case of a sequence of vectors, we can now measure the convergence of a sequence of matrices $\mathbf{A}_1, \mathbf{A}_2, \mathbf{A}_3, \ldots, \mathbf{A}_k$ to a matrix $\mathbf{A}$. For convergence it is necessary and sufficient that

$$\lim_{k \to \infty} \|\mathbf{A}_k - \mathbf{A}\| = 0 \tag{2.161}$$

for any one of the given matrix norms.

In the definition of a matrix norm we needed relation (2.157) to be able to use norms when we encounter matrix products. Similarly, we also want to use norms when products of matrices with vectors occur. In such a case, in order to obtain useful information by applying norms, we need to employ only specific vector norms with specific matrix norms. Which matrix and vector norms should only be used together is determined by the condition that the following relation hold for any matrix $\mathbf{A}$ and vector $\mathbf{v}$:

$$\|\mathbf{A}\mathbf{v}\| \le \|\mathbf{A}\| \|\mathbf{v}\| \tag{2.162}$$

where $\|\mathbf{Av}\|$ and $\|\mathbf{v}\|$ are evaluated using the vector norm and $\|\mathbf{A}\|$ is evaluated using the matrix norm. We may note the close relationship to the condition (2.157), which was required to hold for a matrix norm. If (2.162) holds for a specific vector and matrix norm, the two norms are said to be compatible and the matrix norm is said to be subordinate to the vector norm. The 1-, 2-, and ∞-norms of a matrix, as defined previously, are subordinate, respectively, to the 1-, 2-, and ∞-norms of a vector given in (2.146) to (2.148). In the following example we give the proof that the ∞-norms are compatible and subordinate. The compatibility of the vector and matrix 1- and 2-norms is proved similarly.

EXAMPLE 2.42: Show that for a matrix $\mathbf{A}$ and vector $\mathbf{v}$, we have

$$\|\mathbf{Av}\|_\infty \le \|\mathbf{A}\|_\infty \|\mathbf{v}\|_\infty \tag{a}$$

Using the definitions of the infinity norms, we have

$$\|\mathbf{Av}\|_\infty = \max_i \left| \sum_{j=1}^n a_{ij}v_j \right|$$

$$\le \max_i \sum_{j=1}^n |a_{ij}||v_j|$$

$$\le \left\{ \max_i \sum_{j=1}^n |a_{ij}| \right\} \{ \max_j |v_j| \}$$

This proves (a).

To show that equality can be reached, we need only to consider the case where $\mathbf{v}$ is a full unit vector and $a_{ij} \ge 0$. In this case, $\|\mathbf{v}\|_\infty = 1$ and $\|\mathbf{Av}\|_\infty = \|\mathbf{A}\|_\infty$.

In later chapters we shall encounter various applications of norms. One valuable application arises in the calculation of eigenvalues of a matrix: if we consider the problem $\mathbf{Av} = \lambda\mathbf{v}$, we obtain, taking norms on both sides,

$$\|\mathbf{Av}\| = \|\lambda\mathbf{v}\| \tag{2.163}$$

and hence using (2.144) and (2.162), we have

$$\|\mathbf{A}\|\|\mathbf{v}\| \ge |\lambda|\|\mathbf{v}\| \tag{2.164}$$

or

$$|\lambda| \le \|\mathbf{A}\| \tag{2.165}$$

Therefore, every eigenvalue of $\mathbf{A}$ is in absolute magnitude smaller than or equal to any norm of $\mathbf{A}$. Defining the *spectral radius* $\rho(\mathbf{A})$ as[3]

$$\rho(\mathbf{A}) = \max_i |\lambda_i| \tag{2.166}$$

we have

$$\rho(\mathbf{A}) \le \|\mathbf{A}\| \tag{2.167}$$

In practice, the ∞-norm of $\mathbf{A}$ is calculated most conveniently and thus used effectively to obtain an upper bound on the largest absolute value reached by the eigenvalues.

[3] Note that for a symmetric matrix $\mathbf{A}$ we have $\rho(\mathbf{A}) = \|\mathbf{A}\|_2$, but this does not hold in general for a nonsymmetric matrix; consider, for example, $\mathbf{A} = \begin{bmatrix} 1 & \alpha \\ 0 & 1 \end{bmatrix}$, $\alpha \ne 0$.

EXAMPLE 2.43:   Calculate the spectral radius of the matrix $\mathbf{A}$ considered in Example 2.38. Then show that $\rho(\mathbf{A}) \leq \|\mathbf{A}\|_\infty$.

The spectral radius is equal to $\max |\lambda_i|$ The eigenvalues of $\mathbf{A}$ have been calculated in Example 2.38.

$$\lambda_1 = -6; \qquad \lambda_2 = 6; \qquad \lambda_3 = 12$$

Hence
$$\rho(\mathbf{A}) = 12$$

In Example 2.40 we calculated $\|\mathbf{A}\|_\infty = 16$. Thus the relation $\rho(\mathbf{A}) \leq \|\mathbf{A}\|_\infty$ is satisfied.

Another important application of norms is encountered when considering the stability of finite element formulations (see Section 4.5). Assume that we have a sequence of finite element discretizations using a specific element and that a typical discretization gives the equation

$$\mathbf{A}\mathbf{x} = \mathbf{b} \tag{2.168}$$

Then, roughly speaking, for stability we want a small change in $\mathbf{b}$ to result in only a small change in $\mathbf{x}$. To measure the magnitude of these changes, assume that we choose a norm $\|\bullet\|_L$ for measuring the size of solutions and a norm $\|\bullet\|_R$ for measuring the size of the right-hand terms.

Definition: Let $\mathbf{A}$ be a nonsingular matrix of size $n \times n$. We define the stability constant *of $\mathbf{A}$ with respect to the norms $\|\bullet\|_L$ and $\|\bullet\|_R$ as the smallest possible constant S_{LR} such that*

$$\frac{\|\Delta\mathbf{x}\|_L}{\|\mathbf{x}\|_L} \leq S_{LR} \frac{\|\Delta\mathbf{b}\|_R}{\|\mathbf{b}\|_R} \tag{2.169}$$

for all vectors $\mathbf{x}$ and perturbations $\Delta\mathbf{x}$ which satisfy $\mathbf{A}\mathbf{x} = \mathbf{b}$ and $\mathbf{A}\,\Delta\mathbf{x} = \Delta\mathbf{b}$.

This relation bounds the relative change in the solution $\mathbf{x}$ (in the norm $\|\bullet\|_L$) as a consequence of a change in the forcing vector $\mathbf{b}$ (in the norm $\|\bullet\|_R$), and we say that a sequence of discretizations is stable with respect to the norms $\|\bullet\|_L$ and $\|\bullet\|_R$ if the constant S_{LR} is uniformly bounded irrespective of how large n is (see Section 4.5.2).

In accordance with (2.162), let[4]

$$\|\mathbf{A}\|_{LR} = \sup_{\mathbf{y}} \frac{\|\mathbf{A}\mathbf{y}\|_R}{\|\mathbf{y}\|_L} \tag{2.170}$$

and
$$\|\mathbf{A}^{-1}\|_{RL} = \sup_{\mathbf{z}} \frac{\|\mathbf{A}^{-1}\mathbf{z}\|_L}{\|\mathbf{z}\|_R} \tag{2.171}$$

Using $\mathbf{y} = \mathbf{x}$ in (2.170), we obtain

$$\|\mathbf{A}\|_{LR} \geq \frac{\|\mathbf{b}\|_R}{\|\mathbf{x}\|_L} \tag{2.172}$$

and using $\mathbf{z} = \Delta\mathbf{b}$ in (2.171), we obtain

$$\|\mathbf{A}^{-1}\|_{RL} \geq \frac{\|\Delta\mathbf{x}\|_L}{\|\Delta\mathbf{b}\|_R} \tag{2.173}$$

---

[4] In the following presentation "sup" means "supremum" and "inf" means "infimum" (see Table 4.5).

Therefore,

$$\frac{\|\Delta\mathbf{x}\|_L}{\|\mathbf{x}\|_L} \leq \|\mathbf{A}\|_{LR}\,\|\mathbf{A}^{-1}\|_{RL}\,\frac{\|\Delta\mathbf{b}\|_R}{\|\mathbf{b}\|_R} \tag{2.174}$$

and hence

$$S_{LR} = \|\mathbf{A}\|_{LR}\,\|\mathbf{A}^{-1}\|_{RL} \tag{2.175}$$

In the evaluation of S_{LR} it is crucial to use appropriate norms, and given a norm $\|\bullet\|_L$ a natural choice for the R norm is the dual norm of $\|\bullet\|_L$ defined as

$$\|\mathbf{z}\|_{DL} = \sup_{\mathbf{y}}\frac{\mathbf{y}^T\mathbf{z}}{\|\mathbf{y}\|_L} \tag{2.176}$$

With this choice we obtain for a symmetric matrix $\mathbf{A}$ (see Exercise 2.22)

$$\|\mathbf{A}\|_{LR} = \sup_{\mathbf{x},\mathbf{y}}\frac{\mathbf{x}^T\mathbf{A}\mathbf{y}}{\|\mathbf{x}\|_L\,\|\mathbf{y}\|_L}$$
$$= k_A \tag{2.177}$$

and

$$(\|\mathbf{A}^{-1}\|_{RL})^{-1} = \inf_{\mathbf{x}}\sup_{\mathbf{y}}\frac{\mathbf{x}^T\mathbf{A}\mathbf{y}}{\|\mathbf{x}\|_L\,\|\mathbf{y}\|_L} \tag{2.178}$$
$$= \gamma_A$$

The stability constant S_{LR} is then given by

$$S_{LR} = \frac{k_A}{\gamma_A} \tag{2.179}$$

As we mentioned earlier, for stability of a discretization we need to show that S_{LR} in (2.179) remains bounded as the finite element mesh is refined. This is a rather general result. Our discussion in Section 4.5 is concerned with a particular form of $\mathbf{A}$, namely, the form arising in our mixed displacement/pressure (u/p) formulations. In this case the stability condition leads to specific expressions that pertain specifically to the u/p formulations, and we give these expressions in Section 4.5.2.

2.8 EXERCISES

2.1. Evaluate the following required result in the most efficient way, that is, with the least number of multiplications. Count the number of multiplications used.

Let

$$\mathbf{A} = \begin{bmatrix} 3 & 4 & 1 \\ 4 & 6 & 2 \\ 1 & 2 & 3 \end{bmatrix}$$

$$\mathbf{B}^T = \begin{bmatrix} 1 & 3 & 2 \end{bmatrix}$$

$$k = 4$$

$$\mathbf{C} = \begin{bmatrix} 4 & 1 & -2 \\ 1 & 8 & -1 \\ -2 & -1 & 6 \end{bmatrix}$$

and calculate $\mathbf{B}^T\mathbf{A}k\,\mathbf{CB}$.

2.2. (a) Evaluate $\mathbf{A}^{-1}$ when

$$\mathbf{A} = \begin{bmatrix} 3 & -1 \\ -1 & 2 \end{bmatrix}$$

and when

$$\mathbf{A} = \begin{bmatrix} 2 & 0 & 1 \\ 0 & 4 & 0 \\ 1 & 0 & 2 \end{bmatrix}$$

(b) Evaluate the determinants of these two matrices.

2.3. Consider the following three vectors.

$$\mathbf{x}_1 = \begin{bmatrix} 1 \\ 3 \\ 4 \\ -1 \\ 2 \end{bmatrix}; \qquad \mathbf{x}_2 = \begin{bmatrix} 4 \\ 1 \\ -1 \\ 0 \\ 1 \end{bmatrix}; \qquad \mathbf{x}_3 = \begin{bmatrix} -7 \\ 1 \\ 6 \\ -1 \\ -1 \end{bmatrix}$$

Use these vectors as the columns of a matrix $\mathbf{A}$ and determine the rank and kernel of $\mathbf{A}$.

2.4. Consider the following matrix $\mathbf{A}$. Determine the constant k such that the rank of $\mathbf{A}$ is 2 and then determine the kernel of $\mathbf{A}$.

$$\mathbf{A} = \begin{bmatrix} 1 & -1 & 0 \\ -1 & 1+k & -1 \\ 0 & -1 & 1 \end{bmatrix}$$

2.5. Consider the following two vectors defined in the three-dimensional Cartesian frame with basis vectors $\mathbf{e}_i$.

$$\mathbf{u} = \begin{bmatrix} 2 \\ 3 \\ 4 \end{bmatrix}; \qquad \mathbf{v} = \begin{bmatrix} 1 \\ 2 \\ 3 \end{bmatrix}$$

(a) Evaluate the angle between these vectors.

(b) Assume that a new basis is to be used, namely, the primed basis in Example 2.24. Evaluate the components of the two vectors in this basis.

(c) Evaluate the angle between the vectors in this new basis.

2.6. A *reflection matrix* is defined as $\mathbf{P} = \mathbf{I} - \alpha\mathbf{v}\mathbf{v}^T$, $\alpha = \dfrac{2}{\mathbf{v}^T\mathbf{v}}$ where $\mathbf{v}$ is a vector (of order n) normal to the plane of reflection.

(a) Show that $\mathbf{P}$ is an orthogonal matrix.

(b) Consider the vector $\mathbf{Pu}$ where $\mathbf{u}$ is also a vector of order n. Show that the action of $\mathbf{P}$ on $\mathbf{u}$ is that the component of $\mathbf{u}$ normal to the plane of reflection has its direction reversed and the component of $\mathbf{u}$ in the plane of reflection is not changed.

2.7. The components of the stress tensor in the x_1, x_2 coordinate system of Fig. E2.25 are at a point

$$\boldsymbol{\tau} = \begin{bmatrix} 10 & -6 \\ -6 & 20 \end{bmatrix}$$

(a) Establish a new basis in which the off-diagonal components are zero, and give the new diagonal components.

(b) The effective stress is defined as $\bar{\sigma} = \sqrt{\dfrac{3}{2} S_{ij} S_{ij}}$ where the S_{ij} are the components of the deviatoric stress tensor, $S_{ij} = \tau_{ij} - \tau_m \delta_{ij}$ and τ_m is the mean stress $\tau_m = \dfrac{\tau_{ii}}{3}$. Prove that $\bar{\sigma}$ is a scalar. Then also show explicitly for the given value of $\boldsymbol{\tau}$ that $\bar{\sigma}$ is the same number in the old and new bases.

2.8. The column **q** is defined as

$$\mathbf{q} = \begin{bmatrix} x_1 \\ x_1 + x_2 \end{bmatrix}$$

where (x_1, x_2) are the coordinates of a point. Prove that **q** is *not* a vector.

2.9. The components of the Green-Lagrange strain tensor in the Cartesian coordinate system are defined as (see Section 6.2.2 for details)

$$\boldsymbol{\epsilon} = \tfrac{1}{2}(\mathbf{X}^T \mathbf{X} - \mathbf{I})$$

where the components of the deformation gradient **X** are

$$X_{ij} = \delta_{ij} + \frac{\partial u_i}{\partial x_j}$$

and u_i, x_j are the displacements and coordinates, respectively. Prove that the Green-Lagrange strain tensor is a second-order tensor.

2.10. The material tensor in (2.66) can be written as [see (6.185)]

$$C_{ijrs} = \lambda \delta_{ij} \delta_{rs} + \mu(\delta_{ir} \delta_{js} + \delta_{is} \delta_{jr}) \tag{a}$$

where λ and μ are the Lamé constants,

$$\lambda = \frac{E\nu}{(1 + \nu)(1 - 2\nu)}; \qquad \mu = \frac{E}{2(1 + \nu)}$$

This stress-strain relation can also be written in the matrix form used in Table 4.3, but in the table the use of engineering strain components is implied. (The tensor normal strain components are equal to the engineering normal strain components, but the tensor shear strain components are one-half the engineering components).

(a) Prove that C_{ijrs} is a fourth-order tensor.

(b) Consider the plane stress case and derive from the expression in (a) the expression in Table 4.3.

(c) Consider the plane stress case and write (2.66) in the matrix form $\mathbf{C}' = \mathbf{T}\mathbf{C}\mathbf{T}^T$, where **C** is given in Table 4.3 and you derive **T**. (See also Exercise 4.39.)

2.11. Prove that (2.70) holds.

2.12. The covariant base vectors expressed in a Cartesian coordinate system are

$$\mathbf{g}_1 = \begin{bmatrix} 1 \\ 0 \end{bmatrix}; \qquad \mathbf{g}_2 = \begin{bmatrix} \dfrac{1}{\sqrt{2}} \\ \dfrac{1}{\sqrt{2}} \end{bmatrix}$$

The force and displacement vectors in this basis are

$$\mathbf{R} = 3\mathbf{g}_1 + 4\mathbf{g}_2; \qquad \mathbf{u} = -2\mathbf{g}_1 + 3\mathbf{g}_2$$

(a) Calculate $\mathbf{R} \cdot \mathbf{u}$ using the covariant basis only.

(b) Calculate $\mathbf{R} \cdot \mathbf{u}$ using the covariant basis for $\mathbf{R}$ and the contravariant basis for $\mathbf{u}$.

2.13. Assume that the covariant basis is given by $\mathbf{g}_1$ and $\mathbf{g}_2$ in Exercise 2.12. Let the stress and strain tensor components in the Cartesian basis be

$$\boldsymbol{\tau} = \begin{bmatrix} 100 & 10 \\ 10 & 200 \end{bmatrix}; \quad \boldsymbol{\epsilon} = \begin{bmatrix} 0.01 & 0.05 \\ 0.05 & 0.02 \end{bmatrix}$$

Evaluate the components $\tilde{\tau}^{mn}$ and $\tilde{\epsilon}_{mn}$ and show explicitly that the product $\boldsymbol{\tau} \cdot \boldsymbol{\epsilon}$ is the same using on the one side the Cartesian stress and strain components and on the other side the contravariant stress and covariant strain components.

2.14. Let $\mathbf{a}$ and $\mathbf{b}$ be second-order tensors and let $\mathbf{A}$ and $\mathbf{B}$ be transformation matrices. Prove that

$$\mathbf{a} \cdot (\mathbf{A}\mathbf{b}\mathbf{B}^T) = (\mathbf{A}^T\mathbf{a}\mathbf{B}) \cdot \mathbf{b}.$$

(*Hint:* This proof is easily achieved by writing the quantities in component forms.)

2.15. Consider the eigenproblem $\mathbf{A}\mathbf{v} = \lambda\mathbf{v}$ with

$$\mathbf{A} = \begin{bmatrix} 2 & -1 \\ -1 & 1 \end{bmatrix}$$

(a) Solve for the eigenvalues and orthonormalized eigenvectors and write $\mathbf{A}$ in the form (2.109).

(b) Calculate $\mathbf{A}^6$, $\mathbf{A}^{-1}$ and $\mathbf{A}^{-2}$.

2.16. Consider the eigenproblem

$$\begin{bmatrix} 2 & 1 & 0 \\ 1 & 3 & 1 \\ 0 & 1 & 2 \end{bmatrix} \mathbf{v} = \lambda\mathbf{v}$$

The smallest eigenvalue and corresponding eigenvector are

$$\lambda_1 = 1; \quad \mathbf{v}_1 = \begin{bmatrix} \dfrac{1}{\sqrt{3}} \\[2mm] -\dfrac{1}{\sqrt{3}} \\[2mm] \dfrac{1}{\sqrt{3}} \end{bmatrix}$$

Also, $\lambda_2 = 2$, $\lambda_3 = 4$. Calculate the Rayleigh quotient $\rho(\mathbf{v})$ with

$$\mathbf{v} = \mathbf{v}_1 + 0.1 \begin{bmatrix} 1 \\ 1 \\ 0 \end{bmatrix}$$

and show that $\rho(\mathbf{v})$ is closer to λ_1 than $\mathbf{v}$ is to $\mathbf{v}_1$.

2.17. Consider the eigenproblem

$$\begin{bmatrix} 2 & -1 & 0 \\ -1 & 4 & -1 \\ 0 & -1 & 8 \end{bmatrix} \mathbf{v} = \lambda\mathbf{v}$$

Evaluate the eigenvalues of the matrices $\mathbf{A}$ and $\mathbf{A}^{(m)}$, $m = 1, 2$, where $\mathbf{A}^{(m)}$ is obtained by omitting the last m rows and columns in $\mathbf{A}$. Sketch the corresponding characteristic polynomials (see Example 2.38).

2.18. Prove that the 1- and 2-norms of a vector $\mathbf{v}$ are equivalent. Then show explicitly this equivalency for the vector

$$\mathbf{v} = \begin{bmatrix} 1 \\ 4 \\ -3 \end{bmatrix}$$

2.19. Prove the relation (2.157) for the 1-norm.

2.20. Prove that $\| \mathbf{A}\mathbf{v} \|_1 \leq \| \mathbf{A} \|_1 \| \mathbf{v} \|_1$.

2.21. Prove that for a symmetric matrix $\mathbf{A}$ we have $\| \mathbf{A} \|_2 = \rho(\mathbf{A})$. (*Hint:* Use (2.108).)

2.22. Prove that (2.177) and (2.178) hold when we use the dual norm of the L-norm for the R-norm.

CHAPTER THREE

Some Basic Concepts of Engineering Analysis and an Introduction to the Finite Element Method

3.1 INTRODUCTION

The analysis of an engineering system requires the idealization of the system into a form that can be solved, the formulation of the mathematical model, the solution of this model, and the interpretation of the results (see Section 1.2). The main objective of this chapter is to discuss some classical techniques used for the formulation and solution of mathematical models of engineering systems (see also S. H. Crandall [A]). This discussion will provide a valuable basis for the presentation of finite element procedures in the next chapters. Two categories of mathematical models are considered: lumped-parameter models and continuum-mechanics-based models. We also refer to these as "discrete-system" and "continuous-system" mathematical models.

In a lumped-parameter mathematical model, the actual system response is directly described by the solution of a finite number of state variables. In this chapter we discuss some general procedures that are employed to obtain the governing equations of lumped-parameter models. We consider steady-state, propagation, and eigenvalue problems and also briefly discuss the nature of the solutions of these problems.

For a continuum-mechanics-based mathematical model, the formulation of the governing equations is achieved as for a lumped-parameter model, but instead of a set of algebraic equations for the unknown state variables, differential equations govern the response. The exact solution of the differential equations satisfying all boundary conditions is possible only for relatively simple mathematical models, and numerical procedures must in general be employed. These procedures, in essence, *reduce the continuous-system mathematical model to a discrete idealization* that can be solved in the same manner as a lumped-parameter model. In this chapter we summarize some important classical procedures that are employed to reduce continuous-system mathematical models to lumped-parameter numerical models and briefly show how these classical procedures provide the basis for modern finite element methods.

In practice, the analyst must decide whether an engineering system should be represented by a lumped-parameter or a continuous-system mathematical model and must choose all specifics of the model. Furthermore, if a certain mathematical model is chosen, the analyst must decide how to solve numerically for the response. This is where much of the value of finite element procedures can be found; that is, finite element techniques used in conjunction with the digital computer have enabled the numerical solution of continuous-system mathematical models in a systematic manner and in effect have made possible the practical extension and application of the classical procedures presented in this chapter to very complex engineering systems.

3.2 SOLUTION OF DISCRETE-SYSTEM MATHEMATICAL MODELS

In this section we deal with *discrete* or *lumped-parameter* mathematical models. The essence of a lumped-parameter mathematical model is that the state of the system can be described *directly* with adequate precision by the magnitudes of a finite (and usually small) number of state variables. The solution requires the following steps:

1. *System idealization:* the actual system is idealized as an assemblage of elements
2. *Element equilibrium:* the equilibrium requirements of each element are established in terms of state variables
3. *Element assemblage:* the element interconnection requirements are invoked to establish a set of simultaneous equations for the unknown state variables
4. *Calculation of response:* the simultaneous equations are solved for the state variables, and using the element equilibrium requirements, the response of each element is calculated.

These steps of solution are followed in the analyses of the different types of problems that we consider: steady-state problems, propagation problems, and eigenvalue problems. The objective in this section is to provide an introduction showing how problems in these particular areas are analyzed and to briefly discuss the nature of the solutions. It should be realized that not all types of analysis problems in engineering are considered; however, a large majority of problems do fall naturally into these problem areas. In the examples in this section we consider structural, electrical, fluid flow, and heat transfer problems, and we emphasize that in each of these analyses the same basic steps of solution are followed.

3.2.1 Steady-State Problems

The main characteristic of a steady-state problem is that the response of the system does not change with time. Thus, the state variables describing the response of the system under consideration can be obtained from the solution of a set of equations that do not involve time as a variable. In the following examples we illustrate the procedure of analysis in the solution of some problems. Five sample problems are presented:

1. Elastic spring system
2. Heat transfer system

3. Hydraulic network
4. Dc network
5. Nonlinear elastic spring system.

The analysis of each problem illustrates the application of the general steps of analysis summarized in Section 3.2. The first four problems involve the analysis of linear systems, whereas the nonlinear elastic spring system responds nonlinearly to the applied loads. All the problems are well defined, and a unique solution exists for each system response.

EXAMPLE 3.1:   Figure E3.1 shows a system of three rigid carts on a horizontal plane that are interconnected by a system of linear elastic springs. Calculate the displacements of the carts and the forces in the springs for the loading shown.

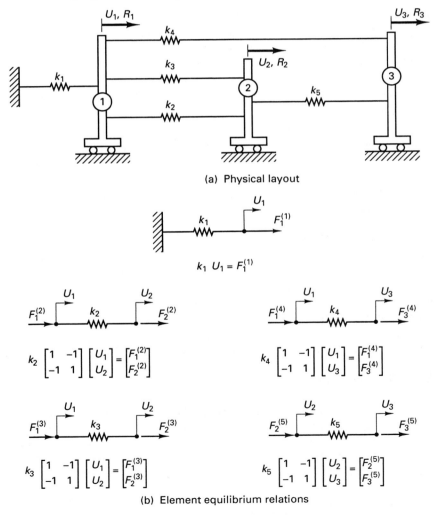

(a) Physical layout

$$k_1 U_1 = F_1^{(1)}$$

$$k_2 \begin{bmatrix} 1 & -1 \\ -1 & 1 \end{bmatrix} \begin{bmatrix} U_1 \\ U_2 \end{bmatrix} = \begin{bmatrix} F_1^{(2)} \\ F_2^{(2)} \end{bmatrix}$$

$$k_4 \begin{bmatrix} 1 & -1 \\ -1 & 1 \end{bmatrix} \begin{bmatrix} U_1 \\ U_3 \end{bmatrix} = \begin{bmatrix} F_1^{(4)} \\ F_3^{(4)} \end{bmatrix}$$

$$k_3 \begin{bmatrix} 1 & -1 \\ -1 & 1 \end{bmatrix} \begin{bmatrix} U_1 \\ U_2 \end{bmatrix} = \begin{bmatrix} F_1^{(3)} \\ F_2^{(3)} \end{bmatrix}$$

$$k_5 \begin{bmatrix} 1 & -1 \\ -1 & 1 \end{bmatrix} \begin{bmatrix} U_2 \\ U_3 \end{bmatrix} = \begin{bmatrix} F_2^{(5)} \\ F_3^{(5)} \end{bmatrix}$$

(b) Element equilibrium relations

Figure E3.1   System of rigid carts interconnected by linear springs

We perform the analysis by following steps 1 to 4 in Section 3.2. As state variables that characterize the response of the system, we choose the displacements U_1, U_2, and U_3. These displacements are measured from the initial positions of the carts, in which the springs are unstretched. The individual spring elements and their equilibrium requirements are shown in Fig. E3.1(b).

To generate the governing equations for the state variables we invoke the element interconnection requirements, which correspond to the static equilibrium of the three carts:

$$F_1^{(1)} + F_1^{(2)} + F_1^{(3)} + F_1^{(4)} = R_1$$

$$F_2^{(2)} + F_2^{(3)} + F_2^{(5)} = R_2 \tag{a}$$

$$F_3^{(4)} + F_3^{(5)} = R_3$$

We can now substitute for the element end forces $F_i^{(j)}$; $i = 1, 2, 3$; $j = 1, \ldots, 5$; using the element equilibrium requirements given in Fig. E3.1(b). Here we recognize that corresponding to the displacement components U_1, U_2, and U_3 we can write for element 1,

$$\begin{bmatrix} k_1 & 0 & 0 \\ 0 & 0 & 0 \\ 0 & 0 & 0 \end{bmatrix} \begin{bmatrix} U_1 \\ U_2 \\ U_3 \end{bmatrix} = \begin{bmatrix} F_1^{(1)} \\ 0 \\ 0 \end{bmatrix}$$

or

$$\mathbf{K}^{(1)} \mathbf{U} = \mathbf{F}^{(1)}$$

for element 2,

$$\begin{bmatrix} k_2 & -k_2 & 0 \\ -k_2 & k_2 & 0 \\ 0 & 0 & 0 \end{bmatrix} \begin{bmatrix} U_1 \\ U_2 \\ U_3 \end{bmatrix} = \begin{bmatrix} F_1^{(2)} \\ F_2^{(2)} \\ 0 \end{bmatrix}$$

or $\mathbf{K}^{(2)} \mathbf{U} = \mathbf{F}^{(2)}$, and so on. Hence the element interconnection requirements in (a) reduce to

$$\mathbf{K} \mathbf{U} = \mathbf{R} \tag{b}$$

where

$$\mathbf{U}^T = [U_1 \quad U_2 \quad U_3]$$

$$\mathbf{K} = \begin{bmatrix} (k_1 + k_2 + k_3 + k_4) & -(k_2 + k_3) & -k_4 \\ -(k_2 + k_3) & (k_2 + k_3 + k_5) & -k_5 \\ -k_4 & -k_5 & (k_4 + k_5) \end{bmatrix}$$

and

$$\mathbf{R}^T = [R_1 \quad R_2 \quad R_3]$$

Here it is noted that the coefficient matrix $\mathbf{K}$ can be obtained using

$$\mathbf{K} = \sum_{i=1}^{5} \mathbf{K}^{(i)} \tag{c}$$

where the $\mathbf{K}^{(i)}$ are the element stiffness matrices. The summation process for obtaining in (c) the total structure stiffness matrix by direct summation of the element stiffness matrices is referred to as the *direct stiffness method*.

The analysis of the system is completed by solving (b) for the state variables U_1, U_2, and U_3 and then calculating the element forces from the element equilibrium relationships in Fig. E3.1.

EXAMPLE 3.2: A wall is constructed of two homogeneous slabs in contact as shown in Fig. E3.2. In steady-state conditions the temperatures in the wall are characterized by the external surface temperatures θ_1 and θ_3 and the interface temperature θ_2. Establish the equi-

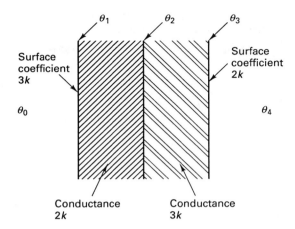

Figure E3.2   Slab subjected to temperature boundary conditions

librium equations of the problem in terms of these temperatures when the ambient temperatures θ_0 and θ_4 are known.

The conductance per unit area for the individual slabs and the surface coefficients are given in Fig. E3.2. The heat conduction law is $q/A = \bar{k} \, \Delta\theta$, where q is the total heat flow, A is the area, $\Delta\theta$ is the temperature drop in the direction of heat flow, and $\bar{k}$ is the conductance or surface coefficient. The state variables in this analysis are θ_1, θ_2, and θ_3. Using the heat conduction law, the element equilibrium equations are

for the left surface, per unit area:

$$q_1 = 3k(\theta_0 - \theta_1)$$

for the left slab:

$$q_2 = 2k(\theta_1 - \theta_2)$$

for the right slab:

$$q_3 = 3k(\theta_2 - \theta_3)$$

for the right surface:

$$q_4 = 2k(\theta_3 - \theta_4)$$

To obtain the governing equations for the state variables, we invoke the heat flow equilibrium requirement $q_1 = q_2 = q_3 = q_4$. Thus,

$$3k(\theta_0 - \theta_1) = 2k(\theta_1 - \theta_2)$$

$$2k(\theta_1 - \theta_2) = 3k(\theta_2 - \theta_3)$$

$$3k(\theta_2 - \theta_3) = 2k(\theta_3 - \theta_4)$$

Writing these equations in matrix form we obtain

$$\begin{bmatrix} 5k & -2k & 0 \\ -2k & 5k & -3k \\ 0 & -3k & 5k \end{bmatrix} \begin{bmatrix} \theta_1 \\ \theta_2 \\ \theta_3 \end{bmatrix} = \begin{bmatrix} 3k\theta_0 \\ 0 \\ 2k\theta_4 \end{bmatrix} \qquad \text{(a)}$$

These equilibrium equations can be also derived in a systematic manner using a direct stiffness procedure. Using this technique, we proceed as in Example 3.1 with the typical element equilibrium relations

$$\bar{k} \begin{bmatrix} 1 & -1 \\ -1 & 1 \end{bmatrix} \begin{bmatrix} \theta_i \\ \theta_j \end{bmatrix} = \begin{bmatrix} q_i \\ q_j \end{bmatrix}$$

where q_i, q_j are the heat flows into the element and θ_i, θ_j are the element-end temperatures. For the system in Fig. E3.2 we have two conduction elements (each slab being one element), hence we obtain

$$
\begin{bmatrix}
2k & -2k & 0 \\
-2k & 5k & -3k \\
0 & -3k & 3k
\end{bmatrix}
\begin{bmatrix}
\theta_1 \\
\theta_2 \\
\theta_3
\end{bmatrix}
=
\begin{bmatrix}
3k(\theta_0 - \theta_1) \\
0 \\
2k(\theta_4 - \theta_3)
\end{bmatrix}
\tag{b}
$$

Since θ_1 and θ_3 are unknown, the equilibrium relations in (b) are rearranged for solution to obtain the relations in (a).

It is interesting to note the analogy between the displacement and force analysis of the spring system in Example 3.1 and the temperature and heat transfer analysis in Example 3.2. The coefficient matrices are very similar in both analyses, and they can both be obtained in a very systematic manner. To emphasize the analogy we give in Fig. 3.1 a spring model that is governed by the coefficient matrix of the heat transfer problem.

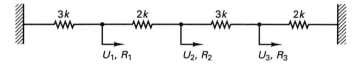

Figure 3.1 Assemblage of springs governed by same coefficient matrix as the heat transfer problem in Fig. E3.2

We next consider the analyses of a simple flow problem and a simple electrical system, both of which are again analyzed in much the same manner as the spring and heat transfer problems.

EXAMPLE 3.3: Establish the equations that govern the steady-state pressure and flow distributions in the hydraulic network shown in Fig. E3.3. Assume the fluid to be incompressible and the pressure drop in a branch to be proportional to the flow q through that branch, $\Delta p = Rq$, where R is the branch resistance coefficient.

In this analysis the elements are the individual branches of the pipe network. As unknown state variables that characterize the flow and pressure distributions in the system we select the

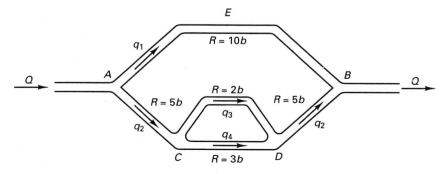

Figure E3.3 Pipe network

pressures at A, C, and D, which we denote as p_A, p_C, and p_D, and we assume that the pressure at B is zero. Thus, we have for the elements

$$q_1 = \frac{p_A}{10b}; \qquad q_3 = \frac{p_C - p_D}{2b}$$

$$q_2|_{AC} = \frac{p_A - p_C}{5b}; \qquad q_2|_{DB} = \frac{p_D}{5b}; \qquad q_4 = \frac{p_C - p_D}{3b}$$

(a)

The element interconnectivity requirements require continuity of flow, hence

$$Q = q_1 + q_2$$

$$q_2|_{AC} = q_3 + q_4; \qquad q_2|_{DB} = q_3 + q_4$$

(b)

Substituting from (a) into (b) and writing the resulting equations in matrix form, we obtain

$$\begin{bmatrix} 3 & -2 & 0 \\ -6 & 31 & -25 \\ -1 & 1 & 1 \end{bmatrix} \begin{bmatrix} p_A \\ p_C \\ p_D \end{bmatrix} = \begin{bmatrix} 10bQ \\ 0 \\ 0 \end{bmatrix}$$

or

$$\begin{bmatrix} 9 & -6 & 0 \\ -6 & 31 & -25 \\ 0 & -25 & 31 \end{bmatrix} \begin{bmatrix} p_A \\ p_C \\ p_D \end{bmatrix} = \begin{bmatrix} 30bQ \\ 0 \\ 0 \end{bmatrix}$$

(c)

The analysis of the pipe network is completed by solving from (c) for the pressures p_A, p_C, and p_D, and then the element equilibrium relations in (a) can be employed to obtain the flow distribution.

The equilibrium relations in (c) can also be derived—as in the preceding spring and heat transfer examples—using a direct stiffness procedure. Using this technique, we proceed as in Example 3.1 with the typical element equilibrium relations

$$\frac{1}{R}\begin{bmatrix} 1 & -1 \\ -1 & 1 \end{bmatrix}\begin{bmatrix} p_i \\ p_j \end{bmatrix} = \begin{bmatrix} q_i \\ q_j \end{bmatrix}$$

where q_i, q_j are the fluid flows into the element and p_i, p_j are the element-end pressures.

EXAMPLE 3.4: Consider the dc network shown in Fig. E3.4. The network with the resistances shown is subjected to the constant-voltage inputs E and $2E$ at A and B, respectively. We are to determine the steady-state current distribution in the network.

In this analysis we use as unknown state variables the currents I_1, I_2, and I_3. The system elements are the resistors, and the element equilibrium requirements are obtained by applying Ohm's law to the resistors. For a resistor $\bar{R}$, carrying current I, we have Ohm's law

$$\Delta E = \bar{R} I$$

where ΔE is the voltage drop across the resistor.

The element interconnection law to be satisfied is Kirchhoff's voltage law for each closed loop in the network,

$$2E = 2RI_1 + 2R(I_1 - I_3)$$

$$E = 4R(I_2 - I_3)$$

$$0 = 6RI_3 + 4R(I_3 - I_2) + 2R(I_3 - I_1)$$

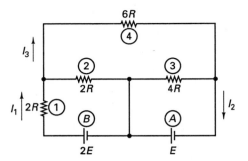

Figure E3.4   Dc network

Writing these equations in matrix form, we obtain

$$
\begin{bmatrix}
4R & 0 & -2R \\
0 & 4R & -4R \\
-2R & -4R & 12R
\end{bmatrix}
\begin{bmatrix}
I_1 \\
I_2 \\
I_3
\end{bmatrix}
=
\begin{bmatrix}
2E \\
E \\
0
\end{bmatrix}
\tag{a}
$$

The analysis is completed by solving these equations for I_1, I_2, and I_3. Note that the equilibrium equations in (a) could also have been established using a direct stiffness procedure, as in Examples 3.1 to 3.3.

We should note once again that the steps of analysis in the preceding structural, heat transfer, fluid flow, and electrical problems are very similar, the basic analogy being possibly best expressed in the use of the direct stiffness procedure for each problem. This indicates that the same basic numerical procedures will be applicable in the analysis of almost any physical problem (see Chapters 4 and 7).

Each of these examples deals with a linear system; i.e., the coefficient matrix is constant and thus, if the right-hand-side forcing functions are multiplied by a constant α, the system response is also α times as large. We consider in this chapter primarily linear systems, but the same steps for solution summarized previously are also applicable in nonlinear analysis, as demonstrated in the following example (see also Chapters 6 and 7).

EXAMPLE 3.5:   Consider the spring-cart system in Fig. E3.1 and assume that spring ① now has the nonlinear behavior shown in Fig. E3.5. Discuss how the equilibrium equations given in Example 3.1 have to be modified for this analysis.

As long as $U_1 \le \Delta y$, the equilibrium equations in Example 3.1 are applicable with $k_1 = k$. However, if the loads are such that $U_1 > \Delta y$, i.e., $F_1^{(1)} > F_y$, we need to use a different value for k_1, and this value depends on the force $F_1^{(1)}$ acting in the element. Denoting the stiffness value by k_s, as shown in Fig. E3.5, the response of the system is described for any load by the equilibrium equations

$$
\mathbf{K}_s \mathbf{U} = \mathbf{R}
\tag{a}
$$

where the coefficient matrix is established exactly as in Example 3.1 but using k_s instead of k_1,

$$
\mathbf{K}_s =
\begin{bmatrix}
(k_s + k_2 + k_3 + k_4) & -(k_2 + k_3) & -k_4 \\
-(k_2 + k_3) & (k_2 + k_3 + k_5) & -k_5 \\
-k_4 & -k_5 & (k_4 + k_5)
\end{bmatrix}
\tag{b}
$$

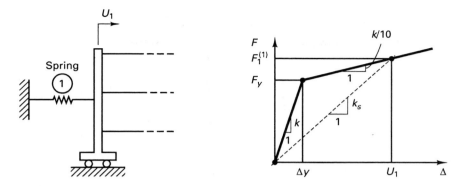

Figure E3.5   Spring ① of the cart-spring system of Fig. E3.1 with nonlinear elastic characteristics

Although the response of the system can be calculated using this approach, in which $\mathbf{K}_s$ is referred to as the secant matrix, we will see in Chapter 6 that in general practical analysis we actually use an incremental procedure with a tangent stiffness matrix.

These analyses demonstrate the general analysis procedure: the selection of unknown state variables that characterize the response of the system under consideration, the identification of elements that together comprise the complete system, the establishment of the element equilibrium requirements, and finally the assemblage of the elements by invoking interelement continuity requirements.

A few observations should be made. First, we need to recognize that there is some choice in the selection of the state variables. For example, in the analysis of the carts in Example 3.1, we could have chosen the unknown forces in the springs as state variables. A second observation is that the equations from which the state variables are calculated can be linear or nonlinear equations and the coefficient matrix can be of a general nature. However, it is most desirable to deal with a symmetric positive definite coefficient matrix because in such cases the solution of the equations is numerically very effective (see Section 8.2).

In general, the physical characteristics of a problem determine whether the numerical solution can actually be cast in a form that leads to a symmetric positive definite coefficient matrix. However, even if possible, a positive definite coefficient matrix is obtained only if appropriate solution variables are selected, and in a nonlinear analysis an appropriate linearization must be performed in the iterative solution. For this reason, in practice, it is valuable to employ general formulations for whole classes of problems (e.g., structural analysis, heat transfer, and so on—see Sections 4.2, 7.2, and 7.3) that for any analysis lead to a symmetric and positive definite coefficient matrix.

In the preceding discussion we employed the direct approach of assembling the system-governing equilibrium equations. An important point is that the governing equilibrium equations for state variables can in many analyses also be obtained using an extremum, or variational formulation. *An extremum problem consists of locating the set (or* *sets) of values (state variables) U_i, $i = 1, \ldots n$, for which a given functional $\Pi(U_1, \ldots, U_n)$ is a maximum, is a minimum, or has a saddle point.* The condition for obtaining the equations for the state variables is

$$\delta\Pi = 0 \tag{3.1}$$

and since

$$\delta\Pi = \frac{\partial\Pi}{\partial U_1}\delta U_1 + \cdots + \frac{\partial\Pi}{\partial U_n}\delta U_n \tag{3.2}$$

we must have

$$\frac{\partial\Pi}{\partial U_i} = 0 \quad \text{for } i = 1, \ldots, n \tag{3.3}$$

We note that δU_i stands for "variations in the state variables U_i that are arbitrary except that they must be zero at and corresponding to the state variable boundary conditions."[1] The second derivatives of Π with respect to the state variables then decide whether the solution corresponds to a maximum, a minimum, or a saddle point. In the solution of lumped-parameter models we can consider that Π *is defined such that the relations in (3.3) generate the governing equilibrium equations.*[2] For example, in linear structural analysis, when displacements are used as state variables, Π is the total potential (or total potential energy)

$$\Pi = \mathcal{U} - \mathcal{W} \tag{3.4}$$

where $\mathcal{U}$ is the strain energy of the system and $\mathcal{W}$ is the total potential of the loads. The solution for the state variables corresponds in this case to the minimum of Π.

EXAMPLE 3.6: Consider a simple spring of stiffness k and applied load P, and discuss the use of (3.1) and (3.4).

Let u be the displacement of the spring under the load P. We then have

$$\mathcal{U} = \tfrac{1}{2}ku^2; \qquad \mathcal{W} = Pu$$

and

$$\Pi = \tfrac{1}{2}ku^2 - Pu$$

Note that for a given P, we could graph Π as a function of u. Using (3.1) we have, with u as the only variable,

$$\delta\Pi = (ku - P)\,\delta u; \qquad \frac{\partial\Pi}{\partial u} = ku - P$$

which gives the equilibrium equation

$$ku = P \tag{a}$$

Using (a) to evaluate $\mathcal{W}$, we have *at equilibrium* $\mathcal{W} = ku^2$; i.e., $\mathcal{W} = 2\mathcal{U}$ and $\Pi = -\tfrac{1}{2}ku^2 = -\tfrac{1}{2}Pu$. Also, $\partial^2\Pi/\partial u^2 = k$ and hence at equilibrium Π is at its minimum.

EXAMPLE 3.7: Consider the analysis of the system of rigid carts in Example 3.1. Determine Π and invoke the condition in (3.1) for obtaining the governing equilibrium equations.

Using the notation defined in Example 3.1, we have

$$\mathcal{U} = \tfrac{1}{2}\mathbf{U}^T\mathbf{K}\mathbf{U} \tag{a}$$

[1] More precisely, the variations in the state variables must be zero *at and corresponding to* the essential boundary conditions, as further discussed in Section 3.3.2.

[2] In this way we consider a specific variational formulation, as further discussed in Chapters 4 and 7.

and $$\mathcal{W} = \mathbf{U}^T \mathbf{R} \tag{b}$$

where it should be noted that the total strain energy in (a) could also be written as

$$\mathcal{U} = \tfrac{1}{2} \mathbf{U}^T \left(\sum_{i=1}^{5} \mathbf{K}^{(i)} \right) \mathbf{U}$$

$$= \tfrac{1}{2} \mathbf{U}^T \mathbf{K}^{(1)} \mathbf{U} + \tfrac{1}{2} \mathbf{U}^T \mathbf{K}^{(2)} \mathbf{U} + \cdots + \tfrac{1}{2} \mathbf{U}^T \mathbf{K}^{(5)} \mathbf{U}$$

$$= \mathcal{U}_1 + \mathcal{U}_2 + \cdots + \mathcal{U}_5$$

where $\mathcal{U}_i$ is the strain energy stored in the ith element.

Using (a) and (b), we now obtain

$$\Pi = \tfrac{1}{2} \mathbf{U}^T \mathbf{K} \mathbf{U} - \mathbf{U}^T \mathbf{R} \tag{c}$$

Applying (3.1) gives

$$\mathbf{K} \mathbf{U} = \mathbf{R}$$

Solving for $\mathbf{U}$ and then substituting into (c), we find that Π corresponding to the displacements at system equilibrium is

$$\Pi = -\tfrac{1}{2} \mathbf{U}^T \mathbf{R}$$

Since the same equilibrium equations are generated using the direct solution approach and the variational approach, we may ask what the advantages of employing a variational scheme are. Assume that for the problem under consideration Π is defined. The equilibrium equations can then be generated by simply adding the contributions from all elements to Π and invoking the stationarity condition in (3.1). In essence, this condition generates automatically the element interconnectivity requirements. Thus, the variational technique can be very effective because the system-governing equilibrium equations can be generated "quite mechanically." The advantages of a variational approach are even more pronounced when we consider the numerical solution of a continuous system (see Section 3.3.2). However, a main disadvantage of a variational approach is that, in general, less physical insight into a problem formulation is obtained than when using the direct approach. Therefore, it may be critical that we interpret physically the system equilibrium equations, once they have been established using a variational approach, in order to identify possible errors in the solution and in order to gain a better understanding of the physical meaning of the equations.

3.2.2 Propagation Problems

The main characteristic of a propagation or dynamic problem is that the response of the system under consideration changes with time. For the analysis of a system, in principle, the same procedures as in the analysis of a steady-state problem are employed, but now the state variables and element equilibrium relations depend on time. The objective of the analysis is to calculate the state variables for all time t.

Before discussing actual propagation problems, let us consider the case where the time effect on the element equilibrium relations is negligible but the load vector is a function of time. In this case the system response is obtained using the equations governing the steady-state response but substituting the time-dependent load or forcing vector for the load vector employed in the steady-state analysis. Since such an analysis is in essence still a steady-state analysis, but with steady-state conditions considered at any time t, the analysis may be referred to as a pseudo steady-state analysis.

In an actual propagation problem, the element equilibrium relations are time-dependent, and this accounts for major differences in the response characteristics when compared to steady-state problems. In the following we present two examples that demonstrate the formulation of the governing equilibrium equations in propagation problems. Methods for calculating the solution of these equations are given in Chapter 9.

EXAMPLE 3.8: Consider the system of rigid carts that was analyzed in Example 3.1. Assume that the loads are time-dependent and establish the equations that govern the dynamic response of the system.

For the analysis we assume that the springs are massless and that the carts have masses m_1, m_2, and m_3 (which amounts to lumping the distributed mass of each spring to its two end points). Then, using the information given in Example 3.1 and invoking d'Alembert's principle, the element interconnectivity requirements yield the equations

$$F_1^{(1)} + F_1^{(2)} + F_1^{(3)} + F_1^{(4)} = R_1(t) - m_1 \ddot{U}_1$$

$$F_2^{(2)} + F_2^{(3)} + F_2^{(5)} = R_2(t) - m_2 \ddot{U}_2$$

$$F_3^{(4)} + F_3^{(5)} = R_3(t) - m_3 \ddot{U}_3$$

where
$$\ddot{U}_i = \frac{d^2 U_i}{dt^2}; \qquad i = 1, 2, 3$$

Thus we obtain as the system-governing equilibrium equations

$$\mathbf{M\ddot{U}} + \mathbf{KU} = \mathbf{R}(t) \tag{a}$$

where $\mathbf{K}$, $\mathbf{U}$, and $\mathbf{R}$ have been defined in Example 3.1 and $\mathbf{M}$ is the system mass matrix

$$\mathbf{M} = \begin{bmatrix} m_1 & 0 & 0 \\ 0 & m_2 & 0 \\ 0 & 0 & m_3 \end{bmatrix}$$

The equilibrium equations in (a) represent a system of ordinary differential equations of second order in time. For the solution of these equations it is also necessary that the initial conditions on $\mathbf{U}$ and $\dot{\mathbf{U}}$ be given; i.e., we need to have $^0\mathbf{U}$ and $^0\dot{\mathbf{U}}$, where

$$^0\mathbf{U} = \mathbf{U}|_{t=0}; \qquad ^0\dot{\mathbf{U}} = \dot{\mathbf{U}}|_{t=0}$$

Earlier we mentioned the case of a pseudo steady-state analysis. Considering the response of the carts, such analysis implies that the loads change very slowly and hence mass effects can be neglected. Therefore, to obtain the pseudo steady-state response, the equilibrium equations (a) in Example 3.8 should be solved with $\mathbf{M} = \mathbf{0}$.

EXAMPLE 3.9: Figure E3.9 shows an idealized case of the transient heat flow in an electron tube. A filament is heated to a temperature θ_f by an electric current; heat is convected from the filament to the surrounding gas and is radiated to the wall, which also receives heat by convection from the gas. The wall itself convects heat to the surrounding atmosphere, which is at temperature θ_a. It is required to formulate the system-governing heat flow equilibrium equations.

In this analysis we choose as unknown state variables the temperature of the gas, θ_1, and the temperature of the wall, θ_2. The system equilibrium equations are generated by invoking the heat flow equilibrium for the gas and the wall. Using the heat transfer coefficients given in

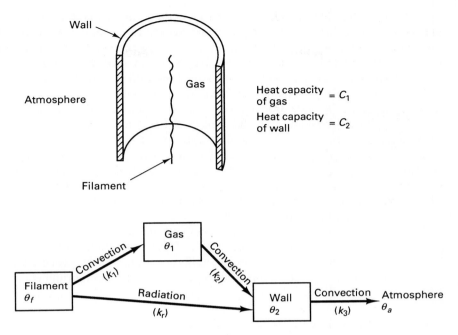

Figure E3.9   Heat transfer idealization of an electron tube

Fig. E3.9, we obtain for the gas

$$C_1 \frac{d\theta_1}{dt} = k_1(\theta_f - \theta_1) - k_2(\theta_1 - \theta_2)$$

and for the wall

$$C_2 \frac{d\theta_2}{dt} = k_r((\theta_f)^4 - (\theta_2)^4) + k_2(\theta_1 - \theta_2) - k_3(\theta_2 - \theta_a)$$

These two equations can be written in matrix form as

$$\mathbf{C\dot{\theta}} + \mathbf{K\theta} = \mathbf{Q} \qquad (a)$$

where
$$\mathbf{C} = \begin{bmatrix} C_1 & 0 \\ 0 & C_2 \end{bmatrix}; \qquad \mathbf{K} = \begin{bmatrix} (k_1 + k_2) & -k_2 \\ -k_2 & (k_2 + k_3) \end{bmatrix}$$

$$\mathbf{\theta} = \begin{bmatrix} \theta_1 \\ \theta_2 \end{bmatrix}; \qquad \mathbf{Q} = \begin{bmatrix} k_1\theta_f \\ k_r((\theta_f)^4 - (\theta_2)^4) + k_3\theta_a \end{bmatrix}$$

We note that because of the radiation boundary condition, the heat flow equilibrium equations are nonlinear in $\mathbf{\theta}$. Here the radiation boundary condition term has been incorporated in the heat flow load vector $\mathbf{Q}$. The solution of the equations can be carried out as described in Section 9.6.

Although, in the previous examples, we considered very specific cases, these examples illustrated in a quite general way how propagation problems of discrete systems are formulated for analysis. In essence, the same procedures are employed as in the analysis of steady-state problems, but "time-dependent loads" are generated that are a result of the "resistance to change" of the elements and thus of the complete system. This resistance to change or *inertia* of the system must be considered in a dynamic analysis.

Based on the preceding arguments and observations, it appears that we can conclude that the analysis of a propagation problem is a very simple extension of the analysis of the corresponding steady-state problem. However, we assumed in the earlier discussion that the discrete system is given and thus the degrees of freedom or state variables can be directly identified. In practice, the selection of an appropriate discrete system that contains all the important characteristics of the actual physical system is usually not straightforward, and in general a different discrete model must be chosen for a dynamic response prediction than is chosen for the steady-state analysis. However, the discussion illustrates that once the discrete model has been chosen for a propagation problem, formulation of the governing equilibrium equations can proceed in much the same way as in the analysis of a steady-state response, except that inertia loads are generated that act on the system in addition to the externally applied loads (see Section 4.2.1). This observation leads us to anticipate that the procedures for solving the dynamic equilibrium equations of a system are largely based on the techniques employed for the solution of steady-state equilibrium equations (see Section 9.2).

3.2.3 Eigenvalue Problems

In our earlier discussion of steady-state and propagation problems we implied the existence of a unique solution for the response of the system. A main characteristic of an eigenvalue problem is that there is no unique solution to the response of the system, and the objective of the analysis is to calculate the various possible solutions. Eigenvalue problems arise in both steady-state and dynamic analyses.

Various different eigenvalue problems can be formulated in engineering analysis. In this book we are primarily concerned with the generalized eigenvalue problem of the form

$$\mathbf{A}\mathbf{v} = \lambda \mathbf{B}\mathbf{v} \tag{3.5}$$

where $\mathbf{A}$ and $\mathbf{B}$ are symmetric matrices, λ is a scalar, and $\mathbf{v}$ is a vector. If λ_i and $\mathbf{v}_i$ satisfy (3.5), they are called an eigenvalue and an eigenvector, respectively.

In steady-state analysis an eigenvalue problem of the form (3.5) is formulated when it is necessary to investigate the physical stability of the system under consideration. The question that is asked and leads to the eigenvalue problem is as follows: *Assuming that the steady-state solution of the system is known, is there another solution into which the system could bifurcate if it were slightly perturbed from its equilibrium position?* The answer to this question depends on the system under consideration and the loads acting on the system. We consider a very simple example to demonstrate the basic idea.

> **EXAMPLE 3.10:** Consider the simple cantilever shown in Fig. E3.10. The structure consists of a rotational spring and a rigid lever arm. Predict the response of the structure for the load applications shown in the figure.
>
> We consider first only the steady-state response as discussed in Section 3.2.1. Since the bar is rigid, the cantilever is a single degree of freedom system and we employ Δ_v as the state variable.

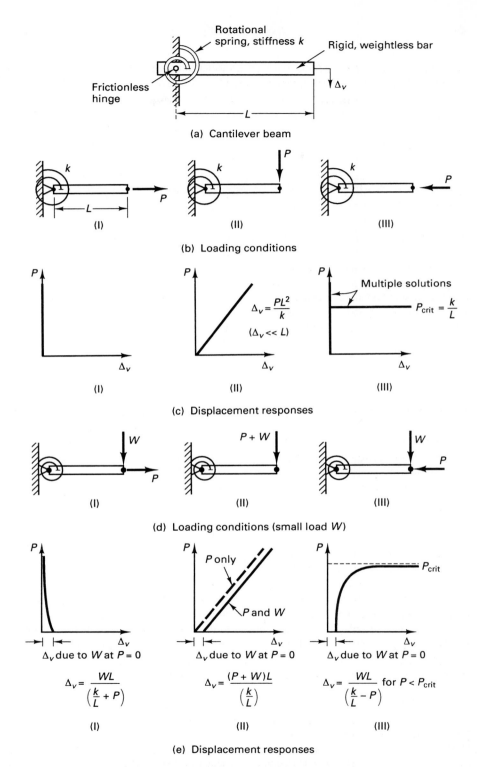

Figure E3.10 Analysis of a simple cantilever model

In loading condition I, the bar is subjected to a longitudinal tensile force P, and the moment in the spring is zero. Since the bar is rigid, we have

$$\Delta_v = 0 \tag{a}$$

Next consider loading condition II. Assuming small displacements we have in this case

$$\Delta_v = \frac{PL^2}{k} \tag{b}$$

Finally, for loading condition III we have, as in condition I,

$$\Delta_v = 0 \tag{c}$$

We now proceed to determine whether the system is stable under these load applications. To investigate the stability we perturb the structure from the equilibrium positions defined in (a), (b), and (c) and ask whether an additional equilibrium position is possible.

Assume that Δ_v is positive but small in loading conditions I and II. If we write the equilibrium equations taking this displacement into account, we observe that in loading condition I the small nonzero Δ_v cannot be sustained, and that in loading condition II the effect of including Δ_v in the analysis is negligible.

Consider next that $\Delta_v > 0$ in loading condition III. In this case, for an equilibrium configuration to be possible with Δ_v nonzero, the following equilibrium equation must be satisfied:

$$P\Delta_v = k\frac{\Delta_v}{L}$$

But this equation is satisfied for any Δ_v, provided $P = k/L$. Hence the critical load P_{crit} at which an equilibrium position in addition to the horizontal one becomes possible is

$$P_{crit} = \frac{k}{L}$$

In summary, we have

$P < P_{crit}$ only the horizontal position of the bar is possible; equilibrium is stable

$P = P_{crit}$ horizontal and deflected positions of the bar are possible; the horizontal equilibrium position is unstable for $P \geq P_{crit}$.

To gain an improved understanding of these results we may assume that in addition to the load P shown in Fig. E3.10(b), a small transverse load W is applied as shown in Fig. E3.10(d). If we then perform an analysis of the cantilever model subjected to P and W, the response curves shown schematically in Fig. E3.10(e) are obtained. Thus, we observe that the effect of the load W decreases and is constant as P increases in loading conditions I and II, but that in loading condition III the transverse displacement Δ_v increases very rapidly as P approaches the critical load, P_{crit}.

The analyses given in Example 3.10 illustrate the main objective of an eigenvalue formulation and solution in instability analysis, namely, to predict whether small disturbances that are imposed on the given equilibrium configuration tend to increase very substantially. The load level at which this situation arises corresponds to the critical loading of the system. In the second solution carried out in Example 3.10 the small disturbance was due to the small load W, which, for example, may simulate the possibility that the horizontal load on the cantilever is not acting perfectly horizontally. In the eigenvalue analysis, we simply assume a deformed configuration and investigate whether there is a load level that indeed admits such a configuration as a possible equilibrium solution. We shall discuss in Section 6.8.2 that the eigenvalue analysis really consists of a linearization of the nonlinear response of the system, and that it depends largely on the system being considered whether a reliable critical load is calculated. The eigenvalue solution is particularly applicable in the analysis of "beam-column-type situations" of beam, plate, and shell structures.

EXAMPLE 3.11:   Experience shows that in structural analysis the critical load on column-type structures can be assessed appropriately using an eigenvalue problem formulation. Consider the system defined in Fig. E3.11. Construct the eigenvalue problem from which the critical loading on the system can be calculated.

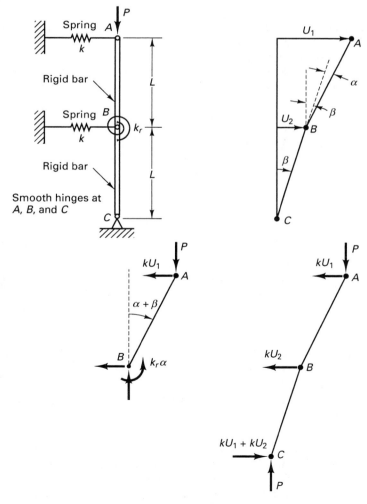

Figure E3.11   Instability analysis of a column

As in the derivation of steady-state equilibrium equations (see Section 3.2.1), we can employ the direct procedure or a variational approach to establish the problem-governing equations, and we describe both techniques in this problem solution.

In the direct approach we establish the governing equilibrium equations directly by considering the equilibrium of the structure in its deformed configuration. Referring to Fig. E3.11, the moment equilibrium of bar AB requires that

$$PL \sin(\alpha + \beta) = kU_1 L \cos(\alpha + \beta) + k_r \alpha \tag{a}$$

Similarly, for bars CBA we need

$$PL[\sin(\alpha + \beta) + \sin \beta] = kU_1 L[\cos(\alpha + \beta) + \cos \beta] + kU_2 L \cos \beta \tag{b}$$

We select U_1 and U_2 as state variables that completely describe the structural response. We also assume small displacements, for which

$$L \sin(\alpha + \beta) = U_1 - U_2; \qquad L \sin \beta = U_2$$

$$L \cos(\alpha + \beta) \doteq L; \qquad L \cos \beta \doteq L; \qquad \alpha \doteq \frac{U_1 - 2U_2}{L}$$

Substituting into (a) and (b) and writing the resulting equations in matrix form, we obtain

$$\begin{bmatrix} kL + \dfrac{k_r}{L} & -2\dfrac{k_r}{L} \\[2mm] 2kL & kL \end{bmatrix} \begin{bmatrix} U_1 \\ U_2 \end{bmatrix} = P \begin{bmatrix} 1 & -1 \\ 1 & 0 \end{bmatrix} \begin{bmatrix} U_1 \\ U_2 \end{bmatrix}$$

We can symmetrize the coefficient matrices by multiplying the first row by -2 and adding the result to row 2, which gives the eigenvalue problem

$$\begin{bmatrix} kL + \dfrac{k_r}{L} & -\dfrac{2k_r}{L} \\[2mm] -\dfrac{2k_r}{L} & kL + \dfrac{4k_r}{L} \end{bmatrix} \begin{bmatrix} U_1 \\ U_2 \end{bmatrix} = P \begin{bmatrix} 1 & -1 \\ -1 & 2 \end{bmatrix} \begin{bmatrix} U_1 \\ U_2 \end{bmatrix} \tag{c}$$

It may be noted that the second equation in (c) can also be obtained by considering the moment equilibrium of bar CB.

Considering next the variational approach, we need to determine the total potential Π of the system in the deformed configuration. Here we have

$$\Pi = \tfrac{1}{2}kU_1^2 + \tfrac{1}{2}kU_2^2 + \tfrac{1}{2}k_r\alpha^2 - PL[1 - \cos(\alpha + \beta) + 1 - \cos \beta] \tag{d}$$

As in the direct approach, we now assume small displacement conditions. Since we want to derive, using (3.1), an eigenvalue problem of form (3.5) in which the coefficient matrices are independent of the state variables, we approximate the trigonometric expressions to second order in the state variables. Thus, we use

$$\cos(\alpha + \beta) \doteq 1 - \frac{(\alpha + \beta)^2}{2}$$

$$\cos \beta \doteq 1 - \frac{\beta^2}{2} \tag{e}$$

and $\qquad \alpha + \beta \doteq \dfrac{U_1 - U_2}{L}; \qquad \alpha \doteq \dfrac{U_1 - 2U_2}{L}; \qquad \beta \doteq \dfrac{U_2}{L} \tag{f}$

Substituting from (e) and (f) into (d) we obtain

$$\Pi = \frac{1}{2}kU_1^2 + \frac{1}{2}kU_2^2 + \frac{1}{2}k_r\left(\frac{U_1 - 2U_2}{L}\right)^2 - \frac{P}{2L}(U_1 - U_2)^2 - \frac{P}{2L}U_2^2$$

Applying the stationarity principle,

$$\frac{\partial \Pi}{\partial U_1} = 0; \qquad \frac{\partial \Pi}{\partial U_2} = 0$$

the equations in (c) are obtained.

Considering now dynamic analysis, an eigenvalue problem may need to be formulated in the solution of the dynamic equilibrium equations. In essence, the objective is then to find a mathematical transformation on the state variables that is employed effectively in the solution of the dynamic response (see Section 9.3). In the analysis of physical problems, it is then most valuable to identify the eigenvalues and vectors with physical quantities (see Section 9.3).

To illustrate how eigenvalue problems are formulated in dynamic analysis, we present the following examples.

EXAMPLE 3.12: Consider the dynamic analysis of the system of rigid carts discussed in Example 3.8. Assume free vibration conditions and that

$$\mathbf{U} = \boldsymbol{\phi} \sin(\omega t - \psi) \tag{a}$$

where $\boldsymbol{\phi}$ is a vector with components independent of time, ω is a circular frequency, and ψ is a phase angle. Show that with this assumption an eigenvalue problem of the form given in (3.5) is obtained when searching for a solution of $\boldsymbol{\phi}$ and ω.

The equilibrium equations of the system when considering free-vibration conditions are

$$\mathbf{M\ddot{U} + KU = 0} \tag{b}$$

where the matrices $\mathbf{M}$ and $\mathbf{K}$ and vector $\mathbf{U}$ have been defined in Examples 3.1 and 3.8. If $\mathbf{U}$ given in (a) is to be a solution of the equations in (b), these equations must be satisfied when substituting for $\mathbf{U}$,

$$-\omega^2 \mathbf{M}\boldsymbol{\phi} \sin(\omega t - \psi) + \mathbf{K}\boldsymbol{\phi} \sin(\omega t - \psi) = \mathbf{0}$$

Thus, for (a) to be a solution of (b) we obtain the condition

$$\mathbf{K}\boldsymbol{\phi} = \omega^2 \mathbf{M}\boldsymbol{\phi} \tag{c}$$

which is an eigenvalue problem of form (3.5). We discuss in Section 9.3 the physical characteristics of a solution, ω_i^2 and $\boldsymbol{\phi}_i$, to the problem in (c).

EXAMPLE 3.13: Consider the electric circuit in Fig. E3.13. Determine the eigenvalue problem from which the resonant frequencies and modes can be calculated when $L_1 = L_2 = L$ and $C_1 = C_2 = C$.

Our first objective is to derive the dynamic equilibrium equations of the system. The element equilibrium equation for an inductor is

$$L\frac{dI}{dt} = V \tag{a}$$

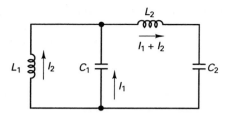

Figure E3.13 Electric circuit

where L is the inductance, I is the current through the inductor, and V is the voltage drop across the inductor. For a capacitor of capacitance C the equilibrium equation is

$$I = C\frac{dV}{dt} \tag{b}$$

As state variables we select the currents I_1 and I_2 shown in Fig. E3.13. The governing equilibrium equations are obtained by invoking the element interconnectivity requirements contained in Kirchhoff's voltage law:

$$V_{C_1} + V_{L_2} + V_{C_2} = 0$$
$$V_{L_1} + V_{L_2} + V_{C_2} = 0 \tag{c}$$

Differentiating (a) and (c) with respect to time and substituting into (c) with $L_1 = L_2 = L$ and $C_1 = C_2 = C$, we obtain

$$L\begin{bmatrix} 1 & 1 \\ 1 & 2 \end{bmatrix}\begin{bmatrix} \ddot{I}_1 \\ \ddot{I}_2 \end{bmatrix} + \frac{1}{C}\begin{bmatrix} 2 & 1 \\ 1 & 1 \end{bmatrix}\begin{bmatrix} I_1 \\ I_2 \end{bmatrix} = \begin{bmatrix} 0 \\ 0 \end{bmatrix} \tag{d}$$

We note that these equations are quite analogous to the free-vibration equilibrium equations of a structural system. Indeed, recognizing the analogy

$$I \rightarrow \text{displacement}; \qquad \frac{1}{C} \rightarrow \text{stiffness}; \qquad L \rightarrow \text{mass}$$

the eigenproblem for the resonant frequencies is established as in Example 3.12 (and an equivalent structural system could be constructed).

3.2.4 On the Nature of Solutions

In the preceding sections we discussed the formulation of steady-state, propagation, and eigenvalue problems, and we gave a number of simple examples. In all cases a system of equations for the unknown state variables was formulated but not solved. For the solution of the equations we refer to the techniques presented in Chapters 8 to 11. The objective in this section is to discuss briefly the nature of the solutions that are calculated when steady-state, propagation, or eigenvalue problems are considered.

For steady-state and propagation problems, it is convenient to distinguish between linear and nonlinear problems. In simple terms, a linear problem is characterized by the fact that the response of the system varies in proportion to the magnitude of the applied loads. All other problems are nonlinear, as discussed in more detail in Section 6.1. To demonstrate in an introductory way some basic response characteristics that are predicted in linear steady-state, propagation, and eigenvalue analyses we consider the following example.

EXAMPLE 3.14: Consider the simple structural system consisting of an assemblage of rigid weightless bars, springs, and concentrated masses shown in Fig. E3.14. The elements are connected at A, B, and C using frictionless pins. It is required to analyze the discrete system for the loading indicated, when the initial displacements and velocities are zero.

The response of the system is described by the two state variables U_1 and U_2 shown in Fig. E3.14(c). To decide what kind of analysis is appropriate we need to have sufficient information on the characteristics of the structure and the applied forces F and P. Let us assume that the structural characteristics and the applied forces are such that the displacements of the element assemblage are relatively small,

$$\frac{U_1}{L} < \frac{1}{10} \quad \text{and} \quad \frac{U_2}{L} < \frac{1}{10}$$

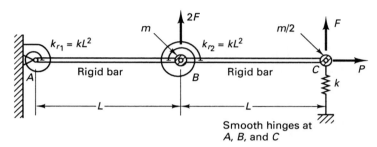

(a) Discrete system

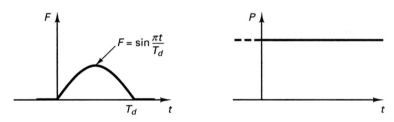

(b) Loading conditions

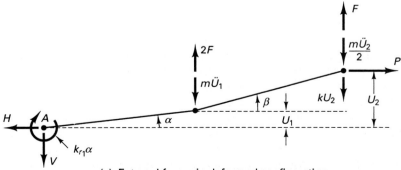

(c) External forces in deformed configuration

Figure E3.14   A two degree of freedom system

We can then assume that

$$\cos \alpha = \cos \beta = \cos(\beta - \alpha) = 1$$

$$\sin \alpha = \alpha; \qquad \sin \beta = \beta \tag{a}$$

$$\alpha = \frac{U_1}{L}; \qquad \beta = \frac{U_2 - U_1}{L}$$

The governing equilibrium equations are derived as in Example 3.11 but we include inertia forces (see Example 3.8); thus we obtain

$$\begin{bmatrix} m & 0 \\ 0 & \dfrac{m}{2} \end{bmatrix} \begin{bmatrix} \ddot{U}_1 \\ \ddot{U}_2 \end{bmatrix} + \begin{bmatrix} \left(5k + \dfrac{2P}{L}\right) & -\left(2k + \dfrac{P}{L}\right) \\ -\left(2k + \dfrac{P}{L}\right) & \left(2k + \dfrac{P}{L}\right) \end{bmatrix} \begin{bmatrix} U_1 \\ U_2 \end{bmatrix} = \begin{bmatrix} 2F \\ F \end{bmatrix} \tag{b}$$

The response of the system must depend on the relative values of k, m, and P/L. In order to obtain a measure of whether a static or dynamic analysis must be performed we calculate the natural frequencies of the system. These frequencies are obtained by solving the eigenvalue problem

$$\begin{bmatrix} \left(5k + \dfrac{2P}{L}\right) & -\left(2k + \dfrac{P}{L}\right) \\ -\left(2k + \dfrac{P}{L}\right) & \left(2k + \dfrac{P}{L}\right) \end{bmatrix} \begin{bmatrix} U_1 \\ U_2 \end{bmatrix} = \omega^2 \begin{bmatrix} m & 0 \\ 0 & \dfrac{m}{2} \end{bmatrix} \begin{bmatrix} U_1 \\ U_2 \end{bmatrix} \tag{c}$$

The solution of (c) gives (see Section 2.5)

$$\omega_1 = \left(\frac{9k}{2m} + \frac{2P}{mL} - \sqrt{\frac{33k^2}{4m^2} + \frac{8Pk}{m^2L} + \frac{2P^2}{m^2L^2}} \right)^{1/2}$$

$$\omega_2 = \left(\frac{9k}{2m} + \frac{2P}{mL} + \sqrt{\frac{33k^2}{4m^2} + \frac{8Pk}{m^2L} + \frac{2P^2}{m^2L^2}} \right)^{1/2}$$

We note that for constant k and m the natural frequencies (radians per unit time) are a function of P/L and increase with P/L as shown in Fig. E3.14(d). The ith natural period, T_i, of the system is given by $T_i = 2\pi/\omega_i$, hence

$$T_1 = \frac{2\pi}{\omega_1}; \qquad T_2 = \frac{2\pi}{\omega_2}$$

The response of the system depends to a large degree on the duration of load application when measured on the natural periods of the system. Since P is constant, the duration of load application is measured by T_d. To illustrate the response characteristics of the system, we assume a specific case $k = m = P/L = 1$ and three different values of T_d.

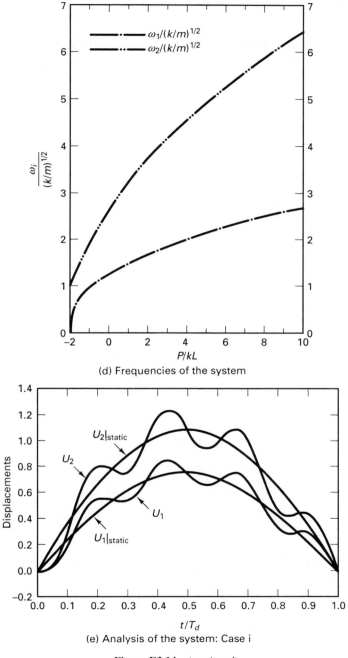

(d) Frequencies of the system

(e) Analysis of the system: Case i

Figure E3.14   *(continued)*

Case (i) $T_d = 4T_1$:   The response of the system is shown for this case of load application in Fig. E3.14(e), Case i. We note that the dynamic response solution is somewhat close to the static response of the system and would be very close if $T_1 \ll T_d$.

Case (ii) $T_d = (T_1 + T_2)/2$:   The response of the system is truly dynamic as shown in Fig. E3.14(e), Case ii. It would be completely inappropriate to neglect the inertia effects.

Case (iii) $T_d = 1/4\ T_2$:   In this case the duration of the loading is relatively short compared to the natural periods of the system. The response of the system is truly dynamic, and inertia effects must be included in the analysis as shown in Fig. E3.14(e), Case iii. The response of the system is somewhat close to the response generated assuming impulse conditions and would be very close if $T_2 \gg T_d$.

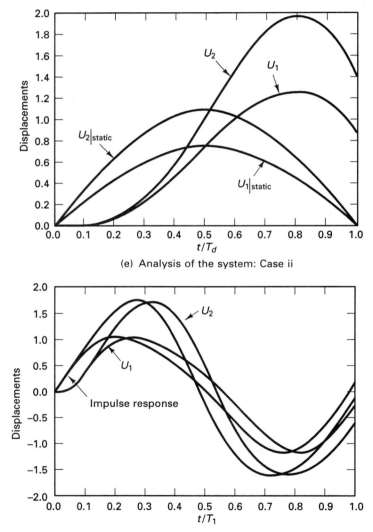

(e) Analysis of the system: Case ii

(e) Analysis of the system: Case iii (here the actual displacements are obtained by multiplying the given values by $2T_d/\pi$; the impulse response was calculated using $^0U_1 = {}^0U_2 = 0$, $^0\dot{U}_1 = {}^0\dot{U}_2 = 4T_d/\pi$ and setting the external loads to zero).

Figure E3.14   *(continued)*

To identify some conditions for which the structure becomes unstable, we note from (b) that the stiffness of the structure increases with increasing values of P/L (which is why the frequencies increase as P/L increases). Therefore, for the structure to become unstable, we need a negative value of P; i.e., P must be compressive. Let us now assume that P is decreased very slowly (P increases in compression) and that F is very small. In this case a static analysis is appropriate, and we can neglect the force F to obtain from (b) the governing equilibrium equations

$$\begin{bmatrix} 5k & -2k \\ -2k & 2k \end{bmatrix} \begin{bmatrix} U_1 \\ U_2 \end{bmatrix} = \frac{P}{L} \begin{bmatrix} -2 & 1 \\ 1 & -1 \end{bmatrix} \begin{bmatrix} U_1 \\ U_2 \end{bmatrix}$$

The solution of this eigenvalue problem gives two values for P/L. Because of the sign convention for P, the larger eigenvalue gives the critical load

$$P_{\text{crit}} = -2kL$$

It may be noted that this is the load at which the smallest frequency of the system is zero [see Fig. E3.14(d)].

Although we considered a structural system in this example, most of the solution characteristics presented are also directly observed in the analysis of other types of problems. As shown in an introductory manner in the example, it is important that an analyst be able to decide what kind of analysis is required: whether a steady-state analysis is sufficient or whether a dynamic analysis should be performed, and whether the system may become unstable. We discuss some important factors that influence this decision in Chapters 6 and 9.

In addition to deciding what kind of analysis should be performed, the analyst must select an appropriate lumped-parameter mathematical model of the actual physical system. The characteristics of this model depend on the analysis to be carried out, but in complex engineering analyses, a simple lumped-parameter model is in many cases not sufficient, and it is necessary to idealize the system by a continuum-mechanics-based mathematical model. We introduce the use of such models in the next section.

3.2.5 Exercises

3.1. Consider the simple cart system in static (steady-state) conditions shown. Establish the governing equilibrium equations.

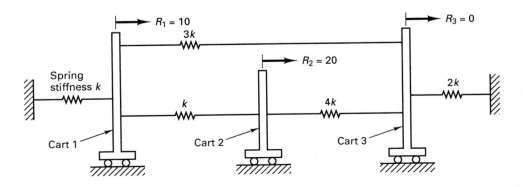

3.2. Consider the wall of three homogeneous slabs in contact as shown. Establish the steady-state heat transfer equilibrium equations of the analysis problem.

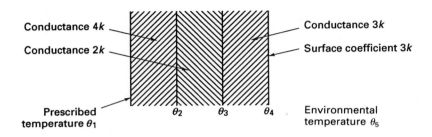

3.3. The hydraulic network shown is to be analyzed. Establish the equilibrium equations of the system when $\Delta p = Rq$ and R is the branch resistance coefficient.

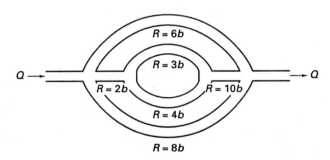

3.4. The dc network shown is to be analyzed. Using Ohm's law, establish the current-voltage drop equilibrium equations of the system.

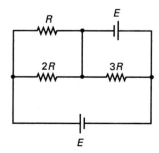

3.5. Consider the spring-cart system in Exercise 3.1. Determine the variational indicator Π of the total potential of this system.

3.6. Consider the slab in Example 3.2. Find a variational indicator Π that has the property that $\delta\Pi = 0$ generates the governing equilibrium equations.

3.7. Establish the dynamic equilibrium equations of the system of carts in Exercise 3.1 when the carts have masses m_1, m_2, and m_3.

3.8. Consider the simple spring-cart system shown initially at rest. Establish the equations governing the dynamic response of the system.

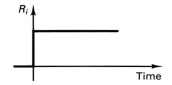

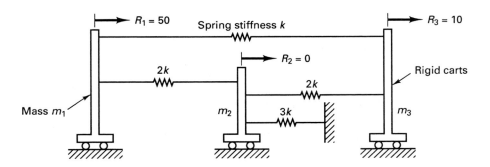

3.9. The rigid bar and cable structure shown is to be analyzed for its dynamic response. Formulate the equilibrium equations of motion.

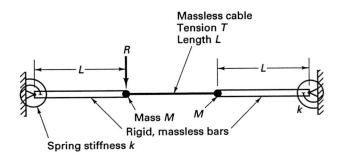

3.10. Consider the structural model shown. Determine the eigenvalue problem from which the critical load can be calculated. Use the direct method and the variational method to obtain the governing equations.

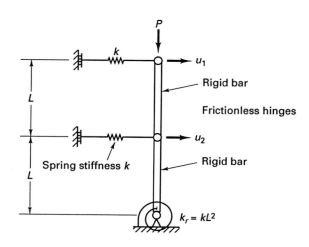

3.11. Establish the eigenproblem governing the stability of the system shown.

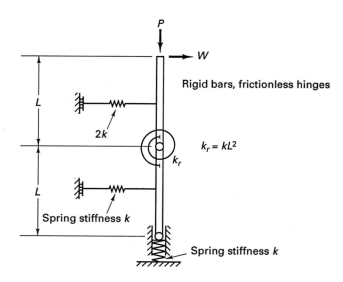

3.12. The column structure in Exercise 3.11 is initially at rest under the constant force P (where P is below the critical load) when suddenly the force W is applied. Establish the governing equations of equilibrium. Assume the springs to be massless and that the bars have mass m per unit length.

3.13. Consider the analysis in Example 3.9. Assume $\boldsymbol{\theta} = \boldsymbol{\phi} e^{-\lambda t}$ and $\mathbf{Q} = \mathbf{0}$ and establish an eigenproblem corresponding to λ, $\boldsymbol{\phi}$.

3.14. Consider the wall of three homogeneous slabs in Exercise 3.2. Formulate the heat transfer equations for a transient analysis in which the initial temperature distribution is given and suddenly θ_1 is changed to θ_1^{new}. Then assume $\boldsymbol{\theta} = \boldsymbol{\phi} e^{-\lambda t}$ and $\mathbf{Q} = \mathbf{0}$, and establish an eigenproblem corresponding to λ, $\boldsymbol{\phi}$. Assume that, for a unit cross-sectional area, each slab has a total heat capacity of c, and that for each slab the heat capacity can be lumped to the faces of the slab.

3.3 SOLUTION OF CONTINUOUS-SYSTEM MATHEMATICAL MODELS

The basic steps in the solution of a continuous-system mathematical model are quite similar to those employed in the solution of a lumped-parameter model (see Section 3.2). However, instead of dealing with discrete elements, we focus attention on typical differential elements with the objective of obtaining differential equations that express the element equilibrium requirements, constitutive relations, and element interconnectivity requirements. These differential equations must hold throughout the domain of the system, and before the solution can be calculated they must be supplemented by boundary conditions and, in dynamic analysis, also by initial conditions.

As in the solution of discrete models, *two different approaches can be followed to generate the system-governing differential equations: the direct method and the variational method.* We discuss both approaches in this section (see also R. Courant and D. Hilbert [A]) and illustrate the variational procedure in some detail because, as introduced in Section 3.3.4, this approach can be regarded as the basis of the finite element method.

3.3.1 Differential Formulation

In the differential formulation we establish the equilibrium and constitutive requirements of typical differential elements in terms of state variables. These considerations lead to a system of differential equations in the state variables, and it is possible that all compatibility requirements (i.e., the interconnectivity requirements of the differential elements) are already contained in these differential equations (e.g., by the mere fact that the solution is to be continuous). However, in general, the equations must be supplemented by additional differential equations that impose appropriate constraints on the state variables in order that all compatibility requirements be satisfied. Finally, to complete the formulation of the problem, all boundary conditions, and in a dynamic analysis the initial conditions, are stated.

For purposes of mathematical analysis it is expedient to classify problem-governing differential equations. Consider the second-order general partial differential equation in the domain x, y,

$$A(x, y)\frac{\partial^2 u}{\partial x^2} + 2B(x, y)\frac{\partial^2 u}{\partial x \partial y} + C(x, y)\frac{\partial^2 u}{\partial y^2} = \phi\left(x, y, u, \frac{\partial u}{\partial x}, \frac{\partial u}{\partial y}\right) \tag{3.6}$$

where u is the unknown state variable. Depending on the coefficients in (3.6) the differential equation is elliptic, parabolic or hyperbolic:

$$B^2 - AC \begin{cases} < 0 & \text{elliptic} \\ = 0 & \text{parabolic} \\ > 0 & \text{hyperbolic} \end{cases}$$

This classification is established when solving (3.6) using the method of characteristics because it is then observed that the character of the solutions is distinctly different for the three categories of equations. These differences are also apparent when the differential equations are identified with the different physical problems that they govern. In their simplest form the three types of equations can be identified with the *Laplace equation,* the *heat conduction equation,* and the *wave equation,* respectively. We demonstrate how these equations arise in the solution of physical problems by the following examples.

EXAMPLE 3.15:   The idealized dam shown in Fig. E3.15 stands on permeable soil. Formulate the differential equation governing the steady-state seepage of water through the soil and give the corresponding boundary conditions.

For a typical element of widths dx and dy (and unit thickness), the total flow into the element must be equal to the total flow out of the element. Hence we have

$$(q|_y - q|_{y+dy})\, dx + (q|_x - q|_{x+dx})\, dy = 0$$

or

$$-\frac{\partial q_y}{\partial y} dy\, dx - \frac{\partial q_x}{\partial x} dx\, dy = 0 \tag{a}$$

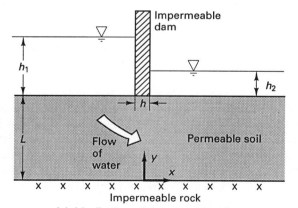

(a) Idealization of dam on soil and rock

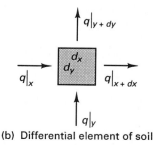

(b) Differential element of soil

Figure E3.15   Two-dimensional seepage problem

Using Darcy's law, the flow is given in terms of the total potential ϕ,

$$q_x = -k \frac{\partial \phi}{\partial x}; \qquad q_y = -k \frac{\partial \phi}{\partial y} \qquad \text{(b)}$$

where we assume a uniform permeability k. Substituting from (b) into (a), we obtain the *Laplace equation*

$$k \left(\frac{\partial^2 \phi}{\partial x^2} + \frac{\partial^2 \phi}{\partial y^2} \right) = 0 \qquad \text{(c)}$$

It may be noted that this same equation is also obtained in heat transfer analysis and in the solution of electrostatic potential and other field problems (see Chapter 7).

The boundary conditions are no-flow boundary conditions in the soil at $x = -\infty$ and $x = +\infty$,

$$\left. \frac{\partial \phi}{\partial x} \right|_{x=-\infty} = 0; \qquad \left. \frac{\partial \phi}{\partial x} \right|_{x=+\infty} = 0 \qquad \text{(d)}$$

at the rock-soil interface,

$$\left. \frac{\partial \phi}{\partial y} \right|_{y=0} = 0 \qquad \text{(e)}$$

and at the dam-soil interface,

$$\frac{\partial \phi}{\partial y}(x, L) = 0 \qquad \text{for } -\frac{h}{2} \leq x \leq +\frac{h}{2} \qquad \text{(f)}$$

In addition, the total potential is prescribed at the water-soil interface,

$$\phi(x, L)|_{x<-(h/2)} = h_1; \qquad \phi(x, L)|_{x>(h/2)} = h_2 \qquad \text{(g)}$$

The differential equation in (c) and the boundary conditions in (d) to (g) define the seepage flow steady-state response.

EXAMPLE 3.16:   The very long slab shown in Fig. E3.16 is at a constant initial temperature θ_i when the surface at $x = 0$ is suddenly subjected to a constant uniform heat flow input. The surface at $x = L$ of the slab is kept at the temperature θ_i, and the surfaces parallel to the x, z plane are insulated. Assuming one-dimensional heat flow conditions, show that the problem-governing differential equation is the *heat conduction equation*

$$k \frac{\partial^2 \theta}{\partial x^2} = \rho c \frac{\partial \theta}{\partial t}$$

where the parameters are defined in Fig. E3.16, and the temperature θ is the state variable. State also the boundary and initial conditions.

We consider a typical differential element of the slab [see Fig. E3.16(b)]. The element equilibrium requirement is that the net heat flow input to the element must equal the rate of heat stored in the element. Thus

$$qA|_x - \left(qA|_x + A \left. \frac{\partial q}{\partial x} \right|_x dx \right) = \rho A \left. c \frac{\partial \theta}{\partial t} \right|_x dx \qquad \text{(a)}$$

The constitutive relation is given by Fourier's law of heat conduction

$$q = -k \frac{\partial \theta}{\partial x} \qquad \text{(b)}$$

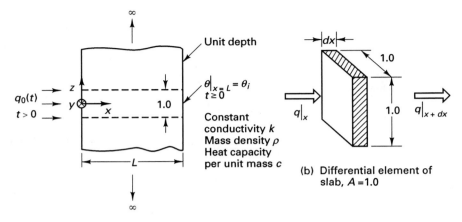

(a) Idealization of very long slab

Figure E3.16   One-dimensional heat conduction problem

Substituting from (b) into (a) we obtain

$$k\frac{\partial^2\theta}{\partial x^2} = \rho c\frac{\partial\theta}{\partial t} \tag{c}$$

In this case the element interconnectivity requirements are contained in the assumption that the temperature θ be a continuous function of x and no additional compatibility conditions are applicable.

The boundary conditions are

$$\frac{\partial\theta}{\partial x}(0, t) = -\frac{q_0(t)}{k}$$
$$\qquad ; \qquad t > 0 \tag{d}$$
$$\theta(L, t) = \theta_i$$

and the initial condition is $$\theta(x, 0) = \theta_i \tag{e}$$

The formulation of the problem is now complete, and the solution of (c) subject to the boundary and initial conditions in (d) and (e) yields the temperature response of the slab.

EXAMPLE 3.17:   The rod shown in Fig. E3.17 is initially at rest when a load $R(t)$ is suddenly applied at its free end. Show that the problem-governing differential equation is the *wave equation*

$$\frac{\partial^2 u}{\partial x^2} = \frac{1}{c^2}\frac{\partial^2 u}{\partial t^2}; \qquad c = \sqrt{\frac{E}{\rho}}$$

where the variables are defined in Fig. E3.17 and the displacement of the rod, u, is the state variable. Also state the boundary and initial conditions.

The element force equilibrium requirements of a typical differential element are, using d'Alembert's principle,

$$\sigma A\Big|_x + A\frac{\partial\sigma}{\partial x}\Big|_x dx - \sigma A\Big|_x = \rho A\frac{\partial^2 u}{\partial t^2}\Big|_x dx \tag{a}$$

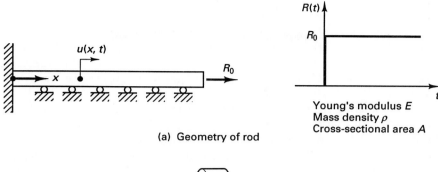

(a) Geometry of rod

(b) Differential element

Figure E3.17   Rod subjected to step load

The constitutive relation is

$$\sigma = E\frac{\partial u}{\partial x}$$ (b)

Combining (a) and (b) we obtain

$$\frac{\partial^2 u}{\partial x^2} = \frac{1}{c^2}\frac{\partial^2 u}{\partial t^2}$$ (c)

The element interconnectivity requirements are satisfied because we assume that the displacement u is continuous, and no additional compatibility conditions are applicable.

The boundary conditions are

$$u(0, t) = 0$$
$$EA\frac{\partial u}{\partial x}(L, t) = R_0$$; $t > 0$ (d)

and the initial conditions are

$$u(x, 0) = 0$$
$$\frac{\partial u}{\partial t}(x, 0) = 0$$ (e)

With the conditions in (d) and (e) the formulation of the problem is complete, and (c) can be solved for the displacement response of the rod.

Although we considered in these examples specific problems that are governed by elliptic, parabolic, and hyperbolic differential equations, the problem formulations illustrate in a quite general way some basic characteristics. In elliptic problems (see Example 3.15) the values of the unknown state variables (or their normal derivatives) are given on the boundary. These problems are for this reason also called *boundary value problems,* where we should note that the solution at a general interior point depends on the data at every point of the boundary. A change in only one boundary value affects the complete solution; for instance, in Example 3.15 the complete solution for ϕ depends on the actual value of h_1. Elliptic differential equations generally govern the steady-state response of systems.

Comparing the governing differential equations given in Examples 3.15 to 3.17 it is noted that in contrast to the elliptic equation, the parabolic and hyperbolic equations (Examples 3.16 and 3.17, respectively) include time as an independent variable and thus define propagation problems. These problems are also called *initial value problems* because the solution depends on the initial conditions. We may note that analogous to the derivation of the dynamic equilibrium equations of lumped-parameter models, the governing differential equations of propagation problems are obtained from the steady-state equations by including the "resistance to change" (inertia) of the differential elements. Conversely, the parabolic and hyperbolic differential equations in Examples 3.16 and 3.17 would become elliptic equations if the time-dependent terms were neglected. In this way the initial value problems would be converted to boundary value problems with steady-state solutions.

We stated earlier that the solution of a boundary value problem depends on the data at all points of the boundary. Here lies a significant difference in the analysis of a propagation problem, namely, considering propagation problems the solution at an interior point may depend only on the boundary conditions of part of the boundary and the initial conditions over part of the interior domain.

3.3.2 Variational Formulations

The variational approach of establishing the governing equilibrium equations of a system was already introduced as an alternative to the direct approach when we discussed the analysis of discrete systems (see Section 3.2.1). As described, the essence of the approach is to calculate the total potential Π of the system and to invoke the stationarity of Π, i.e., $\delta\Pi = 0$, with respect to the state variables. We pointed out that the variational technique can be effective in the analysis of discrete systems; however, we shall now observe that the variational approach provides a particularly powerful mechanism for the analysis of continuous systems. The main reason for this effectiveness lies in the way by which some boundary conditions (namely, the natural boundary conditions defined below) can be generated and taken into account when using the variational approach.

To demonstrate the variational formulation in the following examples, we assume that the total potential Π is given and defer the description of how an appropriate Π can be determined until after the presentation of the examples.

The total potential Π is also called the *functional* of the problem. Assume that in the functional the highest derivative of a state variable (with respect to a space coordinate) is of order m; i.e., the operator contains at most mth-order derivatives. We call such a problem a C^{m-1} *variational problem.* Considering the boundary conditions of the problem, we identify two classes of boundary conditions, called *essential* and *natural boundary conditions.*

The essential boundary conditions are also called *geometric boundary conditions* because in structural mechanics the essential boundary conditions correspond to prescribed displacements and rotations. The order of the derivatives in the essential boundary conditions is, in a C^{m-1} problem, at most $m - 1$.

The second class of boundary conditions, namely, the natural boundary conditions, are also called *force boundary conditions* because in structural mechanics the natural boundary conditions correspond to prescribed boundary forces and moments. The highest derivatives in these boundary conditions are of order m to $2m - 1$.

We will see later that this classification of variational problems and associated boundary conditions is most useful in the design of numerical solutions.

In the variational formulations we will use the variational symbol δ, already briefly employed in (3.1). Let us recall some important operational properties of this symbol; for more details, see, for example, R. Courant and D. Hilbert [A]. Assume that a function F for a given value of x depends on v (the state variable), $dv/dx, \ldots, d^p v/dx^p$, where $p = 1, 2, \ldots$. Then the first variation of F is defined as

$$\delta F = \frac{\partial F}{\partial v} \delta v + \frac{\partial F}{\partial (dv/dx)} \delta\left(\frac{dv}{dx}\right) + \cdots + \frac{\partial F}{\partial (d^p v/dx^p)} \delta\left(\frac{d^p v}{dx^p}\right) \tag{3.7a}$$

This expression is explained as follows. We associate with $v(x)$ a function $\epsilon \, \eta(x)$ where ϵ is a constant (independent of x) and $\eta(x)$ is an arbitrary but sufficiently smooth function *that is zero at and corresponding to the essential boundary conditions.* We call $\eta(x)$ a variation in v, that is $\eta(x) = \delta v(x)$ [and of course $\epsilon \, \eta(x)$ is then also a variation in v] and also have for the required derivatives

$$\frac{d^n \eta}{dx^n} = \frac{d^n \delta v}{dx^n} = \delta\left(\frac{d^n v}{dx^n}\right)$$

that is, the variation of a derivative of v is equal to the derivative of the variation in v. The expression (3.7a) then follows from evaluating

$$\delta F = \lim_{\epsilon \to 0} \frac{F\left[v + \epsilon\eta, \dfrac{d(v + \epsilon\eta)}{dx}, \ldots, \dfrac{d^p(v + \epsilon\eta)}{dx^p}\right] - F\left(v, \dfrac{dv}{dx}, \ldots, \dfrac{d^p v}{dx^p}\right)}{\epsilon} \tag{3.7b}$$

Considering (3.7a) we note that the expression for δF looks like the expression for the total differential dF; that is, the variational operator δ acts like the differential operator with respect to the variables $v, dv/dx, \ldots, d^p v/dx^p$. These equations can be extended to multiple functions and state variables, and we find that the laws of variations of sums, products, and so on, are completely analogous to the corresponding laws of differentiation. For example, let F and Q be two functions possibly dependent on different state variables; then

$$\delta(F + Q) = \delta F + \delta Q; \qquad \delta(FQ) = (\delta F)Q + F(\delta Q); \qquad \delta(F)^n = n(F)^{n-1} \, \delta F$$

In our applications the functions usually appear within an integral sign; and so, for example, we also use

$$\delta \int F(x) \, dx = \int \delta F(x) \, dx$$

We shall employ these rules extensively in the variational derivations and will use one important condition (which corresponds to the properties of η stated earlier), namely, that *the variations of the state variables and of their $(m - 1)$st derivatives must be zero at and* *corresponding to the essential boundary conditions,* but otherwise the variations can be arbitrary.

Consider the following examples.

EXAMPLE 3.18: The functional governing the temperature distribution in the slab considered in Example 3.16 is

$$\Pi = \int_0^L \frac{1}{2} k \left(\frac{\partial \theta}{\partial x} \right)^2 dx - \int_0^L \theta q^B \, dx - \theta_0 q_0 \tag{a}$$

and the essential boundary condition is

$$\theta_L = \theta_i \tag{b}$$

where $\theta_0 = \theta(0, t)$ and $\theta_L = \theta(L, t)$

q^B is the heat generated per unit volume, and otherwise the same notation as in Example 3.16 is used. Invoke the stationarity condition on Π to derive the governing heat conduction equation and the natural boundary condition.

This is a C^0 variational problem; i.e., the highest derivative in the functional in (a) is of order 1, or $m = 1$. An essential boundary condition, here given in (b), can therefore correspond only to a prescribed temperature, and a natural boundary condition must correspond to a prescribed temperature gradient or boundary heat flow input.

To invoke the stationarity condition $\delta\Pi = 0$, we can directly use the fact that variations and differentiations are performed with the same rules. That is, using (3.7a) we obtain

$$\int_0^L \left(k \frac{\partial \theta}{\partial x} \right) \left(\delta \frac{\partial \theta}{\partial x} \right) dx - \int_0^L \delta\theta \, q^B \, dx - \delta\theta_0 q_0 = 0 \tag{c}$$

where also $\delta(\partial\theta/\partial x) = \partial\delta\theta/\partial x$. The same result is also obtained when using (3.7b), which gives here

$$\delta\Pi = \lim_{\epsilon \to 0} \left[\frac{\left\{ \int_0^L \frac{1}{2} k \left(\frac{\partial \theta}{\partial x} + \epsilon \frac{\partial \eta}{\partial x} \right)^2 dx - \int_0^L (\theta + \epsilon\eta) q^B \, dx - (\theta_0 + \epsilon\eta \,|_{x=0}) q_0 \right\}}{\epsilon} \right.$$
$$\left. - \frac{\left\{ \int_0^L \frac{1}{2} k \left(\frac{\partial \theta}{\partial x} \right)^2 dx - \int_0^L \theta q^B \, dx - \theta_0 q_0 \right\}}{\epsilon} \right]$$

$$= \lim_{\epsilon \to 0} \frac{\int_0^L \left[\epsilon k \frac{\partial \theta}{\partial x} \frac{\partial \eta}{\partial x} + \frac{1}{2} \epsilon^2 k \left(\frac{\partial \eta}{\partial x} \right)^2 \right] dx - \int_0^L \epsilon\eta q^B \, dx - \epsilon\eta|_{x=0} \, q_0}{\epsilon}$$

$$= \int_0^L k \frac{\partial \theta}{\partial x} \frac{\partial \eta}{\partial x} dx - \int_0^L \eta q^B \, dx - \eta_0 \, q_0$$

$$= 0$$

where $\eta_0 = \eta|_{x=0}$ and we would now substitute $\delta\theta$ for η.

Now using integration by parts,[2] we obtain from (c) the following equation:

$$\underbrace{-\int_0^L \left(k \frac{\partial^2 \theta}{\partial x^2} + q^B \right) \delta\theta \, dx}_{①} + \underbrace{k \frac{\partial \theta}{\partial x} \bigg|_{x=L} \delta\theta_L}_{②} - \underbrace{\left[k \frac{\partial \theta}{\partial x} \bigg|_{x=0} + q_0 \right] \delta\theta_0}_{③} = 0 \tag{d}$$

---

[2] The divergence theorem is used (see Examples 4.2 and 7.1).

To extract from (d) the governing differential equation and natural boundary condition, we use the argument that the variations on θ are completely arbitrary, except that there can be no variations on the prescribed essential boundary conditions. Hence, because θ_L is prescribed, we have $\delta\theta_L = 0$ and term ② in (d) vanishes.

Considering next terms ① and ③, assume that $\delta\theta_0 = 0$ but that $\delta\theta$ is otherwise nonzero (except at $x = 0$, where we have a sudden jump to a zero value). If (d) is to hold for any nonzero $\delta\theta$, we need to have[3]

$$ k \frac{\partial^2 \theta}{\partial x^2} + q^B = 0 \tag{e} $$

Conversely, assume that $\delta\theta$ is zero everywhere except at $x = 0$; i.e., we have $\delta\theta_0 \neq 0$; then (d) is valid only if

$$ k \left. \frac{\partial \theta}{\partial x} \right|_{x=0} + q_0 = 0 \tag{f} $$

The expression in (f) represents the natural boundary condition.

The governing differential equation of the propagation problem is obtained from (e), specifying here that

$$ q^B = -\rho c \frac{\partial \theta}{\partial t} \tag{g} $$

Hence (e) reduces to
$$ k \frac{\partial^2 \theta}{\partial x^2} = \rho c \frac{\partial \theta}{\partial t} $$

We may note that until the heat capacity effect was introduced in the formulation in (g), the equations were derived as if a steady-state problem (and with q^B time-dependent a pseudo steady-state problem) was being considered. Hence, as noted previously, the formulation of the propagation problem can be obtained from the equation governing the steady-state response by simply taking into account the time-dependent "inertia term."

EXAMPLE 3.19:   The functional and essential boundary condition governing the wave propagation in the rod considered in Example 3.17 are

$$ \Pi = \int_0^L \frac{1}{2} EA \left(\frac{\partial u}{\partial x} \right)^2 dx - \int_0^L u f^B \, dx - u_L R \tag{a} $$

and
$$ u_0 = 0 \tag{b} $$

where the same notation as in Example 3.17 is used, $u_0 = u(0, t)$, $u_L = u(L, t)$, and f^B is the body force per unit length of the rod. Show that by invoking the stationarity condition on Π the governing differential equation of the propagation problem and the natural boundary condition can be derived.

We proceed as in Example 3.18. The stationarity condition $\delta\Pi = 0$ gives

$$ \int_0^L \left(EA \frac{\partial u}{\partial x} \right) \left(\delta \frac{\partial u}{\partial x} \right) dx - \int_0^L \delta u \, f^B \, dx - \delta u_L R = 0 $$

Writing $\partial \delta u / \partial x$ for $\delta(\partial u / \partial x)$, recalling that EA is constant, and using integration by parts yields

$$ -\int_0^L \left(EA \frac{\partial^2 u}{\partial x^2} + f^B \right) \delta u \, dx + \left[EA \left. \frac{\partial u}{\partial x} \right|_{x=L} - R \right] \delta u_L - EA \left. \frac{\partial u}{\partial x} \right|_{x=0} \delta u_0 = 0 $$

---

[3] We in effect imply here that the limits of integration are not 0 to L but 0^+ to L^-.

To obtain the governing differential equation and natural boundary condition we use, in essence, the same argument as in Example 3.18; i.e., since δu_0 is zero but δu is arbitrary at all other points, we must have

$$EA\,\frac{\partial^2 u}{\partial x^2} + f^B = 0 \tag{c}$$

and

$$\left. EA\,\frac{\partial u}{\partial x}\right|_{x=L} = R \tag{d}$$

In this problem we have $f^B = -A\rho\,\partial^2 u/\partial t^2$ and hence (c) reduces to the problem-governing differential equation

$$\frac{\partial^2 u}{\partial x^2} = \frac{1}{c^2}\,\frac{\partial^2 u}{\partial t^2}; \qquad c = \sqrt{\frac{E}{\rho}}$$

The natural boundary condition was stated in (d).

Finally, it may be noted that the problem in (a) and (b) is a C^0 variational problem; i.e., $m = 1$ in this case.

EXAMPLE 3.20:   The functional governing static buckling of the column in Fig. E3.20 is

$$\Pi = \frac{1}{2}\int_0^L EI\left(\frac{d^2 w}{dx^2}\right)^2 dx - \frac{P}{2}\int_0^L \left(\frac{dw}{dx}\right)^2 dx + \frac{1}{2}kw_L^2 \tag{a}$$

where $w_L = w|_{x=L}$ and the essential boundary conditions are

$$w|_{x=0} = 0, \qquad \left.\frac{dw}{dx}\right|_{x=0} = 0 \tag{b}$$

Invoke the stationarity condition $\delta\Pi = 0$ to derive the problem-governing differential equation and the natural boundary conditions.

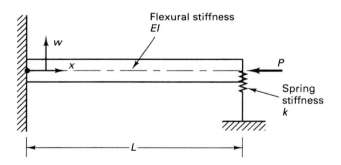

Figure E3.20   Column subjected to a compressive load

This problem is a C^1 variational problem, i.e., $m = 2$, because the highest derivative in the functional is of order 2.

The stationarity condition $\delta\Pi = 0$ yields

$$\int_0^L EIw''\,\delta w''\,dx - P\int_0^L w'\,\delta w'\,dx + kw_L\,\delta w_L = 0$$

where we use the notation $w' = dw/dx$, and so on. But $\delta w'' = d(\delta w')/dx$, and EI is constant; hence, using integration by parts, we obtain

$$\int_0^L EIw'' \, \delta w'' \, dx = EIw'' \, \delta w'|_0^L - EI \int_0^L w''' \, \delta w' \, dx$$

If we continue to integrate by parts $\int_0^L w''' \, \delta w' \, dx$ and also integrate by parts $\int_0^L w' \, \delta w' \, dx$, we obtain

$$\underbrace{\int_0^L (EIw^{iv} + Pw'') \, \delta w \, dx}_{①} + \underbrace{(EIw'' \, \delta w')|_L}_{②} - \underbrace{(EIw'' \, \delta w')|_0}_{③}$$

$$- \underbrace{[(EIw''' + Pw') \, \delta w]|_L}_{④} + \underbrace{[(EIw''' + Pw') \, \delta w]|_0}_{⑤} + \underbrace{kw_L \, \delta w_L}_{⑥} = 0 \qquad \text{(c)}$$

Since the variations on w and w' must be zero at the essential boundary conditions, we have $\delta w_0 = 0$ and $\delta w_0' = 0$. It follows that terms ③ and ⑤ are zero. The variations on w and w' are arbitrary at all other points, hence to satisfy (c) we conclude, using the earlier arguments (see Example 3.18), that the following equations must be satisfied:

$$\text{term 1:} \qquad EIw^{iv} + Pw'' = 0 \qquad\qquad \text{(d)}$$

$$\text{term 2:} \qquad EIw''|_{x=L} = 0 \qquad\qquad \text{(e)}$$

$$\text{terms 4 and 6:} \qquad (EIw''' + Pw' - kw)|_{x=L} = 0 \qquad\qquad \text{(f)}$$

The problem-governing differential equation is given in (d), and the natural boundary conditions are the relations in (e) and (f). We should note that these boundary conditions correspond to the physical conditions of moment and shear equilibrium at $x = L$.

We have illustrated in the preceding examples how the problem-governing differential equation and the natural boundary conditions can be derived by invoking the stationarity of the functional of the problem. At this point a number of observations should be made.

First, considering a C^{m-1} variational problem, the order of the highest derivative present in the problem-governing differential equation is $2m$. The reason for obtaining a derivative of order $2m$ in the problem-governing differential equation is that integration by parts is employed m times.

A second observation is that the effect of the natural boundary conditions was always included as a potential in the expression for Π. Hence the natural boundary conditions are implicitly contained in Π, whereas the essential boundary conditions have been stated separately.

Our objective in Examples 3.18 to 3.20 was to derive the governing differential equations and natural boundary conditions by invoking the stationarity of a functional, and for this purpose the appropriate functional was given in each case. However, an important question then arises: How can we establish an appropriate functional corresponding to a given problem? The two previous observations and the mathematical manipulations in Examples 3.18 to 3.20 suggest that to derive a functional for a given problem we could start with the governing differential equation, establish an integral equation, and then proceed backward in the mathematical manipulations. In this derivation it is necessary to use integration by parts, i.e., the divergence theorem, and the final check would be that the stationarity condition on the Π derived does indeed yield the governing differential equations. This procedure is employed to derive appropriate functionals in many cases (see Section 3.3.4 and Chapters 4 and 7, and for further treatment see, for example, R. Courant and D. Hilbert [A], S. G. Mikhlin [A], K. Washizu [B], and J. T. Oden and J. N. Reddy [A]). In this context, it should also be noted that in considering a specific problem, there does not generally exist a unique appropriate functional, but a number of functionals are applicable. For instance, in the solution of structural mechanics problems, we can employ the principle of minimum potential energy, other displacement-based variational formulations, the Hu-Washizu or Hellinger-Reissner principles, and so on (see Section 4.4.2).

Another important observation is that once a functional has been established for a certain class of problems, the functional can be employed to generate the governing equations for *all* problems in that class and therefore provides a general analysis tool. For example, the principle of minimum potential energy is general and is applicable to all problems in linear elasticity theory.

Based simply on a utilitarian point of view, the following observations can be made in regard to variational formulations.

1. The variational method may provide a relatively easy way to construct the system-governing equations. This ease of use of a variational principle depends largely on the fact that in the variational formulation scalar quantities (energies, potentials, and so on) are considered rather than vector quantities (forces, displacements, and so on).

2. A variational approach may lead more directly to the system-governing equations and boundary conditions. For example, if a complex system is being considered, it is of advantage that some variables that need to be included in a direct formulation are not considered in a variational formulation (such as internal forces that do no net work).

3. The variational approach provides some additional insight into a problem and gives an independent check on the formulation of the problem.

4. For approximate solutions, a larger class of trial functions can be employed in many cases if the analyst operates on the variational formulation rather than on the differential formulation of the problem; for example, the trial functions need not satisfy the natural boundary conditions because these boundary conditions are implicitly contained in the functional (see Section 3.3.4).

This last consideration has most important consequences, and much of the success of the finite element method hinges on the fact that by employing a variational formulation, a larger class of functions can be used. We examine this point in more detail in the next section and in Section 3.3.4.

3.3.3 Weighted Residual Methods; Ritz Method

In previous sections we have discussed differential and variational formulations of the governing equilibrium equations of continuous systems. In dealing with relatively simple systems, these equations can be solved in closed form using techniques of integration, separation of variables, and so on. For more complex systems, approximate procedures of solution must be employed. The objective in this section is to survey some classical techniques in which a family of trial functions is used to obtain an approximate solution. We shall see later that these techniques are very closely related to the finite element method of analysis and that indeed the finite element method can be regarded as an extension of these classical procedures.

Consider the analysis of a steady-state problem using its differential formulation

$$L_{2m}[\phi] = r \tag{3.8}$$

in which L_{2m} is a linear differential operator, ϕ is the state variable to be calculated, and r is the forcing function. The solution to the problem must also satisfy the boundary conditions

$$B_i[\phi] = q_i|_{\text{at boundary } S_i}; \qquad i = 1, 2, \ldots \tag{3.9}$$

We shall be concerned, in particular, with symmetric and positive definite operators that satisfy the symmetry condition

$$\int_D (L_{2m}[u])v \ dD = \int_D (L_{2m}[v])u \ dD \tag{3.10}$$

and the condition of positive definiteness

$$\int_D (L_{2m}[u])u \ dD > 0 \tag{3.11}$$

where D is the domain of the operator and u and v are any functions that satisfy homogeneous essential and natural boundary conditions. To clarify the meaning of relations (3.8) to (3.11), we consider the following example.

EXAMPLE 3.21:   The steady-state response of the bar shown in Fig. E3.17 is calculated by solving the differential equation

$$-EA \frac{\partial^2 u}{\partial x^2} = 0 \tag{a}$$

subject to the boundary conditions

$$u|_{x=0} = 0; \qquad EA \frac{\partial u}{\partial x}\bigg|_{x=L} = R \tag{b}$$

Identify the operators and functions of (3.8) and (3.9) and check whether the operator L_{2m} is symmetric and positive definite.

Comparing (3.8) with (a), we see that in this problem

$$L_{2m} = -EA \frac{\partial^2}{\partial x^2}; \qquad \phi = u; \qquad r = 0$$

Similarly, comparing (3.9) with (b), we obtain

$$B_1 = 1; \qquad\qquad q_1 = 0$$

$$B_2 = EA \frac{\partial}{\partial x}; \qquad q_2 = R$$

To identify whether the operator L_{2m} is symmetric and positive definite, we consider the case $R = 0$. This means physically that we are concerned only with the structure itself and not with the loading applied to it. For (3.10) we have

$$
\int_0^L -EA\frac{\partial^2 u}{\partial x^2}\, v\, dx = -EA\frac{\partial u}{\partial x}\, v\, \bigg|_0^L + \int_0^L EA\frac{\partial u}{\partial x}\frac{\partial v}{\partial x}\, dx
$$

$$
= -EA\frac{\partial u}{\partial x}\, v\, \bigg|_0^L + EAu\frac{\partial v}{\partial x}\, \bigg|_0^L - \int_0^L EA\frac{\partial^2 v}{\partial x^2}\, u\, dx
$$

(c)

Since the boundary conditions are $u = v = 0$ at $x = 0$ and $\partial u/\partial x = \partial v/\partial x = 0$ at $x = L$, we have

$$
\int_0^L -EA\frac{\partial^2 u}{\partial x^2}\, v\, dx = \int_0^L -EA\frac{\partial^2 v}{\partial x^2}\, u\, dx
$$

and the operator is symmetric. We can also directly conclude that the operator is positive definite because from (c) we obtain

$$
\int_0^L -EA\frac{\partial^2 u}{\partial x^2}\, u\, dx = \int_0^L EA\left(\frac{\partial u}{\partial x}\right)^2 dx
$$

In the following we discuss the use of classical weighted residual methods and the Ritz method in the solution of linear steady-state problems as in (3.8) and (3.9), but the same concepts can also be employed in the analysis of propagation problems and eigenproblems and in the analysis of nonlinear response (see Examples 3.23 and 3.24).

The basic step in the weighted residual and Ritz analyses is to assume a solution of the form

$$
\overline{\phi} = \sum_{i=1}^n a_i f_i
$$

(3.12)

where the f_i are linearly independent trial functions and the a_i are multipliers to be determined in the solution.

Consider first the *weighted residual methods*. These techniques operate directly on (3.8) and (3.9). Using these methods, we choose the functions f_i in (3.12) so as to satisfy all boundary conditions in (3.9), and we then calculate the residual

$$
R = r - L_{2m}\left[\sum_{i=1}^n a_i f_i\right]
$$

(3.13)

For the exact solution this residual is of course zero. A good approximation to the exact solution would imply that R is small at all points of the solution domain. The various weighted residual methods differ in the criteria that they employ to calculate the a_i such that R is small. However, in all techniques we determine the a_i so as to make a weighted average of R vanish.

Galerkin method. In this technique the parameters a_i are determined from the n equations

$$
\int_D f_i R\, dD = 0; \qquad i = 1, 2, \ldots, n
$$

(3.14)

where D is the solution domain.

Least squares method.   In this technique the integral of the square of the residual is minimized with respect to the parameters a_i,

$$\frac{\partial}{\partial a_i} \int_D R^2 \, dD = 0; \qquad i = 1, 2, \ldots, n \tag{3.15}$$

Substituting from (3.13), we thus obtain the following n simultaneous equations for the parameters a_i,

$$\int_D R L_{2m}[f_i] \, dD = 0; \qquad i = 1, 2, \ldots, n \tag{3.16}$$

Collocation method.   In this method the residual R is set equal to zero at n distinct points in the solution domain to obtain n simultaneous equations for the parameters a_i. The location of the n points can be somewhat arbitrary, and a uniform pattern may be appropriate, but usually the analyst should use some judgment to employ appropriate locations.

Subdomain method.   The complete domain of solution is subdivided into n subdomains, and the integral of the residual in (3.13) over each subdomain is set equal to zero to generate n equations for the parameters a_i.

An important step in using a weighted residual method is the solution of the simultaneous equations for the parameters a_i. We note that since L_{2m} is a linear operator, in all the procedures mentioned, a linear set of equations in the parameters a_i is generated. In the Galerkin method, the coefficient matrix is symmetric (and also positive definite) if L_{2m} is a symmetric (and also positive definite) operator. In the least squares method we always generate a symmetric coefficient matrix irrespective of the properties of the operator L_{2m}. However, in the collocation and subdomain methods, nonsymmetric coefficient matrices may be generated. In practical analysis, therefore, the Galerkin and least squares methods are usually preferable.

Using weighted residual methods, we operate directly on (3.8) and (3.9) to minimize the error between the trial solution in (3.12) and the actual solution to the problem. Considering next the *Ritz analysis method* (due to W. Ritz [A]), the fundamental difference from the weighted residual methods is that in the Ritz method we operate on the functional corresponding to the problem in (3.8) and (3.9). Let Π be the functional of the C^{m-1} variational problem that is equivalent to the differential formulation given in (3.8) and (3.9); in the Ritz method we substitute the trial functions $\overline{\phi}$ given in (3.12) into Π and generate n simultaneous equations for the parameters a_i using the stationarity condition of Π, $\delta\Pi = 0$ [see (3.1)], which now gives

$$\frac{\partial \Pi}{\partial a_i} = 0; \qquad i = 1, 2, \ldots, n \tag{3.17}$$

An important consideration is the selection of the trial (or Ritz) functions f_i in (3.12). In the Ritz analysis these functions need only satisfy the essential boundary conditions and not the natural boundary conditions. The reason for this relaxed requirement on the trial functions is that the natural boundary conditions are implicitly contained in the functional Π. Assume that the L_{2m} operator corresponding to the variational problem is symmetric and positive definite. In this case the actual extremum of Π is its minimum, and by invoking

(3.17) we minimize (in some sense) the violation of the internal equilibrium requirements and the violation of the natural boundary conditions (see Section 4.3). Therefore, for convergence in a Ritz analysis, the trial functions need only satisfy the essential boundary conditions, which is a fact that may not be anticipated because we know that the exact solution also satisfies the natural boundary conditions. Actually, assuming a given number of trial functions, it can be expected that in most cases the solution will be more accurate if these functions also satisfy the natural boundary conditions. However, it can be very difficult to find such trial functions, and it is generally more effective to use instead a larger number of functions that satisfy only the essential boundary conditions. We demonstrate the use of the Ritz method in the following examples.

EXAMPLE 3.22: Consider a simple bar fixed at one end ($x = 0$) and subjected to a concentrated force at the other end ($x = 180$) as shown in Fig. E3.22. Using the notation given in the figure, the total potential of the structure is

$$\Pi = \int_0^{180} \frac{1}{2} EA \left(\frac{du}{dx} \right)^2 dx - 100u \big|_{x=180} \tag{a}$$

and the essential boundary condition is $u \big|_{x=0} = 0$.

1. Calculate the exact displacement and stress distributions in the bar.
2. Calculate the displacement and stress distributions using the Ritz method with the following displacement assumptions:

$$u = a_1 x + a_2 x^2 \tag{b}$$

and
$$u = \frac{x u_B}{100}; \qquad 0 \le x \le 100 \tag{c}$$

$$u = \left(1 - \frac{x - 100}{80} \right) u_B + \left(\frac{x - 100}{80} \right) u_C; \qquad 100 \le x \le 180$$

where u_B and u_C are the displacements at points B and C.

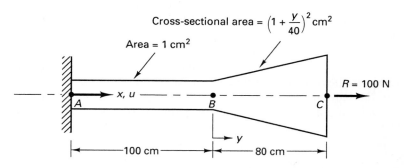

Figure E3.22 Bar subjected to a concentrated end force

In order to calculate the exact displacements in the structure, we use the stationarity condition of Π and generate the governing differential equation and the natural boundary condition. We have

$$\delta\Pi = \int_0^{180} \left(EA \frac{du}{dx} \right) \delta\left(\frac{du}{dx} \right) dx - 100 \, \delta u \big|_{x=180} \tag{d}$$

Setting $\delta\Pi = 0$ and using integration by parts, we obtain (see Example 3.19)

$$\frac{d}{dx}\left(EA\frac{du}{dx}\right) = 0 \tag{e}$$

$$EA\frac{du}{dx}\bigg|_{x=180} = 100 \tag{f}$$

The solution of (e) subject to the natural boundary condition in (f) and the essential boundary condition $u|_{x=0} = 0$ gives

$$u = \frac{100}{E}x; \qquad 0 \le x \le 100$$

$$u = \frac{10000}{E} + \frac{4000}{E} - \frac{4000}{E\left(1 + \dfrac{x - 100}{40}\right)}; \qquad 100 \le x \le 180$$

The exact stresses in the bar are

$$\sigma = 100; \qquad 0 \le x \le 100$$

$$\sigma = \frac{100}{\left(1 + \dfrac{x - 100}{40}\right)^2}; \qquad 100 \le x \le 180$$

Next, to perform the Ritz analyses, we note that the displacement assumptions in (b) and (c) satisfy the essential boundary condition but not the natural boundary condition. Substituting from (b) into (a), we obtain

$$\Pi = \frac{E}{2}\int_0^{100}(a_1 + 2a_2x)^2\,dx + \frac{E}{2}\int_{100}^{180}\left(1 + \frac{x - 100}{40}\right)^2(a_1 + 2a_2x)^2\,dx - 100u|_{x=180}$$

Invoking $\delta\Pi = 0$, we obtain the following equations for a_1 and a_2:

$$E\begin{bmatrix} 0.4467 & 115.6 \\ 115.6 & 34075.7 \end{bmatrix}\begin{bmatrix} a_1 \\ a_2 \end{bmatrix} = \begin{bmatrix} 18 \\ 3240 \end{bmatrix} \tag{g}$$

and

$$a_1 = \frac{129}{E}; \qquad a_2 = -\frac{0.341}{E}$$

This Ritz analysis therefore yields the approximate solution

$$u = \frac{129}{E}x - \frac{0.341}{E}x^2 \tag{h}$$

$$\sigma = 129 - 0.682x; \qquad 0 \le x \le 180 \tag{i}$$

Using next the Ritz functions in (c), we have

$$\Pi = \frac{E}{2}\int_0^{100}\left(\frac{1}{100}u_B\right)^2\,dx + \frac{E}{2}\int_{100}^{180}\left(1 + \frac{x - 100}{40}\right)^2\left(-\frac{1}{80}u_B + \frac{1}{80}u_C\right)^2\,dx - 100u_C$$

Invoking again $\delta\Pi = 0$, we obtain

$$\frac{E}{240}\begin{bmatrix} 15.4 & -13 \\ -13 & 13 \end{bmatrix}\begin{bmatrix} u_B \\ u_C \end{bmatrix} = \begin{bmatrix} 0 \\ 100 \end{bmatrix} \tag{j}$$

Hence we now have

$$u_B = \frac{10{,}000}{E}; \qquad u_C = \frac{11{,}846.2}{E}$$

and

$$\sigma = 100; \qquad 0 \le x \le 100$$

$$\sigma = \frac{1846.2}{80} = 23.08; \qquad 100 \le x \le 180$$

We shall see in Chapter 4 (see Example 4.5) that this Ritz analysis can be regarded to be a finite element analysis.

EXAMPLE 3.23: Consider the slab in Example 3.16. Assume that

$$\theta(t) = \theta_1(t) + \theta_2(t)x + \theta_3(t)x^2 \qquad \text{(a)}$$

where $\theta_1(t)$, $\theta_2(t)$, and $\theta_3(t)$ are the undetermined parameters. Use the Ritz analysis procedure to generate the governing heat transfer equilibrium equations.

The functional governing the temperature distribution in the slab is (see Example 3.18)

$$\Pi = \int_0^L \frac{1}{2}k\left(\frac{\partial\theta}{\partial x}\right)^2 dx - \int_0^L \theta q^B\, dx - \theta|_{x=0}\, q_0 \qquad \text{(b)}$$

with the essential boundary condition

$$\theta|_{x=L} = \theta_i$$

Substituting the temperature assumption of (a) into (b), we obtain

$$\Pi = \int_0^L \frac{1}{2}k((\theta_2)^2 + 4\theta_2\theta_3 x + 4(\theta_3)^2 x^2)dx - \int_0^L (\theta_1 + \theta_2 x + \theta_3 x^2)q^B dx - \theta_1 q_0$$

Invoking the stationarity condition of Π, i.e., $\delta\Pi = 0$, we use

$$\frac{\partial\Pi}{\partial\theta_1} = 0; \qquad \frac{\partial\Pi}{\partial\theta_2} = 0; \qquad \frac{\partial\Pi}{\partial\theta_3} = 0$$

and obtain

$$k\begin{bmatrix} 0 & 0 & 0 \\ 0 & L & L^2 \\ 0 & L^2 & \frac{4}{3}L^3 \end{bmatrix}\begin{bmatrix} \theta_1 \\ \theta_2 \\ \theta_3 \end{bmatrix} = \begin{bmatrix} \int_0^L q^B\, dx + q_0 \\ \int_0^L xq^B\, dx \\ \int_0^L x^2 q^B\, dx \end{bmatrix} \qquad \text{(c)}$$

In this analysis q_0 varies with time, so that the temperature varies with time, and heat capacity effects can be important. Using

$$q^B = -\rho c\frac{\partial\theta}{\partial t} \qquad \text{(d)}$$

because no other heat is generated, substituting for θ in (d) from (a), and then substituting into (c), we obtain as the equilibrium equations,

$$k\begin{bmatrix} 0 & 0 & 0 \\ 0 & L & L^2 \\ 0 & L^2 & \frac{4}{3}L^3 \end{bmatrix}\begin{bmatrix} \theta_1 \\ \theta_2 \\ \theta_3 \end{bmatrix} + \rho c\begin{bmatrix} L & \frac{1}{2}L^2 & \frac{1}{3}L^3 \\ \frac{1}{2}L^2 & \frac{1}{3}L^3 & \frac{1}{4}L^4 \\ \frac{1}{3}L^3 & \frac{1}{4}L^4 & \frac{1}{5}L^5 \end{bmatrix}\begin{bmatrix} \dot\theta_1 \\ \dot\theta_2 \\ \dot\theta_3 \end{bmatrix} = \begin{bmatrix} q_0 \\ 0 \\ 0 \end{bmatrix} \qquad \text{(e)}$$

The final equilibrium equations are now obtained by imposing on the equations in (e) the condition that $\theta\,|_{x=L} = \theta_i$; i.e.,

$$\theta_1(t) + \theta_2(t)L + \theta_3(t)L^2 = \theta_i$$

which can be achieved by expressing θ_1 in (e) in terms of θ_2, θ_3, and θ_i.

EXAMPLE 3.24:   Consider the static buckling response of the column in Example 3.20. Assume that

$$w = a_1x^2 + a_2x^3 \tag{a}$$

and use the Ritz method to formulate equations from which we can obtain an approximate buckling load.

The functional governing the problem was given in Example 3.20,

$$\Pi = \frac{1}{2} \int_0^L EI\left(\frac{d^2w}{dx^2}\right)^2 dx \; - \; \frac{P}{2} \int_0^L \left(\frac{dw}{dx}\right)^2 dx + \frac{1}{2}k(w\,|_{x=L})^2 \tag{b}$$

We note that the trial function on w in (a) already satisfies the essential boundary conditions (displacement and slope equal to zero at the fixed end). Substituting for w into (b), we obtain

$$\Pi = \frac{1}{2} \int_0^L EI(2a_1 + 6a_2x)^2\,dx \; - \; \frac{P}{2}\int_0^L (2a_1x + 3a_2x^2)^2\,dx + \frac{1}{2}k(a_1L^2 + a_2L^3)^2$$

Invoking the stationarity condition $\delta\Pi = 0$, i.e.,

$$\frac{\partial\Pi}{\partial a_1} = 0; \qquad \frac{\partial\Pi}{\partial a_2} = 0$$

we obtain

$$\left\{ 2EI\begin{bmatrix} 2L & 3L^2 \\ 3L^2 & 6L^3 \end{bmatrix} + kL^4\begin{bmatrix} 1 & L \\ L & L^2 \end{bmatrix} \right\}\begin{bmatrix} a_1 \\ a_2 \end{bmatrix} - PL^3\begin{bmatrix} \dfrac{4}{3} & \dfrac{3L}{2} \\ \dfrac{3L}{2} & \dfrac{9L^2}{5} \end{bmatrix}\begin{bmatrix} a_1 \\ a_2 \end{bmatrix} = \begin{bmatrix} 0 \\ 0 \end{bmatrix}$$

The solution of this eigenproblem gives two values of P for which w in (a) is nonzero. The smaller value of P represents an approximation to the lowest buckling load of the structure.

The weighted residual methods presented in (3.14) to (3.16) are difficult to use in practice because the trial functions must be $2m$-times-differentiable and satisfy all—essential and natural—boundary conditions [see (3.13)]. On the other hand, with the Ritz method, which operates on the functional corresponding to the problem being considered, the trial functions need to be only m-times-differentiable and do not need to satisfy the natural boundary conditions. These considerations are most important for practical analysis, and therefore the Galerkin method is used in practice in a different form, namely, in a form that allows the use of the same functions as used in the Ritz method. In the displacement-based analysis of solids and structures, this form of the Galerkin method is referred to as the *principle of virtual displacements*. If the appropriate variational indicator Π is used, the equations obtained with the Ritz method are then identical to those obtained with the Galerkin method.

We elaborate upon these issues in the next section with the objective of providing further understanding for the introduction of finite element procedures.

3.3.4 An Overview: The Differential and Galerkin Formulations, the Principle of Virtual Displacements, and an Introduction to the Finite Element Solution

In the previous sections we reviewed some classical differential and variational formulations, some classical weighted residual methods, and the Ritz method. We now want to reinforce our understanding of these analysis approaches—by summarizing some important concepts—and briefly introduce a mathematical framework for finite element procedures that we will further use and extend in Chapter 4. Let us pursue this objective by focusing on the analysis of a simple example problem.

Consider the one-dimensional bar in Fig. 3.2. The bar is subjected to a distributed load $f^B(x)$ and a concentrated load R at its right end. As discussed in Section 3.3.1, the differential formulation of the bar gives the governing equations

$$\boxed{\textbf{Differential formulation}} \quad \left\{ \begin{array}{ll} EA\dfrac{d^2u}{dx^2} + f^B = 0 & \text{in the bar} \qquad\qquad (3.18) \\[2mm] \left.u\right|_{x=0} = 0 & \qquad\qquad\qquad (3.19) \\[2mm] \left.EA\dfrac{du}{dx}\right|_{x=L} = R & \qquad\qquad\qquad (3.20) \end{array} \right.$$

Since $f^B = ax$, we obtain the solution

$$u(x) = \frac{-(ax^3/6) + (R + \tfrac{1}{2}aL^2)x}{EA} \qquad\qquad (3.21)$$

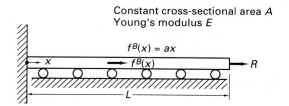

Constant cross-sectional area A
Young's modulus E

$f^B(x) = ax$

$f^B(x)$

R

x

L

Figure 3.2 Uniform bar subjected to body load f^B (force/unit length) and tip load R

We recall that (3.18) is a statement of equilibrium at any point x within the bar, (3.19) is the essential (or geometric) boundary condition (see Section 3.2.2), and (3.20) is the natural (or force) boundary condition. The exact analytical solution (3.21) of course satisfies all three equations (3.18) to (3.20).

We also note that the solution $u(x)$ is a continuous and twice-differentiable function, as required in (3.18). Indeed, we can say that the solutions to (3.18) satisfying (3.19) and (3.20) for any continuous loading f^B lie in the *space* of continuous and twice-differentiable functions that satisfy (3.19) and (3.20).

An alternative approach for the solution of the analysis problem is given by the variational formulation (see Section 3.3.2),

$$
\boxed{\textbf{Variational formulation}}
\begin{cases}
\Pi = \displaystyle\int_0^L \frac{1}{2} EA\left(\frac{du}{dx}\right)^2 dx - \int_0^L uf^B\, dx - Ru\big|_{x=L} & (3.22) \\[2ex]
\qquad\qquad \delta\Pi = 0 & (3.23) \\[2ex]
\text{with} \qquad u\big|_{x=0} = 0 & (3.24) \\[2ex]
\qquad\qquad \delta u\big|_{x=0} = 0 & (3.25)
\end{cases}
$$

where δ means "variation in" and δu is an arbitrary variation on u subject to the condition $\delta u\big|_{x=0} = 0$. We may think of $\delta u(x)$ as any continuous function that satisfies the boundary condition (3.25).[4]

Let us recall that (3.22) to (3.25) are totally equivalent to (3.18) to (3.20) (see Section 3.3.2). That is, invoking (3.23) and then using integration by parts and the boundary condition (3.25) gives (3.18) and (3.20). Therefore, the solution of (3.22) to (3.25) is also (3.21).

The variational formulation can be derived as follows.

Since (3.18) holds for all points within the bar, we also have

$$
\left(EA\frac{d^2u}{dx^2} + f^B\right)\delta u = 0 \qquad (3.26)
$$

where $\delta u(x)$ is an arbitrary variation on u (or an arbitrary continuous function) with $\delta u\big|_{x=0} = 0$. Hence, also

$$
\int_0^L \left(EA\frac{d^2u}{dx^2} + f^B\right)\delta u\, dx = 0 \qquad (3.27)
$$

Integrating by parts, we obtain

$$
\int_0^L \frac{d\delta u}{dx} EA \frac{du}{dx}\, dx = \int_0^L f^B\,\delta u\, dx + EA \frac{du}{dx}\,\delta u\big|_0^L \qquad (3.28)
$$

Substituting from (3.20) and (3.25), we therefore have

$$
\boxed{\textbf{Principle of virtual displacements}}
\begin{cases}
\displaystyle\int_0^L \frac{d\delta u}{dx} EA \frac{du}{dx}\, dx = \int_0^L f^B\,\delta u\, dx + R\,\delta u\big|_{x=L} & (3.29) \\[3ex]
\text{with } u\big|_{x=0} = 0; \qquad \delta u\big|_{x=0} = 0 & (3.30)
\end{cases}
$$

Of course, (3.29) gives

$$
\delta\left\{ \int_0^L \left[\frac{EA}{2}\left(\frac{du}{dx}\right)^2 - f^B u\right] dx - Ru\big|_{x=L}\right\} = 0 \qquad (3.31)
$$

which with (3.30) is the variational statement of (3.22) to (3.25).

The relation (3.29) along with the condition (3.30) is the celebrated principle of virtual displacements (or principle of virtual work) in which $\delta u(x)$ is the virtual displace-

---

[4]In the literature, differential and variational formulations are, respectively, also referred to as strong and weak forms. Variational formulations are also referred to as generalized formulations.

ment. We discuss this principle extensively in Section 4.2 and note that the derivation in (3.26) to (3.30) is a special case of Example 4.2.

It is important to recognize that the above three formulations of the analysis problem are totally equivalent, that is, the solution (3.21) is *the* (unique) solution[5] $u(x)$ of the differential formulation, the variational formulation, and the principle of virtual displacements. However, we note that the variational formulation and the principle of virtual work involve only first-order derivatives of the functions u and δu. Hence the space of functions in which we look for a solution is clearly larger than the space of functions used for the solution of (3.18) [we define the space precisely in (3.35)], and there must be a question as to what it means and how important it is that we use a larger space of functions when solving the problem in Fig. 3.2 with the principle of virtual displacements.

Of course, the space of functions used with the principle of virtual displacements contains the space of functions used with the differential formulation, hence all analysis problems that can be solved with the differential formulation (3.18) to (3.20) can also be solved exactly with the principle of virtual displacements. However, in the analysis of the bar (and the analysis of general bar and beam structures) additional conditions for which the principle of virtual work can be used directly for solution are those where concentrated loads are applied within the bar or discontinuities in the material property or cross-sectional area are present. In these cases the first derivative of $u(x)$ is discontinuous and hence the differential formulation has to be extended to account for such cases (in essence treating separately each section of the bar in which no concentrated loads are applied and in which no discontinuities in the material property and cross-sectional area are present, and connecting the section to the adjoining sections by the boundary conditions; see, for example, S. H. Crandall, N. C. Dahl, and T. J. Lardner [A]). Hence, in these cases the variational formulation and the principle of virtual displacements are somewhat more direct and more powerful for solution.

For general two- and three-dimensional stress situations, we will only consider mathematical models of finite strain energy (meaning for example that concentrated loads should only be applied as enumerated in Section 1.2, see Fig. 1.4, and further discussed in Section 4.3.4), and then the differential and principle of virtual work formulations are also totally equivalent and give the same solutions (see Chapter 4).

These considerations point to a powerful general procedure for formulating the numerical solution of the problem in Fig. 3.2. Consider (3.27) in which we now replace δu with the test function v,

$$\int_0^L \left(EA \frac{d^2u}{dx^2} + f^B \right) v \, dx = 0 \tag{3.32}$$

with $u = 0$ and $v = 0$ at $x = 0$. Integrating by parts and using (3.20), we obtain

$$\int_0^L \frac{dv}{dx} EA \frac{du}{dx} = \int_0^L f^B v \, dx + Rv \big|_{x=L} \tag{3.33}$$

This relation is an application of the Galerkin method or of the principle of virtual displacements and states that "for $u(x)$ to be *the* solution of the problem, the left-hand side of (3.33) (the internal virtual work) must be equal to the right-hand side (the external virtual work)

---

[5]The uniqueness of $u(x)$ follows in this case clearly from the simple integration process for obtaining (3.21), but a general proof that the solution of a linear elasticity problem is always unique is given in (4.80) to (4.82).

for arbitrary test or virtual displacement functions $v(x)$ that are continuous and that satisfy the condition $v = 0$ at $x = 0$."

In Chapter 4 we write the formulation (3.33) in the following form:

$$\text{Find } u \in V \text{ such that}^6 \qquad a(u, v) = (f, v) \qquad \forall v \in V \tag{3.34}$$

where the space V is defined as

$$V = \left\{ v \mid v \in L^2(L), \frac{dv}{dx} \in L^2(L), v\,|_{x=0} = 0 \right\} \tag{3.35}$$

and $L^2(L)$ is the space of square integrable functions over the length of the bar, $0 \leq x \leq L$,

$$L^2(L) = \left\{ w \mid w \text{ is defined over } 0 \leq x \leq L \text{ and } \int_0^L (w)^2 \, dx = \| w \|_{L^2}^2 < \infty \right\} \tag{3.36}$$

Using (3.34) and (3.33), we have

$$a(u, v) = \int_0^L \frac{du}{dx} EA \frac{dv}{dx} \, dx \tag{3.37}$$

and

$$(f, v) = \int_0^L f^B v \, dx + Rv\,|_{x=L} \tag{3.38}$$

where $a(u, v)$ is the bilinear form and (f, v) is the linear form of the problem.

The definition of the space of functions V in (3.35) says that any element v in V is zero at $x = 0$ and

$$\int_0^L v^2 \, dx < \infty; \qquad \int_0^L \left[\frac{dv}{dx} \right]^2 dx < \infty$$

Hence, any element v in V corresponds to a finite strain energy. We note that the elements in V comprise all functions that are candidates for solution of the differential formulation (3.18) to (3.20) with any continuous f^B and also correspond to possible solutions with discontinuous strains [because of concentrated loads, in this one-dimensional analysis case, or discontinuities in the material behavior or cross-sectional area]. This observation underlines the generality of the problem formulation given in (3.34) and (3.35).

For the Galerkin (or finite element) solution we define the space V_h of trial (or finite element) functions v_h,

$$V_h = \left\{ v_h \mid v_h \in L^2(L), \frac{dv_h}{dx} \in L^2(L), v_h\,|_{S_u} = 0 \right\} \tag{3.39}$$

where S_u denotes the surface area on which the zero displacement is prescribed. The subscript h denotes that a particular finite element discretization is being considered (and h actually refers to the size of the elements; see Section 4.3). The finite element formulation of the problem is then

$$\text{Find } u_h \in V_h \text{ such that } \quad a(u_h, v_h) = (f, v_h) \qquad \forall v_h \in V_h \tag{3.40}$$

Of course, (3.40) is the principle of virtual displacements applied with the functions contained in V_h and also corresponds to the minimization of the total potential energy within this space of trial functions. Therefore, (3.40) corresponds to the use of the Ritz method

---

[6] The symbols $\forall$ and $\in$ mean, respectively, "for all" and "an element of."

described in Section 3.3.3. We discuss the finite element formulation extensively in Chapter 4.

However, let us note here that the same solution approach can also be used directly for any analysis problem for which we have the governing differential equation(s). The procedure would be: weigh the governing differential equation(s) in the domain with suitable test function(s); integrate the resulting equation(s) with a transformation using integration by parts (or more generally the divergence theorem; see Example 4.2); and substitute the natural boundary conditions—as we did to find (3.33).

We obtain in this way the principle of virtual displacements for the general analysis of solids and structures (see Example 4.2), the "principle of virtual temperatures" for the general heat flow and temperature analysis of solids (see Example 7.1), and the "principle of virtual velocities" for general fluid flow analysis (see Section 7.4.2).

To demonstrate the use of the above notation, consider the following examples.

EXAMPLE 3.25:   Consider the analysis problem in Example 3.22. Write the problem formulation in the form (3.40) and identify the finite element basis functions used when employing the displacement assumptions (b) and (c) in the example.

Here the bilinear form $a(.,.)$ is

$$a(u_h, v_h) = \int_0^{180} \frac{du_h}{dx} EA \frac{dv_h}{dx} dx$$

and we have the linear form

$$(f, v_h) = 100 v_h|_{x=180}$$

With the displacement assumption (b) we use

$$u_h = a_1 x + a_2 x^2$$

Hence V_h is a two-dimensional space, and the two basis functions are

$$v_h^{(1)} = x \qquad \text{and} \qquad v_h^{(2)} = x^2$$

With the displacement assumption (c) we use

$$u_h = \frac{x}{100} u_B; \qquad 0 \le x \le 100$$

$$u_h = \left(1 - \frac{x - 100}{80}\right) u_B + \frac{(x - 100)}{80} u_C; \qquad 100 \le x \le 180$$

and the two basis functions for V_h are

$$v_h^{(1)} = \begin{cases} \dfrac{x}{100} & \text{for } 0 \le x \le 100 \\[2mm] 1 - \dfrac{x - 100}{80} & \text{for } 100 \le x \le 180 \end{cases}$$

and

$$v_h^{(2)} = \frac{x - 100}{80} \qquad \text{for } 100 \le x \le 180$$

Clearly, all these functions satisfy the conditions in (3.39). If we use (3.40), the equations in (g) and (j) in Example 3.22 are generated.

EXAMPLE 3.26: Consider the analysis problem in Example 3.23. Write the problem formulation in the form (3.40) and identify the element basis functions used when employing the temperature assumption given in the example.

Here the problem formulation is

$$\text{Find } \theta_h \in V_h \text{ such that } a(\theta_h, \psi_h) = (f, \psi_h) \qquad \forall \psi_h \in V_h \tag{a}$$

where

$$a(\theta_h, \psi_h) = \int_0^L \frac{d\psi_h}{dx} k \frac{d\theta_h}{dx} dx$$

$$(f, \psi_h) = \int_0^L \psi_h q^B dx + q_0 \psi_h|_{x=0}$$

Here θ_h and ψ_h correspond to temperature distributions in the slab. With the assumption in Example 3.23 we have for V_h the three basis functions

$$\theta_h^{(1)} = 1; \qquad \theta_h^{(2)} = x; \qquad \theta_h^{(3)} = x^2$$

Using (a) the governing equations given in (c) in Example 3.23 are obtained. Note that in this formulation we have not yet imposed the essential boundary condition (which is achieved later, as in Example 3.23).

3.3.5 Finite Difference Differential and Energy Methods

A classical approach to finding a numerical solution to the governing equations of a mathematical continuum model is to use finite differences (see, for example, L. Collatz [A]), and it is valuable to be familiar with this approach because such knowledge will reinforce our understanding of the finite element procedures. In a finite difference solution, the derivatives are replaced by finite difference approximations and the differential and variational formulations of mathematical models can be solved.

As an example, consider the analysis of the uniform bar in Fig. 3.2 with the governing differential equation (see Example 3.17 and Section 3.3.4),

$$u'' + \frac{f^B}{EA} = 0 \tag{3.41}$$

and the boundary conditions

$$u = 0 \qquad \text{at } x = 0 \tag{3.42}$$

$$EA \frac{du}{dx} = R \qquad \text{at } x = L \tag{3.43}$$

Using an equal spacing h between finite difference stations, we can write (see Fig. 3.3)

$$u'|_{i+1/2} = \frac{u_{i+1} - u_i}{h}; \qquad u'|_{i-1/2} = \frac{u_i - u_{i-1}}{h} \tag{3.44}$$

and

$$u''|_i = \frac{u'|_{i+1/2} - u'|_{i-1/2}}{h} \tag{3.45}$$

so that

$$u''|_i = \frac{1}{h^2}(u_{i+1} - 2u_i + u_{i-1}) \tag{3.46}$$

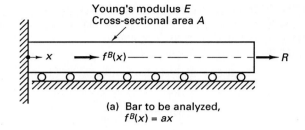

(a) Bar to be analyzed,
$f^B(x) = ax$

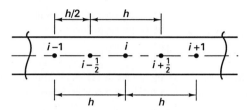

(b) Finite difference stations $i-1$, i, $i+1$
(locations $i-\frac{1}{2}$, $i+\frac{1}{2}$ are not stations)

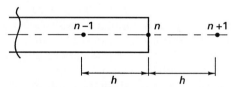

(c) Fictitious finite difference station $n+1$ outside bar

Figure 3.3   Finite difference analysis of a bar

The relation in (3.46) is called the *central difference approximation.* If we substitute (3.46) into (3.41), we obtain

$$\frac{EA}{h}(-u_{i+1} + 2u_i - u_{i-1}) = f_i^B h \tag{3.47}$$

where f_i^B is the load $f^B(x)$ at station i and $f_i^B h$ can be thought of as the total load applied at that finite difference station.

Assume now that we use a total of $n + 1$ finite difference stations on the bar, with station $i = 0$ at the fixed end and station $i = n$ at the other end. Then the boundary conditions are

$$u_0 = 0 \tag{3.48}$$

and

$$EA\frac{u_{n+1} - u_{n-1}}{2h} = R \tag{3.49}$$

where we have introduced the fictitious station $n + 1$ outside the bar [see Fig. 3.3(c)], merely to impose the boundary condition (3.43).

For the finite difference solution we apply (3.47) at all stations $i = 1, \ldots, n$ and use the boundary conditions (3.48) and (3.49) to obtain

$$
\frac{EA}{h}
\begin{bmatrix}
2 & -1 \\
-1 & 2 & -1 \\
 & -1 & 2 & -1 \\
 & & & \ddots \\
 & & & -1 & 2 & -1 \\
 & & & & -1 & 1
\end{bmatrix}
\begin{bmatrix}
u_1 \\
u_2 \\
u_3 \\
\vdots \\
u_{n-1} \\
u_n
\end{bmatrix}
=
\begin{bmatrix}
R_1 \\
R_2 \\
R_3 \\
\vdots \\
R_{n-1} \\
R_n
\end{bmatrix}
\tag{3.50}
$$

where $R_i = f_i^B h$, $i = 1, \ldots, n - 1$, and $R_n = f_n^B h/2 + R$.

We note that the equations in (3.50) are identical to the equations that would be obtained using a series of n spring elements, each of stiffness EA/h. The loads at the nodes corresponding to $f^B(x)$ would be obtained by using the distributed load value at node i and multiplying that value by the contributing length (h for the interior nodes and $h/2$ for the end node.)

The same coefficient matrix is also obtained if we use the Ritz method with the variational formulation of the mathematical model and specific Ritz functions. The variational indicator is (see Example 3.19)

$$
\Pi = \frac{1}{2} \int_0^L EA(u')^2 \, dx - \int_0^L uf^B \, dx - Ru \big|_{x=L}
\tag{3.51}
$$

and the specific Ritz functions are depicted in Fig. 3.4. While the same coefficient matrix is obtained, the load vector is different unless the loading is constant along the length of the bar.

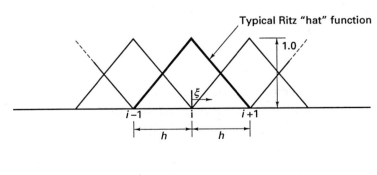

$$
u(\xi) =
\begin{cases}
\left(1 - \dfrac{\xi}{h}\right) u_i & \text{for } 0 \le \xi \le h \\[2mm]
\left(1 + \dfrac{\xi}{h}\right) u_i & \text{for } -h \le \xi \le 0
\end{cases}
$$

Figure 3.4   Typical Ritz function or Galerkin basis function used in analysis of bar problem

The same equations as in the Ritz solution are of course also obtained using the Galerkin method given in Section 3.3.4 (i.e., the principle of virtual work) with the basis functions in Fig. 3.4.

The preceding discussion indicates that the finite difference method can also be used to generate stiffness matrices, and that in some cases the resulting equations obtained in a Ritz analysis and in a finite difference solution are identical or almost identical.

Table 3.1 summarizes some widely used finite difference approximations, also called finite difference stencils or molecules. Let us demonstrate the use of these stencils in two examples.

TABLE 3.1 *Finite difference approximations for various differentiations*

Differentiation	Finite difference approximation	Molecules
$\left. \dfrac{dw}{dx} \right|_i$	$\dfrac{w_{i+1} - w_{i-1}}{2h}$	
$\left. \dfrac{d^2w}{dx^2} \right|_i$	$\dfrac{w_{i+1} - 2w_i + w_{i-1}}{h^2}$	
$\left. \dfrac{d^3w}{dx^3} \right|_i$	$\dfrac{w_{i+2} - 2w_{i+1} + 2w_{i-1} - w_{i-2}}{2h^3}$	
$\left. \dfrac{d^4w}{dx^4} \right|_i$	$\dfrac{w_{i+2} - 4w_{i+1} + 6w_i - 4w_{i-1} + w_{i-2}}{h^4}$	
$\nabla^2 w \big|_{i,j}$	$\dfrac{-4w_{i,j} + w_{i+1,j} + w_{i,j+1} + w_{i-1,j} + w_{i,j-1}}{h^2}$	
$\nabla^4 w \big|_{i,j}$	$[20w_{i,j} - 8(w_{i+1,j} + w_{i-1,j}$ $+ w_{i,j+1} + w_{i,j-1}) + 2(w_{i+1,j+1}$ $+ w_{i-1,j+1} + w_{i-1,j-1} + w_{i+1,j-1})$ $+ w_{i+2,j} + w_{i-2,j} + w_{i,j+2}$ $w_{i,j-2}]/h^4$	

Uniform spacing h; error in each case is $o(h^2)$. Point i or (i, j) is being considered; and $i \pm \cdots$ denotes points in the x-direction; $j \pm \cdots$ denotes points in the y-direction.

EXAMPLE 3.27:   Consider the simply supported beam in Fig. E3.27. Use conventional finite differencing to establish the system equilibrium equations.

The finite difference grid used for the beam analysis is shown in the figure. In the conventional finite difference analysis the differential equation of equilibrium and the geometric and natural boundary conditions are considered; i.e., we approximate by finite differences at each interior station,

$$EI \frac{d^4 w}{dx^4} = q \tag{a}$$

and use the conditions that $w = 0$ and $w'' = 0$ at $x = 0$ and $x = L$.

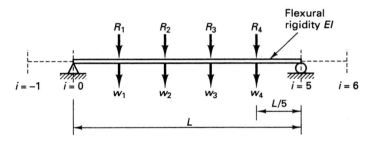

Figure E3.27   Finite difference stations for simply supported beam

Using central differencing, (a) is approximated at station i by

$$\frac{EI}{(L/5)^3} \{ w_{i-2} - 4w_{i-1} + 6w_i - 4w_{i+1} + w_{i+2} \} = R_i \tag{b}$$

where $R_i = q_i L/5$ and is the concentrated load applied at station i. The condition that w'' is zero at station i is approximated using

$$w_{i-1} - 2w_i + w_{i+1} = 0 \tag{c}$$

Applying (b) at each finite difference station, $i = 1, 2, 3, 4$, and using condition (c) at the support points, we obtain the system of equations

$$\frac{125EI}{L^3} \begin{bmatrix} 5 & -4 & 1 & 0 \\ -4 & 6 & -4 & 1 \\ 1 & -4 & 6 & -4 \\ 0 & 1 & -4 & 5 \end{bmatrix} \begin{bmatrix} w_1 \\ w_2 \\ w_3 \\ w_4 \end{bmatrix} = \begin{bmatrix} R_1 \\ R_2 \\ R_3 \\ R_4 \end{bmatrix}$$

where the coefficient matrix of the displacement vector can be regarded as a stiffness matrix.

EXAMPLE 3.28:   Consider the plate shown in Fig. E3.28.

1. Calculate the center point transverse deflection when the plate is uniformly loaded under static conditions with the distributed load p per unit area. Use only one finite difference station in the interior of the plate.
2. If the load p is applied dynamically, i.e., $p = p(t)$, establish an equation of motion governing the behavior of the plate.

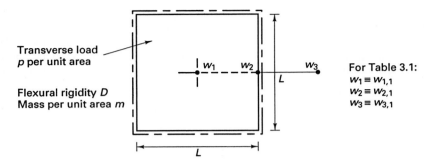

Figure E3.28 Simply supported plate

The governing differential equation of the plate is (see, for example, S. Timoshenko and S. Woinowsky-Krieger [A])

$$\nabla^4 w = \frac{p}{D}$$

where w is the transverse displacement. The boundary conditions are that on each edge of the plate the transverse displacement and the moment across the edge are zero.

We use the finite difference stencil for $\nabla^4 w$ given in Table 3.1, with the center point of the molecule placed at the center of the plate. The displacements corresponding to the coefficients -8 and $+2$ are zero, and the displacements corresponding to the coefficients $+1$ are expressed in terms of the center displacement. For example, the zero moment condition gives (refer to Fig. E3.28)

$$w_1 - 2w_2 + w_3 = 0$$

and because $w_2 = 0$,

$$w_3 = -w_1$$

Therefore, the governing finite difference equation is

$$16w_1 = \frac{p}{D}\left(\frac{L}{2}\right)^4$$

and we obtain

$$\left[\frac{16D}{(L/2)^2}\right] w_1 = R; \qquad R = p\left(\frac{L}{2}\right)^2$$

Note that with this relation we in essence represent the plate by a single spring of stiffness $k = 64D/L^2$, and the total load acting on the spring is given by R. The deflection w_1 thus calculated is only about 4 percent different from the analytically calculated "exact" value.

For the dynamic analysis, we use d'Alembert's principle and subtract from the externally applied load R the inertia load $M\ddot{w}_1$, where M represents a mass in some sense equivalent to the distributed mass of the plate

$$M = m\left(\frac{L}{2}\right)^2$$

Hence the dynamic equilibrium equation is

$$m\frac{L^2}{4}\ddot{w}_1 + \frac{64D}{L^2}w_1 = R$$

In these two examples and in the analysis of the bar in Fig. 3.2, the differential equations of equilibrium have been approximated by finite differences. When the differential equations of equilibrium are used to solve a mathematical model, it is necessary to approximate by finite differences and impose on the coefficient matrix both the essential and the natural boundary conditions. In the analysis of the beam and the plate considered in Examples 3.27 and 3.28, these boundary conditions could easily be imposed (the zero displacements on the boundaries are the essential boundary conditions and the zero moment conditions across the boundaries are the natural boundary conditions). However, for complex geometries the imposition of the natural boundary conditions can be difficult to achieve since the topology of the finite difference mesh restricts the form of differencing that can be carried out, and it may be difficult to obtain a symmetric coefficient matrix in a rigorous manner (see A. Ghali and K. J. Bathe [A]).

The difficulties associated with the use of the differential formulations have given impetus to the development of finite difference analysis procedures based on the principle of minimum total potential energy, referred to as the *finite difference energy method* (see, for example, D. Bushnell, B. O. Almroth, and F. Brogan [A]). In this scheme the displacement derivatives in the total potential energy, Π, of the system are approximated by finite differences, and the minimum condition of Π is used to calculate the unknown displacements at the finite difference stations. Since the variational formulation of the problem under consideration is employed, only the essential (geometric) boundary conditions must be satisfied in the differencing. Furthermore, a symmetric coefficient matrix is always obtained.

As might well be expected, the finite difference energy method is very closely related to the Ritz method, and in some cases the same algebraic equations are generated.

An advantage of the finite difference energy method lies in the effectiveness with which the coefficient matrix of the algebraic equations can be generated. This effectiveness is due to the simple scheme of energy integration employed. However, the Galerkin method implemented in the form of the finite element procedures discussed in the forthcoming chapters is a much more general and powerful technique, and this of course is the reason for the success of the finite element method.

It is instructive to examine the use of the finite difference energy method in some examples.

EXAMPLE 3.29:   Consider the cantilever beam in Fig. E3.29. Evaluate the tip deflection using the conventional finite difference method and the finite difference energy method.

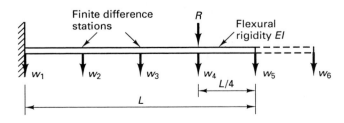

Figure E3.29   Finite difference stations on cantilever beam

The finite difference mesh used is shown in the figure. Using the conventional finite difference procedure and central differencing as in Example 3.27, we obtain the equilibrium equations

$$\frac{64EI}{L^3}\begin{bmatrix} 7 & -4 & 1 & 0 \\ -4 & 6 & -4 & 1 \\ 1 & -4 & 5 & -2 \\ 0 & 1 & -2 & 1 \end{bmatrix}\begin{bmatrix} w_2 \\ w_3 \\ w_4 \\ w_5 \end{bmatrix} = \begin{bmatrix} 0 \\ 0 \\ R \\ 0 \end{bmatrix} \tag{a}$$

It may be noted that in addition to the equations employed in Example 3.27 the conditions $w' = 0$ at the fixed end and $w''' = 0$ at the free end are also used. For w' and w''' equal to zero at station i, we employ, respectively,

$$w_{i+1} - w_{i-1} = 0$$

$$w_{i+2} - 2w_{i+1} + 2w_{i-1} - w_{i-2} = 0$$

Using the finite difference energy method, the total potential energy Π is given as

$$\Pi = \frac{EI}{2}\int_0^L [w''(x)]^2\, dx - \frac{Rw}{x} = \frac{3}{4}L$$

To evaluate the integral we need to approximate $w''(x)$. Using central differencing, we obtain for station i,

$$w_i'' = \frac{1}{(L/4)^2}(w_{i+1} - 2w_i + w_{i-1}) \tag{b}$$

An approximate solution can now be obtained by evaluating Π at the finite difference stations using (b) and replacing the integral by a summation process; i.e., we use the approximation

$$\Pi = \frac{L}{8}\Pi_1 + \frac{L}{4}(\Pi_2 + \Pi_3 + \Pi_4) + \frac{L}{8}\Pi_5 - Rw_4 \tag{c}$$

where
$$\Pi_i = \frac{1}{2}[w_{i-1}\ \ w_i\ \ w_{i+1}]\begin{bmatrix} 1 \\ -2 \\ 1 \end{bmatrix}\frac{EI}{(L/4)^4}[1\ \ -2\ \ 1]\begin{bmatrix} w_{i-1} \\ w_i \\ w_{i+1} \end{bmatrix}$$

Therefore, we can write, in analogy with the finite element analysis procedures (see Section 4.2),

$$\Pi_i = \tfrac{1}{2}\mathbf{U}^T\mathbf{B}_i^T\mathbf{C}_i\mathbf{B}_i\mathbf{U}$$

where $\mathbf{B}_i$ is a generalized strain-displacement transformation matrix, $\mathbf{C}_i$ is the stress-strain matrix, and $\mathbf{U}$ is a vector listing all nodal point displacements. Using the direct stiffness method to calculate the total potential energy as given in (c) and employing the condition that the total potential energy is stationary (i.e., $\delta\Pi = 0$), we obtain the equilibrium equations

$$\frac{64EI}{L^3}\begin{bmatrix} 7 & -4 & 1 & & \\ -4 & 6 & -4 & 1 & \\ 1 & -4 & 5.5 & -3 & 0.5 \\ & 1 & -3 & 3 & -1 \\ & & 0.5 & -1 & 0.5 \end{bmatrix}\begin{bmatrix} w_2 \\ w_3 \\ w_4 \\ w_5 \\ w_6 \end{bmatrix} = \begin{bmatrix} 0 \\ 0 \\ R \\ 0 \\ 0 \end{bmatrix} \tag{d}$$

where the condition of zero slope at the fixed end has already been used.

The close similarity between the equilibrium equations in (a) and (d) should be noted. Indeed, if we eliminate w_6 from the equations in (d), we obtain the equations in (a). Hence, using the finite difference energy method and the conventional finite difference method, we obtain in this case the same equilibrium equations.

As an example, let $R = 1$, $EI = 10^3$, and $L = 10$. Then we obtain, using the equations in (a) or (d),

$$\mathbf{U} = \begin{bmatrix} 0.023437 \\ 0.078125 \\ 0.14843 \\ 0.21875 \end{bmatrix}$$

The exact answer for the tip deflection is $w_5 = 0.2109375$. Hence the finite difference analysis gives a good approximate solution.

EXAMPLE 3.30:   The rod shown in Fig. E3.30 is subjected to a heat flux input of q^S at its right end and a constant temperature θ_0 at its left end and is in steady-state conditions. The variational indicator is

$$\Pi = \frac{1}{2} \int_0^L k \left(\frac{\partial \theta}{\partial x} \right)^2 A \, dx - q^S A_L \theta_L \tag{a}$$

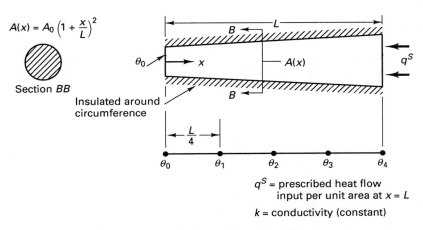

Figure E3.30   Rod in heat transfer condition; finite difference stations used

Use the finite difference method to obtain an approximate solution for the temperature distribution.

Let us use five equally spaced finite difference stations as shown in Fig. E3.30. The finite difference approximation of the integral in (a) is then

$$\Pi = \frac{L}{4} \{ \Pi_{1/2} + \Pi_{3/2} + \Pi_{5/2} + \Pi_{7/2} \} - q^S A_L \theta_L$$

where $\qquad \Pi_{1/2} = \frac{1}{2} [\theta_1 \quad \theta_0] \begin{bmatrix} 1 \\ -1 \end{bmatrix} \dfrac{k(\frac{9}{8})^2 A_0}{(L/4)^2} [1 \quad -1] \begin{bmatrix} \theta_1 \\ \theta_0 \end{bmatrix}$

and the values $\Pi_{3/2}$, $\Pi_{5/2}$, and $\Pi_{7/2}$ are similarly evaluated. Calculating Π, invoking $\delta\Pi = 0$, and imposing the boundary condition that θ_0 is known, we thus obtain

$$\frac{kA_0}{16L}\begin{bmatrix} 202 & -121 & & \\ -121 & 290 & -169 & \\ & -169 & 394 & -225 \\ & & -225 & 225 \end{bmatrix}\begin{bmatrix} \theta_1 \\ \theta_2 \\ \theta_3 \\ \theta_4 \end{bmatrix} = \begin{bmatrix} \frac{81}{16L}kA_0\,\theta_0 \\ 0 \\ 0 \\ 4A_0\,q^S \end{bmatrix}$$

Now assume that $\theta_0 = 0$. Then the solution is

$$\begin{bmatrix} \theta_1 \\ \theta_2 \\ \theta_3 \\ \theta_4 \end{bmatrix} = \begin{bmatrix} 0.79 \\ 1.32 \\ 1.70 \\ 1.98 \end{bmatrix}\frac{Lq^S}{k}$$

which compares as follows with the analytical solution

$$\begin{bmatrix} \theta_1 \\ \theta_2 \\ \theta_3 \\ \theta_4 \end{bmatrix}_{\text{analytical}} = \begin{bmatrix} \frac{4}{5} \\ \frac{4}{3} \\ \frac{12}{7} \\ 2 \end{bmatrix}\frac{Lq^S}{k}$$

3.3.6 Exercises

3.15. Establish the differential equation of equilibrium of the problem shown and the (geometric and force) boundary conditions. Determine whether the operator L_{2m} of the problem is symmetric and positive definite and prove your answer.

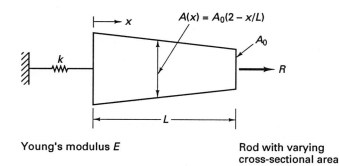

Young's modulus E Rod with varying cross-sectional area

3.16. Consider the cantilever beam shown, which is subjected to a moment M at its tip. Determine the variational indicator Π and state the essential boundary conditions. Invoke the stationarity of Π by using (3.7b) and by using the fact that variations and differentiations are performed using the same rules. Then extract the differential equation of equilibrium and the natural boundary conditions. Determine whether the operator L_{2m} is symmetric and positive definite and prove your answer.

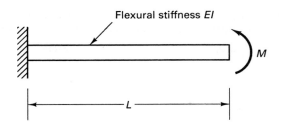

Flexural stiffness EI

M

L

3.17. Consider the heat transfer problem in Example 3.30. Invoke the stationarity of the given variational indicator by using (3.7b) and by using the fact that variations and differentiations are performed using the same rules. Establish the governing differential equation of equilibrium and all boundary conditions. Determine whether the operator L_{2m} is symmetric and positive definite and prove your answer.

3.18. Consider the prestressed cable shown in the figure. The variational indicator is

$$\Pi = \frac{1}{2} \int_0^L T \left(\frac{dw}{dx} \right)^2 dx + \int_0^L \frac{1}{2} k(w)^2 \, dx - Pw_L$$

where w is the transverse displacement and w_L is the transverse displacement at $x = L$. Establish the differential equation of equilibrium and state all boundary conditions. Determine whether the operator L_{2m} is symmetric and positive definite and prove your answer.

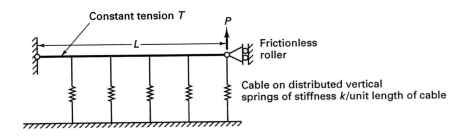

Constant tension T

L

P

Frictionless roller

Cable on distributed vertical springs of stiffness k/unit length of cable

3.19. Consider the prestressed cable in Exercise 3.18.
   (a) Establish a suitable trial function that can be employed in the analysis of the cable using the classical Galerkin and least squares methods. Try $w(x) = a_0 + a_1 x + a_2 x^2$ and modify the function as necessary.
   (b) Establish the governing equations of the system for the selected trial function using the classical Galerkin and least squares methods.

3.20. Consider the prestressed cable in Exercise 3.18. Establish the governing equations using the Ritz method with the trial function $w(x) = a_0 + a_1 x + a_2 x^2$ (i.e., a suitable modification thereof).

3.21. Use the Ritz method to calculate the linearized buckling load of the column shown. Assume that $w = cx^2$, where c is the unknown Ritz parameter.

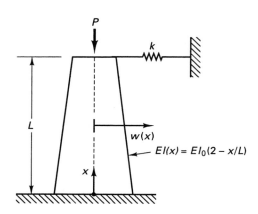

3.22. Consider the structure shown.
   (a) Use the Ritz method to establish the governing equations for the bending response. Use the following functions: (i) $w = a_1 x^2$ and (ii) $w = b_1[1 - \cos(\pi x/2L)]$.
   (b) With $EI_0 = 100, k = 2, L = 1$ estimate the critical load of the column using a Ritz analysis.

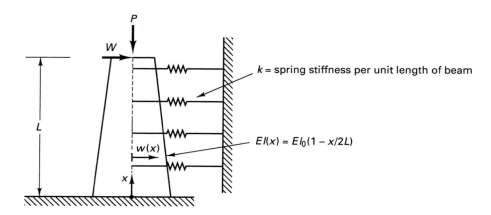

3.23. Consider the slab shown for a heat transfer analysis. The variational indicator for this analysis is

$$\Pi = \int_0^L \frac{1}{2} k \left(\frac{d\theta}{dx}\right)^2 dx - \int_0^L \theta q^B \, dx$$

State the essential and natural boundary conditions. Then perform a Ritz analysis of the problem using two unknown parameters.

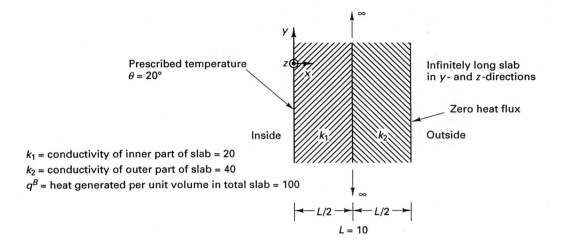

k_1 = conductivity of inner part of slab = 20
k_2 = conductivity of outer part of slab = 40
q^B = heat generated per unit volume in total slab = 100

3.24. The prestressed cable shown is to be analyzed. The governing differential equation of equilibrium is

$$T \frac{\partial^2 w}{\partial x^2} = m \frac{\partial^2 w}{\partial t^2} - p(t)$$

with the boundary conditions

$$w \big|_{x=0} = w \big|_{x=L} = 0$$

and the initial conditions

$$w(x, 0) = 0; \qquad \frac{\partial w}{\partial t}(x, 0) = 0$$

(a) Use the conventional finite difference method to approximate the governing differential equation of equilibrium and thus establish equations governing the response of the cable.

(b) Use the finite difference energy method to establish equations governing the response of the cable.

(c) Use the principle of virtual work to establish equations governing the response of the cable.

When using the finite difference methods, employ two internal finite difference stations. To employ the principle of virtual work, use the two basis functions shown.

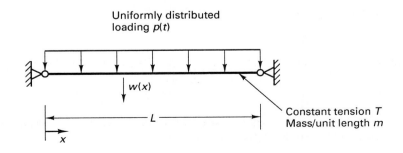

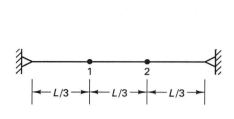

Finite difference stations

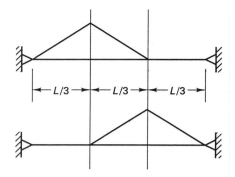

Basis functions for use of
principle of virtual work

3.25. The disk shown is to be analyzed for the temperature distribution. Determine the variational indicator of the problem and obtain an approximate solution using the Ritz method with the basis functions shown in Fig. 3.4. Use two unknown temperatures. Compare your results with the exact analytical solution.

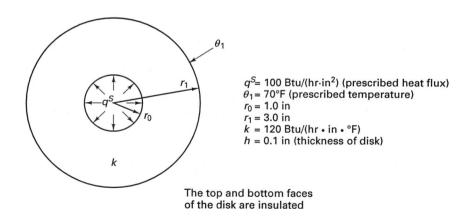

q^S= 100 Btu/(hr·in^2) (prescribed heat flux)
θ_1 = 70°F (prescribed temperature)
r_0 = 1.0 in
r_1 = 3.0 in
k = 120 Btu/(hr · in · °F)
h = 0.1 in (thickness of disk)

The top and bottom faces
of the disk are insulated

3.26. Consider the beam analysis problem shown.
    (a) Use four finite difference stations on the beam with the differential formulation to establish equations governing the response of the beam.
    (b) Use four finite difference stations on the beam with the variational formulation to establish equations governing the response of the beam.

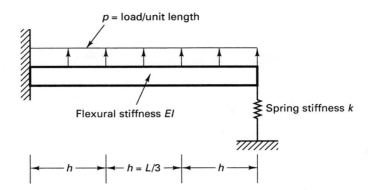

3.27. Use the finite difference energy method with only two unknown temperature values to solve the problem in Exercise 3.23.

3.28. Use the finite difference energy method with only two unknown temperature values to solve the problem in Exercise 3.25.

3.29. The computer program STAP (see Chapter 12) has been written for the analysis of truss structures. However, by using analogies involving variables and equations, the program can also be employed in the analysis of pressure and flow distributions in pipe networks, current distributions in dc networks, and in heat transfer analyses. Use the program STAP to solve the analysis problems in Examples 3.1 to 3.4.

3.30. Use a computer program to solve the problems in Examples 3.1 to 3.4.

3.4 IMPOSITION OF CONSTRAINTS

The analysis of an engineering problem frequently requires that a specific constraint be imposed on certain solution variables. These constraints may need to be imposed on some continuous solution parameters or on some discrete variables and may consist of certain continuity requirements, the imposition of specified values for the solution variables, or conditions to be satisfied between certain solution variables. Two widely used procedures are available, namely, the Lagrange multiplier method and the penalty method (see, for example, D. P. Bertsekas [A]). Applications of these techniques are given in Sections 4.2.2, 4.4.2, 4.4.3, 4.5, 5.4, 6.7.2, and 7.4. Both the Lagrange multiplier and the penalty methods operate on the variational or weighted residual formulations of the problem to be solved.

3.4.1 An Introduction to Lagrange Multiplier and Penalty Methods

As a brief introduction to Lagrange multiplier and penalty methods, consider the variational formulation of a discrete structural model for a steady-state analysis,

$$\Pi = \tfrac{1}{2} \mathbf{U}^T \mathbf{K} \mathbf{U} - \mathbf{U}^T \mathbf{R} \qquad (3.52)$$

with the conditions

$$\frac{\partial \Pi}{\partial U_i} = 0 \qquad \text{for all } i \qquad (3.53)$$

and assume that we want to impose the displacement at the degree of freedom U_i with

$$U_i = U_i^*$$ (3.54)

In the *Lagrange multiplier method* we amend the right-hand side of (3.52) to obtain

$$\Pi^* = \tfrac{1}{2}\mathbf{U}^T\mathbf{K}\mathbf{U} - \mathbf{U}^T\mathbf{R} + \lambda(U_i - U_i^*)$$ (3.55)

where λ is an additional variable, and invoke $\delta\Pi_i^* = 0$, which gives

$$\delta\mathbf{U}^T\mathbf{K}\mathbf{U} - \delta\mathbf{U}^T\mathbf{R} + \lambda\delta U_i + \delta\lambda(U_i - U_i^*) = 0$$ (3.56)

Since $\delta\mathbf{U}$ and $\delta\lambda$ are arbitrary, we obtain

$$\begin{bmatrix} \mathbf{K} & \vdots & \mathbf{e}_i \\ \hline \mathbf{e}_i^T & \vdots & 0 \end{bmatrix} \begin{bmatrix} \mathbf{U} \\ \hline \lambda \end{bmatrix} = \begin{bmatrix} \mathbf{R} \\ \hline U_i^* \end{bmatrix}$$ (3.57)

where $\mathbf{e}_i$ is a vector with all entries equal to zero except its ith entry, which is equal to one. Hence the equilibrium equations without a constraint are amended with an additional equation that embodies the constraint condition.

In the *penalty method* we also amend the right-hand side of (3.52) but without introducing an additional variable. Now we use

$$\Pi^{**} = \frac{1}{2}\mathbf{U}^T\mathbf{K}\mathbf{U} - \mathbf{U}^T\mathbf{R} + \frac{\alpha}{2}(U_i - U_i^*)^2$$ (3.58)

in which α is a constant of relatively large magnitude, $\alpha \gg \max{(k_{ii})}$. The condition $\delta\Pi^{**} = 0$ now yields

$$\delta\mathbf{U}^T\mathbf{K}\mathbf{U} - \delta\mathbf{U}^T\mathbf{R} + \alpha(U_i - U_i^*)\,\delta U_i = 0$$ (3.59)

and

$$(\mathbf{K} + \alpha\mathbf{e}_i\mathbf{e}_i^T)\mathbf{U} = \mathbf{R} + \alpha U_i^*\mathbf{e}_i$$ (3.60)

Hence, using this technique, a large value is added to the ith diagonal element of $\mathbf{K}$ and a corresponding force is added so that the required displacement U_i is approximately equal to U_i^*. This is a general technique that has been used extensively to impose specified displacements or other variables. The method is effective because no additional equation is required, and the bandwidth of the coefficient matrix is preserved (see Section 4.2.2). We demonstrate the Lagrange multiplier method and penalty procedure in the following example.

EXAMPLE 3.31:   Use the Lagrange multiplier method and penalty procedure to analyze the simple spring system shown in Fig. E3.31 with the imposed displacement $U_2 = 1/k$.

The governing equilibrium equations without the imposed displacement U_2 are

$$\begin{bmatrix} 2k & -k \\ -k & k \end{bmatrix} \begin{bmatrix} U_1 \\ U_2 \end{bmatrix} = \begin{bmatrix} R_1 \\ R_2 \end{bmatrix}$$ (a)

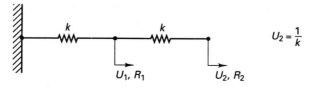

Figure E3.31   A simple spring system

The exact solution is obtained by using the relation $U_2 = 1/k$ and solving from the first equation of (a) for U_1,

$$U_1 = \frac{1 + R_1}{2k} \tag{b}$$

Hence we also have

$$R_2 = 1 - \frac{1 + R_1}{2}$$

which is the force required at the U_2 degree of freedom to impose $U_2 = 1/k$.

Using the Lagrange multiplier method, the governing equations are

$$\begin{bmatrix} 2k & -k & 0 \\ -k & k & 1 \\ 0 & 1 & 0 \end{bmatrix} \begin{bmatrix} U_1 \\ U_2 \\ \lambda \end{bmatrix} = \begin{bmatrix} R_1 \\ 0 \\ \dfrac{1}{k} \end{bmatrix} \tag{c}$$

and we obtain

$$U_1 = \frac{1 + R_1}{2k}; \qquad \lambda = -1 + \frac{1 + R_1}{2}$$

Hence the solution in (b) is obtained, and λ is equal to minus the force that must be applied at the degree of freedom U_2 in order to impose the displacement $U_2 = 1/k$. We may note that with this value of λ the first two equations in (c) reduce to the equations in (a).

Using the penalty method, we obtain

$$\begin{bmatrix} 2k & -k \\ -k & (k + \alpha) \end{bmatrix} \begin{bmatrix} U_1 \\ U_2 \end{bmatrix} = \begin{bmatrix} R_1 \\ \dfrac{\alpha}{k} \end{bmatrix}$$

The solution now depends on α, and we obtain

for $\alpha = 10k$: $U_1 = \dfrac{11R_1 + 10}{21k}$; $U_2 = \dfrac{R_1 + 20}{21k}$

for $\alpha = 100k$: $U_1 = \dfrac{101R_1 + 100}{201k}$; $U_2 = \dfrac{R_1 + 200}{201k}$

and for $\alpha = 1000k$: $U_1 = \dfrac{1001R_1 + 1000}{2001k}$; $U_2 = \dfrac{R_1 + 2000}{2001k}$

In practice, the accuracy obtained using $\alpha = 1000k$ is usually sufficient.

This example gives only a very elementary demonstration of the use of the Lagrange multiplier method and the penalty procedure. Let us now briefly state some more general equations. Assume that we want to impose onto the solution the m linearly independent discrete constraints $\mathbf{B}\mathbf{U} = \mathbf{V}$ where $\mathbf{B}$ is a matrix of order $m \times n$. Then in the Lagrange multiplier method we use

$$\Pi^*(\mathbf{U}, \boldsymbol{\lambda}) = \frac{1}{2}\mathbf{U}^T\mathbf{K}\mathbf{U} - \mathbf{U}^T\mathbf{R} + \boldsymbol{\lambda}^T(\mathbf{B}\mathbf{U} - \mathbf{V}) \tag{3.61}$$

where $\boldsymbol{\lambda}$ is a vector of m Lagrange multipliers. Invoking $\delta\Pi^* = 0$ we now obtain

$$\begin{bmatrix} \mathbf{K} & \mathbf{B}^T \\ \mathbf{B} & \mathbf{0} \end{bmatrix} \begin{bmatrix} \mathbf{U} \\ \boldsymbol{\lambda} \end{bmatrix} = \begin{bmatrix} \mathbf{R} \\ \mathbf{V} \end{bmatrix} \tag{3.62}$$

In the penalty method we use

$$\Pi^{**}(\mathbf{U}) = \frac{1}{2}\mathbf{U}^T\mathbf{K}\mathbf{U} - \mathbf{U}^T\mathbf{R} + \frac{\alpha}{2}(\mathbf{B}\mathbf{U} - \mathbf{V})^T(\mathbf{B}\mathbf{U} - \mathbf{V}) \tag{3.63}$$

and invoking $\delta\Pi^{**} = 0$ we obtain

$$(\mathbf{K} + \alpha\mathbf{B}^T\mathbf{B})\mathbf{U} = \mathbf{R} + \alpha\mathbf{B}^T\mathbf{V} \tag{3.64}$$

Of course, (3.57) and (3.60) are special cases of (3.62) and (3.64).

The above relations are written for discrete systems. When a continuous system is considered, the usual variational indicator Π (see, for example, Examples 3.18 to 3.20) is amended in the Lagrange multiplier method with integral(s) of the continuous constraint(s) times the Lagrange multiplier(s) and in the penalty method with integral(s) of the penalty factor(s) times the square of the constraint(s). If the continuous variables are then expressed through trial functions or finite difference expressions, relations of the form (3.62) and (3.64) are obtained (see Section 4.4).

Although the above introduction to the Lagrange multiplier method and penalty procedure is brief, some basic observations can be made that are quite generally applicable. First, we observe that in the Lagrange multiplier method the diagonal elements in the coefficient matrix corresponding to the Lagrange multipliers are zero. Hence for the solution it is effective to arrange the equations as given in (3.62). Considering the equilibrium equations with the Lagrange multipliers, we also find that these multipliers have the same units as the forcing functions; for example, in (3.57) the Lagrange multiplier is a force.

Using the penalty method, an important consideration is the choice of an appropriate penalty number. In the analysis leading to (3.64) the penalty number α is explicitly specified (such as in Example 3.31), and this is frequently the case (see Section 4.2.2). However, in other analyses, the penalty number is defined by the problem itself using a specific formulation (see Section 5.4.1). The difficulty with the use of a very high penalty number lies in that the coefficient matrix can become ill-conditioned when the off-diagonal elements are multiplied by a large number. If the off-diagonal elements are affected by the penalty number, it is necessary to use enough digits in the computer arithmetical operations to ensure an accurate solution of the problem (see Section 8.2.6).

Finally, we should note that the penalty and Lagrange multiplier methods are quite closely related (see Exercise 3.35) and that the basic ideas of imposing the constraints can also be combined as is done in the augmented Lagrange multiplier method (see M. Fortin and R. Glowinski [A] and Exercise 3.36).

3.4.2 Exercises

3.31. Consider the system of equations

$$\begin{bmatrix} 2 & -1 \\ -1 & 2 \end{bmatrix} \begin{bmatrix} U_1 \\ U_2 \end{bmatrix} = \begin{bmatrix} 10 \\ -1 \end{bmatrix}$$

Use the Lagrange multiplier method and the penalty method to impose the condition $U_2 = 0$. Solve the equations and interpret the solution.

3.32. Consider the system of carts in Example 3.1 with $k_i = k$, $R_1 = 1$, $R_2 = 0$, $R_3 = 1$. Develop the governing equilibrium equations, imposing the condition $U_2 = U_3$.
(a) Use the Lagrange multiplier method.
(b) Use the penalty method with an appropriate penalty factor.

In each case solve for the displacements and the constraining force.

3.33. Consider the heat transfer problem in Example 3.2 with $k = 1$ and $\theta_0 = 10$, $\theta_4 = 20$. Impose the condition that $\theta_3 = 4\theta_2$ and physically interpret the solution. Use the Lagrange multiplier method and then the penalty method with a reasonable penalty parameter.

3.34. Consider the fluid flow in the hydraulic network in Example 3.3. Develop the governing equations for use of the Lagrange multiplier method to impose the condition $p_C = 2p_D$. Solve the equations and interpret the solution.

Repeat the solution using the penalty method with an appropriate penalty factor.

3.35. Consider the problem $\mathbf{KU} = \mathbf{R}$ with the m linearly independent constraints $\mathbf{BU} = \mathbf{V}$ (see (3.61) and (3.62)). Show that the stationarity of the following variational indicator gives the equations of the penalty method (3.64),

$$\tilde{\Pi}^{**}(\mathbf{U}, \boldsymbol{\lambda}) = \frac{1}{2}\mathbf{U}^T\mathbf{KU} - \mathbf{U}^T\mathbf{R} + \boldsymbol{\lambda}^T(\mathbf{BU} - \mathbf{V}) - \frac{\boldsymbol{\lambda}^T\boldsymbol{\lambda}}{2\alpha}$$

where $\boldsymbol{\lambda}$ is a vector of the m Lagrange multipliers and α is the penalty parameter, $\alpha > 0$. Evaluate the Lagrange multipliers in general to be $\boldsymbol{\lambda} = \alpha(\mathbf{BU} - \mathbf{V})$, and show that for the specific case considered in (3.60) $\lambda = \alpha(U_i - U_i^*)$.

3.36. In the *augmented Lagrangian method* the following functional is used for the problem stated in Exercise 3.35:

$$\tilde{\Pi}^*(\mathbf{U}, \boldsymbol{\lambda}) = \frac{1}{2}\mathbf{U}^T\mathbf{KU} - \mathbf{U}^T\mathbf{R} + \frac{\alpha}{2}(\mathbf{BU} - \mathbf{V})^T(\mathbf{BU} - \mathbf{V}) + \boldsymbol{\lambda}^T(\mathbf{BU} - \mathbf{V}); \ \alpha \geq 0$$

(a) Invoke the stationarity of $\tilde{\Pi}^*$ and obtain the governing equations.
(b) Use the augmented Lagrangian method to solve the problem posed in Example 3.31 for $\alpha = 0$, k, and $1000k$. Show that, actually, for any value of α the constraint is accurately satisfied. (The augmented Lagrangian method is used in iterative solution procedures, in which case using an efficient value for α can be important.)

Formulation of the Finite Element Method— Linear Analysis in Solid and Structural Mechanics

4.1 INTRODUCTION

A very important application area for finite element analysis is the linear analysis of solids and structures. This is where the first practical finite element procedures were applied and where the finite element method has obtained its primary impetus of development.

Today many types of linear analyses of structures can be performed in a routine manner. Finite element discretization schemes are well established and are used in standard computer programs. However, there are two areas in which effective finite elements have been developed only recently, namely, the analysis of general plate and shell structures and the solution of (almost) incompressible media.

The standard formulation for the finite element solution of solids is the displacement method, which is widely used and effective except in these two areas of analysis. For the analysis of plate and shell structures and the solution of incompressible solids, mixed formulations are preferable.

In this chapter we introduce the displacement-based method of analysis in detail. The principle of virtual work is the basic relationship used for the finite element formulation. We first establish the governing finite element equations and then discuss the convergence properties of the method. Since the displacement-based solution is not effective for certain applications, we then introduce the use of mixed formulations in which not only the displacements are employed as unknown variables. The use of a mixed method, however, requires a careful selection of appropriate interpolations, and we address this issue in the last part of the chapter.

Various displacement-based and mixed formulations have been presented in the literature, and as pointed out before, our aim is not to survey all these formulations. Instead, we will concentrate in this chapter on some important useful principles of formulating finite elements. Some efficient applications of the principles discussed in this chapter are then presented in Chapter 5.

4.2 FORMULATION OF THE DISPLACEMENT-BASED FINITE ELEMENT METHOD

The displacement-based finite element method can be regarded as an extension of the displacement method of analysis of beam and truss structures, and it is therefore valuable to review this analysis process. The basic steps in the analysis of a beam and truss structure using the displacement method are the following.

1. Idealize the total structure as an assemblage of beam and truss elements that are interconnected at structural joints.
2. Identify the unknown joint displacements that completely define the displacement response of the structural idealization.
3. Formulate force balance equations corresponding to the unknown joint displacements and solve these equations.
4. With the beam and truss element end displacements known, calculate the internal element stress distributions.
5. Interpret, based on the assumptions used, the displacements and stresses predicted by the solution of the structural idealization.

In practical analysis and design the most important steps of the complete analysis are the proper idealization of the actual problem, as performed in step 1, and the correct interpretation of the results, as in step 5. Depending on the complexity of the actual system to be analyzed, considerable knowledge of the characteristics of the system and its mechanical behavior may be required in order to establish an appropriate idealization, as briefly discussed in Chapter 1.

These analysis steps have already been demonstrated to some degree in Chapter 3, but it is instructive to consider another more complex example.

> **EXAMPLE 4.1:**   The piping system shown in Fig. E4.1(a) must be able to carry a large transverse load P applied accidentally to the flange connecting the small- and large-diameter pipes. "Analyze this problem."
>
> The study of this problem may require a number of analyses in which the local kinematic behavior of the pipe intersection is properly modeled, the nonlinear material and geometric behaviors are taken into account, the characteristics of the applied load are modeled accurately, and so on. In such a study, it is usually most expedient to start with a simple analysis in which gross assumptions are made and then work toward a more refined model as the need arises (see Section 6.8.1).

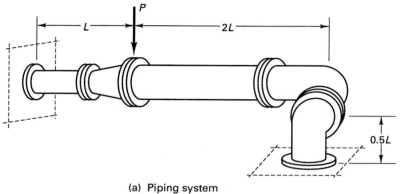

(a) Piping system

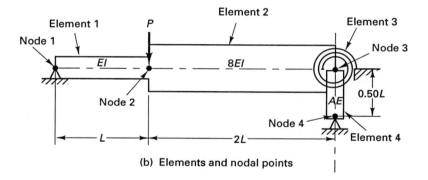

(b) Elements and nodal points

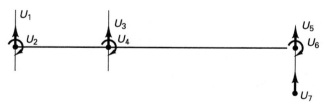

(c) Global degrees of freedom of unrestraint structure

Figure E4.1   Piping system and idealization

Assume that in a first analysis we primarily want to calculate the transverse displacement at the flange when the transverse load is applied slowly. In this case it is reasonable to model the structure as an assemblage of beam, truss, and spring elements and perform a static analysis.

The model chosen is shown in Fig. E4.1(b). The structural idealization consists of two beams, one truss, and a spring element. For the analysis of this idealization we first evaluate the element stiffness matrices that correspond to the global structural degrees of freedom shown in Fig. E4.1(c). For the beam, spring, and truss elements, respectively, we have in this case

$$\mathbf{K}_1^e = \frac{EI}{L}\begin{bmatrix} \dfrac{12}{L^2} & -\dfrac{6}{L} & -\dfrac{12}{L^2} & -\dfrac{6}{L} \\[2mm] & 4 & \dfrac{6}{L} & 2 \\[2mm] \text{symmetric} & & \dfrac{12}{L^2} & \dfrac{6}{L} \\[2mm] & & & 4 \end{bmatrix}; \qquad U_1, U_2, U_3, U_4$$

$$\mathbf{K}_2^e = \frac{EI}{L}\begin{bmatrix} \dfrac{12}{L^2} & -\dfrac{12}{L} & -\dfrac{12}{L^2} & -\dfrac{12}{L} \\[2mm] & 16 & \dfrac{12}{L} & 8 \\[2mm] \text{symmetric} & & \dfrac{12}{L^2} & \dfrac{12}{L} \\[2mm] & & & 16 \end{bmatrix}; \qquad U_3, U_4, U_5, U_6$$

$$\mathbf{K}_3^e = k_s; \qquad U_6$$

$$\mathbf{K}_4^e = \frac{EA}{L}\begin{bmatrix} 2 & -2 \\ -2 & 2 \end{bmatrix}; \qquad U_5, U_7$$

where the subscript on $\mathbf{K}^e$ indicates the element number, and the global degrees of freedom that correspond to the element stiffnesses are written next to the matrices. It should be noted that in this example the element matrices are independent of direction cosines since the centerlines of the elements are aligned with the global axes. If the local axis of an element is not in the direction of a global axis, the local element stiffness matrix must be transformed to obtain the required global element stiffness matrix (see Example 4.10).

The stiffness matrix of the complete element assemblage is effectively obtained from the stiffness matrices of the individual elements using the *direct stiffness method* (see Examples 3.1 and 4.11). In this procedure the structure stiffness matrix $\mathbf{K}$ is calculated by direct addition of the element stiffness matrices; i.e.,

$$\mathbf{K} = \sum_i \mathbf{K}_i^e$$

where the summation includes all elements. To perform the summation, each element matrix $\mathbf{K}_i^e$ is written as a matrix $\mathbf{K}^{(i)}$ of the same order as the stiffness matrix $\mathbf{K}$, where all entries in $\mathbf{K}^{(i)}$ are zero except those which correspond to an element degree of freedom. For example, for element 4 we have

$$
\mathbf{K}^{(4)} = \begin{array}{c} \\ 1 \\ 2 \\ 3 \\ 4 \\ 5 \\ 6 \\ 7 \end{array} \begin{array}{c} \begin{array}{ccccccc} 1 & 2 & 3 & 4 & 5 & 6 & 7 \end{array} \leftarrow \text{Degree of freedom} \\ \begin{bmatrix} 0 & 0 & 0 & 0 & 0 & 0 & 0 \\ 0 & 0 & 0 & 0 & 0 & 0 & 0 \\ 0 & 0 & 0 & 0 & 0 & 0 & 0 \\ 0 & 0 & 0 & 0 & 0 & 0 & 0 \\ 0 & 0 & 0 & 0 & \dfrac{2AE}{L} & 0 & -\dfrac{2EA}{L} \\ 0 & 0 & 0 & 0 & 0 & 0 & 0 \\ 0 & 0 & 0 & 0 & -\dfrac{2AE}{L} & 0 & \dfrac{2EA}{L} \end{bmatrix} \end{array}
$$

Therefore, the stiffness matrix of the structure is

$$
\mathbf{K} =
\begin{bmatrix}
\dfrac{12EI}{L^3} & -\dfrac{6EI}{L^2} & -\dfrac{12EI}{L^3} & \dfrac{6EI}{L^2} & 0 & 0 & 0 \\[2ex]
& \dfrac{4EI}{L} & \dfrac{6EI}{L^2} & \dfrac{2EI}{L} & 0 & 0 & 0 \\[2ex]
& & \dfrac{24EI}{L^3} & -\dfrac{6EI}{L^2} & -\dfrac{12EI}{L^3} & -\dfrac{12EI}{L^2} & 0 \\[2ex]
& & & \dfrac{20EI}{L} & \dfrac{12EI}{L^2} & \dfrac{8EI}{L} & 0 \\[2ex]
& \text{symmetric} & & & \dfrac{12EI}{L^3}+\dfrac{2AE}{L} & \dfrac{12EI}{L^2} & -\dfrac{2AE}{L} \\[2ex]
& & & & & \dfrac{16EI}{L}+k_s & 0 \\[2ex]
& & & & & & \dfrac{2AE}{L}
\end{bmatrix}
$$

and the equilibrium equations for the system are

$$\mathbf{KU} = \mathbf{R}$$

where $\mathbf{U}$ is a vector of the system global displacements and $\mathbf{R}$ is a vector of forces acting in the direction of these displacements:

$$\mathbf{U}^T = [U_1, \ldots, U_7]; \qquad \mathbf{R}^T = [R_1, \ldots, R_7]$$

Before solving for the displacements of the structure, we need to impose the boundary conditions that $U_1 = 0$ and $U_7 = 0$. This means that we may consider only five equations in five unknown displacements; i.e.,

$$\tilde{\mathbf{K}}\tilde{\mathbf{U}} = \tilde{\mathbf{R}} \tag{a}$$

where $\tilde{\mathbf{K}}$ is obtained by eliminating from $\mathbf{K}$ the first and seventh rows and columns, and

$$\tilde{\mathbf{U}}^T = [U_2 \quad U_3 \quad U_4 \quad U_5 \quad U_6]; \qquad \tilde{\mathbf{R}}^T = [0 \quad -P \quad 0 \quad 0 \quad 0]$$

The solution of (a) gives the structure displacements and therefore the element nodal point displacements. The element nodal forces are obtained by multiplying the element stiffness matrices $\mathbf{K}_i^e$ by the element displacements. If the forces at any section of an element are required, we can evaluate them from the element end forces by use of simple statics.

Considering the analysis results it should be recognized, however, that although the structural idealization in Fig. E4.1(b) was analyzed accurately, *the displacements and stresses are only a prediction of the response of the actual physical structure.* Surely this prediction will be accurate only if the model used was appropriate, and in practice a specific model is in general adequate for predicting certain quantities but inadequate for predicting others. For instance, in this analysis the required transverse displacement under the applied load is quite likely predicted accurately using the idealization in Fig. E4.1(b) (provided the load is applied slowly enough, the stresses are small enough not to cause yielding, and so on), but the stresses directly under the load are probably predicted very inaccurately. Indeed, a different and more refined finite element model would need to be used in order to accurately calculate the stresses (see Section 1.2).

This example demonstrates some important aspects of the displacement method of analysis and the finite element method. As summarized previously, the basic process is that the complete structure is idealized as an assemblage of individual structural elements. The element stiffness matrices corresponding to the global degrees of freedom of the structural idealization are calculated, and the total stiffness matrix is formed by the addition of the element stiffness matrices. The solution of the equilibrium equations of the assemblage of elements yields the element displacements, which are then used to calculate the element stresses. Finally, the element displacements and stresses must be interpreted as an estimate of the actual structural behavior, taking into account that a truss and beam idealization was solved.

Considering the analysis of truss and beam assemblages such as in Example 4.1, originally these solutions were not called finite element analyses because there is one major difference in these solutions when compared to a more general finite element analysis of a two- or three-dimensional problem, namely, in the analysis performed in Example 4.1 the exact element stiffness matrices ("exact" within beam theory) could be calculated. The stiffness properties of a beam element are physically the element end forces that correspond to unit element end displacements. These forces can be evaluated by solving the differential equations of equilibrium of the element when it is subjected to the appropriate boundary conditions. Since by virtue of the solution of the differential equations of equilibrium, all three requirements of an exact solution—namely, the stress equilibrium, the compatibility, and the constitutive requirements—throughout each element are fulfilled, the exact element internal displacements and stiffness matrices are calculated. In an alternative approach, these element end forces could also be evaluated by performing a variational solution based on the Ritz method or Galerkin method, as discussed in Section 3.3.4. Such solutions would give the exact element stiffness coefficients if the exact element internal displacements (as calculated in the solution of the differential equations of equilibrium) are used as trial functions (see Examples 3.22 and 4.8). However, approximate stiffness coefficients are obtained if other trial functions (which may be more suitable in practice) are employed.

When considering more general two- and three-dimensional finite element analyses, we use the variational approach with trial functions that approximate the actual displacements because we do not know the exact displacement functions as in the case of truss and beam elements. The result is that the differential equations of equilibrium are not satisfied in general, but this error is reduced as the finite element idealization of the structure or the continuum is refined.

The general formulation of the displacement-based finite element method is based on the use of the principle of virtual displacements which, as discussed in Section 3.3.4, is equivalent to the use of the Galerkin method, and also equivalent to the use of the Ritz method to minimize the total potential of the system.

4.2.1 General Derivation of Finite Element Equilibrium Equations

In this section we first state the general elasticity problem to be solved. We then discuss the principle of virtual displacements, which is used as the basis of our finite element solution, and we derive the finite element equations. Next we elaborate on some important considerations regarding the satisfaction of stress equilibrium, and finally we discuss some details of the process of assemblage of element matrices.

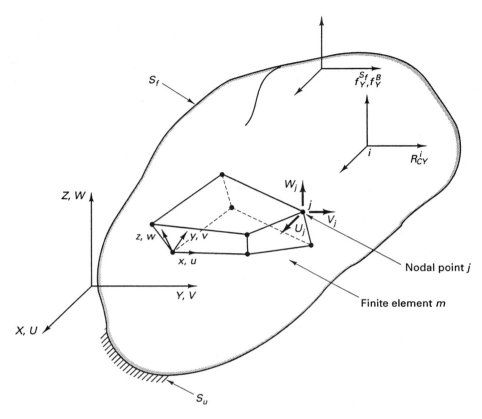

Figure 4.1 General three-dimensional body with an 8-node three-dimensional element

Problem Statement

Consider the equilibrium of a general three-dimensional body such as that shown in Fig. 4.1. The body is located in the fixed (stationary) coordinate system X, Y, Z. Considering the body surface area, the body is supported on the area S_u with prescribed displacements $\mathbf{U}^{S_u}$ and is subjected to surface tractions $\mathbf{f}^{S_f}$ (forces per unit surface area) on the surface area S_f.[1]

[1] We may assume here, for simplicity, that all displacement components on S_u are prescribed, in which case $S_u \cup S_f = S$ and $S_u \cap S_f = 0$. However, in practice, it may well be that at a surface point the displacement(s) corresponding to some direction(s) is (are) imposed, while corresponding to the remaining direction(s) the force component(s) is (are) prescribed. For example, a roller boundary condition on a three-dimensional body would correspond to an imposed zero displacement only in the direction normal to the body surface, while tractions are applied (which are frequently zero) in the remaining directions tangential to the body surface. In such cases, the surface point would belong to S_u and S_f. However, later, in our finite element formulation, we shall first remove all displacement constraints (support conditions) and assume that the reactions are known, and thus consider $S_f = S$ and $S_u = 0$, and then, only after the derivation of the governing finite element equations, impose the displacement constraints. Hence, the assumption that all displacement components on S_u are prescribed may be used here for ease of exposition and does not in any way restrict our formulation.

In addition, the body is subjected to externally applied body forces $\mathbf{f}^B$ (forces per unit volume) and concentrated loads $\mathbf{R}_C^i$ (where i denotes the point of load application). We introduce the forces $\mathbf{R}_C^i$ as separate quantities, although each such force could also be considered surface tractions $\mathbf{f}^{S_f}$ over a very small area (which would usually model the actual physical situation more accurately). In general, the externally applied forces have three components corresponding to the X, Y, Z coordinate axes:

$$
\mathbf{f}^B = \begin{bmatrix} f_X^B \\ f_Y^B \\ f_Z^B \end{bmatrix}; \qquad
\mathbf{f}^{S_f} = \begin{bmatrix} f_X^{S_f} \\ f_Y^{S_f} \\ f_Z^{S_f} \end{bmatrix}; \qquad
\mathbf{R}_C^i = \begin{bmatrix} R_{CX}^i \\ R_{CY}^i \\ R_{CZ}^i \end{bmatrix}
\tag{4.1}
$$

where we note that the components of $\mathbf{f}^B$ and $\mathbf{f}^{S_f}$ vary as a function of X, Y, Z (and for $\mathbf{f}^{S_f}$ the specific X, Y, Z coordinates of S_f are considered).

The displacements of the body from the unloaded configuration are measured in the coordinate system X, Y, Z and are denoted by $\mathbf{U}$, where

$$
\mathbf{U}(X, Y, Z) = \begin{bmatrix} U \\ V \\ W \end{bmatrix}
\tag{4.2}
$$

and $\mathbf{U} = \mathbf{U}^{S_u}$ on the surface area S_u. The strains corresponding to $\mathbf{U}$ are

$$
\boldsymbol{\epsilon}^T = \begin{bmatrix} \epsilon_{XX} & \epsilon_{YY} & \epsilon_{ZZ} & \gamma_{XY} & \gamma_{YZ} & \gamma_{ZX} \end{bmatrix}
\tag{4.3}
$$

where

$$
\epsilon_{XX} = \frac{\partial U}{\partial X}; \qquad \epsilon_{YY} = \frac{\partial V}{\partial Y}; \qquad \epsilon_{ZZ} = \frac{\partial W}{\partial Z}
$$

$$
\gamma_{XY} = \frac{\partial U}{\partial Y} + \frac{\partial V}{\partial X}; \qquad \gamma_{YZ} = \frac{\partial V}{\partial Z} + \frac{\partial W}{\partial Y}; \qquad \gamma_{ZX} = \frac{\partial W}{\partial X} + \frac{\partial U}{\partial Z}
\tag{4.4}
$$

The stresses corresponding to $\boldsymbol{\epsilon}$ are

$$
\boldsymbol{\tau}^T = \begin{bmatrix} \tau_{XX} & \tau_{YY} & \tau_{ZZ} & \tau_{XY} & \tau_{YZ} & \tau_{ZX} \end{bmatrix}
\tag{4.5}
$$

where

$$
\boldsymbol{\tau} = \mathbf{C}\boldsymbol{\epsilon} + \boldsymbol{\tau}^I
\tag{4.6}
$$

In (4.6), $\mathbf{C}$ is the stress-strain material matrix and the vector $\boldsymbol{\tau}^I$ denotes given initial stresses [with components ordered as in (4.5)].

The analysis problem is now the following.

Given

the geometry of the body, the applied loads $\mathbf{f}^{S_f}$, $\mathbf{f}^B$, $\mathbf{R}_C^i$, $i = 1, 2, \ldots$, the support conditions on S_u, the material stress-strain law, and the initial stresses in the body.

Calculate

the displacements $\mathbf{U}$ of the body and the corresponding strains $\boldsymbol{\epsilon}$ and stresses $\boldsymbol{\tau}$.

In the problem solution considered here, we assume linear analysis conditions, which require that

> The displacements be infinitesimally small so that (4.4) is valid and the equilibrium of the body can be established (and is solved for) with respect to its unloaded configuration.
>
> The stress-strain material matrix can vary as a function of X, Y, Z but is constant otherwise (e.g., $\mathbf{C}$ does not depend on the stress state).

We consider nonlinear analysis conditions in which one or more of these assumptions are not satisfied in Chapters 6 and 7.

To calculate the response of the body, we could establish the governing differential equations of equilibrium, which then would have to be solved subject to the boundary conditions (see Section 3.3). However, closed-form analytical solutions are possible only when relatively simple geometries are considered.

The Principle of Virtual Displacements

The basis of the displacement-based finite element solution is the principle of virtual displacements (which we also call the principle of virtual work). This principle states that the equilibrium of the body in Fig. 4.1 requires that for any compatible small[2] virtual displacements (which are zero at and corresponding to the prescribed displacements)[3] imposed on the body in its state of equilibrium, the total internal virtual work is equal to the total external virtual work:

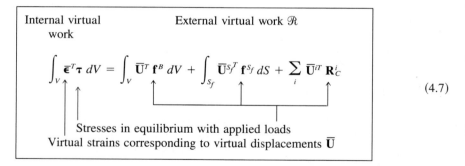

$$\underbrace{\int_V \bar{\boldsymbol{\epsilon}}^T \boldsymbol{\tau} \, dV}_{} = \int_V \bar{\mathbf{U}}^T \mathbf{f}^B \, dV + \int_{S_f} \bar{\mathbf{U}}^{S_f T} \mathbf{f}^{S_f} \, dS + \sum_i \bar{\mathbf{U}}^{iT} \mathbf{R}_C^i \tag{4.7}$$

where the $\bar{\mathbf{U}}$ are the virtual displacements and the $\bar{\boldsymbol{\epsilon}}$ are the *corresponding* virtual strains (the overbar denoting virtual quantities).

The adjective "virtual" denotes that the virtual displacements (and corresponding virtual strains) are not "real" displacements which the body actually undergoes as a consequence of the loading on the body. Instead, the virtual displacements are totally independent

---

[2] We stipulate here that the virtual displacements be "small" because the virtual strains corresponding to these displacements are calculated using the small strain measure (see Example 4.2). Actually, provided this small strain measure is used, the virtual displacements can be of any magnitude and indeed we later on choose convenient magnitudes for solution.

[3] We use the wording "at and corresponding to the prescribed displacements" to mean "at the points and surfaces and corresponding to the components of displacements that are prescribed at those points and surfaces."

from the actual displacements and are used by the analyst in a thought experiment to establish the integral equilibrium equation in (4.7).

Let us emphasize that in (4.7),

The stresses $\boldsymbol{\tau}$ are assumed to be known quantities and are the unique stresses[4] that exactly balance the applied loads.

The virtual strains $\bar{\boldsymbol{\epsilon}}$ are calculated by the differentiations given in (4.4) from the assumed virtual displacements $\bar{\mathbf{U}}$.

The virtual displacements $\bar{\mathbf{U}}$ must represent a continuous virtual displacement field (to be able to evaluate $\bar{\boldsymbol{\epsilon}}$), with $\bar{\mathbf{U}}$ equal to zero at and corresponding to the prescribed displacements on S_u; also, the components in $\bar{\mathbf{U}}^{S_f}$ are simply the virtual displacements $\bar{\mathbf{U}}$ evaluated on the surface S_f.

All integrations are performed over the original volume and surface area of the body, unaffected by the imposed virtual displacements.

To exemplify the use of the principle of virtual displacements, assume that we believe (but are not sure) to have been given the exact solution displacement field of the body. This given displacement field is continuous and satisfies the displacement boundary conditions on S_u. Then we can calculate $\boldsymbol{\epsilon}$ and $\boldsymbol{\tau}$ (corresponding to this displacement field). The vector $\boldsymbol{\tau}$ lists the correct stresses if and only if the equation (4.7) holds for any arbitrary virtual displacements $\bar{\mathbf{U}}$ that are continuous and zero at and corresponding to the prescribed displacements on S_u. In other words, if we can pick one virtual displacement field $\bar{\mathbf{U}}$ for which the relation in (4.7) is not satisfied, then this is proof that $\boldsymbol{\tau}$ is not the correct stress vector (and hence the given displacement field is not the exact solution displacement field).

We derive and demonstrate the principle of virtual displacements in the following examples.

> **EXAMPLE 4.2:** Derive the principle of virtual displacements for the general three-dimensional body in Fig. 4.1.
>
> To simplify the presentation we use indicial notation with the summation convention (see Section 2.4), with x_i denoting the ith coordinate axis ($x_1 \equiv X, x_2 \equiv Y, x_3 \equiv Z$), u_i denoting the ith displacement component ($u_1 \equiv U, u_2 \equiv V, u_3 \equiv W$), and a comma denoting differentiation.
>
> The given displacement boundary conditions are $u_i^{S_u}$ on S_u, and let us assume that we have no concentrated surface loads, that is, all surface loads are contained in the components $f_i^{S_f}$.
>
> The solution to the problem must satisfy the following differential equations (see, for example, S. Timoshenko and J. N. Goodier [A]):
>
> $$\tau_{ij,j} + f_i^B = 0 \qquad \text{throughout the body} \qquad\qquad \text{(a)}$$
>
> with the natural (force) boundary conditions
>
> $$\tau_{ij} n_j = f_i^{S_f} \qquad \text{on } S_f \qquad\qquad \text{(b)}$$
>
> and the essential (displacement) boundary conditions
>
> $$u_i = u_i^{S_u} \qquad \text{on } S_u \qquad\qquad \text{(c)}$$
>
> where $S = S_u \cup S_f, S_u \cap S_f = 0$, and the n_j are the components of the unit normal vector to the surface S of the body.

---

[4] For a proof that these stresses are unique, see Section 4.3.4.

Consider now *any* arbitrarily chosen continuous displacements $\bar{u}_i$ satisfying

$$\bar{u}_i = 0 \qquad \text{on } S_u \tag{d}$$

Then

$$(\tau_{ij,j} + f_i^B)\bar{u}_i = 0$$

and therefore,

$$\int_V (\tau_{ij,j} + f_i^B)\bar{u}_i \, dV = 0 \tag{e}$$

We call the $\bar{u}_i$ *virtual displacements*. Note that since the $\bar{u}_i$ are arbitrary, (e) can be satisfied if (and only if) the quantity in the parentheses vanishes. Hence (e) is equivalent to (a).

Using the mathematical identity $(\tau_{ij}\bar{u}_i)_{,j} = \tau_{ij,j}\bar{u}_i + \tau_{ij}\bar{u}_{i,j}$, we obtain from (e),

$$\int_V [(\tau_{ij}\bar{u}_i)_{,j} - \tau_{ij}\bar{u}_{i,j} + f_i^B \bar{u}_i] \, dV = 0$$

Next, using the identity $\int_V (\tau_{ij}\bar{u}_i)_{,j} \, dV = \int_S (\tau_{ij}\bar{u}_i)n_j \, dS$, which follows from the divergence theorem[5] (see, for example, G. B. Thomas and R. L. Finney [A]), we have

$$\int_V (-\tau_{ij}\bar{u}_{i,j} + f_i^B\bar{u}_i) \, dV + \int_S (\tau_{ij}\bar{u}_i)n_j \, dS = 0 \tag{f}$$

In light of (b) and (d), we obtain

$$\int_V (-\tau_{ij}\bar{u}_{i,j} + f_i^B\bar{u}_i) \, dV + \int_{S_f} f_i^{S_f} \bar{u}_i^{S_f} \, dS = 0 \tag{g}$$

Also, because of the symmetry of the stress tensor ($\tau_{ij} = \tau_{ji}$), we have

$$\tau_{ij}\bar{u}_{i,j} = \tau_{ij}[\tfrac{1}{2}(\bar{u}_{i,j} + \bar{u}_{j,i})] = \tau_{ij}\bar{\epsilon}_{ij}$$

and hence we obtain from (g) the required result, (4.7),

$$\int_V \tau_{ij}\bar{\epsilon}_{ij} \, dV = \int_V f_i^B \bar{u}_i \, dV + \int_{S_f} f_i^{S_f} \bar{u}_i^{S_f} \, dS \tag{h}$$

Note that in (h) we use the tensor notation for the strains; hence, the engineering shear strains used in (4.7) are obtained by adding the appropriate tensor shear strain components, e.g., $\bar{\gamma}_{XY} = \bar{\epsilon}_{12} + \bar{\epsilon}_{21}$. Also note that by using (b) [and (d)] in (f), we explicitly introduced the natural boundary conditions into the principle of virtual displacements (h).

EXAMPLE 4.3:   Consider the bar shown in Figure E4.3.

(a) Specialize the equation of the principle of virtual displacements (4.7) to this problem.
(b) Solve for the exact response of the mechanical model.
(c) Show that for the exact displacement response the principle of virtual displacements is satisfied with the displacement patterns (i) $\bar{u} = ax$ and (ii) $\bar{u} = ax^2$, where a is a constant.
(d) Assume that the stress solution is

$$\tau_{xx} = \frac{F}{\frac{3}{2}A_0}$$

[5] The divergence theorem states: Let $\mathbf{F}$ be a vector field in volume V; then

$$\int_V F_{i,i} \, dV = \int_S \mathbf{F} \cdot \mathbf{n} \, dS$$

where $\mathbf{n}$ is the unit outward normal on the surface S of V.

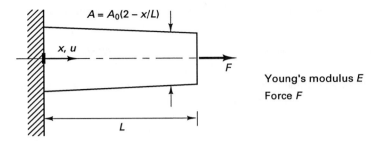

Figure E4.3   Bar subjected to concentrated load F

i.e., that τ_{xx} is the force F divided by the average cross-sectional area, and investigate whether the principle of virtual displacements is satisfied for the displacement patterns given in **(c)**.

The principle of virtual displacements (4.7) specialized to this bar problem gives

$$\int_0^L \frac{d\bar{u}}{dx} EA \frac{du}{dx} dx = \bar{u} \bigg|_{x=L} F \tag{a}$$

The governing differential equations are obtained using integration by parts (see Example 3.19):

$$\bar{u}EA \frac{du}{dx} \bigg|_0^L - \int_0^L \bar{u} \frac{d}{dx}\left(EA \frac{du}{dx}\right) dx = \bar{u} \bigg|_{x=L} F \tag{b}$$

Since $\bar{u}\,|_{x=0} = 0$ and $\bar{u}$ is arbitrary otherwise, we obtain from (b),

$$\frac{d}{dx}\left(EA \frac{du}{dx}\right) = 0 \qquad \text{differential equation of equilibrium} \tag{c}$$

$$EA \frac{du}{dx} \bigg|_{x=L} = F \qquad \text{force or natural boundary condition} \tag{d}$$

Of course, in addition we have the displacement boundary condition $u\,|_{x=0} = 0$. Integrating (c) and using the boundary conditions, we obtain as the exact solution of the mathematical model,

$$u = \frac{FL}{EA_0} \ln\left(\frac{2}{2 - x/L}\right) \tag{e}$$

Next, using (e) and $\bar{u} = ax$ and $\bar{u} = ax^2$ in equation (a), we obtain

$$\int_0^L a \frac{F}{A_0(2 - x/L)} A_0\left(2 - \frac{x}{L}\right) dx = aLF \tag{f}$$

and

$$\int_0^L 2ax \frac{F}{A_0(2 - x/L)} A_0\left(2 - \frac{x}{L}\right) dx = aL^2F \tag{g}$$

Equations (f) and (g) show that for the exact displacement /stress response the principle of virtual displacements is satisfied with the assumed virtual displacements.

Now let us employ the principle of virtual displacements with $\tau_{xx} = \frac{2}{3}(F/A_0)$ and use first $\bar{u} = ax$ and then $\bar{u} = ax^2$. We obtain with $\bar{u} = ax$,

$$\int_0^L a \frac{2}{3} \frac{F}{A_0} A_0 \left(2 - \frac{x}{L}\right) dx = aLF$$

which shows that the principle of virtual displacements is satisfied with this virtual displacement field. For $\bar{u} = ax^2$, we obtain

$$\int_0^L 2ax \frac{2}{3} \frac{F}{A_0} A_0 \left(2 - \frac{x}{L}\right) dx \neq aL^2F$$

and this equation shows that $\tau_{xx} = \frac{2}{3}(F/A_0)$ is not the correct stress solution.

The principle of virtual displacements can be directly related to the principle that the total potential Π of the system must be stationary (see Sections 3.3.2 and 3.3.4). We study this relationship in the following example.

EXAMPLE 4.4:   Show how for a linear elastic continuum the principle of virtual displacements relates to the principle of stationarity of the total potential.

Assuming a linear elastic continuum with zero initial stresses, the total potential of the body in Fig. 4.1 is

$$\Pi = \frac{1}{2} \int_V \boldsymbol{\epsilon}^T \mathbf{C} \boldsymbol{\epsilon} \, dV - \int_V \mathbf{U}^T \mathbf{f}^B \, dV - \int_{S_f} \mathbf{U}^{S_f^T} \mathbf{f}^{S_f} \, dS - \sum_i \mathbf{U}^{i^T} \mathbf{R}_C^i \qquad \text{(a)}$$

where the notation was defined earlier, and we have

$$\boldsymbol{\tau} = \mathbf{C} \boldsymbol{\epsilon}$$

with $\mathbf{C}$ the stress-strain matrix of the material.

Invoking the stationarity of Π, i.e., evaluating $\delta\Pi = 0$ with respect to the displacements (which now appear in the strains) and using the fact that $\mathbf{C}$ is symmetric, we obtain

$$\int_V \delta\boldsymbol{\epsilon}^T \mathbf{C} \boldsymbol{\epsilon} \, dV = \int_V \delta\mathbf{U}^T \mathbf{f}^B \, dV + \int_{S_f} \delta\mathbf{U}^{S_f^T} \mathbf{f}^{S_f} \, dS + \sum_i \delta\mathbf{U}^{i^T} \mathbf{R}_C^i \qquad \text{(b)}$$

However, to evaluate Π in (a) the displacements must satisfy the displacement boundary conditions. Hence in (b) we consider any variations on the displacements but with zero values at and corresponding to the displacement boundary conditions, and the corresponding variations in strains. It follows that invoking the stationarity of Π is equivalent to using the principle of virtual displacements, and indeed we may write

$$\delta\boldsymbol{\epsilon} \equiv \bar{\boldsymbol{\epsilon}}; \qquad \delta\mathbf{U} \equiv \bar{\mathbf{U}}; \qquad \delta\mathbf{U}^{S_f} \equiv \bar{\mathbf{U}}^{S_f}; \qquad \delta\mathbf{U}^i \equiv \bar{\mathbf{U}}^i$$

so that (b) reduces to (4.7).

It is important to realize that when the principle of virtual displacements (4.7) is satisfied for all admissible virtual displacements with the stresses $\boldsymbol{\tau}$ "properly obtained" from a continuous displacement field $\mathbf{U}$ that satisfies the displacement boundary conditions on S_u, all three fundamental requirements of mechanics are fulfilled:

1. *Equilibrium* holds because the principle of virtual displacements is an expression of equilibrium as shown in Example 4.2.

2. *Compatibility* holds because the displacement field **U** is continuous and satisfies the displacement boundary conditions.
3. *The stress-strain law* holds because the stresses **τ** have been calculated using the constitutive relationships from the strains **ε** (which have been evaluated from the displacements **U**).

So far we have assumed that the body being considered is properly supported, i.e., that there are sufficient support conditions for a unique displacement solution. However, the principle of virtual displacements also holds when all displacement supports are removed and the correct reactions (then assumed known) are applied instead. In this case the surface area S_f on which known tractions are applied is equal to the complete surface area S of the body (and S_u is zero)[6]. We use this basic observation in developing the governing finite element equations. That is, it is conceptually expedient to first not consider any displacement boundary conditions, develop the governing finite element equations accordingly, and then prior to solving these equations impose all displacement boundary conditions.

Finite Element Equations

Let us now derive the governing finite element equations. We first consider the response of the general three-dimensional body shown in Fig. 4.1 and later specialize this general formulation to specific problems (see Section 4.2.3).

In the finite element analysis we approximate the body in Fig. 4.1 as an assemblage of discrete finite elements interconnected at nodal points on the element boundaries. The displacements measured in a local coordinate system x, y, z (to be chosen conveniently) within each element are assumed to be a function of the displacements at the N finite element nodal points. Therefore, for element m we have

$$\mathbf{u}^{(m)}(x, y, z) = \mathbf{H}^{(m)}(x, y, z)\,\hat{\mathbf{U}} \qquad (4.8)$$

where $\mathbf{H}^{(m)}$ is the displacement interpolation matrix, the superscript m denotes element m, and $\hat{\mathbf{U}}$ is a vector of the three global displacement components U_i, V_i, and W_i at all nodal points, including those at the supports of the element assemblage; i.e., $\hat{\mathbf{U}}$ is a vector of dimension $3N$,

$$\hat{\mathbf{U}}^T = [U_1\,V_1\,W_1 \quad U_2\,V_2\,W_2 \quad \dots \quad U_N\,V_N\,W_N] \qquad (4.9)$$

We may note here that more generally, we write

$$\hat{\mathbf{U}}^T = [U_1 \quad U_2 \quad U_3 \quad \dots \quad U_n] \qquad (4.10)$$

where it is understood that U_i may correspond to a displacement in any direction X, Y, or Z, or even in a direction not aligned with these coordinate axes (but aligned with the axes of another local coordinate system), and may also signify a rotation when we consider beams, plates, or shells (see Section 4.2.3). Since $\hat{\mathbf{U}}$ includes the displacements (and rota-

---

[6] For this reason, and for ease of notation, we shall now mostly (i.e., until Section 4.4.2) no longer use the superscripts S_f and S_u but simply the superscript S on the surface tractions and displacements.

tions) at the supports of the element assemblage, we need to impose, at a later time, the known values of $\hat{\mathbf{U}}$ prior to solving for the unknown nodal point displacements.

Figure 4.1 shows a typical finite element of the assemblage. This element has eight nodal points, one at each of its corners, and can be thought of as a "brick" element. We should imagine that the complete body is represented as an assemblage of such brick elements put together so as to not leave any gaps between the element domains. We show this element here merely as an example; in practice, elements of different geometries and nodal points on faces and in the element interiors may be used.

The choice of element and the construction of the corresponding entries in $\mathbf{H}^{(m)}$ (which depend on the element geometry, the number of element nodes/degrees of freedom, and convergence requirements) constitute the basic steps of a finite element solution and are discussed in detail later.

Although all nodal point displacements are listed in $\hat{\mathbf{U}}$, it should be realized that for a given element only the displacements at the nodes of the element affect the displacement and strain distributions within the element.

With the assumption on the displacements in (4.8) we can now evaluate the corresponding element strains,

$$\boldsymbol{\epsilon}^{(m)}(x, y, z) = \mathbf{B}^{(m)}(x, y, z)\hat{\mathbf{U}} \qquad (4.11)$$

where $\mathbf{B}^{(m)}$ is the strain-displacement matrix; the rows of $\mathbf{B}^{(m)}$ are obtained by appropriately differentiating and combining rows of the matrix $\mathbf{H}^{(m)}$.

The purpose of defining the element displacements and strains in terms of the complete array of finite element assemblage nodal point displacements may not be obvious now. However, we will see that by proceeding in this way, the use of (4.8) and (4.11) in the principle of virtual displacements will automatically lead to an effective assemblage process of all element matrices into the governing structure matrices. This assemblage process is referred to as the direct stiffness method.

The stresses in a finite element are related to the element strains and the element initial stresses using

$$\boldsymbol{\tau}^{(m)} = \mathbf{C}^{(m)}\boldsymbol{\epsilon}^{(m)} + \boldsymbol{\tau}^{I(m)} \qquad (4.12)$$

where $\mathbf{C}^{(m)}$ is the elasticity matrix of element m and $\boldsymbol{\tau}^{I(m)}$ are the given element initial stresses. The material law specified in $\mathbf{C}^{(m)}$ for each element can be that for an isotropic or an anisotropic material and can vary from element to element.

Using the assumption on the displacements within each finite element, as expressed in (4.8), we can now derive equilibrium equations that correspond to the nodal point displacements of the assemblage of finite elements. First, we rewrite (4.7) as a sum of integrations over the volume and areas of all finite elements:

$$\sum_m \int_{V^{(m)}} \bar{\boldsymbol{\epsilon}}^{(m)T} \boldsymbol{\tau}^{(m)} \, dV^{(m)} = \sum_m \int_{V^{(m)}} \bar{\mathbf{u}}^{(m)T} \mathbf{f}^{B(m)} \, dV^{(m)}$$

$$+ \sum_m \int_{S_1^{(m)}, \ldots, S_q^{(m)}} \bar{\mathbf{u}}^{S(m)T} \mathbf{f}^{S(m)} \, dS^{(m)} + \sum_i \bar{\mathbf{u}}^{iT} \mathbf{R}_C^i \qquad (4.13)$$

where $m = 1, 2, \ldots, k$, where k = number of elements, and $S_1^{(m)}, \ldots, S_q^{(m)}$ denotes the element surfaces that are part of the body surface S. For elements totally surrounded by other elements no such surfaces exist, whereas for elements on the surface of the body one or more such element surfaces are included in the surface force integral. Note that we assume in (4.13) that nodal points have been placed at the points where concentrated loads are applied, although a concentrated load can of course also be included in the surface force integrals.

It is important to note that *since the integrations in* (4.13) *are performed over the element volumes and surfaces, for efficiency we may use a different and any convenient coordinate system for each element in the calculations.* After all, for a given virtual displacement field, the internal virtual work is a number, as is the external virtual work, and this number can be evaluated by integrations in any coordinate system. Of course, it is assumed that for each integral in (4.13) only a single coordinate system for all variables is employed; e.g., $\overline{\mathbf{u}}^{(m)}$ is defined in the same coordinate system as $\mathbf{f}^{B(m)}$. The use of different coordinate systems is in essence the reason why each of the integrals can be evaluated very effectively in general element assemblages.

The relations in (4.8) and (4.11) have been given for the unknown (real) element displacements and strains. In our use of the principle of virtual displacements we employ the same assumptions for the virtual displacements and strains

$$\boxed{\overline{\mathbf{u}}^{(m)}(x, y, z) = \mathbf{H}^{(m)}(x, y, z)\overline{\hat{\mathbf{U}}}} \tag{4.14}$$

$$\boxed{\overline{\boldsymbol{\epsilon}}^{(m)}(x, y, z) = \mathbf{B}^{(m)}(x, y, z)\overline{\hat{\mathbf{U}}}} \tag{4.15}$$

In this way the element stiffness (and mass) matrices will be *symmetric* matrices.

If we now substitute into (4.13), we obtain

$$\overline{\hat{\mathbf{U}}}^T \left[\sum_m \int_{V^{(m)}} \mathbf{B}^{(m)T} \mathbf{C}^{(m)} \mathbf{B}^{(m)} \, dV^{(m)} \right] \hat{\mathbf{U}} = \overline{\hat{\mathbf{U}}}^T \left[\left\{ \sum_m \int_{V^{(m)}} \mathbf{H}^{(m)T} \mathbf{f}^{B(m)} \, dV^{(m)} \right\} \right.$$
$$+ \left\{ \sum_m \int_{S_1^{(m)}, \ldots, S_q^{(m)}} \mathbf{H}^{S(m)T} \mathbf{f}^{S(m)} \, dS^{(m)} \right\} \tag{4.16}$$
$$\left. - \left\{ \sum_m \int_{V^{(m)}} \mathbf{B}^{(m)T} \boldsymbol{\tau}^{I(m)} \, dV^{(m)} \right\} + \mathbf{R}_C \right]$$

where the surface displacement interpolation matrices $\mathbf{H}^{S(m)}$ are obtained from the displacement interpolation matrices $\mathbf{H}^{(m)}$ in (4.8) by substituting the appropriate element surface coordinates (see Examples 4.7 and 5.12) and $\mathbf{R}_C$ is a vector of concentrated loads applied to the nodes of the element assemblage.

We should note that the ith component in $\mathbf{R}_C$ is the concentrated nodal force that corresponds to the ith displacement component in $\hat{\mathbf{U}}$. In (4.16) the nodal point displacement vectors $\hat{\mathbf{U}}$ and $\overline{\hat{\mathbf{U}}}$ of the element assemblage are independent of element m and are therefore taken out of the summation signs.

To obtain from (4.16) the equations for the unknown nodal point displacements, we apply the principle of virtual displacements n times by imposing unit virtual displacements in turn for all components of $\overline{\mathbf{U}}$. In the first application $\overline{\mathbf{U}} = \mathbf{e}_1$,[7] in the second application $\overline{\mathbf{U}} = \mathbf{e}_2$, and so on, until in the nth application $\overline{\mathbf{U}} = \mathbf{e}_n$, so that the result is

$$\boxed{\mathbf{KU} = \mathbf{R}} \tag{4.17}$$

where we do not show the identity matrices $\mathbf{I}$ due to the virtual displacements on each side of the equation and

$$\boxed{\mathbf{R} = \mathbf{R}_B + \mathbf{R}_S - \mathbf{R}_I + \mathbf{R}_C} \tag{4.18}$$

and, as we shall do from now on, we denote the unknown nodal point displacements as $\mathbf{U}$; i.e., $\mathbf{U} \equiv \hat{\mathbf{U}}$.

The matrix $\mathbf{K}$ is the stiffness matrix of the element assemblage,

$$\boxed{\mathbf{K} = \sum_m \underbrace{\int_{V^{(m)}} \mathbf{B}^{(m)T} \mathbf{C}^{(m)} \mathbf{B}^{(m)} \, dV^{(m)}}_{= \mathbf{K}^{(m)}}} \tag{4.19}$$

The load vector $\mathbf{R}$ includes the effect of the element body forces,

$$\boxed{\mathbf{R}_B = \sum_m \underbrace{\int_{V^{(m)}} \mathbf{H}^{(m)T} \mathbf{f}^{B(m)} \, dV^{(m)}}_{= \mathbf{R}_B^{(m)}}} \tag{4.20}$$

the effect of the element surface forces,

$$\boxed{\mathbf{R}_S = \sum_m \underbrace{\int_{S_1^{(m)}, \ldots, S_q^{(m)}} \mathbf{H}^{S(m)T} \mathbf{f}^{S(m)} \, dS^{(m)}}_{= \mathbf{R}_S^{(m)}}} \tag{4.21}$$

the effect of the element initial stresses,

$$\boxed{\mathbf{R}_I = \sum_m \underbrace{\int_{V^{(m)}} \mathbf{B}^{(m)T} \boldsymbol{\tau}^{I(m)} \, dV^{(m)}}_{= \mathbf{R}_I^{(m)}}} \tag{4.22}$$

and the nodal concentrated loads $\mathbf{R}_C$.

---

[7] For the definition of the vector $\mathbf{e}_i$, see the text following (2.7).

We note that the summation of the element volume integrals in (4.19) expresses the direct addition of the element stiffness matrices $\mathbf{K}^{(m)}$ to obtain the stiffness matrix of the total element assemblage. In the same way, the assemblage body force vector $\mathbf{R}_B$ is calculated by directly adding the element body force vectors $\mathbf{R}_B^{(m)}$; and $\mathbf{R}_S$ and $\mathbf{R}_I$ are similarly obtained. The process of assembling the element matrices by this direct addition is called the *direct stiffness method*.

This elegant writing of the assemblage process hinges upon two main factors: first, the dimensions of all matrices to be added are the same and, second, the element degrees of freedom are equal to the global degrees of freedom. In practice of course only the nonzero rows and columns of an element matrix $\mathbf{K}^{(m)}$ are calculated (corresponding to the actual element nodal degrees of freedom), and then the assemblage is carried out using for each element a connectivity array LM (see Example 4.11 and Chapter 12). Also, in practice, the element stiffness matrix may first be calculated corresponding to element local degrees of freedom not aligned with the global assemblage degrees of freedom, in which case a transformation is necessary prior to the assemblage [see (4.41)].

Equation (4.17) is a statement of the static equilibrium of the element assemblage. In these equilibrium considerations, the applied forces may vary with time, in which case the displacements also vary with time and (4.17) is a statement of equilibrium for any specific point in time. (In practice, the time-dependent application of loads can thus be used to model multiple-load cases; see Example 4.5.) However, if in actuality the loads are applied rapidly, measured on the natural frequencies of the system, inertia forces need to be considered; i.e., a truly dynamic problem needs to be solved. Using d'Alembert's principle, we can simply include the element inertia forces as part of the body forces. Assuming that the element accelerations are approximated in the same way as the element displacements in (4.8), the contribution from the total body forces to the load vector $\mathbf{R}$ is (with the X, Y, Z coordinate system stationary)

$$\mathbf{R}_B = \sum_m \int_{V^{(m)}} \mathbf{H}^{(m)T}[\mathbf{f}^{B(m)} - \rho^{(m)}\mathbf{H}^{(m)}\ddot{\mathbf{U}}]\, dV^{(m)} \tag{4.23}$$

where $\mathbf{f}^{B(m)}$ no longer includes inertia forces, $\ddot{\mathbf{U}}$ lists the nodal point accelerations (i.e., is the second time derivative of $\mathbf{U}$), and $\rho^{(m)}$ is the mass density of element m. The equilibrium equations are, in this case,

$$\mathbf{M}\ddot{\mathbf{U}} + \mathbf{K}\mathbf{U} = \mathbf{R} \tag{4.24}$$

where $\mathbf{R}$ and $\mathbf{U}$ are time-dependent. The matrix $\mathbf{M}$ is the mass matrix of the structure,

$$\boxed{\mathbf{M} = \sum_m \underbrace{\int_{V^{(m)}} \rho^{(m)}\mathbf{H}^{(m)T}\mathbf{H}^{(m)}\, dV^{(m)}}_{= \mathbf{M}^{(m)}}} \tag{4.25}$$

In actually measured dynamic responses of structures it is observed that energy is dissipated during vibration, which in vibration analysis is usually taken account of by introducing velocity-dependent damping forces. Introducing the damping forces as additional contributions to the body forces, we obtain corresponding to (4.23),

$$\mathbf{R}_B = \sum_m \int_{V^{(m)}} \mathbf{H}^{(m)T}[\mathbf{f}^{B(m)} - \rho^{(m)}\mathbf{H}^{(m)}\ddot{\mathbf{U}} - \kappa^{(m)}\mathbf{H}^{(m)}\dot{\mathbf{U}}]\, dV^{(m)} \tag{4.26}$$

In this case the vectors $\mathbf{f}^{B(m)}$ no longer include inertia and velocity-dependent damping forces, $\dot{\mathbf{U}}$ is a vector of the nodal point velocities (i.e., the first time derivative of $\mathbf{U}$), and $\kappa^{(m)}$ is the damping property parameter of element m. The equilibrium equations are, in this case,

$$\boxed{\mathbf{M}\ddot{\mathbf{U}} + \mathbf{C}\dot{\mathbf{U}} + \mathbf{K}\mathbf{U} = \mathbf{R}} \tag{4.27}$$

where $\mathbf{C}$ is the damping matrix of the structure; i.e., formally,

$$\mathbf{C} = \sum_m \underbrace{\int_{V^{(m)}} \kappa^{(m)} \mathbf{H}^{(m)T} \mathbf{H}^{(m)} \, dV^{(m)}}_{= \ \mathbf{C}^{(m)}} \tag{4.28}$$

In practice it is difficult, if not impossible, to determine for general finite element assemblages the element damping parameters, in particular because the damping properties are frequency dependent. For this reason, the matrix $\mathbf{C}$ is in general not assembled from element damping matrices but is constructed using the mass matrix and stiffness matrix of the complete element assemblage together with experimental results on the amount of damping. Some formulations used to construct physically significant damping matrices are described in Section 9.3.3.

A complete analysis, therefore, consists of calculating the matrix $\mathbf{K}$ (and the matrices $\mathbf{M}$ and $\mathbf{C}$ in a dynamic analysis) and the load vector $\mathbf{R}$, solving for the response $\mathbf{U}$ from (4.17) [or $\mathbf{U}$, $\dot{\mathbf{U}}$, $\ddot{\mathbf{U}}$ from (4.24) or (4.27)], and then evaluating the stresses using (4.12). We should emphasize that the stresses are simply obtained using (4.12)—hence only from the initial stresses and element displacements—and that these values are not corrected for externally applied element pressures or body forces, as is common practice in the analysis of frame structures with beam elements (see Example 4.5 and, for example, S. H. Crandall, N. C. Dahl, and T. J. Lardner [A]). In the analysis of beam structures, each element represents a one-dimensional stress situation, and the stress correction due to distributed loading is performed by simple equilibrium considerations. In static analysis, relatively long beam elements can therefore be employed, resulting in the use of only a few elements (and degrees of freedom) to represent a frame structure. However, a similar scheme would require, in general two- and three-dimensional finite element analysis, the solution of boundary value problems for the (large) element domains used, and the use of fine meshes for an accurate prediction of the displacements and strains is more effective. With such fine discretizations, the benefits of even correcting approximately the stress predictions for the effects of distributed element loadings are in general small, although for specific situations of course the use of a rational scheme can result in notable improvements.

To illustrate the above derivation of the finite element equilibrium equations, we consider the following examples.

EXAMPLE 4.5: Establish the finite element equilibrium equations of the bar structure shown in Fig. E4.5. The mathematical model to be used is discussed in Examples 3.17 and 3.22. Use the two-node bar element idealization given and consider the following two cases:

1. Assume that the loads are applied very slowly when measured on the time constants (natural periods) of the structure.
2. Assume that the loads are applied rapidly. The structure is initially at rest.

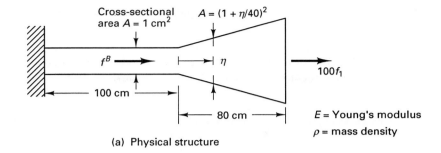

Cross-sectional area $A = 1$ cm^2

$A = (1 + \eta/40)^2$

f^B

η

100 cm

80 cm

$100f_1$

E = Young's modulus

ρ = mass density

(a) Physical structure

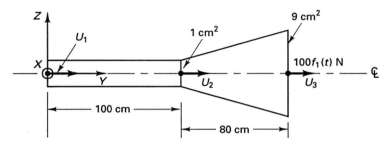

Z

U_1

1 cm^2

9 cm^2

X

Y

U_2

$100f_1(t)$ N

U_3

¢

100 cm

80 cm

(b) Element assemblage in global system

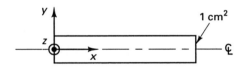

y

z

x

1 cm^2

¢

(c) Element 1, $f_x^B = f_2(t)$ N/cm^3

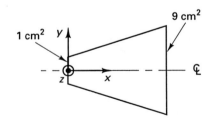

1 cm^2

y

9 cm^2

z

x

¢

(d) Element 2, $f_x^B = 0.1 f_2(t)$ N/cm^3

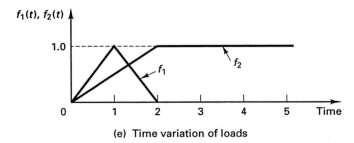

$f_1(t), f_2(t)$

1.0

f_1

f_2

0   1   2   3   4   5   Time

(e) Time variation of loads

Figure E4.5 Two-element bar assemblage

In the formulation of the finite element equilibrium equations we employ the general equations (4.8) to (4.24) but use that the only nonzero stress is the longitudinal stress in the bar. Furthermore, considering the complete bar as an assemblage of 2 two-node bar elements corresponds to assuming a linear displacement variation between the nodal points of each element.

The first step is to construct the matrices $\mathbf{H}^{(m)}$ and $\mathbf{B}^{(m)}$ for $m = 1, 2$. We recall that although the displacement at the left end of the structure is zero, we first include the displacement at that surface in the construction of the finite element equilibrium equations.

Corresponding to the displacement vector $\mathbf{U}^T = [U_1 \quad U_2 \quad U_3]$, we have

$$\mathbf{H}^{(1)} = \left[\left(1 - \frac{x}{100}\right) \quad \frac{x}{100} \quad 0 \right]$$

$$\mathbf{B}^{(1)} = \left[-\frac{1}{100} \quad \frac{1}{100} \quad 0 \right]$$

$$\mathbf{H}^{(2)} = \left[0 \quad \left(1 - \frac{x}{80}\right) \quad \frac{x}{80} \right]$$

$$\mathbf{B}^{(2)} = \left[0 \quad -\frac{1}{80} \quad \frac{1}{80} \right]$$

The material property matrices are

$$\mathbf{C}^{(1)} = E; \qquad \mathbf{C}^{(2)} = E$$

where E is Young's modulus for the material. For the volume integrations we need the cross-sectional areas of the elements. We have

$$A^{(1)} = 1 \text{ cm}^2; \qquad A^{(2)} = \left(1 + \frac{x}{40}\right)^2 \text{ cm}^2$$

When the loads are applied very slowly, a static analysis is required in which the stiffness matrix $\mathbf{K}$ and load vector $\mathbf{R}$ must be calculated. The body forces and loads are given in Fig. E4.5. We therefore have

$$\mathbf{K} = (1)E \int_0^{100} \begin{bmatrix} -\frac{1}{100} \\ \frac{1}{100} \\ 0 \end{bmatrix} \left[-\frac{1}{100} \quad \frac{1}{100} \quad 0 \right] dx + E \int_0^{80} \left(1 + \frac{x}{40}\right)^2 \begin{bmatrix} 0 \\ -\frac{1}{80} \\ \frac{1}{80} \end{bmatrix} \left[0 \quad -\frac{1}{80} \quad \frac{1}{80} \right] dx$$

or

$$\mathbf{K} = \frac{E}{100} \begin{bmatrix} 1 & -1 & 0 \\ -1 & 1 & 0 \\ 0 & 0 & 0 \end{bmatrix} + \frac{13E}{240} \begin{bmatrix} 0 & 0 & 0 \\ 0 & 1 & -1 \\ 0 & -1 & 1 \end{bmatrix}$$

$$= \frac{E}{240} \begin{bmatrix} 2.4 & -2.4 & 0 \\ -2.4 & 15.4 & -13 \\ 0 & -13 & 13 \end{bmatrix} \qquad (a)$$

and also,

$$\mathbf{R}_B = \left\{ (1) \int_0^{100} \begin{bmatrix} 1 - \dfrac{x}{100} \\ \dfrac{x}{100} \\ 0 \end{bmatrix} (1) \, dx + \int_0^{80} \left(1 + \dfrac{x}{40} \right)^2 \begin{bmatrix} 0 \\ 1 - \dfrac{x}{80} \\ \dfrac{x}{80} \end{bmatrix} \left(\dfrac{1}{10} \right) dx \right\} f_2(t)$$

$$= \frac{1}{3} \begin{bmatrix} 150 \\ 186 \\ 68 \end{bmatrix} f_2(t) \tag{b}$$

$$\mathbf{R}_C = \begin{bmatrix} 0 \\ 0 \\ 100 \end{bmatrix} f_1(t) \tag{c}$$

To obtain the solution at a specific time t^*, the vectors $\mathbf{R}_B$ and $\mathbf{R}_C$ must be evaluated corresponding to t^*, and the equation

$$\mathbf{K}\mathbf{U}\big|_{t=t^*} = \mathbf{R}_B\big|_{t=t^*} + \mathbf{R}_C\big|_{t=t^*} \tag{d}$$

yields the displacements at t^*. We should note that in this static analysis the displacements at time t^* depend only on the magnitude of the loads at that time and are independent of the loading history.

Considering now the dynamic analysis, we also need to calculate the mass matrix. Using the displacement interpolations and (4.25), we have

$$\mathbf{M} = (1)\rho \int_0^{100} \begin{bmatrix} 1 - \dfrac{x}{100} \\ \dfrac{x}{100} \\ 0 \end{bmatrix} \left[\left(1 - \dfrac{x}{100} \right) \quad \dfrac{x}{100} \quad 0 \right] dx$$

$$+ \rho \int_0^{80} \left(1 + \dfrac{x}{40} \right)^2 \begin{bmatrix} 0 \\ 1 - \dfrac{x}{80} \\ \dfrac{x}{80} \end{bmatrix} \left[0 \quad \left(1 - \dfrac{x}{80} \right) \quad \dfrac{x}{80} \right] dx$$

Hence

$$\mathbf{M} = \frac{\rho}{6} \begin{bmatrix} 200 & 100 & 0 \\ 100 & 584 & 336 \\ 0 & 336 & 1024 \end{bmatrix}$$

Damping was not specified; thus, the equilibrium equations now to be solved are

$$\mathbf{M}\ddot{\mathbf{U}}(t) + \mathbf{K}\mathbf{U}(t) = \mathbf{R}_B(t) + \mathbf{R}_C(t) \tag{e}$$

where the stiffness matrix $\mathbf{K}$ and load vectors $\mathbf{R}_B$ and $\mathbf{R}_C$ have already been given in (a) to (c). Using the initial conditions

$$\mathbf{U}\big|_{t=0} = \mathbf{0}; \qquad \dot{\mathbf{U}}\big|_{t=0} = \mathbf{0} \tag{f}$$

these dynamic equilibrium equations must be integrated from time 0 to time t^* in order to obtain the solution at time t^* (see Chapter 9).

To actually solve for the response of the structure in Fig. E4.5(a), we need to impose $U_1 = 0$ for all time t. Hence, the equations (d) and (e) must be amended by this condition (see Section 4.2.2). The solution of (d) and (e) then yields $U_2(t)$, $U_3(t)$, and the stresses are obtained using

$$\tau_{xx}^{(m)} = \mathbf{C}^{(m)}\mathbf{B}^{(m)}\mathbf{U}(t); \qquad m = 1, 2 \tag{g}$$

These stresses will be discontinuous between the elements because constant element strains are assumed. Of course, in this example, since the exact solution to the mathematical model can be computed, stresses more accurate than those given by (g) could be evaluated within each element.

In static analysis, this increase in accuracy could simply be achieved, as in beam theory, by adding a stress correction for the distributed element loading to the values given in (g). However, such a stress correction is not straightforward in general dynamic analysis (and in any two- and three-dimensional practical analysis), and if a large number of elements is used to represent the structure, the stresses using (g) are sufficiently accurate (see Section 4.3.6).

EXAMPLE 4.6: Consider the analysis of the cantilever plate shown in Fig. E4.6. To illustrate the analysis technique, use the coarse finite element idealization given in the figure (in a practical analysis more finite elements must be employed (see Section 4.3)). Establish the matrices $\mathbf{H}^{(2)}$, $\mathbf{B}^{(2)}$, and $\mathbf{C}^{(2)}$.

The cantilever plate is acting in plane stress conditions. For an isotropic linear elastic material the stress-strain matrix is defined using Young's modulus E and Poisson's ratio ν (see Table 4.3),

$$\mathbf{C}^{(2)} = \frac{E}{1-\nu^2}\begin{bmatrix} 1 & \nu & 0 \\ \nu & 1 & 0 \\ 0 & 0 & \frac{1-\nu}{2} \end{bmatrix}$$

The displacement transformation matrix $\mathbf{H}^{(2)}$ of element 2 relates the element internal displacements to the nodal point displacements,

$$\begin{bmatrix} u(x, y) \\ v(x, y) \end{bmatrix}^{(2)} = \mathbf{H}^{(2)}\mathbf{U} \tag{a}$$

where $\mathbf{U}$ is a vector listing all nodal point displacements of the structure,

$$\mathbf{U}^T = [U_1 \quad U_2 \quad U_3 \quad U_4 \quad \ldots \quad U_{17} \quad U_{18}] \tag{b}$$

(As mentioned previously, in this phase of analysis we are considering the structural model without displacement boundary conditions.) In considering element 2, we recognize that only the displacements at nodes 6, 3, 2, and 5 affect the displacements in the element. For computational purposes it is convenient to use a convention to number the element nodal points and corresponding element degrees of freedom as shown in Fig E4.6(c). In the same figure the global structure degrees of freedom of the vector $\mathbf{U}$ in (b) are also given.

To derive the matrix $\mathbf{H}^{(2)}$ in (a) we recognize that there are four nodal point displacements each for expressing $u(x, y)$ and $v(x, y)$. Hence, we can assume that the local element displacements u and v are given in the following form of polynomials in the local coordinate variables x and y:

$$u(x, y) = \alpha_1 + \alpha_2 x + \alpha_3 y + \alpha_4 xy$$
$$v(x, y) = \beta_1 + \beta_2 x + \beta_3 y + \beta_4 xy \tag{c}$$

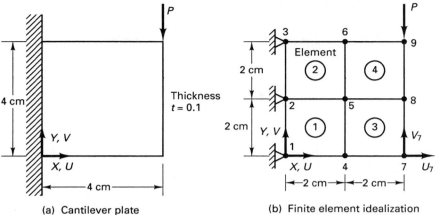

(a) Cantilever plate

(b) Finite element idealization
(plane stress condition)

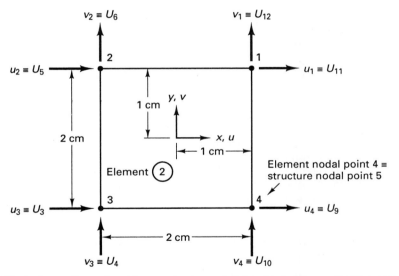

(c) Typical two-dimensional four-node element defined in local coordinate system

Figure E4.6   Finite element plane stress analysis

The unknown coefficients $\alpha_1, \ldots, \beta_4$, which are also called the generalized coordinates, will be expressed in terms of the unknown element nodal point displacements $u_1, \ldots, u_4$ and $v_1, \ldots, v_4$. Defining

$$\hat{\mathbf{u}}^T = \begin{bmatrix} u_1 & u_2 & u_3 & u_4 & \vdots & v_1 & v_2 & v_3 & v_4 \end{bmatrix} \tag{d}$$

we can write (c) in matrix form:

$$\begin{bmatrix} u(x, y) \\ v(x, y) \end{bmatrix} = \mathbf{\Phi}\boldsymbol{\alpha} \tag{e}$$

where
$$\mathbf{\Phi} = \begin{bmatrix} \boldsymbol{\phi} & \mathbf{0} \\ \mathbf{0} & \boldsymbol{\phi} \end{bmatrix}; \quad \boldsymbol{\phi} = \begin{bmatrix} 1 & x & y & xy \end{bmatrix}$$

and
$$\boldsymbol{\alpha}^T = \begin{bmatrix} \alpha_1 & \alpha_2 & \alpha_3 & \alpha_4 \ \vdots \ \beta_1 & \beta_2 & \beta_3 & \beta_4 \end{bmatrix}$$

Equation (e) must hold for all nodal points of the element; therfore, using (d), we have

$$\hat{\mathbf{u}} = \mathbf{A}\boldsymbol{\alpha} \tag{f}$$

in which
$$\mathbf{A} = \begin{bmatrix} \mathbf{A}_1 & \mathbf{0} \\ \mathbf{0} & \mathbf{A}_1 \end{bmatrix}$$

and
$$\mathbf{A}_1 = \begin{bmatrix} 1 & 1 & 1 & 1 \\ 1 & -1 & 1 & -1 \\ 1 & -1 & -1 & 1 \\ 1 & 1 & -1 & -1 \end{bmatrix}$$

Solving from (f) for $\boldsymbol{\alpha}$ and substituting into (e), we obtain

$$\mathbf{H} = \mathbf{\Phi}\mathbf{A}^{-1} \tag{g}$$

where the fact that no superscript is used on $\mathbf{H}$ indicates that the displacement interpolation matrix is defined corresponding to the element nodal point displacements in (d),

$$\mathbf{H} = \frac{1}{4}\begin{bmatrix} (1+x)(1+y) & (1-x)(1+y) & (1-x)(1-y) & (1+x)(1-y) \\ 0 & 0 & 0 & 0 \\ 0 & 0 & 0 & 0 \\ (1+x)(1+y) & (1-x)(1+y) & (1-x)(1-y) & (1+x)(1-y) \end{bmatrix} \tag{h}$$

The displacement functions in $\mathbf{H}$ could also have been established by inspection. Let H_{ij} be the (i, j)th element of $\mathbf{H}$; then H_{11} corresponds to a function that varies linearly in x and y [as required in (c)], is unity at $x = 1, y = 1$, and is zero at the other three element nodes. We discuss the construction of the displacement functions in $\mathbf{H}$ based on these thoughts in Section 5.2.

With $\mathbf{H}$ given in (h) we have

$$
\mathbf{H}^{(2)} =
\begin{array}{c}
\begin{matrix} & & u_3 & v_3 & & u_2 & v_2 & & & & u_4 & v_4 & \\ U_1 & U_2 & U_3 & U_4 & U_5 & U_6 & & U_7 & U_8 & U_9 & U_{10} & \end{matrix} \\
\begin{bmatrix} 0 & 0 & H_{13} & H_{17} & H_{12} & H_{16} & 0 & 0 & H_{14} & H_{18} \\ 0 & 0 & H_{23} & H_{27} & H_{22} & H_{26} & 0 & 0 & H_{24} & H_{28} \end{bmatrix}
\end{array}
$$

$$u_1 \quad v_1 \leftarrow \text{Element degrees of freedom} \tag{i}$$

$$
\begin{matrix} U_{11} & U_{12} & U_{13} & U_{14} & & U_{18}\leftarrow\text{Assemblage degrees} \\ H_{11} & H_{15} & 0 & 0 & \ldots\text{zeros}\ldots 0 & \text{of freedom} \\ H_{21} & H_{25} & 0 & 0 & \ldots\text{zeros}\ldots 0 \end{matrix}
$$

The strain-displacement matrix can now directly be obtained from (g). In plane stress conditions the element strains are

$$\boldsymbol{\epsilon}^T = \begin{bmatrix} \epsilon_{xx} & \epsilon_{yy} & \gamma_{xy} \end{bmatrix}$$

where
$$\epsilon_{xx} = \frac{\partial u}{\partial x}; \quad \epsilon_{yy} = \frac{\partial v}{\partial y}; \quad \gamma_{xy} = \frac{\partial u}{\partial y} + \frac{\partial v}{\partial x}$$

Using (g) and recognizing that the elements in $\mathbf{A}^{-1}$ are independent of x and y, we obtain

$$\mathbf{B} = \mathbf{EA}^{-1}$$

where

$$\mathbf{E} = \begin{bmatrix} 0 & 1 & 0 & y & 0 & 0 & 0 & 0 \\ 0 & 0 & 0 & 0 & 0 & 0 & 1 & x \\ 0 & 0 & 1 & x & 0 & 1 & 0 & y \end{bmatrix}$$

Hence, the strain-displacement matrix corresponding to the local element degrees of freedom is

$$\mathbf{B} = \frac{1}{4} \begin{bmatrix} (1+y) & -(1+y) & -(1-y) & (1-y) \\ 0 & 0 & 0 & 0 \\ (1+x) & (1-x) & -(1-x) & -(1+x) \end{bmatrix}$$

$$\left. \begin{matrix} 0 & 0 & 0 & 0 \\ (1+x) & (1-x) & -(1-x) & -(1+x) \\ (1+y) & -(1+y) & -(1-y) & (1-y) \end{matrix} \right] \qquad (j)$$

The matrix $\mathbf{B}$ could also have been calculated directly by operating on the rows of the matrix $\mathbf{H}$ in (h).

Let B_{ij} be the (i, j)th element of $\mathbf{B}$; then we now have

$$\mathbf{B}^{(2)} = \begin{bmatrix} 0 & 0 & \vdots & B_{13} & B_{17} & \vdots & B_{12} & B_{16} & \vdots & 0 & 0 & \vdots & B_{14} & B_{18} & \vdots & B_{11} & B_{15} & \vdots & 0 & 0 & \vdots \\ 0 & 0 & \vdots & B_{23} & B_{27} & \vdots & B_{22} & B_{26} & \vdots & 0 & 0 & \vdots & B_{24} & B_{28} & \vdots & B_{21} & B_{25} & \vdots & 0 & 0 & \vdots \\ 0 & 0 & \vdots & B_{33} & B_{37} & \vdots & B_{32} & B_{36} & \vdots & 0 & 0 & \vdots & B_{34} & B_{38} & \vdots & B_{31} & B_{35} & \vdots & 0 & 0 & \vdots \end{bmatrix}$$

$$\left. \begin{matrix} 0 \\ \ldots \text{ zeroes } \ldots\, 0 \\ 0 \end{matrix} \right]$$

where the element degrees of freedom and assemblage degrees of freedom are ordered as in (d) and (b).

EXAMPLE 4.7: A linearly varying surface pressure distribution as shown in Fig. E4.7 is applied to element (m) of an element assemblage. Evaluate the vector $\mathbf{R}_S^{(m)}$ for this element.

The first step in the calculation of $\mathbf{R}_S^{(m)}$ is the evaluation of the matrix $\mathbf{H}^{S(m)}$. This matrix can be established using the same approach as in Example 4.6. For the surface displacements we assume

$$u^S = \alpha_1 + \alpha_2 x + \alpha_3 x^2$$
$$v^S = \beta_1 + \beta_2 x + \beta_3 x^2 \qquad (a)$$

where (as in Example 4.6) the unknown coefficients $\alpha_1, \ldots, \beta_3$ are evaluated using the nodal point displacements. We thus obtain

$$\begin{bmatrix} u^S(x) \\ v^S(x) \end{bmatrix} = \mathbf{H}^S \hat{\mathbf{u}}$$

$$\hat{\mathbf{u}}^T = \begin{bmatrix} u_1 & u_2 & u_3 & \vdots & v_1 & v_2 & v_3 \end{bmatrix}$$

and

$$\mathbf{H}^S = \begin{bmatrix} \frac{1}{2}x(1+x) & -\frac{1}{2}x(1-x) & (1-x^2) & 0 & 0 & 0 \\ 0 & 0 & 0 & \frac{1}{2}x(1+x) & -\frac{1}{2}x(1-x) & (1-x^2) \end{bmatrix}$$

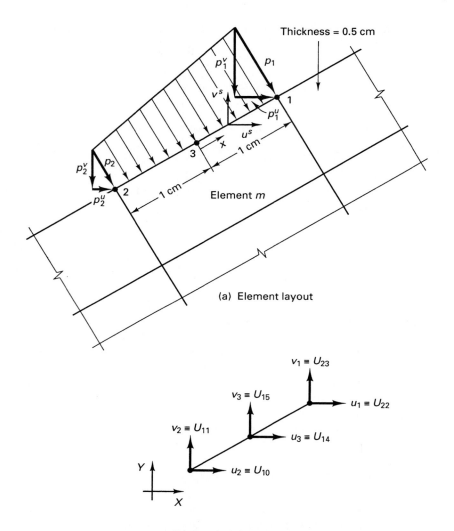

(a) Element layout

(b) Local-global degrees of freedom

Figure E4.7   Pressure loading on element (m)

The vector of surface loads is (with p_1 and p_2 positive)

$$\mathbf{f}^S = \begin{bmatrix} \frac{1}{2}(1+x)p_1^u + \frac{1}{2}(1-x)p_2^u \\ -\frac{1}{2}(1+x)p_1^v - \frac{1}{2}(1-x)p_2^v \end{bmatrix}$$

To obtain $\mathbf{R}_S^{(m)}$ we first evaluate

$$\mathbf{R}_S = 0.5 \int_{-1}^{+1} \mathbf{H}^{S^T} \mathbf{f}^S \, dx$$

to obtain
$$\mathbf{R}_S = \frac{1}{3} \begin{bmatrix} p_1^u \\ p_2^u \\ 2(p_1^u + p_2^u) \\ -p_1^v \\ -p_2^v \\ -2(p_1^v + p_2^v) \end{bmatrix}$$

Thus, corresponding to the global degrees of freedom given in Fig. E4.7, we have

$$\begin{array}{ccccccccc} & & U_{10} & U_{11} & U_{12} & U_{13} & U_{14} & & U_{15} \\ \mathbf{R}_S^{(m)T} = \tfrac{1}{3}[0 & \cdots & 0 & \vdots & p_2^u & -p_2^v & \vdots & 0 & 0 & \vdots & 2(p_1^u + p_2^u) & -2(p_1^v + p_2^v) & \vdots & 0 & \cdots \end{array}$$

$$\begin{array}{cc} U_{22} & U_{23} \leftarrow \text{Assemblage degrees of freedom} \\ \cdots \quad 0 \vdots \quad p_1^u \quad -p_1^v \vdots \quad 0 \quad \cdots \quad 0] \end{array}$$

The Assumption About Stress Equilibrium

We noted earlier that the analyses of truss and beam assemblages were originally not considered to be finite element analysis because the "exact" element stiffness matrices can be employed in the analyses. These stiffness matrices are obtained in the application of the principle of virtual displacements if the assumed displacement interpolations are in fact the exact displacements that the element undergoes when subjected to the unit nodal point displacements. Here the word "exact" refers to the fact that by imposing these displacements on the element, all pertinent differential equations of equilibrium and compatibility and the constitutive requirements (and also the boundary conditions) are fully satisfied in static analysis.

In considering the analysis of the truss assemblage in Example 4.5, we obtained the exact stiffness matrix of element 1. However, for element 2 an approximate stiffness matrix was calculated as shown in the next example.

EXAMPLE 4.8:   Calculate for element 2 in Example 4.5 the exact element internal displacements that correspond to a unit element end displacement u_2 and evaluate the corresponding stiffness matrix. Also, show that using the element displacement assumption in Example 4.5, internal element equilibrium is not satisfied.

Consider element 2 with a unit displacement imposed at its right end as shown in Fig. E4.8. The element displacements are calculated by solving the differential equation (see Example 3.22),

$$E \frac{d}{dx}\left(A \frac{du}{dx} \right) = 0 \tag{a}$$

subject to the boundary conditions $u|_{x=0} = 0$ and $u|_{x=80} = 1.0$. Substituting for the area A and integrating the relation in (a), we obtain

$$u = \frac{3}{2}\left(1 - \frac{1}{1 + x/40} \right) \tag{b}$$

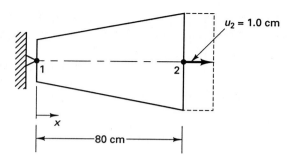

Figure E4.8   Element 2 of bar analyzed in Example 4.5

These are the exact element internal displacements. The element end forces required to subject the bar to these displacements are

$$k_{12} = -EA \left.\frac{du}{dx}\right|_{x=0}$$

$$k_{22} = EA \left.\frac{du}{dx}\right|_{x=L}$$

(c)

Substituting from (b) into (c) we have

$$k_{22} = \frac{3E}{80}; \qquad k_{12} = -\frac{3E}{80}$$

Hence we have, using the symmetry of the element matrix and equilibrium to establish k_{21} and k_{11},

$$\mathbf{K} = \frac{3}{80} E \begin{bmatrix} 1 & -1 \\ -1 & 1 \end{bmatrix}$$

(d)

The same result is of course obtained using the principle of virtual displacements with the displacement (b).

We note that the stiffness coefficient in (d) is smaller than the corresponding value obtained in Example 4.5 ($3E/80$ instead of $13E/240$). The finite element solution in Example 4.5 overestimates the stiffness of the structure because the assumed displacements artificially constrain the motion of the material particles (see Section 4.3.4). To check that the internal equilibrium is indeed not satisfied, we substitute the finite element solution (given by the displacement assumption in Example 4.5) into (a) and obtain

$$E \frac{d}{dx} \left\{ \left(1 + \frac{x}{40}\right)^2 \frac{1}{80} \right\} \neq 0$$

The solution of truss and beam structures, using the exact displacements corresponding to unit nodal point displacements and rotations to evaluate the stiffness matrices, gives analysis results that for the selected mathematical model satisfy all three requirements of mechanics exactly: differential equilibrium for every point of the structure (including nodal point equilibrium), compatibility, and the stress-strain relationships. Hence, the exact (unique) solution for the selected mathematical model is obtained.

We may note that such an exact solution is usually pursued in static analysis, in which the exact stiffness relationships are obtained as described in Example 4.8, but an exact solution is much more difficult to reach in dynamic analysis because in this case the distributed mass and damping effects must be included (see, for example, R. W. Clough and J. Penzien [A]).

However, although in a general (static or dynamic) finite element analysis, differential equilibrium is not exactly satisfied at all points of the continuum considered, two important properties are always satisfied by the finite element solution using a coarse or a fine mesh. These properties are (see Fig. 4.2)

1. Nodal point equilibrium
2. Element equilibrium.

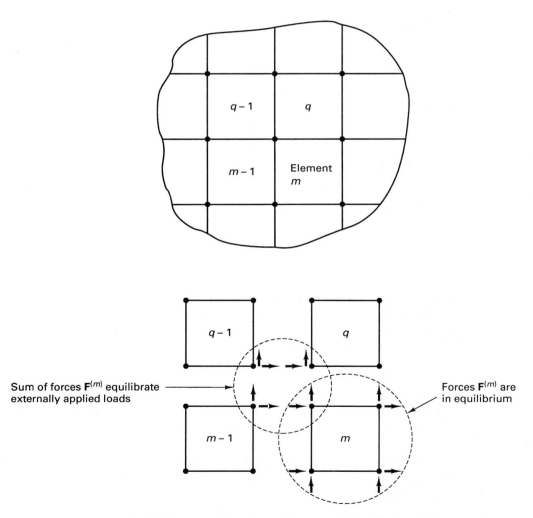

Figure 4.2   Nodal point and element equilibrium in a finite element analysis

Namely, consider that a finite element analysis has been performed and that we calculate for each finite element m the element nodal point force vectors

$$\mathbf{F}^{(m)} = \int_{V^{(m)}} \mathbf{B}^{(m)T} \boldsymbol{\tau}^{(m)} \, dV^{(m)} \tag{4.29}$$

where $\boldsymbol{\tau}^{(m)} = \mathbf{C}^{(m)} \boldsymbol{\epsilon}^{(m)}$. Then we observe that according to property 1,

> At any node, the sum of the element nodal point forces is in equilibrium with the externally applied nodal loads (which include all effects due to body forces, surface tractions, initial stresses, concentrated loads, inertia and damping forces, and reactions).

And according to property 2,

> Each element m is in equilibrium under its forces $\mathbf{F}^{(m)}$.

Property 1 follows simply because (4.27) expresses the nodal point equilibrium and we have

$$\sum_m \mathbf{F}^{(m)} = \mathbf{K}\mathbf{U} \tag{4.30}$$

The element equilibrium stated in property 2 is satisfied provided the finite element displacement interpolations in $\mathbf{H}^{(m)}$ satisfy the basic convergence requirements, which include the condition that the element must be able to represent the rigid body motions (see Section 4.3). Namely, let us consider element m subjected to the nodal point forces $\mathbf{F}^{(m)}$ and impose virtual nodal point displacements corresponding to the rigid body motions. Then for each virtual element rigid body motion with nodal point displacements $\bar{\bar{\mathbf{u}}}$, we have

$$\bar{\bar{\mathbf{u}}}^{\,T} \mathbf{F}^{(m)} = \int_{V^{(m)}} (\mathbf{B}^{(m)} \bar{\bar{\mathbf{u}}})^T \boldsymbol{\tau}^{(m)} \, dV^{(m)} = \int_{V^{(m)}} \bar{\bar{\boldsymbol{\epsilon}}}^{\,(m)T} \boldsymbol{\tau}^{(m)} \, dV^{(m)} = 0$$

because here $\bar{\bar{\boldsymbol{\epsilon}}}^{\,(m)} = \mathbf{0}$. Using all applicable rigid body motions we therefore find that the forces $\mathbf{F}^{(m)}$ are in equilibrium.

Hence, a finite element analysis can be interpreted as a process in which

1. The structure or continuum is idealized as an assemblage of discrete elements connected at nodes pertaining to the elements.
2. The externally applied forces (body forces, surface tractions, initial stresses, concentrated loads, inertia and damping forces, and reactions) are lumped to these nodes using the virtual work principle to obtain equivalent externally applied nodal point forces.
3. The equivalent externally applied nodal point forces (calculated in 2) are equilibrated by the element nodal point forces that are equivalent (in the virtual work sense) to the element internal stresses; i.e., we have

$$\sum_m \mathbf{F}^{(m)} = \mathbf{R}$$

4. Compatibility and the stress-strain material relationship are satisfied exactly, but instead of equilibrium on the differential level, only global equilibrium for the com-

plete structure, at the nodes, and of each element m under its nodal point forces $\mathbf{F}^{(m)}$ is satisfied.

Consider the following example.

EXAMPLE 4.9:   The finite element solution to the problem in Fig. E4.6, with $P = 100$, $E = 2.7 \times 10^6$, $\nu = 0.30$, $t = 0.1$, is given in Fig. E4.9. Clearly, the stresses are not continuous between elements, and equilibrium on the differential level is not satisfied. However,

1. Show that $\Sigma_m \, \mathbf{F}^{(m)} = \mathbf{R}$ and calculate the reactions.
2. Show that the element forces $\mathbf{F}^{(4)}$ for element 4 are in equilibrium.

The fact that $\Sigma_m \, \mathbf{F}^{(m)} = \mathbf{R}$ follows from the solution of (4.17), and $\mathbf{R}$ consists of the sum of all nodal point forces. Hence, this relation can also be used to evaluate the reactions.

Referring to the nodal point numbering in Fig. E4.6(b), we find for node 1:

$$\text{reactions } R_x = 100.15$$

$$R_y = 41.36$$

for node 2:

$$\text{reactions } R_x = 2.58 - 2.88 = -0.30$$

$$R_y = 16.79 + 5.96 = 22.74 \text{ (because of rounding)}$$

for node 3:

$$\text{reactions } R_x = -99.85$$

$$R_y = 35.90$$

for node 4:

$$\text{horizontal force equilibrium: } -42.01 + 42.01 = 0$$

$$\text{vertical force equilibrium: } -22.90 + 22.90 = 0$$

for node 5:

$$\text{horizontal force equilibrium: } -60.72 - 12.04 + 44.73 + 28.03 = 0$$

$$\text{vertical force equilibrium: } -35.24 - 35.04 + 19.10 + 51.18 = 0$$

for node 6:

$$\text{horizontal force equilibrium: } 57.99 - 57.99 = 0$$

$$\text{vertical force equilibrium: } -6.81 + 6.81 = 0$$

And for nodes 7, 8, and 9, force equilibrium is obviously also satisfied, where at node 9 the element nodal force balances the applied load $P = 100$.

Finally, let us check the overall force equilibrium of the model: horizontal equilibrium:

$$100.15 - 0.30 - 99.85 = 0$$

vertical equilibrium:

$$41.36 + 22.74 + 35.90 - 100 = 0$$

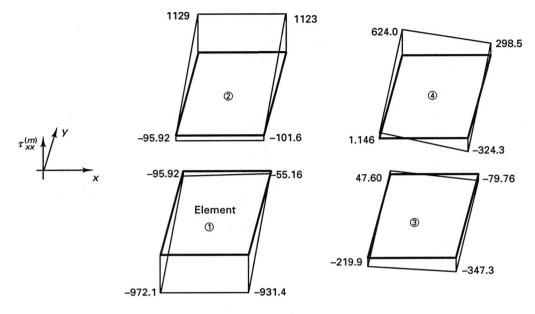

(a) Exploded view of elements showing stresses $\tau_{xx}^{(m)}$.
    Note the stress discontinuities between elements
    and the nonzero stresses along the free edges

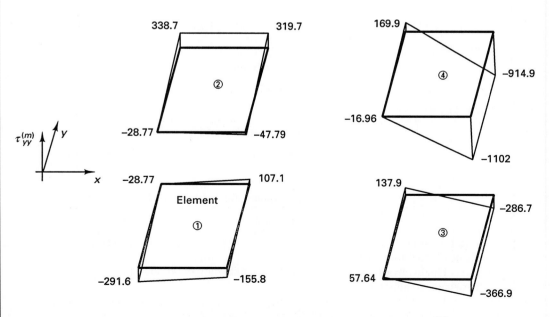

(b) Exploded view of elements showing stresses $\tau_{yy}^{(m)}$

Figure E4.9   Solution results for problem considered in Example 4.6 (rounded to digits shown)

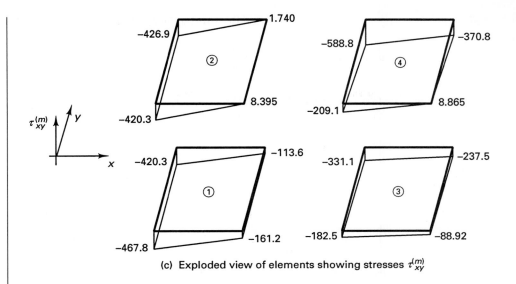

(c) Exploded view of elements showing stresses $\tau_{xy}^{(m)}$

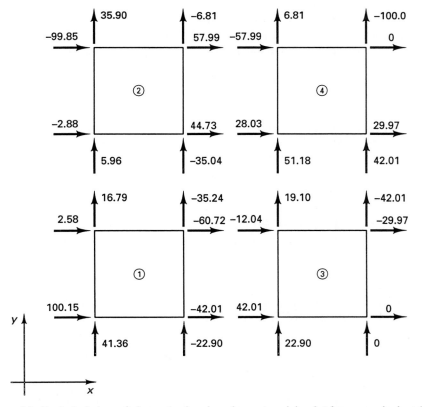

(d) Exploded view of elements showing element nodal point forces equivalent (in the virtual work sense) to the element stresses. The nodal point forces are at each node in equilibrium with the applied forces (including the reactions)

Figure E4.9 (*continued*)

moment equilibrium (about node 2):

$$-100 \times 4 + 100.15 \times 2 + 99.85 \times 2 = 0$$

It is important to realize that this force equilibrium will hold for *any* finite element mesh, however coarse the mesh may be, provided properly formulated elements are used (see Section 4.3).

Now consider element 4:

horizontal equilibrium:

$$0 - 57.99 + 28.03 + 29.97 = 0 \text{ (because of rounding)}$$

vertical equilibrium:

$$-100 + 6.81 + 51.18 + 42.01 = 0$$

moment equilibrium (about its local node 3):

$$-100 \times 2 + 57.99 \times 2 + 42.01 \times 2 = 0$$

Hence the element nodal forces are in equilibrium.

Element Local and Structure Global Degrees of Freedom

The derivations of the element matrices in Example 4.6 and 4.7 show that it is expedient to first establish the matrices corresponding to the local element degrees of freedom. The construction of the finite element matrices, which correspond to the global assemblage degrees of freedom [used in (4.19) to (4.25)] can then be directly achieved by identifying the global degrees of freedom that correspond to the local element degrees of freedom. However, considering the matrices $\mathbf{H}^{(m)}$, $\mathbf{B}^{(m)}$, $\mathbf{K}^{(m)}$, and so on, corresponding to the global assemblage degrees of freedom, only those rows and columns that correspond to element degrees of freedom have nonzero entries, and the main objective in defining these specific matrices was to be able to express the assemblage process of the element matrices in a theoretically elegant manner. In the practical implementation of the finite element method, this elegance is also present, but all element matrices are calculated corresponding only to the element degrees of freedom and are then directly assembled using the correspondence between the local element and global assemblage degrees of freedom. Thus, with only the element local nodal point degrees of freedom listed in $\hat{\mathbf{u}}$, we now write (as in Example 4.6)

$$\boxed{\mathbf{u} = \mathbf{H}\hat{\mathbf{u}}} \tag{4.31}$$

where the entries in the vector $\mathbf{u}$ are the element displacements measured in any convenient local coordinate system. We then also have

$$\boxed{\boldsymbol{\epsilon} = \mathbf{B}\hat{\mathbf{u}}} \tag{4.32}$$

Considering the relations in (4.31) and (4.32), the fact that no superscript is used on the interpolation matrices indicates that the matrices are defined with respect to the local element degrees of freedom. Using the relations for the element stiffness matrix, mass matrix, and load vector calculations as before, we obtain

$$\mathbf{K} = \int_V \mathbf{B}^T \mathbf{C} \mathbf{B} \; dV \qquad (4.33)$$

$$\mathbf{M} = \int_V \rho \mathbf{H}^T \mathbf{H} \; dV \qquad (4.34)$$

$$\mathbf{R}_B = \int_V \mathbf{H}^T \mathbf{f}^B \; dV \qquad (4.35)$$

$$\mathbf{R}_S = \int_S \mathbf{H}^{S^T} \mathbf{f}^S \; dS \qquad (4.36)$$

$$\mathbf{R}_I = \int_V \mathbf{B}^T \boldsymbol{\tau}^I \; dV \qquad (4.37)$$

where all variables are defined as in (4.19) to (4.25), but corresponding to the local element degrees of freedom. In the derivations and discussions to follow, we shall refer extensively to the relations in (4.33) to (4.37). Once the matrices given in (4.33) to (4.37) have been calculated, they can be assembled directly using the procedures described in Example 4.11 and Chapter 12.

In this assemblage process it is assumed that the directions of the element nodal point displacements $\hat{\mathbf{u}}$ in (4.31) are the same as the directions of the global nodal point displacements $\mathbf{U}$. However, in some analyses it is convenient to start the derivation with element nodal point degrees of freedom $\tilde{\mathbf{u}}$ that are not aligned with the global assemblage degrees of freedom. In this case we have

$$\mathbf{u} = \tilde{\mathbf{H}} \tilde{\mathbf{u}} \qquad (4.38)$$

and

$$\tilde{\mathbf{u}} = \mathbf{T} \hat{\mathbf{u}} \qquad (4.39)$$

where the matrix $\mathbf{T}$ transforms the degrees of freedom $\hat{\mathbf{u}}$ to the degrees of freedom $\tilde{\mathbf{u}}$ and (4.39) corresponds to a first-order tensor transformation (see Section 2.4); the entries in column j of the matrix $\mathbf{T}$ are the direction cosines of a unit vector corresponding to the jth degree of freedom in $\hat{\mathbf{u}}$ when measured in the directions of the $\tilde{\mathbf{u}}$ degrees of freedom. Substituting (4.39) into (4.38), we obtain

$$\mathbf{H} = \tilde{\mathbf{H}} \mathbf{T} \qquad (4.40)$$

Thus, identifying all finite element matrices corresponding to the degrees of freedom $\tilde{\mathbf{u}}$ with a curl placed over them, we obtain from (4.40) and (4.33) to (4.37),

$$\mathbf{K} = \mathbf{T}^T\tilde{\mathbf{K}}\mathbf{T}; \qquad \mathbf{M} = \mathbf{T}^T\tilde{\mathbf{M}}\mathbf{T}$$

$$\mathbf{R}_B = \mathbf{T}^T\tilde{\mathbf{R}}_B; \qquad \mathbf{R}_S = \mathbf{T}^T\tilde{\mathbf{R}}_S; \qquad \mathbf{R}_I = \mathbf{T}^T\tilde{\mathbf{R}}_I \tag{4.41}$$

We note that such transformations are also used when boundary displacements must be imposed that do not correspond to the global assemblage degrees of freedom (see Section 4.2.2). Table 4.1 summarizes some of the notation that we have employed.

We demonstrate the presented concepts in the following examples.

TABLE 4.1 *Summary of some notation used*

(a) $\mathbf{u}^{(m)} = \mathbf{H}^{(m)}\hat{\mathbf{U}}$ or $\mathbf{u}^{(m)} = \mathbf{H}^{(m)}\mathbf{U}$
   where $\mathbf{u}^{(m)}$ = displacements within element m as a function of the element coordinates
      $\mathbf{U}$ = nodal point displacements of the total element assemblage [from equation (4.17) onward we simply use $\mathbf{U}$].

(b) $\mathbf{u} = \mathbf{H}\hat{\mathbf{u}}$
   where $\mathbf{u} \equiv \mathbf{u}^{(m)}$ and it is implied that a specific element is considered
      $\hat{\mathbf{u}}$ = nodal point displacements of the element under consideration; the entries of $\hat{\mathbf{u}}$ are those displacements in $\hat{\mathbf{U}}$ that belong to the element.

(c) $\mathbf{u} = \tilde{\mathbf{H}}\tilde{\mathbf{u}}$
   where $\tilde{\mathbf{u}}$ = nodal point displacements of an element in a coordinate system other than the global system (in which $\hat{\mathbf{U}}$ is defined).

EXAMPLE 4.10: Establish the matrix $\mathbf{H}$ for the truss element shown in Fig. E4.10. The directions of local and global degrees of freedom are shown in the figure.

Here we have

$$\begin{bmatrix} u(x) \\ v(x) \end{bmatrix} = \frac{1}{L}\begin{bmatrix} \left(\frac{L}{2}-x\right) & 0 & \left(\frac{L}{2}+x\right) & 0 \\ 0 & \left(\frac{L}{2}-x\right) & 0 & \left(\frac{L}{2}+x\right) \end{bmatrix}\begin{bmatrix} \tilde{u}_1 \\ \tilde{v}_1 \\ \tilde{u}_2 \\ \tilde{v}_2 \end{bmatrix} \tag{a}$$

and

$$\begin{bmatrix} \tilde{u}_1 \\ \tilde{v}_1 \\ \tilde{u}_2 \\ \tilde{v}_2 \end{bmatrix} = \begin{bmatrix} \cos\alpha & \sin\alpha & 0 & 0 \\ -\sin\alpha & \cos\alpha & 0 & 0 \\ 0 & 0 & \cos\alpha & \sin\alpha \\ 0 & 0 & -\sin\alpha & \cos\alpha \end{bmatrix}\begin{bmatrix} u_1 \\ v_1 \\ u_2 \\ v_2 \end{bmatrix}$$

Thus, we have

$$\mathbf{H} = \frac{1}{L}\begin{bmatrix} \left(\frac{L}{2}-x\right) & 0 & \left(\frac{L}{2}+x\right) & 0 \\ 0 & \left(\frac{L}{2}-x\right) & 0 & \left(\frac{L}{2}+x\right) \end{bmatrix}\begin{bmatrix} \cos\alpha & \sin\alpha & 0 & 0 \\ -\sin\alpha & \cos\alpha & 0 & 0 \\ 0 & 0 & \cos\alpha & \sin\alpha \\ 0 & 0 & -\sin\alpha & \cos\alpha \end{bmatrix}$$

It should be noted that for the construction of the strain-displacement matrix $\mathbf{B}$ (in linear analysis), only the first row of $\mathbf{H}$ is required because only the normal strain $\epsilon_{xx} = \partial u/\partial x$ is

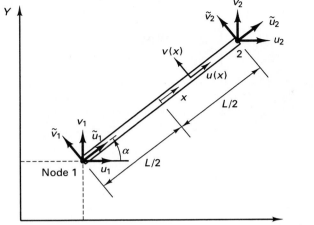

Figure E4.10   Truss element

considered in the derivation of the stiffness matrix. In practice, it is effective to use only the first row of the matrix $\tilde{\mathbf{H}}$ in (a) and then transform the matrix $\tilde{\mathbf{K}}$ as given in (4.41).

EXAMPLE 4.11:   Assume that the element stiffness matrices corresponding to the element displacements shown in Fig. E4.11 have been calculated and denote the elements as shown (Ⓐ), (Ⓑ), (Ⓒ), and (Ⓓ). Assemble these element matrices directly into the global structure stiffness matrix with the displacement boundary conditions shown in Fig. E4.11(a). Also, give the connectivity arrays LM for the elements.

In this analysis all element stiffness matrices have already been established corresponding to the degrees of freedom aligned with the global directions. Therefore, no transformation as given in (4.41) is required, and we can directly assemble the complete stiffness matrix.

Since the displacements at the supports are zero, we need only assemble the structure stiffness matrix corresponding to the unknown displacement components in **U**. The connectivity array (LM array) for each element lists the global structure degrees of freedom in the order of the element local degrees of freedom, with a zero signifying that the corresponding column and row of the element stiffness matrix are not assembled (the column and row correspond to a zero structure degree of freedom) (see also Chapter 12).

$$
\mathbf{K}_A =
\begin{array}{c}
\begin{array}{cccccccc}
U_2 & U_3 & & & & U_1 & U_4 & U_5 \\
u_1 & v_1 & u_2 & v_2 & u_3 & v_3 & u_4 & v_4 \\
\end{array} \\
\begin{bmatrix}
a_{11} & a_{12} & \cdots & & & a_{16} & a_{17} & a_{18} \\
a_{21} & a_{22} & \cdots & & & a_{26} & a_{27} & a_{28} \\
\vdots & & & & & & & \vdots \\
& & \cdots & & & & & \\
\vdots & & & & & & & \vdots \\
a_{61} & a_{62} & \cdots & & & a_{66} & a_{67} & a_{68} \\
a_{71} & a_{72} & \cdots & & & a_{76} & a_{77} & a_{78} \\
a_{81} & a_{82} & & & & a_{86} & a_{87} & a_{88} \\
\end{bmatrix}
\begin{array}{ll}
u_1 & U_2 \\
v_1 & U_3 \\
u_2 & \\
v_2 & \\
u_3 & \\
v_3 & U_1 \\
u_4 & U_4 \\
v_4 & U_5 \\
\end{array}
\end{array}
$$

with, above the matrix, arrows indicating "Global displacements" (for U_2, U_3, U_1, U_4, U_5) and "Local displacements" (for u_1, v_1, u_2, v_2, u_3, v_3, u_4, v_4).

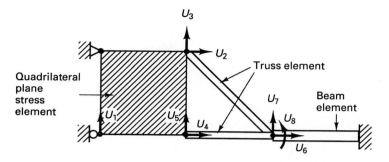

(a) Structural assemblage and degrees of freedom

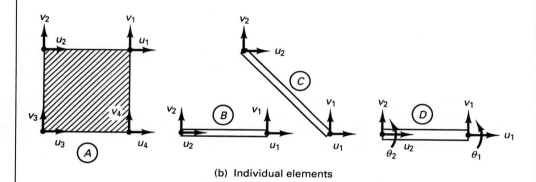

(b) Individual elements

Figure E4.11   A simple element assemblage

$$
\mathbf{K}_B = \begin{array}{cccc} \overset{U_6}{u_1} & \overset{U_7}{v_1} & \overset{U_4}{u_2} & \overset{U_5}{v_2} \\ \begin{bmatrix} b_{11} & b_{12} & b_{13} & b_{14} \\ b_{21} & b_{22} & b_{23} & b_{24} \\ b_{31} & b_{32} & b_{33} & b_{34} \\ b_{41} & b_{42} & b_{43} & b_{44} \end{bmatrix} & \begin{array}{l} u_1 \;\; U_6 \\ v_1 \;\; U_7 \\ u_2 \;\; U_4 \\ v_2 \;\; U_5 \end{array} \end{array}
$$

$$
\mathbf{K}_C = \begin{array}{cccc} \overset{U_6}{u_1} & \overset{U_7}{v_1} & \overset{U_2}{u_2} & \overset{U_3}{v_2} \\ \begin{bmatrix} c_{11} & c_{12} & c_{13} & c_{14} \\ c_{21} & c_{22} & c_{23} & c_{24} \\ c_{31} & c_{32} & c_{33} & c_{34} \\ c_{41} & c_{42} & c_{43} & c_{44} \end{bmatrix} & \begin{array}{l} u_1 \;\; U_6 \\ v_1 \;\; U_7 \\ u_2 \;\; U_2 \\ v_2 \;\; U_3 \end{array} \end{array}
$$

$$
\mathbf{K}_D = \begin{array}{cccccc} u_1 & v_1 & \theta_1 & \overset{U_6}{u_2} & \overset{U_7}{v_2} & \overset{U_8}{\theta_2} \\ \begin{bmatrix} \cdots & \cdot & \cdot & \cdot & \cdot & \cdots \\ \cdots & \cdot & \cdot & \cdot & \cdot & \cdots \\ \cdots & \cdot & \cdot & \cdot & \cdot & \cdots \\ \cdots & \cdot & \cdots & d_{44} & d_{45} & d_{46} \\ \cdots & \cdot & \cdots & d_{54} & d_{55} & d_{56} \\ \cdots & \cdot & \cdots & d_{64} & d_{65} & d_{66} \end{bmatrix} & \begin{array}{l} u_1 \\ v_1 \\ \theta_1 \\ u_2 \;\; U_6 \\ v_2 \;\; U_7 \\ \theta_2 \;\; U_8 \end{array} \end{array}
$$

and the equation $\mathbf{K} = \Sigma_m \mathbf{K}^{(m)}$ gives

$$
\mathbf{K} =
\begin{array}{c}
\begin{array}{cccccccc}
U_1 & U_2 & U_3 & U_4 & U_5 & U_6 & U_7 & U_8
\end{array} \\
\left[
\begin{array}{cccccccc}
a_{66} & a_{61} & a_{62} & a_{67} & a_{68} & \multicolumn{3}{c}{\text{zeros}} \\
a_{16} & a_{11} + c_{33} & a_{12} + c_{34} & a_{17} & a_{18} & c_{31} & c_{32} & \\
a_{26} & a_{21} + c_{43} & a_{22} + c_{44} & a_{27} & a_{28} & c_{41} & c_{42} & \\
a_{76} & a_{71} & a_{72} & a_{77} + b_{33} & a_{78} + b_{34} & b_{31} & b_{32} & \\
a_{86} & a_{81} & a_{82} & a_{87} + b_{43} & a_{88} + b_{44} & b_{41} & b_{42} & \\
 & c_{13} & c_{14} & b_{13} & b_{14} & b_{11} + c_{11} + d_{44} & b_{12} + c_{12} + d_{45} & d_{46} \\
 & c_{23} & c_{24} & b_{23} & b_{24} & b_{21} + c_{21} + d_{54} & b_{22} + c_{22} + d_{55} & d_{56} \\
 & \multicolumn{4}{c}{\text{symmetric about diagonal}} & d_{64} & d_{65} & d_{66}
\end{array}
\right]
\begin{array}{c}
U_1 \\ U_2 \\ U_3 \\ U_4 \\ U_5 \\ U_6 \\ U_7 \\ U_8
\end{array}
\end{array}
$$

The LM arrays for the elements are

for element A: $\text{LM} = [2 \ \ 3 \ \ 0 \ \ 0 \ \ 0 \ \ 1 \ \ 4 \ \ 5]$

for element B: $\text{LM} = [6 \ \ 7 \ \ 4 \ \ 5]$

for element C: $\text{LM} = [6 \ \ 7 \ \ 2 \ \ 3]$

for element D: $\text{LM} = [0 \ \ 0 \ \ 0 \ \ 6 \ \ 7 \ \ 8]$

We note that if the element stiffness matrices and LM arrays are known, the total structure stiffness matrix can be obtained directly in an automated manner (see also Chapter 12).

4.2.2 Imposition of Displacement Boundary Conditions

We discussed in Section 3.3.2 that in the analysis of a continuum we have displacement (also called essential) boundary conditions and force (also called natural) boundary conditions. Using the displacement-based finite element method, the force boundary conditions are taken into account in evaluating the externally applied nodal point force vector. The vector $\mathbf{R}_C$ assembles the concentrated loads including the reactions, and the vector $\mathbf{R}_S$ contains the effect of the distributed surface loads and distributed reactions.

Assume that the equilibrium equations of a finite element system without the imposition of the displacement boundary conditions as derived in Section 4.2.1 are, neglecting damping,

$$
\begin{bmatrix} \mathbf{M}_{aa} & \mathbf{M}_{ab} \\ \mathbf{M}_{ba} & \mathbf{M}_{bb} \end{bmatrix}
\begin{bmatrix} \ddot{\mathbf{U}}_a \\ \ddot{\mathbf{U}}_b \end{bmatrix}
+
\begin{bmatrix} \mathbf{K}_{aa} & \mathbf{K}_{ab} \\ \mathbf{K}_{ba} & \mathbf{K}_{bb} \end{bmatrix}
\begin{bmatrix} \mathbf{U}_a \\ \mathbf{U}_b \end{bmatrix}
=
\begin{bmatrix} \mathbf{R}_a \\ \mathbf{R}_b \end{bmatrix}
\tag{4.42}
$$

where the $\mathbf{U}_a$ are the unknown displacements and the $\mathbf{U}_b$ are the known, or prescribed, displacements. Solving for $\mathbf{U}_a$, we obtain

$$
\mathbf{M}_{aa}\ddot{\mathbf{U}}_a + \mathbf{K}_{aa}\mathbf{U}_a = \mathbf{R}_a - \mathbf{K}_{ab}\mathbf{U}_b - \mathbf{M}_{ab}\ddot{\mathbf{U}}_b
\tag{4.43}
$$

Hence, in this solution for $\mathbf{U}_a$, only the stiffness and mass matrices of the complete assemblage corresponding to the unknown degrees of freedom $\mathbf{U}_a$ need to be assembled (see

Example 4.11), but the load vector $\mathbf{R}_a$ must be modified to include the effect of imposed nonzero displacements. Once the displacements $\mathbf{U}_a$ have been evaluated from (4.43), the reactions can be calculated by first writing [(using (4.18)]

$$\mathbf{R}_b = \mathbf{R}_B^b + \mathbf{R}_S^b - \mathbf{R}_I^b + \mathbf{R}_C^b + \mathbf{R}_r \tag{4.44}$$

where $\mathbf{R}_B^b$, $\mathbf{R}_S^b$, $\mathbf{R}_I^b$, and $\mathbf{R}_C^b$ are the known externally applied nodal point loads not including the reactions and $\mathbf{R}_r$ denotes the unknown reactions. The superscript b indicates that of $\mathbf{R}_B$, $\mathbf{R}_S$, $\mathbf{R}_I$, and $\mathbf{R}_C$ in (4.17) only the components corresponding to the $\mathbf{U}_b$ degrees of freedom are used in the force vectors. Note that the vector $\mathbf{R}_r$ may be thought of as an unknown correction to the concentrated loads. Using (4.44) and the second set of equations in (4.42), we thus obtain

$$\mathbf{R}_r = \mathbf{M}_{ba}\ddot{\mathbf{U}}_a + \mathbf{M}_{bb}\ddot{\mathbf{U}}_b + \mathbf{K}_{ba}\mathbf{U}_a + \mathbf{K}_{bb}\mathbf{U}_b - \mathbf{R}_B^b - \mathbf{R}_S^b + \mathbf{R}_I^b - \mathbf{R}_C^b \tag{4.45}$$

Here, the last four terms are a correction due to known internal and surface element loading and any concentrated loading, all directly applied to the supports.

We demonstrate these relations in the following example.

EXAMPLE 4.12: Consider the structure shown in Fig. E4.12. Solve for the displacement response and calculate the reactions.

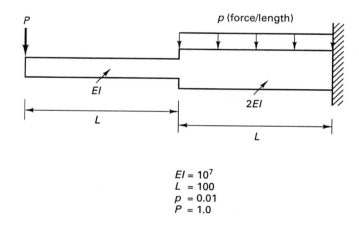

$EI = 10^7$
$L = 100$
$p = 0.01$
$P = 1.0$

(a) Cantilever beam

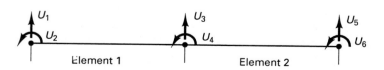

(b) Discretization

Figure E4.12   Analysis of cantilever beam

We consider the cantilever beam as an assemblage of two beam elements. The governing equations of equilibrium (4.42) are (using the matrices in Example 4.1)

$$
\frac{EI}{L}
\begin{bmatrix}
\dfrac{12}{L^2} & \dfrac{6}{L} & -\dfrac{12}{L^2} & \dfrac{6}{L} & & \\[2mm]
\dfrac{6}{L} & 4 & -\dfrac{6}{L} & 2 & & \\[2mm]
-\dfrac{12}{L^2} & -\dfrac{6}{L} & \dfrac{36}{L^2} & \dfrac{6}{L} & -\dfrac{24}{L^2} & \dfrac{12}{L} \\[2mm]
\dfrac{6}{L} & 2 & \dfrac{6}{L} & 12 & -\dfrac{12}{L} & 4 \\[2mm]
& & -\dfrac{24}{L^2} & -\dfrac{12}{L} & \dfrac{24}{L^2} & -\dfrac{12}{L} \\[2mm]
& & \dfrac{12}{L} & 4 & -\dfrac{12}{L} & 8
\end{bmatrix}
\begin{bmatrix}
U_1 \\[2mm] U_2 \\[2mm] U_3 \\[2mm] U_4 \\[2mm] U_5 \\[2mm] U_6
\end{bmatrix}
=
\begin{bmatrix}
-P \\[2mm]
0 \\[2mm]
-\dfrac{pL}{2} \\[2mm]
-\dfrac{pL^2}{12} \\[2mm]
-\dfrac{pL}{2} + R_r\big|_{U_5} \\[2mm]
\dfrac{pL^2}{12} + R_r\big|_{U_6}
\end{bmatrix}
$$

Here $\mathbf{U}_b^T = [U_5 \quad U_6]$ and $\mathbf{U}_b = \mathbf{0}$. Using (4.43), we obtain, for the case of $EI = 10^7$, $L = 100$, $p = 0.01$, $P = 1.0$,

$$\mathbf{U}_a^T = [-165 \quad 1.33 \quad -47.9 \quad 0.83] \times 10^{-3}$$

and then using (4.45), we have

$$\mathbf{R}_r = \begin{bmatrix} 2 \\ -250 \end{bmatrix}$$

In using (4.42) we assume that the displacement components employed in Section 4.2.1 actually contain all prescribed displacements [denoted as $\mathbf{U}_b$ in (4.42)]. If this is not the case, we need to identify all prescribed displacements that do not correspond to defined assemblage degrees of freedom and transform the finite element equilibrium equations to correspond to the prescribed displacements. Thus, we write

$$\mathbf{U} = \mathbf{T}\bar{\mathbf{U}} \qquad (4.46)$$

where $\bar{\mathbf{U}}$ is the vector of nodal point degrees of freedom in the required directions. The transformation matrix $\mathbf{T}$ is an identity matrix that has been altered by the direction cosines of the components in $\bar{\mathbf{U}}$ measured in the original displacement directions [see (2.58)]. Using (4.46) in (4.42), we obtain

$$\bar{\mathbf{M}}\ddot{\bar{\mathbf{U}}} + \bar{\mathbf{K}}\bar{\mathbf{U}} = \bar{\mathbf{R}} \qquad (4.47)$$

where $\qquad \bar{\mathbf{M}} = \mathbf{T}^T\mathbf{M}\mathbf{T}; \qquad \bar{\mathbf{K}} = \mathbf{T}^T\mathbf{K}\mathbf{T}; \qquad \bar{\mathbf{R}} = \mathbf{T}^T\mathbf{R} \qquad (4.48)$

We should note that the matrix multiplications in (4.48) involve changes only in those columns and rows of $\mathbf{M}$, $\mathbf{K}$, and $\mathbf{R}$ that are actually affected and that this transformation is equivalent to the calculations performed in (4.41) on a single element matrix. In practice, the transformation is carried out effectively on the element level just prior to adding the element matrices to the matrices of the total assemblage. Figure 4.3 gives the transformation matrices $\mathbf{T}$ for a typical nodal point in two- and three-dimensional analysis when displacements are constrained in skew directions. The unknown displacements can now be calculated from (4.47) using the procedure in (4.42) and (4.43).

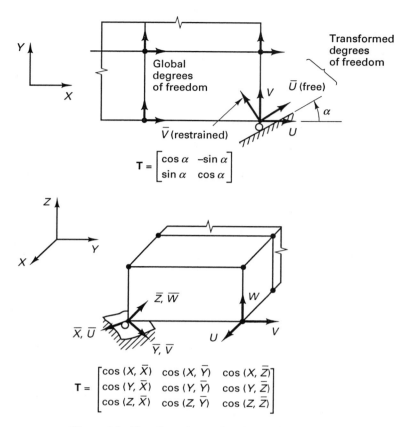

$$T = \begin{bmatrix} \cos \alpha & -\sin \alpha \\ \sin \alpha & \cos \alpha \end{bmatrix}$$

$$T = \begin{bmatrix} \cos (X, \bar{X}) & \cos (X, \bar{Y}) & \cos (X, \bar{Z}) \\ \cos (Y, \bar{X}) & \cos (Y, \bar{Y}) & \cos (Y, \bar{Z}) \\ \cos (Z, \bar{X}) & \cos (Z, \bar{Y}) & \cos (Z, \bar{Z}) \end{bmatrix}$$

Figure 4.3 Transformation to skew boundary conditions

In an alternative approach, the required displacements can also be imposed by adding to the finite element equilibrium equations (4.47) the constraint equations that express the prescribed displacement conditions. Assume that the displacement is to be specified at degree of freedom i, say $\bar{U}_i = b$; then the constraint equation

$$k\bar{U}_i = kb \tag{4.49}$$

is added to the equilibrium equations (4.47), where $k \gg \bar{k}_{ii}$. Therefore, the solution of the modified equilibrium equations must now give $\bar{U}_i = b$, and we note that because (4.47) was used, only the diagonal element in the stiffness matrix was affected, resulting in a numerically stable solution (see Section 8.2.6). Physically, this procedure can be interpreted as adding at the degree of freedom i a spring of large stiffness k and specifying a load which, because of the relatively flexible element assemblage, produces at this degree of freedom the required displacement b (see Fig. 4.4). Mathematically, the procedure corresponds to an application of the penalty method discussed in Section 3.4.

In addition to specified nodal point displacement conditions, some nodal point displacements may also be subjected to constraint conditions. Considering (4.24), a typical constraint equation would be

$$U_i = \sum_{j=1}^{r_i} \alpha_{q_j} U_{q_j} \tag{4.50}$$

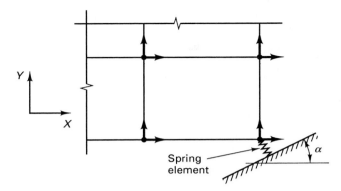

Figure 4.4   Skew boundary condition imposed using spring element

where the U_i is a dependent nodal point displacement and the U_{qj} are r_i independent nodal point displacements. Using all constraint equations of the form (4.50) and recognizing that these constraints must hold in the application of the principle of virtual work for the actual nodal point displacements as well as for the virtual displacements, the imposition of the constraints corresponds to a transformation of the form (4.46) and (4.47), in which $\mathbf{T}$ is now a rectangular matrix and $\bar{\mathbf{U}}$ contains all independent degrees of freedom. This transformation corresponds to adding α_{qj} times the ith columns and rows to the q_jth columns and rows, for $j = 1, \ldots, r_i$ and all i considered. In the actual implementation the transformation is performed effectively on the element level during the assemblage process.

Finally, it should be noted that combinations of the above displacement boundary conditions are possible, where, for example, in (4.50) an independent displacement component may correspond to a skew boundary condition with a specified displacement. We demonstrate the imposition of displacement constraints in the following examples.

EXAMPLE 4.13:   Consider the truss assemblage shown in Fig. E4.13. Establish the stiffness matrix of the structure that contains the constraint conditions given.

The independent degrees of freedom in this analysis are U_1, U_2, and U_4. The element stiffness matrices are given in Fig. E4.13, and we recognize that corresponding to (4.50), we

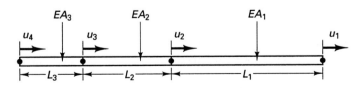

Displacement conditions: $u_3 = 2u_1$
$$u_4 = \delta$$

$$K_i = \frac{EA_i}{L_i} \begin{bmatrix} 1 & -1 \\ -1 & 1 \end{bmatrix}$$

Figure E4.13   Truss assemblage

have $i = 3$, $\alpha_1 = 2$, and $q_1 = 1$. Establishing the complete stiffness matrix directly during the assemblage process, we have

$$
\mathbf{K} = \begin{bmatrix} \dfrac{EA_1}{L_1} & -\dfrac{EA_1}{L_1} & 0 \\[2mm] -\dfrac{EA_1}{L_1} & \dfrac{EA_1}{L_1} & 0 \\[2mm] 0 & 0 & 0 \end{bmatrix} + \begin{bmatrix} \dfrac{4EA_2}{L_2} & -\dfrac{2EA_2}{L_2} & 0 \\[2mm] -\dfrac{2EA_2}{L_2} & \dfrac{EA_2}{L_2} & 0 \\[2mm] 0 & 0 & 0 \end{bmatrix}
$$

$$
+ \begin{bmatrix} \dfrac{4EA_3}{L_3} & 0 & -\dfrac{2EA_3}{L_3} \\[2mm] 0 & 0 & 0 \\[2mm] -\dfrac{2EA_3}{L_3} & 0 & \dfrac{EA_3}{L_3} \end{bmatrix} + \begin{bmatrix} 0 & 0 & 0 \\ 0 & 0 & 0 \\ 0 & 0 & k \end{bmatrix}
$$

where

$$
k \gg \frac{EA_3}{L_3}
$$

EXAMPLE 4.14:   The frame structure shown in Fig. E4.14(a) is to be analyzed. Use symmetry and constraint conditions to establish a suitable model for analysis.

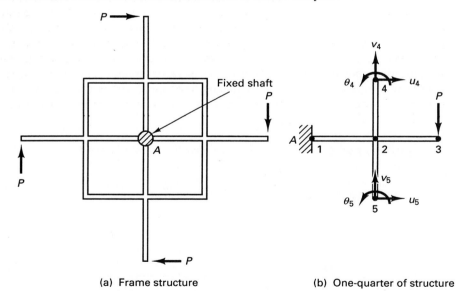

(a) Frame structure   (b) One-quarter of structure

Figure E4.14   Analysis of a cyclicly symmetric structure

The complete structure and applied loading display cyclic symmetry, so that only one-quarter of the structure need be considered, as shown in Fig. E4.14(b), with the following constraint conditions:

$$
u_5 = v_4
$$

$$
v_5 = -u_4
$$

$$
\theta_5 = \theta_4
$$

This is a simple example demonstrating how the analysis effort can be reduced considerably through the use of symmetry conditions. In practice, the saving through the use of cyclic symmetry conditions can in some cases be considerable, and indeed only by use of such conditions may the analysis be possible.

In this analysis, the structure *and* loading show cyclic symmetry. An analysis capability can also be developed in which only a part of the structure is modeled for the case of a geometrically cyclic symmetric structure with arbitrary loading (see, for example, W. Zhong and C. Qiu [A]).

4.2.3 Generalized Coordinate Models for Specific Problems

In Section 4.2.1 the finite element discretization procedure and derivation of the equilibrium equations was presented in general; i.e., a general three-dimensional body was considered. As shown in the examples, the general equations derived must be specialized in specific analyses to the specific stress and strain conditions considered. The objective in this section is to discuss and summarize how the finite element matrices that correspond to specific problems can be obtained from the general finite element equations (4.8) to (4.25).

Although in theory any body may be understood to be three-dimensional, for practical analysis it is in many cases imperative to reduce the dimensionality of the problem. The first step in a finite element analysis is therefore to decide what kind of problem[8] is at hand. This decision is based on the assumptions used in the theory of elasticity mathematical models for specific problems. The classes of problems that are encountered may be summarized as (1) truss, (2) beam, (3) plane stress, (4) plane strain, (5) axisymmetric, (6) plate bending, (7) thin shell, (8) thick shell, and (9) general three-dimensional. For each of these problem cases, the general formulation is applicable; however, only the appropriate displacement, stress, and strain variables must be used. These variables are summarized in Tables 4.2 and 4.3 together with the stress-strain matrices to be employed when considering an isotropic material. Figure 4.5 shows various stress and strain conditions considered in the formulation of finite element matrices.

TABLE 4.2   *Corresponding kinematic and static variables in various problems*

Problem	Displacement components	Strain vector ϵ^T	Stress vector τ^T
Bar	u	$[\epsilon_{xx}]$	$[\tau_{xx}]$
Beam	w	$[\kappa_{xx}]$	$[M_{xx}]$
Plane stress	u, v	$[\epsilon_{xx} \; \epsilon_{yy} \; \gamma_{xy}]$	$[\tau_{xx} \; \tau_{yy} \; \tau_{xy}]$
Plane strain	u, v	$[\epsilon_{xx} \; \epsilon_{yy} \; \gamma_{xy}]$	$[\tau_{xx} \; \tau_{yy} \; \tau_{xy}]$
Axisymmetric	u, v	$[\epsilon_{xx} \; \epsilon_{yy} \; \gamma_{xy} \; \epsilon_{zz}]$	$[\tau_{xx} \; \tau_{yy} \; \tau_{xy} \; \tau_{zz}]$
Three-dimensional	u, v, w	$[\epsilon_{xx} \; \epsilon_{yy} \; \epsilon_{zz} \; \gamma_{xy} \; \gamma_{yz} \; \gamma_{zx}]$	$[\tau_{xx} \; \tau_{yy} \; \tau_{zz} \; \tau_{xy} \; \tau_{yz} \; \tau_{zx}]$
Plate bending	w	$[\kappa_{xx} \; \kappa_{yy} \; \kappa_{xy}]$	$[M_{xx} \, M_{yy} \, M_{xy}]$

Notation: $\epsilon_{xx} = \dfrac{\partial u}{\partial x}$, $\epsilon_{yy} = \dfrac{\partial v}{\partial y}$, $\gamma_{xy} = \dfrac{\partial u}{\partial y} + \dfrac{\partial v}{\partial x}, \dots, \kappa_{xx} = \dfrac{\partial^2 w}{\partial x^2}$, $\kappa_{yy} = \dfrac{\partial^2 w}{\partial y^2}$, $\kappa_{xy} = 2\dfrac{\partial^2 w}{\partial x \, \partial y}$.

In Examples 4.5 to 4.10 we already developed some specific finite element matrices. Referring to Example 4.6, in which we considered a plane stress condition, we used for the u and v displacements simple linear polynomial assumptions, where we identified the

---

[8] We use here the parlance commonly used in engineering analysis but recognize that "choice of problem" really corresponds to "choice of mathematical model" (see Section 1.2).

TABLE 4.3 *Generalized stress-strain matrices for isotropic materials and the problems in Table 4.2*

Problem	Material matrix $\mathbf{C}$
Bar	E
Beam	EI
Plane stress	$\dfrac{E}{1-\nu^2}\begin{bmatrix} 1 & \nu & 0 \\ \nu & 1 & 0 \\ 0 & 0 & \dfrac{1-\nu}{2} \end{bmatrix}$
Plane strain	$\dfrac{E(1-\nu)}{(1+\nu)(1-2\nu)}\begin{bmatrix} 1 & \dfrac{\nu}{1-\nu} & 0 \\[2mm] \dfrac{\nu}{1-\nu} & 1 & 0 \\[2mm] 0 & 0 & \dfrac{1-2\nu}{2(1-\nu)} \end{bmatrix}$
Axisymmetric	$\dfrac{E(1-\nu)}{(1+\nu)(1-2\nu)}\begin{bmatrix} 1 & \dfrac{\nu}{1-\nu} & 0 & \dfrac{\nu}{1-\nu} \\[2mm] \dfrac{\nu}{1-\nu} & 1 & 0 & \dfrac{\nu}{1-\nu} \\[2mm] 0 & 0 & \dfrac{1-2\nu}{2(1-\nu)} & 0 \\[2mm] \dfrac{\nu}{1-\nu} & \dfrac{\nu}{1-\nu} & 0 & 1 \end{bmatrix}$
Three-dimensional	$\dfrac{E(1-\nu)}{(1+\nu)(1-2\nu)}\begin{bmatrix} 1 & \dfrac{\nu}{1-\nu} & \dfrac{\nu}{1-\nu} & & & \\[2mm] \dfrac{\nu}{1-\nu} & 1 & \dfrac{\nu}{1-\nu} & & & \\[2mm] \dfrac{\nu}{1-\nu} & \dfrac{\nu}{1-\nu} & 1 & & & \\[2mm] & & & \dfrac{1-2\nu}{2(1-\nu)} & & \\[2mm] & & & & \dfrac{1-2\nu}{2(1-\nu)} & \\[2mm] & & & & & \dfrac{1-2\nu}{2(1-\nu)} \end{bmatrix}$ Elements not shown are zeros
Plate bending	$\dfrac{Eh^3}{12(1-\nu^2)}\begin{bmatrix} 1 & \nu & 0 \\ \nu & 1 & 0 \\ 0 & 0 & \dfrac{1-\nu}{2} \end{bmatrix}$

Notation: E = Young's modulus, ν = Poisson's ratio, h = thickness of plate, I = moment of inertia

unknown coefficients in the polynomials as generalized coordinates. The number of unknown coefficients in the polynomials was equal to the number of element nodal point displacements. Expressing the generalized coordinates in terms of the element nodal point displacements, we found that, in general, each polynomial coefficient is not an actual physical displacement but is equal to a linear combination of the element nodal point displacements.

Finite element matrices that are formulated by assuming that the displacements vary in the form of a function whose unknown coefficients are treated as generalized coordinates are referred to as generalized coordinate finite element models. A rather natural class of functions to use for approximating element displacements are polynomials because they are commonly employed to approximate unknown functions, and the higher the degree of the polynomial, the better the approximation that we can expect. In addition, polynomials are easy to differentiate; i.e., if the polynomials approximate the displacements of the structure, we can evaluate the strains with relative ease.

Using polynomial displacement assumptions, a very large number of finite elements for practically all problems in structural mechanics have been developed.

The objective in this section is to describe the formulation of a variety of generalized coordinate finite element models that use polynomials to approximate the displacement fields. Other functions could in principle be used in the same way, and their use can be effective in specific applications (see Example 4.20). In the presentation, emphasis is given to the general formulation rather than to numerically effective finite elements. Therefore, this section serves primarily to enhance our general understanding of the finite element method. More effective finite elements for general application are the isoparametric and related elements described in Chapter 5.

In the following derivations the displacements of the finite elements are always described in the local coordinate systems shown in Fig. 4.5. Also, since we consider one specific element, we shall leave out the superscript (m) used in Section 4.2.1 [see (4.31)].

For one-dimensional bar elements (truss elements) we have

$$u(x) = \alpha_1 + \alpha_2 x + \alpha_3 x^2 + \cdots \tag{4.51}$$

where x varies over the length of the element, u is the local element displacement, and α_1, $\alpha_2, \ldots$, are the generalized coordinates. The displacement expansion in (4.51) can also be used for the transverse and longitudinal displacements of a beam.

For two-dimensional elements (i.e., plane stress, plane strain, and axisymmetric elements), we have for the u and v displacements as a function of the element x and y coordinates,

$$u(x, y) = \alpha_1 + \alpha_2 x + \alpha_3 y + \alpha_4 xy + \alpha_5 x^2 + \cdots$$
$$v(x, y) = \beta_1 + \beta_2 x + \beta_3 y + \beta_4 xy + \beta_5 x^2 + \cdots \tag{4.52}$$

where $\alpha_1, \alpha_2, \ldots$, and $\beta_1, \beta_2, \ldots$, are the generalized coordinates.

In the case of a plate bending element, the transverse deflection w is assumed as a function of the element coordinates x and y; i.e.,

$$w(x, y) = \gamma_1 + \gamma_2 x + \gamma_3 y + \gamma_4 xy + \gamma_5 x^2 + \cdots \tag{4.53}$$

where $\gamma_1, \gamma_2, \ldots$, are the generalized coordinates.

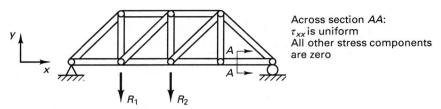

(a) Uniaxial stress condition: frame under concentrated loads

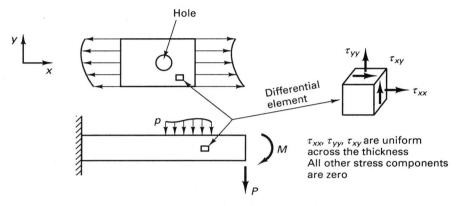

(b) Plane stress conditions: membrane and beam under in-plane actions

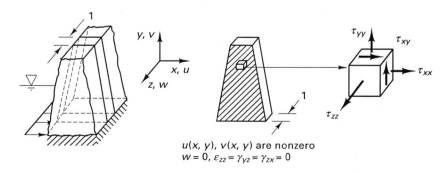

(c) Plane strain condition: long dam subjected to water pressure

Figure 4.5 Various stress and strain conditions with illustrative examples

Finally, for elements in which the u, v, and w displacements are measured as a function of the element x, y, and z coordinates, we have, in general,

$$
\begin{aligned}
u(x, y, z) &= \alpha_1 + \alpha_2 x + \alpha_3 y + \alpha_4 z + \alpha_5 xy + \cdots \\
v(x, y, z) &= \beta_1 + \beta_2 x + \beta_3 y + \beta_4 z + \beta_5 xy + \cdots \\
w(x, y, z) &= \gamma_1 + \gamma_2 x + \gamma_3 y + \gamma_4 z + \gamma_5 xy + \cdots
\end{aligned}
\tag{4.54}
$$

where $\alpha_1, \alpha_2, \ldots, \beta_1, \beta_2, \ldots,$ and $\gamma_1, \gamma_2, \ldots$ are now the generalized coordinates.

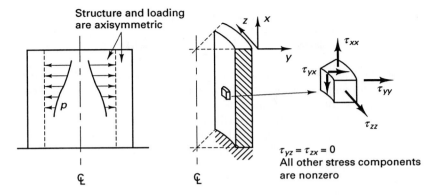

$\tau_{yz} = \tau_{zx} = 0$
All other stress components
are nonzero

(d) Axisymmetric condition: cylinder under internal pressure

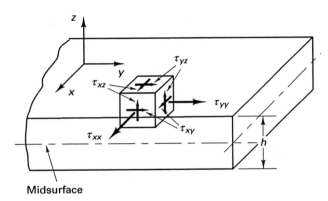

Plate

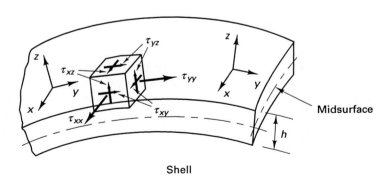

Shell

$\tau_{zz} = 0$
All other stress components
are nonzero

(e) Plate and shell structures

Figure 4.5   *(continued)*

As in the discussion of the plane stress element in Example 4.6, the relations (4.51) to (4.54) can be written in matrix form,

$$\mathbf{u} = \boldsymbol{\Phi}\boldsymbol{\alpha} \tag{4.55}$$

where the vector $\mathbf{u}$ corresponds to the displacements used in (4.51) to (4.54), the elements of $\boldsymbol{\Phi}$ are the corresponding polynomial terms, and $\boldsymbol{\alpha}$ is a vector of the generalized coordinates arranged in the appropriate order.

To evaluate the generalized coordinates in terms of the element nodal point displacements, we need to have as many nodal point displacements as assumed generalized coordinates. Then, evaluating (4.55) specifically for the nodal point displacements $\hat{\mathbf{u}}$ of the element, we obtain

$$\hat{\mathbf{u}} = \mathbf{A}\boldsymbol{\alpha} \tag{4.56}$$

Assuming that the inverse of $\mathbf{A}$ exists, we have

$$\boldsymbol{\alpha} = \mathbf{A}^{-1}\hat{\mathbf{u}} \tag{4.57}$$

The element strains to be considered depend on the specific problem to be solved. Denoting by $\boldsymbol{\epsilon}$ a generalized strain vector, whose components are given for specific problems in Table 4.2, we have

$$\boldsymbol{\epsilon} = \mathbf{E}\boldsymbol{\alpha} \tag{4.58}$$

where the matrix $\mathbf{E}$ is established using the displacement assumptions in (4.55). A vector of generalized stresses $\boldsymbol{\tau}$ is obtained using the relation

$$\boldsymbol{\tau} = \mathbf{C}\boldsymbol{\epsilon} \tag{4.59}$$

where $\mathbf{C}$ is a generalized elasticity matrix. The quantities $\boldsymbol{\tau}$ and $\mathbf{C}$ are defined for some problems in Tables 4.2 and 4.3. We may note that except in bending problems, the generalized $\boldsymbol{\tau}$, $\boldsymbol{\epsilon}$, and $\mathbf{C}$ matrices are those that are used in the theory of elasticity. The word "generalized" is employed merely to include curvatures and moments as strains and stresses, respectively. The advantage of using curvatures and moments in bending analysis is that in the stiffness evaluation an integration over the thickness of the corresponding element is not required because this stress and strain variation has already been taken into account (see Example 4.15).

Referring to Table 4.3, it should be noted that all stress-strain matrices can be derived from the general three-dimensional stress-strain relationship. The plane strain and axisymmetric stress-strain matrices are obtained simply by deleting in the three-dimensional stress-strain matrix the rows and columns that correspond to the zero strain components. The stress-strain matrix for plane stress analysis is then obtained from the axisymmetric stress-strain matrix by using the condition that τ_{zz} is zero (see the program QUADS in Section 5.6). To calculate the generalized stress-strain matrix for plate bending analysis, the stress-strain matrix corresponding to plane stress conditions is used, as shown in the following example.

EXAMPLE 4.15: Derive the stress-strain matrix $\mathbf{C}$ used for plate bending analysis (see Table 4.3).

The strains at a distance z measured upward from the midsurface of the plate are

$$\left[-z\,\frac{\partial^2 w}{\partial x^2} \quad -z\,\frac{\partial^2 w}{\partial y^2} \quad -z\,\frac{2\partial^2 w}{\partial x\,\partial y} \right]$$

In plate bending analysis it is assumed that each layer of the plate acts in plane stress condition and positive curvatures correspond to positive moments (see Section 5.4.2). Hence, integrating the normal stresses in the plate to obtain moments per unit length, the generalized stress-strain matrix is

$$\mathbf{C} = \int_{-h/2}^{+h/2} z^2 \frac{E}{1-\nu^2} \begin{bmatrix} 1 & \nu & 0 \\ \nu & 1 & 0 \\ 0 & 0 & \dfrac{1-\nu}{2} \end{bmatrix} dz$$

or

$$\mathbf{C} = \frac{Eh^3}{12(1-\nu^2)} \begin{bmatrix} 1 & \nu & 0 \\ \nu & 1 & 0 \\ 0 & 0 & \dfrac{1-\nu}{2} \end{bmatrix}$$

Considering (4.55) to (4.59), we recognize that, in general terms, all relationships for evaluation of the finite element matrices corresponding to the local finite element nodal point displacements have been defined, and using the notation of Section 4.2.1, we have

$$\mathbf{H} = \mathbf{\Phi}\mathbf{A}^{-1} \tag{4.60}$$

$$\mathbf{B} = \mathbf{E}\mathbf{A}^{-1} \tag{4.61}$$

Let us now consider briefly various types of finite elements encountered, which are subject to certain static or kinematic assumptions.

Truss and beam elements.   Truss and beam elements are very widely used in structural engineering to model, for example, building frames and bridges [see Fig. 4.5(a) for an assemblage of truss elements].

As discussed in Section 4.2.1, the stiffness matrices of these elements can in many cases be calculated by solving the differential equations of equilibrium (see Example 4.8), and much literature has been published on such derivations. The results of these derivations have been employed in the displacement method of analysis and the corresponding approximate solution techniques, such as the method of moment distribution. However, it can be effective to evaluate the stiffness matrices using the finite element formulation, i.e., the virtual work principle, particularly when considering complex beam geometries and geometric nonlinear analysis (see Section 5.4.1).

Plane stress and plane strain elements.   Plane stress elements are employed to model membranes, the in-plane action of beams and plates as shown in Fig. 4.5(b), and so on. In each of these cases a two-dimensional stress situation exists in an xy plane with the stresses τ_{zz}, τ_{yz}, and τ_{zx} equal to zero. Plane strain elements are used to represent a slice (of unit thickness) of a structure in which the strain components ϵ_{zz}, γ_{yz}, and γ_{zx} are zero. This situation arises in the analysis of a long dam as illustrated in Fig. 4.5(c).

Axisymmetric elements.   Axisymmetric elements are used to model structural components that are rotationally symmetric about an axis. Examples of application are pressure vessels and solid rings. If these structures are also subjected to axisymmetric loads, a two-dimensional analysis of a unit radian of the structure yields the complete stress and strain distributions as illustrated in Fig. 4.5(d).

On the other hand, if the axisymmetric structure is loaded nonaxisymmetrically, the choice lies between a fully three-dimensional analysis, in which substructuring (see Section 8.2.4) or cyclic symmetry (see Example 4.14) is used, and a Fourier decomposition of the loads for a superposition of harmonic solutions (see Example 4.20).

Plate bending and shell elements.   The basic proposition in plate bending and shell analyses is that the structure is thin in one dimension, and therefore the following assumptions can be made [see Fig. 4.5(e)]:

1. The stress through the thickness (i.e., perpendicular to the midsurface) of the plate/shell is zero.
2. Material particles that are originally on a straight line perpendicular to the midsurface of the plate/shell remain on a straight line during deformations. In the Kirchhoff theory, shear deformations are neglected and the straight line remains perpendicular to the midsurface during deformations. In the Reissner/Mindlin theory, shear deformations are included, and therefore the line originally normal to the midsurface in general does not remain perpendicular to the midsurface during the deformations (see Section 5.4.2).

The first finite elements developed to model thin plates in bending and shells were based on the Kirchhoff plate theory (see R. H. Gallagher [A]). The difficulties in these approaches are that the elements must satisfy the convergence requirements *and* be relatively effective in their applications. Much research effort was spent on the development of such elements; however, it was recognized that more effective elements can frequently be formulated using the Reissner/Mindlin plate theory (see Section 5.4.2).

To obtain a shell element a simple approach is to superimpose a plate bending stiffness and a plane stress membrane stiffness. In this way flat shell elements are obtained that can be used to model flat components of shells (e.g., folded plates) and that can also be employed to model general curved shells as an assemblage of flat elements. We demonstrate the development of a plate bending element based on the Kirchhoff plate theory and the construction of an associated flat shell element in Examples 4.18 and 4.19.

> **EXAMPLE 4.16:**   Discuss the derivation of the displacement and strain-displacement interpolation matrices of the beam shown in Fig. E4.16.
>
> The exact stiffness matrix (within beam theory) of this beam could be evaluated by solving the beam differential equations of equilibrium, which are for the bending behavior
>
> $$\frac{d^2}{d\xi^2}\left(EI\,\frac{d^2w}{d\xi^2}\right) = 0; \qquad EI = E\,\frac{bh^3}{12} \tag{a}$$
>
> and for the axial behavior
>
> $$\frac{d}{d\xi}\left(EA\,\frac{du}{d\xi}\right) = 0; \qquad A = bh \tag{b}$$
>
> where E is Young's modulus. The procedure is to impose a unit end displacement, with all other end displacements equal to zero, and solve the appropriate differential equation of equilibrium of the beam subject to these boundary conditions. Once the element internal displacements for these boundary conditions have been calculated, appropriate derivatives give the element end

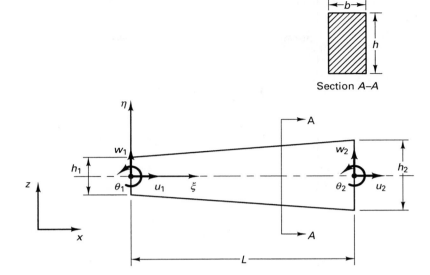

Figure E4.16   Beam element with varying section

forces that together constitute the column of the stiffness matrix corresponding to the imposed end displacement. It should be noted that this stiffness matrix is only "exact" for static analysis because in dynamic analysis the stiffness coefficients are frequency-dependent.

Alternatively, the formulation given in (4.8) to (4.17) can be used. The same stiffness matrix as would be evaluated by the above procedure is obtained if the exact element internal displacements [that satisfy (a) and (b)] are employed to construct the strain-displacement matrix. However, in practice it is frequently expedient to use the displacement interpolations that correspond to a uniform cross-section beam, and this yields an approximate stiffness matrix. The approximation is generally adequate when h_2 is not very much larger than h_1 (hence when a sufficiently large number of beam elements is employed to model the complete structure). The errors encountered in the analysis are those discussed in Section 4.3, because this formulation corresponds to displacement-based finite element analysis.

Using the variables defined in Fig. E4.16 and the "exact" displacements (Hermitian functions) corresponding to a prismatic beam, we have

$$u = \left(1 - \frac{\xi}{L}\right)u_1 + \frac{6\eta}{L}\left(\frac{\xi}{L} - \frac{\xi^2}{L^2}\right)w_1 - \eta\left(1 - 4\frac{\xi}{L} + 3\frac{\xi^2}{L^2}\right)\theta_1$$

$$+ \frac{\xi}{L}u_2 - \frac{6\eta}{L}\left(\frac{\xi}{L} - \frac{\xi^2}{L^2}\right)w_2 + \eta\left(2\frac{\xi}{L} - 3\frac{\xi^2}{L^2}\right)\theta_2$$

Hence,

$$\mathbf{H} = \left[\left(1 - \frac{\xi}{L}\right) \; \middle| \; \frac{6\eta}{L}\left(\frac{\xi}{L} - \frac{\xi^2}{L^2}\right) \; \middle| \; -\eta\left(1 - \frac{4\xi}{L} + 3\frac{\xi^2}{L^2}\right) \; \middle| \; \frac{\xi}{L} \; \middle| \right.$$

$$\left. -\frac{6\eta}{L}\left(\frac{\xi}{L} - \frac{\xi^2}{L^2}\right) \; \middle| \; \eta\left(\frac{2\xi}{L} - 3\frac{\xi^2}{L^2}\right)\right] \qquad \text{(c)}$$

For (c) we ordered the nodal point displacements as follows

$$\hat{\mathbf{u}}^T = [u_1 w_1 \theta_1 \quad u_2 w_2 \theta_2]$$

Considering only normal strains and stresses in the beam, i.e., neglecting shearing deformations, we have as the only strain and stress components

$$\epsilon_{\xi\xi} = \frac{du}{d\xi}; \qquad \tau_{\xi\xi} = E\epsilon_{\xi\xi}$$

and hence

$$\mathbf{B} = \left[-\frac{1}{L} \vdots \frac{6\eta}{L}\left(\frac{1}{L} - \frac{2\xi}{L^2}\right) \vdots -\eta\left(\frac{-4}{L} + \frac{6\xi}{L^2}\right) \vdots \frac{1}{L} \vdots -\frac{6\eta}{L}\left(\frac{1}{L} - \frac{2\xi}{L^2}\right) \vdots \eta\left(\frac{2}{L} - \frac{6\xi}{L^2}\right)\right] \tag{d}$$

The relations in (c) and (d) can be used directly to evaluate the element matrices defined in (4.33) to (4.37); e.g.,

$$\mathbf{K} = Eb \int_0^L \int_{-h/2}^{h/2} \mathbf{B}^T\mathbf{B} \, d\eta \, d\xi$$

where

$$h = h_1 + (h_2 - h_1)\frac{\xi}{L}$$

This formulation can be directly extended to develop the element matrices corresponding to the three-dimensional action of the beam element and to include shear deformations (see K. J. Bathe and S. Bolourchi [A]).

EXAMPLE 4.17: Discuss the derivation of the stiffness, mass, and load matrices of the axisymmetric three-node finite element in Fig. E4.17.

This element was one of the first finite elements developed. For most practical applications, much more effective finite elements are presently available (see Chapter 5), but the element is conveniently used for instructional purposes because the equations to be dealt with are relatively simple.

The displacement assumption used is

$$u(x, y) = \alpha_1 + \alpha_2 x + \alpha_3 y$$
$$v(x, y) = \beta_1 + \beta_2 x + \beta_3 y$$

Therefore, a linear displacement variation is assumed, just as for the derivation of the four-node plane stress element considered in Example 4.6 where the fourth node required that the term xy be included in the displacement assumption. Referring to the derivations carried out in Example 4.6, we can directly establish the following relationships:

$$\begin{bmatrix} u(x, y) \\ v(x, y) \end{bmatrix} = \mathbf{H}\begin{bmatrix} u_1 \\ u_2 \\ u_3 \\ v_1 \\ v_2 \\ v_3 \end{bmatrix}$$

where

$$\mathbf{H} = \begin{bmatrix} 1 & x & y & 0 & 0 & 0 \\ 0 & 0 & 0 & 1 & x & y \end{bmatrix}\mathbf{A}^{-1}$$

$$\mathbf{A}^{-1} = \begin{bmatrix} \mathbf{A}_1^{-1} & \mathbf{0} \\ \mathbf{0} & \mathbf{A}_1^{-1} \end{bmatrix}; \qquad \mathbf{A}_1 = \begin{bmatrix} 1 & x_1 & y_1 \\ 1 & x_2 & y_2 \\ 1 & x_3 & y_3 \end{bmatrix}$$

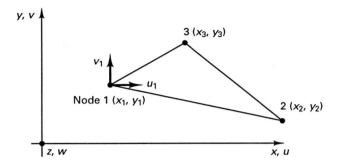

(a) Nodal points

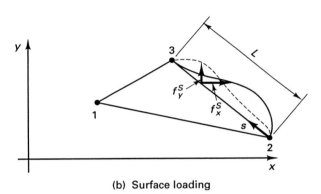

(b) Surface loading

Figure E4.17 Axisymmetric three-node element

Hence

$$A_1^{-1} = \frac{1}{\det A_1} \begin{bmatrix} x_2 y_3 - x_3 y_2 & x_3 y_1 - x_1 y_3 & x_1 y_2 - x_2 y_1 \\ y_2 - y_3 & y_3 - y_1 & y_1 - y_2 \\ x_3 - x_2 & x_1 - x_3 & x_2 - x_1 \end{bmatrix}$$

where

$$\det A_1 = x_1(y_2 - y_3) + x_2(y_3 - y_1) + x_3(y_1 - y_2)$$

We may note that $\det A_1$ is zero only if the three element nodal points lie on a straight line. The strains are given in Table 4.2 and are

$$\epsilon_{xx} = \frac{\partial u}{\partial x}; \qquad \epsilon_{yy} = \frac{\partial v}{\partial y}; \qquad \gamma_{xy} = \frac{\partial u}{\partial y} + \frac{\partial v}{\partial x}; \qquad \epsilon_{zz} = \frac{\partial w}{\partial z} = \frac{u}{x}$$

Using the assumed displacement polynomials, we obtain

$$\begin{bmatrix} \epsilon_{xx} \\ \epsilon_{yy} \\ \gamma_{xy} \\ \epsilon_{zz} \end{bmatrix} = B \begin{bmatrix} u_1 \\ u_2 \\ u_3 \\ v_1 \\ v_2 \\ v_3 \end{bmatrix}; \qquad B = \begin{bmatrix} 0 & 1 & 0 & 0 & 0 & 0 \\ 0 & 0 & 0 & 0 & 0 & 1 \\ 0 & 0 & 1 & 0 & 1 & 0 \\ \frac{1}{x} & 1 & \frac{y}{x} & 0 & 0 & 0 \end{bmatrix} A^{-1} = EA^{-1}$$

Using the relations (4.33) to (4.37), we thus have

$$
\mathbf{K} = \mathbf{A}^{-T}\left\{ \int_A \frac{E(1-\nu)}{(1+\nu)(1-2\nu)}
\begin{bmatrix}
0 & 0 & 0 & \dfrac{1}{x} \\
1 & 0 & 0 & 1 \\
0 & 0 & 1 & \dfrac{y}{x} \\
0 & 0 & 0 & 0 \\
0 & 0 & 1 & 0 \\
0 & 1 & 0 & 0
\end{bmatrix}
\begin{bmatrix}
1 & \dfrac{\nu}{1-\nu} & 0 & \dfrac{\nu}{1-\nu} \\
\dfrac{\nu}{1-\nu} & 1 & 0 & \dfrac{\nu}{1-\nu} \\
0 & 0 & \dfrac{1-2\nu}{2(1-\nu)} & 0 \\
\dfrac{\nu}{1-\nu} & \dfrac{\nu}{1-\nu} & 0 & 1
\end{bmatrix}
\right.
$$

$$
\left.
\begin{bmatrix}
0 & 1 & 0 & 0 & 0 & 0 \\
0 & 0 & 0 & 0 & 0 & 1 \\
0 & 0 & 1 & 0 & 1 & 0 \\
\dfrac{1}{x} & 1 & \dfrac{y}{x} & 0 & 0 & 0
\end{bmatrix}
x \, dx \, dy
\right\} \mathbf{A}^{-1} \qquad \text{(a)}
$$

where 1 radian of the axisymmetric element is considered in the volume integration. Similarly, we have

$$
\mathbf{R}_B = \mathbf{A}^{-T} \int_A
\begin{bmatrix}
1 & 0 \\
x & 0 \\
y & 0 \\
0 & 1 \\
0 & x \\
0 & y
\end{bmatrix}
\begin{bmatrix} f_x^B \\ f_y^B \end{bmatrix}
x \, dx \, dy
$$

$$
\mathbf{R}_I = \mathbf{A}^{-T} \int_A
\begin{bmatrix}
0 & 0 & 0 & \dfrac{1}{x} \\
1 & 0 & 0 & 1 \\
0 & 0 & 1 & \dfrac{y}{x} \\
0 & 0 & 0 & 0 \\
0 & 0 & 1 & 0 \\
0 & 1 & 0 & 0
\end{bmatrix}
\begin{bmatrix} \tau_{xx}^I \\ \tau_{yy}^I \\ \tau_{xy}^I \\ \tau_{zz}^I \end{bmatrix}
x \, dx \, dy \qquad \text{(b)}
$$

$$
\mathbf{M} = \rho \mathbf{A}^{-T} \left\{ \int_A
\begin{bmatrix}
1 & 0 \\
x & 0 \\
y & 0 \\
0 & 1 \\
0 & x \\
0 & y
\end{bmatrix}
\begin{bmatrix}
1 & x & y & 0 & 0 & 0 \\
0 & 0 & 0 & 1 & x & y
\end{bmatrix}
x \, dx \, dy \right\} \mathbf{A}^{-1}
$$

where the mass density ρ is assumed to be constant.

For calculation of the surface load vector $\mathbf{R}_S$, it is expedient in practice to introduce auxiliary coordinate systems located along the loaded sides of the element. Assume that the side 2–3 of the element is loaded as shown in Fig. E4.17. The load vector $\mathbf{R}_S$ is then evaluated using as the variable s,

$$\mathbf{R}_S = \int_S \begin{bmatrix} 0 & 0 \\ 1 - \dfrac{s}{L} & 0 \\ \dfrac{s}{L} & 0 \\ 0 & 0 \\ 0 & 1 - \dfrac{s}{L} \\ 0 & \dfrac{s}{L} \end{bmatrix} \begin{bmatrix} f_x^S \\ f_y^S \end{bmatrix} \left[x_2 \left(1 - \dfrac{s}{L} \right) + x_3 \dfrac{s}{L} \right] ds$$

Considering these finite element matrix evaluations the following observations can be made. First, to evaluate the integrals, it is possible to obtain closed-form solutions; alternatively, numerical integration (discussed in Section 5.5) can be used. Second, we find that the stiffness, mass, and load matrices corresponding to plane stress and plane strain finite elements can be obtained simply by (1) not including the fourth row in the strain-displacement matrix $\mathbf{E}$ used in (a) and (b), (2) employing the appropriate stress-strain matrix $\mathbf{C}$ in (a), and (3) using as the differential volume element $h\,dx\,dy$ instead of $x\,dx\,dy$, where h is the thickness of the element (conveniently taken equal to 1 in plane strain analysis). Therefore, axisymmetric, plane stress, and plane strain analyses can effectively be implemented in a single computer program. Also, the matrix $\mathbf{E}$ shows that constant-strain conditions ϵ_{xx}, ϵ_{yy}, and γ_{xy} are assumed in either analysis.

The concept of performing axisymmetric, plane strain, and plane stress analysis in an effective manner in one computer program is, in fact, presented in Section 5.6, where we discuss the efficient implementation of isoparametric finite element analysis.

EXAMPLE 4.18: Derive the matrices $\boldsymbol{\phi}(x, y)$, $\mathbf{E}(x, y)$, and $\mathbf{A}$ for the rectangular plate bending element in Fig. E4.18.

This element is one of the first plate bending elements derived, and more effective plate bending elements are already in use (see Section 5.4.2).

As shown in Fig. E4.18, the plate bending element considered has three degress of freedom per node. Therefore, it is necessary to have 12 unknown generalized coordinates, $\alpha_1, \ldots, \alpha_{12}$,

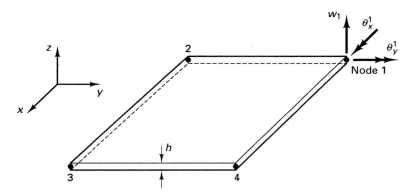

Figure E4.18   Rectangular plate bending element.

in the displacement assumption for w. The polynomial used is

$$w = \alpha_1 + \alpha_2 x + \alpha_3 y + \alpha_4 x^2 + \alpha_5 xy + \alpha_6 y^2 + \alpha_7 x^3 + \alpha_8 x^2 y$$
$$+ \alpha_9 xy^2 + \alpha_{10} y^3 + \alpha_{11} x^3 y + \alpha_{12} xy^3$$

Hence,

$$\mathbf{\Phi}(x, y) = \begin{bmatrix} 1 & x & y & x^2 & xy & y^2 & x^3 & x^2 y & xy^2 & y^3 & x^3 y & xy^3 \end{bmatrix} \qquad \text{(a)}$$

We can now calculate $\partial w / \partial x$ and $\partial w / \partial y$:

$$\frac{\partial w}{\partial x} = \alpha_2 + 2\alpha_4 x + \alpha_5 y + 3\alpha_7 x^2 + 2\alpha_8 xy + \alpha_9 y^2 + 3\alpha_{11} x^2 y + \alpha_{12} y^3 \qquad \text{(b)}$$

and

$$\frac{\partial w}{\partial y} = \alpha_3 + \alpha_5 x + 2\alpha_6 y + \alpha_8 x^2 + 2\alpha_9 xy + 3\alpha_{10} y^2 + \alpha_{11} x^3 + 3\alpha_{12} xy^2 \qquad \text{(c)}$$

Using the conditions

$$\left. \begin{array}{c} w_i = (w)_{x_i, y_i}; \qquad \theta_x^i = \left(\dfrac{\partial w}{\partial y} \right)_{x_i, y_i} \\[2em] \theta_y^i = \left(-\dfrac{\partial w}{\partial x} \right)_{x_i, y_i} \end{array} \right\} \quad i = 1, \ldots, 4$$

we can construct the matrix $\mathbf{A}$, obtaining

$$\begin{bmatrix} w_1 \\ \vdots \\ \vdots \\ w_4 \\ \theta_x^1 \\ \vdots \\ \theta_x^4 \\ \theta_y^1 \\ \vdots \\ \theta_y^4 \end{bmatrix} = \mathbf{A} \begin{bmatrix} \alpha_1 \\ \alpha_2 \\ \vdots \\ \\ \\ \\ \\ \\ \\ \alpha_{12} \end{bmatrix}$$

where

$$\mathbf{A} = \begin{bmatrix} 1 & x_1 & y_1 & x_1^2 & x_1 y_1 & y_1^2 & x_1^3 & x_1^2 y_1 & x_1 y_1^2 & y_1^3 & x_1^3 y_1 & x_1 y_1^3 \\ & & & \vdots & & & & \vdots & & & & \\ 1 & x_4 & y_4 & x_4^2 & x_4 y_4 & y_4^2 & x_4^3 & x_4^2 y_4 & x_4 y_4^2 & y_4^3 & x_4^3 y_4 & x_4 y_4^3 \\ 0 & 0 & 1 & 0 & x_1 & 2y_1 & 0 & x_1^2 & 2x_1 y_1 & 3y_1^2 & x_1^3 & 3x_1 y_1^2 \\ & & & \vdots & & & & \vdots & & & & \\ 0 & 0 & 1 & 0 & x_4 & 2y_4 & 0 & x_4^2 & 2x_4 y_4 & 3y_4^2 & x_4^3 & 3x_4 y_4^2 \\ 0 & -1 & 0 & -2x_1 & -y_1 & 0 & -3x_1^2 & -2x_1 y_1 & -y_1^2 & 0 & -3x_1^2 y_1 & -y_1^3 \\ & & & \vdots & & & & \vdots & & & & \\ 0 & -1 & 0 & -2x_4 & -y_4 & 0 & -3x_4^2 & -2x_4 y_4 & -y_4^2 & 0 & -3x_4^2 y_4 & -y_4^3 \end{bmatrix} \qquad \text{(d)}$$

which can be shown to be always nonsingular.

To evaluate the matrix $\mathbf{E}$, we recall that in plate bending analysis curvatures and moments are used as generalized strains and stresses (see Tables 4.2 and 4.3). Calculating the required derivatives of (b) and (c), we obtain

$$\frac{\partial^2 w}{\partial x^2} = 2\alpha_4 + 6\alpha_7 x + 2\alpha_8 y + 6\alpha_{11} xy$$

$$\frac{\partial^2 w}{\partial y^2} = 2\alpha_6 + 2\alpha_9 x + 6\alpha_{10} y + 6\alpha_{12} xy \tag{e}$$

$$2\frac{\partial^2 w}{\partial x\, \partial y} = 2\alpha_5 + 4\alpha_8 x + 4\alpha_9 y + 6\alpha_{11} x^2 + 6\alpha_{12} y^2$$

Hence we have

$$\mathbf{E} = \begin{bmatrix} 0 & 0 & 0 & 2 & 0 & 0 & 6x & 2y & 0 & 0 & 6xy & 0 \\ 0 & 0 & 0 & 0 & 0 & 2 & 0 & 0 & 2x & 6y & 0 & 6xy \\ 0 & 0 & 0 & 0 & 2 & 0 & 0 & 4x & 4y & 0 & 6x^2 & 6y^2 \end{bmatrix} \tag{f}$$

With the matrices $\boldsymbol{\Phi}$, $\mathbf{A}$, and $\mathbf{E}$ given in (a), (d), and (f) and the material matrix $\mathbf{C}$ in Table 4.3, the element stiffness matrix, mass matrix, and load vectors can now be calculated.

An important consideration in the evaluation of an element stiffness matrix is whether the element is complete and compatible. The element considered in this example is complete as shown in (e) (i.e., the element can represent constant curvature states), but the element is not compatible. The compatibility requirements are violated in a number of plate bending elements, meaning that convergence in the analysis is in general not monotonic (see Section 4.3).

EXAMPLE 4.19: Discuss the evaluation of the stiffness matrix of a flat rectangular shell element.

A simple rectangular flat shell element can be obtained by superimposing the plate bending behavior considered in Example 4.18 and the plane stress behavior of the element used in Example 4.6. The resulting element is shown in Fig. E4.19. The element can be employed to model assemblages of flat plates (e.g., folded plate structures) and also curved shells. For actual analyses more effective shell elements are available, and we discuss here only the element in Fig. E4.19 in order to demonstrate some basic analysis approaches.

Let $\tilde{\mathbf{K}}_B$ and $\tilde{\mathbf{K}}_M$ be the stiffness matrices, in the local coordinate system, corresponding to the bending and membrane behavior of the element, respectively. Then the shell element stiffness matrix $\tilde{\mathbf{K}}_S$ is

$$\underset{20\times20}{\tilde{\mathbf{K}}_S} = \begin{bmatrix} \underset{12\times12}{\tilde{\mathbf{K}}_B} & \mathbf{0} \\ \mathbf{0} & \underset{8\times8}{\tilde{\mathbf{K}}_M} \end{bmatrix} \tag{a}$$

The matrices $\tilde{\mathbf{K}}_M$ and $\tilde{\mathbf{K}}_B$ were discussed in Examples 4.6 and 4.18, respectively.

This shell element can now be directly employed in the analysis of a variety of shell structures. Consider the structures in Fig. E4.19, which might be idealized as shown. Since we deal in these analyses with six degrees of freedom per node, the element stiffness matrices corresponding to the global degrees of freedom are calculated using the transformation given in (4.41)

$$\underset{24\times24}{\mathbf{K}_S} = \mathbf{T}^T \tilde{\mathbf{K}}_S^* \mathbf{T} \tag{b}$$

where

$$\underset{24\times24}{\tilde{\mathbf{K}}_S^*} = \begin{bmatrix} \underset{20\times20}{\tilde{\mathbf{K}}_S} & \mathbf{0} \\ \mathbf{0} & \underset{4\times4}{\mathbf{0}} \end{bmatrix} \tag{c}$$

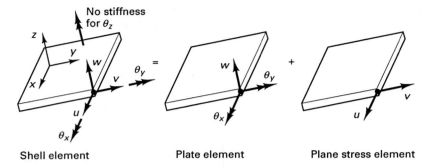

(a) Basic shell element with local five degrees of freedom at a node

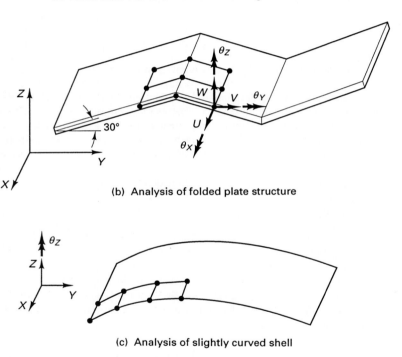

(b) Analysis of folded plate structure

(c) Analysis of slightly curved shell

Figure E4.19   Use of a flat shell element

and $\mathbf{T}$ is the transformation matrix between the local and global element degrees of freedom. To define $\tilde{\mathbf{K}}_S^*$ corresponding to six degrees of freedom per node, we have amended $\tilde{\mathbf{K}}_S$ on the right-hand side of (c) to include the stiffness coefficients corresponding to the local rotations θ_z (rotations about the z-axis) at the nodes. These stiffness coefficients have been set equal to zero in (c). The reason for doing so is that these degrees of freedom have not been included in the formulation of the element; thus the element rotation θ_z at a node is not measured and does not contribute to the strain energy stored in the element.

The solution of a model can be obtained using $\tilde{\mathbf{K}}_S^*$ in (c) as long as the elements surrounding a node are not coplanar. This does not hold for the folded plate model, and considering the analysis of the slightly curved shell in Fig. E4.19(c), the elements may be almost coplanar (depending on the curvature of the shell and the idealization used). In these cases, the global stiffness matrix is singular or ill-conditioned because of the zero diagonal elements in $\tilde{\mathbf{K}}_S^*$ and difficulties arise in solving the global equilibrium equations (see Section 8.2.6). To avoid this problem it is possible to add a small stiffness coefficient corresponding to the θ_z rotation; i.e., instead of $\hat{\mathbf{K}}_S^*$ in (c) we use

$$\tilde{\mathbf{K}}_S^{*\prime} = \begin{bmatrix} \tilde{\mathbf{K}}_S \\ {\scriptstyle 20\times20} & \mathbf{0} \\ \mathbf{0} & k\,\mathbf{I} \\ & {\scriptstyle 4\times4} \end{bmatrix} \tag{d}$$

where k is about one-thousandth of the smallest diagonal element of $\tilde{\mathbf{K}}_S$. The stiffness coefficient k must be large enough to allow accurate solution of the finite element system equilibrium equations and small enough not to affect the system response significantly. Therefore, a large enough number of digits must be used in the floating-point arithmetic (see Section 8.2.6).

A more effective way to circumvent the problem is to use curved shell elements with five degrees of freedom per node where these are defined corresponding to a plane tangent to the midsurface of the shell. In this case the rotation normal to the shell surface is not a degree of freedom (see Section 5.4.2).

In the above element formulations we used polynomial functions to express the displacements. We should briefly note, however, that for certain applications the use of other functions such as trigonometric expressions can be effective. Trigonometric functions, for example, are used in the analysis of axisymmetric structures subjected to nonaxisymmetric loading (see E. L. Wilson [A]), and in the finite strip method (see Y. K. Cheung [A]). The advantage of the trigonometric functions lies in their orthogonality properties. Namely, if sine and cosine products are integrated over an appropriate interval, the integral can be zero. This then means that there is no coupling in the equilibrium equations between the generalized coordinates that correspond to the sine and cosine functions, and the equilibrium equations can be solved more effectively. In this context it may be noted that the best functions that we could use in the finite element analysis would be given by the eigenvectors of the problem because they would give a diagonal stiffness matrix. However, these functions are not known, and for general applications, the use of polynomial, trigonometric, or other assumptions for the finite element displacements is most natural.

The use of special interpolation functions can of course also lead to efficient solution schemes in the analysis of certain fluid flows (see, for example, A. T. Patera [A]).

We demonstrate the use of trigonometric functions in the following example.

EXAMPLE 4.20: Figure E4.20 shows an axisymmetric structure subjected to a nonaxisymmetric loading in the radial direction. Discuss the analysis of this structure using the three-node axisymmetric element in Example 4.17 when the loading is represented as a superposition of Fourier components.

The stress distribution in the structure is three-dimensional and could be calculated using a three-dimensional finite element idealization. However, it is possible to take advantage of the axisymmetric geometry of the structure and, depending on the exact loading applied, reduce the computational effort very significantly.

The key point in this analysis is that we expand the externally applied loads $R_r(\theta,y)$ in the Fourier series:

$$R_r = \sum_{p=1}^{p_c} R_p^c \cos p\theta + \sum_{p=1}^{p_s} R_p^s \sin p\theta \tag{a}$$

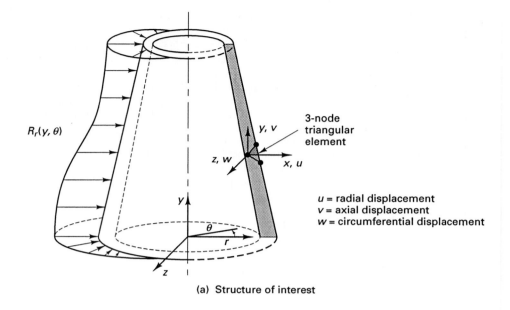

$R_r(y, \theta)$

y, v

3-node triangular element

z, w

x, u

y

θ

r

z

u = radial displacement
v = axial displacement
w = circumferential displacement

(a) Structure of interest

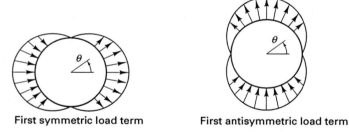

θ

θ

First symmetric load term   First antisymmetric load term

(b) Representation of nonaxisymmetric loading

Figure E4.20   Axisymmetric structure subjected to nonaxisymmetric loading

where p_c and p_s are the total number of symmetric and antisymmetric load contributions about $\theta = 0$, respectively. Figure E4.20(b) illustrates the first terms in the expansion of (a).

The complete analysis can now be performed by superimposing the responses due to the symmetric and antisymmetric load contributions defined in (a). For example, considering the symmetric response, we use for an element

$$u(x, y, \theta) = \sum_{p=1}^{p_c} \cos p\theta \ \mathbf{H}\hat{\mathbf{u}}^p$$

$$v(x, y, \theta) = \sum_{p=1}^{p_c} \cos p\theta \ \mathbf{H}\hat{\mathbf{v}}^p \qquad (b)$$

$$w(x, y, \theta) = \sum_{p=1}^{p_c} \sin p\theta \ \mathbf{H}\hat{\mathbf{w}}^p$$

where for the triangular elements, referring to Example 4.17,

$$\mathbf{H} = \begin{bmatrix} 1 & x & y \end{bmatrix} \mathbf{A}_1^{-1} \tag{c}$$

and the $\hat{\mathbf{u}}^p$, $\hat{\mathbf{v}}^p$, and $\hat{\mathbf{w}}^p$ are the element unknown generalized nodal point displacements corresponding to mode p.

We should note that we superimpose in (b) the response measured in individual harmonic displacement distributions. Using (b), we can now establish the strain-displacement matrix of the element. Since we are dealing with a three-dimensional stress distribution, we use the expression for three-dimensional strain distributions in cylindrical coordinates:

$$\boldsymbol{\epsilon} = \begin{bmatrix} \dfrac{\partial u}{\partial r} \\[2mm] \dfrac{\partial v}{\partial y} \\[2mm] \dfrac{u}{r} + \dfrac{1}{r}\dfrac{\partial w}{\partial \theta} \\[2mm] \dfrac{\partial u}{\partial y} + \dfrac{\partial v}{\partial r} \\[2mm] \dfrac{\partial w}{\partial y} + \dfrac{1}{r}\dfrac{\partial v}{\partial \theta} \\[2mm] \dfrac{\partial w}{\partial r} + \dfrac{1}{r}\dfrac{\partial u}{\partial \theta} - \dfrac{w}{r} \end{bmatrix} \tag{d}$$

where

$$\boldsymbol{\epsilon}^T = \begin{bmatrix} \epsilon_{rr} & \epsilon_{yy} & \epsilon_{\theta\theta} & \gamma_{ry} & \gamma_{y\theta} & \gamma_{\theta r} \end{bmatrix} \tag{e}$$

Substituting from (b) into (d) we obtain a strain-displacement matrix $\mathbf{B}_p$ for each value of p, and the total strains can be thought of as the superposition of the strain distributions contained in each harmonic.

The unknown nodal point displacements can now be evaluated using the usual procedures. The equilibrium equations corresponding to the generalized nodal point displacements U_i^p, V_i^p, W_i^p, $i = 1, \ldots, N$ (N is equal to the total number of nodes) and $p = 1, \ldots, p_c$ are evaluated as given in (4.17) to (4.22), where we now have

$$\mathbf{U}^T = \begin{bmatrix} \mathbf{U}^{1T} & \mathbf{U}^{2T} & \cdots & \mathbf{U}^{p_c T} \end{bmatrix} \tag{f}$$

and

$$\mathbf{U}^{pT} = \begin{bmatrix} U_1^p & V_1^p & W_1^p & \vdots & U_2^p & \cdots & W_N^p \end{bmatrix} \tag{g}$$

In the calculations of $\mathbf{K}$ and $\mathbf{R}_S$ we note that because of the orthogonality properties

$$\int_0^{2\pi} \sin n\theta \sin m\theta \, d\theta = 0 \qquad n \neq m$$

$$\int_0^{2\pi} \cos n\theta \cos m\theta \, d\theta = 0 \qquad n \neq m \tag{h}$$

the stiffness matrices corresponding to the different harmonics are decoupled from each other. Hence, we have the following equilibrium equations for the structure:

$$\mathbf{K}^p \mathbf{U}^p = \mathbf{R}_S^p \qquad p = 1, \ldots, p_c \tag{i}$$

where $\mathbf{K}^p$ and $\mathbf{R}_S^p$ are the stiffness matrix and load vector corresponding to the pth harmonic.

Solution of the equations in (i) gives the generalized nodal point displacements of each element, and (b) then yields all element internal displacements.

In the above displacement solution we considered only the symmetric load contributions. But an analogous analysis can be performed for the antisymmetric load harmonics of (a) by simply replacing in (b) to (i) all sine and cosine terms by cosine and sine terms, respectively. The complete structural response is then obtained by superimposing the displacements corresponding to all harmonics.

Although we have considered only surface loading in the discussion, the analysis can be extended using the same approach to include body force loading and initial stresses.

Finally, we note that the computational effort required in the analysis is directly proportional to the number of load harmonics used. Hence, the solution procedure is very efficient if the loading can be represented using only a few harmonics (e.g., wind loading) but may be inefficient when many harmonics must be used to represent the loading (e.g., a concentrated force).

4.2.4 Lumping of Structure Properties and Loads

A physical interpretation of the finite element procedure of analysis as presented in the previous sections is that the structure properties—stiffness and mass—and the loads, internal and external, are lumped to the discrete nodes of the element assemblage using the virtual work principle. *Because the same interpolation functions are employed in the*

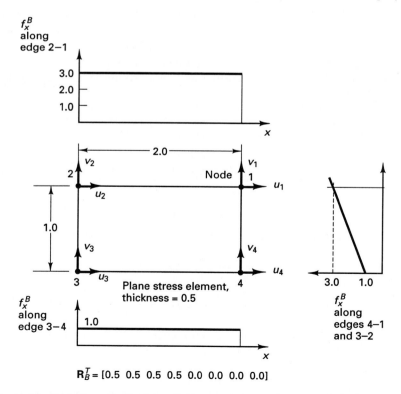

$$\mathbf{R}_B^T = [0.5 \quad 0.5 \quad 0.5 \quad 0.5 \quad 0.0 \quad 0.0 \quad 0.0 \quad 0.0]$$

Figure 4.6 Body force distribution and corresponding lumped body force vector $\mathbf{R}_B$ of a rectangular element

calculation of the load vectors and the mass matrix as in the evaluation of the stiffness matrix, we say that "consistent" load vectors and a consistent mass matrix are evaluated. In this case, provided certain conditions are fulfilled (see Section 4.3.3), the finite element solution is a Ritz analysis.

It may now be recognized that instead of performing the integrations leading to the consistent load vector, we may evaluate an approximate load vector by simply adding to the actually applied concentrated nodal forces $\mathbf{R}_C$ additional forces that are in some sense equivalent to the distributed loads on the elements. A somewhat obvious way of constructing approximate load vectors is to calculate the total body and surface forces corresponding to an element and to assign equal parts to the appropriate element nodal degrees of freedom. Consider as an example the rectangular plane stress element in Fig. 4.6 with the variation of the body force shown. The total body force is equal to 2.0, and hence we obtain the lumped body force vector given in the figure.

In considering the derivation of an element mass matrix, we recall that the inertia forces have been considered part of the body forces. Hence we may also establish an approximate mass matrix by lumping equal parts of the total element mass to the nodal points. Realizing that each nodal mass essentially corresponds to the mass of an element contributing volume around the node, we note that using this procedure of lumping mass, we assume in essence that the accelerations of the contributing volume to a node are constant and equal to the nodal values.

An important advantage of using a lumped mass matrix is that the matrix is diagonal, and, as will be seen later, the numerical operations for the solution of the dynamic equations of equilibrium are in some cases reduced very significantly.

EXAMPLE 4.21:   Evaluate the lumped body force vector and the lumped mass matrix of the element assemblage in Fig. E4.5.

The lumped mass matrix is

$$\mathbf{M} = \rho \int_0^{100} (1) \begin{bmatrix} \frac{1}{2} & 0 & 0 \\ 0 & \frac{1}{2} & 0 \\ 0 & 0 & 0 \end{bmatrix} dx + \rho \int_0^{80} \left(1 + \frac{x}{40}\right)^2 \begin{bmatrix} 0 & 0 & 0 \\ 0 & \frac{1}{2} & 0 \\ 0 & 0 & \frac{1}{2} \end{bmatrix} dx$$

or

$$\mathbf{M} = \frac{\rho}{3} \begin{bmatrix} 150 & 0 & 0 \\ 0 & 670 & 0 \\ 0 & 0 & 520 \end{bmatrix}$$

Similarly, the lumped body force vector is

$$\mathbf{R}_B = \left(\int_0^{100} (1) \begin{bmatrix} \frac{1}{2} \\ \frac{1}{2} \\ 0 \end{bmatrix} (1) \, dx + \int_0^{80} \left(1 + \frac{x}{40}\right)^2 \begin{bmatrix} 0 \\ \frac{1}{2} \\ \frac{1}{2} \end{bmatrix} \left(\frac{1}{10}\right) dx \right) f_2(t)$$

$$= \frac{1}{3} \begin{bmatrix} 150 \\ 202 \\ 52 \end{bmatrix} f_2(t)$$

It may be noted that, as required, the sums of the elements in $\mathbf{M}$ and $\mathbf{R}_B$ in both this example and in Example 4.5 are the same.

When using the load lumping procedure it should be recognized that the nodal point loads are, in general, calculated only approximately, and if a coarse finite element mesh is employed, the resulting solution may be very inaccurate. Indeed, in some cases when higher-order finite elements are used, surprising results are obtained. Figure 4.7 demonstrates such a case (see also Example 5.12).

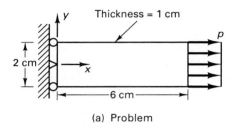

$p = 300 \text{ N/cm}^2$
$E = 3 \times 10^7 \text{ N/cm}^2$
$v = 0.3$

(a) Problem

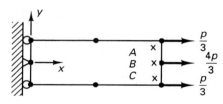

Integration point	τ_{xx}	τ_{yy}	τ_{xy}
A	300.00	0.0	0.0
B	300.00	0.0	0.0
C	300.00	0.0	0.0

(b) Finite element model
with consistent loading

(All stresses have units of N/cm²)

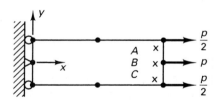

Integration point	τ_{xx}	τ_{yy}	τ_{xy}
A	301.41	−7.85	−24.72
B	295.74	−9.55	0.0
C	301.41	−7.85	24.72

(c) Finite element model
with lumped loading

(All stresses have units of N/cm²)
(3 × 3 Gauss points are used, see Table 5.7)

Figure 4.7   Some sample analysis results with and without consistent loading

Considering dynamic analysis, the inertia effects can be thought of as body forces. Therefore, if a lumped mass matrix is employed, little might be gained by using a consistent load vector, whereas consistent nodal point loads should be used if a consistent mass matrix is employed in the analysis.

4.2.5 Exercises

4.1. Use the procedure in Example 4.2 to formally derive the principle of virtual work for the one-dimensional bar shown.

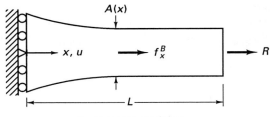

$$E = \text{Young's modulus}$$

The differential equations of equilibrium are

$$E \frac{\partial}{\partial x}\left(A \frac{\partial u}{\partial x} \right) + f_x^B = 0$$

$$EA \left. \frac{\partial u}{\partial x} \right|_{x=L} = R$$

4.2. Consider the structure shown.

 (a) Write down the principle of virtual displacements by specializing the general equation (4.7) to this case.

 (b) Use the principle of virtual work to check whether the exact solution is

$$\tau(x) = \left(\frac{72}{73} + \frac{24x}{73L} \right) \frac{F}{A_0}$$

Use the following three virtual displacements: (i) $\bar{u}(x) = a_0 x$, (ii) $\bar{u}(x) = a_0 x^2$, (iii) $\bar{u}(x) = a_0 x^3$.

 (c) Solve the governing differential equations of equilibrium,

$$E \frac{\partial}{\partial x}\left(A \frac{\partial u}{\partial x} \right) = 0$$

$$EA \left. \frac{\partial u}{\partial x} \right|_{x=L} = F$$

 (d) Use the three different virtual displacement patterns given in part (b), substitute into the principle of virtual work using the exact solution for the stress [from part (c)], and explicitly show that the principle holds.

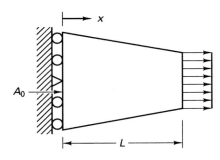

F = total force exerted on right end
E = Young's modulus
$A(x) = A_0(1 - x/4L)$

4.3. Consider the bar shown.
   (a) Solve for the exact displacement response of the structure.
   (b) Show explicitly that the principle of virtual work is satisfied with the displacement patterns
      (i) $\bar{u} = ax$ and (ii) $\bar{u} = ax^2$.
   (c) Identify a stress τ_{xx} for which the principle of virtual work is satisfied with pattern (ii) but
      not with pattern (i).

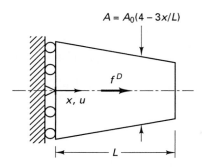

f^D = constant force per unit length
Young's modulus E

4.4. For the two-dimensional body shown, use the principle of virtual work to show that the body
forces are in equilibrium with the applied concentrated nodal loads.

$$f_x^B = 10(1 + 2x) \text{ N/m}^3$$

$$f_y^B = 20(1 + y) \text{ N/m}^3$$

$$R_1 = 60 \text{ N}$$

$$R_2 = 45 \text{ N}$$

$$R_3 = 15 \text{ N}$$

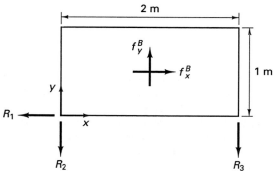

4.5. Idealize the bar structure shown as an assemblage of 2 two-node bar elements.
   (a) Calculate the equilibrium equations $\mathbf{KU} = \mathbf{R}$.
   (b) Calculate the mass matrix of the element assemblage.

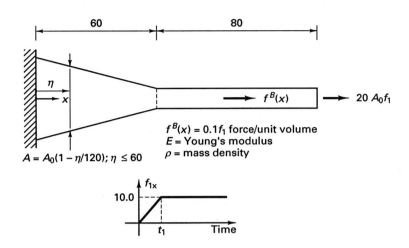

$f^B(x) = 0.1f_1$ force/unit volume
E = Young's modulus
ρ = mass density
$A = A_0(1 - \eta/120); \; \eta \leq 60$

4.6. Consider the disk with a centerline hole of radius 20 shown spinning at a rotational velocity of ω radians/second.

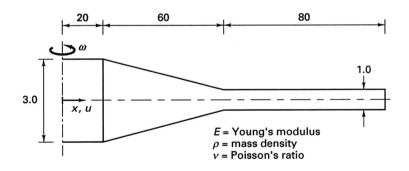

E = Young's modulus
ρ = mass density
v = Poisson's ratio

Idealize the structure as an assemblage of 2 two-node elements and calculate the steady-state (pseudostatic) equilibrium equations. (Note that the strains are now $\partial u/\partial x$ and u/x, where u/x is the hoop strain.)

4.7. Consider Example 4.5 and the state at time $t = 2.0$ with $U_1(t) = 0$ at all times.
   (a) Use the finite element formulation given in the example to calculate the static nodal point displacements and the element stresses.
   (b) Calculate the reaction at the support.

(c) Let the calculated finite element solution be u^{FE}. Calculate and plot the error r measured in satisfying the differential equation of equilibrium, i.e.,

$$r = E\left[\frac{\partial}{\partial x}\left(A\frac{\partial u^{FE}}{\partial x}\right)\right] + f_x^B A$$

(d) Calculate the strain energy of the structure as evaluated in the finite element solution and compare this strain energy with the exact strain energy of the mathematical model.

4.8. The two-node truss element shown, originally at a uniform temperature, 20°C, is subjected to a temperature variation

$$\theta = (10x + 20)°C$$

Calculate the resulting stress and nodal point displacement. Also obtain the analytical solution, assuming a continuum, and briefly discuss your results.

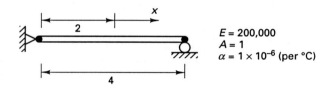

$E = 200,000$
$A = 1$
$\alpha = 1 \times 10^{-6}$ (per °C)

4.9. Consider the finite element analysis illustrated.

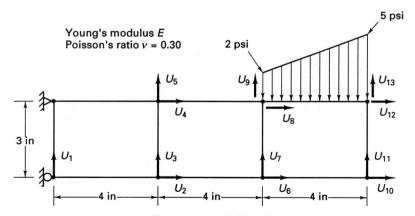

Plane stress condition (thickness t).
All elements are 4-node elements

(a) Begin by establishing the typical matrix **B** of an element for the vector $\hat{\mathbf{u}}^T = \begin{bmatrix} u_1 & v_1 & u_2 & v_2 & u_3 & v_3 & u_4 & v_4 \end{bmatrix}$.

(b) Calculate the elements of the **K** matrix, $K_{U_2 U_2}$, $K_{U_6 U_7}$, $K_{U_7 U_6}$, and $K_{U_5 U_{12}}$ of the structural assemblage.

(c) Calculate the nodal load R_9 due to the linearly varying surface pressure distribution.

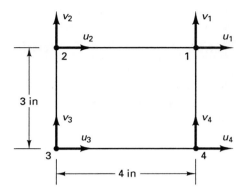

4.10. Consider the simply supported beam shown.

(a) Assume that usual beam theory is employed and use the principle of virtual work to evaluate the reactions R_1 and R_2.

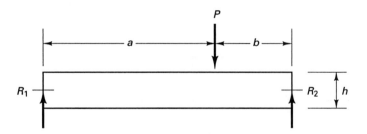

(b) Now assume that the beam is modeled by a four-node finite element. Show that to be able to evaluate R_1 and R_2 as in part (a) it is necessary that the finite element displacement functions can represent the rigid body mode displacements.

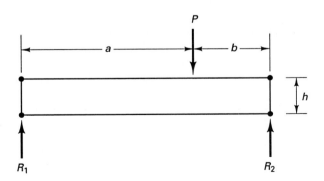

4.11. The four-node plane stress element shown carries the initial stresses

$$\tau_{xx}^I = 0 \text{ MPa}$$

$$\tau_{yy}^I = 10 \text{ MPa}$$

$$\tau_{xy}^I = 20 \text{ MPa}$$

(a) Calculate the corresponding nodal point forces $\mathbf{R}_I$.

(b) Evaluate the nodal point forces $\mathbf{R}_S$ equivalent to the surface tractions that correspond to the element stresses. Check your results using elementary statics and show that $\mathbf{R}_S$ is equal to $\mathbf{R}_I$ evaluated in part (a). Explain why this result makes sense.

(c) Derive a general result: Assume that any stresses are given, and $\mathbf{R}_I$ and $\mathbf{R}_S$ are calculated. What conditions must the given stresses satisfy in order that $\mathbf{R}_I = \mathbf{R}_S$, where the surface tractions in $\mathbf{R}_S$ are obtained from equation (b) in Example 4.2?

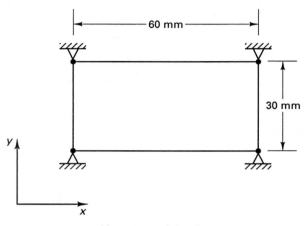

Young's modulus E
Poisson's ratio ν
Thickness = 0.5 mm

4.12. The four-node plane strain element shown is subjected to the constant stresses

$$\tau_{xx} = 20 \text{ psi}$$

$$\tau_{yy} = 10 \text{ psi}$$

$$\tau_{xy} = 10 \text{ psi}$$

Calculate the nodal point displacements of the element.

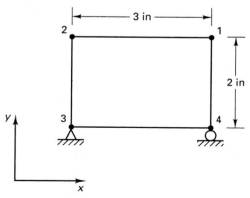

Young's modulus $E = 30 \times 10^6$ psi
Poisson's ratio $\nu = 0.30$

4.13. Consider element 2 in Fig. E4.9.
   (a) Show explicitly that

$$\mathbf{F}^{(2)} = \int_{V^{(2)}} \mathbf{B}^{(2)T} \, \boldsymbol{\tau}^{(2)} \, dV^{(2)}$$

   (b) Show that the element nodal point forces $\mathbf{F}^{(2)}$ are in equilibrium.

4.14. Assume that the element stiffness matrices $\mathbf{K}_A$ and $\mathbf{K}_B$ corresponding to the element displacements shown have been calculated. Assemble these element matrices directly into the global structure stiffness matrix with the displacement boundary conditions shown.

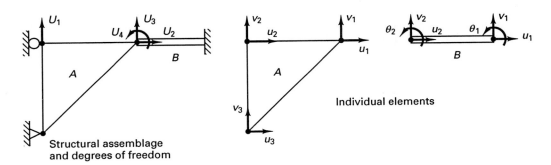

Structural assemblage
and degrees of freedom

Individual elements

$$\mathbf{K}_A = \begin{bmatrix} a_{11} & a_{12} & a_{13} & a_{14} & a_{15} & a_{16} \\ a_{21} & a_{22} & a_{23} & a_{24} & a_{25} & a_{26} \\ a_{31} & a_{32} & a_{33} & a_{34} & a_{35} & a_{36} \\ a_{41} & a_{42} & a_{43} & a_{44} & a_{45} & a_{46} \\ a_{51} & a_{52} & a_{53} & a_{54} & a_{55} & a_{56} \\ a_{61} & a_{62} & a_{63} & a_{64} & a_{65} & a_{66} \end{bmatrix} \begin{matrix} u_1 \\ v_1 \\ u_2 \\ v_2 \\ u_3 \\ v_3 \end{matrix} \qquad \mathbf{K}_B = \begin{bmatrix} b_{11} & b_{12} & b_{13} & b_{14} & b_{15} & b_{16} \\ b_{21} & b_{22} & b_{23} & b_{24} & b_{25} & b_{26} \\ b_{31} & b_{32} & b_{33} & b_{34} & b_{35} & b_{36} \\ b_{41} & b_{42} & b_{43} & b_{44} & b_{45} & b_{46} \\ b_{51} & b_{52} & b_{53} & b_{54} & b_{55} & b_{56} \\ b_{61} & b_{62} & b_{63} & b_{64} & b_{65} & b_{66} \end{bmatrix} \begin{matrix} u_1 \\ v_1 \\ \theta_1 \\ u_2 \\ v_2 \\ \theta_2 \end{matrix}$$

4.15. Assume that the element stiffness matrices $\mathbf{K}_A$ and $\mathbf{K}_B$ corresponding to the element displacements shown have been calculated. Assemble these element matrices directly into the global structure stiffness matrix with the displacement boundary conditions shown.

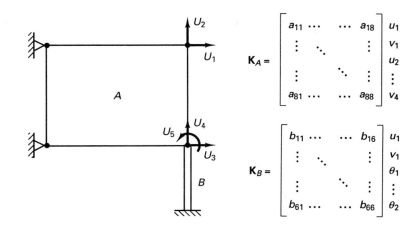

$$\mathbf{K}_A = \begin{bmatrix} a_{11} & \cdots & & \cdots & a_{18} \\ & \ddots & & & \vdots \\ \vdots & & \ddots & & \vdots \\ & & & \ddots & \vdots \\ a_{81} & \cdots & & \cdots & a_{88} \end{bmatrix} \begin{matrix} u_1 \\ v_1 \\ u_2 \\ \vdots \\ v_4 \end{matrix}$$

$$\mathbf{K}_B = \begin{bmatrix} b_{11} & \cdots & & \cdots & b_{16} \\ & \ddots & & & \vdots \\ \vdots & & \ddots & & \vdots \\ & & & \ddots & \vdots \\ b_{61} & \cdots & & \cdots & b_{66} \end{bmatrix} \begin{matrix} u_1 \\ v_1 \\ \theta_1 \\ \vdots \\ \theta_2 \end{matrix}$$

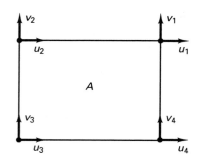
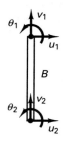

4.16. Consider Example 4.11. Assume that at the support A, the roller allows a displacement only along a slope of 30 degrees to the horizontal direction. Determine the modifications necessary in the solution in Example 4.11 to obtain the structure matrix $\mathbf{K}$ for this situation.
  (a) Consider imposing the zero displacement condition exactly.
  (b) Consider imposing the zero displacement condition using the penalty method.

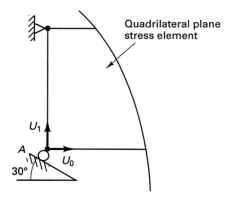

Quadrilateral plane stress element

4.17. Consider the beam element shown. Evaluate the stiffness coefficients k_{11} and k_{12}.
  (a) Obtain the exact coefficients from the solution of the differential equation of equilibrium (using the mathematical model of Bernoulli beam theory).
  (b) Obtain the coefficients using the principle of virtual work with the Hermitian beam functions (see Example 4.16).

$$h(x) = h_0 (1 + x/L)$$

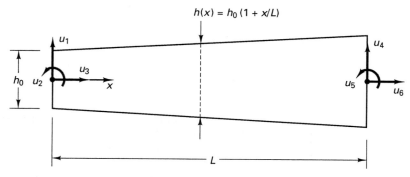

Young's modulus E
Unit thickness

4.18. Consider the two-element assemblage shown.
    (a) Evaluate the stiffness coefficients K_{11}, K_{14} for the finite element idealization.
    (b) Calculate the load vector of the element assemblage.

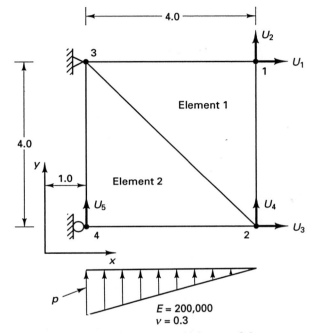

E = 200,000
ν = 0.3

Plane stress, thickness = 0.1

4.19. Consider the two-element assemblage in Exercise 4.18 but now assume axisymmetric conditions. The y-axis is the axis of revolution.
    (a) Evaluate the stiffness coefficients K_{11}, K_{14} for the finite element idealization.
    (b) Evaluate the corresponding load vector.

4.20. Consider Example 4.20 and let the loading on the structure be $R_r = f_1(t) \cos \theta$.
    (a) Establish the stiffness matrix, mass matrix, and load vector of the three-node element

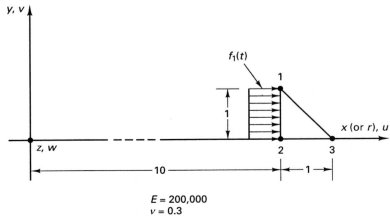

E = 200,000
ν = 0.3
ρ = mass density

shown. Establish explicitly all matrices you need but do not perform any multiplications and integrations.

(b) Explain (by physical reasoning) that your assumptions on u, v, w make sense.

4.21. An inviscid fluid element (for acoustic motions) can be obtained by considering only volumetric strain energy (since inviscid fluids provide no resistance to shear). Formulate the finite element fluid stiffness matrix for the four-node plane element shown and write out all matrices required. Do not actually perform any integrations or matrix multiplications. *Hint:* Remember that $p = -\beta\,\Delta V/V$ and $\boldsymbol{\tau}^T = [\tau_{xx}\quad \tau_{yy}\quad \tau_{xy}\quad \tau_{zz}] = [-p\quad -p\quad 0\quad -p]$ and $\Delta V/V = \epsilon_{xx} + \epsilon_{yy}$.

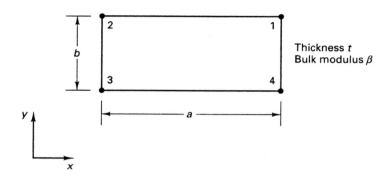

Thickness t
Bulk modulus β

4.22. Consider the element assemblages in Exercises 4.18 and 4.19. For each case, evaluate a lumped mass matrix (using a uniform mass density ρ) and a lumped load vector.

4.23. Use a finite element program to solve the model shown of the problem in Example 4.6.

(a) Print out the element stresses and element nodal point forces and draw the "exploded element views" for the stresses and nodal point forces as in Example 4.9.

(b) Show that the element nodal point forces of element 5 are in equilibrium and that the element nodal point forces of elements 5 and 6 equilibrate the applied load.

(c) Print out the reactions and show that the element nodal point forces equilibrate these reactions.

(d) Calculate the strain energy of the finite element model.

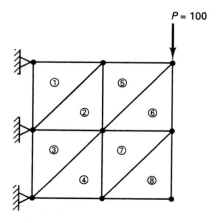

Eight constant-strain triangles

4.24. Use a finite element program to solve the model shown of the problem in Example 4.6. Print out the element stresses and reactions and calculate the strain energy of the model. Draw the "exploded element views" for the stresses and nodal point forces. Compare your results with those for Exercise 4.23 and discuss why we should not be surprised to have obtained different results (although the same kind and same number of elements are used in both idealizations).

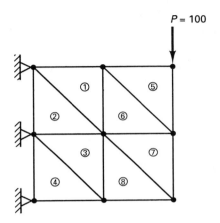

Eight constant-strain triangles

4.3 CONVERGENCE OF ANALYSIS RESULTS

Since the finite element method is a numerical procedure for solving complex engineering problems, important considerations pertain to the accuracy of the analysis results and the convergence of the numerical solution. The objective in this section is to address these issues. We start by defining in Section 4.3.1 what we mean by convergence. Then we consider in a rather physical manner the criteria for monotonic convergence and relate these criteria to the conditions in a Ritz analysis (introduced in Section 3.3.3). Next, some important properties of the finite element solution are summarized (and proven) and the rate of convergence is discussed. Finally, we consider the calculation of stresses and the evaluation of error measures that indicate the magnitude of the error in stresses at the completion of an analysis.

We consider in this section displacement-based finite elements leading to monotonically convergent solutions. Formulations that lead to a nonmonotonic convergence are considered in Sections 4.4 and 4.5.

4.3.1 The Model Problem and a Definition of Convergence

Based on the preceding discussions, we can now say that, in general, a finite element analysis requires the idealization of an actual physical problem into a mathematical model and then the finite element solution of that model (see Section 1.2). Figure 4.8 summarizes these concepts. The distinction given in the figure is frequently not recognized in practical analysis because the differential equations of motion of the mathematical model are not dealt with, and indeed the equations may be unknown in the analysis of a complex problem,

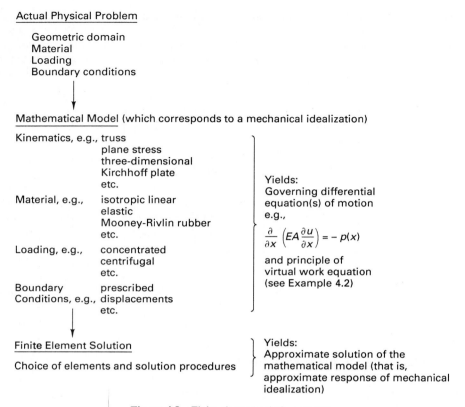

Actual Physical Problem

- Geometric domain
- Material
- Loading
- Boundary conditions

Mathematical Model (which corresponds to a mechanical idealization)

Kinematics, e.g.,   truss
                     plane stress
                     three-dimensional
                     Kirchhoff plate
                     etc.

Material, e.g.,   isotropic linear
                     elastic
                     Mooney-Rivlin rubber
                     etc.

Loading, e.g.,   concentrated
                     centrifugal
                     etc.

Boundary   prescribed
Conditions, e.g.,   displacements
                     etc.

Yields:
Governing differential
equation(s) of motion
e.g.,

$$\frac{\partial}{\partial x}\left(EA\frac{\partial u}{\partial x}\right) = -p(x)$$

and principle of
virtual work equation
(see Example 4.2)

Finite Element Solution

Choice of elements and solution procedures

Yields:
Approximate solution of the
mathematical model (that is,
approximate response of mechanical
idealization)

Figure 4.8   Finite element solution process

such as the response prediction of a three-dimensional shell. Instead, in a practical analysis, a finite element idealization of the physical problem is established directly. However, to study the convergence of the finite element solution as the number of elements increases, it is valuable to recognize that a mathematical model is actually implied in the finite element representation of the physical problem. That is, a proper finite element solution should converge (as the number of elements is increased) to the analytical (exact) solution of the differential equations that govern the response of the mathematical model. Furthermore, the convergence behavior displays all the characteristics of the finite element scheme because the differential equations of motion of the mathematical model express in a very precise and compact manner all basic conditions that the solution variables (stress, displacement, strain, and so on) must satisfy. If the differential equations of motion are not known, as in a complex shell analysis, and/or analytical solutions cannot be obtained, the convergence of the finite element solutions can be measured only on the fact that all basic kinematic, static, and constitutive conditions contained in the mathematical model must ultimately (at convergence) be satisfied. Therefore, in all discussions of the convergence of finite element solutions we imply that the convergence to the exact solution of a mathematical model is meant.

Here it is important to recognize that in linear elastic analysis there is a unique exact solution to the mathematical model. Hence if we have *a* solution that satisfies the governing mathematical equations exactly, then this is *the* exact solution to the problem (see Section 4.3.4).

In considering the approximate finite element solution to the exact response of the mathematical model, we need to recognize that different sources of errors affect the finite element solution results. Table 4.4 summarizes various general sources of errors. Round-off errors are a result of the finite precision arithmetic of the computer used; solution errors in the constitutive modeling are due to the linearization and integration of the constitutive relations; solution errors in the calculation of the dynamic response arise in the numerical integration of the equations of motion or because only a few modes are used in a mode superposition analysis; and solution errors arise when an iterative solution is obtained because convergence is measured on increments in the solution variables that are small but not zero. In this section, we will discuss only the finite element discretization errors, which are due to interpolation of the solution variables. Thus, in essence, *we consider in this section a model problem in which the other solution errors referred to above do not arise: a linear elastic static problem with the geometry represented exactly with the exact calculation of the element matrices and solution of equations, i.e., also negligible round-off errors.* For ease of presentation, we assume that the prescribed displacements are zero. Nonzero displacement boundary conditions would be imposed as discussed in Section 4.2.2, and such boundary conditions do not change the properties of the finite element solution.

For this model problem, let us restate for purposes of our discussion the basic equation of the principle of virtual work governing the exact solution of the mathematical model

$$\int_V \bar{\boldsymbol{\epsilon}}^T \boldsymbol{\tau} \, dV = \int_{S_f} \bar{\mathbf{u}}^{S_f T} \mathbf{f}^{S_f} \, dS + \int_V \bar{\mathbf{u}}^T \mathbf{f}^B \, dV \tag{4.62}$$

TABLE 4.4   *Finite element solution errors*

Error	Error occurrence in	See section
Discretization	Use of finite element interpolations for geometry and solution variables	4.2.1 4.2.3, 5.3
Numerical integration in space	Evaluation of finite element matrices using numerical integration	5.5 6.8.4
Evaluation of constitutive relations	Use of nonlinear material models	6.6.3 6.6.4
Solution of dynamic equilibrium equations	Direct time integration, mode superposition	9.2–9.4
Solution of finite element equations by iteration	Gauss-Seidel, conjugate gradient, Newton-Raphson, quasi-Newton methods, eigensolutions	8.3, 8.4 9.5 10.4
Round-off	Setting up equations and their solution	8.2.6

We recall that for $\boldsymbol{\tau}$ to be the exact solution of the mathematical model, (4.62) must hold for arbitrary virtual displacements $\bar{\mathbf{u}}$ (and corresponding virtual strains $\bar{\boldsymbol{\epsilon}}$), with $\bar{\mathbf{u}}$ zero at and corresponding to the prescribed displacements. A short notation for (4.62) is

> Find the displacements $\mathbf{u}$ (and corresponding stresses $\boldsymbol{\tau}$) such that
>
> $$a(\mathbf{u}, \mathbf{v}) = (\mathbf{f}, \mathbf{v}) \qquad \text{for all admissible } \mathbf{v}$$

(4.63)

Here $a(\cdot,\cdot)$ is a bilinear form and $(\mathbf{f},\cdot)$ is a linear form[9]—these forms depend on the mathematical model considered—$\mathbf{u}$ is the exact displacement solution, $\mathbf{v}$ is any admissible virtual displacement ["admissible" because the functions $\mathbf{v}$ must be continuous and zero at and corresponding to actually prescribed displacements (see (4.7))], and $\mathbf{f}$ represents the forcing functions (loads $\mathbf{f}^{S_f}$ and $\mathbf{f}^B$). Note that the notation in (4.63) implies an integration process. The bilinear forms $a(\cdot,\cdot)$ that we consider in this section are symmetric in the sense that $a(\mathbf{u}, \mathbf{v}) = a(\mathbf{v}, \mathbf{u})$.

From (4.63) we have that the strain energy corresponding to the exact solution $\mathbf{u}$ is $1/2\, a(\mathbf{u}, \mathbf{u})$. We assume that the material properties and boundary conditions of our model problem are such that this strain energy is finite. This is not a serious restriction in practice but requires the proper choice of a mathematical model. In particular, the material properties must be physically realistic and the load distributions (externally applied or due to displacement constraints) must be sufficiently smooth. We have discussed the need of modeling the applied loads properly already in Section 1.2 and will comment further on it in Section 4.3.4.

Assume that the finite element solution is $\mathbf{u}_h$: this solution lies of course in the finite element space given by the displacement interpolation functions (h denoting here the size of the generic element and hence denoting a specific mesh). Then we define "convergence" to mean that

$$a(\mathbf{u} - \mathbf{u}_h, \mathbf{u} - \mathbf{u}_h) \to 0 \qquad \text{as } h \to 0$$

(4.64)

or, equivalently [see (4.90)], that

$$a(\mathbf{u}_h, \mathbf{u}_h) \to a(\mathbf{u}, \mathbf{u}) \qquad \text{as } h \to 0$$

Physically, this statement means that the strain energy calculated by the finite element solution converges to the exact strain energy of the mathematical model as the finite element mesh is refined. Let us consider a simple example to show what we mean by the bilinear form $a(\cdot,\cdot)$.

---

[9] The bilinearity of $a(\cdot,\cdot)$ refers to the fact that for any constants γ_1 and γ_2,

$$a(\gamma_1 \mathbf{u}_1 + \gamma_2 \mathbf{u}_2, \mathbf{v}) = \gamma_1 a(\mathbf{u}_1, \mathbf{v}) + \gamma_2 a(\mathbf{u}_2, \mathbf{v})$$

$$a(\mathbf{u}, \gamma_1 \mathbf{v}_1 + \gamma_2 \mathbf{v}_2) = \gamma_1 a(\mathbf{u}, \mathbf{v}_1) + \gamma_2 a(\mathbf{u}, \mathbf{v}_2)$$

and the linearity of $(\mathbf{f},\cdot)$ refers to the fact that for any constants γ_1 and γ_2,

$$(\mathbf{f}, \gamma_1 \mathbf{v}_1 + \gamma_2 \mathbf{v}_2) = \gamma_1 (\mathbf{f}, \mathbf{v}_1) + \gamma_2 (\mathbf{f}, \mathbf{v}_2).$$

EXAMPLE 4.22:   Assume that a simply supported prestressed membrane, with (constant) prestress tension T, subjected to transverse loading p is to be analyzed (see Fig. E4.22). Establish for this problem the form (4.63) of the principle of virtual work.

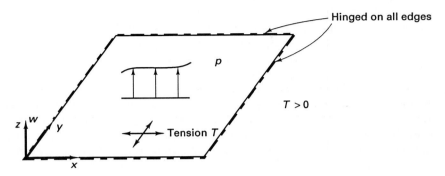

Figure E4.22   Prestressed membrane

The principle of virtual work gives for this problem

$$
\int_A
\begin{bmatrix} \dfrac{\partial \overline{w}}{\partial x} \\[2mm] \dfrac{\partial \overline{w}}{\partial y} \end{bmatrix}^T
T
\begin{bmatrix} \dfrac{\partial w}{\partial x} \\[2mm] \dfrac{\partial w}{\partial y} \end{bmatrix}
dx \, dy = \int_A p\overline{w} \, dx \, dy
$$

where $w(x, y)$ is the transverse displacement. The left-hand side of this equation gives the bilinear form $a(v, u)$, with $v = \overline{w}$, $u = w$, and the integration on the right-hand side gives (f, v).

Depending on the specific (properly formulated) displacement-based finite elements used in the analysis of the model problem defined above, we may converge monotonically or nonmonotonically to the exact solution as the number of finite elements is increased. In the following discussion we consider the criteria for the monotonic convergence of solutions. Finite element analysis conditions that lead to nonmonotonic convergence are discussed in Section 4.4.

4.3.2 Criteria for Monotonic Convergence

For monotonic convergence, the elements must be complete and the elements and mesh must be compatible. If these conditions are fulfilled, the accuracy of the solution results will increase continuously as we continue to refine the finite element mesh. This mesh refinement should be performed by subdividing a previously used element into two or more elements; thus, the old mesh will be "embedded" in the new mesh. This means mathematically that the new space of finite element interpolation functions will contain the previously used space, and as the mesh is refined, the dimension of the finite element solution space will be continuously increased to contain ultimately the exact solution.

The requirement of completeness of an element means that the displacement functions of the element must be able to represent *the rigid body displacements* and the *constant strain states.*

The rigid body displacements are those displacement modes that the element must be able to undergo as a rigid body without stresses being developed in it. As an example, a two-dimensional plane stress element must be able to translate uniformly in either direction of its plane and to rotate without straining. The reason that the element must be able to undergo these displacements without developing stresses is illustrated in the analysis of the cantilever shown in Fig. 4.9: the element at the tip of the beam—for any element size— must translate and rotate stress-free because by simple statics the cantilever is not subjected to stresses beyond the point of load application.

The number of rigid body modes that an element must be able to undergo can usually be identified without difficulty by inspection, but it is instructive to note that the number of element rigid body modes is equal to the number of element degrees of freedom minus the number of element straining modes (or natural modes). As an example, a two-noded truss has one straining mode (constant strain state), and thus one, three, and five rigid body modes in one-, two-, and three-dimensional conditions, respectively. For more complex finite

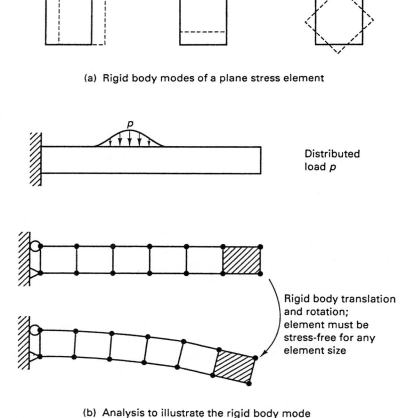

(a) Rigid body modes of a plane stress element

Distributed load p

Rigid body translation and rotation; element must be stress-free for any element size

(b) Analysis to illustrate the rigid body mode conditon

Figure 4.9 Use of plane stress element in analysis of cantilever

elements the individual straining modes and rigid body modes are displayed effectively by representing the stiffness matrix in the basis of eigenvectors. Thus, solving the eigenproblem

$$\mathbf{K}\boldsymbol{\phi} = \lambda\boldsymbol{\phi} \tag{4.65}$$

we have (see Section 2.5)

$$\mathbf{K}\boldsymbol{\Phi} = \boldsymbol{\Phi}\boldsymbol{\Lambda} \tag{4.66}$$

where $\boldsymbol{\Phi}$ is a matrix storing the eigenvectors $\boldsymbol{\phi}_1, \ldots, \boldsymbol{\phi}_n$ and $\boldsymbol{\Lambda}$ is a diagonal matrix storing the corresponding eigenvalues, $\boldsymbol{\Lambda} = \text{diag}(\lambda_i)$. Using the eigenvector orthonormality property we thus have

$$\boldsymbol{\Phi}^T\mathbf{K}\boldsymbol{\Phi} = \boldsymbol{\Lambda} \tag{4.67}$$

We may look at $\boldsymbol{\Lambda}$ as being the stiffness matrix of the element corresponding to the eigenvector displacement modes. The stiffness coefficients $\lambda_1, \ldots, \lambda_n$ display directly how stiff the element is in the corresponding displacement mode. Thus, the transformation in (4.67) shows clearly whether the rigid body modes and what additional straining modes are present.[10] As an example, the eight eigenvectors and corresponding eigenvalues of a four-node element are shown in Fig. 4.10.

The necessity for the constant strain states can be physically understood if we imagine that more and more elements are used in the assemblage to represent the structure. Then in the limit as each element approaches a very small size, the strain in each element approaches a constant value, and any complex variation of strain within the structure can be approximated. As an example, the plane stress element used in Fig. 4.9 must be able to represent two constant normal stress conditions and one constant shearing stress condition. Figure 4.10 shows that the element can represent these constant stress conditions and, in addition, contains two flexural straining modes.

The rigid body modes and constant strain states that an element can represent can also be directly identified by studying the element strain-displacement matrix (see Example 4.23).

The requirement of compatibility means that the displacements within the elements and across the element boundaries must be continuous. Physically, compatibility ensures that no gaps occur between elements when the assemblage is loaded. When only translational degrees of freedom are defined at the element nodes, only continuity in the displacements u, v, or w, whichever are applicable, must be preserved. However, when rotational degrees of freedom are also defined that are obtained by differentiation of the transverse displacement (such as in the formulation of the plate bending element in Example 4.18), it is also necessary to satisfy element continuity in the corresponding first displacement derivatives. This is a consequence of the kinematic assumption on the displacements over the depth of the plate bending element; that is, the continuity in the displacement w and the derivatives $\partial w/\partial x$ and/or $\partial w/\partial y$ along the respective element edges ensures continuity of displacements over the thickness of adjoining elements.

Compatibility is automatically ensured between truss and beam elements because they join only at the nodal points, and compatibility is relatively easy to maintain in

---

[10] Note also that since the finite element analysis overestimates the stiffness, as discussed in Section 4.3.4, the "smaller" the eigenvalues, the more effective the element.

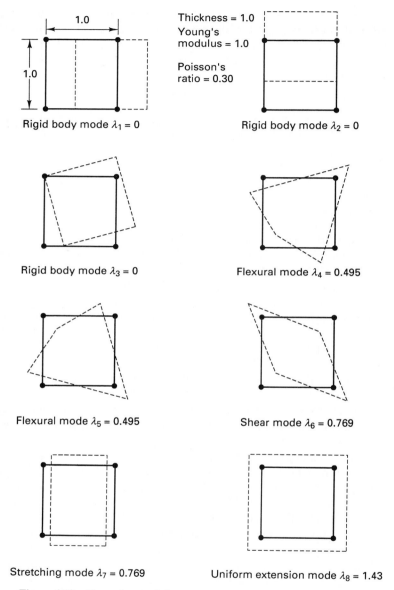

Figure 4.10 Eigenvalues and eigenvectors of four-node plane stress element

two-dimensional plane strain, plane stress, and axisymmetric analysis and in three-dimensional analysis, when only u, v, and w degrees of freedom are used as nodal point variables. However, the requirements of compatibility are difficult to satisfy in plate bending analysis, and particularly in thin shell analysis if the rotations are derived from the transverse displacements. For this reason, much emphasis has been directed toward the development of plate and shell elements, in which the displacements and rotations are variables (see Section 5.4). With such elements the compatibility requirements are just as easy to fulfill as in the case of dealing only with translational degrees of freedom.

Whether a specific element is complete and compatible depends on the formulation used, and each formulation need be analyzed individually. Consider the following simple example.

EXAMPLE 4.23:   Investigate if the plane stress element used in Example 4.6 is compatible and complete.

We have for the displacements of the element,

$$u(x, y) = \alpha_1 + \alpha_2 x + \alpha_3 y + \alpha_4 xy$$

$$v(x, y) = \beta_1 + \beta_2 x + \beta_3 y + \beta_4 xy$$

Observing that the displacements within an element are continuous, in order to show that the element is compatible, we need only investigate if interelement continuity is also preserved when an element assemblage is loaded. Consider two elements interconnected at two node points (Fig. E4.23) on which we impose two arbitrary displacements. It follows from the displacement assumptions that the points (i.e., the material particles) on the adjoining element edges displace linearly, and therefore continuity between the elements is preserved. Hence the element is compatible.

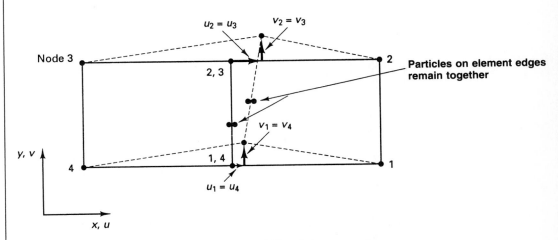

Figure E4.23   Compatibility of plane stress element

Considering completeness, the displacement functions show that a rigid body translation in the x direction is achieved if only α_1 is nonzero. Similarly, a rigid body displacement in the y direction is imposed by having only β_1 nonzero, and for a rigid body rotation α_3 and β_2 must be nonzero only with $\beta_2 = -\alpha_3$. The same conclusion can also be arrived at using the matrix **E** that relates the strains to the generalized coordinates (see Example 4.6). This matrix also shows that the constant strain states are possible. Therefore the element is complete.

4.3.3 The Monotonically Convergent Finite Element Solution: A Ritz Solution

We observed earlier that the application of the principle of virtual work is identical to using the stationarity condition of the total potential of the system (see Example 4.4). Considering also the discussion of the Ritz method in Section 3.3.3, we can conclude that monotonically convergent displacement-based finite element solutions are really only applications of this method. In the finite element analysis the Ritz functions are contained in the element displacement interpolation matrices $\mathbf{H}^{(m)}$, $m = 1, 2, \ldots$, and the Ritz parameters are the unknown nodal point displacements stored in $\mathbf{U}$. As we discuss further below, the mathematical conditions on the displacement interpolation functions in the matrices $\mathbf{H}^{(m)}$, in order that the finite element solution be a Ritz analysis, are exactly those that we identified earlier using physical reasoning. The correspondence between the analysis methods is illustrated in Examples 3.22 and 4.5.

Considering the Ritz method of analysis with the finite element interpolations, we have

$$\Pi = \tfrac{1}{2}\mathbf{U}^T\mathbf{K}\mathbf{U} - \mathbf{U}^T\mathbf{R} \tag{4.68}$$

where Π is the total potential of the system. Invoking the stationarity of Π with respect to the Ritz parameters U_i stored in $\mathbf{U}$ and recognizing that the matrix $\mathbf{K}$ is symmetric, we obtain

$$\mathbf{K}\mathbf{U} = \mathbf{R} \tag{4.69}$$

The solution of (4.69) yields the Ritz parameters, and then the displacement solution in the domain considered is

$$\mathbf{u}^{(m)} = \mathbf{H}^{(m)}\mathbf{U}; \qquad m = 1, 2, \ldots \tag{4.70}$$

The relations in (4.68) to (4.70) represent a Ritz analysis provided the functions used satisfy certain conditions. We defined in Section 3.3.2 a C^{m-1} variational problem as one in which the variational indicator of the problem contains derivatives of order m and lower. We then noted that for convergence the Ritz functions must satisfy the essential (or geometric) boundary conditions of the problem involving derivatives up to order $(m - 1)$, but that the functions do not need to satisfy the natural (or force) boundary conditions involving derivatives of order m to $(2m - 1)$ because these conditions are implicitly contained in the variational indicator Π. Therefore, in order for a finite element solution to be a Ritz analysis, the essential boundary conditions must be completely satisfied by the finite element nodal point displacements and the displacement interpolations between the nodal points. However, in selecting the finite element displacement functions, no special attention need be given to the natural boundary conditions because these conditions are imposed with the load vector and are satisfied approximately in the Ritz solution. The accuracy with which the natural or force boundary conditions are satisfied depends on the specific Ritz functions employed, but this accuracy can always be increased by using a larger number of functions, i.e., a larger number of finite elements to model the problem.

In the classical Ritz analysis the Ritz functions extend over the complete domain considered, whereas in the finite element analysis the individual Ritz functions extend only over subdomains (finite elements) of the complete region. Hence, there must be a question as to what conditions must be fulfilled by the finite element interpolations with regard to continuity requirements *between* adjacent subdomains. To answer this question we consider the integrations that must be performed to evaluate the coefficient matrix $\mathbf{K}$. We recognize that in considering a C^{m-1} problem we need continuity in at least the $(m - 1)$st derivatives of the Ritz trial functions in order that we can perform the integrations across the element boundaries. However, this continuity requirement corresponds entirely to the element compatibility conditions that we discussed in Section 4.3.2. For example, in the analysis of fully three-dimensional problems only the displacements between elements must be continuous, whereas in the analysis of plate problems formulated using the Kirchhoff plate theory we also need continuity in the first derivatives of the displacement functions.

In summary, therefore, for a C^{m-1} problem $[C^{m-1} \equiv$ continuity on trial functions and their derivatives up to order $(m - 1)]$, in the classical Ritz analysis the trial functions are selected to satisfy exactly all boundary conditions that involve derivatives up to order $(m - 1)$. The same holds in finite element analysis, but in addition, continuity in the trial functions and their derivatives up to order $(m - 1)$ must be satisfied between elements in order for the finite element solution to correspond to a Ritz analysis.

Although the classical Ritz analysis procedure and the displacement-based finite element method are theoretically identical, in practice, the finite element method has important advantages over a conventional Ritz analysis. One disadvantage of the conventional Ritz analysis is that the Ritz functions are defined over the whole region considered. For example, in the analysis of the cantilever in Example 3.24, the Ritz functions spanned from $x = 0$ to $x = L$. Therefore, in the conventional Ritz analysis, the matrix $\mathbf{K}$ is a full matrix, and as pointed out in Section 8.2.3, the numerical operations required for solution of the resulting algebraic equations are considerable if many functions are used.

A particular difficulty in a conventional Ritz analysis is the selection of appropriate Ritz functions since the solution is a linear combination of these functions. In order to solve accurately for large displacement or stress gradients, many functions may be needed. However, these functions also unnecessarily extend over the regions in which the displacements and stresses vary rather slowly and where not many functions are needed.

Another difficulty arises in the conventional Ritz analysis when the total region of interest is made up of subregions with different kinds of strain distributions. As an example, consider a plate that is supported by edge beams and columns. In such a case, the Ritz functions used for one region (e.g., the plate) are not appropriate for the other regions (i.e., the edge beams and columns), and special displacement continuity conditions or boundary relations must be introduced.

The few reasons given already show that the conventional Ritz analysis is, in general, not particularly computer-oriented, except in some cases for the development of special-purpose programs. On the other hand, the finite element method has to a large extent removed the practical difficulties while retaining the advantageous properties of the conventional Ritz method. With regard to the difficulties mentioned above, the selection of Ritz functions is handled by using an adequate element library in the computer program. The use of relatively many functions in regions of high stress and displacement gradients is possible simply by using many elements, and the combination of domains with different kinds of strain distributions is possible by using different kinds of elements to idealize the domains. It is this generality of the finite element method, and the good mathematical foundation, that have made the finite element method the very widely used analysis tool in today's engineering environments.

4.3.4 Properties of the Finite Element Solution

Let us consider the general linear elasticity problem and its finite element solution and identify certain properties that are useful for an understanding of the finite element method. We shall use the notation summarized in Table 4.5.

The elasticity problem can be written as follows (see, for example, G. Strang and G. F. Fix [A], P. G. Ciarlet [A], or F. Brezzi and M. Fortin [A]).

$$
\boxed{
\begin{array}{l}
\text{Find } \mathbf{u} \in V \text{ such that} \\[2mm]
\qquad a(\mathbf{u}, \mathbf{v}) = (\mathbf{f}, \mathbf{v}) \qquad \forall \, \mathbf{v} \in V
\end{array}
}
\tag{4.71}
$$

where the space V is defined as

$$
\boxed{
V = \left\{ \mathbf{v} \mid \mathbf{v} \in L^2(\text{Vol}); \; \frac{\partial v_i}{\partial x_j} \in L^2(\text{Vol}), \, i, j = 1, 2, 3; \, v_i |_{S_u} = 0, \, i = 1, 2, 3 \right\}
}
\tag{4.72}
$$

Here $L^2(\text{Vol})$ is the space of square integrable functions in the volume, "Vol", of the body being considered,

$$
\boxed{
L^2(\text{Vol}) = \left\{ \mathbf{w} \mid \mathbf{w} \text{ is defined in Vol and } \int_{\text{Vol}} \left(\sum_{i=1}^{3} (w_i)^2 \right) d\,\text{Vol} = \| \mathbf{w} \|_{L^2(\text{Vol})}^2 < +\infty \right\}
}
\tag{4.73}
$$

TABLE 4.5 *Notation used in discussion of the properties and convergence of finite element solutions*

Symbol	Meaning
$a(.,.)$	Bilinear form corresponding to model problem being considered (see Example 4.22)
$\mathbf{f}$	Load vector
$\mathbf{u}$	Exact displacement solution to mathematical model; an element of the space V
$\mathbf{v}$	Displacements; an element of the space V
$\mathbf{u}_h$	Finite element solution, an element of the space V_h
$\mathbf{v}_h$	Finite element displacements; an element of the space V_h
$\forall$	For all
$\in$	An element of
V, V_h	Spaces of functions [see (4.72) and (4.84)]
Vol	Volume of body considered
L^2	Space of a square integrable functions [see (4.73)]
$\mathbf{e}_h$	Error between exact and finite element solution, $\mathbf{e}_h = \mathbf{u} - \mathbf{u}_h$
$\exists$	There exists
$\subset$	Contained in
$\subsetneq$	Contained in but not equal to
$\| \ \|_E$	Energy norm [see (4.74)]
inf	We take the infimum.
sup	We take the supremum.

Hence, (4.72) defines a space of functions corresponding to a general three-dimensional analysis. The functions in the space vanish on the boundary S_u, and the squares of the functions and of their first derivatives are integrable. Corresponding to V, we use the energy norm

$$\| \mathbf{v} \|_E^2 = a(\mathbf{v}, \mathbf{v}) \tag{4.74}$$

which actually corresponds to twice the strain energy stored in the body when the body is subjected to the displacement field $\mathbf{v}$.

We assume in our discussion that the structure considered in (4.71) is properly supported, corrresponding to the zero displacement conditions on S_u, so that $\| \mathbf{v} \|_E^2$ is greater than zero for any $\mathbf{v}$ different from zero.

In addition, we shall also use the Sobolev norms of order $m = 0$ and $m = 1$ defined as

$m = 0$:

$$(\| \mathbf{v} \|_0)^2 = \int_{\text{Vol}} \left(\sum_{i=1}^{3} (v_i)^2 \right) d\,\text{Vol} \tag{4.75}$$

$m = 1$:

$$(\| \mathbf{v} \|_1)^2 = (\| \mathbf{v} \|_0)^2 + \int_{\text{Vol}} \left[\sum_{i=1, j=1}^{3} \left(\frac{\partial v_i}{\partial x_j} \right)^2 \right] d\,\text{Vol} \tag{4.76}$$

For our elasticity problem the norm of order 1 is used,[11] and we have the following two important properties for our bilinear form a.

Continuity:

$$\exists\, M > 0 \text{ such that } \forall\, \mathbf{v}_1, \mathbf{v}_2 \in V, \qquad |a(\mathbf{v}_1, \mathbf{v}_2)| \leq M \| \mathbf{v}_1 \|_1 \| \mathbf{v}_2 \|_1 \tag{4.77}$$

Ellipticity:

$$\exists\, \alpha > 0 \text{ such that } \forall\, \mathbf{v} \in V, \qquad a(\mathbf{v}, \mathbf{v}) \geq \alpha \| \mathbf{v} \|_1^2 \tag{4.78}$$

where the constants α and M depend on the actual elasticity problem being considered, including the material constants used, but are independent of $\mathbf{v}$.

---

[11] In our discussion, we shall also use the Poincaré-Friedrichs inequality, namely, that for the analysis problems we consider, for any $\mathbf{v}$ we have

$$\int_{\text{Vol}} \left(\sum_{i=1}^{3} (v_i)^2 \right) d\,\text{Vol} \leq c \int_{\text{Vol}} \left(\sum_{i, j=1}^{3} \left(\frac{\partial v_i}{\partial x_j} \right)^2 \right) d\,\text{Vol}$$

where c is a constant (see, for example, P. G. Ciarlet [A]).

The continuity property is satisfied because reasonable norms are used in (4.77), and the ellipticity property is satisfied because a properly supported (i.e., stable) structure is being considered (see P. G. Ciarlet [A] for a mathematical proof). Based on these properties we have

$$c_1 \| \mathbf{v} \|_1 \leq (a(\mathbf{v}, \mathbf{v}))^{1/2} \leq c_2 \| \mathbf{v} \|_1 \qquad (4.79)$$

where c_1 and c_2 are constants independent of $\mathbf{v}$, and we therefore have that the energy norm is equivalent to the 1-norm (see Section 2.7). In mathematical analysis the Sobolev norms are commonly used to measure rates of convergence (see Section 4.3.5), but in practice the energy norm is frequently more easily evaluated [see (4.97)]. Because of (4.79), we can say that convergence can also be defined, instead of using (4.64), as

$$\| \mathbf{u} - \mathbf{u}_h \|_1 \to 0 \qquad \text{as } h \to 0$$

and the energy norm in problem solutions will converge with the same order as the 1-norm. We examine the continuity and ellipticity of a bilinear form a in the following example.

EXAMPLE 4.24: Consider the problem in Example 4.22. Show that the bilinear form a satisfies the continuity and ellipticity conditions.

Continuity follows because[12]

$$a(w_1, w_2) = \int_A T \left(\frac{\partial w_1}{\partial x} \frac{\partial w_2}{\partial x} + \frac{\partial w_1}{\partial y} \frac{\partial w_2}{\partial y} \right) dx \, dy$$

$$\leq \int_A T \left[\left(\frac{\partial w_1}{\partial x} \right)^2 + \left(\frac{\partial w_1}{\partial y} \right)^2 \right]^{1/2} \left[\left(\frac{\partial w_2}{\partial x} \right)^2 + \left(\frac{\partial w_2}{\partial y} \right)^2 \right]^{1/2} dx \, dy$$

$$\leq \left\{ \int_A T \left[\left(\frac{\partial w_1}{\partial x} \right)^2 + \left(\frac{\partial w_1}{\partial y} \right)^2 \right] dx \, dy \right\}^{1/2}$$

$$\times \left\{ \int_A T \left[\left(\frac{\partial w_2}{\partial x} \right)^2 + \left(\frac{\partial w_2}{\partial y} \right)^2 \right] dx \, dy \right\}^{1/2} \leq c \| w_1 \|_1 \, \| w_2 \|_1$$

Ellipticity requires that

$$a(w, w) = \int_A T \left[\left(\frac{\partial w}{\partial x} \right)^2 + \left(\frac{\partial w}{\partial y} \right)^2 \right] dx \, dy$$

$$\geq \alpha \int_A \left[w^2 + \left(\frac{\partial w}{\partial x} \right)^2 + \left(\frac{\partial w}{\partial y} \right)^2 \right] dx \, dy = \alpha \| w \|_1^2$$

(a)

However, the Poincaré-Friedrichs inequality,

$$\int_A w^2 \, dx \, dy \leq c \int_A \left[\left(\frac{\partial w}{\partial x} \right)^2 + \left(\frac{\partial w}{\partial y} \right)^2 \right] dx \, dy$$

where c is a constant, ensures that (a) is satisfied.

---

[12] Here we use the Schwarz inequality, which says that for vectors $\mathbf{a}$ and $\mathbf{b}$, $| \mathbf{a} \cdot \mathbf{b} | \leq \| \mathbf{a} \|_2 \| \mathbf{b} \|_2$, where $\| \cdot \|_2$ is defined in (2.148).

The above statements on the elasticity problem encompass one important point already mentioned earlier: the exact solution to the problem must correspond to a finite strain energy, see (4.64) and (4.79). Therefore, for example,—strictly—we do not endeavor to solve general two- or three-dimensional elasticity problems with the mathematical idealization of point loads (the solution for a point load on a half space corresponds to infinite strain energy, see for instance S. Timoshenko and J. N. Goodier [A]). Instead, we represent the loads in the elasticity problem closer to how they actually act in nature, namely as smoothly distributed loads, which however can have high magnitudes and act over very small areas. Then the solution of the variational formulation in (4.71) is the same as the solution of the differential formulation. Of course, in our finite element analysis so long as the finite elements are much larger than the area of load application, we can replace the distributed load over the area with an equivalent point load, merely for efficiency of solution; see Section 1.2 and the example in Fig. 1.4.

An important observation is that the exact solution to our elasticity problem is unique. Namely, assume that $\mathbf{u}_1$ and $\mathbf{u}_2$ *are* two different solutions; then we would have

$$a(\mathbf{u}_1, \mathbf{v}) = (\mathbf{f}, \mathbf{v}) \qquad \forall \mathbf{v} \in V \tag{4.80}$$

and

$$a(\mathbf{u}_2, \mathbf{v}) = (\mathbf{f}, \mathbf{v}) \qquad \forall \mathbf{v} \in V \tag{4.81}$$

Subtracting, we obtain

$$a(\mathbf{u}_1 - \mathbf{u}_2, \mathbf{v}) = 0 \qquad \forall \mathbf{v} \in V \tag{4.82}$$

and taking $\mathbf{v} = \mathbf{u}_1 - \mathbf{u}_2$, we have $a(\mathbf{u}_1 - \mathbf{u}_2, \mathbf{u}_1 - \mathbf{u}_2) = 0$. Using (4.79) with $\mathbf{v} = \mathbf{u}_1 - \mathbf{u}_2$, we obtain $\| \mathbf{u}_1 - \mathbf{u}_2 \|_1 = 0$, which means $\mathbf{u}_1 \equiv \mathbf{u}_2$, and hence we have proven that our assumption of two different solutions is untenable.

Now let V_h be the space of finite element displacement functions (which correspond to the displacement interpolations contained in all element displacement interpolation matrices $\mathbf{H}^{(m)}$) and let $\mathbf{v}_h$ be any element in that space (i.e., any displacement pattern that can be obtained by the displacement interpolations). Let $\mathbf{u}_h$ be the finite element solution; hence $\mathbf{u}_h$ is also an element in V_h and the specific element that we seek. Then the finite element solution of the problem in (4.71) can be written as

$$\boxed{\begin{array}{l} \text{Find } \mathbf{u}_h \in V_h \text{ such that} \\[1em] a(\mathbf{u}_h, \mathbf{v}_h) = (\mathbf{f}, \mathbf{v}_h) \qquad \forall \mathbf{v}_h \in V_h \end{array}} \tag{4.83}$$

The space V_h is defined as

$$\boxed{V_h = \left\{ \mathbf{v}_h \mid \mathbf{v}_h \in L^2(\text{Vol}); \frac{\partial (v_h)_i}{\partial x_j} \in L^2(\text{Vol}), i,j = 1, 2, 3; (v_h)_i \big|_{S_u} = 0, i = 1, 2, 3 \right\}} \tag{4.84}$$

and for the elements of this space we use the energy norm (4.74) and the Sobolev norm (4.76). Of course, $V_h \subset V$.

The relation in (4.83) is the principle of virtual work for the finite element discretization corresponding to V_h. With this solution space, the continuity and ellipticity conditions (4.77) and (4.78) are satisfied, using $\mathbf{v}_h \in V_h$, and a positive definite stiffness matrix is obtained for any V_h.

We should note that V_h corresponds to a given mesh, where h denotes the generic element size, and that in the discussion of convergence we of course consider a sequence of spaces V_h (a sequence of meshes with decreasing h). We illustrate in Figure 4.11 the elements of V_h for the discretization dealt with in Example 4.6.

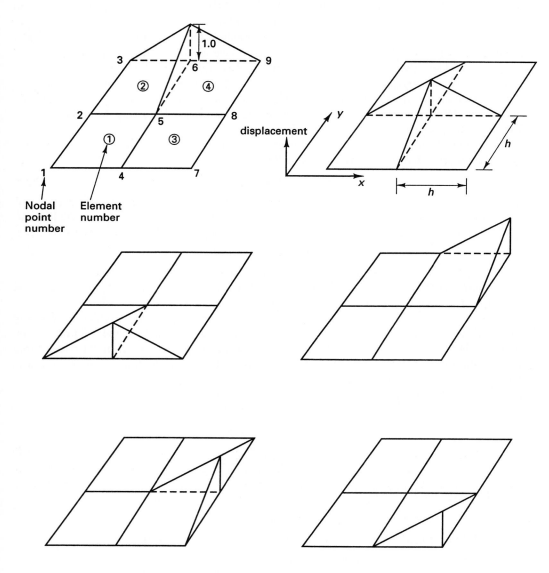

Figure 4.11 Aerial view of basis functions for space V_h used in analysis of cantilever plate of Example 4.6. The displacement functions are plotted upwards for ease of display, but each function shown is applicable to the u and v displacements. An element of V_h is any linear combination of the 12 displacement functions. Note that the functions correspond to the element displacement interpolation matrices $\mathbf{H}^{(m)}$, discussed in Example 4.6, and that the displacements at nodes 1, 2 and 3 are zero.

Considering the finite element solution $\mathbf{u}_h$ and the exact solution $\mathbf{u}$ to the problem, we have the following important properties.

Property 1.   Let the error between the exact solution $\mathbf{u}$ and the finite element solution $\mathbf{u}_h$ be $\mathbf{e}_h$,

$$\mathbf{e}_h = \mathbf{u} - \mathbf{u}_h \tag{4.85}$$

Then the first property is

$$a(\mathbf{e}_h, \mathbf{v}_h) = 0 \qquad \forall \ \mathbf{v}_h \in V_h \tag{4.86}$$

The proof is obtained by realizing that the principle of virtual work gives

$$a(\mathbf{u}, \mathbf{v}_h) = (\mathbf{f}, \mathbf{v}_h) \qquad \forall \ \mathbf{v}_h \in V_h \tag{4.87}$$

and

$$a(\mathbf{u}_h, \mathbf{v}_h) = (\mathbf{f}, \mathbf{v}_h) \qquad \forall \ \mathbf{v}_h \in V_h \tag{4.88}$$

so that by subtraction we obtain (4.86). We may say that the error is "orthogonal in $a(.\,,\,.)$" to all $\mathbf{v}_h$ in V_h. Clearly, as the space V_h increases, with the larger space always containing the smaller space, the solution accuracy will increase continuously. The next two properties are based on Property 1.

Property 2.   The second property is

$$a(\mathbf{u}_h, \mathbf{u}_h) \le a(\mathbf{u}, \mathbf{u}) \tag{4.89}$$

We prove this property by considering

$$\begin{aligned}
a(\mathbf{u}, \mathbf{u}) &= a(\mathbf{u}_h + \mathbf{e}_h, \mathbf{u}_h + \mathbf{e}_h) \\
&= a(\mathbf{u}_h, \mathbf{u}_h) + 2a(\mathbf{u}_h, \mathbf{e}_h) + a(\mathbf{e}_h, \mathbf{e}_h) \\
&= a(\mathbf{u}_h, \mathbf{u}_h) + a(\mathbf{e}_h, \mathbf{e}_h)
\end{aligned} \tag{4.90}$$

where we have used (4.86) with $\mathbf{v}_h = \mathbf{u}_h$. The relation (4.89) follows because $a(\mathbf{e}_h, \mathbf{e}_h) > 0$ for any $\mathbf{e}_h \ne \mathbf{0}$ (since for the properly supported structure $\|\mathbf{v}\|_E > 0$ for any nonzero $\mathbf{v}$).

Hence, the strain energy corresponding to the finite element solution is always smaller than or equal to the strain energy corresponding to the exact solution.

Property 3.   The third property is

$$a(\mathbf{e}_h, \mathbf{e}_h) \le a(\mathbf{u} - \mathbf{v}_h, \mathbf{u} - \mathbf{v}_h) \qquad \forall \ \mathbf{v}_h \in V_h \tag{4.91}$$

For the proof we use that for any $\mathbf{w}_h$ in V_h, we have

$$a(\mathbf{e}_h + \mathbf{w}_h, \mathbf{e}_h + \mathbf{w}_h) = a(\mathbf{e}_h, \mathbf{e}_h) + a(\mathbf{w}_h, \mathbf{w}_h) \tag{4.92}$$

Hence,
$$a(\mathbf{e}_h, \mathbf{e}_h) \le a(\mathbf{e}_h + \mathbf{w}_h, \mathbf{e}_h + \mathbf{w}_h) \tag{4.93}$$

Choosing $\mathbf{w}_h = \mathbf{u}_h - \mathbf{v}_h$ gives (4.91).

This third property says that the finite element solution $\mathbf{u}_h$ is chosen from all the possible displacement patterns $\mathbf{v}_h$ in V_h such that the strain energy corresponding to $\mathbf{u} - \mathbf{u}_h$ is the minimum. Hence, in that sense, the "energy distance" between $\mathbf{u}$ and the elements in V_h is minimized by the solution $\mathbf{u}_h$ in V_h.

Using (4.91) and the ellipticity and continuity of the bilinear form, we further obtain

$$
\begin{aligned}
\alpha \|\mathbf{u} - \mathbf{u}_h\|_1^2 &\le a(\mathbf{u} - \mathbf{u}_h, \mathbf{u} - \mathbf{u}_h) \\
&= \inf_{\mathbf{v}_h \in V_h} a(\mathbf{u} - \mathbf{v}_h, \mathbf{u} - \mathbf{v}_h) \\
&\le M \inf_{\mathbf{v}_h \in V_h} \|\mathbf{u} - \mathbf{v}_h\|_1 \|\mathbf{u} - \mathbf{v}_h\|_1
\end{aligned}
\tag{4.94}
$$

where "inf" denotes the infimum (see Table 4.5). If we let $d(\mathbf{u}, V_h) = \lim_{\mathbf{v}_h \in V_h} \|\mathbf{u} - \mathbf{v}_h\|_1$, we recognize that we have the *property*

$$\boxed{\|\mathbf{u} - \mathbf{u}_h\|_1 \le c\, d(\mathbf{u}, V_h)} \tag{4.95}$$

where c is a constant, $c = \sqrt{M/\alpha}$, independent of h but dependent on the material properties.[13] This result is referred to as Cea's lemma (see, for example, P. G. Ciarlet [A]).

The above three properties give valuable insight into how the finite element solution is chosen from the displacement patterns possible within a given finite element mesh and what we can expect as the mesh is refined.

We note, in particular, that (4.95), which is based on Property 3, states that a sufficient condition for convergence with our sequence of finite element spaces is that for any $\mathbf{u} \in V$ we have $\lim_{h \to 0} \inf \|\mathbf{u} - \mathbf{v}_h\|_1 = 0$. Also, (4.95) can be used to measure the rate of convergence as the mesh is refined by introducing an upper bound on how $d(\mathbf{u}, V_h)$ changes with the mesh refinement (see Section 4.3.5).

Further, Properties 2 and 3 say that *at* the finite element solution the error in strain energy is minimized within the possible displacement patterns of a given mesh and that the strain energy corresponding to the finite element solution will approach the exact strain energy (from below) as increasingly finer meshes are used (with the displacement patterns of the finer mesh containing the displacement patterns of the previous coarser mesh).

We can also relate these statements to earlier observations that in a finite element solution the stationarity of the total potential is established (see Section 4.3.2). That is, for a *given* mesh and *any* nodal displacements $\mathbf{U}_{\text{any}}$, we have

$$\boxed{\Pi|_{\mathbf{U}_{\text{any}}} = \tfrac{1}{2}\mathbf{U}_{\text{any}}^T \mathbf{K} \mathbf{U}_{\text{any}} - \mathbf{U}_{\text{any}}^T \mathbf{R}} \tag{4.96}$$

[13] There is a subtle point in considering the *property* (4.95) and the *condition* (4.156) discussed later; namely, while (4.95) is always valid for any values of bulk and shear moduli, the constant c becomes very large as the bulk modulus increases, and the property (4.95) is no longer useful. For this reason, when the bulk modulus κ is very large, we *need* the new property (4.156) in which the constant is independent of κ, and this leads to the inf-sup condition.

The finite element solution $\mathbf{U}$ is obtained by invoking the stationarity of Π to obtain

$$\mathbf{KU} = \mathbf{R}$$

At the finite element displacement solution $\mathbf{U}$ we have the total potential Π and strain energy $\mathcal{U}$

$$\boxed{\Pi = -\tfrac{1}{2}\mathbf{U}^T\mathbf{R}; \qquad \mathcal{U} = \tfrac{1}{2}\mathbf{U}^T\mathbf{R}} \tag{4.97}$$

Therefore, to evaluate the strain energy corresponding to the finite element solution, we only need to perform a vector multiplication.

To show with this notation that within the given possible finite element displacements (i.e., within the space V_h) Π is minimized at the finite element solution $\mathbf{U}$, let us calculate Π at $\mathbf{U} + \boldsymbol{\epsilon}$, where $\boldsymbol{\epsilon}$ is any arbitrary vector,

$$
\begin{aligned}
\Pi\big|_{\mathbf{U}+\boldsymbol{\epsilon}} &= \tfrac{1}{2}(\mathbf{U} + \boldsymbol{\epsilon})^T\mathbf{K}(\mathbf{U} + \boldsymbol{\epsilon}) - (\mathbf{U} + \boldsymbol{\epsilon})^T\mathbf{R} \\
&= \Pi\big|_{\mathbf{U}} + \boldsymbol{\epsilon}^T(\mathbf{KU} - \mathbf{R}) + \tfrac{1}{2}\boldsymbol{\epsilon}^T\mathbf{K}\boldsymbol{\epsilon} \\
&= \Pi\big|_{\mathbf{U}} + \tfrac{1}{2}\boldsymbol{\epsilon}^T\mathbf{K}\boldsymbol{\epsilon}
\end{aligned}
\tag{4.98}
$$

where we used that $\mathbf{KU} = \mathbf{R}$ and the fact that $\mathbf{K}$ is a symmetric matrix. However, since $\mathbf{K}$ is positive definite, $\Pi\big|_{\mathbf{U}}$ is the minimum of Π for the given finite element mesh. As the mesh is refined, Π will decrease and according to (4.97) $\mathcal{U}$ will correspondingly increase.

Considering (4.89), (4.91), and (4.97), we observe that in the finite element solution the displacements are (on the "whole") underestimated and hence the stiffness of the mathematical model is (on the "whole") overestimated. This overestimation of the stiffness is (physically) a result of the "internal displacement constraints" that are implicitly imposed on the solution as a result of the displacement assumptions. As the finite element discretization is refined, these "internal displacement constraints" are reduced, and convergence to the exact solution (and stiffness) of the mathematical model is obtained.

To exemplify the preceding discussion, Figure 4.12 shows the results obtained in the analysis of an ad hoc test problem for two-dimensional finite element discretizations. The problem is constructed so as to have no singularities. As we discuss in the next section, in this case the full (maximum) order of convergence is obtained with a given finite element in a sequence of uniform finite element meshes (in each mesh all elements are of equal square size).

Figure 4.12 shows the convergence in strain energy when a sequence of uniform meshes of nine-node elements is employed for the solutions. The meshes are constructed by starting with a 2×2 mesh of square elements of unit side length (for which $h = 1$), then subdividing each element into four equal square elements (for which $h = \tfrac{1}{2}$,) to obtain the second mesh, and continuing this process. We clearly see that the error in the strain energy decreases with decreasing element size h, as we would expect according to (4.91). We compare the order of convergence seen in the finite element computations with a theoretically established value in the next section.

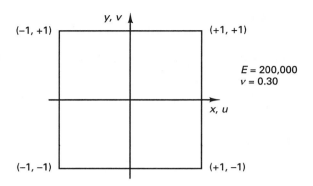

N elements per side, $N = 2, 4, 8,...$

(a) Square domain considered

$$u = c_1 (1 - x^2)(1 - y^2) e^{ky} \cos kx$$
$$v = c_1 (1 - x^2)(1 - y^2) e^{ky} \sin kx$$
$$c_1 = \text{constant; } k = 5$$

(b) Exact in-plane displacements

Obtain the finite element solution for the body loads f_x^B and f_y^B, where

$$f_x^B = -\left(\frac{\partial \tau_{xx}}{\partial x} + \frac{\partial \tau_{xy}}{\partial y}\right)$$

$$f_y^B = -\left(\frac{\partial \tau_{yy}}{\partial y} + \frac{\partial \tau_{yx}}{\partial x}\right)$$

and $\tau_{xx}, \tau_{yy}, \tau_{xy}$ are the stresses corresponding to the exact in-plane displacements given in (b).

(c) Test problem

Figure 4.12   Ad-hoc test problem for plane stress (or plane strain, axisymmetric) elements. We use, for h small, $E - E_h = c\,h^\alpha$ and hence $\log (E - E_h) = \log c + \alpha \log h$ (see also (4.101)). The numerical solutions give $\alpha = 3.91$.

4.3.5 Rate of Convergence

In the previous sections we considered the conditions required for monotonic convergence of the finite element analysis results and discussed how in general convergence is reached, but we did not mention the rate at which convergence occurs.

As must be expected, the rate of convergence depends on the order of the polynomials used in the displacement assumptions. In this context the notion of *complete* polynomials is useful.

Figure 4.13 shows the polynomial terms that should be included to have complete polynomials in x and y for two-dimensional analysis. It is seen that all possible terms of the form $x^\alpha y^\beta$ are present, where $\alpha + \beta = k$ and k is the degree to which the polynomial is complete. For example, we may note that the element investigated in Example 4.6 uses a

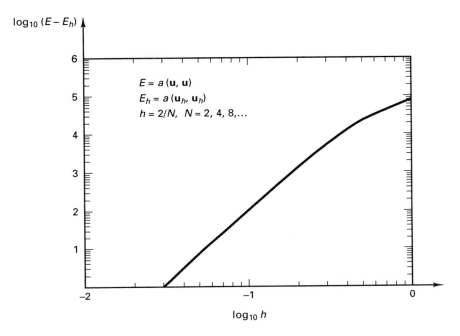

(d) Solution for plane stress problem

Figure 4.12   (*continued*)

polynomial displacement that is complete to degree 1 only. Figure 4.13 also shows important notation for polynomial spaces. The spaces P_k correspond to the complete polynomials up to degree k. They can also be thought of as the basis functions of triangular elements: the functions in P_1 correspond to the functions of the linear displacement (constant strain) triangle (see Example 4.17); the functions in P_2 correspond to the functions of the parabolic displacement (linear strain) triangle (see Section 5.3.2); and so on.

In addition, Fig. 4.13 shows the polynomial spaces Q_k, $k = 1, 2, 3$, which correspond to the 4-node, 9-node, and 16-node elements, referred to as Lagrangian elements because the displacement functions of these elements are Lagrangian functions (see also Section 5.5.1).

In considering three-dimensional analysis of course a figure analogous to Fig. 4.13 could be drawn in which the variable z would be included.

Let us think about a sequence of uniform meshes idealizing the complete volume of the body being considered. A mesh of a sequence of uniform meshes consists of elements of equal size—square elements when the polynomial spaces Q_k are used. Hence, the parameter h can be taken to be a typical length of an element side. The sequence is obtained by taking a starting mesh of elements and subdividing each element with a natural pattern to obtain the next mesh, and then repeating this process. We did this in solving the ad hoc test problem in Fig. 4.12. However, considering an additional analysis problem, for example, the problem in Example 4.6, we would in Fig. 4.11 subdivide each four-node element into four equal new four-node elements to obtain the first refined mesh; then we would

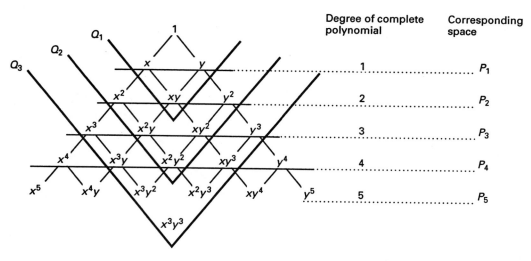

Figure 4.13 Polynomial terms in two-dimensional analysis, Pascal triangle

subdivide each element of the first refined mesh into four equal new four-node elements to obtain the second refined mesh; and so on. The continuation of this subdivision process would give the complete sequence of meshes.

To obtain an expression for the rate of convergence, we would ideally use a formula giving $d(\mathbf{u}, V_h)$ in (4.95) as a function of h. However, such a formula is difficult to obtain, and it is more convenient to use interpolation theory and work with an upper bound on $d(\mathbf{u}, V_h)$.

Let us assume that we employ elements with complete polynomials of degree k and that the exact solution $\mathbf{u}$ to our elasticity problem is "smooth" in the sense that the solution satisfies the relation[14]

$$\| \mathbf{u} \|_{k+1} = \left\{ \int_{\text{Vol}} \left[\sum_{i=1}^{3} (u_i)^2 + \sum_{i=1}^{3} \sum_{j=1}^{3} \left(\frac{\partial u_i}{\partial x_j} \right)^2 \right. \right.$$
$$\left. \left. + \sum_{n=2}^{k+1} \sum_{i=1}^{3} \sum_{r+s+t=n} \left(\frac{\partial^n u_i}{\partial x_1^r \, \partial x_2^s \, \partial x_3^t} \right)^2 \right] d\,\text{Vol} \right\}^{1/2} < \infty \tag{4.99}$$

where of course $k \geq 1$.

Therefore, we assume that all derivatives of the exact solution up to order $(k + 1)$ in (4.99) can be calculated.

A basic result of interpolation theory is that there exists an interpolation function $\mathbf{u}_I \in V_h$ such that

$$\| \mathbf{u} - \mathbf{u}_I \|_1 \leq \hat{c} \, h^k \, \| \mathbf{u} \|_{k+1} \tag{4.100}$$

where h is the mesh size parameter indicating the "size" of the elements and $\hat{c}$ is a constant independent of h. Typically, h is taken to be the length of the side of a generic element or the diameter of a circle encompassing that element. Note that $\mathbf{u}_I$ *is not the finite element solution* in V_h but merely an element in V_h that geometrically corresponds to a function

[14] We then have $\mathbf{u}$ is an element of the Hilbert space H^{k+1}.

close to $\mathbf{u}$. Frequently, as here, we let $\mathbf{u}_I$, at the finite element nodes, take the value of the exact solution $\mathbf{u}$.

Using (4.100) and Property 3 discussed in Section 4.3.4 [see (4.91)], we can now show that the rate of convergence of the finite element solution $\mathbf{u}_h$ to the exact theory of elasticity solution $\mathbf{u}$ is given by the error estimate

$$\boxed{\| \mathbf{u} - \mathbf{u}_h \|_1 \leq c\, h^k\, \| \mathbf{u} \|_{k+1}} \tag{4.101}$$

where c is a constant independent of h but dependent on the material properties. Namely, using (4.95) and (4.100), we have

$$\| \mathbf{u} - \mathbf{u}_h \|_1 \leq c\, d(\mathbf{u}, V_h)$$
$$\leq c\, \| \mathbf{u} - \mathbf{u}_I \|_1 \tag{4.101a}$$
$$\leq c\, \hat{c}\, h^k \| \mathbf{u} \|_{k+1}$$

which gives (4.101) with a new constant c. For (4.101), we say that the *rate of convergence* is given by the complete right-hand-side expression, and we say that the *order of convergence* is k or, equivalently, that we have $o(h^k)$ convergence.

Another way to look at the derivation of (4.101)—which is of course closely related to the previous derivation—is to use (4.79) and (4.91). Then we have

$$\| \mathbf{u} - \mathbf{u}_h \|_1 \leq \frac{1}{c_1} [a(\mathbf{u} - \mathbf{u}_h, \mathbf{u} - \mathbf{u}_h)]^{1/2}$$

$$\leq \frac{1}{c_1} [a(\mathbf{u} - \mathbf{u}_I, \mathbf{u} - \mathbf{u}_I)]^{1/2}$$

$$\leq \frac{c_2}{c_1} \| \mathbf{u} - \mathbf{u}_I \|_1 \tag{4.101b}$$

$$\leq c\, h^k \| \mathbf{u} \|_{k+1}$$

Hence, we see directly that to obtain the rate of convergence, we really only expressed the distance $d(\mathbf{u}, V_h)$ in terms of an upper bound given by (4.100).

In practice, we frequently simply write (4.101) as

$$\boxed{\| \mathbf{u} - \mathbf{u}_h \|_1 \leq c\, h^k} \tag{4.102}$$

and we now recognize that the constant c used here is independent of h but depends on the solution *and* the material properties [because c in (4.101a) and c_2, c_1 in (4.101b) depend on the material properties]. This dependence on the material properties is detrimental when (almost) incompressible material conditions are considered because the constant then becomes very large and the order of convergence k results in good accuracy only at very small (impractical) values of h. For this reason we need in that case the property (4.95) with the constant independent of the material properties, and this requirement leads to the condition (4.156) (see Section 4.5).

The constant c also depends on the kind of element used. While we have assumed that the element is based on a complete polynomial of order k, different kinds of elements within that class in general display a different constant c for the same analysis problem (e.g., triangular and quadrilateral elements). Hence, the actual magnitude of the error may be considerably different for a given h, while the order with which the error decreases as the mesh is refined is the same. Clearly, the magnitude of the constant c can be crucial in practical analysis because it largely determines how small h actually has to be in order to reach an acceptable error.

These derivations of course represent theoretical results, and we may question in how far these results are applicable in practice. Experience shows that the theoretical results indeed closely represent the actual convergence behavior of the finite element discretizations being considered. Indeed, to measure the order of convergence, we may simply consider the equal sign in (4.102) to obtain

$$\log \left(\| \mathbf{u} - \mathbf{u}_h \|_1 \right) = \log c + k \log h \tag{4.103}$$

Then, if we plot from our computed results the graph of $\log \left(\| \mathbf{u} - \mathbf{u}_h \|_1 \right)$ versus $\log h$, we find that the resulting curve indeed has the approximate slope k when h is sufficiently small.

Evaluating the Sobolev norm may require considerable effort, and in practice, we may use the equivalence of the energy norm with the 1-norm. Namely, because of (4.79), we see that (4.101) also holds for the energy norm on the left side, and this norm can frequently be evaluated more easily [see (4.97)]. Figure 4.12 shows an application. Note that the error in strain energy can be evaluated simply by subtracting the current strain energy from the strain energy of the limit solution (or, if known, the exact solution) [see (4.90)]. In the solution in Fig. 4.12 we obtained an order of convergence (of the numerical results) of 3.91, which compares very well with the theoretical value of 4 (here $k = 2$ and the strain energy is the energy norm squared). Further results of convergence for this ad hoc problem are given in Fig. 5.39 (where distorted elements with numerically integrated stiffness matrices are considered).

The relation in (4.101) gives, in essence, an error estimate for the displacement gradient, hence for the strains and stresses, because the primary contribution in the 1-norm will be due to the error in the derivatives of the displacements. We will primarily use (4.101) and (4.102) but also note that the error in the displacements is given by

$$\| \mathbf{u} - \mathbf{u}_h \|_0 \leq c \, h^{k+1} \| \mathbf{u} \|_{k+1} \tag{4.104}$$

Hence, the order of convergence for the displacements is one order higher than for the strains.

These results are intuitively reasonable. Namely, let us think in terms of a Taylor series analysis. Then, since a finite element of "dimension h" with a complete displacement expansion of order k can represent displacement variations up to that order exactly, the local error in representing arbitrary displacements with a uniform mesh should be $o(h^{k+1})$. Also, for a C^{m-1} problem the stresses are calculated by differentiating the displacements m times, and therefore the error in the stresses is $o(h^{k+1-m})$. For the theory of elasticity problem considered above, $m = 1$, and hence the relations in (4.101) and (4.104) are what we might expect.

EXAMPLE 4.25: Consider the problem shown in Figure E4.25. Estimate the error of the finite element solution if linear two-node finite elements are used.

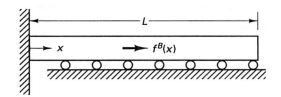

Constant cross-sectional area A
Young's modulus E

(a) Bar subjected to load per unit length $f^B(x) = ax$

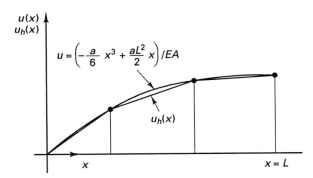

**(b) Solutions (for finite element
solution three elements are used)**

Figure E4.25   Analysis of bar

The finite element problem in this case is to calculate $u_h \in V_h$ such that

$$(EA\, u'_h, v'_h) = (f^B, v_h) \qquad \forall\, v_h \in V_h$$

with
$$V_h = \left\{ v_h \mid v_h \in L^2(\text{Vol}), \frac{\partial v_h}{\partial x} \in L^2(\text{Vol}), v_h|_{x=0} = 0 \right\}$$

To estimate the error we use (4.91) and can directly say for this simple problem

$$\int_0^L (u' - u'_h)^2 \, dx \leq \int_0^L (u' - u'_I)^2 \, dx \tag{a}$$

where u is the exact solution, u_h is the finite element solution, and u_I is the interpolant, meaning that u_I is considered to be equal to u at the nodal points. Hence, our aim is now to obtain an upper bound on $\int_0^L (u' - u'_I)^2 \, dx$.

Consider an arbitrary element with end points x_i and x_{i+1} in the mesh. Then we can say that for the exact solution $u(x)$ and $x_i \leq x \leq x_{i+1}$,

$$u'(x) = u'|_{x_c} + (x - x_c)u''\,|_{x=\bar{x}}$$

where $x = x_c$ denotes a chosen point in the element and $\bar{x}$ is also a point in the element. Let us choose an x_c where $u'|_{x_c} = u'_I$, which can always be done because

$$u_I(x_i) = u(x_i), \quad u_I(x_{i+1}) = u(x_{i+1})$$

Then we have for the element

$$\left| u'(x) - u'_I \right| \leq h \left(\max_{0 \leq x \leq L} |u''| \right) \tag{b}$$

where we have introduced the largest absolute value of the second derivative of the exact solution to obtain an upper bound.

With (b) we have

$$\int_0^L (u' - u'_I)^2 \, dx \leq Lh^2 \left(\max_{0 \leq x \leq L} |u''| \right)^2$$

and hence

$$\left(\int_0^L (u' - u'_h)^2 \, dx \right)^{1/2} \leq ch \tag{c}$$

where the constant c depends on A, E, L, and f^B but is independent of h.

We should recognize that this analysis is quite general but assumes that the exact solution is smooth so that its second derivative can be calculated (in this example given by $-f^B/EA$). Of course the result in (c) is just the error estimate (4.102).

An interesting additional result is that the nodal point displacements of the finite element solution are for two reasons the exact displacements. First, the exact solution at the nodes due to the distributed loading is the same as that due to the equivalent concentrated loading (the "equivalent" loading calculated by the principle of virtual work). Second, the finite element space V_h contains the exact solution corresponding to the equivalent concentrated loading. Of course, this nice result is a special property of the solution of one-dimensional problems and does not exist in general two- or three-dimensional analysis.

In the above convergence study it is assumed that uniform discretizations are used (that, for example, in two-dimensional analysis the elements are square and of equal size) and that the exact solution is smooth. Also, implicitly, the degree of the element polynomial displacement expansions is not varied. In practice, these conditions are generally not encountered, and we need to ask what the consequences might be.

If the solution is not smooth—for example, because of sudden changes in the geometry, in loads, or in material properties or thicknesses—and the uniform mesh subdivision is used, the order of convergence decreases; hence, the exponent of h in (4.102) is not k but a smaller value dependent on the degree of "loss of smoothness."

In practice of course graded meshes are used in such analyses, with small elements in the areas of high stress variation and larger elements away from these regions. The order of convergence of the solutions is then still given by (4.101) but rewritten as

$$\| \mathbf{u} - \mathbf{u}_h \|_1^2 \leq c \sum_m h_m^{2k} \| \mathbf{u} \|_{k+1,m}^2 \tag{4.101c}$$

where m denotes an individual element and h_m is a measure of the size of the element. Hence the total error is now estimated by summing the local contributions in (4.101) from each element. A good grading of elements means that the error density in each element is about the same.

In practice when mesh grading is employed, geometrically distorted elements are invariably used. Hence, for example, general quadrilateral elements are very frequently encountered in two-dimensional analyses. We discuss elements of general geometric shapes in Chapter 5 and point out in Section 5.3.3 that the same orders of convergence are applicable to these elements so long as the magnitude of the geometric distortions is reasonable.

In the above sequence of meshes the same kind of elements are used and the element sizes are uniformly decreased. This approach is referred to as the *h*-method of analysis. Alternatively, an initial mesh of relatively large and low-order elements may be chosen, and then the polynomial displacement expansions in the elements may be successively increased. For example, a mesh of elements with a bilinear displacement assumption may be used (here $k = 1$), and then the degree of the polynomial expansion is increased to order $2, 3, \ldots p$, where p may be 10 or even higher. This approach is referred to as the *p*-method of analysis. To achieve this increase in element polynomial order efficiently, special interpolation functions have been proposed that allow the calculation of the element stiffness matrix corresponding to a higher interpolation by using the previously calculated stiffness matrix and simply amending this matrix, and that have valuable orthogonality properties (see B. Szabó and I. Babuška [A]). However, unfortunately, these functions lack the internal element displacement variations which are important when elements are geometrically distorted (see K. Kato, N. S. Lee, and K. J. Bathe [A] and Section 5.3.3). We demonstrate the use of these functions in the following example.

EXAMPLE 4.26:   Consider the one-dimensional bar element shown in Fig. E4.26. Let $(\mathbf{K}_p)$ be the stiffness matrix corresponding to the order of displacement interpolation p, where $p = 1, 2, 3, \ldots$, and let the interpolation functions corresponding to $p = 1$ be

$$h_1 = \tfrac{1}{2}(1 - x); \qquad h_2 = \tfrac{1}{2}(1 + x) \tag{a}$$

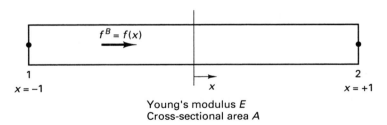

Young's modulus E
Cross-sectional area A

Figure E4.26   Bar element subjected to varying body force

For the higher-order interpolations use

$$h_i(x) = \phi_{i-1}(x) \qquad i = 3, 4, \ldots \tag{b}$$

where

$$\phi_j = \frac{1}{[2(2j - 1)]^{1/2}} [P_j(x) - P_{j-2}(x)] \tag{c}$$

and the P_j are the Legendre polynomials (see, for example, E. Kreyszig [A]),

$$P_0 = 1$$
$$P_1 = x$$
$$P_2 = \tfrac{1}{2}(3x^2 - 1)$$
$$P_3 = \tfrac{1}{2}(5x^3 - 3x)$$
$$P_4 = \tfrac{1}{8}(35x^4 - 30x^2 + 3)$$
$$\vdots$$
$$(n + 1)P_{n+1} = (2n + 1)xP_n - nP_{n-1}$$

Calculate the stiffness matrix $(\mathbf{K})_p$ and corresponding load vector of the element for $p \geq 1$.

Let us first note that these interpolation functions fulfill the requirements of monotonic convergence: the displacement continuity between elements is enforced, and the functions are complete (they can represent the rigid body mode and the constant strain state). This follows because the functions in (a) fulfill these requirements and the functions in (b) merely add higher-order displacement variations within the element with $h_i = 0$ at $x = \pm 1$, $i \geq 3$.

The stiffness matrix and load vector of the element are obtained using (4.19) and (4.20). Hence, typical elements of the stiffness matrix and load vector are

$$K_{ij} = \int_{-1}^{+1} AE \frac{dh_i}{dx}\frac{dh_j}{dx} dx \tag{d}$$

$$R_i^B = \int_{-1}^{+1} f(x)h_i \, dx$$

The evaluation of (d) gives

$$(\mathbf{K})_p = \frac{AE}{2} \begin{bmatrix} 1 & -1 & & & \text{zero} \\ -1 & 1 & & & \text{entries} \\ & & 2 & & \\ & & & 2 & \\ & & & & \ddots \\ & & & & & 2 \end{bmatrix}_{(p+1)\times(p+1)} \tag{e}$$

where we note that, in essence, the usual 2×2 stiffness matrix corresponding to the interpolation functions (a) has been amended by diagonal entries corresponding to the internal element displacement modes (b). In this specific case, each such entry is uncoupled from all other entries because of the orthogonality properties of the Legendre functions. Hence, as the order of the element is increased, additional diagonal entries are simply computed and all other stiffness coefficients are unchanged.

This structure of the matrix $(\mathbf{K})_p$ makes the solution of the governing equations of an element assemblage simple, and the conditioning of the coefficient matrix is always good irrespective of how high an order of element matrices is used. Note also that if the finite element solution is known for elements with a given order of interpolation, then the solution for an increased order of interpolation within the elements is obtained simply by calculating and adding the additional displacements due to the additional internal element modes.

Since the sets of displacement functions corresponding to the matrix $(\mathbf{K})_{p+1}$ contain the sets of functions corresponding to the matrix $(\mathbf{K})_p$, we refer to the displacement functions and the stiffness matrices as hierarchical functions and matrices. This hierarchical property is generally available when the interpolation order is increased (see Exercise 4.29 and Section 5.2).

The concept given in Example 4.26 is also used to establish the displacement functions for higher-order two- and three-dimensional elements. For example, in the two-dimensional case, the basic functions are h_i, $i = 1, 2, 3, 4$, used in Example 4.6, and the additional functions are due to side modes and internal modes (see Exercises 4.30 and 4.31).

We noted that in the analysis of a bar structure idealized by elements of the kind discussed in Example 4.26, the coupling between elements is due only to the nodal point displacements with the functions h_1 and h_2, and this leads to the very efficient solution. However, in the two- and three-dimensional cases this computational efficiency is not present because the element side modes couple the displacements of adjacent elements and the governing equations of the finite element assemblage have, in fact, a large bandwith (see Section 8.2.3).

A very high rate of convergence in the solution of general stress conditions can be obtained if we increase the number of elements and at the same time increase the order of displacement variations in the elements. This approach of mesh/element refinement is referred to as the h/p method and can yield an exponential rate of convergence of the form (see B. Szabó and I. Babuška [A])

$$\| \mathbf{u} - \mathbf{u}_h \|_1 \leq \frac{c}{\exp\left[\beta(N)^{\gamma}\right]} \tag{4.105}$$

where c, β, and γ are positive constants and N is the number of nodes in the mesh. If for comparison with (4.105) we write (4.101) in the same form, we obtain for the h method the algebraic rate of convergence

$$\| \mathbf{u} - \mathbf{u}_h \|_1 \leq \frac{c}{(N)^{k/d}}$$

where $d = 1, 2, 3$, respectively, in one-, two-, and three-dimensional problems. The effectiveness of the h/p method lies in that it combines the two attractive properties of the h and p methods: using the p method, an exponential rate of convergence is obtained when the exact solution is smooth, and using the h method, the optimal rate of convergence is maintained by proper mesh grading independent of the smoothness of the exact solution.

While the rate of convergence can be very high in the h/p solution approach, of course, whether the solution procedure is effective depends on the total computational effort expended to reach a specified error (which also depends on the constant c).

A key feature of a finite element solution using the h, p, or h/p methods must therefore be the "proper" mesh grading. The above expressions indicate a priori how convergence to the exact solution will be obtained as the density of elements and the order of interpolations are increased, but the meshes used in the successive solutions must be properly graded. By this we mean that the local error density in each element should be about constant. We discuss the evaluation of errors in the next section.

We also assumed in the above discussion on convergence—considering the linear static model problem—that the finite element matrices are calculated exactly and that the governing equilibrium equations are solved without error. In practice, numerical integration is employed in the evaluation of the element matrices (see Section 5.5), and finite precision arithmetic is used to solve the governing equilibrium equations (see Section 8.2.6); hence some error will clearly be introduced in the solution steps. However, the numerical integration errors will not reduce the order of convergence, provided a reliable integration scheme of high enough order is used (see Section 5.5.5), and the errors in the solution of equations are normally small unless a very ill-conditioned set of equations is solved (see Section 8.2.6).

4.3.6 Calculation of Stresses and the Assessment of Error

We discussed above that for monotonic convergence to the exact results ("exact" within the mechanical, i.e., mathematical, assumptions made) the elements must be complete and compatible. Using compatible (or conforming) elements means that in the finite element representation of a C^{m-1} variational problem, the displacements and their $(m-1)$st derivatives are continuous across the element boundaries. Hence, for example, in a plane stress analysis the u and v displacements are continuous, and in the analysis of a plate bending problem using the transverse displacement w as the only unknown variable, this displacement w and its derivatives, $\partial w/\partial x$ and $\partial w/\partial y$, are continuous. However, this continuity does not mean that the element stresses are continuous across element boundaries.

The element stresses are calculated using derivatives of the displacements [see (4.11) and (4.12)], and the stresses obtained at an element edge (or face) when calculated in adjacent elements may differ substantially if a coarse finite element mesh is used. The stress differences at the element boundaries decrease as the finite element mesh is refined, and the rate at which this decrease occurs is of course determined by the order of the elements in the discretization.

For the same mathematical reason that the element stresses are, in general, not continuous across element boundaries, the element stresses at the surface of the structure that is modeled are, in general, not in equilibrium with the externally applied tractions. However, as for the stress jumps between elements, the difference between the externally applied tractions and the element stresses decreases as the number of elements used to model the structure increases.

The stress jumps across element boundaries and stress imbalances at the boundary of the body are of course a consequence of the fact that stress equilibrium is not accurately satisfied at the differential level unless a very fine finite element discretization is used: we recall the derivation of the principle of virtual work in Example 4.2. The development in this example shows that the differential equations of equilibrium are fulfilled only if the virtual work equation is satisfied for *any* arbitrary virtual displacements that are zero on the surface of the displacement boundary conditions. In the finite element analysis, the number of "real" and virtual displacement patterns is equal to the number of nodal degrees of freedom, and hence only an approximate solution in terms of satisfying the stress equilibrium at the differential level is obtained (while the compatibility and constitutive conditions are satisfied exactly). The error in the solution can therefore be measured by substituting the finite element solution for the stresses τ_{ij}^h into the basic equations of equilibrium to find that for each geometric domain represented by a finite element,

$$\tau_{ij,j}^h + f_i^B \neq 0 \tag{4.106}$$

$$\tau_{ij}^h n_j - t_i \neq 0 \tag{4.107}$$

where n_j represents the direction cosines of the normal to the element domain boundary and the t_i are the components of the exact traction vector along that boundary (see Fig. 4.14). Of course, this traction vector of the exact solution is not known, and that the left-hand side of (4.107) is not zero simply shows that we must expect stress jumps between elements.

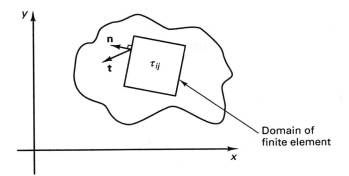

(a) Exact solution to mathematical model

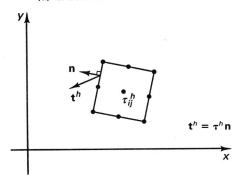

$$t^h = \tau^h n$$

(b) Finite element solution

Figure 4.14 Finite element representing subdomain of continuum

It can be proven that for low-order elements the imbalance in (4.107) is larger than the imbalance in (4.106), and that for high-order elements the imbalance in (4.106) becomes predominant. In practice, (4.107) can be used to obtain an indication of the accuracy of the stress solution and is easily applied by using the isobands of stresses as proposed by T. Sussman and K. J. Bathe [A]. These isobands are constructed using the calculated stresses without stress smoothing as follows:

Choose a stress measure; typically, pressure or the effective (von Mises) stress is chosen, but of course any stress component may be selected.

Divide the entire range over which the stress measure varies into stress intervals, assign each interval a color (or use black and white shading or simply alternate black and white intervals).

A point in the mesh is given the color of the interval corresponding to the value of the stress measure at that point.

If all stresses are continuous across the element boundaries, then this procedure will yield unbroken isobands of stresses. However, in practice, stress discontinuities arise across the element boundaries, resulting in "breaks" in the bands. The magnitude of the intervals of the stress bands together with the severity of the breaks in the bands indicate directly the magnitude of stress discontinuities (see Fig. 4.15). Hence, the isobands represent an

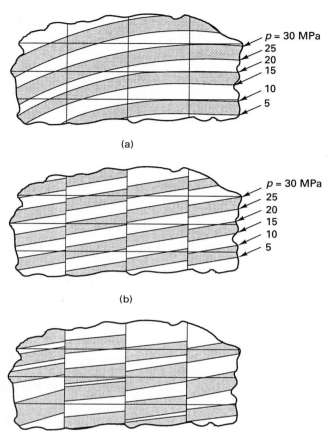

(a)

(b)

(c)

Figure 4.15 Schematic of estimating stress discontinuities using pressure bands, width of bands = 5 MPa; black and white intervals are used; (a) negligible discontinuities, $\Delta p \ll 5$ MPa; (b) visible discontinuities but bands still distinguishable, $\Delta p \simeq 2$ MPa; (c) visible discontinuities, bands not distinguishable, $\Delta p > 5$ MPa.

"eyeball norm" for the accuracy of the stress prediction τ_{ij}^h achieved with a given finite element mesh.

In linear analysis, the finite element stress values can be calculated using the relation $\boldsymbol{\tau}^h = \mathbf{CB\hat{u}}$ at any point in the element; however, this evaluation is relatively expensive and hardly possible in general nonlinear analysis (including material nonlinear effects). An adequate approach is to use the integration point values to bilinearly interpolate over the corresponding domain of the element. Figure 4.16 illustrates an example in two-dimensional analysis.

An alternative procedure for obtaining an approximation to the error in the calculated stresses τ_{ij}^h is to first find some improved values $(\tau_{ij}^h)_{\text{impr.}}$ and then evaluate and display

$$\Delta \tau_{ij} = \tau_{ij}^h - (\tau_{ij}^h)_{\text{impr.}} \tag{4.108}$$

The display can again be achieved effectively using the isoband procedure discussed above.

Improved values might be found by simply averaging the stress values obtained at the nodes using the procedure indicated in Fig. 4.16 or by using a least squares fit over the integration point values of the elements (see E. Hinton and J. S. Campbell [A]). The least squares procedure might be applied over patches of adjacent elements or even globally over

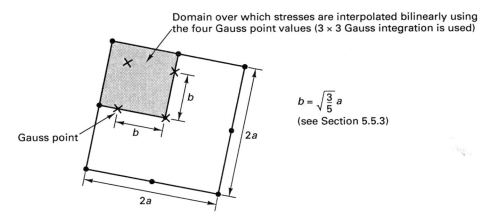

Domain over which stresses are interpolated bilinearly using the four Gauss point values (3 × 3 Gauss integration is used)

$$b = \sqrt{\frac{3}{5}}\,a$$

(see Section 5.5.3)

Gauss point

Figure 4.16   Interpolation of stresses from Gauss point stresses

a whole mesh. However, if the domain over which the least squares fit is applied involves many stress points, the solution will be expensive and, in addition, a large error in one part of the domain may affect rather strongly the least squares prediction in the other parts. Another consideration is that when using the direct stress evaluation in (4.12), the stresses are frequently more accurate at the numerical integration points used to evaluate the element matrices (see Section 5.5) than at the nodal points. Hence, for a least squares fit, it can be of value to use functions of order higher than that of the stress variations obtained from the assumed displacement functions because in this way improved values can be expected.

We demonstrate the nodal point and least squares stress averaging in the following example.

EXAMPLE 4.27:   Consider the mesh of nine-node elements shown in Fig. E4.27. Propose reasonable schemes for improving the stress results by nodal point averaging and least squares fitting.

Let τ be a typical stress component. One simple and frequently effective way of improving the stress results is to bilinearly extrapolate the calculated stress components from the integration points of each element to node i. In this way, for the situation and node i in Fig. E4.27, four values for each stress component are obtained. The mean value, say $(\tau^h)^i_{\text{mean}}$, of these four values is then taken as the value at nodal point i. After performing similar calculations for each nodal point, the improved value of the stress component over a typical element is

$$(\tau^h)_{\text{impr.}} = \sum_{i=1}^{9} h_i (\tau^h)^i_{\text{mean}} \tag{a}$$

where the h_i are the displacement interpolation functions because the averaged nodal values are deemed to be more accurate than the values obtained simply from the derivatives of the displacements (which would imply that an interpolation of one order lower is more appropriate).

The key step in this scheme is the calculation of $(\tau^h)^i_{\text{mean}}$. Such an improved value can also be extracted by using a procedure based on least squares.

Consider the eight nodes closest to node i, plus node i, and the values of the stress component of interest at the 16 integration points closest to node i (shown in Fig. E4.27). Let $(\tau^h)^i_{\text{integr.}}$ be the known values of the stress component at the integration points, $j = 1, \ldots, 16$, and let $(\tau^h)^k_{\text{nodes}}$ be the unknown values at the nine nodes (of the domain corresponding to the

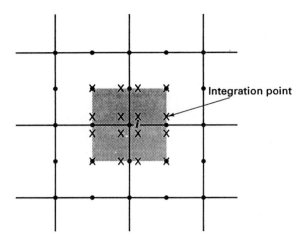

Figure E4.27   Mesh of nine-node elements. Integration points near node *i* are also shown.

integration points). We can use the least squares procedure (see Section 3.3.3) to calculate the values $(\tau^h)^k_{\text{nodes}}$ by minimizing the errors between the given integration point values and the values calculated at the same points by interpolation from the nodal point values $(\tau^h)^k_{\text{nodes}}$,

$$\frac{\partial}{\partial(\tau^h)^k_{\text{nodes}}}\left[\sum_{j=1}^{16}((\tau^h)^i_{\text{integr.}} - (\hat{\tau}^h)^i_{\text{integr.}})^2\right] = 0 \tag{b}$$

$$k = 1, \ldots, 9$$

where
$$(\hat{\tau}^h)^i_{\text{integr.}} = \sum_{k=1}^{9} h_k \bigg|_{\substack{\text{at integr.} \\ \text{point } j}} (\tau^h)^k_{\text{nodes}} \tag{c}$$

Note that in (c) we evaluate the interpolation functions at the 16 integration stations shown in Fig. E4.27. The relations in (b) and (c) give nine equations for the values $(\tau^h)^k_{\text{nodes}}, k = 1, \ldots, 9$. We solve for these values but accept only the value at node *i* as the improved stress value, which is now our value for $(\tau^h)^i_{\text{mean}}$ in (a). The same basic procedure is used for all nodes to arrive at nodal "mean" values, so that (a) can be used for all elements.

A least squares procedure clearly involves more computations, and in many cases the simpler scheme of merely extrapolating the Gauss values and averaging at the nodes as described above is adequate.

Of course, we presented in Fig. E4.27 a situation of four equal square elements. In practice, the elements are generally distorted and fewer or more elements may couple into the node *i*. Also, element non-corner nodes and special mesh topologies at boundaries need to be considered.

We emphasize that the calculation of an error measure and its display is a most important aspect of a finite element solution. The quality of the finite element stress solution τ^h_{ij} should be known. Once the error is acceptably small, values of stresses that have been smoothed, for example, by nodal point or least squares averaging, can be used with confidence.

These error measures are based on the discontinuities of stresses between elements. However, for high-order elements (of order 4 and higher), such discontinuities can be small and yet the solution is not accurate because the differential equations of equilibrium of stresses within the elements are not satisfied to sufficient accuracy. In this case the error measure should also include the element internal stress imbalance (4.106).

Once an error measure for the stresses has been calculated in a finite element solution and the errors are deemed to be too large, a procedure needs to be used to establish a new mesh (with a refined discretization in certain areas, derefinement in other areas, and possibly new element interpolation orders). This process of new mesh selection can be automatized to a large degree and is important for the widespread use of finite element analysis in CAD (see Section 1.3).

4.3.7 Exercises

4.25. Calculate the eight smallest eigenvalues of the four-node shell element stiffness matrix available in a finite element program and interpret each eigenvalue and corresponding eigenvector. (*Hint:* The eigenvalues of the element stiffness matrix can be obtained by carrying out a frequency solution with a mass matrix corresponding to unit masses for each degree of freedom.)

4.26. Show that the strain energy corresponding to the displacement error e_h, where $e_h = u - u_h$, is equal to the difference in the strain energies, corresponding to the exact displacement solution u and the finite element solution u_h.

4.27. Consider the analysis problem in Example 4.6. Use a finite element program to perform the convergence study shown in Fig. 4.12 with the nine-node and four-node (Lagrangian) elements. That is, measure the rate of convergence in the energy norm and compare this rate with the theoretical results given in Section 4.3.5. Use $N = 2, 4, 8, 16, 32$; consider $N = 32$ to be the limit solution, and use uniform and graded meshes.

4.28. Perform an analysis of the cantilever problem shown using a finite element program. Use a two-dimensional plane stress element idealization to solve for the static response.

(a) Use meshes of four-node elements.

(b) Use meshes of nine-node elements.

In each case construct a sequence of meshes and identify the rate of convergence of strain energy.

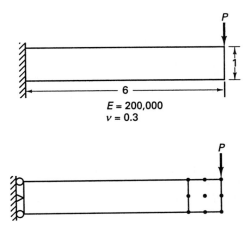

P

6

$E = 200,000$
$v = 0.3$

P

Also, compare your finite element solutions with the solutions using Bernoulli-Euler and Timoshenko beam theories (see S. H. Crandall, N. C. Dahl, and T. J. Lardner [A] and Section 5.4.1).

4.29. Consider the three-node bar element shown. Construct and plot the displacement functions of the element for the following two cases:

for case 1: $h_i = 1$ at node i, $i = 1, 2, 3$
                       $= 0$ at node $j \neq i$

for case 2: $h_i = 1$ at node i, $i = 1, 2$
                       $= 0$ at node $j \neq i$, $j = 1, 2$
                       $h_3 = 1$ at node 3
                       $h_3 = 0$ at node 1, 2

We note that the functions for case 1 and case 2 contain the same displacement variations, and hence correspond to the same displacement space. Also, the sets of functions are hierarchical because the three-node element contains the functions of the two-node element.

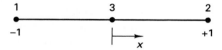

4.30. Consider the eight-node element shown. Identify the terms of the Pascal triangle present in the element interpolations.

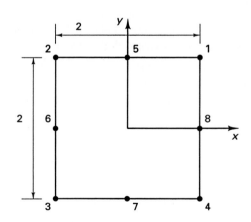

$$h_1 = \tfrac{1}{4}(1 + x)(1 + y), \quad h_2 = \tfrac{1}{4}(1 - x)(1 + y)$$

$$h_3 = \tfrac{1}{4}(1 - x)(1 - y), \quad h_4 = \tfrac{1}{4}(1 + x)(1 - y)$$

$$h_5 = \tfrac{1}{2}(1 + y)\phi_2(x), \quad h_6 = \tfrac{1}{2}(1 - x)\phi_2(y)$$

$$h_7 = \tfrac{1}{2}(1 - y)\phi_2(x), \quad h_8 = \tfrac{1}{2}(1 + x)\phi_2(y)$$

where ϕ_2 is defined in Example 4.26.

4.31. A p-element of order $p = 4$ is obtained by using the following displacement functions.

h_i, $i = 1, 2, 3, 4$, as for the basic four-node element (with corner nodes only; see Example 4.6).

h_i, $i = 5, \ldots , 16$ to represent side modes.

side 1:	$h_i^{(1)} = \frac{1}{2}(1 + y)\phi_j(x)$;	$i = 5, 9, 13; j = 2, 3, 4$
side 2:	$h_i^{(2)} = \frac{1}{2}(1 - x)\phi_j(y)$;	$i = 6, 10, 14; j = 2, 3, 4$
side 3:	$h_i^{(3)} = \frac{1}{2}(1 - y)\phi_j(x)$;	$i = 7, 11, 15; j = 2, 3, 4$
side 4:	$h_i^{(4)} = \frac{1}{2}(1 + x)\phi_j(y)$;	$i = 8, 12, 16; j = 2, 3, 4$

where ϕ_2, ϕ_3, and ϕ_4 have been defined in Example 4.26. h_{17} to represent an internal mode

$$h_{17} = (1 - x^2)(1 - y^2)$$

Identify the terms of the Pascal triangle present in the element interpolations.

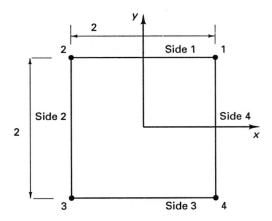

4.32. Consider the analysis problem in Example 4.6. Use a finite element program to solve the problem with the meshes of nine-node elements in Exercise 4.27 and plot isobands of the von Mises stress and the pressure (without using stress smoothing). Hence, the isobands will display stress discontinuities between elements. Show how the bands converge to continuous stress bands over the cantilever plate.

4.4 INCOMPATIBLE AND MIXED FINITE ELEMENT MODELS

In the previous sections we considered the displacement-based finite element method, and the conditions imposed so far on the assumed displacement (or field) functions were completeness and compatibility. If these conditions are satisfied, the calculated solution converges in the strain energy monotonically (i.e., one-sided) to the exact solution. The completeness condition can, in general, be satisfied with relative ease. The compatibility condition can also be satisfied without major difficulties in C^0 problems, for example, in plane stress and plane strain problems or in the analysis of three-dimensional solids such as dams. Yet, in the analysis of shell problems, and in complex analyses in which completely different finite elements must be used to idealize different regions of the structure, compatibility may be quite impossible to maintain. However, although the compatibility requirements are violated, experience shows that good results are frequently obtained.

Also, in the search for finite element it was realized that for shell analysis and the analysis of incompressible media, the pure displacement-based method is not efficient. The difficulties in developing compatible displacement-based finite elements for these problems that are computationally effective, and the realization that by using variational approaches many more finite element discretizations can be developed, led to large research efforts. In these activities various classes of new types of elements have been proposed, and the amount of information available on these elements is voluminous. We shall not present the various formulations in detail but only briefly outline some of the major ideas that have been used and then concentrate upon a formulation for a large class of problems—the analysis of almost incompressible media. The analysis of plate and shell structures using many of the concepts outlined below is then further addressed in Chapter 5.

4.4.1 Incompatible Displacement-Based Models

In practice, a frequently made observation is that satisfactory finite element analysis results have been obtained although some continuity requirements between displacement-based elements in the mesh employed were violated. In some instances the nodal point layout was such that interelement continuity was not preserved, and in other cases elements were used that contained interelement incompatibilities (see Example 4.28). The final result was the same in either case, namely, that the displacements or their derivatives between elements were not continuous to the degree necessary to satisfy all compatibility conditions discussed in Section 4.3.2.

Since in finite element analysis using incompatible (nonconforming) elements the requirements presented in Section 4.3.2 are not satisfied, the calculated total potential energy is not necessarily an upper bound to the exact total potential energy of the system, and consequently, monotonic convergence is not ensured. However, having relaxed the objective of monotonic convergence in the analysis, we still need to establish conditions that will ensure at least a nonmonotonic convergence.

Referring to Section 4.3, the element completeness condition must always be satisfied, and it may be noted that this condition is not affected by the size of the finite element. We recall that an element is complete if it can represent the physical rigid body modes (but the element matrix has no spurious zero eigenvalues) and the constant strain states.

However, the compatibility condition can be relaxed somewhat at the expense of not obtaining a monotonically convergent solution, provided that when relaxing this requirement, the essential ingredients of the completeness condition are not lost. We recall that as the finite element mesh is refined (i.e., the size of the elements gets smaller), each element should approach a constant strain condition. Therefore, the second condition on convergence of an assemblage of incompatible finite elements, where the elements may again be of any size, is that the elements together can represent constant strain conditions. We should note that *this is not a condition on a single individual element but on an assemblage of elements.* That is, although an individual element is able to represent all constant strain states, when the element is used in an assemblage, the incompatibilities between elements may prohibit constant strain states from being represented. We may call this condition the *completeness condition on an element assemblage.*

As a test to investigate whether an assemblage of nonconforming elements is complete, the *patch test* has been proposed (see B. M. Irons and A. Razzaque [A]). In this test a specific element is considered and a patch of elements is subjected to the minimum displacement boundary conditions to eliminate all rigid body modes and to the boundary nodal point forces that by an analysis should result in constant stress conditions. If for *any* patch of elements the element stresses actually represent the constant stress conditions and all nodal point displacements are correctly predicted, we say that the element passes the patch test. Since a patch may also consist of only a single element, this test ensures that the element itself is complete and that the completeness condition is also satisfied by any element assemblage.

The number of constant stress states in a patch test depends of course on the actual number of constant stress states that pertain to the mathematical model; for example, in plane stress analysis three constant stress states must be considered in the patch test, whereas in a fully three-dimensional analysis six constant stress states should be possible.

Fig. 4.17 shows a typical patch of elements used in numerical investigations for various problems. Here of course only one mesh with distorted elements is considered, whereas in fact any patch of distorted elements should be analyzed. This, however, requires an analytical solution. If in practice the element is complete and the specific analyses shown here produce the correct results, then it is quite likely that the element passes the patch test.

When considering displacement-based elements with incompatibilities, if the patch test is passed, convergence is ensured (although convergence may not be monotonic and convergence may be slow).

The patch test is used to assess incompatible finite element meshes, and we may note that when properly formulated displacement-based elements are used in compatible meshes, the patch test is automatically passed.

Figure 4.18(a) shows a patch of eight-node elements (which are discussed in detail in Section 5.2). The tractions corresponding to the plane stress patch test are also shown. The elements form a compatible mesh, and hence the patch test is passed.

However, if we next assign to nodes 1 to 8 individual degrees of freedom for the adjacent elements [e.g., at node 2 we assign two u and v degrees of freedom each for elements 1 and 2] such that the displacements are not tied together at these nodes (and therefore displacement incompatibilities exist along the edges), the patch test is not passed. Figure 4.18(b) gives some results of the solution.

The example in Fig. 4.18(b) uses, in essence, an element that was proposed by E. L. Wilson, R. L. Taylor, W. P. Doherty, and J. Ghaboussi [A]. Since the degrees of freedom of the midside nodes of an element are not connected to the adjacent elements, they can be statically condensed out at the element level (see Section 8.2.4) and a four-node element is obtained. However, as indicated in Fig. 4.18(b), this element does not pass the patch test. In the following example, we consider the element in more detail, first as a square element

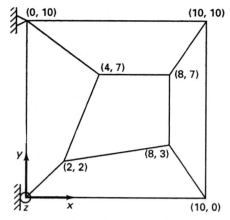

(a) Patch of elements, two-dimensional elements, plate bending elements, or side view of three-dimensional elements. Each quadrilateral domain represents an element; for triangular and tetrahedral elements, each quadrilateral domain is further subdivided

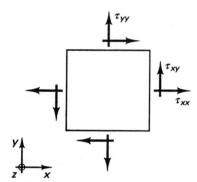

Plane stress and plane strain: τ_{xx}, τ_{yy}, τ_{xy} constant; in three-dimensional analysis the additional three stress conditions τ_{zz}, τ_{zx}, τ_{yz} constant are tested

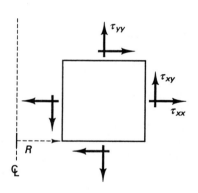

Axisymmetric; here perform the test with $R \rightarrow \infty$

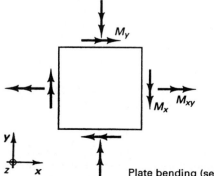

Plate bending (see Section 5.4.2)

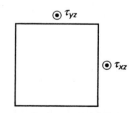

(This test also produces bending)

(b) Stress conditions to be tested

Figure 4.17 Patch tests

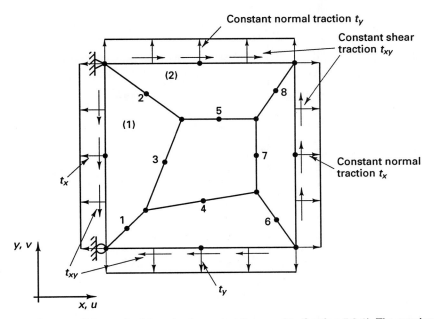

(a) Patch test of compatible mesh of 8-node elements (discussed in Section 5.3.1). The patch test is passed; that is, all calculated element stresses are equal to the applied tractions

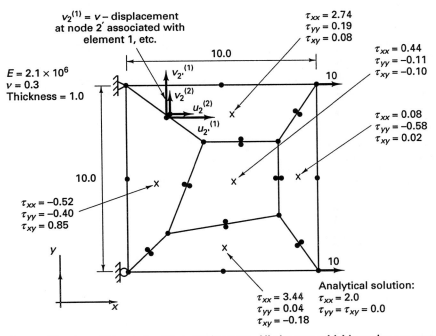

(b) Patch test of incompatible mesh of 8-node elements. All element midside nodes are now element individual nodes with degrees of freedom not coupled to the adjacent element. Hence, two nodes are located where in Fig. 4.18(a) only one node was located. Patch test results are shown at center of elements for external traction applied in the x-direction. (Note that only the corner nodes of the complete patch are subjected to externally applied loads)

Figure 4.18 Patch test results using the patch and element geometries of Fig. 4.17

and then as a general quadrilateral element. We also present a remedy to correct the element so that it will always pass the patch test (see E. L. Wilson and A. Ibrahimbegovic [A]).

EXAMPLE 4.28: Consider the four-node square element with incompatible modes in Fig. E4.28(a) and determine whether the patch test is passed. Then consider the general quadrilateral element in Fig. E4.28(b) and repeat the investigation.

We notice that the square element is really a special case of the general quadrilateral element. In fact, the quadrilateral element is formulated using the square element as a basis and using the natural coordinates (r, s) in the interpolations as discussed in Section 5.2.

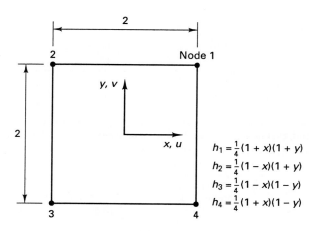

$$h_1 = \frac{1}{4}(1 + x)(1 + y)$$
$$h_2 = \frac{1}{4}(1 - x)(1 + y)$$
$$h_3 = \frac{1}{4}(1 - x)(1 - y)$$
$$h_4 = \frac{1}{4}(1 + x)(1 - y)$$

Displacement interpolation functions

$$u = \sum_{i=1}^{4} h_i u_i + \alpha_1 \phi_1 + \alpha_2 \phi_2$$
$$v = \sum_{i=1}^{4} h_i v_i + \alpha_3 \phi_1 + \alpha_4 \phi_2$$
$$\phi_1 = (1 - x^2); \ \phi_2 = (1 - y^2)$$

(a) Square element

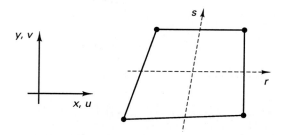

(b) General quadrilateral element (here h_i and ϕ_i are used with r, s coordinates; see Section 5.2)

Figure E4.28 Four-node plane stress element with incompatible modes, constant thickness

For this element formulation we can analytically investigate whether, or under which conditions, the patch test is passed. First, we recall that the patch test is passed for the four-node compatible element (i.e., when the ϕ_1, ϕ_2 displacement interpolations are not used).

Next, let us consider that the element is placed in a condition of constant stresses $\boldsymbol{\tau}^c$. Then the requirement for passing the patch test is that, in these constant stress conditions, the element should behave in the same way as the four-node compatible element.

The formal mathematical condition can be derived by considering the stiffness matrix of the element with incompatible modes.

Let

$$\hat{\mathbf{u}}^* = \begin{bmatrix} \hat{\mathbf{u}} \\ \boldsymbol{\alpha} \end{bmatrix}$$

with

$$\hat{\mathbf{u}}^T = [u_1 \quad \ldots \quad u_4 \vdots v_1 \quad \ldots \quad v_4]$$

and

$$\boldsymbol{\alpha}^T = [\alpha_1 \quad \ldots \quad \alpha_4]$$

Then

$$\boldsymbol{\epsilon} = [\mathbf{B} \vdots \mathbf{B}_{\text{IC}}] \begin{bmatrix} \hat{\mathbf{u}} \\ \cdots \\ \boldsymbol{\alpha} \end{bmatrix}$$

where $\mathbf{B}$ is the usual strain-displacement matrix of the four-node element and $\mathbf{B}_{\text{IC}}$ is the contribution due to the incompatible modes.

Hence, with our usual notation, we have

$$\begin{bmatrix} \int_V \mathbf{B}^T \, \mathbf{CB} \, dV & \vdots & \int_V \mathbf{B}^T \, \mathbf{CB}_{\text{IC}} \, dV \\ \cdots\cdots\cdots\cdots\cdots\cdots & \vdots & \cdots\cdots\cdots\cdots\cdots\cdots \\ \int_V \mathbf{B}_{\text{IC}}^T \, \mathbf{CB} \, dV & \vdots & \int_V \mathbf{B}_{\text{IC}}^T \, \mathbf{CB}_{\text{IC}} \, dV \end{bmatrix} \begin{bmatrix} \hat{\mathbf{u}} \\ \boldsymbol{\alpha} \end{bmatrix} = \begin{bmatrix} \mathbf{R} \\ \mathbf{0} \end{bmatrix} \qquad (a)$$

In practice, the incompatible displacement parameters $\boldsymbol{\alpha}$ would now be statically condensed out to obtain the element stiffness matrix corresponding to only the $\hat{\mathbf{u}}$ degrees of freedom.

If the nodal point displacements are the physically correct values $\hat{\mathbf{u}}^c$ for the constant stresses $\boldsymbol{\tau}^c$, we have

$$\int_V \mathbf{B}_{\text{IC}}^T \, \mathbf{CB} \, dV \, \hat{\mathbf{u}}^c = \int_V \mathbf{B}_{\text{IC}}^T \boldsymbol{\tau}^c \, dV \qquad (b)$$

To now force the element to behave under constant stress conditions in the same way as the four-node compatible element, we require that (since the entries $\boldsymbol{\tau}^c$ are independent of each other)

$$\int_V \mathbf{B}_{\text{IC}}^T \, dV = \mathbf{0} \qquad (c)$$

Namely, when (c) is satisfied, we find from (a):

> If the nodal point forces of the element are those of the compatible four-node element, the solution is $\hat{\mathbf{u}} = \hat{\mathbf{u}}^c$ and $\boldsymbol{\alpha} = \mathbf{0}$. Also, of course, if we set $\hat{\mathbf{u}} = \hat{\mathbf{u}}^c$ and $\boldsymbol{\alpha} = \mathbf{0}$, we obtain from (a) the nodal point forces of the compatible four-node element and no forces corresponding to the incompatible modes.

Hence, under constant stress conditions the element behaves as if the incompatible modes were not present.

We can now easily check that the condition in (c) is satisfied for the square element:

$$\int_V \begin{bmatrix} -2x & 0 & 0 & 0 \\ 0 & 0 & 0 & -2y \\ 0 & -2y & -2x & 0 \end{bmatrix} dV = \mathbf{0}$$

However, we can also check that the condition is not satisfied for the general quadrilateral element (here the Jacobian transformation of Section 5.2 is used to evaluate $\mathbf{B}_{IC}$). In order to satisfy (c) we therefore modify the $\mathbf{B}_{IC}$ matrix by a correction $\mathbf{B}_{IC}^C$ and use

$$\mathbf{B}_{IC}^{new} = \mathbf{B}_{IC} + \mathbf{B}_{IC}^C$$

The condition (c) on $\mathbf{B}_{IC}^{new}$ gives

$$\mathbf{B}_{IC}^C = -\frac{1}{V} \int_V \mathbf{B}_{IC} \, dV$$

The element stiffness matrix is then obtained by using $\mathbf{B}_{IC}^{new}$ in (a) instead of $\mathbf{B}_{IC}$. In practice, the element stiffness matrix is evaluated by numerical integration (see Chapter 5), and $\mathbf{B}_{IC}^C$ is calculated by numerical integration prior to the evaluation of (a).

With the above patch test we test only for the constant stress conditions. Any patch of elements with incompatibilities must be able to represent these conditions if convergence is to be ensured.

In essence, this patch test is a boundary value problem in which the external forces are prescribed (the forces $\mathbf{f}^B$ are zero and the tractions $\mathbf{f}^S$ are constant) and the deformations and internal stresses are calculated (the rigid body modes are merely suppressed to render the solution possible). If the deformations and constant stresses are correctly predicted, the patch test is passed, and (because at least constant stresses can be correctly predicted) convergence in stresses will be at least $o(h)$.

This interpretation of the patch test suggests that we may in an analogous manner also test for the order of convergence of a discretization. Namely, using the same concept, we may instead apply the external forces that correspond to higher-order variations of internal stresses and test whether these stresses are correctly predicted. For example, in order to test whether a discretization will give a quadratic order of stress convergence, that is, whether the stresses converge $o(h^2)$, a linear stress variation needs to be correctly represented. We infer from the basic differential equations of equilibrium that the corresponding patch test is to apply a constant value of internal forces and the corresponding boundary tractions. While numerical results are again of interest and are valuable as in the test for constant stress conditions, only analytical results can ensure that for all geometric element distortions in the patch the correct stresses and deformations are obtained (see Section 5.3.3 for further discussion and results).

Of course, in practice, when testing element formulations, this formal procedure of evaluating the order of convergence frequently is not followed, and instead a sequence of simple test problems is used to identify the predictive capability of an element.

4.4.2 Mixed Formulations

To formulate the displacement-based finite elements we have used the principle of virtual displacements, which is equivalent to invoking the stationarity of the total potential energy Π (see Example 4.4). The essential theory used can be summarized briefly as follows.

1. We use[15]

$$\Pi(\mathbf{u}) = \frac{1}{2} \int_V \boldsymbol{\epsilon}^T \mathbf{C}\boldsymbol{\epsilon} \, dV - \int_V \mathbf{u}^T \mathbf{f}^B \, dV - \int_{S_f} \mathbf{u}^{S_f^T} \mathbf{f}^{S_f} \, dS$$

$$= \text{stationary} \tag{4.109}$$

with the conditions

$$\boldsymbol{\epsilon} = \boldsymbol{\partial}_\epsilon \mathbf{u} \tag{4.110}$$

$$\mathbf{u}^{S_u} - \mathbf{u}_p = \mathbf{0} \tag{4.111}$$

where $\boldsymbol{\partial}_\epsilon$ represents the differential operator on $\mathbf{u}$ to obtain the strain components, the vector $\mathbf{u}_p$ contains the prescribed displacements, and the vector $\mathbf{u}^{S_u}$ lists the corresponding displacement components of $\mathbf{u}$.

If the strain components are ordered as in (4.3), we have

$$\mathbf{u} = \begin{bmatrix} u\,(x,\,y,\,z) \\ v\,(x,\,y,\,z) \\ w\,(x,\,y,\,z) \end{bmatrix}; \qquad \boldsymbol{\partial}_\epsilon = \begin{bmatrix} \dfrac{\partial}{\partial x} & 0 & 0 \\[2mm] 0 & \dfrac{\partial}{\partial y} & 0 \\[2mm] 0 & 0 & \dfrac{\partial}{\partial z} \\[2mm] \dfrac{\partial}{\partial y} & \dfrac{\partial}{\partial x} & 0 \\[2mm] 0 & \dfrac{\partial}{\partial z} & \dfrac{\partial}{\partial y} \\[2mm] \dfrac{\partial}{\partial z} & 0 & \dfrac{\partial}{\partial x} \end{bmatrix}$$

2. The equilibrium equations are obtained by invoking the stationarity of Π (with respect to the displacements which appear in the strains),

$$\int_V \delta\boldsymbol{\epsilon}^T \mathbf{C}\boldsymbol{\epsilon} \, dV = \int_V \delta\mathbf{u}^T \mathbf{f}^B \, dV + \int_{S_f} \delta\mathbf{u}^{S_f^T} \mathbf{f}^{S_f} \, dS \tag{4.112}$$

The variations on $\mathbf{u}$ must be zero at and corresponding to the prescribed displacements on the surface area S_u. We recall that to obtain from (4.112) the differential equations of equilibrium and the stress (natural) boundary conditions we substitute $\mathbf{C}\boldsymbol{\epsilon} = \boldsymbol{\tau}$ and reverse the process of transformation employed in Example 4.2 (see Sections 3.3.2 and 3.3.4). Therefore, the stress-strain relationship, the strain-displacement conditions [in (4.110)], and the displacement boundary conditions [in (4.111)] are directly fulfilled, and the condition of differential equilibrium (in the interior and on the boundary) is a consequence of the stationarity condition of Π.

3. In the displacement-based finite element solution the stress-strain relationship, the strain-displacement conditions [in (4.110)], and the displacement boundary conditions [in (4.111)] are satisfied exactly, but the differential equations of equilibrium in the interior and the stress (natural) boundary conditions are satisfied only in the limit as the number of elements increases.

---

[15] In this section, as in equation (4.7), we use the notation $\mathbf{f}^{S_f}$ instead of the usual $\mathbf{f}^S$ to explicitly denote that these are tractions applied to S_f. Similarly, we have in this section also the tractions $\mathbf{f}^{S_u}$ and the surface displacements $\mathbf{u}^{S_f}$ and $\mathbf{u}^{S_u}$. For definitions of these quantities, see Section 4.2.1.

The important point to note concerning the use of (4.109) to (4.112) for a finite element solution is that the only solution variables are the displacements which must satisfy the displacement boundary conditions in (4.111) and appropriate interelement conditions. Once we have calculated the displacements, other variables of interest such as strains and stresses can be directly obtained.

In practice, the displacement-based finite element formulation is used most frequently; however, other techniques have also been employed successfully and in some cases are much more effective (see Section 4.4.3).

Some very general finite element formulations are obtained by using variational principles that can be regarded as extensions of the principle of stationarity of total potential. These extended variational principles use not only the displacements but also the strains and/or stresses as primary variables. In the finite element solutions, the unknown variables are therefore then also displacements and strains and/or stresses. These finite element formulations are referred to as *mixed finite element formulations*.

Various extended variational principles can be used as the basis of a finite element formulation, and the use of many different finite element interpolations can be pursued. While a large number of mixed finite element formulations has consequently been proposed (see, for example, H. Kardestuncer and D. H. Norrie (eds.) [A] and F. Brezzi and M. Fortin [A]), our objective here is only to present briefly some of the basic ideas, which we shall then use to formulate some efficient solution schemes (see Sections 4.4.3 and 5.4).

To arrive at a very general and powerful variational principle we rewrite (4.109) in the form

$$\Pi^* = \Pi - \int_V \boldsymbol{\lambda}_\epsilon^T(\boldsymbol{\epsilon} - \boldsymbol{\partial}_\epsilon \mathbf{u}) \, dV - \int_{S_u} \boldsymbol{\lambda}_u^T(\mathbf{u}^{S_u} - \mathbf{u}_p) \, dS$$
$$= \text{stationary}$$

(4.113)

where $\boldsymbol{\lambda}_\epsilon$ and $\boldsymbol{\lambda}_u$ are Lagrange multipliers and S_u is the surface on which displacements are prescribed. The Lagrange multipliers are used here to enforce the conditions (4.110) and (4.111) (see Section 3.4). The variables in (4.113) are $\mathbf{u}$, $\boldsymbol{\epsilon}$, $\boldsymbol{\lambda}_\epsilon$, and $\boldsymbol{\lambda}_u$. By invoking $\delta\Pi^* = 0$ the Lagrange multipliers $\boldsymbol{\lambda}_\epsilon$ and $\boldsymbol{\lambda}_u$ are identified, respectively, as the stresses $\boldsymbol{\tau}$ and tractions over S_u, $\mathbf{f}^{S_u}$, so that the variational indicator in (4.113) can be written as

$$\Pi_{\text{HW}} = \Pi - \int_V \boldsymbol{\tau}^T(\boldsymbol{\epsilon} - \boldsymbol{\partial}_\epsilon \mathbf{u}) \, dV - \int_{S_u} \mathbf{f}^{S_u T}(\mathbf{u}^{S_u} - \mathbf{u}_p) \, dS$$

(4.114)

This functional is referred to as the Hu-Washizu functional (see H. C. Hu [A] and K. Washizu [A, B]). The independent variables in this functional are the displacements $\mathbf{u}$, strains $\boldsymbol{\epsilon}$, stresses $\boldsymbol{\tau}$, and surface tractions $\mathbf{f}^{S_u}$. The functional can be used to derive a number of other functionals, such as the Hellinger-Reissner functionals (see E. Hellinger [A] and E. Reissner [A], Examples 4.30 and 4.31, and Exercise 4.36) and the minimum complementary energy functional, and can be regarded as the foundation of many finite element methods (see H. Kardestuncer and D. H. Norrie (eds.) [A], T. H. H. Pian and P. Tong [A], and W. Wunderlich [A]).

Invoking the stationarity of Π_{HW} with respect to $\mathbf{u}$, $\boldsymbol{\epsilon}$, $\boldsymbol{\tau}$, and $\mathbf{f}^{S_u}$, we obtain

$$\int_V \delta\boldsymbol{\epsilon}^T \mathbf{C}\boldsymbol{\epsilon} \, dV - \int_V \delta\mathbf{u}^T \mathbf{f}^B \, dV - \int_{S_f} \delta\mathbf{u}^{S_f T} \mathbf{f}^{S_f} \, dS - \int_V \delta\boldsymbol{\tau}^T(\boldsymbol{\epsilon} - \boldsymbol{\partial}_\epsilon \mathbf{u}) \, dV$$

$$- \int_V \boldsymbol{\tau}^T (\delta\boldsymbol{\epsilon} - \boldsymbol{\partial}_\epsilon \delta\mathbf{u}) \, dV - \int_{S_u} \delta\mathbf{f}^{S_u T}(\mathbf{u}^{S_u} - \mathbf{u}_p) \, dS - \int_{S_u} \mathbf{f}^{S_u T} \, \delta\mathbf{u}^{S_u} \, dS = 0 \qquad (4.115)$$

where S_f is the surface on which known tractions are prescribed.

The above discussion shows that the Hu-Washizu variational formulation may be regarded as a generalization of the principle of virtual displacements, in which the displacement boundary conditions and strain compatibility conditions have been relaxed but then imposed by Lagrange multipliers, and variations are performed on all unknown displacements, strains, stresses, and unknown surface tractions. That this principle is indeed a valid and most general description of the static and kinematic conditions of the body under consideration follows because (4.115) yields, since (4.115) must hold for the individual variations used, the following.

For the volume of the body:

The stress-strain condition,

$$\boldsymbol{\tau} = \mathbf{C}\boldsymbol{\epsilon} \qquad (4.116)$$

The compatibility condition,

$$\boldsymbol{\epsilon} = \boldsymbol{\partial}_\epsilon \mathbf{u} \qquad (4.117)$$

The equilibrium conditions,

$$\frac{\partial \tau_{xx}}{\partial x} + \frac{\partial \tau_{xy}}{\partial y} + \frac{\partial \tau_{xz}}{\partial z} + f_x^B = 0$$

$$\frac{\partial \tau_{yx}}{\partial x} + \frac{\partial \tau_{yy}}{\partial y} + \frac{\partial \tau_{yz}}{\partial z} + f_y^B = 0 \qquad (4.118)$$

$$\frac{\partial \tau_{zx}}{\partial x} + \frac{\partial \tau_{zy}}{\partial y} + \frac{\partial \tau_{zz}}{\partial z} + f_z^B = 0$$

For the surface of the body:

The applied tractions are equilibrated by the stresses,

$$\mathbf{f}^{S_f} = \bar{\boldsymbol{\tau}}\mathbf{n} \qquad \text{on } S_f \qquad (4.119)$$

The reactions are equilibrated by the stresses,

$$\mathbf{f}^{S_u} = \bar{\boldsymbol{\tau}}\mathbf{n} \qquad \text{on } S_u \qquad (4.120)$$

where $\mathbf{n}$ represents the unit normal vector to the surface and $\bar{\boldsymbol{\tau}}$ contains in matrix form the components of the vector $\boldsymbol{\tau}$.

The displacements on S_u are equal to the prescribed displacements,

$$\mathbf{u}^{S_u} = \mathbf{u}_p \qquad \text{on } S_u \qquad (4.121)$$

The variational formulation in (4.115) represents a very general continuum mechanics formulation of the problems in elasticity.

Considering now the possibilities for finite element solution procedures, the Hu-Washizu variational principle and principles derived therefrom can be directly employed to derive various finite element discretizations. In these finite element solution procedures the applicable continuity requirements of the finite element variables between elements and on the boundaries need to be satisfied either directly or to be imposed by Lagrange multipliers. It now becomes apparent that with this added flexibility in formulating finite element methods a large number of different finite element discretizations can be devised, depending on which variational principle is used as the basis of the formulation, which finite element interpolations are employed, and how the continuity requirements are enforced. The various different discretization procedures have been classified as hybrid and mixed finite element formulations (see H. Kardestuncer and D. H. Norrie (eds.) [A] and T. H. H. Pian and P. Tong [A]).

We demonstrate the use of the Hu-Washizu principle in the following examples.

EXAMPLE 4.29: Consider the three-node truss element shown in Fig. E4.29. Assume a parabolic variation for the displacement and a linear variation in strain and stress. Also, let the stress and strain variables correspond to internal element degrees of freedom so that only the displacements at nodes 1 and 2 connect to the adjacent elements. Use the Hu-Washizu variational principle to calculate the element stiffness matrix.

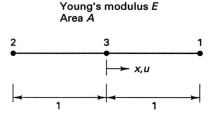

Figure E4.29   Three-node truss element

We can start directly with (4.115) to obtain

$$\underbrace{\int_V \delta\epsilon^T (C\epsilon - \tau)\, dV}_{①} - \underbrace{\int_V \delta\tau^T (\epsilon - \partial_\epsilon u)\, dV}_{②}$$

$$+ \underbrace{\int_V (\partial_\epsilon \delta u)^T \tau\, dV}_{③} - \int_V \delta u^T f^B\, dV + \text{boundary terms} = 0 \qquad \text{(a)}$$

where $\epsilon = \epsilon_{xx}; \qquad \partial_\epsilon = \dfrac{\partial}{\partial x}; \qquad \tau = \tau_{xx}; \qquad C = E; \qquad f^B = f_x^B$

and the boundary terms correspond to expressions for S_f and S_u and are not needed to evaluate the element stiffness matrix.

We now use the following interpolations:

$$u = \mathbf{H}\hat{u}; \qquad \mathbf{H} = \left[\frac{(1 + x)x}{2} \quad -\frac{(1 - x)x}{2} \quad 1 - x^2 \right]$$

$$\hat{u}^T = [u_1 \quad u_2 \quad u_3]$$

$$\tau = \mathbf{E}\hat{\boldsymbol{\tau}}; \qquad \mathbf{E} = \left[\frac{1+x}{2} \quad \frac{1-x}{2} \right]$$

$$\epsilon = \mathbf{E}\hat{\boldsymbol{\epsilon}}$$

$$\hat{\boldsymbol{\tau}}^T = [\tau_1 \quad \tau_2]; \qquad \hat{\boldsymbol{\epsilon}}^T = [\epsilon_1 \quad \epsilon_2]$$

Substituting the interpolations into (a), we obtain corresponding to term 1:

$$\delta\hat{\boldsymbol{\epsilon}}^T \left[\left(\int_V \mathbf{E}^T \mathbf{C}\mathbf{E} \, dV \right) \hat{\boldsymbol{\epsilon}} - \left(\int_V \mathbf{E}^T \mathbf{E} \, dV \right) \hat{\boldsymbol{\tau}} \right]$$

corresponding to term 2:

$$\delta\hat{\boldsymbol{\tau}}^T \left[-\left(\int_V \mathbf{E}^T \mathbf{E} \, dV \right) \hat{\boldsymbol{\epsilon}} + \left(\int_V \mathbf{E}^T \mathbf{B} \, dV \right) \hat{\mathbf{u}} \right]$$

corresponding to term 3: $\qquad \delta\hat{\mathbf{u}}^T \left(\int_V \mathbf{B}^T \mathbf{E} \, dV \right) \hat{\boldsymbol{\tau}}$

where $\qquad\qquad\qquad \mathbf{B} = [(\tfrac{1}{2} + x) \quad (-\tfrac{1}{2} + x) \quad -2x]$

Hence, we obtain

$$\begin{bmatrix} \mathbf{0} & \mathbf{0} & \mathbf{K}_{u\tau} \\ \mathbf{0} & \mathbf{K}_{\epsilon\epsilon} & \mathbf{K}_{\epsilon\tau} \\ \mathbf{K}_{u\tau}^T & \mathbf{K}_{\epsilon\tau}^T & \mathbf{0} \end{bmatrix} \begin{bmatrix} \hat{\mathbf{u}} \\ \hat{\boldsymbol{\epsilon}} \\ \hat{\boldsymbol{\tau}} \end{bmatrix} = \cdots \qquad\qquad \text{(b)}$$

where $\qquad\qquad\qquad \mathbf{K}_{\epsilon\epsilon} = \int_V \mathbf{E}^T \mathbf{C}\mathbf{E} \, dV$

$$\mathbf{K}_{u\tau} = \int_V \mathbf{B}^T \mathbf{E} \, dV$$

and $\qquad\qquad\qquad \mathbf{K}_{\epsilon\tau} = -\int_V \mathbf{E}^T \mathbf{E} \, dV$

If we now substitute the expressions for $\mathbf{B}$ and $\mathbf{E}$ and eliminate the ϵ_i and τ_i degrees of freedom (because they are assumed to pertain only to this element, thus allowing jumps in stresses and strains between adjacent elements), we obtain from (b)

$$\frac{EA}{6} \begin{bmatrix} 7 & 1 & -8 \\ 1 & 7 & -8 \\ -8 & -8 & 16 \end{bmatrix} \begin{bmatrix} u_1 \\ u_2 \\ u_3 \end{bmatrix} = \cdots$$

This stiffness matrix is identical to the matrix of a three-node displacement-based truss element—as should be expected using a linear strain and parabolic displacement assumption.

However, we should note that if the element stress and strain variables are not eliminated on the element level and instead are used to impose continuity in stress and strain between elements, then clearly with the element stiffness matrix in (b) the stiffness matrix of the complete element assemblage is not positive definite.

This derivation could of course be extended to obtain the stiffness matrices of truss elements with various displacement, stress, and strain assumptions. However, a useful element is obtained only if the interpolations are "judiciously" chosen and actually fulfill specific requirements (see Section 4.5).

EXAMPLE 4.30:   Consider the two-node beam element shown in Fig. E4.30. Assume linear variations in the transverse displacement w and section rotation θ and a constant element transverse shear strain γ. Establish the finite element equations.

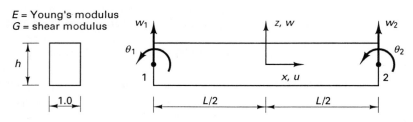

E = Young's modulus
G = shear modulus

Figure E4.30   Two-node beam element

We assume that the stresses are given by the strains, and so we can substitute $\tau = \mathbf{C}\boldsymbol{\epsilon}$ into (4.114) and obtain

$$\Pi^*_{HR} = \int_V \left(-\frac{1}{2}\boldsymbol{\epsilon}^T\mathbf{C}\boldsymbol{\epsilon} + \boldsymbol{\epsilon}^T\mathbf{C}\partial_\epsilon\mathbf{u} - \mathbf{u}^T\mathbf{f}^B \right) dV + \text{boundary terms} \qquad (a)$$

This variational indicator is also a Hellinger-Reissner functional, but comparing (a) with the functional in Exercise 4.36, we note that here strains and displacements are the independent variables (instead of the stresses and displacements in Exercise 4.36).

In our beam formulation the variables are u, w, and γ^{AS}_{xz} (the superscript AS denotes the assumed constant value). Hence, the bending strain ϵ_{xx} is calculated from the displacement, and we can specialize (a) further:

$$\tilde{\Pi}^*_{HR} = \int_V \left(\frac{1}{2}\epsilon_{xx}E\epsilon_{xx} - \frac{1}{2}\gamma^{AS}_{xz}G\gamma^{AS}_{xz} + \gamma^{AS}_{xz}G\gamma_{xz} - \mathbf{u}^T\mathbf{f}^B \right) dV + \text{boundary terms}$$

where

$$\mathbf{u} = \begin{bmatrix} u \\ w \end{bmatrix}; \qquad \epsilon_{xx} = \frac{\partial u}{\partial x}; \qquad \gamma_{xz} = \frac{\partial w}{\partial x} + \frac{\partial u}{\partial z}$$

Now invoking $\delta\tilde{\Pi}^*_{HR} = 0$, we obtain corresponding to $\delta\mathbf{u}$, (not including boundary terms)

$$\int_V (\delta\epsilon_{xx}E\epsilon_{xx} + \delta\gamma_{xz}G\gamma^{AS}_{xz})\, dV = \int_V \delta\mathbf{u}^T\mathbf{f}^B\, dV \qquad (b)$$

and corresponding to $\delta\gamma^{AS}_{xz}$,

$$\int_V \delta\gamma^{AS}_{xz}G(\gamma_{xz} - \gamma^{AS}_{xz})\, dV = 0 \qquad (c)$$

Let

$$\hat{\mathbf{u}} = \begin{bmatrix} w_1 \\ \theta_1 \\ w_2 \\ \theta_2 \end{bmatrix}; \qquad \hat{\boldsymbol{\epsilon}} = [\gamma^{AS}]$$

Then we can write

$$\mathbf{u} = \mathbf{H}\hat{\mathbf{u}}; \qquad \epsilon_{xx} = \mathbf{B}_b\hat{\mathbf{u}}$$

$$\gamma_{xz} = \mathbf{B}_s\hat{\mathbf{u}}; \qquad \gamma^{AS}_{xz} = \mathbf{B}^{AS}_s\hat{\boldsymbol{\epsilon}}$$

Substituting into (b) and (c), we obtain

$$\begin{bmatrix} \mathbf{K}_{uu} & \mathbf{K}_{u\epsilon} \\ \mathbf{K}_{u\epsilon}^T & \mathbf{K}_{\epsilon\epsilon} \end{bmatrix} \begin{bmatrix} \hat{\mathbf{u}} \\ \hat{\boldsymbol{\epsilon}} \end{bmatrix} = \begin{bmatrix} \mathbf{R}_B \\ \mathbf{0} \end{bmatrix} \tag{d}$$

where

$$\mathbf{K}_{uu} = \int_V \mathbf{B}_b^T E \mathbf{B}_b \, dV; \qquad \mathbf{K}_{u\epsilon} = \int_V \mathbf{B}_s^T G \mathbf{B}_s^{AS} \, dV$$

$$\mathbf{K}_{\epsilon\epsilon} = -\int_V (\mathbf{B}_s^{AS})^T G \mathbf{B}_s^{AS} \, dV; \qquad \mathbf{R}_B = \int_V \mathbf{H}^T \mathbf{f}^B \, dV$$

We can now use static condensation on $\hat{\boldsymbol{\epsilon}}$ to obtain the final element stiffness matrix:

$$\mathbf{K} = \mathbf{K}_{uu} - \mathbf{K}_{u\epsilon} \mathbf{K}_{\epsilon\epsilon}^{-1} \mathbf{K}_{u\epsilon}^T$$

In our case, we have

$$\mathbf{H} = \begin{bmatrix} 0 & -\dfrac{z}{L}\left(\dfrac{L}{2} - x\right) & 0 & -\dfrac{z}{L}\left(\dfrac{L}{2} + x\right) \\ \dfrac{1}{L}\left(\dfrac{L}{2} - x\right) & 0 & \dfrac{1}{L}\left(\dfrac{L}{2} + x\right) & 0 \end{bmatrix}$$

$$\mathbf{B}_b = \begin{bmatrix} 0 & \dfrac{z}{L} & 0 & -\dfrac{z}{L} \end{bmatrix}$$

$$\mathbf{B}_s = \begin{bmatrix} -\dfrac{1}{L} & -\dfrac{1}{L}\left(\dfrac{L}{2} - x\right) & \dfrac{1}{L} & -\dfrac{1}{L}\left(\dfrac{L}{2} + x\right) \end{bmatrix}$$

$$\mathbf{B}_s^{AS} = [1]$$

so that

$$\mathbf{K} = \begin{bmatrix} \dfrac{Gh}{L} & \dfrac{Gh}{2} & \dfrac{-Gh}{L} & \dfrac{Gh}{2} \\[2mm] \dfrac{Gh}{2} & \left(\dfrac{GhL}{4}\right) + \dfrac{Eh^3}{12L} & \dfrac{-Gh}{2} & \left(\dfrac{GhL}{4}\right) - \dfrac{Eh^3}{12L} \\[2mm] \dfrac{-Gh}{L} & \dfrac{-Gh}{2} & \dfrac{Gh}{L} & \dfrac{-Gh}{2} \\[2mm] \dfrac{Gh}{2} & \left(\dfrac{GhL}{4}\right) - \dfrac{Eh^3}{12L} & \dfrac{-Gh}{2} & \left(\dfrac{GhL}{4}\right) + \dfrac{Eh^3}{12L} \end{bmatrix} \tag{e}$$

It is interesting to note that a pure displacement formulation would give a very similar stiffness matrix. The only difference is that the circled terms would be $GhL/3$ on the diagonal and $GhL/6$ in the off-diagonal locations. However, the element predictive capability of the pure displacement-based formulation is drastically different, displaying a behavior that is much too stiff when the element is thin (we discuss this phenomenon in Sections 4.5.7 and 5.4.1).

Note that if we assume a displacement vector corresponding to section rotations only,

$$\hat{\mathbf{u}} = \begin{bmatrix} 0 & \alpha & 0 & -\alpha \end{bmatrix}$$

then using (e) the element displays bending stiffness only, whereas the pure displacement-based element shows an erroneous shear contribution.

Let us finally note that the stiffness matrix in (e) corresponds to the matrix obtained in the mixed interpolation approach discussed in detail in Section 5.4.1. Namely, if we use the last equation in (d), which corresponds to the equation (c), we obtain

$$\gamma_{XZ}^{AS} = \frac{w_2 - w_1}{L} - \frac{\theta_1 + \theta_2}{2}$$

which shows that the assumed shear strain value is equal to the shear strain value at the midpoint of the beam calculated from the nodal point displacements.

As pointed out above, the Hu-Washizu principle provides the basis for the derivation of various variational principles, and many different mixed finite element discretizations can be designed. However, whether a specific finite element discretization is effective for practical analysis depends on a number of factors, particularly on whether the method is general for a certain class of applications, whether the method is stable with a sufficiently high rate of convergence, how efficient the method is computationally, and how the method compares to alternative schemes. While mixed finite element discretizations can offer some advantages in certain analyses, compared to the standard displacement-based discretization, there are two large areas in which the use of mixed elements is much more efficient than the use of pure displacement-based elements. These two areas are the analysis of almost incompressible media and the analysis of plate and shell structures (see the following sections and Section 5.4).

4.4.3 Mixed Interpolation—Displacement/Pressure Formulations for Incompressible Analysis

The displacement-based finite element procedure described in Section 4.2 is very widely used because of its simplicity and general effectiveness. However, there are two problem areas in which the pure displacement-based finite elements are not sufficiently effective, namely, the analysis of incompressible (or almost incompressible) media and the analysis of plates and shells. In each of these cases, a mixed interpolation approach—which can be thought of as a special use of the Hu-Washizu variational principle (see Example 4.30)—is far more efficient.

We discuss the mixed interpolation for beam, plate, and shell analyses in Section 5.4, and we address here the analysis of incompressible media.

Although we are dealing with the solution of incompressible solid media, the same basic observations are also directly applicable to the analysis of incompressible fluids (see Section 7.4). For example, the elements summarized in Tables 4.6 and 4.7 (later in this section) are also used effectively in fluid flow solutions.

The Basic Differential Equations for Incompressible Analysis

In the analysis of solids, it is frequently necessary to consider that the material is almost incompressible. For example, some rubberlike materials, and materials in inelastic conditions, may exhibit an almost incompressible response. Indeed, the compressibility effects may be so small that they could be neglected, in which case the material would be idealized as totally incompressible.

A basic observation in the analysis of almost incompressible media is that the pressure is difficult to predict accurately. Depending on how close the material is to being incompressible, the displacement-based finite element method may still provide accurate solutions, but the number of elements required to obtain a given solution accuracy is usually far greater than the number of elements required in a comparable analysis involving a compressible material.

To identify the basic difficulty in more detail, let us again consider the three-dimensional body in Fig. 4.1. The material of the body is isotropic and is described by Young's modulus E and Poisson's ratio ν.

Using indicial notation, the governing differential equations for this body are (see Example 4.2)

$$\tau_{ij,j} + f_i^B = 0 \qquad \text{throughout the volume } V \text{ of the body} \tag{4.122}$$

$$\tau_{ij} n_j = f_i^{S_f} \qquad \text{on } S_f \tag{4.123}$$

$$u_i = u_i^{S_u} \qquad \text{on } S_u \tag{4.124}$$

If the body is made of an almost incompressible material, we anticipate that the volumetric strains will be small in comparison to the deviatoric strains, and therefore we use the constitutive relations in the form (see Exercise 4.39)

$$\tau_{ij} = \kappa \epsilon_V \delta_{ij} + 2G \epsilon'_{ij} \tag{4.125}$$

where κ is the bulk modulus,

$$\kappa = \frac{E}{3(1 - 2\nu)} \tag{4.126}$$

ϵ_V is the volumetric strain,

$$\epsilon_V = \epsilon_{kk}$$
$$= \frac{\Delta V}{V} (= \epsilon_{xx} + \epsilon_{yy} + \epsilon_{zz} \text{ in Cartesian coordinates}) \tag{4.127}$$

δ_{ij} is the Kronecker delta,

$$\delta_{ij} \begin{cases} = 1; & i = j \\ = 0; & i \neq j \end{cases} \tag{4.128}$$

ϵ'_{ij} are the deviatoric strain components,

$$\epsilon'_{ij} = \epsilon_{ij} - \frac{\epsilon_V}{3} \delta_{ij} \tag{4.129}$$

and G is the shear modulus,

$$G = \frac{E}{2(1 + \nu)} \tag{4.130}$$

We also have for the pressure in the body,

$$p = -\kappa \epsilon_V \tag{4.131}$$

where $\qquad p = -\frac{\tau_{kk}}{3} \left(= -\frac{\tau_{xx} + \tau_{yy} + \tau_{zz}}{3} \text{ in Cartesian coordinates} \right) \tag{4.132}$

Now let us gradually increase κ (by increasing the Poisson ratio ν to approach 0.5). Then, as κ increases, the volumetric strain ϵ_V decreases and becomes very small.

In fact, in total incompressibility ν is exactly equal to 0.5, the bulk modulus is infinite, the volumetric strain is zero, and the pressure is of course finite (and of the order of the applied boundary tractions). The stress components are then expressed as [see (4.125) and (4.131)]

$$\boxed{\tau_{ij} = -p\delta_{ij} + 2G\epsilon'_{ij}}$$
(4.133)

and the solution of the governing differential equations (4.122) to (4.124) now involves using the displacements *and* the pressure as unknown variables.

In addition, special attention need also be given to the boundary conditions in (4.123) and (4.124) when material incompressibility is being considered and the displacements are prescribed on the complete surface of the body, i.e., when we have the special case $S_u = S$, $S_f = 0$. If the material is totally incompressible, *a first condition* is that the prescribed displacements u_i^S must be compatible with the zero volumetric strain throughout the body. This physical observation is expressed as

$$\epsilon_{ii} = 0 \qquad \text{throughout } V$$
(4.134)

hence,
$$\int_V \epsilon_{ii} \, dV = \int_S \mathbf{u}^S \cdot \mathbf{n} \, dS = 0$$
(4.135)

where we used the divergence theorem and $\mathbf{n}$ is the unit normal vector on the surface of the body. Hence, the displacements prescribed normal to the body surface must be such that the volume of the body is preserved. This condition will of course be automatically satisfied if the prescribed surface displacements are zero (the particles on the surface of the body are not displaced).

Assuming that the volumetric strain/boundary displacement compatibility is satisfied, for the case $S_u = S$, *the second condition* is that the pressure must be prescribed at some point in the body. Otherwise, the pressure is not unique because an arbitrary constant pressure does not cause any deformations. Only when both these conditions are fulfilled is the problem well posed for solution.

Of course, the condition of prescribed displacements on the complete surface of the body is a somewhat special case in the analysis of solids, but we encounter an analogous situation frequently in fluid mechanics. Here the velocities may be prescribed on the complete boundary of the fluid domain (see Chapter 7).

Although we considered here a totally incompressible medium, it is clear that these considerations are also important when the material is only almost incompressible—a violation of the conditions discussed will lead to an ill-posed problem statement.

Of course, these observations also pertain to the use of the principle of virtual work. Let us consider the simple example shown in Fig. 4.19. Since only volumetric strain energy is present, the principle of virtual work gives for this case,

$$\int_V \bar{\epsilon}_V \kappa \epsilon_V \, dV = -\int_{S_f} \bar{v}^S p^* \, dS$$
(4.136)

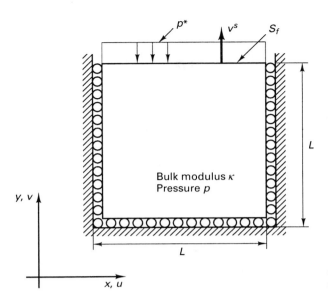

Figure 4.19 Block of material in plane strain condition, subjected to uniform surface pressure p^*

If the bulk modulus κ is finite, we obtain directly from (4.136),

$$v^S = -\frac{p^*L}{\kappa} \tag{4.137}$$

and

$$p = p^* \tag{4.138}$$

However, if κ is infinite, we need to use instead of (4.136) the following form of the principle of virtual work, with the pressure p unknown,

$$\int_V \bar{\epsilon}_V(-p)\,dV = -\int_{S_f} \bar{v}^S p^*\,dS \tag{4.139}$$

and we again obtain $p = p^*$. Of course, the solution of (4.139) does not use the constitutive relation but only the equilibrium condition.

The Finite Element Solution of Almost Incompressible Conditions

The preceding discussion indicates that when pursuing a pure displacement-based finite element analysis of an almost incompressible medium, significant difficulties must be expected. The very small volumetric strain, approaching zero in the limit of total incompressibility, is determined from derivatives of displacements, which are not as accurately predicted as the displacements themselves. Any error in the predicted volumetric strain will appear as a large error in the stresses, and this error will in turn also affect the displacement prediction since the external loads are balanced (using the principle of virtual work) by the stresses. In practice, therefore, a very fine finite element discretization may be required to obtain good solution accuracy.

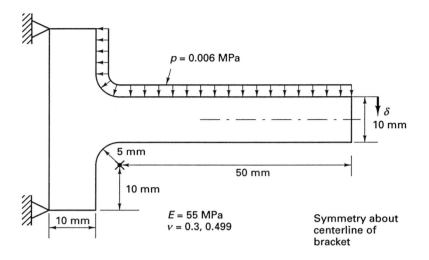

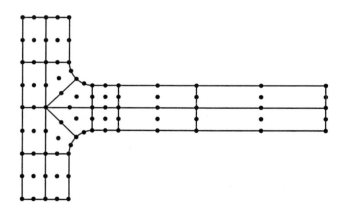

(a) Geometry, material data, applied loading, and the coarse sixteen element mesh

Figure 4.20 Analysis of cantilever bracket in plane strain conditions. Nine-node displacement-based elements are used. The 16 × 64 = 1024-element mesh is obtained by dividing each element of the 16-element mesh into 64 elements. Maximum principal stress results are shown using the band representation of Fig. 4.15. Also, $(\sigma_1)_{max}$ is the predicted maximum value of the maximum principal stress, and δ is defined in (a).

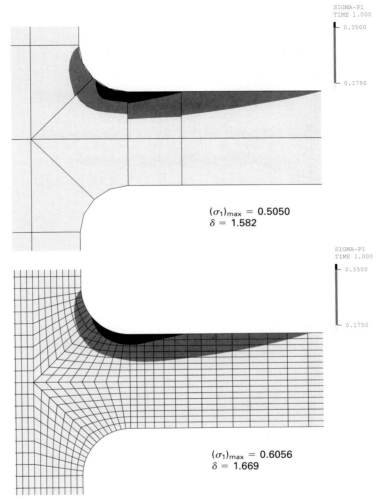

$(\sigma_1)_{max} = 0.5050$
$\delta = 1.582$

$(\sigma_1)_{max} = 0.6056$
$\delta = 1.669$

(b) Displacement-based element solution results for the case Poisson's ratio
$\nu = 0.30$. Sixteen element and 16×64 element mesh results

Figure 4.20   (*continued*)

Figure 4.20 shows some results obtained in the analysis of a cantilever bracket subjected to pressure loading. We consider plane strain conditions and the cases of Poisson's ratio $\nu = 0.30$ and $\nu = 0.499$. In all solutions, nine-node displacement-based elements have been used (with 3×3 Gauss integration; see Section 5.5.5). A coarse mesh and a very fine mesh are used, and Fig. 4.20(a) shows the coarse idealization using only 16 elements. The solution results for the maximum principal stress σ_1 are shown using the isoband representation discussed in Section 4.3.6. Here we have selected the bandwidth so as to be able to see the rather poor performance of the displacement-based element when the Poisson ratio is close to 0.5. Figure 4.20(b) shows that when $\nu = 0.30$, the element stresses are reasonably smooth across boundaries for the coarse mesh and very smooth for the fine mesh. Indeed, the coarse idealization gives a quite reasonable stress prediction. However,

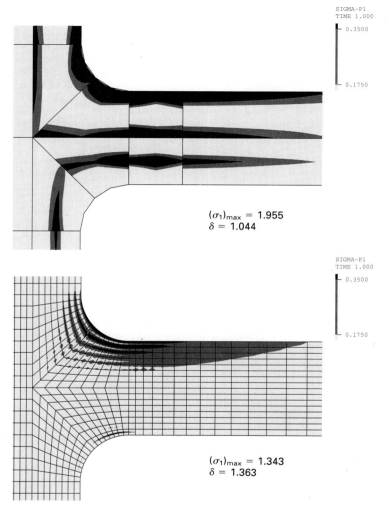

$(\sigma_1)_{max} = 1.955$
$\delta = 1.044$

$(\sigma_1)_{max} = 1.343$
$\delta = 1.363$

(c) Displacement-based element solution results for the case Poisson's ratio
$\nu = 0.499$. Sixteen element and 16×64 element mesh results

Figure 4.20   *(continued)*

when $\nu = 0.499$, the same meshes of nine-node displacement-based elements result into poor stress predictions [see Fig. 4.20(c)]. Large stress fluctuations are seen in the individual elements of the coarse mesh *and* the fine mesh.[16] Hence, in summary, we see here that the displacement-based element used in the analysis is effective when $\nu = 0.3$, but as ν approaches 0.5, the stress prediction becomes very inaccurate.

This discussion indicates what is very desirable, namely, a finite element formulation which gives essentially the same accuracy in results for a given mesh irrespective of what Poisson's ratio is used, even when ν is close to 0.5. Such behavior is observed if for the finite

---

[16] We discuss briefly in Section 5.5.6 the use of "reduced integration." If in this analysis the reduced integration of 2×2 Gauss integration is attempted, the solution cannot be obtained because the resulting stiffness matrix is singular.

element formulation the predictive capability of displacements and stresses is independent of the bulk modulus used.

We refer to finite element formulations with this desirable behavior as *nonlocking,* whereas otherwise the finite elements are *locking.*

The term "locking" is based upon experiences in the analysis of beams, plates, and shells (see Section 5.4.1), where an inappropriate formulation—one that locks—results in displacements very much smaller than those intuitively expected for a given mesh (and calculated with an appropriate formulation; see, for example, Fig. 5.20). In the analysis of almost incompressible behavior, using a formulation that locks, the displacements are not necessarily that much in error but the stresses (the pressure) are very inaccurate. We note that the pure displacement formulation generally locks in almost incompressible analysis. These statements are discussed more precisely in Section 4.5.

Effective finite element formulations for the analysis of almost incompressible behavior that do not lock are obtained by interpolating displacements and pressure. Figure 4.21 shows the results obtained in the analysis of the cantilever bracket in Fig. 4.20 with a displacement/pressure formulation referred to as u/p formulation using the 9/3 element (see below for the explanation of the formulation and the element). We see that the isobands of the maximum principal stress have in all cases the desirable degree of smoothness and that the stress prediction does not deteriorate when Poisson's ratio ν approaches 0.5.

To introduce the displacement/pressure formulations, we recall that in a pure displacement formulation, the evaluation of the pressure from the volumetric strain is difficult when κ is large (in comparison to G) and that when a totally incompressible condition is considered, the pressure must be used as a solution variable [see (4.133)]. It therefore appears reasonable to work with the unknown displacements *and* pressure as solution variables when almost incompressible conditions are analyzed. Such analysis procedures, if properly formulated, should then also be directly applicable to the limit of incompressible conditions.

The basic approach of displacement/pressure finite element formulations is therefore to interpolate the displacements and the pressure. This requires that we express the principle of virtual work in terms of the independent variables $\mathbf{u}$ and p, which gives

$$\int_V \bar{\boldsymbol{\epsilon}}'^T \mathbf{S} \, dV - \int_V \bar{\epsilon}_V p \, dV = \mathfrak{R} \tag{4.140}$$

where, as usual, the overbar indicates virtual quantities, $\mathfrak{R}$ corresponds to the usual external virtual work [$\mathfrak{R}$ is equal to the right-hand side of (4.7)], and $\mathbf{S}$ and $\boldsymbol{\epsilon}'$ are the deviatoric stress and strain vectors,

$$\mathbf{S} = \boldsymbol{\tau} + p\boldsymbol{\delta} \tag{4.141}$$

$$\boldsymbol{\epsilon}' = \boldsymbol{\epsilon} - \frac{1}{3}\epsilon_V \boldsymbol{\delta} \tag{4.142}$$

where $\boldsymbol{\delta}$ is a vector of the Kronecker delta symbol [see (4.128)].

Note that using the definition of p in (4.131), a uniform compressive stress gives a positive pressure and that in the simple example in Fig. 4.19, only the volumetric part of the internal virtual work contributed.

In (4.140) we have separated and then summed the deviatoric strain energy and the bulk strain energy. Since the displacements and pressure are considered independent vari-

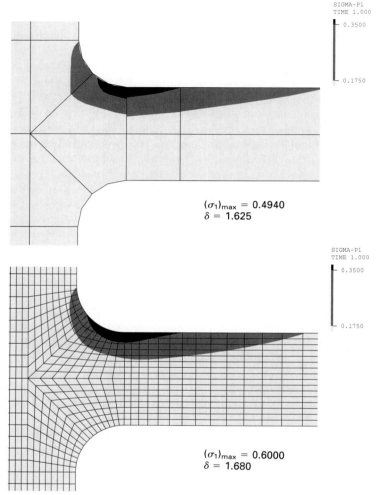

(a) Bands of maximum principal stress. Case of Poisson's ratio $\nu = 0.30$. Sixteen and 16×64 element mesh results

Figure 4.21 Analysis of cantilever bracket in plane strain conditions. Bracket is shown in Fig. 4.20(a). Same meshes as in Fig. 4.20 are used but with the nine-node mixed interpolated element (the 9/3 element). Compare the results shown with those given in Fig. 4.20.

ables, we need another equation to connect these two solution variables. This equation is provided by (4.131) written in integral form (see Example 4.31),

$$\int_V \left(\frac{p}{\kappa} + \epsilon_V\right)\overline{p}\, dV = 0 \tag{4.143}$$

These basic equations can also be derived more formally from variational principles (see L. R. Herrmann [A] and S. W. Key [A]). We derive the basic equations in the following example from the Hu-Washizu functional.

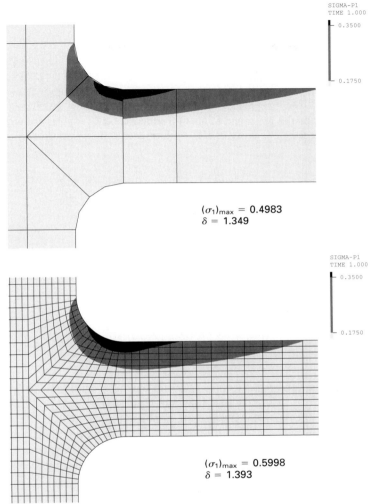

$(\sigma_1)_{\text{max}} = 0.4983$
$\delta = 1.349$

$(\sigma_1)_{\text{max}} = 0.5998$
$\delta = 1.393$

(b) Bands of maximum principal stress. Case of Poisson's ratio $\nu = 0.499$.
Sixteen and 16×64 element mesh results

Figure 4.21   (*continued*)

EXAMPLE 4.31:   Derive the u/p formulation from the Hu-Washizu variational principle.
  The derivation is quite analogous to the presentation in Example 4.30 where we considered
a mixed interpolation for a beam element.
  We start by letting $\boldsymbol{\tau} = \mathbf{C}\boldsymbol{\epsilon}$ in (4.114) to obtain the Hellinger-Reissner functional,

$$\Pi_{\text{HR}}^*(\mathbf{u}, \boldsymbol{\epsilon}) = -\int_V \frac{1}{2}\,\boldsymbol{\epsilon}^T \mathbf{C}\boldsymbol{\epsilon}\,dV + \int_V \boldsymbol{\epsilon}^T \mathbf{C}\,\boldsymbol{\partial}_\epsilon \mathbf{u}\,dV - \int_V \mathbf{u}^T \mathbf{f}^B\,dV - \int_{S_f} \mathbf{u}^{S_f T} \mathbf{f}^{S_f}\,dS \qquad \text{(a)}$$

where we assume that the displacement boundary conditions are satisfied exactly (hence, also the
displacement variations will be zero on the surface of prescribed displacements).

Next we establish the deviatoric and volumetric contributions and postulate that the deviatoric contribution will be evaluated from the displacements. Hence, we can specialize (a) into

$$\tilde{\Pi}^*_{HR}(\mathbf{u}, p) = \int_V \frac{1}{2}\boldsymbol{\epsilon}'^T\mathbf{C}'\boldsymbol{\epsilon}'\,dV - \int_V \frac{1}{2}\frac{p^2}{\kappa}\,dV - \int_V p\epsilon_V\,dV - \int_V \mathbf{u}^T\mathbf{f}^B\,dV - \int_{S_f} \mathbf{u}^{S_f T}\mathbf{f}^{S_f}\,dS \quad (b)$$

where the prime denotes deviatoric quantities, ϵ_V is the volumetric strain evaluated from the displacements, p is the pressure, and κ is the bulk modulus. Note that whereas in (a) the independent variables are $\mathbf{u}$ and $\boldsymbol{\epsilon}$, in (b) the independent variables are $\mathbf{u}$ and p.

Invoking the stationarity of $\tilde{\Pi}^*_{HR}$ with respect to the displacements and the pressure, we obtain

$$\int_V \delta\boldsymbol{\epsilon}'^T\mathbf{C}'\boldsymbol{\epsilon}'\,dV - \int_V p\delta\epsilon_V\,dV = \mathcal{R}$$

and

$$\int_V \left(\frac{p}{\kappa} + \epsilon_V\right)\delta p\,dV = 0$$

where $\mathcal{R}$ corresponds to the virtual work of the externally applied loading [see (4.7)].

It is interesting to note that we may also think of (b) as the total potential in terms of the displacements and the pressure plus a Lagrange multiplier term that enforces the constraint between the volumetric strains and the pressure,

$$\tilde{\tilde{\Pi}}^*_{HR} = -\int_V \frac{1}{2}\boldsymbol{\epsilon}'^T\mathbf{C}'\boldsymbol{\epsilon}'\,dV + \int_V \frac{1}{2}\frac{p^2}{\kappa}\,dV - \int_V \mathbf{u}^T\mathbf{f}^B\,dV$$
$$- \int_{S_f} \mathbf{u}^{S_f T}\mathbf{f}^{S_f}\,dS - \int_V \lambda\left(\epsilon_V + \frac{p}{\kappa}\right)dV \quad (c)$$

In (c) the last integral represents the Lagrange multiplier constraint, and we find $\lambda = p$.

To arrive at the governing finite element equations, we can now use (4.140) and (4.143) as in Section 4.2.1, but in addition to interpolating the displacements we also interpolate the pressure p. The discussion in Section 4.2.1 showed that we need to consider the formulation of only a single element; the matrices of an assemblage of elements are then formed in a standard manner.

Using, as in Section 4.2.1,

$$\mathbf{u} = \mathbf{H}\hat{\mathbf{u}} \quad (4.144)$$

we can calculate

$$\boldsymbol{\epsilon}' = \mathbf{B}_D\hat{\mathbf{u}}; \qquad \epsilon_V = \mathbf{B}_V\hat{\mathbf{u}} \quad (4.145)$$

The additional interpolation assumption is

$$p = \mathbf{H}_p\hat{\mathbf{p}} \quad (4.146)$$

where the vector $\hat{\mathbf{p}}$ lists the pressure variables [(see the discussion following (4.148)].

Substituting from (4.144) to (4.146) into (4.140) and (4.143), we obtain

$$\begin{bmatrix} \mathbf{K}_{uu} & \mathbf{K}_{up} \\ \mathbf{K}_{pu} & \mathbf{K}_{pp} \end{bmatrix}\begin{bmatrix} \hat{\mathbf{u}} \\ \hat{\mathbf{p}} \end{bmatrix} = \begin{bmatrix} \mathbf{R} \\ \mathbf{0} \end{bmatrix} \quad (4.147)$$

where

$$\mathbf{K}_{uu} = \int_V \mathbf{B}_D^T\mathbf{C}'\mathbf{B}_D\,dV$$

$$\mathbf{K}_{up} = \mathbf{K}_{pu}^T = -\int_V \mathbf{B}_V^T \mathbf{H}_p \, dV \qquad (4.148)$$

$$\mathbf{K}_{pp} = -\int_V \mathbf{H}_p^T \frac{1}{\kappa} \mathbf{H}_p \, dV$$

and $\mathbf{C}'$ is the stress-strain matrix for the deviatoric stress and strain components.

The relations in (4.144) to (4.148) give the basic equations for formulating elements with displacements and pressure as variables. The key question for the formulation is now, What pressure and displacement interpolations should be used to arrive at effective elements? For example, if the pressure interpolation is of too high a degree compared to the displacement interpolation, the element may again behave as a displacement-based element and not be effective.

Considering for the moment only the pressure interpolation, the following two main possibilities exist and we label them differently.

The u/p formulation.   In this formulation, the pressure variables pertain only to the specific element being considered. In the analysis of almost incompressible media (as so far discussed), the element pressure variables can be statically condensed out prior to the element assemblage. Continuity of pressure is not enforced between elements but will be a result of the finite element solution if the mesh used is fine enough.

The u/p-c formulation.   The letter "c" denotes continuity in pressure.

In this formulation, the element pressure is defined by nodal pressure variables that pertain to adjacent elements in the assemblage. The pressure variables therefore cannot be statically condensed out prior to the element assemblage. Continuity of pressure between elements is directly enforced and will therefore always be a result of the solution irrespective of whether the mesh used is fine or coarse.

Consider the following two elements, one corresponding to each of the formulations.

EXAMPLE 4.32:   For the four-node plane strain element shown, assume that the displacements are interpolated using the four nodes and assume a constant pressure. Evaluate the matrix expressions used for the u/p formulation.

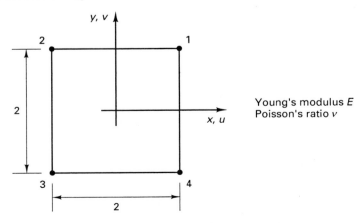

Figure E4.32   A 4/1 element

This element is referred to as the u/p 4/1 element. In plane strain analysis we have

$$\boldsymbol{\epsilon}' = \begin{bmatrix} \epsilon_{xx} - \dfrac{1}{3}(\epsilon_{xx} + \epsilon_{yy}) \\[2mm] \epsilon_{yy} - \dfrac{1}{3}(\epsilon_{xx} + \epsilon_{yy}) \\[2mm] \gamma_{xy} \\[2mm] -\dfrac{1}{3}(\epsilon_{xx} + \epsilon_{yy}) \end{bmatrix} = \begin{bmatrix} \dfrac{2}{3}\dfrac{\partial u}{\partial x} - \dfrac{1}{3}\dfrac{\partial v}{\partial y} \\[2mm] \dfrac{2}{3}\dfrac{\partial v}{\partial y} - \dfrac{1}{3}\dfrac{\partial u}{\partial x} \\[2mm] \dfrac{\partial u}{\partial y} + \dfrac{\partial v}{\partial x} \\[2mm] -\dfrac{1}{3}\left(\dfrac{\partial u}{\partial x} + \dfrac{\partial v}{\partial y}\right) \end{bmatrix} \quad ; \quad \epsilon_V = \epsilon_{xx} + \epsilon_{yy} \qquad \text{(a)}$$

and $\mathbf{S} = \mathbf{C}'\boldsymbol{\epsilon}'$, where

$$\mathbf{C}' = \begin{bmatrix} 2G & 0 & 0 & 0 \\ 0 & 2G & 0 & 0 \\ 0 & 0 & G & 0 \\ 0 & 0 & 0 & 2G \end{bmatrix} \quad ; \quad G = \frac{E}{2(1+\nu)}$$

The displacement interpolation is as in Example 4.6,

$$\mathbf{u} = \mathbf{H}\hat{\mathbf{u}}$$

with $\qquad \mathbf{u}(x, y) = \begin{bmatrix} u(x, y) \\ v(x, y) \end{bmatrix}; \qquad \hat{\mathbf{u}}^T = \begin{bmatrix} u_1 & u_2 & u_3 & u_4 & \vdots & v_1 & v_2 & v_3 & v_4 \end{bmatrix}$

$$\mathbf{H} = \begin{bmatrix} h_1 & h_2 & h_3 & h_4 & \vdots & 0 & 0 & 0 & 0 \\ 0 & 0 & 0 & 0 & \vdots & h_1 & h_2 & h_3 & h_4 \end{bmatrix} \qquad \text{(b)}$$

$$h_1 = \tfrac{1}{4}(1+x)(1+y); \qquad h_2 = \tfrac{1}{4}(1-x)(1+y)$$
$$h_3 = \tfrac{1}{4}(1-x)(1-y); \qquad h_4 = \tfrac{1}{4}(1+x)(1-y)$$

Using (a) and (b), the strain-displacement interpolation matrices are

$$\mathbf{B}_D = \begin{bmatrix} \tfrac{2}{3}h_{1,x} & \tfrac{2}{3}h_{2,x} & \cdots & \vdots & -\tfrac{1}{3}h_{1,y} & -\tfrac{1}{3}h_{2,y} & \cdots \\[2mm] -\tfrac{1}{3}h_{1,x} & -\tfrac{1}{3}h_{2,x} & \cdots & \vdots & \tfrac{2}{3}h_{1,y} & \tfrac{2}{3}h_{2,y} & \cdots \\[2mm] h_{1,y} & h_{2,y} & \cdots & \vdots & h_{1,x} & h_{2,x} & \cdots \\[2mm] -\tfrac{1}{3}h_{1,x} & -\tfrac{1}{3}h_{2,x} & \cdots & \vdots & -\tfrac{1}{3}h_{1,y} & -\tfrac{1}{3}h_{2,y} & \cdots \end{bmatrix}$$

and $\qquad \mathbf{B}_V = \begin{bmatrix} h_{1,x} & h_{2,x} & \cdots & \vdots & h_{1,y} & h_{2,y} & \cdots \end{bmatrix}$

For a constant pressure assumption we have

$$\mathbf{H}_p = [1]; \qquad \hat{\mathbf{p}} = [p_0]$$

Since the degree of freedom $\hat{\mathbf{p}} = [p_0]$ pertains only to this element and not to the adjacent elements, we can use static condensation to obtain from (4.147) the element stiffness matrix corresponding to the nodal point displacement degrees of freedom only;

$$\mathbf{K} = \mathbf{K}_{uu} - \mathbf{K}_{up}\mathbf{K}_{pp}^{-1}\mathbf{K}_{pu}$$

The element is further discussed in Example 4.38.

EXAMPLE 4.33:   Consider the nine-node plane strain element shown in Fig. E4.33. Assume that the displacements are interpolated using the nine nodes and that the pressure is interpolated using only the four corner nodes. Refer to the information given in Example 4.32 and discuss the additional considerations for the evaluation of the matrix expressions of this element.

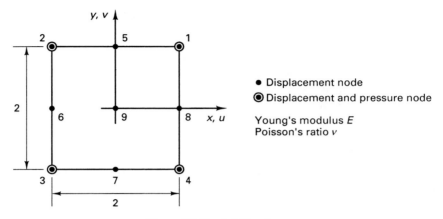

Figure E4.33   A 9/4-c element

This element was proposed by P. Hood and C. Taylor [A]. In the formulation the nodal pressures pertain to adjacent elements, and according to the above element nomination we refer to it as a u/p-c element (it is the 9/4-c element).

The deviatoric and volumetric strains are as given in (a) in Example 4.32. The displacement interpolation corresponds to the nine nodes of the element,

$$\begin{bmatrix} u(x, y) \\ v(x, y) \end{bmatrix} = \begin{bmatrix} h_1^* & \dots & h_9^* & \vdots & 0 & \dots & 0 \\ 0 & \dots & 0 & \vdots & h_1^* & \dots & h_9^* \end{bmatrix} \begin{bmatrix} u_1 \\ \cdot \\ \cdot \\ \cdot \\ u_9 \\ \dots \\ v_1 \\ \cdot \\ \cdot \\ \cdot \\ v_9 \end{bmatrix} \qquad (a)$$

where the interpolation functions h_i^* are constructed as explained in Section 4.2.3 (or see Section 5.3 and Fig. 5.4).

The deviatoric and volumetric strain-displacement matrices are obtained as in Example 4.32.

The pressure interpolation is given by

$$p = [h_1 \quad h_2 \quad h_3 \quad h_4] \begin{bmatrix} p_1 \\ p_2 \\ p_3 \\ p_4 \end{bmatrix}$$

where the h_i are those given in (b) in Example 4.32.

A main computational difference between this element and the four-node element discussed in Example 4.32 is that the pressure degrees of freedom cannot be statically condensed out on the element level because the variables $p_1, \dots, p_4$ pertain to the element we are considering here *and* to the adjacent elements, thus describing a continuous pressure field for the discretization.

Let us now return to the discussion of what pressure and displacement interpolations should be used in order to have an effective element.

For instance, in Example 4.32, we used four nodes to interpolate the displacements and assumed a constant pressure, and we may ask whether a constant pressure is the appropriate choice for the four-node element. Actually, for this element, it is a somewhat natural choice because the volumetric strain calculated from the displacements contains linear variations in x and y and our pressure assumption should be of lower order.

When higher-order displacement interpolations are used, the choice of the appropriate pressure interpolation is not obvious and indeed much more difficult: the pressure should not be interpolated at too low a degree because then the pressure prediction could be of higher order and hence be more accurate, but the pressure should also not be interpolated at too high a degree because then the element would behave like the displacement-based elements and lock. Hence, we want to use the highest degree of pressure interpolation that does not introduce locking into the element.

For example, considering the u/p formulation and biquadratic displacement interpolation (i.e., nine nodes for the description of the displacements), we may naturally try the following cases:

1. Constant pressure, $p = p_0$ (9/1 element)
2. Linear pressure, $p = p_0 + p_1 x + p_2 y$ (9/3 element)
3. Bilinear pressure, $p = p_0 + p_1 x + p_2 y + p_3 xy$ (9/4 element)

and so on, up to a quadratic pressure interpolation (which corresponds to the 9/9 element).

These elements have been analyzed theoretically and by use of numerical experiments. Studies of the elements show that the 9/1 element does not lock, but the rate of convergence of pressure (and hence stresses) as the mesh is refined is only of $o(h)$ because a constant pressure is assumed in each nine-node element. The poor quality of the pressure prediction can of course also have a negative effect on the prediction of the displacements.

Studies also show that the 9/3 element is most attractive because it does not lock and the stress convergence is of $o(h^2)$. Hence, the predictive capability is optimal since if a biquadratic displacement expansion is used, no higher-order convergence in stresses can be expected. Also, the 9/3 element is effective for any Poisson's ratio up to 0.5 (but the static condensation of the pressure degrees of freedom is possible only for values of $v < 0.5$).

Hence, we may be tempted to always use the 9/3 element (instead of the displacement-based nine-node element). However, we find in practice that the 9/3 element is computationally slightly more expensive than the nine-node displacement-based element, and when v is less than 0.48, the additional terms in the pressure expansion of the displacement-based element allow a slightly better prediction of stresses.

The next u/p element of interest is the 9/4 element, and studies show that this element locks when v is close to 0.50; hence it cannot be recommended for almost incompressible analysis.

In an analogous manner, other u/p elements can be constructed, and Table 4.6 summarizes some choices. Regarding these elements, we may note that the four-node two-dimensional and eight-node three-dimensional elements are extensively used in practice. However, the nine-node two-dimensional and 27-node three-dimensional elements are frequently more powerful.

As indicated in Table 4.6, the $Q_2 - P_1$ and $P_2^+ - P_1$ elements are the first members of two families of elements that may be used. That is, the quadrilateral elements $Q_n - P_{n-1}$, and the triangular elements $P_n^+ - P_{n-1}$, $n > 2$, are also effective elements.

In Table 4.6 we refer to the inf-sup condition, which we will discuss in Section 4.5.

From a computational point of view, the u/p elements are attractive because the element pressure degrees of freedom can be statically condensed out before the elements are assembled (assuming $\nu < 0.5$ but possibly very close to 0.5). Hence, the degrees of freedom for the assemblage of elements are only the same nodal point displacements that are also the degrees of freedom in the pure displacement-based solution.

However, the u/p-c formulation has the advantage that a continuous pressure field is always calculated. Table 4.7 lists some effective elements.

The Finite Element Solution of Totally Incompressible Conditions

If we want to consider the material to be totally incompressible, we can still use (4.140) and (4.143), but we then let $\kappa \to \infty$. For this reason, we refer to this case as the *limit problem*. Then (4.143) becomes

$$\int_V \epsilon_V \overline{p} \, dV = 0 \tag{4.149}$$

and (4.147) becomes, correspondingly,

$$\begin{bmatrix} \mathbf{K}_{uu} & \mathbf{K}_{up} \\ \mathbf{K}_{pu} & \mathbf{0} \end{bmatrix} \begin{bmatrix} \hat{\mathbf{u}} \\ \hat{\mathbf{p}} \end{bmatrix} = \begin{bmatrix} \mathbf{R} \\ \mathbf{0} \end{bmatrix} \tag{4.150}$$

Hence, in the coefficient matrix, the diagonal elements corresponding to the pressure degrees of freedom are now zero. It follows that a static condensation of the element pressure degrees of freedom in the u/p formulation is no longer possible and that the solution of the equations of the complete assemblage of elements needs special considerations (beyond those required in the pure displacement-based solution) to avoid encountering a zero pivot element (see Section 8.2.5).

Suitable elements for solution are listed in Tables 4.6 and 4.7. These elements are effective (except for the $Q_1 - P_0$ elements) because they have good predictive capability irrespective of how close the behavior of the medium is to a situation of total incompressibility (but the procedure for solving the governing finite element equations must take into account that the elements in $\mathbf{K}_{pp}$ become increasingly smaller as total incompressibility is approached).

As already noted earlier, we refer to the inf-sup condition in Tables 4.6 and 4.7. This condition is the basic mathematical criterion that determines whether a mixed finite element discretization is stable and convergent (and hence will yield a reliable solution). The condition was introduced as *the* fundamental test for mixed finite element formulations by I. Babuška [A] and F. Brezzi [A] and since then has been used extensively in the analysis of mixed finite element formulations. In addition to the inf-sup condition, there is also the ellipticity condition which has not received as much attention because frequently—as in the analysis of almost incompressible media—the ellipticity condition is automatically satisfied.

TABLE 4.6 *Various effective u/p elements (displacements between elements are continuous and pressure variables pertain to individual elements)*[†]

Element	Nodal points		Remarks
	2-D element	3-D element	
$Q_1 - P_0$ in 2-D: 4/1 in 3-D: 8/1	$p = p_0$	$p = p_0$	The element predicts reasonably good displacements, but stresses may be inaccurate because of the constant pressure assumption and possible pressure fluctuations. The element does not satisfy the inf-sup condition (see discussion of element in Section 4.5.5).
$Q_2 - P_0$; $Q_2^- = Q_2 \cap P_3$ in 2-D: 8/1 in 3-D: 20/1	$p = p_0$		The element satisfies the inf-sup condition, but the constant pressure assumption may require fine discretizations for accurate stress prediction.

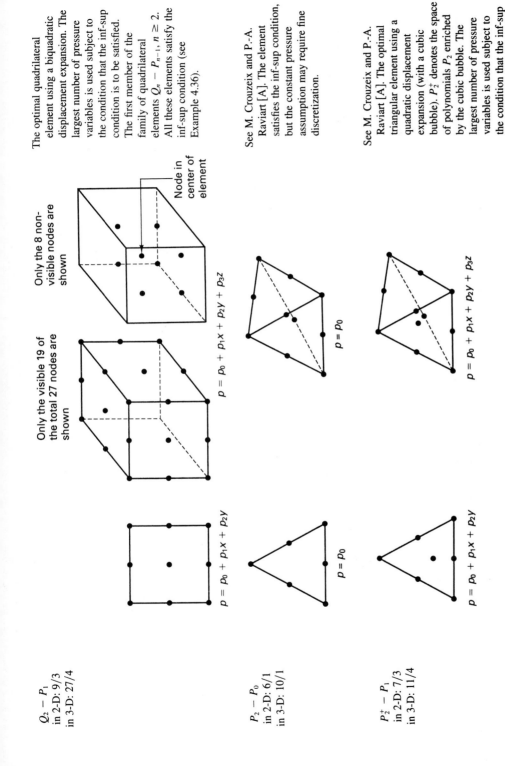

$Q_2 - P_1$
in 2-D: 9/3
in 3-D: 27/4

$p = p_0 + p_1x + p_2y$

Only the visible 19 of the total 27 nodes are shown

Only the 8 non-visible nodes are shown

Node in center of element

$p = p_0 + p_1x + p_2y + p_3z$

The optimal quadrilateral element using a biquadratic displacement expansion. The largest number of pressure variables is used subject to the condition that the inf-sup condition is to be satisfied. The first member of the family of quadrilateral elements $Q_n - P_{n-1}$, $n \geq 2$. All these elements satisfy the inf-sup condition (see Example 4.36).

$P_2 - P_0$
in 2-D: 6/1
in 3-D: 10/1

$p = p_0$

$p = p_0$

See M. Crouzeix and P.-A. Raviart [A]. The element satisfies the inf-sup condition, but the constant pressure assumption may require fine discretization.

$P_2^+ - P_1$
in 2-D: 7/3
in 3-D: 11/4

$p = p_0 + p_1x + p_2y$

$p = p_0 + p_1x + p_2y + p_3z$

See M. Crouzeix and P.-A. Raviart [A]. The optimal triangular element using a quadratic displacement expansion (with a cubic bubble). P_2^+ denotes the space of polynomials P_2 enriched by the cubic bubble. The largest number of pressure variables is used subject to the condition that the inf-sup condition is to be satisfied. The first member of the family of triangular elements $P_n^+ - P_{n-1}$, $n \geq 2$. All these elements satisfy the inf-sup condition.

† For the interpolation functions, see Figs. 4.13, 5.4, 5.5, 5.11, and 5.13.

TABLE 4.7 *Various effective u/p-c elements (displacements and pressure between elements are continuous and all elements satisfy the inf-sup condition)*[†]

Element	Nodal points		Remarks
	2-D element	3-D element	
$Q_2 - Q_1$ in 2-D: 9/4-c in 3-D: 27/8-c		Only the 8 non-visible nodes are shown	See P. Hood and C. Taylor [A]. The first member of the $Q_n - Q_{n-1}$ family of quadrilateral elements, $n \geq 2$.
	Only the visible 19 of the total 27 nodes are shown		

Node in center of element

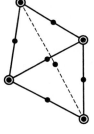

$P_2 - P_1$
in 2-D: 6/3-c
in 3-D: 10/4-c

See P. Hood and C. Taylor [A]. The first member of the $P_n - P_{n-1}$ family of triangular elements, $n \geq 2$.

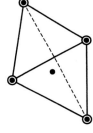

$P_1^+ - P_1$
in 2-D: 4/3-c
in 3-D: 5/4-c

See D. N. Arnold, F. Brezzi, and M. Fortin [A]. P_1^+ denotes the space of polynomials P_1 enriched by the cubic bubble. Also referred to as MINI elements.

● Node with displacement variables

◎ Node with displacement and pressure variables

† For the interpolation functions, see Figs. 4.13, 5.4, 5.5, 5.11, and 5.13.

We may ask whether in practice it is really important to satisfy the inf-sup condition, that is, whether perhaps this condition is too strong and elements that do not satisfy it can still be used reliably. Our experience is that if the inf-sup condition is satisfied, the element will be, for the interpolations used, as effective as we can reasonably expect and in that sense optimal. For example, the 9/3 element for plane strain analysis in Table 4.6 is based on a parabolic interpolation of displacements and a linear interpolation of pressure. The element does not lock, and the order of convergence of displacements is always $o(h^3)$, and of stresses, $o(h^2)$, which is surely the best behavior we can obtain with the interpolations used.

On the other hand, if the inf-sup condition is not satisfied, the element will not always display for all analysis problems (pertaining to the mathematical model considered) the convergence characteristics that we would expect and indeed require in practice. The element is therefore not robust and reliable.

Since the inf-sup condition is of great fundamental importance, we present in the following section a derivation that although not mathematically complete does yield valuable insight. In this discussion we will also encounter and briefly exemplify the ellipticity condition. For a mathematically complete derivation of the ellipticity and inf-sup conditions and many more details, we refer the reader to the book by F. Brezzi and M. Fortin [A].

In the derivation in the next section we examine the problem of incompressible elasticity, but our considerations are also directly applicable to the problem of incompressible fluid flow, and as shown in Section 4.5.7, to the formulations of structural elements.

4.4.4 Exercises

4.33. Use the four-node and eight-node shell elements available in a finite element program and perform the patch tests in Fig. 4.17.

4.34. Consider the three-dimensional eight-node element shown. Design the patch test and identify analytically whether it is passed for the element.

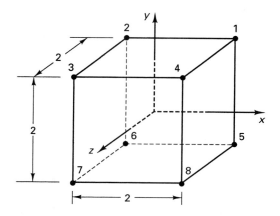

$$u = \sum_{i=1}^{8} h_i u_i + \alpha_1 \phi_1 + \alpha_2 \phi_2 + \alpha_3 \phi_3$$

$$v = \sum_{i=1}^{8} h_i v_i + \alpha_4 \phi_1 + \alpha_5 \phi_2 + \alpha_6 \phi_3$$

$$w = \sum_{i=1}^{8} h_i w_i + \alpha_7 \phi_1 + \alpha_8 \phi_2 + \alpha_9 \phi_3$$

$$h_i = \frac{1}{8}(1 + x_i x)(1 + y_i y)(1 + z_i z)$$

$$\phi_1 = 1 - x^2; \phi_2 = 1 - y^2; \phi_3 = 1 - z^2$$

Displacement interpolation functions

4.35. Consider the Hu-Washizu functional Π_{HW} in (4.114) and derive in detail the equations (4.116) to (4.121).

4.36. The following functional is referred to as the Hellinger-Reissner functional[17]

$$\Pi_{HR}(\mathbf{u}, \boldsymbol{\tau}) = \int_V -\frac{1}{2}\boldsymbol{\tau}^T \mathbf{C}^{-1}\boldsymbol{\tau} \, dV + \int_V \boldsymbol{\tau}^T \, \boldsymbol{\partial}_\epsilon \mathbf{u} \, dV$$

$$- \int_V \mathbf{u}^T \mathbf{f}^B \, dV - \int_{S_f} \mathbf{u}^{S_f T}\mathbf{f}^{S_f} \, dS - \int_{S_u} \mathbf{f}^{S_u T}(\mathbf{u}^{S_u} - \mathbf{u}_p) \, dS$$

where the prescribed (not to be varied) quantities are $\mathbf{f}^B$ in V, $\mathbf{u}_p$ on S_u, and $\mathbf{f}^{S_f}$ on S_f.

Derive this functional from the Hu-Washizu functional by imposing $\boldsymbol{\epsilon} = \mathbf{C}^{-1}\boldsymbol{\tau}$. Then invoke the stationarity of Π_{HR} and establish all remaining differential conditions for the volume and surface of the body.

4.37. Consider the functional

$$\Pi_1 = \Pi - \int_{S_u} \mathbf{f}^{S_u T}(\mathbf{u}^{S_u} - \mathbf{u}_p) \, dS$$

where Π is given in (4.109) and $\mathbf{u}_p$ are the displacements to be prescribed on the surface S_u. Hence, the vector $\mathbf{f}^{S_u}$ represents the Lagrange multipliers (surface tractions) used to enforce the surface displacement conditions. Invoke the stationarity of Π_1 and show that the Lagrange multiplier term will enforce the displacement boundary conditions on S_u.

4.38. Consider the three-node truss element in Fig. E4.29. Use the Hu-Washizu variational principle and establish the stiffness matrices for the following assumptions:
(a) Parabolic displacement, linear strain, and constant stress
(b) Parabolic displacement, constant strain, and constant stress
Discuss your results in terms of whether the choices of interpolations are sensible (see Example 4.29).

4.39. Show that the following stress-strain expressions of an isotropic material are equivalent.

$$\tau_{ij} = \kappa\epsilon_V\delta_{ij} + 2G\epsilon'_{ij} \tag{a}$$

$$\tau_{ij} = C_{ijrs}\epsilon_{rs} \tag{b}$$

$$\boldsymbol{\tau} = \mathbf{C}\boldsymbol{\epsilon} \tag{c}$$

where κ is the bulk modulus, G is the shear modulus,

$$\kappa = \frac{E}{3(1-2\nu)}; \qquad G = \frac{E}{2(1+\nu)}$$

E is Young's modulus, ν is Poisson's ratio, ϵ_V is the volumetric strain, and ϵ'_{ij} are the deviatoric strain components,

$$\epsilon_V = \epsilon_{kk}; \qquad \epsilon'_{ij} = \epsilon_{ij} - \frac{\epsilon_V}{3}\delta_{ij}$$

Also,
$$C_{ijrs} = \lambda\delta_{ij}\delta_{rs} + \mu(\delta_{ir}\delta_{js} + \delta_{is}\delta_{jr})$$

---

[17] This functional is sometimes given in a different form by applying the divergence theorem to the second term.

where λ and μ are the Lamé constants,

$$\lambda = \frac{E\nu}{(1 + \nu)(1 - 2\nu)}; \qquad \mu = \frac{E}{2(1 + \nu)}$$

In (a) and (b) tensorial quantities are used, whereas in (c) the vector of strains contains the engineering shear strains (which are equal to twice the tensor components; e.g., $\gamma_{xy} = \epsilon_{12} + \epsilon_{21}$). Also, the stress-strain matrix $\mathbf{C}$ in (c) is given in Table 4.3.

4.40. Identify the order of pressure interpolation that should be used in the u/p formulation in order to obtain the same stiffness matrix as in the pure displacement formulation. Consider the following elements of 2×2 geometry.
  (a) Four-node element in plane strain
  (b) Four-node element in axisymmetric conditions
  (c) Nine-node element in plane strain.

4.41. Consider the 4/1 element in Example 4.32 and assume that the displacement boundary condition to be imposed is $u_1 = \bar{u}$. Show formally that imposing this boundary condition prior to or after the static condensation of the pressure degree of freedom, yields the same element contribution to the stiffness matrix of the assemblage.

4.42. Consider the axisymmetric 4/1 u/p element shown. Construct the matrices $\mathbf{B}_D$, $\mathbf{B}_V$, $\mathbf{C}'$, and $\mathbf{H}_p$ for this element.

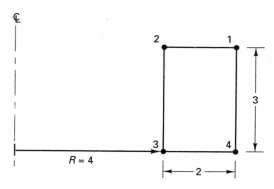

4.43. Consider the 4/3-c element in plane strain conditions shown. Formulate all displacement and strain interpolation matrices for this element (see Table 4.7).

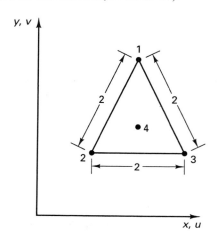

4.44. Consider the 9/3 plane strain u/p element shown. Calculate the matrix $\mathbf{K}_{pp}$.

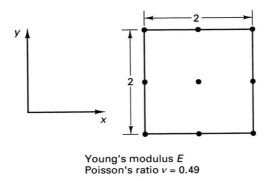

Young's modulus E
Poisson's ratio $v = 0.49$

4.45. Consider the plate with the circular hole shown. Use a finite element program to solve for the stress distribution along section AA for the two cases of Poisson's ratios $v = 0.3$ and $v = 0.499$. Assess the accuracy of your results by means of an error measure. (*Hint:* For the analysis with $v = 0.499$, the 9/3 element is effective.)

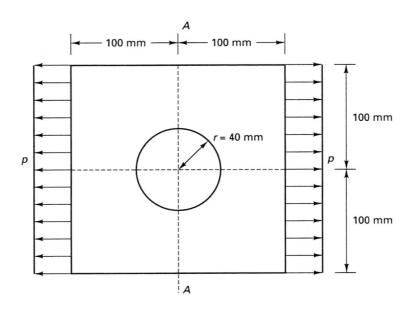

Plane strain condition
Young's modulus $E = 200,000$ MPa

4.46. The static response of the thick cylinder shown is to be calculated with a finite element program.

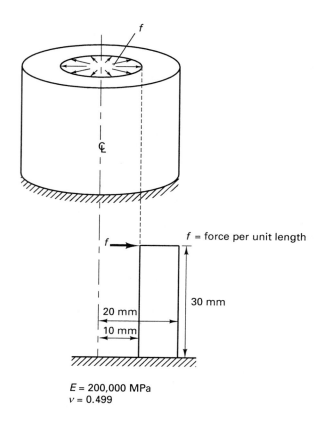

f = force per unit length

30 mm

20 mm

10 mm

$E = 200,000$ MPa
$v = 0.499$

Use idealizations based on the following elements to analyze the cylinder.
(a) Four-node displacement-based element
(b) Nine-node displacement-based element
(c) 4/1 u/p element.
(d) 9/3 u/p element.
In each case use a sequence of meshes and identify the convergence rate of the strain energy.

4.5 THE INF-SUP CONDITION FOR ANALYSIS OF INCOMPRESSIBLE MEDIA AND STRUCTURAL PROBLEMS

As we pointed out in the previous section, it is important that the finite element discretization for the analysis of almost, and of course totally, incompressible media satisfy the inf-sup condition. The objective in this section is to present this condition. We first consider the pure displacement formulation for the analysis of solids and then the displacement/pressure formulations. Finally, we also briefly discuss the inf-sup condition as applicable to structural elements.

In our discussion we apply the displacement and displacement/pressure formulations to a solid medium. However, the basic observations and conclusions are also directly applicable to the solution of incompressible fluid flows if velocities are used instead of displacements (see Section 7.4).

4.5.1 The Inf-Sup Condition Derived from Convergence Considerations

We want to solve a general linear elasticity problem (see Section 4.2.1) in which a body is subjected to body forces $\mathbf{f}^B$, surface tractions $\mathbf{f}^{S_f}$ on the surface S_f, and displacement boundary conditions $\mathbf{u}^{S_u}$ on the surface S_u. Without loss of generality of the conclusions that we want to reach in this section, we can assume that the prescribed displacements $\mathbf{u}^{S_u}$ and prescribed tractions $\mathbf{f}^{S_f}$ are zero. Of course, we assume that the body is properly supported, so that no rigid body motions are possible. We can then write our analysis problem as a problem of minimization,

$$\min_{\mathbf{v} \in V} \left\{ \frac{1}{2} a(\mathbf{v}, \mathbf{v}) + \frac{\kappa}{2} \int_{\text{Vol}} (\text{div } \mathbf{v})^2 \, d\text{Vol} - \int_{\text{Vol}} \mathbf{f}^B \cdot \mathbf{v} \, d\text{Vol} \right\} \tag{4.151}$$

where using indicial notation and tensor quantities (see Sections 4.3.4 and 4.4.3),

$$a(\mathbf{u}, \mathbf{v}) = 2G \int_{\text{Vol}} \sum_{i,j}^{3} \epsilon'_{ij}(\mathbf{u}) \, \epsilon'_{ij}(\mathbf{v}) \, d\text{Vol}$$

$$\epsilon'_{ij}(\mathbf{u}) = \epsilon_{ij}(\mathbf{u}) - \tfrac{1}{3} \text{div } \mathbf{u} \delta_{ij} \tag{4.152}$$

$$\epsilon_{ij}(\mathbf{u}) = \frac{1}{2}\left(\frac{\partial u_i}{\partial x_j} + \frac{\partial u_j}{\partial x_i} \right); \qquad \text{div } \mathbf{v} = v_{i,i}$$

where $\kappa = E/[3(1 - 2\nu)]$ (bulk modulus), $G = E/[2(1 + \nu)]$ (shear modulus), $E =$ Young's modulus, $\nu =$ Poisson's ratio.

$$V = \left\{ \mathbf{v} \,\middle|\, \frac{\partial v_i}{\partial x_j} \in L^2(\text{Vol}), \, i, j = 1, 2, 3; \, v_i|_{S_u} = 0, \, i = 1, 2, 3 \right\}$$

In these expressions we use the notation defined earlier (see Section 4.3) and we denote by "Vol" the domain over which we integrate so as to avoid any confusion with the vector space V. Also, we use for the vector $\mathbf{v}$ and scalar q the norms

$$\| \mathbf{v} \|_{\tilde{V}}^2 = \sum_{i,j} \left\| \frac{\partial v_i}{\partial x_j} \right\|_{L^2(\text{Vol})}^2 ; \qquad \| q \|_0^2 = \| q \|_{L^2(\text{Vol})}^2 \tag{4.153}$$

where the vector norm $\| \cdot \|_{\tilde{V}}$ is somewhat easier to work with but is equivalent to the Sobolev norm $\| \cdot \|_1$ defined in (4.76) (by the Poincaré-Friedrichs inequality).

In the following discussion we will not explicitly give the subscripts on the norms but always imply that a vector $\mathbf{w}$ has norm $\| \mathbf{w} \|_V$ and a scalar γ has norm $\| \gamma \|_0$.

Let $\mathbf{u}$ be the minimizer of (4.151) (i.e., the exact solution to the problem) and let V_h be a space of a sequence of finite element spaces that we choose to solve the problem. These spaces are defined in (4.84). Of course, each discrete problem,

$$\lim_{\mathbf{v}_h \in V_h} \left\{ \frac{1}{2} a(\mathbf{v}_h, \mathbf{v}_h) + \frac{\kappa}{2} \int_{\mathrm{Vol}} (\mathrm{div}\ \mathbf{v}_h)^2\ d\mathrm{Vol} - \int_{\mathrm{Vol}} \mathbf{f}^B \cdot \mathbf{v}_h\ d\mathrm{Vol} \right\} \qquad (4.154)$$

has a unique finite element solution $\mathbf{u}_h$. We considered the properties of this solution in Section 4.3.4, and in particular we presented the properties (4.95) and (4.101). However, we also stated that the constants c in these relations are dependent on the material properties. The important point now is that when the bulk modulus κ is very large, the relations (4.95) and (4.101) are no longer useful because the constants are too large. Therefore, we want our finite element space V_h to satisfy another property, still of the form (4.95) but in which the constant c, in addition to being independent of h, is also independent of κ.

To state this new desired property, let us first define the "distance" between the exact solution $\mathbf{u}$ and the finite element space V_h (see Fig. 4.22),

$$d(\mathbf{u}, V_h) = \inf_{\mathbf{v}_h \in V_h} \| \mathbf{u} - \mathbf{v}_h \| = \| \mathbf{u} - \tilde{\mathbf{u}}_h \| \qquad (4.155)$$

where $\tilde{\mathbf{u}}_h$ is an element in V_h but is in general not the finite element solution.

The Basic Requirements

In engineering practice, the bulk modulus κ may vary from values of the order of G to very large values, and indeed to infinity when complete incompressibility is considered. Our objective is to use finite elements that are uniformly effective irrespective of what value κ

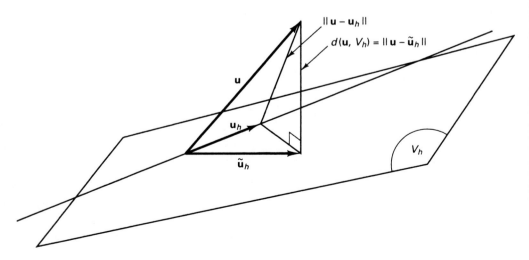

Figure 4.22 Schematic representation of solutions and distances; for optimal convergence $\| \mathbf{u} - \mathbf{u}_h \| \leq c\ d(\mathbf{u}, V_h)$ with c independent of h and κ.

takes. Mathematically, therefore, our purpose is to find conditions on V_h such that

$$\|\mathbf{u} - \mathbf{u}_h\| \le c\, d(\mathbf{u}, V_h)$$
$$\textit{with a constant c independent of h and } \kappa. \tag{4.156}$$

These conditions shall guide us in our choice of effective finite elements and discretizations.

The inequality (4.156) means that the distance between the continuous solution $\mathbf{u}$ and the finite element solution $\mathbf{u}_h$ will be smaller than a (reasonably sized) constant c times $d(\mathbf{u}, V_h)$ and that this relationship will be satisfied with the *same* constant c irrespective of the bulk modulus used. Note that this *independence* of c from the bulk modulus is the key property we did not have in Section 4.3.4 when we derived a relation such as (4.156) [see (4.95)].

Assume that the condition (4.156) holds (with a reasonably sized constant c). Then if $d(\mathbf{u}, V_h)$ is $o(h^k)$, we know that $\|\mathbf{u} - \mathbf{u}_h\|$ is also $o(h^k)$, and since c is reasonably sized and independent of κ, we will in fact observe the same solution accuracy and improvement in accuracy as h is decreased irrespective of the bulk modulus in the problem. In this case the finite element spaces have good approximation properties for any value of κ, and the finite element discretization is reliable (see Section 1.3).

The relationship in (4.156) expresses our fundamental requirement for the finite element discretization, and finite element formulations that satisfy (4.156) do not lock (see Section 4.4.3). In the following discussion, we write (4.156) only in forms with which we can work more easily in choosing effective finite elements. One of these forms uses an inf-sup value and is the celebrated inf-sup condition.

To proceed further, we define the spaces K and D,

$$K(q) = \{\mathbf{v} \mid \mathbf{v} \in V, \operatorname{div} \mathbf{v} = q\} \tag{4.157}$$

$$D = \{q \mid q = \operatorname{div} \mathbf{v} \text{ for some } \mathbf{v} \in V\} \tag{4.158}$$

and the corresponding spaces for our discretizations,

$$K_h(q_h) = \{\mathbf{v}_h \mid \mathbf{v}_h \in V_h, \operatorname{div} \mathbf{v}_h = q_h\} \tag{4.159}$$

$$D_h = \{q_h \mid q_h = \operatorname{div} \mathbf{v}_h \text{ for some } \mathbf{v}_h \in V_h\} \tag{4.160}$$

Hence the space $K_h(q_h)$, for a given q_h, corresponds to all the elements $\mathbf{v}_h$ in V_h that satisfy $\operatorname{div} \mathbf{v}_h = q_h$. Also, the space D_h corresponds to all the elements q_h with $q_h = \operatorname{div} \mathbf{v}_h$ that are reached by the elements $\mathbf{v}_h$ in V_h; that is, for any q_h an element of D_h there is at least one element $\mathbf{v}_h$ in V_h such that $q_h = \operatorname{div} \mathbf{v}_h$. Similar thoughts are applicable to the spaces K and D.

We recall that when κ is large, the quantity $\|\operatorname{div} \mathbf{u}_h\|$ will be small; the larger κ, the smaller $\|\operatorname{div} \mathbf{u}_h\|$, and it is difficult to obtain an accurate pressure prediction $p_h = -\kappa \operatorname{div} \mathbf{u}_h$. In the limit $\kappa \to \infty$ we have $\operatorname{div} \mathbf{u}_h = 0$, but the pressure p_h is still finite (and of course of order of the applied tractions) and therefore $\kappa(\operatorname{div} \mathbf{u}_h)^2 = 0$.

Before developing the inf-sup condition, let us state the ellipticity condition for the problem of total incompressibility: there is a constant α greater than zero and independent of h such that

$$a(\mathbf{v}_h, \mathbf{v}_h) \geq \alpha \|\mathbf{v}_h\|^2 \qquad \forall \ \mathbf{v}_h \in K_h(0) \qquad (4.161)$$

This condition in essence states that the deviatoric strain energy is to be bounded from below, a condition that is clearly satisfied. We further refer to and explain the ellipticity condition for the incompressible elasticity problem in Section 4.5.2.

Let us emphasize that in this finite element formulation the only variables are the displacements.

Obtaining the Inf-Sup Condition

The inf-sup condition—which when satisfied ensures that (4.156) holds—can now be developed as follows. Since the condition of total incompressibility clearly represents the most severe constraint, we consider this case. Then $q = 0$, $\mathbf{u}$ belongs to $K(q)$ for $q = 0$ [that is, $K(0)$], and the continuous problem (4.151) becomes

$$\min_{\mathbf{v} \in K(0)} \left\{ \frac{1}{2} a(\mathbf{v}, \mathbf{v}) - \int_{\text{Vol}} \mathbf{f}^B \cdot \mathbf{v} \, d\text{Vol} \right\} \qquad (4.162)$$

with the solution $\mathbf{u}$, while the discrete problem is

$$\min_{\mathbf{v}_h \in K_h(0)} \left\{ \frac{1}{2} a(\mathbf{v}_h, \mathbf{v}_h) - \int_{\text{Vol}} \mathbf{f}^B \cdot \mathbf{v}_h \, d\text{Vol} \right\} \qquad (4.163)$$

with the solution $\mathbf{u}_h$.

Now consider condition (4.156). We notice that in this condition we compare distances. In the following discussion *we characterize a distance as "small" if it remains of the same order of magnitude as $d(\mathbf{u}, V_h)$ as h decreases.* Similarly, we will say that a vector is small if its length satisfies this definition and that a vector is "close" to another vector if the vector difference in the two vectors is small.

Since $\mathbf{u}_h \in K_h(0)$, and therefore always $\|\mathbf{u} - \mathbf{u}_h\| \leq \tilde{c} \, d[\mathbf{u}, K_h(0)]$ (see Exercise 4.47), we can also write condition (4.156) in the form

$$\boxed{d[\mathbf{u}, K_h(0)] \leq c \, d(\mathbf{u}, V_h)} \qquad (4.164)$$

which means that we want the distance from $\mathbf{u}$ to $K_h(0)$ to be small. This relation expresses the requirement that if the distance between $\mathbf{u}$ and V_h (the complete finite element displacement space) decreases at a certain rate as $h \to 0$, then the distance between $\mathbf{u}$ and the space in which the actual solution lies [because $\mathbf{u}_h \in K_h(0)$] decreases at the same rate.

Figure 4.23 shows schematically the spaces and vectors that we use. Let $\mathbf{u}_{h0}$ be a vector of our choice in $K_h(0)$ and let $\mathbf{w}_h$ be the corresponding vector such that

$$\tilde{\mathbf{u}}_h = \mathbf{u}_{h0} + \mathbf{w}_h \qquad (4.165)$$

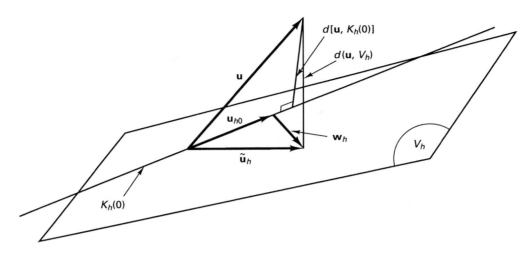

Figure 4.23 Spaces and vectors considered in deriving the inf-sup condition

We can then prove that the condition in (4.164) is fulfilled provided that

> for all $q_h \in D_h$, there is a $\mathbf{w}_h \in K_h(q_h)$ such that
>
> $$\| \mathbf{w}_h \| \leq c' \, \| q_h \|$$ (4.166)
>
> where c' is independent of h and the bulk modulus κ.

First, we always have (see Exercise 4.48)

$$\| \operatorname{div}(\mathbf{u} - \tilde{\mathbf{u}}_h) \| \leq \alpha \| \mathbf{u} - \tilde{\mathbf{u}}_h \|$$ (4.167)

and hence,

$$\| \operatorname{div} \tilde{\mathbf{u}}_h \| \leq \alpha \, d(\mathbf{u}, V_h)$$ (4.168)

where α is a constant and we used div $\mathbf{u} = 0$.

Second, we consider

$$\| \mathbf{u} - \mathbf{u}_{h0} \| = \| \mathbf{u} - \tilde{\mathbf{u}}_h + \mathbf{w}_h \|$$

$$\leq \| \mathbf{u} - \tilde{\mathbf{u}}_h \| + \| \mathbf{w}_h \|$$

Now assume that (4.166) holds with $q_h = \operatorname{div} \tilde{\mathbf{u}}_h$. Because div $\mathbf{u}_{h0} = 0$, we have div $\tilde{\mathbf{u}}_h = \operatorname{div} \mathbf{w}_h$, where we note that $\tilde{\mathbf{u}}_h$ is fixed by (4.155) and therefore q_h is fixed, but by choosing different values of $\mathbf{u}_{h0}$ different values of $\mathbf{w}_h$ are also obtained. Then it follows that

$$\| \mathbf{u} - \mathbf{u}_{h0} \| \leq d(\mathbf{u}, V_h) + c' \, \| q_h \|$$

$$= d(\mathbf{u}, V_h) + c' \, \| \operatorname{div} \tilde{\mathbf{u}}_h \|$$ (4.169)

$$\leq d(\mathbf{u}, V_h) + c'\alpha \, d(\mathbf{u}, V_h)$$

We emphasize that we have used the condition (4.166) in this derivation and have assumed that $\mathbf{u}_{h0}$ is an element in $K_h(0)$ such that $\mathbf{w}_h$ satisfies (4.166). Also, note that (4.168) established only that $\| \operatorname{div} \tilde{\mathbf{u}}_h \|$ is small, but then (4.169) established that $\| \mathbf{u} - \mathbf{u}_{h0} \|$ is small.

Third, since $\mathbf{u}_{h0} \in K_h(0)$, we obtain from (4.169),

$$d[\mathbf{u}, K_h(0)] \leq \|\mathbf{u} - \mathbf{u}_{h0}\| \leq (1 + \alpha c') d(\mathbf{u}, V_h) \tag{4.170}$$

which is (4.164) with $c = 1 + \alpha c'$, and we note that c is independent of h and the bulk modulus.

The crucial step in the derivation of (4.164) is that using (4.166) with $q_h = \text{div } \tilde{\mathbf{u}}_h$, we can choose a vector $\mathbf{w}_h$ that is small [which follows by using (4.166) and (4.168)]. We note that (4.166) is the only condition we need in order to prove (4.164) and is therefore the fundamental requirement to be satisfied in order to have a finite element discretization that will give an optimal rate of convergence.

The optimal rate of convergence requires in (4.164) that the constant c' in (4.166) be independent of h. Assume, for example, that instead of (4.166) we have $\|\mathbf{w}_h\| \leq (1/\beta_h)\|q_h\|$ with β_h decreasing with h. Then (4.170) will read

$$d[\mathbf{u}, K_h(0)] \leq \left(1 + \frac{\alpha}{\beta_h}\right) d(\mathbf{u}, V_h) \tag{4.171}$$

and hence the distance between $\mathbf{u}$ and $K_h(0)$ will not decrease at the same rate as $d(\mathbf{u}, V_h)$. However, convergence, although not optimal, will still occur if $d(\mathbf{u}, V_h)$ decreases faster than β_h. This shows that the condition in (4.166) is a strong guarantee for good convergence properties of our discretization.

Let us now rewrite (4.166) in the form of the inf-sup condition. From (4.166) we obtain, with q_h and $\mathbf{w}_h$ variables, $\mathbf{w}_h \in K_h(q_h)$, the condition

$$\|\mathbf{w}_h\| \|q_h\| \leq c' \|q_h\|^2 = c' \int_{\text{Vol}} q_h \text{ div } \mathbf{w}_h \, d\text{Vol} \tag{4.172}$$

or the condition is that for all $q_h \in D_h$, there is a $\mathbf{w}_h \in K_h(q_h)$ such that

$$\frac{1}{c'} \|q_h\| \leq \frac{\int_{\text{Vol}} q_h \text{ div } \mathbf{w}_h \, d\text{Vol}}{\|\mathbf{w}_h\|} \tag{4.173}$$

Hence, we want
$$\frac{1}{c'} \|q_h\| \leq \sup_{\mathbf{v}_h \in V_h} \frac{\int_{\text{Vol}} q_h \text{ div } \mathbf{v}_h \, d\text{Vol}}{\|\mathbf{v}_h\|} \tag{4.174}$$

and the inf-sup condition follows,

$$\inf_{q_h \in D_h} \sup_{\mathbf{v}_h \in V_h} \frac{\int_{\text{Vol}} q_h \text{ div } \mathbf{v}_h \, d\text{Vol}}{\|\mathbf{v}_h\| \|q_h\|} \geq \beta > 0$$

with β a constant independent of κ and h $\tag{4.175}$

We note that $\beta = 1/c'$.

Therefore, (4.166) implies (4.175), and it can also be proven that (4.175) implies (4.166) (see Example 4.42). (We will not present this proof until later because we must first discuss certain additional basic facts.) Hence, we may also refer to (4.166) as one form of the inf-sup condition.

The inf-sup condition says that for a finite element discretization to be effective, we must have that, for a sequence of finite element spaces, if we take any $q_h \in D_h$, there must be a $\mathbf{v}_h \in V_h$ such that the quotient in (4.175) is $\geq \beta > 0$. If the inf-sup condition is satisfied by the sequence of finite element spaces, then our finite element discretization scheme will exhibit the good approximation property that we seek, namely, (4.156) will be fulfilled.

Note that if β is dependent on h, say (4.175) is satisfied with β_h instead of β, then the expression in (4.171) will be applicable (for an example, see the three-node isoparametric beam element in Section 4.5.7).

Whether the inf-sup condition is satisfied depends, in general, on the specific finite element we use, the mesh topology, and the boundary conditions. If a discretization using a specific finite element always satisfies (4.175), for any mesh topology and boundary conditions, we simply say that the element satisfies the inf-sup condition. If, on the other hand, we know of one mesh topology and/or one set of (physically realistic) boundary conditions for which the discretization does not satisfy (4.175), then we simply say that the element does not satisfy the inf-sup condition.

Another Form of the Inf-Sup Condition

To analyze whether an element satisfies the inf-sup condition (4.175), another form of this condition is very useful, namely

> For all $\mathbf{u}$ there is a $\mathbf{u}_I \in V_h$ (a vector that interpolates $\mathbf{u}$) such that
> $$\int_{\text{Vol}} \text{div}(\mathbf{u} - \mathbf{u}_I) q_h \, d\text{Vol} = 0 \qquad \text{for all } q_h \in D_h$$
> $$\|\mathbf{u}_I\| \leq c \|\mathbf{u}\|$$
> with the constant c independent of $\mathbf{u}$, $\mathbf{u}_I$, and h.

(4.176)

The equivalence of (4.176) and (4.175) [and hence (4.166)] can be formally proven (see F. Brezzi and M. Fortin [A] and F. Brezzi and K. J. Bathe [A, B]), but to simply relate the statements in (4.176) to our earlier discussion, we note that two fundamental requirements emerged in the derivation of the inf-sup condition; namely, that there is a vector $\mathbf{w}_h$ such that (see Figure 4.23)

$$\text{div } \mathbf{w}_h = \text{div } \tilde{\mathbf{u}}_h \tag{4.177}$$

and [see (4.166) and (4.168)]

$$\|\mathbf{w}_h\| \leq c^* d(\mathbf{u}, V_h) \tag{4.178}$$

where c^* is a constant.

We note that (4.176) corresponds to (4.177) and (4.178) if we consider the vector $\tilde{\mathbf{u}}_h - \mathbf{u}$ (the vector of difference between the best approximation in V_h and the exact solution) the *solution vector* and the vector $\mathbf{w}_h$ the *interpolation vector*.

Hence, the conditions are that the interpolation vector $\mathbf{w}_h$ shall satisfy the above divergence and "small-size" conditions *for and measured on* the vector $(\tilde{\mathbf{u}}_h - \mathbf{u})$ in order to have an effective discretization scheme.

The three expressions of the inf-sup condition, (4.166), (4.175), and (4.176), are useful in different ways but of course all express the same requirement. In mathematical analyses the forms (4.166) and (4.175) are usually employed, whereas (4.176) is frequently most easily used to prove whether a specific element satisfies the condition (see Example 4.36).

Considering the inf-sup condition, we recognize that the richer the space $K_h(0)$, the greater the capacity to satisfy (4.175) [that is, (4.164)]. However, unfortunately, using the standard displacement-based elements, the constraint is generally too strong for the elements and meshes (i.e., spaces V_h) of interest and the discretizations lock (see Fig. 4.20). We therefore turn to mixed formulations that do not lock and that exhibit the desired rates of convergence. Excellent candidates are the displacement/pressure formulations already introduced in Section 4.4.3. However, whereas the pure displacement formulation is (always) stable but generally locks, for any mixed formulation, a main additional concern is that it be stable. We shall see in the following discussion that the conditions of no locking and stability are fulfilled if by appropriate choice of the displacement and pressure interpolations the inf-sup condition is satisfied, and the desired (optimal) convergence rate is also obtained if the interpolations for the displacements and pressure are chosen appropriately.

Weakening the Constraint

Let us consider the u/p formulation. The variational discrete problem in the u/p formulation [corresponding to (4.140) and (4.143)] is

$$\min_{\mathbf{v}_h \in V_h} \left\{ \frac{1}{2} a(\mathbf{v}_h, \mathbf{v}_h) + \frac{\kappa}{2} \int_{\text{Vol}} [P_h(\text{div } \mathbf{v}_h)]^2 \, d\text{Vol} - \int_{\text{Vol}} \mathbf{f}^B \cdot \mathbf{v}_h \, d\text{Vol} \right\} \tag{4.179}$$

where the projection operator P_h is defined by

$$\int_{\text{Vol}} [P_h(\text{div } \mathbf{v}_h) - \text{div } \mathbf{v}_h] q_h \, d\text{Vol} = 0 \qquad \text{for all } q_h \in Q_h \tag{4.180}$$

and Q_h is a "pressure space" to be chosen. We see that Q_h always contains $P_h(D_h)$ but that Q_h is sometimes larger than $P_h(D_h)$, which is a case that we shall discuss later.

To recognize that (4.179) and (4.180) are indeed equivalent to the u/p formulation, we rewrite (4.179) and (4.180) as

$$2G \int_{\text{Vol}} \epsilon'_{ij}(\mathbf{u}_h) \epsilon'_{ij}(\mathbf{v}_h) \, d\text{Vol} - \int_{\text{Vol}} p_h \text{ div } \mathbf{v}_h \, d\text{Vol} = \int_{\text{Vol}} \mathbf{f}^B \cdot \mathbf{v}_h \, d\text{Vol} \qquad \forall \, \mathbf{v}_h \in V_h \tag{4.181}$$

$$\int_{\text{Vol}} \left(\frac{p_h}{\kappa} + \text{div } \mathbf{u}_h \right) q_h \, d\text{Vol} = 0 \qquad \forall \, q_h \in Q_h \tag{4.182}$$

These equations are (4.140) and (4.143) in Section 4.4.3, and we recall that they are valid for any value of $\kappa > 0$. The key point in the u/p formulation is that (4.180) [i.e., (4.182)] is applied individually for each element and, provided κ is finite, the pressure variables can be statically condensed out on the element level (before assembly of the element stiffness matrix into the global structure stiffness matrix).

Consider the following example.

EXAMPLE 4.34:   Derive $P_h(\text{div } \mathbf{v}_h)$ for the 4/1 element shown in Fig. E4.34. Hence, evaluate the term $(\kappa/2) \int_{\text{vol}} [P_h(\text{div } \mathbf{v}_h)]^2 \, d\text{Vol}$ in (4.179).

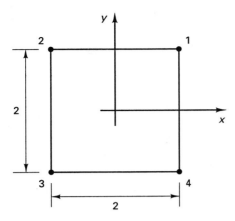

Figure E4.34   A 4/1 plane strain element

We have

$$\text{div } \mathbf{v}_h = \begin{bmatrix} h_{1,x} & \dots & h_{4,x} & \vdots & h_{1,y} & \dots & h_{4,y} \end{bmatrix} \hat{\mathbf{u}}$$

where

$$\hat{\mathbf{u}}^T = \begin{bmatrix} u_1 & \dots & u_4 & \vdots & v_1 & \dots & v_4 \end{bmatrix}$$

We now use (4.180), with q_h an arbitrary nonzero constant (say $q_h = \alpha$), because here Q_h is the space of constant pressures. Since $P_h(\text{div } \mathbf{v}_h)$ is also constant, we have from (4.180),

$$4 P_h(\text{div } \mathbf{v}_h)\alpha = \alpha \int_{\text{vol}} \text{div } \mathbf{v}_h \, d\text{Vol}$$

which gives

$$P_h(\text{div } \mathbf{v}_h) = \tfrac{1}{4}\begin{bmatrix} 1 & -1 & -1 & 1 & \vdots & 1 & 1 & -1 & -1 \end{bmatrix} \hat{\mathbf{u}}$$

$$= \mathbf{D}\hat{\mathbf{u}}$$

Hence,

$$\frac{\kappa}{2} \int_{\text{Vol}} [P_h(\text{div } \mathbf{v}_h)]^2 \, d\text{Vol} = \frac{\kappa}{2} \hat{\mathbf{u}}^T \mathbf{G}_h \, \hat{\mathbf{u}}$$

where

$$\mathbf{G}_h = 4\mathbf{D}^T\mathbf{D}$$

Note that although we have used the pressure space Q_h, the stiffness matrix obtained from (4.179) will correspond to nodal point displacements only.

Also, we may note that the term $P_h(\text{div } \mathbf{v}_h)$ is simply div $\mathbf{v}_h$ at $x = y = 0$.

EXAMPLE 4.35:   Consider the nine-node element shown in Fig. E4.35 and assume that $\mathbf{v}_h$ is given by the nodal point displacements $u_1 = 1$, $u_5 = 0.5$, $u_8 = 0.5$, $u_9 = 0.25$ with all other nodal point displacements equal to zero. Let Q_h be the space corresponding to $\{1, x, y\}$. Evaluate $P_h(\text{div } \mathbf{v}_h)$.

To evaluate $P_h(\text{div } \mathbf{v}_h)$ we use the general relationship

$$\int_{\text{Vol}} (P_h(\text{div } \mathbf{v}_h) - \text{div } \mathbf{v}_h)q_h \, d\text{Vol} = 0 \qquad \forall \, q_h \in Q_h \tag{a}$$

In this example,

$$\text{div } \mathbf{v}_h = \frac{\partial u_h}{\partial x} + \frac{\partial v_h}{\partial y}$$

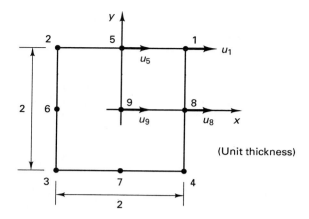

Figure E4.35 A 9/3 element subjected to nodal point displacements

where u_h and v_h are given by the element nodal point displacements. Hence,

$$u_h = \tfrac{1}{4}(1 + x)(1 + y)$$

$$v_h = 0$$

and

$$\text{div } \mathbf{v}_h = \tfrac{1}{4}(1 + y)$$

Let

$$P_h(\text{div } \mathbf{v}_h) = a_1 + a_2 x + a_3 y$$

then (a) gives

$$\int_{\text{Vol}} \left[(a_1 + a_2 x + a_3 y) - \frac{1}{4}(1 + y) \right] q_h \, dx \, dy = 0 \qquad \text{(b)}$$

for $q_h = 1$, x, and y. Hence, (b) gives the set of equations

$$
\begin{bmatrix}
\displaystyle\int_{\text{Vol}} dx \, dy & \displaystyle\int_{\text{Vol}} x \, dx \, dy & \displaystyle\int_{\text{Vol}} y \, dx \, dy \\[2ex]
 & \displaystyle\int_{\text{Vol}} x^2 \, dx \, dy & \displaystyle\int_{\text{Vol}} xy \, dx \, dy \\[2ex]
\text{Symmetric} & & \displaystyle\int_{\text{Vol}} y^2 \, dx \, dy
\end{bmatrix}
\begin{bmatrix} a_1 \\[2ex] a_2 \\[2ex] a_3 \end{bmatrix}
=
\begin{bmatrix}
\displaystyle\int_{\text{Vol}} \frac{1}{4}(1 + y) \, dx \, dy \\[2ex]
\displaystyle\int_{\text{Vol}} \frac{1}{4}(1 + y) x \, dx \, dy \\[2ex]
\displaystyle\int_{\text{Vol}} \frac{1}{4}(1 + y) y \, dx \, dy
\end{bmatrix}
$$

or

$$
\begin{bmatrix}
4 & 0 & 0 \\
 & \tfrac{4}{3} & 0 \\
\text{Sym.} & & \tfrac{4}{3}
\end{bmatrix}
\begin{bmatrix} a_1 \\ a_2 \\ a_3 \end{bmatrix}
=
\begin{bmatrix} 1 \\ 0 \\ \tfrac{1}{3} \end{bmatrix}
\qquad \text{(c)}
$$

The solution of (c) gives $a_1 = \tfrac{1}{4}$, $a_2 = 0$, $a_3 = \tfrac{1}{4}$, and hence,

$$P_h(\text{div } \mathbf{v}_h) = \tfrac{1}{4}(1 + y)$$

This result is correct because div $\mathbf{v}_h$ can be represented exactly in Q_h and in such a case the projection gives of course the value of div $\mathbf{v}_h$.

The inf-sup condition corresponding to (4.179) is now like the inf-sup condition we discussed earlier but using the term $P_h(\text{div } \mathbf{v}_h)$ instead of div $\mathbf{v}_h$. Hence our condition is now

$$\inf_{q_h \in P_h(D_h)} \sup_{\mathbf{v}_h \in V_h} \frac{\int_{\text{Vol}} q_h \, \text{div} \, \mathbf{v}_h \, d\text{Vol}}{\| \mathbf{v}_h \| \, \| q_h \|} \geq \beta > 0 \tag{4.183}$$

In other words, the inf-sup condition now corresponds to any element in V_h and $P_h(D_h)$. Hence, when applying (4.166), (4.175), or (4.176) to the mixed interpolated u/p elements, we now need to consider the finite element spaces V_h and $P_h(D_h)$, where $P_h(D_h)$ is used instead of D_h.

EXAMPLE 4.36: Prove that the inf-sup condition is satisfied by the 9/3 two-dimensional u/p element presented in Section 4.4.3.

For this proof we use the form of the inf-sup condition given in (4.176) (see F. Brezzi and K. J. Bathe [A]). Given $\mathbf{u}$ smooth we must find an interpolation, $\mathbf{u}_I \in V_h$, such that for each element m,

$$\int_{\text{Vol}^{(m)}} (\text{div} \, \mathbf{u} - \text{div} \, \mathbf{u}_I) q_h \, d\text{Vol}^{(m)} = 0 \tag{a}$$

for all q_h polynomials of degree ≤ 1 in $\text{Vol}^{(m)}$. To define $\mathbf{u}_I$ we prescribe the values of each displacement at the nine element nodes (corner nodes, midside nodes, and the center node). We start with the corner nodes and require for these nodes $i = 1, 2, 3, 4$,

$$\mathbf{u}_I |_i = \mathbf{u} |_i \qquad \text{eight conditions} \tag{b}$$

Then we adjust the values at the midside nodes $j = 5, 6, 7, 8$ in such a way that

$$\int_{S_j} (\mathbf{u} - \mathbf{u}_I) \cdot \mathbf{n} \, dS = \int_{S_j} (\mathbf{u} - \mathbf{u}_I) \cdot \boldsymbol{\tau} \, dS = 0 \qquad \text{eight conditions} \tag{c}$$

for every edge $S_1, \ldots, S_4$ of the element with $\mathbf{n}$ the unit normal vector and $\boldsymbol{\tau}$ the unit tangential vector to the edge.

Next we note that (a) in particular implies, for every constant q_h,

$$\int_{\text{Vol}^{(m)}} \text{div}(\mathbf{u} - \mathbf{u}_I) q_h \, d\text{Vol}^{(m)} = q_h \sum_{S_1, \ldots, S_4} \int_{S_j} (\mathbf{u} - \mathbf{u}_I) \cdot \mathbf{n} \, dS \tag{d}$$

We are left to use the two degrees of freedom at the element center node. We choose these in such a way that

$$\int_{\text{Vol}^{(m)}} \text{div}(\mathbf{u} - \mathbf{u}_I) x \, d\text{Vol}^{(m)} = \int_{\text{Vol}^{(m)}} \text{div}(\mathbf{u} - \mathbf{u}_I) y \, d\text{Vol}^{(m)} = 0 \tag{e}$$

We note now that (d) and (e) imply (a) and that $\mathbf{u}_I$, constructed element by element through (b) and (c), will be continuous from element to element. Finally, note that clearly if $\mathbf{u}$ is a (vector) polynomial of degree ≤ 2 on the element, we obtain $\mathbf{u}_I \equiv \mathbf{u}$ and this ensures optimal bounds for $\| \mathbf{u} - \mathbf{u}_I \|$ and implies the condition $\| \mathbf{u}_I \| \leq c \| \mathbf{u} \|$ in (4.176) for all $\mathbf{u}$.

While in the u/p formulation the projection (4.180) is carried out for each element individually, in the u/p-c formulation a continuous pressure interpolation is assumed and then (4.181) and (4.182) are applied. The relation (4.182) with the continuous pressure interpolation gives a set of equations coupling the displacements and pressures for adjacent elements. In this case the inf-sup condition is still given by (4.183), but now the pressure space corresponds to the nodal point continuous pressure interpolations.

In dealing with the inf-sup condition, we recognize that the ability to satisfy the condition depends on how the space $P_h(D_h)$ relates to the space of displacements V_h. Here again, P_h is the projection operator onto the space Q_h [see (4.180) and (4.182)], and, in general, the smaller the space Q_h, the easier it is to satisfy the condition. Of course, if for a given space V_h the inf-sup condition is satisfied with Q_h smaller than necessary, we have a stable element but the predictive capability is not as high as possible (namely, as high as it would be using the larger space Q_h but still satisfying the inf-sup condition).

For example, consider the nine-node isoparametric element (see Section 4.4.3). Using the u/p formulation with $P_h = I$ (the identity operator), the displacement-based formulation is obtained and the element locks. Reducing the constraint to obtain the 9/3 element, the inf-sup condition is satisfied (see Example 4.36) and optimal convergence rates are obtained for the displacements and the pressure; that is, the convergence rate for the displacements is $o(h^3)$ and for the stress is $o(h^2)$, which is all that we can expect with a parabolic interpolation of displacements and a linear interpolation of pressure. Reducing the constraint further to obtain the 9/1 element, the inf-sup condition is also satisfied, and while the element behavior for the interpolations used is still optimal, the predictive capability of this nine-node element is not the best possible (because a constant element pressure is assumed, whereas a linear pressure variation could be used).

This observation (about the quality of the solution) is explained by the error bounds (see, for example, F. Brezzi and K. J. Bathe [B]). Let $\mathbf{u}_I \in V_h$ be an interpolant of $\mathbf{u}$ satisfying

$$\left. \begin{aligned} \int_{\text{Vol}} [\text{div}(\mathbf{u} - \mathbf{u}_I)]q_h \, d\text{Vol} = 0 \qquad \forall \, q_h \in P_h(D_h) \\[6pt] \text{and} \qquad \|\mathbf{u}_I\| \le c\|\mathbf{u}\| \end{aligned} \right\} \qquad (4.184)$$

If (4.184) holds for all possible solutions $\mathbf{u}$, then

$$\|\mathbf{u} - \mathbf{u}_h\| \le c_1(\|\mathbf{u} - \mathbf{u}_I\| + \|(I - P_h)p\|) \qquad (4.185)$$

and

$$\|p + \kappa P_h(\text{div } \mathbf{u}_h)\| \le c_2(\|\mathbf{u} - \mathbf{u}_I\| + \|(I - P_h)p\|) \qquad (4.186)$$

where $p = -\kappa \, \text{div } \mathbf{u}$ and c_1, c_2 are constants independent of h and κ. We note of course that (4.184) is the inf-sup condition with the weakened constraint $q_h \in P_h(D_h)$ [see (4.176)] and that the right-hand sides of (4.185) and (4.186) are smaller the closer P_h is to I.

4.5.2 The Inf-Sup Condition Derived from the Matrix Equations

Further insight into the inf-sup condition is obtained by studying the governing algebraic finite element equations. Let us consider the case of total incompressibility (it being the most severe case),

$$\begin{bmatrix} (\mathbf{K}_{uu})_h & (\mathbf{K}_{up})_h \\ (\mathbf{K}_{pu})_h & \mathbf{0} \end{bmatrix} \begin{bmatrix} \mathbf{U}_h \\ \mathbf{P}_h \end{bmatrix} = \begin{bmatrix} \mathbf{R}_h \\ \mathbf{0} \end{bmatrix} \qquad (4.187)$$

where $\mathbf{U}_h$ lists all the unknown nodal point displacements and $\mathbf{P}_h$ lists the unknown pressure variables. Since the material is assumed to be totally incompressible, we have a square null matrix equal in size to the number of pressure variables in the lower right of the coefficient matrix.

The mathematical analysis of the formulation resulting in (4.187) consists of a study of the *solvability* and the *stability* of the equations, where the stability of the equations implies their solvability.

The solvability of (4.187) simply refers to the fact that (4.187) can actually be solved for unique vectors $\mathbf{U}_h$ and $\mathbf{P}_h$ when $\mathbf{R}_h$ is given.

The conditions for solvability (see Exercise 4.54) are

Condition i:

$$\mathbf{V}_h^T (\mathbf{K}_{uu})_h \mathbf{V}_h > 0 \qquad \text{for all } \mathbf{V}_h \text{ satisfying } (\mathbf{K}_{pu})_h \mathbf{V}_h = \mathbf{0} \qquad (4.188)$$

Condition ii:

$$(\mathbf{K}_{up})_h \mathbf{Q}_h = \mathbf{0} \qquad \text{implies that } \mathbf{Q}_h \text{ must be zero} \qquad (4.189)$$

The space of displacement vectors $\mathbf{V}_h$ that satisfy $(\mathbf{K}_{pu})_h \mathbf{V}_h = \mathbf{0}$ represents the kernel of $(\mathbf{K}_{pu})_h$.

The *stability* of the formulation is studied by considering a sequence of problems of the form (4.187) with increasingly finer meshes. Let S be the smallest constant such that

$$\frac{\| \Delta \mathbf{u}_h \|_V + \| \Delta p_h \|_0}{\| \mathbf{u}_h \|_V + \| p_h \|_0} \leq S \frac{\| \Delta \mathbf{f}^B \|_{DV}}{\| \mathbf{f}^B \|_{DV}} \qquad (4.190)$$

for all $\mathbf{u}_h, p_h, \mathbf{f}^B, \Delta \mathbf{u}_h, \Delta p_h, \Delta \mathbf{f}^B$, where $\| \cdot \|_V$ and $\| \cdot \|_0$ are the norms defined in (4.153), $\| \cdot \|_{DV}$ means the dual norm of $\| \cdot \|_V$ (see Section 2.7), and $\Delta \mathbf{f}^B$, $\Delta \mathbf{u}_h$, and Δp_h denote a prescribed perturbation on the load function $\mathbf{f}^B$ and the resulting perturbations on the displacement vector $\mathbf{u}_h$ and pressure p_h. Of course, we have

$$\begin{bmatrix} (\mathbf{K}_{uu})_h & (\mathbf{K}_{up})_h \\ (\mathbf{K}_{pu})_h & \mathbf{0} \end{bmatrix} \begin{bmatrix} \Delta \mathbf{U}_h \\ \Delta \mathbf{P}_h \end{bmatrix} = \begin{bmatrix} \Delta \mathbf{R}_h \\ \mathbf{0} \end{bmatrix} \qquad (4.191)$$

where $\Delta \mathbf{R}_h$ corresponds to the load variation $\Delta \mathbf{f}^B$ and the norms of the finite element variables in (4.190) are given by the nodal point values listed in the solution vectors. Hence (4.190) expresses that for a given relative perturbation in the load vector, the corresponding relative perturbation in the solution is bounded by S times the relative perturbation in the loads.

For any given fixed mesh, satisfying the conditions of solvability (4.188) and (4.189) implies that (4.190) is satisfied for some S, the value of which depends on the mesh.

The formulation is stable if for any sequence of meshes the stability constant S is uniformly bounded. Hence, our question of stability reduces to asking for the conditions on the matrices $(\mathbf{K}_{uu})_h$ and $(\mathbf{K}_{up})_h$ that ensure that S remains uniformly bounded when using any sequence of meshes.

We considered briefly in Section 2.7 the stability conditions as related to a formulation that leads to a general coefficient matrix $\mathbf{A}$ [see (2.169) to (2.179)]. If we specialize these considerations to the specific coefficient matrix used in the displacement/pressure formulations, we will find a rather natural result (see F. Brezzi and K. J. Bathe [B]), namely, that the stability conditions are an extension of the solvability conditions (4.188) and (4.189) in that stability in the use of these relations with increasingly finer meshes must be preserved.

The stability condition corresponding to the solvability condition (4.188) is that there is an $\alpha > 0$ independent of the mesh size such that

$$\mathbf{V}_h^T(\mathbf{K}_{uu})_h\mathbf{V}_h \geq \alpha \parallel \mathbf{v}_h \parallel_V^2 \qquad \text{for all } \mathbf{V}_h \in \text{kernel } [(\mathbf{K}_{pu})_h] \qquad (4.192)$$

This condition is the ellipticity condition already mentioned briefly in Section 4.5.1. The relation states that, for any fineness of mesh, the Rayleigh quotient obtained with any vector $\mathbf{V}_h$ satisfying $(\mathbf{K}_{pu})_h\mathbf{V}_h = \mathbf{0}$, will be bounded from below by the constant α (which is independent of element mesh size). This ellipticity condition is always (i.e., for any choice of element interpolation) fulfilled by our displacement/pressure formulations. We elaborate upon this fact in the following example.

> **EXAMPLE 4.37:**   Consider the ellipticity condition in (4.192) and discuss that it is satisfied for any (practical) displacement/pressure formulation.
>
> To understand that the ellipticity condition is fulfilled, we need to recall that (4.187) is the result of the finite element discretization in (4.179). Hence,
>
> $$\mathbf{V}_h^T(\mathbf{K}_{uu})_h\mathbf{V}_h; \qquad \mathbf{V}_h \in \text{kernel } (\mathbf{K}_{pu})_h \qquad (a)$$
>
> corresponds to twice the strain energy stored in the finite element discretization when $\mathbf{v}_h$ corresponds to an element in V_h that satisfies $P_h(\text{div } \mathbf{v}_h) = 0$. However, unless we select the pressure space $Q_h = \{0\}$, that is, unless we totally remove the incompressibility constraint and the formulation does not contain strain energy due to compression—an impractical and trivial case—the expression in (a) will always be greater than zero (and bounded from below).
>
> If (4.192) is not satisfied, we could easily stabilize the solution. This is achieved by considering the almost incompressible case and using the variational formulation
>
> $$\min_{\mathbf{v}_h\in V_h} \left\{ \frac{1}{2} a(\mathbf{v}_h, \mathbf{v}_h) + \frac{\kappa^*}{2} \int_{\text{Vol}} (\text{div } \mathbf{v}_h)^2 \, d\text{Vol} + \frac{\kappa - \kappa^*}{2} \int [P_h(\text{div } \mathbf{v}_h)]^2 \, d\text{Vol} - \int_{\text{Vol}} \mathbf{f}^B \cdot \mathbf{v}_h \, d\text{Vol} \right\}$$
>
> where κ^* is a bulk modulus of the order of the shear modulus and does not lead to locking. Of course, we could now assume $(\kappa - \kappa^*) \to \infty$.
>
> This procedure amounts to evaluating a portion of the bulk energy as in the displacement method and using a projection for the remaining portion. Note that when κ is equal to κ^*, the part to be projected is zero. Hence the essence of the scheme is that a well-behaved part of the term that is difficult to deal with has been moved to be evaluated without the projection. This kind of stabilization to satisfy the ellipticity condition can be important in the design of formulations (see F. Brezzi and M. Fortin [A]). The procedure has been proposed to stabilize a displacement/pressure formulation for the analysis of inviscid fluids (see C. Nitikitpaiboon and K. J. Bathe [A]) and for the development of plate and shell elements (see D. N. Arnold and F. Brezzi [A]). However, the difficulty with this approach can be in selecting the portions of energies to be evaluated with and without projection, in particular when the various kinematic actions are fully coupled as, for instance, in the analysis of shell structures (see Section 5.4.2).

The stability condition corresponding to the solvability condition (4.189) is that there is a $\beta > 0$ independent of the mesh size h such that

$$\inf_{\mathbf{Q}_h} \sup_{\mathbf{V}_h} \frac{\mathbf{Q}_h^T(\mathbf{K}_{pu})_h\mathbf{V}_h}{\parallel q_h \parallel \parallel \mathbf{v}_h \parallel} \geq \beta > 0 \qquad (4.193)$$

for every problem in the sequence.

Note that here we take the sup using the elements in $\mathbf{V}_h$ and the inf using the elements in $\mathbf{Q}_h$. Of course, this relation is our inf-sup condition (4.183) in algebraic form, but we now have $q_h \in Q_h$, where Q_h is not necessarily equal to $P_h(D_h)$.

We note that a simple test consisting of counting displacement and pressure variables and comparing the number of such variables is not adequate to identify whether a mixed formulation is stable. The above discussion shows that such a test is certainly not sufficient to ensure the stability of a formulation and in general does not even ensure that condition (4.189) for solvability is satisfied (see also Exercises 4.60 and 4.64).

4.5.3 The Constant (Physical) Pressure Mode

Let us assume in this section that our finite element discretization contains no spurious pressure modes (which we discuss in the next section) and that the inf-sup condition for $q_h \in P_h(D_h)$ is satisfied.

We mentioned earlier (see Section 4.4.3) that when our elasticity problem corresponds to total incompressibility (i.e., we consider $q = \text{div } \mathbf{u} = 0$) and all displacements normal to the surface of the body are prescribed (i.e., S_u is equal to S), special considerations are necessary. Actually, we can consider the following two cases.

Case i: *All displacements normal to the body surface are prescribed to be zero.* In this case, the pressure is undetermined unless it is prescribed at one point in the body. Namely, assume that p_0 is a constant pressure. Then

$$\int_{\text{Vol}} p_0 \text{ div } \mathbf{v}_h \, d\text{Vol} = p_0 \int_S \mathbf{v}_h \cdot \mathbf{n} \, dS = 0 \qquad \forall \; \mathbf{v}_h \in V_h \qquad (4.194)$$

where $\mathbf{n}$ is the unit normal vector to the body surface. Hence, if the pressure is not prescribed at one point, we can add an arbitrary constant pressure p_0 to any proposed solution. A consequence is that the equations (4.187) cannot be solved unless the pressure is prescribed at one point, which amounts to eliminating one pressure degree of freedom [one column in $(\mathbf{K}_{up})_h$ and the corresponding row in $(\mathbf{K}_{pu})_h$]. If this pressure degree of freedom is not eliminated, Q_h is larger than $P_h(D_h)$, the solvability condition (4.189) is not satisfied, and the inf-sup value including this pressure mode is zero. For a discussion of the case Q_h larger that $P_h(D_h)$ but pertaining to spurious pressure modes, see Section 4.5.4.

Of course, instead of eliminating one pressure degree of freedom, it may be more expedient in practice to release some displacement degrees of freedom normal to the body surface.

Case ii: *All displacements normal to the body surface are prescribed with some nonzero values.* The difficulty in this case is that the incompressibility condition must be fulfilled

$$\int_{\text{Vol}} \text{div } \mathbf{v}_h \, d\text{Vol} = \int_S \mathbf{v}_h \cdot \mathbf{n} \, dS = 0 \qquad \forall \; \mathbf{v}_h \in V_h \qquad (4.195)$$

A constant pressure mode will also be present, which can be eliminated as discussed for Case i. If the body geometry is complex, it can be difficult to satisfy exactly the surface integral condition in (4.195). Since any error in fulfilling this condition can result in a large error in pressure prediction, it may be best in practice to leave the displacement(s) normal to the surface free at some node(s).

Let us next consider that the body is only almost incompressible, that κ is large but finite, and that the u/p formulation is used. In Case i, the arbitrary constant pressure p_0 will then automatically be set to zero (in the same way as spurious modes are set to zero; see Section 4.5.4). This is a most convenient result because we do not need to be concerned with the elimination of a pressure degree of freedom. Of course, in practice we could also leave some nodal point displacement degree(s) of freedom normal to the body surface free, which would eliminate the constant pressure mode.

With the constant pressure mode present in the model, Q_h is (by one basis vector) larger than $P_h(D_h)$ and the inf-sup value corresponding to this mode is zero. Nevertheless, we can solve the algebraic equations and obtain a reliable solution (unless κ is so large that the ill-conditioning of the coefficient matrix results in significant round-off errors, see Section 8.2.6).

In Case ii, it is probably best to proceed as recommended above, namely, to leave some nodal displacement(s) normal to the surface free, in order to give the material the freedom to satisfy the constraint of near incompressibility. Then the constant pressure mode is not present in the finite element model.

An important point in these considerations is that if all displacements normal to the surface of the body are prescribed, the pressure space will be larger than $P_h(D_h)$, but only by the constant pressure mode. This mode is of course a physical phenomenon and not a spurious mode. If the inf-sup condition for $q_h \in P_h(D_h)$ is satisfied, then the solution is rendered stable and accurate by simply eliminating the constant pressure mode (or using the u/p formulation with a not too large value of κ to automatically set the value of the constant pressure to zero). We consider in the next section the case of Q_h larger than $P_h(D_h)$ as a result of spurious pressure modes.

4.5.4 Spurious Pressure Modes—The Case of Total Incompressibility

We consider in this section the condition of total incompressibility and, merely for simplicity of discussion, that the physical constant pressure mode mentioned earlier is not present in the model. If it were actually present, the considerations given above would apply in addition to those we shall now present.

With this provision, we recall that in our discussion of the inf-sup condition we assumed that the space Q_h is equal to the space $P_h(D_h)$ [see (4.183)], whereas in (4.193) we have no such restriction. In an actual finite element solution we may well have $P_h(D_h) \subsetneq Q_h$, and it is important to recognize the consequences.

If the space Q_h is larger than the space $P_h(D_h)$, the solution will exhibit spurious pressure modes. These modes are a result of the numerical solution procedure only, namely, the specific finite elements and mesh patterns used, and have no physical explanation.

We define a spurious pressure mode as a (nonzero) pressure distribution p_s that satisfies the relation

$$\int_{\text{Vol}} p_s \operatorname{div} \mathbf{v}_h \, d\text{Vol} = 0 \qquad \forall \, \mathbf{v}_h \in V_h \tag{4.196}$$

In the matrix formulation (4.187) a spurious pressure mode corresponds to the case

$$(\mathbf{K}_{up})_h \mathbf{P}_s = \mathbf{0} \tag{4.197}$$

where $\mathbf{P}_s$ is the (nonzero) vector of pressure variables corresponding to p_s. Hence, the solvability condition (4.189) is not satisfied when spurious pressure modes are present, and of course the inf-sup value when testing over the complete space Q_h in (4.193) is zero.

Let us show that if Q_h is equal to $P_h(D_h)$, there can be no spurious pressure mode. Assume that $\hat{p}_h$ is proposed to be a spurious pressure mode. If $Q_h = P_h(D_h)$, there is always a vector $\hat{\mathbf{v}}_h$ such that $\hat{p}_h = -P_h (\text{div } \hat{\mathbf{v}}_h)$. However, using $\hat{\mathbf{v}}_h$ in (4.196), we obtain

$$-\int_{\text{Vol}} \hat{p}_h \text{ div } \hat{\mathbf{v}}_h \, d\text{Vol} = -\int_{\text{Vol}} \hat{p}_h P_h(\text{div } \hat{\mathbf{v}}_h) \, d\text{Vol} = \int_{\text{Vol}} \hat{p}_h^2 \, d\text{Vol} > 0 \tag{4.198}$$

meaning that (4.196) is not satisfied. On the other hand, if Q_h is greater than $P_h(D_h)$, notably $P_h(D_h) \not\subseteq Q_h$, then we can find a pressure distribution in the space orthogonal to $P_h(D_h)$, and hence for that pressure distribution (4.196) is satisfied (see Example 4.38).

Hence, we now recognize that in essence we have two phenomena that may occur when testing a specific finite element discretization using displacements and pressure as variables:

1. The *locking phenomenon,* which is detected by the smallest value of the inf-sup expression not being bounded from below by a value $\beta > 0$ [see discussion following (4.156)]

2. The *spurious modes phenomenon,* which corresponds to a zero value of the inf-sup expression when we test with $q_h \in Q_h$.

Of course, when a discretization with spurious modes is considered, we might still be interested in the smallest nonzero value of the inf-sup expression, and we can focus on this value by only testing with $q_h \in P_h(D_h)$, in other words, by ignoring all spurious pressure modes.

The numerical inf-sup test described in Section 4.5.6 actually gives the smallest nonzero value of the inf-sup expression and also evaluates the number of spurious pressure modes.

Let us note here, as a side remark, that the spurious pressure modes have no relationship to the spurious zero energy modes mentioned in Section 5.5.6 (and which are a result of using reduced or selective numerical integration in the evaluation of element stiffness matrices). In the displacement/pressure formulations considered here, each element stiffness matrix is accurately calculated and exhibits only the correct physical rigid body modes. The spurious pressure modes in the *complete* mesh are a result of the specific displacement and pressure spaces used for the *complete* discretization.

One way to gain more insight into the relation (4.193) is to imagine the matrix $(\mathbf{K}_{up})_h$ [or $(\mathbf{K}_{pu})_h = (\mathbf{K}_{up})_h^T$] in diagonalized form (choosing the appropriate basis for displacements and pressure variables), in which case we would have

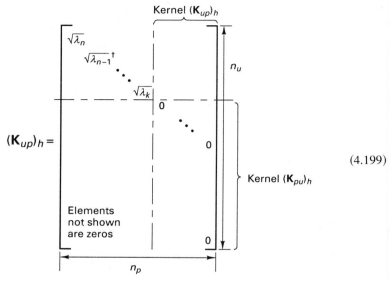

$$\tag{4.199}$$

† We call the elements $\sqrt{\lambda_i}$ in anticipation of our discussion in Section 4.5.6.

In this representation the zero columns define the kernel of $(\mathbf{K}_{up})_h$ and each zero column corresponds to a spurious pressure mode. Also, since for any displacement vector $\hat{\mathbf{U}}_h$ we need

$$(\mathbf{K}_{pu})_h \hat{\mathbf{U}}_h = \mathbf{0} \tag{4.200}$$

and $(\mathbf{K}_{pu})_h = (\mathbf{K}_{up})_h^T$, the size of the kernel of $(\mathbf{K}_{pu})_h$ determines whether the solution is overconstrained. Whereas, on one hand, we want the kernel of $(\mathbf{K}_{up})_h$ to be zero (no spurious pressure modes), on the other hand, we want the kernel of $(\mathbf{K}_{pu})_h$ to be large so as to admit many linearly independent vectors $\hat{\mathbf{U}}_h$ that satisfy (4.200). Our actual displacement solution to the problem (4.187) will lie in the subspace spanned by these vectors, and if that subspace is too small, as a result of the pressure space Q_h being too large, the solution will be overconstrained. The theory on the inf-sup condition [see the discussion in Section 4.5.1 and (4.193)] showed that this overconstraint is detected by $\sqrt{\lambda_k}$ decreasing to zero as the mesh is refined. Vice versa, if $\sqrt{\lambda_k} \geq \beta > 0$, for any mesh, as the size of the elements is decreased, with β independent of the mesh, the solution space is not overconstrained and the discretization yields a reliable solution (with the optimal rate of convergence in the displacements and pressure, provided the pressure space is largest without violating the inf-sup condition; see Section 4.5.1).

4.5.5 Spurious Pressure Modes—The Case of Near Incompressibility

In the above discussion we assumed conditions of total incompressibility, and the use of either the u/p or the u/p-c formulation. Consider now that we have a finite (but large) κ and that the u/p formulation with static condensation on the pressure degrees of freedom (as is typical) is used. In this case, the governing finite element equations are, for a typical element (or the complete mesh),

$$\begin{bmatrix} (\mathbf{K}_{uu})_h & (\mathbf{K}_{up})_h \\ (\mathbf{K}_{pu})_h & (\mathbf{K}_{pp})_h \end{bmatrix} \begin{bmatrix} \mathbf{U}_h \\ \mathbf{P}_h \end{bmatrix} = \begin{bmatrix} \mathbf{R}_h \\ \mathbf{0} \end{bmatrix} \tag{4.201}$$

or

$$[(\mathbf{K}_{uu})_h - (\mathbf{K}_{up})_h (\mathbf{K}_{pp})_h^{-1} (\mathbf{K}_{pu})_h] \mathbf{U}_h = \mathbf{R}_h \tag{4.202}$$

So far we have assumed that no nonzero displacements are prescribed. It is an important observation that in this case any spurious pressure mode has no effect on the predicted displacements and pressure. The reason can be shown by considering $(\mathbf{K}_{up})_h$ in (4.199) with some zero columns. Since $(\mathbf{K}_{pp})_h$ is, in the same basis, diagonal with the bulk modulus $-\kappa^{-1}$ as diagonal elements and the corresponding right-hand-side is a zero vector, the solution for the spurious pressure mode values is zero (see also Example 4.39).

A different observation is that the coefficient matrix in (4.201) contains a large bulk modulus which, when κ^{-1} is close to zero, results in ill-conditioning—but this ill-conditioning is observed whether or not spurious pressure modes are present.

The spurious pressure modes can, however, have a drastic effect when nonzero displacements are prescribed. In this case, we recognize that the right-hand side corresponding to the pressure degrees of freedom may not be zero (see Section 4.2.2 on how nonzero displacements are imposed), and a large spurious pressure may be generated.

Clearly, a reliable element should not lock and ideally should not lead to any spurious pressure mode in any chosen mesh.

The elements listed in Tables 4.6 and 4.7 are of such a nature—except for the 4/1 two-dimensional u/p element (and the analogous 8/1 three-dimensional element). Using the 4/1 element, specific meshes with certain boundary conditions exhibit a spurious pressure mode, and the 4/1 element does not satisfy the inf-sup condition (4.183) unless used in special geometric arrangements of macroelements (see P. Le Tallec and V. Ruas [A] for an example). However, because of its simplicity, the 4/1 element is quite widely used in practice. We examine this element in more detail in the following example.

EXAMPLE 4.38: Consider the finite element discretization of 4/1 elements shown in Fig. E4.38 and show that the spurious checkerboard mode of pressure indicated in the figure exists.

We note that for this model all tangential displacements on the boundary are set to zero. In order to show that the pressure distribution indicated in Fig. E4.38 corresponds to a spurious pressure mode, we need to prove that (4.196) holds. Consider a single element as shown in Fig. E4.38(a). We have

$$\int_{\text{Vol}} p^{e_i} \, \text{div} \, \mathbf{v}_h^e \, d\text{Vol} = p^{e_i} [1 \quad -1 \quad -1 \quad 1 \quad \vdots \quad 1 \quad 1 \quad -1 \quad -1] \, \hat{\mathbf{u}}$$

where p^{e_i} is the constant pressure in the element and

If a patch of four adjacent elements is then considered, we note that for the displacement u_i shown in Fig. E4.38(b) we have

$$\int_{\text{Vol}} p \, \text{div} \, \mathbf{v}_h \, d\text{Vol} = [p^{e_1}(1) + p^{e_2}(1) + p^{e_3}(-1) + p^{e_4}(-1)] \, u_i = 0 \tag{a}$$

provided the pressure distribution corresponds to $p^{e_1} = -p^{e_2} = p^{e_3} = -p^{e_4}$. Similarly, for any displacement v_i we have

$$\int_{\text{Vol}} p \, \text{div} \, \mathbf{v}_h \, d\text{Vol} = [p^{e_1}(-1) + p^{e_2}(1) + p^{e_3}(1) + p^{e_4}(-1)] \, v_i = 0 \tag{b}$$

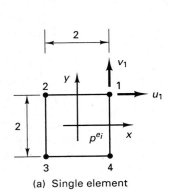

(a) Single element

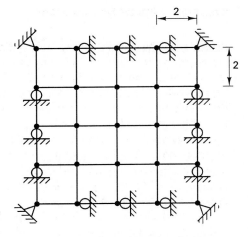

(c) 4 × 4 mesh of equal square elements

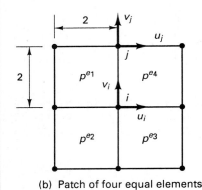

(b) Patch of four equal elements

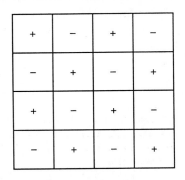

(d) Checkerboard pressure distribution. + and − mean +Δp and −Δp, where Δp is an arbitrary value.

Figure E4.38 4/1 elements

For the normal displacement v_j on an edge of the patch, we similarly obtain

$$\int_{\text{Vol}} p \operatorname{div} \mathbf{v}_h \, d\text{Vol} = [p^{e_1}(1) + p^{e_2}(1)]v_j = 0 \qquad (c)$$

On the other hand, for a tangential displacement u_j, the integral

$$\int_{\text{Vol}} p \operatorname{div} \mathbf{v}_h \, d\text{Vol} \neq 0$$

However, in the model in Fig. E4.38(c) all tangential displacements are constrained to zero. Hence, by superposition, using expressions (a) to (c), the relation (4.196) is satisfied for any nodal point displacements when the pressure distribution is the indicated checkerboard pressure.

Note that the same checkerboard pressure distribution is also a spurious pressure mode when more nodal point displacements than those given in Fig. E4.38(c) are constrained to zero. Also note that the (assumed) pressure distribution in Fig. E4.38(d) cannot be obtained by any nodal point displacements, hence this pressure distribution does not correspond to an element in $P_h(D_h)$.

In the above example, we showed that a spurious pressure mode is present when the 4/1 element is used in discretizations of equal-size square elements with certain boundary conditions. The spurious pressure mode no longer exists when nonhomogeneous meshes are employed or at least one tangential displacement on the surface is released to be free.

Consider now that a force is applied to any one of the free degrees of freedom in Fig. E4.38(c). The solution is then obtained by solving (4.201) and, as pointed out before, the spurious pressure mode will not enter the solution (it will not be observed).

The spurious pressure mode, however, has a very significant effect on the calculated stresses when, for example, one tangential boundary displacement is prescribed to be nonzero while all other tangential boundary displacements are kept at zero.[18] In this case the prescribed nodal point displacement results in a nonzero forcing vector for the pressure degrees of freedom, and the spurious pressure mode is excited. Hence, in practice, it is expedient to not constrain all tangential nodal point displacements on the body considered.

Let us conclude this section by considering the following example because it illustrates, in a simple manner, some of the important general observations we have made.

EXAMPLE 4.39:[19]   Assume that the governing equations (4.187) are

$$\begin{bmatrix} \alpha_1 & 0 & 0 & \vdots & \beta_1 & 0 \\ 0 & \alpha_2 & 0 & \vdots & 0 & \beta_2 \\ 0 & 0 & \alpha_3 & \vdots & 0 & 0 \\ \hdashline \beta_1 & 0 & 0 & \vdots & 0 & 0 \\ 0 & \beta_2 & 0 & \vdots & 0 & 0 \end{bmatrix} \begin{bmatrix} u_1 \\ u_2 \\ u_3 \\ \hdashline p_1 \\ p_2 \end{bmatrix} = \begin{bmatrix} r_1 \\ r_2 \\ r_3 \\ \hdashline g_1 \\ g_2 \end{bmatrix} \tag{a}$$

Of course, such simple equations are not obtained in practical finite element analysis, but the essential ingredients are those of the general equations (4.187). We note that the coefficient matrix corresponds to a fully incompressible material condition and that the entries g_1 and g_2 correspond to prescribed boundary displacements.

These equations can also be written as

$$\alpha_i u_i + \beta_i p_i = r_i; \qquad \beta_i u_i = g_i; \qquad i = 1, 2; \qquad \alpha_3 u_3 = r_3$$

Assume that $\alpha_i > 0$ for all i (as we would have in practice). Then, $u_3 = r_3/\alpha_3$, and we need only consider the typical equations

$$\alpha u + \beta p = r; \qquad \beta u = g \tag{b}$$

(where we have dropped the subscript i).

When the material is considered almost incompressible, u_3 is unchanged but (b) becomes

$$\alpha u_\epsilon + \beta p_\epsilon = r; \qquad \beta u_\epsilon - \epsilon p_\epsilon = g \tag{c}$$

where $\epsilon = 1/\kappa$ (ϵ is very small when the bulk modulus κ is very large) and u_ϵ, p_ϵ is the solution sought. Equations (c) give

$$u_\epsilon = \frac{\epsilon r + \beta g}{\epsilon \alpha + \beta^2}; \qquad p_\epsilon = \frac{\beta r - \alpha g}{\epsilon \alpha + \beta^2} \tag{d}$$

We can now make the following observations.
First, we consider the case of a spurious pressure mode, i.e., $\beta = 0$.

Case i: $\beta = g = 0$

This case corresponds to a spurious pressure mode and zero prescribed displacements.

The solution of (b) gives $u = r/\alpha$, with p undetermined.
The solution of (c) gives $u_\epsilon = r/\alpha$, $p_\epsilon = 0$.

---

[18] We may note that these analysis conditions and results are similar to the conditions and results obtained when all displacements normal to the surface of a body are constrained to zero, except for one, at which a normal displacement is prescribed [see (4.195)].

[19] This example was presented by F. Brezzi and K. J. Bathe [B].

Hence, we notice that the use of a finite bulk modulus allows us to solve the equations and suppresses the spurious pressure.

Case ii: $\beta = 0$, $g \neq 0$

This case corresponds to a spurious pressure mode and nonzero prescribed displacements (corresponding to this mode).

Now (b) has no solution for u and p.

The solution of (c) is $u_\epsilon = r/\alpha$, $p_\epsilon = -g/\epsilon$.

Hence, the spurious pressure becomes large as κ increases.

Next we consider the case of β very small.

Hence, we have no spurious pressure mode. Of course, the inf-sup condition is not passed if $\beta \to 0$.

Case iii: β is small

Let us also assume that $g = 0$.

Now (b) gives the solution $u = 0$, $p = r/\beta$.

The solution of (c) is $u_\epsilon \to 0$ and $p_\epsilon \to r/\beta$ for $\epsilon \to 0$ (β fixed, and hence we have $\beta^2 \gg \epsilon\alpha$), which is consistent with the solution of (b). Hence, the displacement approaches zero and the pressure becomes large when β is small and the bulk modulus increases. Of course, we test for this behavior with the inf-sup condition. For an actual finite element solution, this observation may be interpreted as taking a fixed mesh (β is fixed) and increasing κ. The result is that the pressure in the mode for which β is small increases while the displacements in this mode decrease.

However, (c) also gives $u_\epsilon \to r/\alpha$ and $p_\epsilon \to 0$ for $\beta \to 0$ (ϵ fixed, and hence we have $\beta^2 \ll \epsilon\alpha$), which is the behavior noted earlier in Case i. For an actual finite element solution this observation may be interpreted as taking a fixed κ and increasing the fineness of the mesh. As β is decreased as a result of mesh refinement, the pressure corresponding to this mode becomes small. Hence, the behavior of this pressure mode is when β is sufficiently small (which may mean a very fine mesh when κ is large) like the behavior of a spurious mode.

4.5.6 The Inf-Sup Test

The results of analytical studies of the inf-sup characteristics of various displacement/pressure elements are summarized in Tables 4.6 and 4.7 (see also F. Brezzi and M. Fortin [A]). However, an analytical proof of whether the inf-sup condition is satisfied by a specific element can be difficult, and for this reason a numerical test is valuable. Such a test can be applied to newly proposed elements and also to discretizations with elements of distorted geometries (recall that analytical studies assume homogeneous meshes of square elements). Of course, a numerical test cannot be completely affirmative (as an analytical proof is), but if a properly designed numerical test is passed, the formulation is very likely to be effective. The same idea is used when performing the patch test only in numerical form (to study incompatible displacement formulations and the effect of element geometric distortions) because an analytical evaluation is not achieved (see Section 4.4.1).

In the following discussion we present the numerical inf-sup test proposed by D. Chapelle and K. J. Bathe [A].

First consider the u/p formulation. In this case the inf-sup condition (4.183) can be written in the form

$$\inf_{\mathbf{w}_h \in V_h} \sup_{\mathbf{v}_h \in V_h} \frac{\int_{\text{Vol}} P_h(\text{div } \mathbf{w}_h) \text{ div } \mathbf{v}_h \, d\text{Vol}}{\| P_h(\text{div } \mathbf{w}_h) \| \| \mathbf{v}_h \|} \geq \beta > 0 \tag{4.203}$$

or
$$\inf_{\mathbf{w}_h \in V_h} \sup_{\mathbf{v}_h \in V_h} \frac{b'(\mathbf{w}_h, \mathbf{v}_h)}{[b'(\mathbf{w}_h, \mathbf{w}_h)]^{1/2} \|\mathbf{v}_h\|} \geq \beta > 0 \tag{4.204}$$

where
$$b'(\mathbf{w}_h, \mathbf{v}_h) = \int_{\text{Vol}} P_h (\text{div } \mathbf{w}_h) P_h(\text{div } \mathbf{v}_h) \, d\text{Vol} = \int_{\text{Vol}} P_h(\text{div } \mathbf{w}_h) \, \text{div } \mathbf{v}_h \, d\text{Vol} \tag{4.205}$$

The relation (4.204) is in matrix form

$$\inf_{\mathbf{W}_h} \sup_{\mathbf{V}_h} \frac{\mathbf{W}_h^T \mathbf{G}_h \mathbf{V}_h}{[\mathbf{W}_h^T \mathbf{G}_h \mathbf{W}_h]^{1/2} [\mathbf{V}_h^T \mathbf{S}_h \mathbf{V}_h]^{1/2}} \geq \beta > 0 \tag{4.206}$$

where $\mathbf{W}_h$ and $\mathbf{V}_h$ are vectors of the nodal displacement values corresponding to $\mathbf{w}_h$ and $\mathbf{v}_h$, and $\mathbf{G}_h$, $\mathbf{S}_h$ are matrices corresponding to the operator b' and the norm $\|\cdot\|_V$, respectively. The matrices $\mathbf{G}_h$ and $\mathbf{S}_h$ are, respectively, positive semidefinite and positive definite (for the problem we consider, see Section 4.5.1).

EXAMPLE 4.40: In Example 4.34 we calculated the matrix $\mathbf{G}_h$ of a 4/1 element. Now also establish the matrix $\mathbf{S}_h$ of this element.

To evaluate $\mathbf{S}_h$ we recall that the norm of $\mathbf{w}$ is given by [see (4.153)]

$$\|\mathbf{w}\|_V^2 = \sum_{i,j} \left\| \frac{\partial w_i}{\partial x_j} \right\|_{L^2(\text{Vol})}^2$$

Hence, for our case

$$\|\mathbf{w}_h\|_V^2 = \int_{-1}^{+1} \int_{-1}^{+1} \left[\left(\frac{\partial u}{\partial x}\right)^2 + \left(\frac{\partial u}{\partial y}\right)^2 + \left(\frac{\partial v}{\partial x}\right)^2 + \left(\frac{\partial v}{\partial y}\right)^2 \right] dx \, dy \tag{a}$$

where u, v are the components w_i, $i = 1, 2$.

Let us order the nodal point displacements in $\hat{\mathbf{u}}$ as in Example 4.34,

$$\hat{\mathbf{u}}^T = [u_1 \quad u_2 \quad u_3 \quad u_4 \quad \vdots \quad v_1 \quad v_2 \quad v_3 \quad v_4]$$

By definition, $\|\mathbf{w}_h\|_V^2 = \hat{\mathbf{u}}^T \mathbf{S}_h \hat{\mathbf{u}}$. Also, we have

$$\frac{\partial u}{\partial x} = \sum_{i=1}^{4} h_{i,x} u_i; \qquad \frac{\partial u}{\partial y} = \sum_{i=1}^{4} h_{i,y} u_i \tag{b}$$

and we write in (a)

$$\left(\frac{\partial u}{\partial x}\right)^2 = \left(\frac{\partial u}{\partial x}\right)^T \left(\frac{\partial u}{\partial x}\right)$$
$$\left(\frac{\partial u}{\partial y}\right)^2 = \left(\frac{\partial u}{\partial y}\right)^T \left(\frac{\partial u}{\partial y}\right) \tag{c}$$

Substituting from (c) and (b) into (a) we obtain

$$S_h(1, 1) = \int_{-1}^{+1} \int_{-1}^{+1} [(h_{1,x})^2 + (h_{1,y})^2] \, dx \, dy = \frac{2}{3}$$

$$S_h(1, 2) = \int_{-1}^{+1} \int_{-1}^{+1} [h_{1,x}h_{2,x} + h_{1,y}h_{2,y}] \, dx \, dy = -\frac{1}{6}$$

and so on.

Similarly, the terms corresponding to the v_i degrees of freedom are calculated, and we obtain

$$\mathbf{S}_h = \begin{bmatrix} \tilde{\mathbf{S}}_h & \mathbf{0} \\ \mathbf{0} & \tilde{\mathbf{S}}_h \end{bmatrix}; \qquad \tilde{\mathbf{S}}_h = \frac{1}{6}\begin{bmatrix} 4 & -1 & -2 & -1 \\ -1 & 4 & -1 & -2 \\ -2 & -1 & 4 & -1 \\ -1 & -2 & -1 & 4 \end{bmatrix}$$

Let us now consider the u/p-c formulation. In this case the same expression as in (4.206) applies, but we need to use $\mathbf{G}_h = (\mathbf{K}_{pu})_h^T \mathbf{T}_h^{-1}(\mathbf{K}_{pu})_h$, where $\mathbf{T}_h$ is the matrix of the L^2-norm of p_h (see Exercise 4.59); i.e., for any vector of pressure nodal values $\mathbf{P}_h$, we have $\|p_h\| = \mathbf{P}_h^T \mathbf{T}_h \mathbf{P}_h$.

The form (4.206) of the inf-sup condition is effective because we can numerically evaluate the inf-sup value of the left-hand side and do so for a sequence of meshes. If the left-hand-side inf-sup value approaches (asymptotically) a value greater than zero (and there are no spurious pressure modes, further discussed below), the inf-sup condition is satisfied. In practice, only a sequence of about three meshes needs to be considered (see examples given below).

The key is the evaluation of the inf-sup value of the expression in (4.206). We can show that this value is given by the square root of the smallest nonzero eigenvalue of the problem

$$\mathbf{G}_h \boldsymbol{\phi}_h = \lambda \mathbf{S}_h \boldsymbol{\phi}_h \tag{4.207}$$

Hence, if there are $(k - 1)$ zero eigenvalues (because $\mathbf{G}_h$ is a positive semidefinite matrix) and we order the eigenvalues in ascending order, we find that the inf-sup value of the expression in (4.206) is $\sqrt{\lambda_k}$. We prove this result in the following example.

EXAMPLE 4.41:   Consider the function $f(\mathbf{U}, \mathbf{V})$ defined as

$$f(\mathbf{U}, \mathbf{V}) = \frac{\mathbf{U}^T\mathbf{G}\mathbf{V}}{(\mathbf{U}^T\mathbf{G}\mathbf{U})^{1/2}(\mathbf{V}^T\mathbf{S}\mathbf{V})^{1/2}} \tag{a}$$

where $\mathbf{G}$ is an $n \times n$ symmetric positive semidefinite matrix, $\mathbf{S}$ is an $n \times n$ positive definite matrix, and $\mathbf{U}, \mathbf{V}$ are vectors of order n. Show that

$$\inf_{\mathbf{U}} \sup_{\mathbf{V}} f(\mathbf{U}, \mathbf{V}) = \sqrt{\lambda_k} \tag{b}$$

where λ_k is the smallest nonzero eigenvalue of the problem

$$\mathbf{G}\boldsymbol{\phi} = \lambda \mathbf{S}\boldsymbol{\phi} \tag{c}$$

Let the eigenvalues of (c) be

$$\lambda_1 = \lambda_2 = \cdots = \lambda_{k-1} = 0 < \lambda_k \le \lambda_{k+1} \cdots \le \lambda_n$$

and the corresponding eigenvectors be $\boldsymbol{\phi}_1, \boldsymbol{\phi}_2, \ldots, \boldsymbol{\phi}_n$.

To evaluate $f(\mathbf{U}, \mathbf{V})$, we represent $\mathbf{U}$ and $\mathbf{V}$ as

$$\mathbf{U} = \sum_{i=1}^{n} \tilde{u}_i \boldsymbol{\phi}_i; \qquad \mathbf{V} = \sum_{i=1}^{n} \tilde{v}_i \boldsymbol{\phi}_i$$

Therefore, for any $\mathbf{U}$,

$$\sup_{\mathbf{V}} f(\mathbf{U}, \mathbf{V}) = \sup_{\tilde{v}_i} \frac{\displaystyle\sum_{i=1}^{n} \lambda_i \tilde{u}_i \tilde{v}_i}{\left(\displaystyle\sum_{i=1}^{n} \lambda_i \tilde{u}_i^2\right)^{1/2} \left(\displaystyle\sum_{i=1}^{n} \tilde{v}_i^2\right)^{1/2}}$$

$$= \frac{1}{\left(\displaystyle\sum_{i=1}^{n} \lambda_i \tilde{u}_i^2\right)^{1/2}} \sup_{\tilde{v}_i} \frac{\displaystyle\sum_{i=1}^{n} \lambda_i \tilde{u}_i \tilde{v}_i}{\left(\displaystyle\sum_{i=1}^{n} \tilde{v}_i^2\right)^{1/2}} \tag{d}$$

To evaluate the supremum value in (d), let us define $\alpha_i = \lambda_i \tilde{u}_i$; then we note that

$$\sum_{i=1}^{n} \lambda_i \tilde{u}_i \tilde{v}_i = \sum_{i=1}^{n} \alpha_i \tilde{v}_i \leq \sqrt{\sum_{i=1}^{n} \alpha_i^2 \sum_{i=1}^{n} \tilde{v}_i^2} \tag{e}$$

(by the Schwarz inequality), and equality is reached when $\tilde{v}_i = \alpha_i$. Substituting from (e) into (d) and using $\lambda_1 = \cdots = \lambda_{k-1} = 0$, we thus obtain

$$\sup_{\mathbf{V}} f(\mathbf{U}, \mathbf{V}) = \sqrt{\frac{\displaystyle\sum_{i=1}^{n} \lambda_i^2 \tilde{u}_i^2}{\displaystyle\sum_{i=1}^{n} \lambda_i \tilde{u}_i^2}} = \sqrt{\frac{\displaystyle\sum_{i=k}^{n} \lambda_i^2 \tilde{u}_i^2}{\displaystyle\sum_{i=k}^{n} \lambda_i \tilde{u}_i^2}}$$

If we now let $\sqrt{\lambda_i}\,\tilde{u}_i = \beta_i$, we can write

$$\inf_{\mathbf{U}} \sup_{\mathbf{V}} f(\mathbf{U}, \mathbf{V}) = \inf_{(\tilde{u}_i)_1^n} \sqrt{\frac{\displaystyle\sum_{i=k}^{n} \lambda_i^2 \tilde{u}_i^2}{\displaystyle\sum_{i=k}^{n} \lambda_i \tilde{u}_i^2}} = \inf_{(\beta_i)_k^n} \sqrt{\frac{\displaystyle\sum_{i=k}^{n} \lambda_i \beta_i^2}{\displaystyle\sum_{i=k}^{n} \beta_i^2}} \tag{f}$$

The last expression in (f) has the form of a Rayleigh quotient (see Section 2.6), and we know that the smallest value is $\sqrt{\lambda_k}$, achieved for $\beta_k \neq 0$ and $\beta_i = 0$, for $i \neq k$, which gives the required result.

In practice, to calculate the inf-sup value $\sqrt{\lambda_k}$ an eigenvalue solution routine should be used that can skip over all zero eigenvalues and then calculate λ_k. A Sturm sequence test (see Section 11.4.3) will then also give the value of k, and then we can conclude directly whether the model contains spurious pressure modes. Namely, let n_p be the number of pressure degrees of freedom and n_u be the number of displacement degrees of freedom. Then the number of pressure modes, k_{pm}, is

$$k_{pm} = k - (n_u - n_p + 1)$$

If $k_{pm} > 0$, the finite element discretization contains the constant pressure mode or spurious pressure modes [the inf-sup value in (4.193) is zero, although λ_k (the first nonzero eigenvalue) may asymptotically approach a value greater than zero]. This formula follows because for there to be no pressure mode, the kernel $(\mathbf{K}_{up})_h$ must be zero [see (4.199)].

To demonstrate this inf-sup test, we show in Fig. 4.24 results obtained for the four-node and nine-node elements. We see that a sequence of three meshes used to calculate $\sqrt{\lambda_k}$ for each discretization was, in these cases, sufficient to identify whether the element locks. We note that, clearly, the four-node and the nine-node displacement-based elements do not satisfy the inf-sup condition and that the distortions of elements have a negligible effect on the results. In each of these tests k_{pm} was zero, hence, as expected, the idealizations do not contain any pressure modes. Of course, a spurious pressure mode would be found for the 4/1 element if the boundary conditions of Example 4.38 were used. That is, in the general testing of elements for spurious modes the condition of zero displacements on the complete boundary should be considered [the smaller the dimension of V_h, for a given Q_h, the greater the possibility that (4.196) is satisfied].

The solutions in Fig. 4.24 are numerical results pertaining to only one problem and one mesh topology. However, if the inf-sup condition is not satisfied in these results, then we can conclude that it is not satisfied in general.

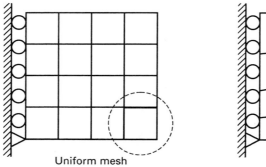 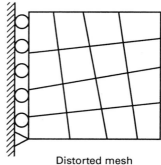

Uniform mesh   Distorted mesh

(a) Problem considered in inf-sup test. N = number of elements along each side; we show $N = 4$, plane strain case

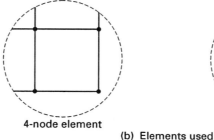 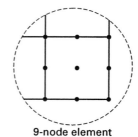

4-node element   9-node element

(b) Elements used

Figure 4.24   The inf-sup test applied in a simple problem

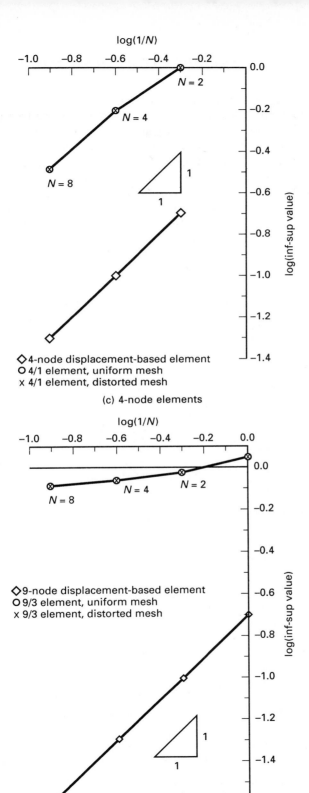

Figure 4.24 (*continued*)

327

Figure 4.25 shows results pertaining to the three-node triangular constant pressure element, formulated as a u/p element (see Exercise 4.50). The results show that the inf-sup condition is not satisfied by this element. Further, it is interesting to note that the meshes with pattern B do not contain spurious pressure modes, whereas the other meshes in general do contain spurious pressure modes.

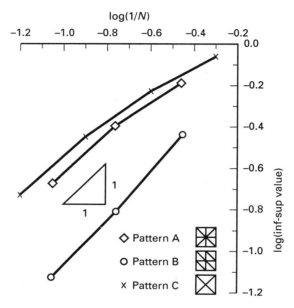

Figure 4.25   Inf-sup test of triangular elements, using problem of Fig.4.24(a). The patterns A and C result in spurious modes.

Additional results are given in Table 4.8 (see D. Chapelle and K. J. Bathe [A]). This table gives a summary of the results of the numerical evaluations of the inf-sup condition and analytical results, given, for example, by F. Brezzi and M. Fortin [A]. The numerical evaluation is useful because the same procedure applies to all u/p and u/p-c elements, in uniform or distorted meshes, and elements can be evaluated for which no analytical results are (yet) available. Also, the effects of constructing macroelements from the basic elements can be easily evaluated (see D. Chapelle and K. J. Bathe [A] for some results regarding the 4/1 element used in a macroelement).

A similar numerical evaluation of the inf-sup condition for other constraint problems, in particular mixed formulations, can be performed (see, for example, Exercise 4.63).

Finally, we recall that in the derivation of the inf-sup condition (see Section 4.5.1), we showed that if (4.166) holds, then the inf-sup condition (4.175) follows. However, as we pointed out, the equivalence of (4.166) and (4.175) also requires that we prove that if (4.175) holds, then (4.166) follows. We deferred this proof to Example 4.42, which we present next.

TABLE 4.8   *Inf-sup numerical predictions*

Element[†]	Inf-sup condition		Remarks
	Analytical proof	Numerical prediction	
3/1[‡]	Fail	Fail	See Fig. 4.25
4/1[‡]	Fail	Fail	See Fig. 4.24
8/3	Fail	Fail	
8/1	Pass	Pass	
9/4	Fail	Fail	
9/3	Pass	Pass	See Example 4.36, Fig. 4.24
4/3-c	Pass	Pass	
9/9-c	Fail	Fail	
9/8-c	Fail	Fail	
9/5-c	?	Fail	
9/4-c	Pass	Pass	
9/(4-c + 1)	?	Pass	For the element see P. M. Gresho, R. L. Lee, S. T. Chan, and J. M. Leone, Jr. [A]

[†] O, Continuous pressure degree of freedom; X, discontinuous pressure degree of freedom.

[‡] 3/1 and 4/1 element discretizations can contain spurious pressure modes.

EXAMPLE 4.42: Assume that the inf-sup condition (4.175) holds. Prove that (4.166) follows.

Let the eigenvectors and corresponding eigenvalues of (4.207) with G_h corresponding to D_h [and not $P_h(D_h)$ because in (4.175) we consider D_h] be $\boldsymbol{\phi}_i$ and λ_i, $i = 1, \ldots, n$. The vectors $\boldsymbol{\phi}_i$ form an orthonormal basis of V_h. Then we can write any vector $\mathbf{w}_h$ in V_h as

$$\mathbf{w}_h = \sum_{i=1}^{n} w_h^i \boldsymbol{\phi}_i \tag{a}$$

and we have by use of the eigenvalue and vector properties (see Section 2.5)

$$\| \operatorname{div} \mathbf{w}_h \|^2 = \sum_{i=1}^{n} \lambda_i (w_h^i)^2 \tag{b}$$

Let us now pick any q_h and any $\tilde{\mathbf{w}}_h$ satisfying $\operatorname{div} \tilde{\mathbf{w}}_h = q_h$. We can decompose $\tilde{\mathbf{w}}_h$ in the form of (a),

$$\tilde{\mathbf{w}}_h = \sum_{i=1}^{k-1} \tilde{w}_h^i \boldsymbol{\phi}_i + \sum_{i=k}^{n} \tilde{w}_h^i \boldsymbol{\phi}_i \tag{b}$$

The first summation sign in (b) defines a vector that belongs to $K_h(0)$ and may be a large component. However, we are concerned only with the component that is not an element of $K_h(0)$, which we call $\mathbf{w}_h$,

$$\mathbf{w}_h = \sum_{i=k}^{n} \tilde{w}_h^i \boldsymbol{\phi}_i$$

With this $\mathbf{w}_h$, we have

$$\frac{\| q_h \|^2}{\| \mathbf{w}_h \|^2} = \frac{\displaystyle\sum_{i=k}^{n} \lambda_i (\tilde{w}_h^i)^2}{\displaystyle\sum_{i=k}^{n} (\tilde{w}_h^i)^2}$$

$$\geq \lambda_k$$
$$= \beta_h^2$$
$$\geq \beta^2$$

and (4.166) follows with $c' = 1/\beta$.

4.5.7 An Application to Structural Elements: The Isoparametric Beam Elements

In the above discussion we considered the general elasticity problem (4.151) and the corresponding variational discrete problem (4.154) subject to the constraint of (near or total) incompressibility. However, the ellipticity and inf-sup conditions are also the basic conditions to be considered in the development of beam, plate, and shell elements that are subject to shear and membrane strain constraints (see Section 5.4). We briefly introduced a mixed two-node beam element in Example 4.30 and we consider this and higher-order elements of the same kind in Section 5.4.1. Let us briefly discuss the ellipticity and inf-sup conditions for mixed interpolated and pure displacement-based beam elements.

General Considerations

The variational discrete problem of the displacement-based formulation is

$$\min_{v_h \in V_h} \left\{ \frac{EI}{2} \int_0^L (\beta_h')^2 \, dx + \frac{GAk}{2} \int_0^L (\gamma_h)^2 \, dx - \int_0^L p w_h \, dx \right\} \tag{4.208}$$

where EI and GAk are the flexural and shear rigidities of the beam (see Section 5.4.1), L is the length of the beam, p is the transverse load per unit length, β_h is the section rotation, γ_h is the transverse shear strain,

$$\gamma_h = \frac{\partial w_h}{\partial x} - \beta_h \tag{4.209}$$

w_h is the transverse displacement, and an element of V_h is

$$\mathbf{v}_h = \begin{bmatrix} w_h \\ \beta_h \end{bmatrix} \tag{4.210}$$

The constraint to be dealt with is now the shear constraint,

$$\gamma_h = \frac{\partial w_h}{\partial x} - \beta_h \to 0 \tag{4.211}$$

In practice, γ_h is usually very small and can of course also be zero. Hence we have, using our earlier notation, the spaces

$$K_h(q_h) = \{\mathbf{v}_h \mid \mathbf{v}_h \in V_h, \ \gamma_h(\mathbf{v}_h) = q_h\} \tag{4.212}$$

$$D_h = \{q_h \mid q_h = \gamma_h(\mathbf{v}_h) \text{ for some } \mathbf{v}_h \in V_h\} \tag{4.213}$$

and the norms

$$\| \mathbf{v}_h \|^2 = \int_{\text{Vol}} \left[\left(\frac{\partial w_h}{\partial x} \right)^2 + L^2 \left(\frac{\partial \beta_h}{\partial x} \right)^2 \right] d\text{Vol}; \qquad \| \gamma_h \|^2 = \int_{\text{Vol}} (\gamma_h)^2 \, d\text{Vol} \tag{4.214}$$

The ellipticity condition is satisfied in this problem formulation because

$$EI \int_0^L (\beta_h')^2 \, dx \geq \alpha \| \mathbf{v}_h \|^2 \qquad \forall \ \mathbf{v}_h \in K_h(0) \tag{4.215}$$

with $\alpha > 0$ and independent of h. To prove this relation we need only to note that

$$\int_0^L \left(\frac{\partial w_h}{\partial x} \right)^2 dx = \int_0^L (\beta_h)^2 \, dx \leq \int_0^L L^2 \left(\frac{\partial \beta_h}{\partial x} \right)^2 dx \tag{4.216}$$

and therefore,

$$\| \mathbf{v}_h \|^2 \leq 2L^2 \int_{\text{Vol}} \left(\frac{\partial \beta_h}{\partial x} \right)^2 d\text{Vol} \tag{4.217}$$

giving $\alpha = EI/2L^2$.

The inf-sup condition for this formulation is

$$\inf_{\gamma_h \in D_h} \ \sup_{\mathbf{v}_h \in V_h} \ \frac{\int_{\text{Vol}} \gamma_h [(\partial w_h / \partial x) - \beta_h] \, d\text{Vol}}{\| \gamma_h \| \ \| \mathbf{v}_h \|} \geq c > 0 \tag{4.218}$$

in which the constant c is independent of h.

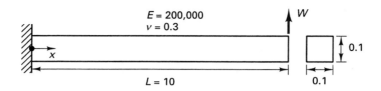

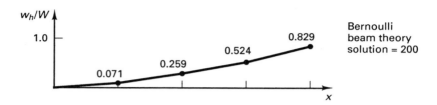

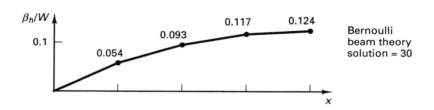

(a) Analysis with pure displacement-based element: w_h and β_h vary linearly over each element, and $\gamma_h = (\partial w_h/\partial x) - \beta_h$; since the values of w_h and β_h are very inaccurate, the shear strains are so too

Figure 4.26 Analysis of cantilever beam using two-node beam elements. Four equal length elements are used. (Shear correction factor k of (5.57) is taken equal to 1.0.)

The two-node element. Let us first consider the two-node displacement-based element for which w_h and β_h are assumed linear over each element [see Fig. 4.26(a) for an example solution]. A comparison of the computed results with the Bernoulli beam theory solution given in Fig. 4.26 shows that the element performs quite badly. In this case $K_h(0) = \{0\}$, and so the inf-sup condition in (4.218) is not satisfied. Refering to (4.164), we can also see that a good convergence behavior is not possible; namely, $d(\mathbf{u}, V_h) \rightarrow 0$ as we increase the space V_h, whereas $d[\mathbf{u}, K_h(0)] = \|\mathbf{u}\|$ (a constant value).

Next, consider the two-node mixed interpolated element for which w_h and β_h are linear and γ_h is constant over each element. Figure 4.26(b) shows the results obtained in the cantilever analysis and indicates the good predictive capability of this element. The ellipticity condition is again satisfied (see Exercise 4.61), and in addition we now need to investi-

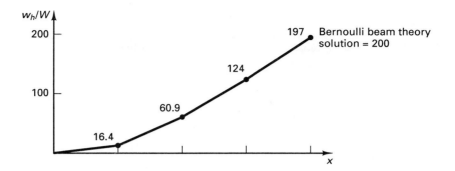

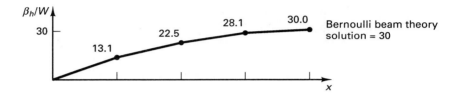

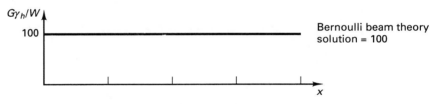

(b) Analysis with mixed interpolated element; w_h and β_h vary linearly over each element, and γ_h is constant in each element

Figure 4.26   (*continued*)

gate whether the following inf-sup condition is satisfied:

$$\inf_{\gamma_h \in P_h(D_h)} \sup_{\mathbf{v}_h \in V_h} \frac{\int_{\text{Vol}} \gamma_h[(\partial w_h / \partial x) - \beta_h]\, d\text{Vol}}{\|\gamma_h\|\, \|\mathbf{v}_h\|} \geq c > 0 \tag{4.219}$$

Now $K_h(0) \neq \{0\}$, and we test for the inf-sup condition by considering a typical γ_h (where γ_h is thought of as a variable). Then with a typical γ_h given, we choose

$$\hat{\mathbf{v}}_h = \begin{bmatrix} \hat{w}_h \\ \hat{\beta}_h \end{bmatrix} \tag{4.220}$$

with $\hat{\beta}_h = 0$ and $\partial \hat{w}_h / \partial x = \gamma_h$.
Now consider

$$\frac{\int_{\text{Vol}} \gamma_h[(\partial \hat{w}_h / \partial x) - \hat{\beta}_h]\, d\text{Vol}}{\|\hat{\mathbf{v}}_h\|} = \sqrt{\int_{\text{Vol}} (\gamma_h)^2\, d\text{Vol}} \tag{4.221}$$

Hence, we have

$$\sup_{v_h \in V_h} \frac{\int_{\text{Vol}} \gamma_h [(\partial w_h / \partial x) - \beta_h] \, d\text{Vol}}{\| v_h \|} \geq \frac{\int_{\text{Vol}} \gamma_h [(\partial \hat{w}_h / \partial x) - \hat{\beta}_h] \, d\text{Vol}}{\| \hat{v}_h \|}$$

$$= \sqrt{\int_{\text{Vol}} (\gamma_h)^2 \, d\text{Vol}} \tag{4.222}$$

with γ_h still a variable. Therefore, for the two-node mixed interpolated beam element we have

$$\inf_{\gamma_h \in P_h(D_h)} \sup_{v_h \in V_h} \frac{\int_{\text{Vol}} \gamma_h [(\partial w_h / \partial x) - \beta_h] \, d\text{Vol}}{\| \gamma_h \| \, \| v_h \|} \geq 1 \tag{4.223}$$

and the inf-sup condition is satisfied.

We can also apply the inf-sup eigenvalue test to the two-node beam elements. The equations used are those presented for the elasticity problem, but we use the spaces of the beam elements (see Exercise 4.63). Figure 4.27 shows the results obtained. We note that in (4.207) the smallest nonzero eigenvalue of the pure displacement-based discretization approaches zero as the mesh is refined, whereas the mixed interpolated beam element meshes give an eigenvalue that equals 1.0 for all meshes [which corresponds to the equal sign in (4.223)].

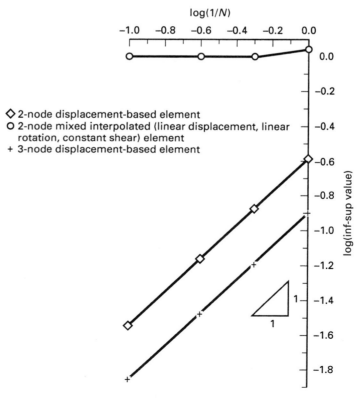

Figure 4.27 Inf-sup test of beam elements
(a cantilever beam is considered)

Higher-order mixed interpolated beam elements can be analyzed in the same way as the two-node elements (see Exercise 4.62). Figure 4.27 also shows the results obtained for the three-node pure displacement-based element with the numerical inf-sup test.

4.5.8 Exercises

4.47. Prove that $\| \mathbf{u} - \mathbf{u}_h \| \leq \tilde{c}\, d[\mathbf{u}, K_h(0)]$ is always true, where $\mathbf{u}_h$ is the finite element solution and $K_h(0)$ is defined in (4.159). Use that

$$\exists\, \alpha > 0 \quad \text{such that} \quad \forall\, \mathbf{v}_h \in K_h(0),\ a(\mathbf{v}_h, \mathbf{v}_h) \geq \alpha \, \| \mathbf{v}_h \|^2$$

$$\exists\, M > 0 \quad \text{such that} \quad \forall\, \mathbf{v}_{h1}, \mathbf{v}_{h2} \in V_h,\ |a(\mathbf{v}_{h2}, \mathbf{v}_{h1})| \leq M \, \| \mathbf{v}_{h1} \| \| \mathbf{v}_{h2} \|$$

and the approach in (4.94). Note that the constant $\tilde{c}$ is independent of the bulk modulus.

4.48. Prove that $\| \operatorname{div}\, (\mathbf{v}_1 - \mathbf{v}_2) \|_0 \leq c \| \mathbf{v}_1 - \mathbf{v}_2 \|_V$. Here $\mathbf{v}_1, \mathbf{v}_2 \in V_h$ and c is a constant.

4.49. Evaluate $P_h(\operatorname{div}\, \mathbf{v}_h)$ for the eight-node element shown assuming a constant pressure field over the element.

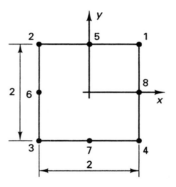

4.50. Evaluate the stiffness matrix of a general $3/1$ triangular u/p element for two-dimensional analysis. Hence, the element has three nodes and a constant discontinuous pressure is assumed. Use the data in Fig. E4.17 and consider plane stress, plane strain, and axisymmetric conditions.

  (a) Establish all required matrices using the general procedure for the u/p elements (see Example 4.32) but do not perform any matrix multiplications. Consider the case κ finite.

  (b) Compare the results obtained in Example 4.17 with the results obtained in part (a).

  (c) Give the u/p element matrix when total incompressibility is assumed (hence static condensation on the pressure degree of freedom cannot be performed).

  (*Note:* This element is not a reliable element for practical analysis of (almost) incompressible conditions but is merely used here in an exercise.)

4.51. Consider the $4/1$ element in Example 4.32. Show that using the term $P_h(\operatorname{div}\, \mathbf{v}_h)$ (evaluated in Example 4.34) in (4.179), we obtain the same element stiffness matrix as that found in Example 4.32.

4.52. Consider the $9/3$ element in Example 4.36; i.e., assume that $Q_h = [1, x, y]$. Assume that corresponding to $\mathbf{v}_h$ the nodal point displacements are

$$u_1 = 1; \qquad u_2 = -1; \qquad u_3 = -1; \qquad u_4 = 1; \qquad u_6 = -1; \qquad u_8 = 1$$

$$v_1 = 1; \qquad v_2 = -1; \qquad v_3 = -1; \qquad v_4 = 1; \qquad v_6 = -1; \qquad v_8 = 1$$

with all other nodal point displacements zero. Calculate the projection $P_h(\operatorname{div}\, \mathbf{v}_h)$.

4.53. Show that the $8/1$ u/p element satisfies the inf-sup condition (and hence discretizations using this element will not display a spurious pressure mode). For the proof refer to Example 4.36.

4.54. Consider the solution of (4.187) and show that the conditions i and ii in (4.188) and (4.189) are necessary and sufficient for a unique solution.

4.55. Consider the ellipticity condition in (4.192). Prove that this condition is satisfied for the $4/1$ element in two-dimensional plane stress and plane strain analyses.

4.56. The constant pressure mode, $p_0 \in Q_h$, in a two-dimensional square plane strain domain of an incompressible material modeled using four $9/3$ elements with all boundary displacements set to zero is not a spurious mode (because it physically should exist). Show that this mode is not an element of $P_h(D_h)$.

4.57. Consider the $4/1$ element. Can you construct a two-element model with appropriate boundary conditions that contains a spurious pressure mode? Explain your answer.

4.58. Consider the nine $4/1$ elements shown. Assume that all boundary displacements are zero.
(a) Pick a pressure distribution $\hat{p}_h$ for which there exists a vector $\mathbf{v}_h$ such that

$$\int_{\text{Vol}} \hat{p}_h \, \text{div} \, \mathbf{v}_h \, d\text{Vol} > 0$$

(b) Pick a pressure distribution $\hat{p}_h$ for which any displacement distribution $\mathbf{v}_h$ in V_h will give

$$\int_{\text{Vol}} \hat{p}_h \, \text{div} \, \mathbf{v}_h \, d\text{Vol} = 0$$

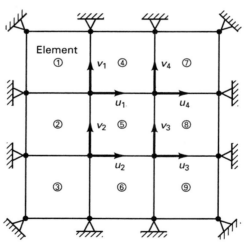

4.59. Consider the u/p-c formulation.
(a) Show that the inf-sup condition can be written as in (4.206) but that $\mathbf{G}_h = (\mathbf{K}_{up})_h \mathbf{T}_h^{-1}(\mathbf{K}_{pu})_h$.
(b) Also, show that, alternatively, the eigenproblem

$$\mathbf{G}_h' \mathbf{Q}_h = \lambda' \mathbf{T}_h \mathbf{Q}_h \tag{a}$$

can be considered, where $\mathbf{G}_h' = (\mathbf{K}_{pu})_h \mathbf{S}_h^{-1}(\mathbf{K}_{up})_h$, and that the smallest nonzero eigenvalues of (a) and (4.207) are the same.

Here $\mathbf{T}_h$ is the matrix of the L^2-norm of p_h; that is, for any vector of nodal pressures $\mathbf{P}_h$, we have $\|p_h\| = \mathbf{P}_h^T \mathbf{T}_h \mathbf{P}_h$; hence $\mathbf{T}_h = -\kappa(\mathbf{K}_{pp})_h$.

4.60. Consider the analysis of the cantilever plate in plane strain conditions shown. Assume that the $3/1$ u/p element is to be used in a sequence of uniform mesh refinements. Let n_u be the number of nodal point displacements and n_p the number of pressure variables. Show that as the mesh is refined, the ratio n_u/n_p approaches 1. (This clearly indicates solution difficulties.)

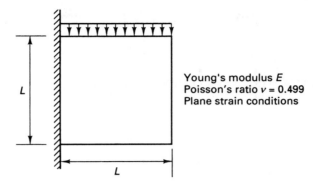

Young's modulus E
Poisson's ratio $v = 0.499$
Plane strain conditions

Calculate the same ratio when the 9/3 and 9/8-c elements are used (the 9/8-c element is defined in Table 4.8) and discuss your result.

4.61. Show that the mixed interpolated two-, three-, and four-node beam elements satisfy the ellipticity condition. The two-node element was considered in Section 4.5.7, and the three- and four-node elements are discussed in Secton 5.4.1 (see also Exercise 4.62).

4.62. Show analytically that the inf-sup condition is not satisfied for the three- and four-node displacement-based beam elements and that the condition is satisfied for the mixed interpolated beam elements with γ_h varying, respectively, linearly and parabolically (see Section 5.4.1).

4.63. Establish the eigenvalue problem of the numerical inf-sup test for the beam elements considered in Section 4.5.7. Use the form (4.207) and define all matrices in detail.

4.64. Consider the problem in Fig. 4.24 and the elements mentioned in Table 4.8. Calculate, for each of these elements, the constraint ratio defined as the number of displacement degrees of freedom divided by the number of pressure degrees of freedom as the mesh is refined, that is, as $h \rightarrow 0$. Hence note that this constraint ratio alone does not show whether or not the inf-sup condition is satisfied.

CHAPTER FIVE

Formulation and Calculation of Isoparametric Finite Element Matrices

5.1 INTRODUCTION

A very important phase of a finite element solution is the calculation of the finite element matrices. In Chapter 4 we discussed the formulation and calculation of generalized coordinate finite element models. The aim in the presentation of the generalized coordinate finite elements was primarily to enhance our understanding of the finite element method. We have already pointed out that in most practical analyses the use of isoparametric finite elements is more effective. For the original developments of these elements, see I. C. Taig [A] and B. M. Irons [A, B].

Our objective in this chapter is to present the formulation of isoparametric finite elements and describe effective implementations. In the derivation of generalized coordinate finite element models, we used local element coordinate systems x, y, z and assumed the element displacements $u(x, y, z)$, $v(x, y, z)$, and $w(x, y, z)$ (and in the case of mixed methods also the element stress and strain variables) in the form of polynomials in x, y, and z with undetermined constant coefficients α_i, β_i, and γ_i, $i = 1, 2, \ldots$, identified as generalized coordinates. It was not possible to associate a priori a physical meaning with the generalized coordinates; however, on evaluation we found that the generalized coordinates determining the displacements are linear combinations of the element nodal point displacements. The principal idea of the isoparametric finite element formulation is to achieve the relationship between the element displacements at any point and the element nodal point displacements directly through the use of *interpolation functions* (also called *shape functions*). This means that the transformation matrix $\mathbf{A}^{-1}$ [see (4.57)] is not evaluated; instead, the element matrices corresponding to the required degrees of freedom are obtained directly.

5.2 ISOPARAMETRIC DERIVATION OF BAR ELEMENT STIFFNESS MATRIX

Consider the example of a bar element to illustrate the procedure of an isoparametric stiffness formulation. In order to simplify the explanation, assume that the bar lies in the global X-coordinate axis, as shown in Fig. 5.1. The first step is to relate the actual global coordinates X to a *natural coordinate system* with variable r, $-1 \le r \le 1$ (Fig. 5.1). This transformation is given by

$$X = \tfrac{1}{2}(1 - r)X_1 + \tfrac{1}{2}(1 + r)X_2 \tag{5.1}$$

or

$$X = \sum_{i=1}^{2} h_i X_i \tag{5.2}$$

where $h_1 = \tfrac{1}{2}(1 - r)$ and $h_2 = \tfrac{1}{2}(1 + r)$ are the interpolation or shape functions. Note that (5.2) establishes a unique relationship between the coordinates X and r on the bar.

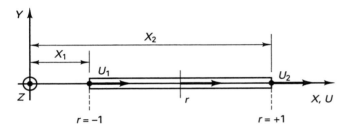

Figure 5.1   Element in global and natural coordinate system

The bar global displacements are expressed in the same way as the global coordinates:

$$U = \sum_{i=1}^{2} h_i U_i \tag{5.3}$$

where in this case a linear displacement variation is specified. *The interpolation of the element coordinates and element displacements using the same interpolation functions, which are defined in a natural coordinate system, is the basis of the isoparametric finite element formulation.*

For the calculation of the element stiffness matrix we need to find the element strains $\epsilon = dU/dX$. Here we use

$$\epsilon = \frac{dU}{dr}\frac{dr}{dX} \tag{5.4}$$

where, from (5.3),

$$\frac{dU}{dr} = \frac{U_2 - U_1}{2} \tag{5.5}$$

and using (5.2), we obtain

$$\frac{dX}{dr} = \frac{X_2 - X_1}{2} = \frac{L}{2} \tag{5.6}$$

where L is the length of the bar. Hence, as expected, we have

$$\epsilon = \frac{U_2 - U_1}{L} \tag{5.7}$$

The strain-displacement transformation matrix corresponding to (4.32) is therefore

$$\mathbf{B} = \frac{1}{L}[-1 \quad 1] \tag{5.8}$$

In general, the strain-displacement transformation matrix is a function of the natural coordinates, and we therefore evaluate the stiffness matrix volume integral in (4.33) by integrating over the natural coordinates. Following this general procedure, although in this example it is not necessary, we have

$$\mathbf{K} = \frac{AE}{L^2} \int_{-1}^{1} \begin{bmatrix} -1 \\ 1 \end{bmatrix} [-1 \quad 1] \, J \, dr \tag{5.9}$$

where the bar area A and modulus of elasticity E have been assumed constant and J is the Jacobian relating an element length in the global coordinate system to an element length in the natural coordinate system; i.e.,

$$dX = J \, dr \tag{5.10}$$

From (5.6) we have
$$J = \frac{L}{2} \tag{5.11}$$

Then, evaluating (5.9), we obtain the well-known matrix

$$\mathbf{K} = \frac{AE}{L} \begin{bmatrix} 1 & -1 \\ -1 & 1 \end{bmatrix} \tag{5.12}$$

As stated in the introduction, the isoparametric formulation avoids the construction of the transformation matrix $\mathbf{A}^{-1}$. In order to compare this formulation with the generalized coordinate formulation, we need to solve from (5.1) for r and then substitute for r into (5.3). We obtain

$$r = \frac{X - [(X_1 + X_2)/2]}{L/2} \tag{5.13}$$

and then
$$U = \alpha_0 + \alpha_1 X \tag{5.14}$$

where

$$\left. \begin{aligned} \alpha_0 &= \tfrac{1}{2}(U_1 + U_2) - \frac{X_1 + X_2}{2L}(U_2 - U_1) \\[2mm] \alpha_1 &= \frac{1}{L}(U_2 - U_1) \end{aligned} \right\} \tag{5.15}$$

or
$$\boldsymbol{\alpha} = \begin{bmatrix} \dfrac{1}{2} + \dfrac{X_1 + X_2}{2L} & \dfrac{1}{2} - \dfrac{X_1 + X_2}{2L} \\[3mm] -\dfrac{1}{L} & \dfrac{1}{L} \end{bmatrix} \mathbf{U} \tag{5.16}$$

where
$$\boldsymbol{\alpha}^T = [\alpha_0 \quad \alpha_1]; \qquad \mathbf{U}^T = [U_1 \quad U_2] \tag{5.17}$$

and the matrix relating $\boldsymbol{\alpha}$ to $\mathbf{U}$ in (5.16) is $\mathbf{A}^{-1}$. It should be noted that in this example the generalized coordinates α_0 and α_1 relate the global element displacement to the global element coordinate [see (5.14)].

5.3 FORMULATION OF CONTINUUM ELEMENTS

For a continuum finite element, it is in most cases effective to calculate directly the element matrices corresponding to the global degrees of freedom. However, we shall first present the formulation of the matrices that correspond to the element local degrees of freedom because additional considerations may be necessary when the element matrices that correspond to the global degrees of freedom are calculated directly (see Section 5.3.4). In the following we consider the derivation of the element matrices of straight truss elements; two-dimensional plane stress, plane strain, and axisymmetric elements; and three-dimensional elements that all have a variable number of nodes. Typical elements are shown in Fig. 5.2.

We direct our discussion to the calculation of displacement-based finite element matrices. However, the same procedures are also used in the calculation of the element matrices of mixed formulations, and in particular of the displacement/pressure-based formulations for incompressible analysis, as briefly discussed in Section 5.3.5.

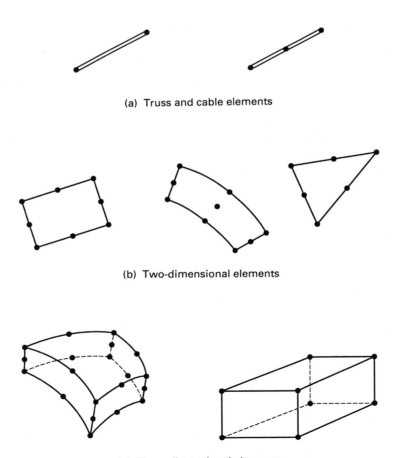

(a) Truss and cable elements

(b) Two-dimensional elements

(c) Three-dimensional elements

Figure 5.2   Some typical continuum elements

5.3.1 Quadrilateral Elements

The basic procedure in the isoparametric finite element formulation is to express the element coordinates and element displacements in the form of interpolations using the natural coordinate system of the element. This coordinate system is one-, two-, or three-dimensional, depending on the dimensionality of the element. The formulation of the element matrices is the same whether we deal with a one, two-, or three-dimensional element. For this reason we use in the following general presentation the equations of a three-dimensional element. However, the one- and two-dimensional elements are included by simply using only the relevant coordinate axes and the appropriate interpolation functions.

Considering a general three-dimensional element, the coordinate interpolations are

$$ x = \sum_{i=1}^{q} h_i x_i; \qquad y = \sum_{i=1}^{q} h_i y_i; \qquad z = \sum_{i=1}^{q} h_i z_i \qquad (5.18) $$

where x, y, and z are the coordinates at any point of the element (here local coordinates) and x_i, y_i, z_i, $i = 1, \ldots , q$, are the coordinates of the q element nodes. The interpolation functions h_i are defined in the natural coordinate system of the element, which has variables r, s, and t that each vary from -1 to $+1$. For one- or two-dimensional elements, only the relevant equations in (5.18) would be employed, and the interpolation functions would depend only on the natural coordinate variables r and r, s, respectively.

The unknown quantities in (5.18) are so far the interpolation functions h_i. The fundamental property of the interpolation function h_i is that its value in the natural coordinate system is unity at node i and zero at all other nodes. Using these conditions, the functions h_i corresponding to a specific nodal point layout could be solved for in a systematic manner. However, it is convenient to construct them by inspection, which is demonstrated in the following simple example.

EXAMPLE 5.1: Construct the interpolation functions corresponding to the three-node truss element in Fig. E5.1.

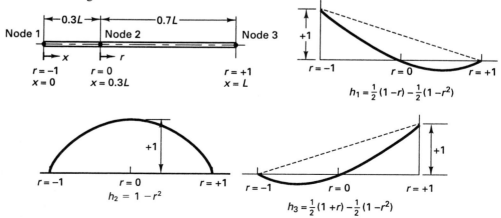

Figure E5.1 One-dimensional interpolation functions of a truss element

A first observation is that for the three-node truss element we want interpolation polynomials that involve r^2 as the highest power of r; in other words, the interpolation functions shall be parabolas. The function h_2 can thus be constructed without much effort. Namely, the parabola that satisfies the conditions to be equal to zero at $r = \pm 1$ and equal to 1 at $r = 0$ is given by $(1 - r^2)$. The other two interpolation functions h_1 and h_3 are constructed by superimposing a linear function and a parabola. Consider the interpolation function h_3. Using $\frac{1}{2}(1 + r)$, the conditions that the function shall be zero at $r = -1$ and 1 at $r = +1$ are satisfied. To ensure that h_3 is also zero at $r = 0$, we need to use $h_3 = \frac{1}{2}(1 + r) - \frac{1}{2}(1 - r^2)$. The interpolation function h_1 is obtained in a similar manner.

The procedure used in Example 5.1 of constructing the final required interpolation functions suggests an attractive formulation of an element with a variable number of nodes. This formulation is achieved by constructing first the interpolations corresponding to a basic two-node element. The addition of another node then results in an additional interpolation function and a correction to be applied to the already existing interpolation functions. Figure 5.3 gives the interpolation functions of the one-dimensional element considered in Example 5.1, with an additional fourth node possible. As shown, the element can have from two to four nodes. We should note that nodes 3 and 4 are now interior nodes because nodes 1 and 2 are used to define the two-node element.

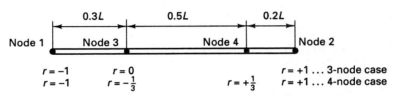

(a) 2 to 4 variable-number-nodes truss element

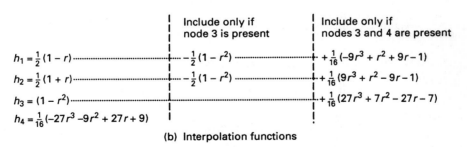

(b) Interpolation functions

Figure 5.3   Interpolation functions of two to four variable-number-nodes one-dimensional element

This procedure of constructing the element interpolation functions for one-dimensional analysis can be directly generalized for use in two and three dimensions. Figure 5.4 shows the interpolation functions of a four to nine variable-number-nodes two-dimensional element, and Fig. 5.5 gives the interpolation functions for three-dimensional 8- to 20-node elements. The two- and three-dimensional interpolations have been established in a manner analogous to the one-dimensional interpolations, where the basic functions used are, in fact, those already employed in Fig. 5.3. We consider in Figs. 5.4 and 5.5 at most parabolic interpolation, but variable-number-nodes elements with interpolations of higher order could be derived in an analogous way.

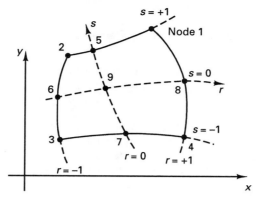

(a) 4 to 9 variable-number-nodes two-dimensional element

Include only if node i is defined

		$i = 5$	$i = 6$	$i = 7$	$i = 8$	$i = 9$
$h_1 =$	$\frac{1}{4}(1+r)(1+s)$	$-\frac{1}{2}h_5$			$-\frac{1}{2}h_8$	$-\frac{1}{4}h_9$
$h_2 =$	$\frac{1}{4}(1-r)(1+s)$	$-\frac{1}{2}h_5$	$-\frac{1}{2}h_6$			$-\frac{1}{4}h_9$
$h_3 =$	$\frac{1}{4}(1-r)(1-s)$		$-\frac{1}{2}h_6$	$-\frac{1}{2}h_7$		$-\frac{1}{4}h_9$
$h_4 =$	$\frac{1}{4}(1+r)(1-s)$			$-\frac{1}{2}h_7$	$-\frac{1}{2}h_8$	$-\frac{1}{4}h_9$
$h_5 =$	$\frac{1}{2}(1-r^2)(1+s)$					$-\frac{1}{2}h_9$
$h_6 =$	$\frac{1}{2}(1-s^2)(1-r)$					$-\frac{1}{2}h_9$
$h_7 =$	$\frac{1}{2}(1-r^2)(1-s)$					$-\frac{1}{2}h_9$
$h_8 =$	$\frac{1}{2}(1-s^2)(1+r)$					$-\frac{1}{2}h_9$
$h_9 =$	$(1-r^2)(1-s^2)$					

(b) Interpolation functions

Figure 5.4 Interpolation functions of four to nine variable-number-nodes two-dimensional element

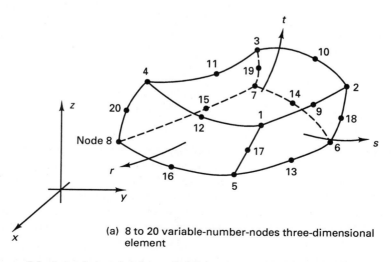

(a) 8 to 20 variable-number-nodes three-dimensional element

Figure 5.5 Interpolation functions of eight to twenty variable-number-nodes three-dimensional element

$$h_1 = g_1 - (g_9 + g_{12} + g_{17})/2 \qquad h_6 = g_6 - (g_{13} + g_{14} + g_{18})/2$$

$$h_2 = g_2 - (g_9 + g_{10} + g_{18})/2 \qquad h_7 = g_7 - (g_{14} + g_{15} + g_{19})/2$$

$$h_3 = g_3 - (g_{10} + g_{11} + g_{19})/2 \qquad h_8 = g_8 - (g_{15} + g_{16} + g_{20})/2$$

$$h_4 = g_4 - (g_{11} + g_{12} + g_{20})/2 \qquad h_j = g_j \text{ for } j = 9, \ldots, 20$$

$$h_5 = g_5 - (g_{13} + g_{16} + g_{17})/2$$

$g_i = 0$ if node i is not included; otherwise,

$$g_i = G(r, r_i)\, G(s, s_i)\, G(t, t_i)$$

$$G(\beta, \beta_i) = \tfrac{1}{2}(1 + \beta_i \beta) \quad \text{for } \beta_i = \pm 1$$

$$G(\beta, \beta_i) = (1 - \beta^2) \qquad \text{for } \beta_i = 0 \qquad ; \beta = r, s, t$$

(b) Interpolation functions

Figure 5.5 (*continued*)

The attractiveness of the elements in Figs. 5.3 to 5.5 lies in that the elements can have any number of nodes between the minimum and the maximum. Also, triangular elements can be formed (see Section 5.3.2). However, in general, to obtain maximum accuracy, the variable-number-nodes elements should be as nearly rectangular (in three-dimensional analysis, rectangular in each local plane) as possible and the noncorner nodes should, in general, be located at their natural coordinate positions; e.g., for the nine-node two-dimensional element the intermediate side nodes should, in general, be located at the midpoints between the corner nodes and the ninth node should be at the center of the element (for some exceptions see Section 5.3.2, and for more details on these observations, see Section 5.3.3).

Considering the geometry of the two- and three-dimensional elements in Figs. 5.4 and 5.5 we note that by means of the coordinate interpolations in (5.18), the elements can have, without any difficulty, curved boundaries. This is an important advantage over the generalized coordinate finite element formulation. Another important advantage is the ease with which the element displacement functions can be constructed.

In the *isoparametric* formulation the element displacements are interpolated in the same way as the geometry; i.e., we use

$$u = \sum_{i=1}^{q} h_i u_i; \qquad v = \sum_{i=1}^{q} h_i v_i; \qquad w = \sum_{i=1}^{q} h_i w_i \qquad (5.19)$$

where u, v, and w are the local element displacements at any point of the element and u_i, v_i, and w_i, $i = 1, \ldots, q$, are the corresponding element displacements at its nodes. Therefore, it is assumed that to each nodal point coordinate necessary to describe the geometry of the element, there corresponds one nodal point displacement.[1]

To be able to evaluate the stiffness matrix of an element, we need to calculate the strain-displacement transformation matrix. The element strains are obtained in terms of

[1] In addition to the isoparametric elements, there are *subparametric* elements, for which the geometry is interpolated to a lower degree than the displacements (see end of this section) and *superparametric* elements for which the reverse is applicable (see Section 5.4).

derivatives of element displacements with respect to the local coordinates. Because the element displacements are defined in the natural coordinate system using (5.19), we need to relate the x, y, z derivatives to the r, s, t derivatives, where we realize that (5.18) is of the form

$$x = f_1(r, s, t); \qquad y = f_2(r, s, t); \qquad z = f_3(r, s, t) \qquad (5.20)$$

where f_i denotes "function of." The inverse relationship is

$$r = f_4(x, y, z); \qquad s = f_5(x, y, z); \qquad t = f_6(x, y, z) \qquad (5.21)$$

We require the derivatives $\partial/\partial x$, $\partial/\partial y$, and $\partial/\partial z$, and it seems natural to use the chain rule in the following form:

$$\frac{\partial}{\partial x} = \frac{\partial}{\partial r}\frac{\partial r}{\partial x} + \frac{\partial}{\partial s}\frac{\partial s}{\partial x} + \frac{\partial}{\partial t}\frac{\partial t}{\partial x} \qquad (5.22)$$

with similar relationships for $\partial/\partial y$ and $\partial/\partial z$. However, to evaluate $\partial/\partial x$ in (5.22), we need to calculate $\partial r/\partial x$, $\partial s/\partial x$, and $\partial t/\partial x$, which means that the explicit inverse relationships in (5.21) would need to be evaluated. These inverse relationships are, in general, difficult to establish explicitly, and it is necessary to evaluate the required derivatives in the following way. Using the chain rule, we have

$$\begin{bmatrix} \dfrac{\partial}{\partial r} \\[2ex] \dfrac{\partial}{\partial s} \\[2ex] \dfrac{\partial}{\partial t} \end{bmatrix} = \begin{bmatrix} \dfrac{\partial x}{\partial r} & \dfrac{\partial y}{\partial r} & \dfrac{\partial z}{\partial r} \\[2ex] \dfrac{\partial x}{\partial s} & \dfrac{\partial y}{\partial s} & \dfrac{\partial z}{\partial s} \\[2ex] \dfrac{\partial x}{\partial t} & \dfrac{\partial y}{\partial t} & \dfrac{\partial z}{\partial t} \end{bmatrix} \begin{bmatrix} \dfrac{\partial}{\partial x} \\[2ex] \dfrac{\partial}{\partial y} \\[2ex] \dfrac{\partial}{\partial z} \end{bmatrix} \qquad (5.23)$$

or, in matrix notation,

$$\frac{\boldsymbol{\partial}}{\boldsymbol{\partial} \mathbf{r}} = \mathbf{J}\frac{\boldsymbol{\partial}}{\boldsymbol{\partial} \mathbf{x}} \qquad (5.24)$$

where $\mathbf{J}$ is the *Jacobian operator* relating the natural coordinate derivatives to the local coordinate derivatives. We should note that the Jacobian operator can easily be found using (5.18). We require $\boldsymbol{\partial}/\boldsymbol{\partial}\mathbf{x}$ and use

$$\frac{\boldsymbol{\partial}}{\boldsymbol{\partial} \mathbf{x}} = \mathbf{J}^{-1}\frac{\boldsymbol{\partial}}{\boldsymbol{\partial} \mathbf{r}} \qquad (5.25)$$

which requires that the inverse of $\mathbf{J}$ exists. This inverse exists provided that there is a one-to-one (i.e., unique) correspondence between the natural and the local coordinates of the element, as expressed in (5.20) and (5.21). In most formulations the one-to-one correspondence between the coordinate systems (i.e., to each r, s, and t there corresponds only one x, y, and z) is obviously given, such as for the elements in Figs. 5.3 to 5.5. However, in cases where the element is much distorted or folds back upon itself, as in Fig. 5.6, the unique relation between the coordinate systems does not exist (see also Section 5.3.2 for singularities in the Jacobian transformation, Example 5.17).

Using (5.19) and (5.25), we evaluate $\partial u/\partial x$, $\partial u/\partial y$, $\partial u/\partial z$, $\partial v/\partial x$, ..., $\partial w/\partial z$ and can therefore construct the strain-displacement transformation matrix $\mathbf{B}$, with

$$\boldsymbol{\epsilon} = \mathbf{B}\hat{\mathbf{u}} \qquad (5.26)$$

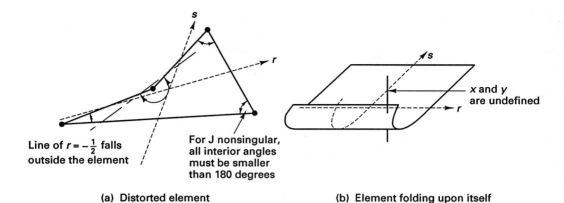

(a) Distorted element   (b) Element folding upon itself

Figure 5.6   Elements with possible singular Jacobian

where $\hat{\mathbf{u}}$ is a vector listing the element nodal point displacements of (5.19), and we note that $\mathbf{J}$ affects the elements in $\mathbf{B}$. The element stiffness matrix corresponding to the local element degrees of freedom is then

$$\mathbf{K} = \int_V \mathbf{B}^T \mathbf{C} \mathbf{B} \, dV \qquad (5.27)$$

We should note that the elements of $\mathbf{B}$ are functions of the natural coordinates r, s, and t. Therefore, the volume integration extends over the natural coordinate volume, and the volume differential dV need also be written in terms of the natural coordinates. In general, we have

$$dV = \det \mathbf{J} \, dr \, ds \, dt \qquad (5.28)$$

where $\det \mathbf{J}$ is the determinant of the Jacobian operator in (5.24) (see Exercise 5.6).

An explicit evaluation of the volume integral in (5.27) is, in general, not effective, particularly when higher-order interpolations are used or the element is distorted. Therefore, numerical integration is employed. Indeed, numerical integration must be regarded as an integral part of isoparametric element matrix evaluations. The details of the numerical integration procedures are described in Section 5.5, but the process can briefly be summarized as follows. First, we write (5.27) in the form

$$\mathbf{K} = \int_V \mathbf{F} \, dr \, ds \, dt \qquad (5.29)$$

where $\mathbf{F} = \mathbf{B}^T \mathbf{C} \mathbf{B} \det \mathbf{J}$ and the integration is performed in the natural coordinate system of the element. As stated above, the elements of $\mathbf{F}$ depend on r, s, and t, but the detailed functional relationship is usually not calculated. Using numerical integration, the stiffness matrix is now evaluated as

$$\mathbf{K} = \sum_{i,\, j,\, k} \alpha_{ijk} \mathbf{F}_{ijk} \qquad (5.30)$$

where $\mathbf{F}_{ijk}$ is the matrix $\mathbf{F}$ evaluated at the point (r_i, s_j, t_k), and α_{ijk} is a given constant that depends on the values of r_i, s_j, and t_k. The sampling points (r_i, s_j, t_k) of the function and the corresponding weighting factors α_{ijk} are chosen to obtain maximum accuracy in the integration. Naturally, the integration accuracy can increase as the number of sampling points is increased.

The purpose of this brief outline of the numerical integration procedure was to complete the description of the general isoparametric formulation. The relative simplicity of the formulation may already be noted. It is the simplicity of the element formulation and the efficiency with which the element matrices can actually be evaluated in a computer that has drawn much attention to the development of the isoparametric and related elements.

The formulation of the element mass matrix and load vectors is now straightforward. Namely, writing the element displacements in the form

$$\mathbf{u}(r, s, t) = \mathbf{H}\hat{\mathbf{u}} \tag{5.31}$$

where $\mathbf{H}$ is a matrix of the interpolation functions, we have, as in (4.34) to (4.37),

$$\mathbf{M} = \int_V \rho \mathbf{H}^T \mathbf{H}\, dV \tag{5.32}$$

$$\mathbf{R}_B = \int_V \mathbf{H}^T \mathbf{f}^B\, dV \tag{5.33}$$

$$\mathbf{R}_S = \int_S \mathbf{H}^{S^T} \mathbf{f}^S\, dS \tag{5.34}$$

$$\mathbf{R}_I = \int_V \mathbf{B}^T \boldsymbol{\tau}^I\, dV \tag{5.35}$$

These matrices are evaluated using numerical integration, as indicated for the stiffness matrix $\mathbf{K}$ in (5.30). In the evaluation we need to use the appropriate function $\mathbf{F}$. To calculate the body force vector $\mathbf{R}_B$ we use $\mathbf{F} = \mathbf{H}^T \mathbf{f}^B \det \mathbf{J}$, for the surface force vector we use $\mathbf{F} = \mathbf{H}^{S^T} \mathbf{f}^S \det \mathbf{J}^S$, for the initial stress load vector we use $\mathbf{F} = \mathbf{B}^T \boldsymbol{\tau}^I \det \mathbf{J}$, and for the mass matrix we have $\mathbf{F} = \rho \mathbf{H}^T \mathbf{H} \det \mathbf{J}$.

This formulation was for one-, two-, or three-dimensional elements. We shall now consider some specific cases and demonstrate the details of the calculation of element matrices.

EXAMPLE 5.2: Derive the displacement interpolation matrix $\mathbf{H}$, strain-displacement interpolation matrix $\mathbf{B}$, and Jacobian operator $\mathbf{J}$ for the three-node truss element shown in Fig. E5.2.

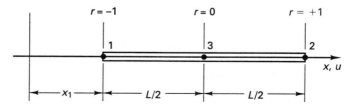

Figure E5.2 Truss element with node 3 at center of element

The interpolation functions of the element were given in Fig. E5.1. Thus, we have

$$\mathbf{H} = \left[-\frac{r}{2}(1 - r) \quad \frac{r}{2}(1 + r) \quad (1 - r^2) \right] \tag{a}$$

The strain-displacement matrix $\mathbf{B}$ is obtained by differentiation of $\mathbf{H}$ with respect to r and premultiplying the result by the inverse of the Jacobian operator,

$$\mathbf{B} = \mathbf{J}^{-1}[(-\tfrac{1}{2} + r) \quad (\tfrac{1}{2} + r) \quad -2r] \tag{b}$$

To evaluate $\mathbf{J}$ formally we use

$$x = -\frac{r}{2}(1 - r)x_1 + \frac{r}{2}(1 + r)(x_1 + L) + (1 - r^2)\left(x_1 + \frac{L}{2}\right)$$

hence,

$$x = x_1 + \frac{L}{2} + \frac{L}{2}r \tag{c}$$

where we may note that because node 3 is at the center of the truss, x is interpolated linearly between nodes 1 and 2. The same result would be obtained using only nodes 1 and 2 for the geometry interpolation. Using now the relation in (c), we have

$$\mathbf{J} = \left[\frac{L}{2}\right] \tag{d}$$

and

$$\mathbf{J}^{-1} = \left[\frac{2}{L}\right]; \qquad \det \mathbf{J} = \frac{L}{2}$$

With the relations in (a) to (d), we can now evaluate all finite element matrices and vectors given in (5.27) to (5.35).

EXAMPLE 5.3:   Establish the Jacobian operator $\mathbf{J}$ of the two-dimensional elements shown in Fig. E5.3.

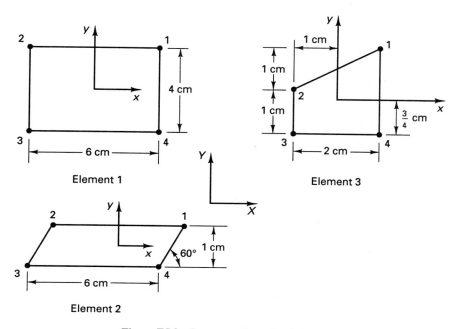

Figure E5.3   Some two-dimensional elements

The Jacobian operator is the same for the global X, Y and the local x, y coordinate systems. For convenience we therefore use the local coordinate systems. Substituting into (5.18) and (5.23) using the interpolation functions given in Fig. 5.4, we obtain for element 1:

$$x = 3r; \qquad y = 2s$$

$$\mathbf{J} = \begin{bmatrix} 3 & 0 \\ 0 & 2 \end{bmatrix}$$

Similarly, for element 2, we have

$$x = \tfrac{1}{4}\{(1 + r)(1 + s)[3 + 1/(2\sqrt{3})] + (1 - r)(1 + s)[-(3 - 1/(2\sqrt{3}))]$$
$$+ (1 - r)(1 - s)[-(3 + 1/(2\sqrt{3}))] + (1 + r)(1 - s)[3 - 1/(2\sqrt{3})]\}$$
$$y = \tfrac{1}{4}\{(1 + r)(1 + s)(\tfrac{1}{2}) + (1 - r)(1 + s)(\tfrac{1}{2}) + (1 - r)(1 - s)(-\tfrac{1}{2})$$
$$+ (1 + r)(1 - s)(-\tfrac{1}{2})\}$$

and hence,

$$\mathbf{J} = \begin{bmatrix} 3 & 0 \\ \dfrac{1}{2\sqrt{3}} & 2 \end{bmatrix}$$

Also, for element 3,

$$x = \tfrac{1}{4}[(1 + r)(1 + s)(1) + (1 - r)(1 + s)(-1) + (1 - r)(1 - s)(-1)$$
$$+ (1 + r)(1 - s)(+1)]$$
$$y = \tfrac{1}{4}[(1 + r)(1 + s)(\tfrac{5}{4}) + (1 - r)(1 + s)(\tfrac{1}{4}) + (1 - r)(1 - s)(-\tfrac{3}{4})$$
$$+ (1 + r)(1 - s)(-\tfrac{3}{4})]$$

therefore,

$$\mathbf{J} = \frac{1}{4}\begin{bmatrix} 4 & (1 + s) \\ 0 & (3 + r) \end{bmatrix}$$

We may recognize that the Jacobian operator of a 2 × 2 square element is the identity matrix, and that the entries in the operator $\mathbf{J}$ of a general element express the amount of distortion from that 2 × 2 square element. Since the distortion is constant at any point (r, s) of elements 1 and 2, the operator $\mathbf{J}$ is constant for these elements.

EXAMPLE 5.4:   Establish the interpolation functions of the two-dimensional element shown in Fig. E5.4.

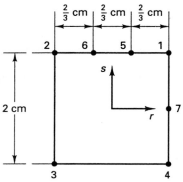

(a)

Figure E5.4   A seven-node element

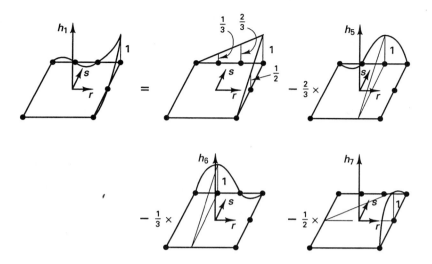

(b) Construction of h_1

Figure E5.4   (*continued*)

The individual functions are obtained by combining the basic linear, parabolic, and cubic interpolations corresponding to the r and s directions. Thus, using the functions in Figure 5.3, we obtain

$$h_5 = [\tfrac{1}{16}(-27r^3 - 9r^2 + 27r + 9)][\tfrac{1}{2}(1 + s)]$$

$$h_6 = [(1 - r^2) + \tfrac{1}{16}(27r^3 + 7r^2 - 27r - 7)][\tfrac{1}{2}(1 + s)]$$

$$h_2 = [\tfrac{1}{2}(1 - r) - \tfrac{1}{2}(1 - r^2) + \tfrac{1}{16}(-9r^3 + r^2 + 9r - 1)][\tfrac{1}{2}(1 + s)]$$

$$h_3 = \tfrac{1}{4}(1 - r)(1 - s)$$

$$h_7 = \tfrac{1}{2}(1 - s^2)(1 + r)$$

$$h_4 = \tfrac{1}{4}(1 + r)(1 - s) - \tfrac{1}{2}h_7$$

$$h_1 = \tfrac{1}{4}(1 + r)(1 + s) - \tfrac{2}{3}h_5 - \tfrac{1}{3}h_6 - \tfrac{1}{2}h_7$$

where h_1 is constructed as indicated in an oblique/aerial view in Fig. E5.4.

EXAMPLE 5.5: Derive the expressions needed for the evaluation of the stiffness matrix of the isoparametric four-node finite element in Fig. E5.5. Assume plane stress or plane strain conditions.

Using the interpolation function h_1, h_2, h_3, and h_4 defined in Fig. 5.4, the coordinate interpolation given in (5.18) is, for this element,

$$x = \tfrac{1}{4}(1 + r)(1 + s)x_1 + \tfrac{1}{4}(1 - r)(1 + s)x_2 + \tfrac{1}{4}(1 - r)(1 - s)x_3 + \tfrac{1}{4}(1 + r)(1 - s)x_4$$

$$y = \tfrac{1}{4}(1 + r)(1 + s)y_1 + \tfrac{1}{4}(1 - r)(1 + s)y_2 + \tfrac{1}{4}(1 - r)(1 - s)y_3 + \tfrac{1}{4}(1 + r)(1 - s)y_4$$

The displacement interpolation given in (5.19) is

$$u = \tfrac{1}{4}(1 + r)(1 + s)u_1 + \tfrac{1}{4}(1 - r)(1 + s)u_2 + \tfrac{1}{4}(1 - r)(1 - s)u_3 + \tfrac{1}{4}(1 + r)(1 - s)u_4$$

$$v = \tfrac{1}{4}(1 + r)(1 + s)v_1 + \tfrac{1}{4}(1 - r)(1 + s)v_2 + \tfrac{1}{4}(1 - r)(1 - s)v_3 + \tfrac{1}{4}(1 + r)(1 - s)v_4$$

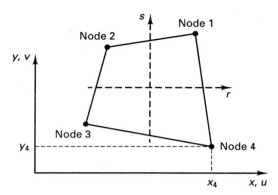

Figure E5.5   Four-node two-dimensional element

The element strains are given by

$$\boldsymbol{\epsilon}^T = \begin{bmatrix} \epsilon_{xx} & \epsilon_{yy} & \gamma_{xy} \end{bmatrix}$$

where

$$\epsilon_{xx} = \frac{\partial u}{\partial x}; \qquad \epsilon_{yy} = \frac{\partial v}{\partial y}; \qquad \gamma_{xy} = \frac{\partial u}{\partial y} + \frac{\partial v}{\partial x}$$

To evaluate the displacement derivatives, we need to evaluate (5.23):

$$\begin{bmatrix} \dfrac{\partial}{\partial r} \\[2mm] \dfrac{\partial}{\partial s} \end{bmatrix} = \begin{bmatrix} \dfrac{\partial x}{\partial r} & \dfrac{\partial y}{\partial r} \\[2mm] \dfrac{\partial x}{\partial s} & \dfrac{\partial y}{\partial s} \end{bmatrix} \begin{bmatrix} \dfrac{\partial}{\partial x} \\[2mm] \dfrac{\partial}{\partial y} \end{bmatrix} \qquad \text{or} \qquad \frac{\partial}{\partial \mathbf{r}} = \mathbf{J} \frac{\partial}{\partial \mathbf{x}}$$

where

$$\frac{\partial x}{\partial r} = \frac{1}{4}(1 + s)x_1 - \frac{1}{4}(1 + s)x_2 - \frac{1}{4}(1 - s)x_3 + \frac{1}{4}(1 - s)x_4$$

$$\frac{\partial x}{\partial s} = \frac{1}{4}(1 + r)x_1 + \frac{1}{4}(1 - r)x_2 - \frac{1}{4}(1 - r)x_3 - \frac{1}{4}(1 + r)x_4$$

$$\frac{\partial y}{\partial r} = \frac{1}{4}(1 + s)y_1 - \frac{1}{4}(1 + s)y_2 - \frac{1}{4}(1 - s)y_3 + \frac{1}{4}(1 - s)y_4$$

$$\frac{\partial y}{\partial s} = \frac{1}{4}(1 + r)y_1 + \frac{1}{4}(1 - r)y_2 - \frac{1}{4}(1 - r)y_3 - \frac{1}{4}(1 + r)y_4$$

Therefore, for any value r and s, $-1 \le r \le +1$ and $-1 \le s \le +1$, we can form the Jacobian operator $\mathbf{J}$ by using the expressions shown for $\partial x/\partial r$, $\partial x/\partial s$, and $\partial y/\partial r$, $\partial y/\partial s$. Assume that we evaluate $\mathbf{J}$ at $r = r_i$ and $s = s_j$ and denote the operator by $\mathbf{J}_{ij}$ and its determinant by $\det \mathbf{J}_{ij}$. Then we have

$$\begin{bmatrix} \dfrac{\partial}{\partial x} \\[2mm] \dfrac{\partial}{\partial y} \end{bmatrix}_{\substack{\text{at } r=r_i \\ s=s_j}} = \mathbf{J}_{ij}^{-1} \begin{bmatrix} \dfrac{\partial}{\partial r} \\[2mm] \dfrac{\partial}{\partial s} \end{bmatrix}_{\substack{\text{at } r=r_i \\ s=s_j}}$$

To evaluate the element strains we use

$$\frac{\partial u}{\partial r} = \frac{1}{4}(1 + s)u_1 - \frac{1}{4}(1 + s)u_2 - \frac{1}{4}(1 - s)u_3 + \frac{1}{4}(1 - s)u_4$$

$$\frac{\partial u}{\partial s} = \frac{1}{4}(1 + r)u_1 + \frac{1}{4}(1 - r)u_2 - \frac{1}{4}(1 - r)u_3 - \frac{1}{4}(1 + r)u_4$$

$$\frac{\partial v}{\partial r} = \frac{1}{4}(1 + s)v_1 - \frac{1}{4}(1 + s)v_2 - \frac{1}{4}(1 - s)v_3 + \frac{1}{4}(1 - s)v_4$$

$$\frac{\partial v}{\partial s} = \frac{1}{4}(1 + r)v_1 + \frac{1}{4}(1 - r)v_2 - \frac{1}{4}(1 - r)v_3 - \frac{1}{4}(1 + r)v_4$$

Therefore,

$$\begin{bmatrix} \dfrac{\partial u}{\partial x} \\ \dfrac{\partial u}{\partial y} \end{bmatrix}_{\substack{\text{at } r=r_i \\ s=s_j}} = \frac{1}{4}\mathbf{J}_{ij}^{-1} \begin{bmatrix} 1 + s_j & 0 & -(1 + s_j) & 0 & -(1 - s_j) & 0 & 1 - s_j & 0 \\ 1 + r_i & 0 & 1 - r_i & 0 & -(1 - r_i) & 0 & -(1 + r_i) & 0 \end{bmatrix} \hat{\mathbf{u}} \tag{a}$$

and

$$\begin{bmatrix} \dfrac{\partial v}{\partial x} \\ \dfrac{\partial v}{\partial y} \end{bmatrix}_{\substack{\text{at } r=r_i \\ s=s_j}} = \frac{1}{4}\mathbf{J}_{ij}^{-1} \begin{bmatrix} 0 & 1 + s_j & 0 & -(1 + s_j) & 0 & -(1 - s_j) & 0 & 1 - s_j \\ 0 & 1 + r_i & 0 & 1 - r_i & 0 & -(1 - r_i) & 0 & -(1 + r_i) \end{bmatrix} \hat{\mathbf{u}} \tag{b}$$

where

$$\hat{\mathbf{u}}^T = \begin{bmatrix} u_1 & v_1 & u_2 & v_2 & u_3 & v_3 & u_4 & v_4 \end{bmatrix}$$

Evaluating the relations in (a) and (b), we can establish the strain-displacement transformation matrix at the point (r_i, s_j); i.e., we obtain

$$\boldsymbol{\epsilon}_{ij} = \mathbf{B}_{ij}\hat{\mathbf{u}}$$

where the subscripts i and j indicate that the strain-displacement transformation is evaluated at the point (r_i, s_j). For example, if $x = r$, $y = s$ (i.e., the stiffness matrix of a square element is required that has side lengths equal to 2), the Jacobian operator is the identity matrix, and hence hence

$$B_{ij} = \frac{1}{4} \begin{bmatrix} 1 + s_j & 0 & -(1 + s_j) & 0 & -(1 - s_j) & 0 & 1 - s_j & 0 \\ 0 & 1 + r_i & 0 & 1 - r_i & 0 & -(1 - r_i) & 0 & -(1 + r_i) \\ 1 + r_i & 1 + s_j & 1 - r_i & -(1 + s_j) & -(1 - r_i) & -(1 - s_j) & -(1 + r_i) & 1 - s_j \end{bmatrix}$$

The matrix $\mathbf{F}_{ij}$ in (5.30) is now simply

$$\mathbf{F}_{ij} = \mathbf{B}_{ij}^T \mathbf{C} \mathbf{B}_{ij} \det \mathbf{J}_{ij}$$

where the material property matrix $\mathbf{C}$ is given in Table 4.3. In the case of plane stress or plane strain conditions, we integrate in the r, s plane and assume that the function $\mathbf{F}$ is constant through the thickness of the element. The stiffness matrix of the element is therefore

$$\mathbf{K} = \sum_{i,j} t_{ij}\alpha_{ij}\mathbf{F}_{ij}$$

where t_{ij} is the thickness of the element at the sampling point (r_i, s_j) $(t_{ij} = 1.0$ in plane strain analysis). With the matrices $\mathbf{F}_{ij}$ as given and the weighting factors α_{ij} available, the required stiffness matrix can readily be evaluated.

For the actual implementation it should be noted that in the evaluation of $\mathbf{J}_{ij}$ and of the matrices defining the displacement derivatives in (a) and (b), only the eight possible derivatives of the interpolation functions $h_1, \ldots, h_4$ are required. Therefore, it is expedient to calculate these derivatives corresponding to the point (r_i, s_j) once at the start of the evaluation of $\mathbf{B}_{ij}$ and use them whenever they are required.

It should also be realized that considering the specific point (r_i, s_j), the relations in (a) and (b) may be written, respectively, as

$$
\left.
\begin{aligned}
\frac{\partial u}{\partial x} &= \sum_{i=1}^{4} \frac{\partial h_i}{\partial x} u_i \\
\frac{\partial u}{\partial y} &= \sum_{i=1}^{4} \frac{\partial h_i}{\partial y} u_i
\end{aligned}
\right\} \tag{c}
$$

and

$$
\left.
\begin{aligned}
\frac{\partial v}{\partial x} &= \sum_{i=1}^{4} \frac{\partial h_i}{\partial x} v_i \\
\frac{\partial v}{\partial y} &= \sum_{i=1}^{4} \frac{\partial h_i}{\partial y} v_i
\end{aligned}
\right\} \tag{d}
$$

Hence, we have

$$
\mathbf{B} = \begin{bmatrix}
\dfrac{\partial h_1}{\partial x} & 0 & \dfrac{\partial h_2}{\partial x} & 0 & \dfrac{\partial h_3}{\partial x} & 0 & \dfrac{\partial h_4}{\partial x} & 0 \\[2ex]
0 & \dfrac{\partial h_1}{\partial y} & 0 & \dfrac{\partial h_2}{\partial y} & 0 & \dfrac{\partial h_3}{\partial y} & 0 & \dfrac{\partial h_4}{\partial y} \\[2ex]
\dfrac{\partial h_1}{\partial y} & \dfrac{\partial h_1}{\partial x} & \dfrac{\partial h_2}{\partial y} & \dfrac{\partial h_2}{\partial x} & \dfrac{\partial h_3}{\partial y} & \dfrac{\partial h_3}{\partial x} & \dfrac{\partial h_4}{\partial y} & \dfrac{\partial h_4}{\partial x}
\end{bmatrix} \tag{e}
$$

where it is implied that in (c) and (d), the derivatives are evaluated at point (r_i, s_j), and therefore in (e), we have, in fact, the matrix $\mathbf{B}_{ij}$.

EXAMPLE 5.6: Derive the expressions needed for the evaluation of the mass matrix of the element considered in Example 5.5.

The mass matrix of the element is given by

$$
\mathbf{M} = \sum_{i,j} \alpha_{ij} t_{ij} \mathbf{F}_{ij}
$$

where

$$
\mathbf{F}_{ij} = \rho_{ij} \mathbf{H}_{ij}^T \mathbf{H}_{ij} \det \mathbf{J}_{ij}
$$

and $\mathbf{H}_{ij}$ is the displacement interpolation matrix. The displacement interpolation functions for u and v of the four-node element have been given in Example 5.5, and we have

$$
\mathbf{H}_{ij} = \frac{1}{4}\begin{bmatrix}
(1 + r_i)(1 + s_j) & 0 & (1 - r_i)(1 + s_j) & 0 \\
0 & (1 + r_i)(1 + s_j) & 0 & (1 - r_i)(1 + s_j) \\
(1 - r_i)(1 - s_j) & 0 & (1 + r_i)(1 - s_j) & 0 \\
0 & (1 - r_i)(1 - s_j) & 0 & (1 + r_i)(1 - s_j)
\end{bmatrix}
$$

The determinant of the Jacobian matrix, det $\mathbf{J}_{ij}$, was given in Example 5.5, and ρ_{ij} is the mass density at the sampling point (r_i, s_j). Therefore, all required variables for the evaluation of the mass matrix have been defined.

EXAMPLE 5.7: Derive the expressions needed for the evaluation of the body force vector $\mathbf{R}_B$ and the initial stress vector $\mathbf{R}_I$ of the element considered in Example 5.5.

These vectors are obtained using the matrices $\mathbf{H}_{ij}$, $\mathbf{B}_{ij}$, and $\mathbf{J}_{ij}$ defined in Examples 5.5 and 5.6; i.e., we have

$$\mathbf{R}_B = \sum_{i,j} \alpha_{ij} t_{ij} \mathbf{H}_{ij}^T \mathbf{f}_{ij}^B \, \det \mathbf{J}_{ij}$$

$$\mathbf{R}_I = \sum_{i,j} \alpha_{ij} t_{ij} \mathbf{B}_{ij}^T \boldsymbol{\tau}_{ij}^I \, \det \mathbf{J}_{ij}$$

where $\mathbf{f}_{ij}^B$ and $\boldsymbol{\tau}_{ij}^I$ are the body force vector and initial stress vector evaluated at the integration sampling points.

EXAMPLE 5.8: Derive the expressions needed in the calculation of the surface force vector $\mathbf{R}_S$ when the element edge 1-2 of the four-node isoparametric element considered in Example 5.5 is loaded as shown in Fig. E5.8.

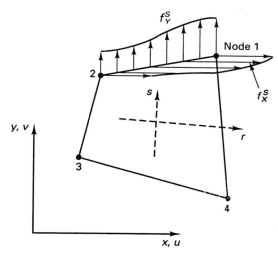

Figure E5.8   Traction distribution along edge 1-2 of a four-node element

The first step is to establish the displacement interpolations. Since $s = +1$ at the edge 1-2, we have, using the interpolation functions given in Example 5.5,

$$u^S = \tfrac{1}{2}(1 + r)u_1 + \tfrac{1}{2}(1 - r)u_2$$

$$v^S = \tfrac{1}{2}(1 + r)v_1 + \tfrac{1}{2}(1 - r)v_2$$

Hence, to evaluate $\mathbf{R}_S$ in (5.34) we can use

$$\mathbf{H}^S = \begin{bmatrix} \tfrac{1}{2}(1+r) & 0 & \tfrac{1}{2}(1-r) & 0 & 0 & 0 & 0 & 0 \\ 0 & \tfrac{1}{2}(1+r) & 0 & \tfrac{1}{2}(1-r) & 0 & 0 & 0 & 0 \end{bmatrix}$$

and

$$\mathbf{f}^S = \begin{bmatrix} f_x^S \\ f_y^S \end{bmatrix}$$

where f_x^S and f_y^S are the x and y components of the applied surface force. These components may have been given as a function of r.

For the evaluation of the integral in (5.34), we also need the differential surface area dS expressed in the r, s natural coordinate system. If t_r is the thickness, $dS = t_r \, dl$, where dl is a differential length,

$$dl = \det \mathbf{J}^S \, dr; \qquad \det \mathbf{J}^S = \left[\left(\frac{\partial x}{\partial r} \right)^2 + \left(\frac{\partial y}{\partial r} \right)^2 \right]^{1/2}$$

But the derivatives $\partial x / \partial r$ and $\partial y / \partial r$ have been given in Example 5.5. Using $s = +1$, we have, in this case,

$$\frac{\partial x}{\partial r} = \frac{x_1 - x_2}{2}; \qquad \frac{\partial y}{\partial r} = \frac{y_1 - y_2}{2}$$

Although the vector $\mathbf{R}_S$ could in this case be evaluated in a closed-form solution (provided that the functions used in $\mathbf{f}^S$ are simple), in order to keep generality in the program that calculates $\mathbf{R}_S$, it is expedient to use numerical integration. This way, variable-number-nodes elements can be implemented in an elegant manner in one program. Thus, using the notation defined in this section, we have

$$\mathbf{R}_S = \sum_i \alpha_i t_{ri} \mathbf{F}_i$$

$$\mathbf{F}_i = \mathbf{H}_i^{S^T} \mathbf{f}_i^S \det \mathbf{J}_i^S$$

It is noted that in this case only one-dimensional numerical integration is required because s is not a variable.

EXAMPLE 5.9:   Explain how the expressions given in Examples 5.5 to 5.7 need be modified when the element considered is an axisymmetric element.

In this case two modifications are necessary. First, we consider 1 radian of the structure. Hence, the thickness to be employed in all integrations is that corresponding to 1 radian, which means that at an integration point the thickness is equal to the radius at that point:

$$t_{ij} = \sum_{k=1}^{4} h_k \bigg|_{r_i, s_j} x_k \tag{a}$$

Second, it is recognized that also circumferential strains and stresses are developed (see Table 4.2). Hence, the strain-displacement matrix must be augmented by one row for the hoop strain u/R; i.e., we have

$$\mathbf{B} = \begin{bmatrix} \cdots & & & & & & & \cdots \\ \dfrac{h_1}{t} & 0 & \dfrac{h_2}{t} & 0 & \dfrac{h_3}{t} & 0 & \dfrac{h_4}{t} & 0 \end{bmatrix} \tag{b}$$

where the first three rows have already been defined in Example 5.5 and t is equal to the radius. To obtain the strain-displacement matrix at integration point (i, j) we use (a) to evaluate t and substitute into (b).

EXAMPLE 5.10:   Calculate the nodal point forces of the four-node axisymmetric finite element shown in Fig. E5.10 when the element is subjected to centrifugal loading.

Here we want to evaluate

$$\mathbf{R}_B = \int_V \mathbf{H}^T \mathbf{f}^B \, dV$$

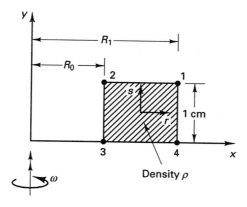

Figure E5.10 Four-node axisymmetric element rotating at angular velocity ω (rad/sec)

Density ρ

where
$$f_x^B = \rho\omega^2 R; \qquad f_y^B = 0$$
$$R = \tfrac{1}{2}(1 - r)R_0 + \tfrac{1}{2}(1 + r)R_1$$

$$\mathbf{H} = \begin{bmatrix} h_1 & 0 & h_2 & 0 & h_3 & 0 & h_4 & 0 \\ 0 & h_1 & 0 & h_2 & 0 & h_3 & 0 & h_4 \end{bmatrix}; \qquad \mathbf{J} = \begin{bmatrix} \dfrac{R_1 - R_0}{2} & 0 \\ 0 & \dfrac{1}{2} \end{bmatrix}$$

and the h_i are defined in Fig. 5.4. Also, considering 1 radian,

$$dV = \det \mathbf{J} \, dr \, ds \, R = \left(\frac{R_1 - R_0}{4}\right) dr \, ds \left(\frac{R_1 + R_0}{2} + \frac{R_1 - R_0}{2} r\right)$$

Hence,

$$\mathbf{R}_B = \frac{\rho\omega^2(R_1 - R_0)}{64} \int_{r=-1}^{+1} \int_{s=-1}^{+1} \begin{bmatrix} (1 + r)(1 + s) & 0 \\ 0 & (1 + r)(1 + s) \\ (1 - r)(1 + s) & 0 \\ 0 & (1 - r)(1 + s) \\ (1 - r)(1 - s) & 0 \\ 0 & (1 - r)(1 - s) \\ (1 + r)(1 - s) & 0 \\ 0 & (1 + r)(1 - s) \end{bmatrix}$$
$$\left[(R_1 + R_0) + (R_1 - R_0)r\right]^2 \begin{bmatrix} 1 \\ 0 \end{bmatrix} dr \, ds$$

If we let $A = R_1 + R_0$ and $B = R_1 - R_0$, we have

$$\mathbf{R}_B = \frac{\rho\omega^2 B}{64} \begin{bmatrix} \tfrac{2}{3}(6A^2 + 4AB + 2B^2) \\ 0 \\ \tfrac{2}{3}(6A^2 - 4AB + 2B^2) \\ 0 \\ \tfrac{2}{3}(6A^2 - 4AB + 2B^2) \\ 0 \\ \tfrac{2}{3}(6A^2 + 4AB + 2B^2) \\ 0 \end{bmatrix}$$

EXAMPLE 5.11:   The four-node plane stress element shown in Fig. E5.11 is subjected to the given temperature distribution. If the temperature corresponding to the stress-free state is θ_0, evaluate the nodal point forces to which the element must be subjected so that there are no nodal point displacements.

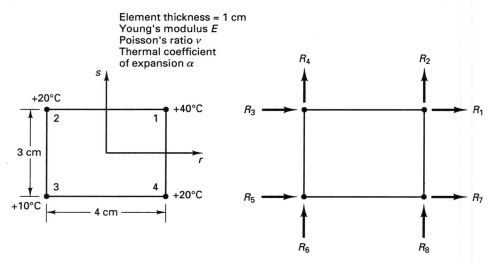

Element thickness = 1 cm
Young's modulus E
Poisson's ratio ν
Thermal coefficient
of expansion α

Figure E5.11   Nodal point forces due to initial temperature distribution

In this case we have for the total stresses, due to total strains $\boldsymbol{\epsilon}$ and thermal strains $\boldsymbol{\epsilon}^{\text{th}}$,

$$\boldsymbol{\tau} = \mathbf{C}(\boldsymbol{\epsilon} - \boldsymbol{\epsilon}^{\text{th}}) \tag{a}$$

where $\epsilon_{xx}^{\text{th}} = \alpha(\theta - \theta_0)$, $\epsilon_{yy}^{\text{th}} = \alpha(\theta - \theta_0)$, $\gamma_{xy}^{\text{th}} = 0$. If the nodal point displacements are zero, we have $\boldsymbol{\epsilon} = \mathbf{0}$, and the stresses due to the thermal strains can be thought of as initial stresses. Thus, the nodal point forces are

$$\mathbf{R}_I = \int_V \mathbf{B}^T \boldsymbol{\tau}^I \, dV$$

$$\boldsymbol{\tau}^I = -\frac{E\alpha}{1 - \nu^2}
\begin{bmatrix}
1 & \nu & 0 \\
\nu & 1 & 0 \\
0 & 0 & \dfrac{1 - \nu}{2}
\end{bmatrix}
\begin{bmatrix}
1 \\
1 \\
0
\end{bmatrix}
\left\{ \left(\sum_{i=1}^{4} h_i \theta_i \right) - \theta_0 \right\}$$

and the h_i are the interpolation functions defined in Fig. 5.4. Also,

$$\mathbf{J} = \begin{bmatrix} 2 & 0 \\ 0 & 1.5 \end{bmatrix}; \qquad \mathbf{J}^{-1} = \begin{bmatrix} \frac{1}{2} & 0 \\ 0 & \frac{2}{3} \end{bmatrix}; \qquad \det \mathbf{J} = 3$$

$$\mathbf{B} = \begin{bmatrix}
\dfrac{1 + s}{8} & 0 & -\dfrac{1 + s}{8} & 0 & -\dfrac{1 - s}{8} & 0 & \dfrac{1 - s}{8} & 0 \\
0 & \dfrac{1 + r}{6} & 0 & \dfrac{1 - r}{6} & 0 & -\dfrac{1 - r}{6} & 0 & -\dfrac{1 + r}{6} \\
\dfrac{1 + r}{6} & \dfrac{1 + s}{8} & \dfrac{1 - r}{6} & -\dfrac{1 + s}{8} & -\dfrac{1 - r}{6} & -\dfrac{1 - s}{8} & -\dfrac{1 + r}{6} & \dfrac{1 - s}{8}
\end{bmatrix}$$

Hence,

$$\mathbf{R}_I = \int_{-1}^{+1} \int_{-1}^{+1} - \begin{bmatrix} \dfrac{1+s}{8} & 0 & \dfrac{1+r}{6} \\[2mm] 0 & \dfrac{1+r}{6} & \dfrac{1+s}{8} \\[2mm] -\dfrac{1+s}{8} & 0 & \dfrac{1-r}{6} \\[2mm] 0 & \dfrac{1-r}{6} & -\dfrac{1+s}{8} \\[2mm] -\dfrac{1-s}{8} & 0 & -\dfrac{1-r}{6} \\[2mm] 0 & -\dfrac{1-r}{6} & -\dfrac{1-s}{8} \\[2mm] \dfrac{1-s}{8} & 0 & -\dfrac{1+r}{6} \\[2mm] 0 & -\dfrac{1+r}{6} & \dfrac{1-s}{8} \end{bmatrix} \begin{bmatrix} 1+\nu \\ 1+\nu \\ 0 \end{bmatrix} \dfrac{E\alpha}{1-\nu^2}$$

$$[2.5(s+3)(r+3) - \theta_0]3 \; dr \; ds$$

$$\mathbf{R}_I = -\dfrac{E\alpha}{(1-\nu)} \begin{bmatrix} 37.5 - 1.5\theta_0 \\ 50 - 2\theta_0 \\ -37.5 + 1.5\theta_0 \\ 40 - 2\theta_0 \\ -30 + 1.5\theta_0 \\ -40 + 2\theta_0 \\ +30 - 1.5\theta_0 \\ -50 + 2\theta_0 \end{bmatrix}$$

The calculation of the initial stress force vector as performed here is a typical step in a thermal stress analysis. In a complete thermal stress analysis the temperatures are calculated as described in Section 7.2, the element load vectors due to the thermal effects are evaluated as illustrated in this example, and the solution of the equilibrium equations (4.17) of the complete element assemblage then yields the nodal point displacements. The element total strains $\boldsymbol{\epsilon}$ are evaluated from the nodal point displacements and then, using (a), the final element stresses are calculated.

EXAMPLE 5.12:   Consider the elements in Fig. E5.12. Evaluate the consistent nodal point forces corresponding to the surface loading (assuming that the nodal point forces are positive when acting in the direction of the pressure).

Here we want to evaluate

$$\mathbf{R}_S = \int_S \mathbf{H}^{S^T} \mathbf{f}^S \; dS$$

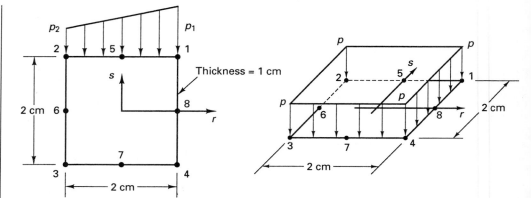

(a) Two-dimensional element subjected to linearly varying pressure along one side

(b) Flat surface of three-dimensional element subjected to constant pressure p

Figure E5.12   Two- and three-dimensional elements subjected to pressure loading

Consider first the two-dimensional element. Since $s = +1$ at the edge 1-2, we have, using the interpolation functions for the eight-node element (see Fig. 5.4),

$$h_5 = \tfrac{1}{2}(1 - r^2)(1 + s)|_{s=+1} = 1 - r^2$$

$$h_1 = \tfrac{1}{4}(1 + r)(1 + s)(r + s - 1)|_{s=+1} = \tfrac{1}{2}r(1 + r)$$

$$h_2 = \tfrac{1}{4}(1 - r)(1 + s)(s - r - 1)|_{s=+1} = -\tfrac{1}{2}r(1 - r)$$

which are equal to the interpolation functions of the three-node bar in Fig. E5.2. Hence

$$\begin{bmatrix} u^S \\ v^S \end{bmatrix} = \begin{bmatrix} \tfrac{1}{2}r(1 + r) & 0 & -\tfrac{1}{2}r(1 - r) & 0 & (1 - r^2) & 0 \\ 0 & \tfrac{1}{2}r(1 + r) & 0 & -\tfrac{1}{2}r(1 - r) & 0 & (1 - r^2) \end{bmatrix} \begin{bmatrix} u_1 \\ v_1 \\ u_2 \\ v_2 \\ u_5 \\ v_5 \end{bmatrix}$$

Also, $$\mathbf{f}^S = \begin{bmatrix} f_r^S \\ f_s^S \end{bmatrix} = \begin{bmatrix} 0 \\ \tfrac{1}{2}(1 + r)p_1 + \tfrac{1}{2}(1 - r)p_2 \end{bmatrix}; \qquad \det \mathbf{J}^S = 1$$

Hence,

$$\mathbf{R}_S = \int_{-1}^{+1} \frac{t}{2} \begin{bmatrix} r(1 + r) & 0 \\ 0 & r(1 + r) \\ -r(1 - r) & 0 \\ 0 & -r(1 - r) \\ 2(1 - r^2) & 0 \\ 0 & 2(1 - r^2) \end{bmatrix} \frac{1}{2}\begin{bmatrix} 0 \\ (1 + r)p_1 + (1 - r)p_2 \end{bmatrix} dr$$

$$\mathbf{R}_S = \frac{1}{3} \begin{bmatrix} 0 \\ p_1 \\ 0 \\ p_2 \\ 0 \\ 2(p_1 + p_2) \end{bmatrix} \tag{a}$$

For the three-dimensional element we proceed similarly. Since the surface is flat and the loading is normal to it, only the nodal point forces normal to the surface are nonzero [see also (a)]. Also, by symmetry, we know that the forces at nodes 1, 2, 3, 4 and 5, 6, 7, 8 are equal, respectively. Using the interpolation functions of Fig. 5.4, we have for the force at node 1,

$$R_1 = p \int_{-1}^{+1} \int_{-1}^{+1} \frac{1}{4}(1 + r)(1 + s)(r + s - 1) \, dr \, ds = -\frac{1}{3}p$$

and for the force at node 5,

$$R_5 = p \int_{-1}^{+1} \int_{-1}^{+1} \frac{1}{2}(1 - r^2)(1 + s) \, dr \, ds = \frac{4}{3}p$$

The total pressure loading on the surface is $4p$, which, as a check, is equal to the sum of all the nodal point forces. However, it should be noted that the consistent nodal point forces at the corners of the element act in the direction opposite that of the pressure!

EXAMPLE 5.13: Calculate the deflection u_A of the structural model shown in Fig. E5.13.

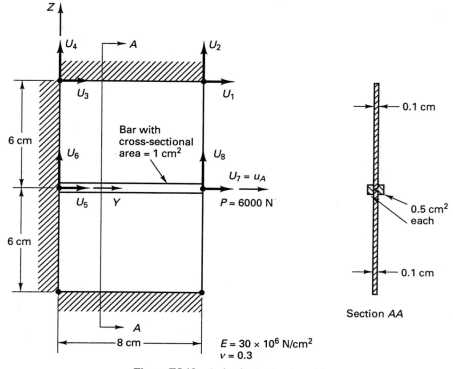

Figure E5.13 A simple structural model

Because of the symmetry and boundary conditions, we need to evaluate only the stiffness coefficient corresponding to u_A. Here we have for the four-node element,

$$\mathbf{J} = \begin{bmatrix} 4 & 0 \\ 0 & 3 \end{bmatrix}; \qquad \mathbf{B} = \frac{1}{48} \left[\cdots \begin{array}{c} 3(1-s) \\ 0 \\ -4(1+r) \end{array} \cdots \right]$$

$$k_{77} = \int_{-1}^{+1} \int_{-1}^{+1} \left(\frac{1}{48}\right)^2 \frac{E}{1-\nu^2} [3(1-s) \mid 0 \mid -4(1+r)] \begin{bmatrix} 3(1-s) \\ 3\nu(1-s) \\ -2(1-\nu)(1+r) \end{bmatrix}$$

$$(12)(0.1) \; dr \; ds$$

or
$$k_{77} = 1,336,996.34 \text{ N/cm}$$

Also, the stiffness of the truss is AE/L, or

$$k = \frac{(1)(30 \times 10^6)}{8} = 3,750,000 \text{ N/cm}$$

Hence
$$k_{\text{total}} = 6.424 \times 10^6 \text{ N/cm}$$

and
$$u_A = 9.34 \times 10^{-4} \text{ cm}$$

EXAMPLE 5.14:   Consider the five-node element in Fig. E5.14. Evaluate the consistent nodal point forces corresponding to the stresses given.

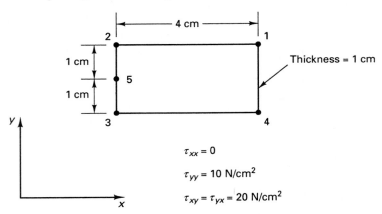

$\tau_{xx} = 0$

$\tau_{yy} = 10 \text{ N/cm}^2$

$\tau_{xy} = \tau_{yx} = 20 \text{ N/cm}^2$

Figure E5.14   Five-node element with stresses given

Using the interpolation functions in Fig. 5.4, we can evaluate the strain-displacement matrix of the element:

$$\mathbf{B} = \frac{1}{8} \begin{bmatrix} (1+s) & 0 & -s(1+s) & 0 & s(1-s) \\ 0 & 2(1+r) & 0 & 2(1-r)(1+2s) & 0 \\ 2(1+r) & (1+s) & 2(1-r)(1+2s) & -s(1+s) & -2(1-r)(1-2s) \end{bmatrix}$$

$$\begin{bmatrix} 0 & (1-s) & 0 & -2(1-s^2) & 0 \\ -2(1-r)(1-2s) & 0 & -2(1+r) & 0 & -8(1-r)s \\ s(1-s) & -2(1+r) & (1-s) & -8(1-r)s & -2(1-s^2) \end{bmatrix}$$

where we used
$$\mathbf{J} = \begin{bmatrix} 2 & 0 \\ 0 & 1 \end{bmatrix}$$

The required nodal point forces can now be evaluated using (5.35); hence,

$$\mathbf{R}_I = \int_{-1}^{+1} \int_{-1}^{+1} \mathbf{B}^T \begin{bmatrix} 0 \\ 10 \\ 20 \end{bmatrix} (2) \, dr \, ds$$

which gives

$$\mathbf{R}_I^T = \begin{bmatrix} 40 & 40 & 40 & \frac{40}{3} & -40 & -\frac{80}{3} & -40 & 0 & 0 & -\frac{80}{3} \end{bmatrix}$$

It should be noted that the forces in this vector are also equal to the nodal point consistent forces that correspond to the (constant) surface tractions, which are in equilibrium with the internal stresses given in Fig. E.5.14.

Earlier we mentioned briefly the possible use of *subparametric* elements: here the geometry is interpolated to a lower degree than the displacements. In the above examples, the nodes corresponding to the higher-order interpolation functions (nodes 5 and higher for the two-dimensional elements) were always placed at their "natural" positions so that the Jacobian matrix would be the same if, for the geometry interpolation, only the "basic" lower-order functions were used. Hence, in this case the subparametric two-dimensional element, using only the four corner nodes for the interpolation of the geometry, gives the same element matrices as the isoparametric element. For instance, in Example 5.14, the Jacobian matrix $\mathbf{J}$ would be the same using only the basic four-node interpolation functions, and hence the vector $\mathbf{R}_I$ for the subparametric element (using the four corner nodes for the geometry interpolation and the five nodes for the displacement interpolation) would be the same as for the isoparametric five-node element.

However, while the use of subparametric elements decreases somewhat the computational effort, such use also limits the generality of the finite element discretization and in addition complicates the solution procedures considerably in geometrically nonlinear analysis (where the new geometry of an element is obtained by adding the displacements to the previous geometry; see Chapter 6).

5.3.2 Triangular Elements

In the previous section we discussed quadrilateral isoparametric elements that can be used to model very general geometries. However, in some cases the use of triangular or wedge elements may be attractive. Triangular elements can be formulated using different approaches, which we briefly discuss in this section.

Triangular Elements Formulated by Collapsing Quadrilateral Elements

Since the elements discussed in Section 5.3.1 can be distorted, as shown for example in Fig. 5.2, a natural way of generating triangular elements appears to be to simply distort the basic quadrilateral element into the required triangular form (see Fig. 5.7). This is achieved in practice by assigning the same global node to two corner nodes of the element. We demonstrate this procedure in the following example.

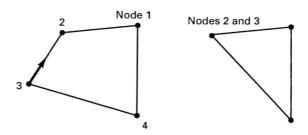

(a) Degeneration of 4-node to 3-node two-
dimensional element

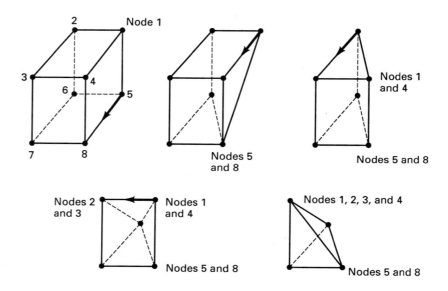

(b) Degenerate forms of 8-node three-
dimensional element

Figure 5.7   Degenerate forms of four- and eight-node elements of Figs. 5.4 and 5.5

EXAMPLE 5.15:   Show that by collapsing the side 1-2 of the four-node quadrilateral element in Fig. E5.15 a constant strain triangle is obtained.

Using the interpolation functions of Fig. 5.4, we have

$$x = \tfrac{1}{4}(1 + r)(1 + s)x_1 + \tfrac{1}{4}(1 - r)(1 + s)x_2 + \tfrac{1}{4}(1 - r)(1 - s)x_3 + \tfrac{1}{4}(1 + r)(1 - s)x_4$$

$$y = \tfrac{1}{4}(1 + r)(1 + s)y_1 + \tfrac{1}{4}(1 - r)(1 + s)y_2 + \tfrac{1}{4}(1 - r)(1 - s)y_3 + \tfrac{1}{4}(1 + r)(1 - s)y_4$$

Thus, using the conditions $x_1 = x_2$ and $y_1 = y_2$, we obtain

$$x = \tfrac{1}{2}(1 + s)x_2 + \tfrac{1}{4}(1 - r)(1 - s)x_3 + \tfrac{1}{4}(1 + r)(1 - s)x_4$$

$$y = \tfrac{1}{2}(1 + s)y_2 + \tfrac{1}{4}(1 - r)(1 - s)y_3 + \tfrac{1}{4}(1 + r)(1 - s)y_4$$

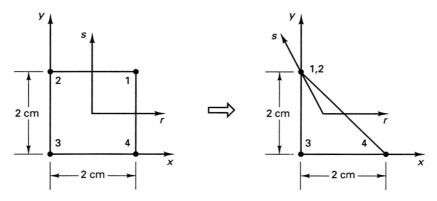

Figure E5.15   Collapsing a plane stress four-node element to a triangular element

and hence with the nodal coordinates given in Fig. E5.15,

$$x = \tfrac{1}{2}(1 + r)(1 - s)$$

$$y = 1 + s$$

It follows that

$$\frac{\partial x}{\partial r} = \frac{1}{2}(1 - s) \qquad \frac{\partial y}{\partial r} = 0$$

$$\frac{\partial x}{\partial s} = -\frac{1}{2}(1 + r) \qquad \frac{\partial y}{\partial s} = 1$$

$$; \qquad \mathbf{J} = \frac{1}{2}\begin{bmatrix} (1 - s) & 0 \\ -(1 + r) & 2 \end{bmatrix}; \qquad \mathbf{J}^{-1} = \begin{bmatrix} \dfrac{2}{1 - s} & 0 \\ \dfrac{1 + r}{1 - s} & 1 \end{bmatrix}$$

Using the isoparametric assumption, we also have

$$u = \tfrac{1}{2}(1 + s)u_2 + \tfrac{1}{4}(1 - r)(1 - s)u_3 + \tfrac{1}{4}(1 + r)(1 - s)u_4$$

$$v = \tfrac{1}{2}(1 + s)v_2 + \tfrac{1}{4}(1 - r)(1 - s)v_3 + \tfrac{1}{4}(1 + r)(1 - s)v_4$$

$$\frac{\partial u}{\partial r} = -\frac{1}{4}(1 - s)u_3 + \frac{1}{4}(1 - s)u_4; \qquad \frac{\partial v}{\partial r} = -\frac{1}{4}(1 - s)v_3 + \frac{1}{4}(1 - s)v_4$$

$$\frac{\partial u}{\partial s} = \frac{1}{2}u_2 - \frac{1}{4}(1 - r)u_3 - \frac{1}{4}(1 + r)u_4; \qquad \frac{\partial v}{\partial s} = \frac{1}{2}v_2 - \frac{1}{4}(1 - r)v_3 - \frac{1}{4}(1 + r)v_4$$

$$\begin{bmatrix} \dfrac{\partial}{\partial x} \\[2ex] \dfrac{\partial}{\partial y} \end{bmatrix} = \mathbf{J}^{-1}\begin{bmatrix} \dfrac{\partial}{\partial r} \\[2ex] \dfrac{\partial}{\partial s} \end{bmatrix}$$

Hence,

$$\begin{bmatrix} \dfrac{\partial u}{\partial x} \\[2ex] \dfrac{\partial u}{\partial y} \end{bmatrix} = \begin{bmatrix} \dfrac{2}{1 - s} & 0 \\[2ex] \dfrac{1 + r}{1 - s} & 1 \end{bmatrix}\begin{bmatrix} 0 & 0 & -\dfrac{1}{4}(1 - s) & 0 & \dfrac{1}{4}(1 - s) & 0 \\[2ex] \dfrac{1}{2} & 0 & -\dfrac{1}{4}(1 - r) & 0 & -\dfrac{1}{4}(1 + r) & 0 \end{bmatrix}\begin{bmatrix} u_2 \\ v_2 \\ u_3 \\ v_3 \\ u_4 \\ v_4 \end{bmatrix}$$

and

$$\begin{bmatrix} \dfrac{\partial u}{\partial x} \\[2mm] \dfrac{\partial u}{\partial y} \end{bmatrix} = \begin{bmatrix} 0 & 0 & -\dfrac{1}{2} & 0 & \dfrac{1}{2} & 0 \\[2mm] \dfrac{1}{2} & 0 & -\dfrac{1}{2} & 0 & 0 & 0 \end{bmatrix} \begin{bmatrix} u_2 \\ \vdots \\ \vdots \\ u_4 \\ v_4 \end{bmatrix}$$

Similarly,

$$\begin{bmatrix} \dfrac{\partial v}{\partial x} \\[2mm] \dfrac{\partial v}{\partial y} \end{bmatrix} = \begin{bmatrix} 0 & 0 & 0 & -\dfrac{1}{2} & 0 & \dfrac{1}{2} \\[2mm] 0 & \dfrac{1}{2} & 0 & -\dfrac{1}{2} & 0 & 0 \end{bmatrix} \begin{bmatrix} u_2 \\ \vdots \\ \vdots \\ u_4 \\ v_4 \end{bmatrix}$$

So we obtain

$$\boldsymbol{\epsilon} = \begin{bmatrix} 0 & 0 & -\frac{1}{2} & 0 & \frac{1}{2} & 0 \\[1mm] 0 & \frac{1}{2} & 0 & -\frac{1}{2} & 0 & 0 \\[1mm] \frac{1}{2} & 0 & -\frac{1}{2} & -\frac{1}{2} & 0 & \frac{1}{2} \end{bmatrix} \begin{bmatrix} u_2 \\ v_2 \\ u_3 \\ v_3 \\ u_4 \\ v_4 \end{bmatrix}$$

For any values of u_2, v_2, u_3, v_3, and u_4, v_4 the strain vector is constant and independent of r, s. Thus, the triangular element is a constant strain triangle.

In the preceding example we considered only one specific case. However, using the same approach it is apparant that collapsing any one side of a four-node plane stress or plane strain element will always result in a constant strain triangle.

In considering the process of collapsing an element side, it is interesting to note that in the formulation used in Example 5.15 the matrix $\mathbf{J}$ is singular at $s = +1$, but that this singularity disappears when the strain-displacement matrix is calculated. A practical consequence is that if in a computer program the general formulation of the four-node element is employed to generate a constant strain triangle (as in Example 5.15), the stresses should not be calculated at the two local nodes that have been assigned the same global node. (Since the stresses are constant throughout the element, they are conveniently evaluated at the center of the element, i.e., at $r = 0$, $s = 0$.)

The same procedure can also be employed in three-dimensional analysis in order to obtain, from the basic eight-node element, wedge or tetrahedral elements. The procedure is illustrated in Fig. 5.7 and in the following example.

EXAMPLE 5.16:   Show that the three-dimensional tetrahedral element generated in Fig. E5.16 from the eight-node three-dimensional brick element is a constant strain element.

Here we proceed as in Example 5.15. Thus, using the interpolation functions of the brick element (see Fig. 5.5) and substituting the nodal point coordinates of the tetrahedron, we obtain

$$x = \tfrac{1}{4}(1 + r)(1 - s)(1 - t)$$

$$y = \tfrac{1}{2}(1 + s)(1 - t)$$

$$z = 1 + t$$

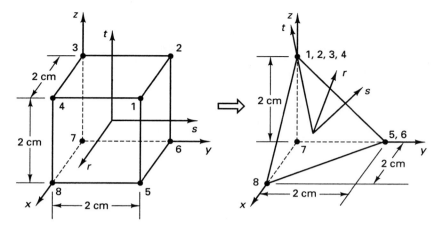

Figure E5.16   Collapsing an eight-node brick element into a tetrahedral element

Hence,
$$\mathbf{J} = \begin{bmatrix} \frac{1}{4}(1-s)(1-t) & 0 & 0 \\ -\frac{1}{4}(1+r)(1-t) & \frac{1}{2}(1-t) & 0 \\ -\frac{1}{4}(1+r)(1-s) & -\frac{1}{2}(1+s) & 1 \end{bmatrix};$$

$$\mathbf{J}^{-1} = \begin{bmatrix} \dfrac{4}{(1-s)(1-t)} & 0 & 0 \\ \dfrac{2(1+r)}{(1-s)(1-t)} & \dfrac{2}{1-t} & 0 \\ \dfrac{2(1+r)}{(1-s)(1-t)} & \dfrac{1+s}{1-t} & 1 \end{bmatrix} \tag{a}$$

Using the same interpolation functions for u, and the conditions that $u_1 = u_2 = u_3 = u_4$ and $u_5 = u_6$, we obtain

$$u = h_4^* u_4 + h_5^* u_5 + h_7^* u_7 + h_8^* u_8$$

with

$$h_4^* = \tfrac{1}{2}(1+t); \qquad h_5^* = \tfrac{1}{4}(1+s)(1-t);$$
$$h_7^* = \tfrac{1}{8}(1-r)(1-s)(1-t); \qquad h_8^* = \tfrac{1}{8}(1+r)(1-s)(1-t)$$

Similarly, we also have

$$v = h_4^* v_4 + h_5^* v_5 + h_7^* v_7 + h_8^* v_8$$
$$w = h_4^* w_4 + h_5^* w_5 + h_7^* w_7 + h_8^* w_8$$

Evaluating now the derivatives of the displacements u, v, and w with respect to r, s, and t, and using $\mathbf{J}^{-1}$ of (a), we obtain

$$
\begin{bmatrix}
\dfrac{\partial u}{\partial x} \\[2mm]
\dfrac{\partial v}{\partial y} \\[2mm]
\dfrac{\partial w}{\partial z} \\[2mm]
\dfrac{\partial u}{\partial y}+\dfrac{\partial v}{\partial x} \\[2mm]
\dfrac{\partial v}{\partial z}+\dfrac{\partial w}{\partial y} \\[2mm]
\dfrac{\partial u}{\partial z}+\dfrac{\partial w}{\partial x}
\end{bmatrix}
=
\begin{bmatrix}
0 & 0 & 0 & 0 & 0 & 0 & -\tfrac{1}{2} & 0 & 0 & \tfrac{1}{2} & 0 & 0 \\[1mm]
0 & 0 & 0 & 0 & \tfrac{1}{2} & 0 & 0 & -\tfrac{1}{2} & 0 & 0 & 0 & 0 \\[1mm]
0 & 0 & \tfrac{1}{2} & 0 & 0 & 0 & 0 & 0 & -\tfrac{1}{2} & 0 & 0 & 0 \\[1mm]
0 & 0 & 0 & \tfrac{1}{2} & 0 & 0 & -\tfrac{1}{2} & -\tfrac{1}{2} & 0 & 0 & \tfrac{1}{2} & 0 \\[1mm]
0 & \tfrac{1}{2} & 0 & 0 & 0 & \tfrac{1}{2} & 0 & -\tfrac{1}{2} & -\tfrac{1}{2} & 0 & 0 & 0 \\[1mm]
\tfrac{1}{2} & 0 & 0 & 0 & 0 & 0 & -\tfrac{1}{2} & 0 & -\tfrac{1}{2} & 0 & 0 & \tfrac{1}{2}
\end{bmatrix}
\begin{bmatrix}
u_4 \\ v_4 \\ w_4 \\ \hline u_5 \\ v_5 \\ w_5 \\ \hline u_7 \\ v_7 \\ w_7 \\ \hline u_8 \\ v_8 \\ w_8
\end{bmatrix}
$$

Hence, the strains are constant for any nodal point displacements, which means that the element can represent only constant strain conditions.

The process of collapsing an element side, or in three-dimensional analysis a number of element sides, may directly yield a desired element, but when higher-order two- or three-dimensional elements are employed, some special considerations may be necessary regarding the interpolation functions used. Specifically, when the lower-order elements displayed in Fig. 5.7 are employed, spatially isotropic triangular and wedge elements are automatically generated, but this is not necessarily the case when using higher-order elements.

As an example, we consider the six-node triangular two-dimensional element obtained by collapsing one side of an eight-node element as shown in Fig. 5.8. If the triangular element has sides of equal length, we may want the element to be spatially isotropic; i.e.,

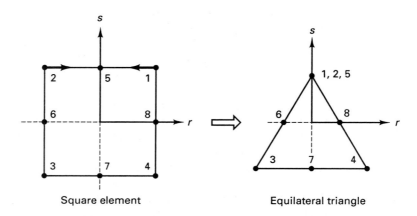

Square element   Equilateral triangle

Figure 5.8   Collapsing an eight-node element into a triangle

we may wish the internal element displacements u and v to vary in the same manner for each corner nodal displacement and each midside nodal displacement, respectively. However, the interpolation functions that are generated for the triangle when the side 1-2-5 of the square is simply collapsed do not fulfill the requirement that we should be able to change the numbering of the vertices without a change in the displacement assumptions. In order to fulfill this requirement, corrections need be applied to the interpolation functions of the nodes 3, 4, and 7 to obtain the final interpolations h_i^* of the triangular element (see Exercise 5.25),

$$h_1^* = \tfrac{1}{2}(1 + s) - \tfrac{1}{2}(1 - s^2)$$

$$h_3^* = \tfrac{1}{4}(1 - r)(1 - s) - \tfrac{1}{4}(1 - s^2)(1 - r) - \tfrac{1}{4}(1 - r^2)(1 - s) + \Delta h$$

$$h_4^* = \tfrac{1}{4}(1 + r)(1 - s) - \tfrac{1}{4}(1 - r^2)(1 - s) - \tfrac{1}{4}(1 - s^2)(1 + r) + \Delta h$$

$$h_6^* = \tfrac{1}{2}(1 - s^2)(1 - r) \qquad\qquad\qquad\qquad (5.36)$$

$$h_7^* = \tfrac{1}{2}(1 - r^2)(1 - s) - 2\Delta h$$

$$h_8^* = \tfrac{1}{2}(1 - s^2)(1 + r)$$

where we added the appropriate interpolations given in Fig. 5.4 and

$$\Delta h = \frac{(1 - r^2)(1 - s^2)}{8} \qquad\qquad\qquad\qquad (5.37)$$

Thus, to generate higher-order triangular elements by collapsing sides of square elements, it may be necessary to apply a correction to the interpolation functions used.

Triangular Elements in Fracture Mechanics

In the preceding considerations, we assumed that a spatially isotropic element was desirable because the element was to be employed in a finite element assemblage used to predict a somewhat homogeneous stress field. However, in some cases, very specific stress variations are to be predicted, and in such analyses a spatially nonisotropic element may be more effective. One area of analysis in which specific spatially nonisotropic elements are employed is the field of fracture mechanics. Here it is known that specific stress singularities exist at crack tips, and for the calculation of stress intensity factors or limit loads, the use of finite elements that contain the required stress singularities can be effective. Various elements of this sort have been designed, but very simple and attractive elements can be obtained by distorting the higher-order isoparametric elements (see R. D. Henshell and K. G. Shaw [A] and R. S. Barsoum [A, B]). Figure 5.9 shows two-dimensional isoparametric elements that have been employed with much success in linear and nonlinear fracture mechanics because they contain the $1/\sqrt{R}$ and $1/R$ strain singularities, respectively. We should note that these elements have the interpolation functions given in (5.36) but with $\Delta h = 0$. The same node-shifting and side-collapsing procedures can also be employed with higher-order three-dimensional elements in order to generate the required singularities. We demonstrate the procedure of node shifting to generate a strain singularity in the following example.

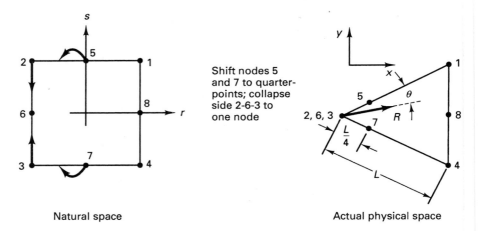

(a) Quarter-point triangular element with $1/\sqrt{R}$ strain singularity at node 2-6-3

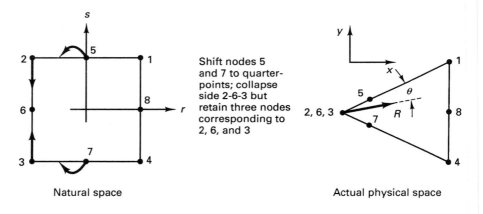

(b) Quarter-point triangular element with $1/\sqrt{R}$ and $1/R$ strain singularities at nodes 2, 6, and 3

Figure 5.9 Two-dimensional distorted (quarter point) isoparametric elements useful in fracture mechanics. Strain singularities are within the element for any angle θ. [Note that in (a) the one node (2-6-3) has two degrees of freedom, and that in (b) nodes 2, 3, and 6 each have two degrees of freedom.]

EXAMPLE 5.17: Consider the three-node truss element in Fig. E5.17. Show that when node 3 is specified to be at the quarter-point, the strain has a singularity of $1/\sqrt{x}$ at node 1.

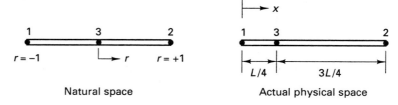

Figure E5.17 Quarter-point one-dimensional element

We have already considered a three-node truss in Example 5.2. Proceeding as before, we now have

$$x = \frac{r}{2}(1+r)L + (1 - r^2)\frac{L}{4}$$

or

$$x = \frac{L}{4}(1 + r)^2 \tag{a}$$

Hence,

$$\mathbf{J} = \left[\frac{L}{2} + \frac{r}{2}L\right]$$

and the strain-displacement matrix is [using (b) in Example 5.2]

$$\mathbf{B} = \left[\frac{1}{L/2 + rL/2}\right]\left[\left(-\frac{1}{2} + r\right)\quad\left(\frac{1}{2} + r\right)\quad -2r\right] \tag{b}$$

To show the $1/\sqrt{x}$ singularity we need to express r in terms of x. Using (a), we have

$$r = 2\sqrt{\frac{x}{L}} - 1$$

Substituting this value for r into (b), we obtain

$$\mathbf{B} = \left[\left(\frac{2}{L} - \frac{3}{2\sqrt{L}}\frac{1}{\sqrt{x}}\right)\quad\left(\frac{2}{L} - \frac{1}{2\sqrt{L}}\frac{1}{\sqrt{x}}\right)\quad\left(\frac{2}{\sqrt{L}}\frac{1}{\sqrt{x}} - \frac{4}{L}\right)\right]$$

Hence at $x = 0$ the quarter-point element in Fig. E5.17 has a strain singularity of order $1/\sqrt{x}$.

Triangular Elements by Area Coordinates

Although the procedure of distorting a rectangular isoparametric element to generate a triangular element can be effective in some cases as discussed above, triangular elements (and in particular spatially isotropic elements) can be constructed directly by using area coordinates. For the triangle in Fig. 5.10, the position of a typical interior point P with coordinates x and y is defined by the area coordinates

$$L_1 = \frac{A_1}{A}; \qquad L_2 = \frac{A_2}{A}; \qquad L_3 = \frac{A_3}{A} \tag{5.38}$$

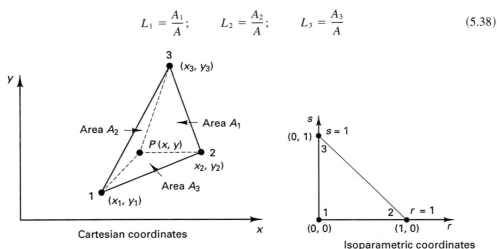

Figure 5.10 Description of three-node triangle

where the areas A_i, $i = 1, 2, 3$, are defined in the figure and A is the total area of the triangle. Thus, we also have

$$L_1 + L_2 + L_3 = 1 \tag{5.39}$$

Since element strains are obtained by taking derivatives with respect to the Cartesian coordinates, we need a relation that gives the area coordinates in terms of the coordinates x and y. Here we have

$$x = L_1 x_1 + L_2 x_2 + L_3 x_3 \tag{5.40}$$

$$y = L_1 y_1 + L_2 y_2 + L_3 y_3 \tag{5.41}$$

because these relations hold at points 1, 2, and 3 and x and y vary linearly in between. Using (5.39) to (5.41), we have

$$\begin{bmatrix} 1 \\ x \\ y \end{bmatrix} = \begin{bmatrix} 1 & 1 & 1 \\ x_1 & x_2 & x_3 \\ y_1 & y_2 & y_3 \end{bmatrix} \begin{bmatrix} L_1 \\ L_2 \\ L_3 \end{bmatrix} \tag{5.42}$$

which gives

$$L_i = \frac{1}{2A} (a_i + b_i x + c_i y); \qquad i = 1, 2, 3$$

where

$$2A = x_1 y_2 + x_2 y_3 + x_3 y_1 - y_1 x_2 - y_2 x_3 - y_3 x_1$$

$$a_1 = x_2 y_3 - x_3 y_2; \qquad a_2 = x_3 y_1 - x_1 y_3; \qquad a_3 = x_1 y_2 - x_2 y_1$$

$$b_1 = y_2 - y_3; \qquad b_2 = y_3 - y_1; \qquad b_3 = y_1 - y_2 \tag{5.43}$$

$$c_1 = x_3 - x_2; \qquad c_2 = x_1 - x_3; \qquad c_3 = x_2 - x_1$$

As must have been expected, these L_i are equal to the interpolation functions of a constant strain triangle. Thus, in summary we have for the three-node triangular element in Fig. 5.10,

$$u = \sum_{i=1}^{3} h_i u_i; \qquad x \equiv \sum_{i=1}^{3} h_i x_i$$

$$v = \sum_{i=1}^{3} h_i v_i; \qquad y \equiv \sum_{i=1}^{3} h_i y_i \tag{5.44}$$

where $h_i = L_i$, $i = 1, 2, 3$, and the h_i are functions of the coordinates x and y.

Using the relations in (5.44), the various finite element matrices of (5.27) to (5.35) can be directly evaluated. However, just as in the formulation of the quadrilateral elements (see Section 5.3.1), in practice, it is frequently expedient to use a natural coordinate space in order to describe the element coordinates and displacements. Using the natural coordinate system shown in Fig. 5.10, we have

$$h_1 = 1 - r - s; \qquad h_2 = r; \qquad h_3 = s \tag{5.45}$$

and the evaluation of the element matrices now involves a Jacobian transformation. Furthermore, all integrations are carried out over the natural coordinates; i.e., the r integrations go from 0 to 1 and the s integrations go from 0 to $(1 - r)$.

EXAMPLE 5.18: Using the isoparametric natural coordinate system in Fig. 5.10, establish the displacement and strain-displacement interpolation matrices of a three-node triangular element with

$$x_1 = 0; \qquad x_2 = 4; \qquad x_3 = 1$$
$$y_1 = 0; \qquad y_2 = 0; \qquad y_3 = 3$$

In this case we have, using (5.44),

$$x = 4r + s$$
$$y = 3s$$

Hence, using (5.23),

$$\mathbf{J} = \begin{bmatrix} 4 & 0 \\ 1 & 3 \end{bmatrix}$$

and

$$\frac{\partial}{\partial \mathbf{x}} = \frac{1}{12} \begin{bmatrix} 3 & 0 \\ -1 & 4 \end{bmatrix} \frac{\partial}{\partial \mathbf{r}}$$

It follows that

$$\mathbf{H} = \begin{bmatrix} (1 - r - s) & 0 & \vdots & r & 0 & \vdots & s & 0 \\ 0 & (1 - r - s) & \vdots & 0 & r & \vdots & 0 & s \end{bmatrix}$$

and

$$\mathbf{B} = \frac{1}{12} \begin{bmatrix} -3 & 0 & \vdots & 3 & 0 & \vdots & 0 & 0 \\ 0 & -3 & \vdots & 0 & -1 & \vdots & 0 & 4 \\ -3 & -3 & \vdots & -1 & 3 & \vdots & 4 & 0 \end{bmatrix}$$

By analogy to the formulation of higher-order quadrilateral elements, we can also directly formulate higher-order triangular elements. Using the natural coordinate system in Fig. 5.10, which reduces to

$$L_1 = 1 - r - s; \qquad L_2 = r; \qquad L_3 = s \qquad (5.46)$$

where the L_i are the area coordinates of the "unit triangle," the interpolation functions of a 3 to 6 variable-number-nodes element are given in Fig. 5.11. These functions are constructed in the usual way, namely, h_i must be unity at node i and zero at all other nodes (see Example 5.1).[2] The interpolation functions of still higher-order triangular elements are obtained in a similar manner. Then the "cubic bubble function" $L_1L_2L_3$ is also employed.

Using this approach we can now also directly construct the interpolation functions of three-dimensional tetrahedral elements. First, we note that in analogy to (5.46) we now employ *volume coordinates*

$$L_1 = 1 - r - s - t; \qquad L_2 = r$$
$$L_3 = s; \qquad L_4 = t \qquad (5.47)$$

where we may check that $L_1 + L_2 + L_3 + L_4 = 1$. The L_i in (5.47) are the interpolation functions of the four-node element in Fig. 5.12 in its natural space. The interpolation

---

[2] It is interesting to note that the functions of the six-node triangle in Fig. 5.11 are exactly those given in (5.36), provided the variables r and s in Fig. 5.11 are replaced by $\frac{1}{4}(1 + r)(1 - s)$ and $\frac{1}{2}(1 + s)$, respectively, in order to account for the different natural coordinate systems. Hence, the correction Δh in (5.36) can be evaluated from the functions in Fig. 5.11.

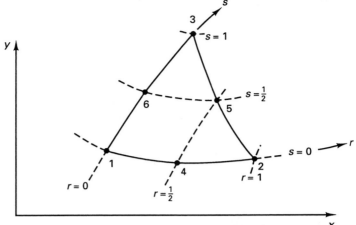

(a) Coordinate system and nodal points

			Include only if node i is defined		
			$i = 4$	$i = 5$	$i = 6$
$h_1 =$	$1 - r - s$		$-\frac{1}{2}h_4$	....	$-\frac{1}{2}h_6$
$h_2 =$	r		$-\frac{1}{2}h_4$	$-\frac{1}{2}h_5$	
$h_3 =$	s		....	$-\frac{1}{2}h_5$	$-\frac{1}{2}h_6$
$h_4 =$	$4r(1 - r - s)$				
$h_5 =$	$4rs$				
$h_6 =$	$4s(1 - r - s)$				

(b) Interpolation functions

Figure 5.11 Interpolation functions of three to six variable-number-nodes two-dimensional triangle

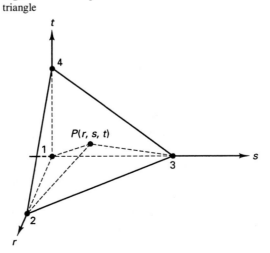

Figure 5.12 Natural coordinate system of tetrahedral element

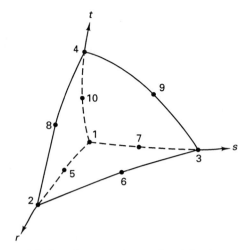

(a) Coordinate system and nodal points

Include only if node *i* is defined

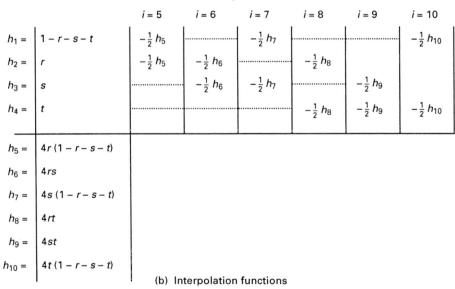

$h_1 =$	$1 - r - s - t$	$-\frac{1}{2}h_5$		$-\frac{1}{2}h_7$			$-\frac{1}{2}h_{10}$
		i = 5	*i* = 6	*i* = 7	*i* = 8	*i* = 9	*i* = 10
$h_1 =$	$1 - r - s - t$	$-\frac{1}{2}h_5$		$-\frac{1}{2}h_7$			$-\frac{1}{2}h_{10}$
$h_2 =$	r	$-\frac{1}{2}h_5$	$-\frac{1}{2}h_6$		$-\frac{1}{2}h_8$		
$h_3 =$	s		$-\frac{1}{2}h_6$	$-\frac{1}{2}h_7$		$-\frac{1}{2}h_9$	
$h_4 =$	t				$-\frac{1}{2}h_8$	$-\frac{1}{2}h_9$	$-\frac{1}{2}h_{10}$

$h_5 =$	$4r(1 - r - s - t)$
$h_6 =$	$4rs$
$h_7 =$	$4s(1 - r - s - t)$
$h_8 =$	$4rt$
$h_9 =$	$4st$
$h_{10} =$	$4t(1 - r - s - t)$

(b) Interpolation functions

Figure 5.13   Interpolation functions of four to ten variable-number-nodes three-dimensional tetrahedral element

functions of a 4 to 10 three-dimensional variable-number-nodes element are given in Fig. 5.13.

To evaluate the element matrices, it is necessary to include the Jacobian transformation as given in (5.24) and to perform the *r* integrations from 0 to 1, the *s* integrations from 0 to $(1 - r)$, and the *t* integrations from 0 to $(1 - r - s)$. As for the quadrilateral elements, these integrations are carried out effectively in general analysis using numerical integration, but the integration rules employed are different from those used for quadrilateral elements (see Section 5.5.4).

EXAMPLE 5.19:   The triangular element shown in Fig. E5.19 is subjected to the body force vector $\mathbf{f}^B$ per unit volume. Calculate the consistent nodal point load vector.

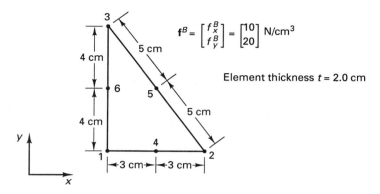

Figure E5.19   Six-node triangular element

Let us use the displacement vector

$$\hat{\mathbf{u}}^T = \begin{bmatrix} u_1 & v_1 & u_2 & v_2 & u_3 & v_3 & \ldots & v_6 \end{bmatrix}$$

Hence, the load vector corresponding to the applied body force loading is

$$\mathbf{R}_B = \int_V \begin{bmatrix} h_1 \, f_x^B \\ h_1 \, f_y^B \\ \vdots \\ h_6 \, f_y^B \end{bmatrix} dV$$

We have

$$\mathbf{J} = \begin{bmatrix} 6 & 0 \\ 0 & 8 \end{bmatrix}$$

and note that the Jacobian matrix is diagonal and constant and that det $\mathbf{J}$ is equal to twice the area of the triangle. The integrations involve the following term for node i:

$$f_i = \int_{r=0}^{1} \int_{s=0}^{1-r} h_i t \det \mathbf{J} \, ds \, dr$$

which gives $f_1 = f_2 = f_3 = 0$, whereas $f_4 = f_5 = f_6 = (t/6) \det \mathbf{J}$. Hence, we obtain

$$\mathbf{R}_B^T = \begin{bmatrix} 0 & \ldots & 0 & 160 & 320 & 160 & 320 & 160 & 320 \end{bmatrix} \qquad (a)$$

with the consistent nodal forces at the corner nodes equal to zero. Note that the total applied load is of course statically equivalent to the nodal forces listed in (a).

5.3.3 Convergence Considerations

We discussed in Section 4.3 the requirements for monotonic convergence of a finite element discretization. Since isoparametric elements are used very widely, let us address some key issues of convergence specifically for these elements.

Basic Requirements for Convergence

The two requirements for monotonic convergence are that the elements (or the mesh) must be compatible and complete.

To investigate the compatibility of an element assemblage, we need to consider each edge, or rather face, between adjacent elements. For compatibility it is necessary that the coordinates and the displacements of the elements at the common face be the same. We note that for the elements considered here, the coordinates and displacements on an element face are determined only by nodes and nodal degrees of freedom on that face. Therefore, compatibility is satisfied if the elements have the same nodes on the common face and the coordinates and displacements on the common face are in each element defined by the same interpolation functions.

Examples of adjacent elements that do and do not preserve compatibility are shown in Fig. 5.14.

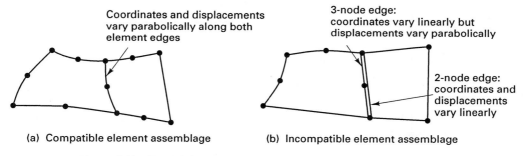

Figure 5.14   Compatible and incompatible two-dimensional element assemblage

In practice, mesh grading is frequently necessary (see Section 4.3), and the isoparametric elements show particular flexibility in achieving compatible graded meshes (see Fig. 5.15).

Completeness requires that the rigid body displacements and constant strain states be possible. One way to investigate whether these criteria are satisfied for an isoparametric element is to follow the considerations given in Section 4.3.2. However, we now want to obtain more insight into the specific conditions that pertain to the isoparametric formulation of a continuum element. For this purpose we consider in the following discussion a three-dimensional continuum element because the one- and two-dimensional elements can be regarded as special cases of these three-dimensional considerations. For the rigid body and constant strain states to be possible, the following displacements defined in the local element coordinate system must be contained in the isoparametric formulation

$$\left. \begin{aligned} u &= a_1 + b_1 x + c_1 y + d_1 z \\ v &= a_2 + b_2 x + c_2 y + d_2 z \\ w &= a_3 + b_3 x + c_3 y + d_3 z \end{aligned} \right\} \qquad (5.48)$$

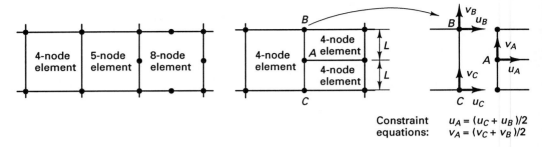

(a) 4-node to 8-node element
    transition region

(b) 4-node to 4-node element transition;
    from one to two layers

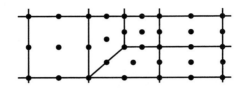

(c) 9-node to 9-node element transition region;
    from one to two layers

Figure 5.15   Some transitions with compatible element layouts

where the a_j, b_j, c_j, and d_j, $j = 1, 2, 3$, are constants. The nodal point displacements corresponding to this displacement field are

$$
\left.\begin{aligned}
u_i &= a_1 + b_1 x_i + c_1 y_i + d_1 z_i \\
v_i &= a_2 + b_2 x_i + c_2 y_i + d_2 z_i \\
w_i &= a_3 + b_3 x_i + c_3 y_i + d_3 z_i
\end{aligned}\right\} \tag{5.49}
$$

where $i = 1, \ldots, q$ and q = number of nodes.

The test for completeness is now as follows: show that the displacements in (5.48) are *in fact* obtained *within* the element when the element nodal point displacements are given by (5.49). In other words, we should find that with the nodal point displacements in (5.49), the displacements *within* the element are actually those given in (5.48).

In the isoparametric formulation we have the displacement interpolation

$$
u = \sum_{i=1}^{q} h_i u_i; \qquad v = \sum_{i=1}^{q} h_i v_i; \qquad w = \sum_{i=1}^{q} h_i w_i
$$

which, using (5.49), reduces to

$$
\left.\begin{aligned}
u &= a_1 \sum_{i=1}^{q} h_i + b_1 \sum_{i=1}^{q} h_i x_i + c_1 \sum_{i=1}^{q} h_i y_i + d_1 \sum_{i=1}^{q} h_i z_i \\
v &= a_2 \sum_{i=1}^{q} h_i + b_2 \sum_{i=1}^{q} h_i x_i + c_2 \sum_{i=1}^{q} h_i y_i + d_2 \sum_{i=1}^{q} h_i z_i \\
w &= a_3 \sum_{i=1}^{q} h_i + b_3 \sum_{i=1}^{q} h_i x_i + c_3 \sum_{i=1}^{q} h_i y_i + d_3 \sum_{i=1}^{q} h_i z_i
\end{aligned}\right\} \tag{5.50}
$$

Since in the isoparametric formulation the coordinates are interpolated in the same way as the displacements, we can use (5.18) to obtain from (5.50),

$$
\left.
\begin{aligned}
u &= a_1 \sum_{i=1}^{q} h_i + b_1 x + c_1 y + d_1 z \\
v &= a_2 \sum_{i=1}^{q} h_i + b_2 x + c_2 y + d_2 z \\
w &= a_3 \sum_{i=1}^{q} h_i + b_3 x + c_3 y + d_3 z
\end{aligned}
\right\}
\tag{5.51}
$$

The displacements defined in (5.51), however, are the same as those given in (5.48), provided that for any point in the element,

$$
\sum_{i=1}^{q} h_i = 1
\tag{5.52}
$$

The relation in (5.52) is the condition on the interpolation functions for the completeness requirements to be satisfied. We may note that (5.52) is certainly satisfied at the nodes of an element because the interpolation function h_i has been constructed to be unity at node i with all other interpolation functions $h_j, j \neq i$, being zero at that node; but in order that an isoparametric element be properly constructed, the condition must be satisfied for all points in the element.

In the preceding discussion, we considered a three-dimensional continuum element, but the conclusions are also directly applicable to the other isoparametric continuum element formulations. For the one- or two-dimensional continuum elements we simply include only the appropriate displacement and coordinate interpolations in the relations (5.48) to (5.52). We demonstrate the convergence considerations in the following example.

> **EXAMPLE 5.20:** Investigate whether the requirements for monotonic convergence are satisfied for the variable-number-nodes elements in Figs. 5.4 and 5.5.
>
> Compatibility is maintained between element edges in two-dimensional analysis and element faces in three-dimensional analysis, provided that the same number of nodes is used on connecting element edges and faces. A typical compatible element layout is shown in Fig. 5.14(a).
>
> The second requirement for monotonic convergence is the completeness condition. Considering first the basic four-node two-dimensional element, we recognize that the arguments leading to the condition in (5.52) are directly applicable, provided that only the x and y coordinates and u and v displacements are considered.
>
> Evaluating $\sum_{i=1}^{4} h_i$ for the element, we find
>
> $$\tfrac{1}{4}(1 + r)(1 + s) + \tfrac{1}{4}(1 - r)(1 + s) + \tfrac{1}{4}(1 - r)(1 - s) + \tfrac{1}{4}(1 + r)(1 - s) = 1$$
>
> Hence, the basic four-node element is complete. We now study the interpolation functions given in Fig. 5.4 for the variable-number-nodes element and find that the total contribution that is added to the basic four-node interpolation functions is always zero for whichever additional node is included. Hence, any one of the possible elements defined by the variable number of nodes in Fig. 5.4 is complete. The proof for the three-dimensional elements in Fig. 5.5 is carried out in an analogous manner.
>
> It follows therefore that the variable-number-nodes continuum elements satisfy the requirements for monotonic convergence.

Order of Convergence, the Effect of Element Distortions

The basic requirements for monotonic convergence, namely, compatibility and completeness, are satisfied by the isoparametric elements, as discussed above, when these elements are of general (but admissible) geometric shape. Therefore, the elements always have the capability to represent the rigid body modes and constant strain states, and convergence is guaranteed.

We discussed in Section 4.3.5 the rates of convergence of sequences of finite element discretizations with the assumptions that the elements are based on polynomial expansions and that uniform meshes of elements with characteristic dimension h are used. For the discussion we used the Pascal triangle to display which polynomial terms are present in various elements. The complete polynomial of highest order in the Pascal triangle determines the order of convergence. Let this degree (now for r, s, t) be k. Then if the exact solution $\mathbf{u}$ is sufficiently smooth and uniform meshes are used, the rate of convergence of the finite element solution $\mathbf{u}_h$ is given by [see (4.102)]

$$\| \mathbf{u} - \mathbf{u}_h \|_1 \leq c\, h^k \tag{5.53}$$

where k is the order of convergence. The constant c is independent of h but depends on the exact solution of the mathematical model and the material properties.

In general practical finite element analysis, the exact solution of the mathematical model is not smooth (e.g., because of rapid load variations, changes in material properties), and with uniform meshes the order of convergence is much reduced. Therefore, mesh grading must be employed with fine discretizations in regions of nonsmooth stress distributions and coarse discretizations in the other regions. The meshes will therefore be nonuniform and based on geometrically distorted elements using, for example, in two-dimensional analysis general quadrilateral and triangular elements; see Fig. 5.16 for an example of a nine-node quadrilateral element.

The aim in such mesh constructions is then to use meshes in which the density of solution error is (nearly) constant over the domain considered and to use *regular* meshes.[3] When regular meshes are used, the rate of convergence is still given by a form such as (5.53) [see (4.101c)], namely,

$$\| \mathbf{u} - \mathbf{u}_h \|_1^2 \leq c \sum_m h_m^{2k} \| \mathbf{u} \|_{k+1,m}^2$$

where h_m denotes the largest dimension of element m (see Fig. 5.16). We note that, in essence, in this relation the interpolation errors over all elements are added to obtain the total interpolation error, which then gives us the usual bound on the actual error of the solution.

The (nearly) constant density of solution error can of course be achieved, in general, only by proper mesh grading and adaptive mesh refinement because the mesh to be used depends on the exact (and unknown) solution. In practice, a refinement of a mesh is constructed on the basis of local error estimates computed from the solution just obtained (with a coarser mesh).

---

[3] In referring to a "regular mesh," we always mean "a mesh from a sequence of meshes that is regular."

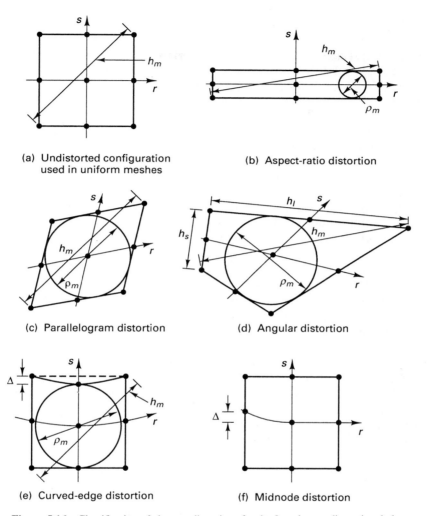

(a) Undistorted configuration used in uniform meshes

(b) Aspect-ratio distortion

(c) Parallelogram distortion

(d) Angular distortion

(e) Curved-edge distortion

(f) Midnode distortion

Figure 5.16 Classification of element distortions for the 9-node two-dimensional element; all midside and interior nodes are placed at their "natural" positions for cases (a) to (e). The value of Δ should be smaller than h_m^2 for (5.53) to be applicable. An actual distortion in practice would be a combination of those shown.

To introduce a measure of mesh regularity, the element geometric parameter σ_m, is used,

$$\sigma_m = \frac{h_m}{\rho_m}$$

where h_m is the largest dimension and ρ_m is the diameter of the largest circle (or sphere) that can be inscribed in element m (see Fig. 5.16). A sequence of meshes is *regular* if $\sigma_m \leq \sigma_0$ for all elements m and meshes used, where σ_0 is a fixed positive value. In addition, when using meshes of quadrilateral elements in two-dimensional analysis and hexahedral elements in three-dimensional analysis, we also require that for each element the ratio of the largest to the smallest side lengths (h_l/h_s in Fig. 5.16) is smaller than a reasonable positive number. These conditions prevent excessive aspect ratios and geometric distortions of the elements. Referring to Fig. 5.16, the elements in (b), (c), and in particularly (d) are used extensively in regular meshes.[4]

The above described mesh grading can in general be achieved with straight-sided elements, and the noncorner nodes can usually be placed at their natural positions (i.e., at the physical x, y, z locations in proportion to the r, s, t distances from the corner nodes); and the most typically used element in Fig. 5.16 is the quadrilateral in Fig. 5.16(d). However, when curved boundaries need to be modeled, the element sides will also be curved [see Fig. 5.16(e)], and we must ask what effect all these geometric distortions will have on the order of convergence.

Whereas the cases in Figs. 5.16(a) to (e) are used extensively in mesh designs, we note that the element distortion shown in Fig. 5.16(f) is avoided, unless specific stress effects need to be modeled, such as in fracture mechanics [where even larger distortions than those shown in Fig. 5.16(f) are used; see Fig. 5.9]. However, the distortion in Fig. 5.16(f) may also arise in geometrically nonlinear analysis.

P. G. Ciarlet and P. -A. Raviart [A] and P. G. Ciarlet [A] have shown in their mathematical analyses that the order of convergence of a sequence of regular meshes with straight element sides is still given as in (5.53) (even though, for example, in two-dimensional analysis, general straight-sided quadrilaterals are used instead of square elements) *and* that the order of convergence is also still given as in (5.53) with curved element sides and when the noncorner nodes are not placed at their natural positions provided these distortions are small, measured on the size of the element. For the element in Fig. 5.16 the distortions must be $o(h^2)$. The element distortions due to curved sides and due to interior nodes not placed at their natural positions must therefore be small, *and* in the refinement process the distortions must decrease much faster than the element size. The order of convergence in (5.53) is reached directly when the exact solution **u** is smooth, whereas when the exact solution is nonsmooth, mesh grading is necessary (to fulfill the requirement that the density of solution error be (almost) constant over the solution domain). We present some solutions to illustrate a few of these results in Section 5.5.5 (see Fig. 5.39).[5]

Of course, the actual accuracy attained with a given mesh is also determined by the constant c in (5.53). This constant depends on the specific elements used (all with the complete polynomial of degree k) and also on the geometric distortions of the elements. We should note that if the constant is large, the order of convergence may be of little interest because the h^k term may decrease the error sufficiently only at very small values of h.

These remarks pertain to the order of convergence reached when element sizes are small. However, interesting observations also pertain to a study of the predictive capability of elements when the element sizes are large. Namely, element geometric distortions can affect the general predictive capabilities to a significant degree.

---

[4] In addition, we can also define a sequence of meshes that is *quasi-uniform*. In such sequence we also have, in addition to the regularity condition that the ratio of the maximum h_m encountered in the mesh over the minimum h_m encountered in that same mesh remains for all meshes below a reasonable positive number. Hence, whereas regularity allows that the ratio of element sizes becomes any value, quasi-uniformity restricts the relative sizes that are permitted. Therefore, the error measure in (4.101c) is also valid when a quasi-uniform sequence of meshes is used.

[5] These solutions are given in Section 5.5.5 because the element matrices of the distorted elements are evaluated using numerical integration and the effect of the numerical integration error must also be considered.

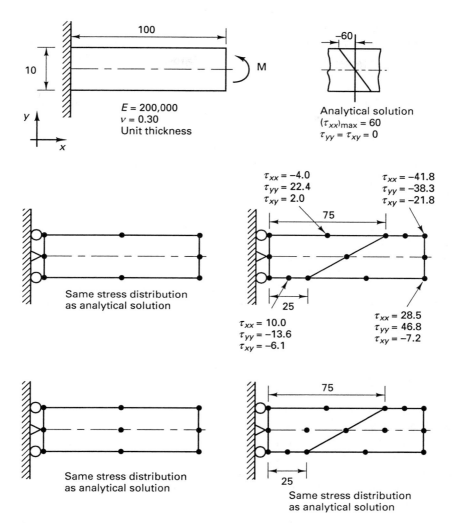

Figure 5.17   Example demonstrating effect of element distortions on predictive capability of elements

As an example to demonstrate a possible loss of predictive capability when an isoparametric element is geometrically distorted, consider the results given in Fig. 5.17. The single undistorted eight-node element gives the exact (beam theory) solution for the beam bending problem. However, when two elements of distorted shape are used, significant solution errors are obtained. On the other hand, when the same problem is analyzed with nine-node elements, the mesh of two distorted elements gives the correct result.

This example shows that in coarse meshes the stress predictive capability of certain elements can be significantly affected by element geometric distortions. Since, in practice, frequently rather coarse meshes are used and complete convergence studies are not performed, surely it is preferable to use those elements that are least sensitive to element geometric distortions.

On studying the cause of loss of predictive capability, we find that this effect is due to the elements no longer being able to represent the same order of polynomials in the physical coordinates x, y, z after the geometric distortion as they did without the distortion. For example, the general quadrilateral nine-node element, shown in Fig. 5.16(d), is able to represent the x^2, xy, y^2 displacement variations *exactly*, whereas the corresponding eight-node quadrilateral element is not able to do so. Hence, the general quadrilateral eight-node element does not contain the quadratic terms in the Pascal triangle of the physical coordinates.

This observation explains the results in Fig. 5.17, and an investigation into this phenomenon for widely used elements and common distortions is of general interest. In such a study, we can measure the loss of predictive capability by identifying which terms in the physical coordinates of the Pascal triangle can no longer be represented exactly, (see N. S. Lee and K. J. Bathe [A]).

Let us consider the two-dimensional element in Fig. 5.16 as an example. For elements with undistorted configurations or with aspect ratio distortions only, the physical coordinates x, y are linearly related to the isoparametric coordinates r, s; i.e., we have $x = c_1 r$, $y = c_2 s$, where c_1 and c_2 are constants. Hence, the Pascal triangle terms in physical coordinates are simply the r, s terms obtained from the interpolation functions h_i replaced by x and y, respectively.

The effects of the parallelogram, general angular, and curved edge distortions shown in Figs. 5.16(c) to (e) can be studied by establishing the physical coordinate variations for these specific cases with the coordinate interpolations (5.18) and then asking what polynomial terms in x and y are contained in the r, s polynomial terms of the displacement variations given in (5.19) (see Example 5.21).

Table 5.1 summarizes the results obtained in such a study for two-dimensional quadrilateral elements (see N. S. Lee and K. J. Bathe [A]). The first column in Table 5.1 gives the terms in the Pascal triangle when the element is undistorted or is subjected to an aspect ratio or parallelogram distortion only. The terms below the dashed line are present only when the element is undistorted, or subjected only to an aspect ratio distortion, *and* also unrotated. Table 5.1 in particular shows that a general angular distortion significantly affects the predictive capability of 8- and 12-node elements; i.e., with such distortions the elements can represent only linear displacement variations in x and y *exactly*, whereas the 9- and 16-node elements can in distorted form still represent the parabolic and cubic displacement fields *exactly*.

On the other hand, curved edge distortions reduce the order of displacement polynomials that can be represented *exactly* for all the elements considered in Table 5.1, and indeed with such distortions only the biquartic 25-node element can still represent the parabolic displacement field exactly.

While the information given in Table 5.1 shows clearly that the Lagrangian elements are preferable to the 8- and 12-node elements in terms of predictive capability, of course, we also need to recall that the Lagrangian elements are computationally slightly more expensive, and for fine meshes the order of convergence is identical [although the constant c in (5.53) is different].

We demonstrate the procedure of analysis to obtain the information given in Table 5.1 in the following example.

TABLE 5.1 *Polynomial displacement fields in physical coordinates that can be solved exactly by various elements in their undistorted and distorted configurations*[†]

Type of element	Fields for undistorted configuration, aspect ratio and/or parallelogram distortions — — — — — — — — — — Additional fields if also unrotated	Angular distortion	Quadratic curved-edge distortion
8-node element	1 $x \quad y$ $x^2 \quad xy \quad y^2$ – – – – – $x^2y \quad xy^2$	1 $x \quad y$	1 $x \quad y$
12-node element	1 $x \quad y$ $x^2 \quad xy \quad y^2$ $x^3 \quad x^2y \quad xy^2 \quad y^3$ – – – – – – – – $x^3y \qquad xy^3$	1 $x \quad y$	1 $x \quad y$
9-node Lagrangian element	1 $x \quad y$ $x^2 \quad xy \quad y^2$ – – – – – $x^2y \quad xy^2$ x^2y^2	1 $x \quad y$ $x^2 \quad xy \quad y^2$	1 $x \quad y$
16-node Lagrangian element	1 $x \quad y$ $x^2 \quad xy \quad y^2$ $x^3 \quad x^2y \quad xy^2 \quad y^3$ – – – – – – – – $x^3y \quad x^2y^2 \quad xy^3$ $x^3y^2 \quad x^2y^3$ x^3y^3	1 $x \quad y$ $x^2 \quad xy \quad y^2$ $x^3 \quad x^2y \quad xy^2 \quad y^3$	1 $x \quad y$
25-node Lagrangian element	1 $x \quad y$ $x^2 \quad xy \quad y^2$ $x^3 \quad x^2y \quad xy^2 \quad y^3$ $x^4 \quad x^3y \quad x^2y^2 \quad xy^3 \quad y^4$ – – – – – – – – $x^4y \quad x^3y^2 \quad x^2y^3 \quad xy^4$ $x^4y^2 \quad x^3y^3 \quad x^2y^4$ $x^4y^3 \quad x^3y^4$ x^4y^4	1 $x \quad y$ $x^2 \quad xy \quad y^2$ $x^3 \quad x^2y \quad xy^2 \quad y^3$ $x^4 \quad x^3y \quad x^2y^2 \quad xy^3 \quad y^4$	1 $x \quad y$ $x^2 \quad xy \quad y^2$

[†] Two-dimensional quadrilateral elements are considered.

EXAMPLE 5.21: Consider the general angularly distorted eight-node element in Fig. E5.21. Evaluate the Pascal triangle terms in x, y for this element.

The physical coordinate variations are obtained by using the interpolation functions in Fig. 5.4, which give for this element with its midside nodes placed halfway between the corner nodes,

$$x = \gamma_1 + \gamma_2 r + \gamma_3 s + \gamma_4 rs \qquad (a)$$

$$y = \delta_1 + \delta_2 r + \delta_3 s + \delta_4 rs \qquad (b)$$

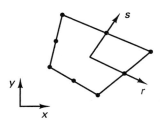

Figure E5.21   Eight-node isoparametric element, with angular distortion

with $\gamma_1, \ldots, \gamma_4$ and $\delta_1, \ldots, \delta_4$ constants. We use (a) and (b) to identify which x and y terms are contained in the displacement interpolations

$$u = \sum_{i=1}^{8} h_i u_i \qquad \text{(c)}$$

$$v = \sum_{i=1}^{8} h_i v_i \qquad \text{(d)}$$

where the h_i are again those in Fig. 5.4.

Consider the u-displacement interpolation. The constant and x and y terms in (a) and (b) are clearly contained in (c) because (c) interpolates u in terms of the functions $(1, r, s, r^2, rs, s^2, r^2s, rs^2)$ multiplied by constants. We discussed this fact earlier when considering the requirements for convergence.

However, if we next consider the term x^2, we notice that the term r^2s^2 [obtained by squaring the right-hand side of (a)] is not present in (c). Similarly, the terms xy, y^2, x^2y, and xy^2 are not present in the displacement interpolation (c).

The analysis for the v-displacement interpolation is of course identical. Hence, when an eight-node isoparametric element is subjected to a general angular distortion, the predictive capability is diminished in that quadratic displacement variations in x and y can no longer be represented exactly (see Table 5.1).

This analysis also shows that the quadratic displacement variations in x and y are retained when the nine-node displacement-based element is subjected to the same angular distortions. These conclusions explain the results shown in Fig. 5.16.

5.3.4 Element Matrices in Global Coordinate System

So far we have considered the calculation of isoparametric element matrices that correspond to local element degrees of freedom. In the evaluation we used local element coordinates x, y, and z, whichever were applicable, and local element degrees of freedom u_i, v_i, and w_i. However, we may note that for the two-dimensional element considered in Examples 5.5 to 5.7 the element matrices could have been evaluated using the global coordinate variables X and Y, and the global nodal point displacements U_i and V_i. Indeed, in the calculations presented, the x and y local coordinates and u and v local displacement components simply needed to be replaced by the X and Y global coordinates and U and V global displacement components, respectively. In such cases the matrices then would correspond directly to the global displacement components.

In general, the calculation of the element matrices should be carried out in the global coordinate system, using global displacement components if the number of natural coordinate variables is equal to the number of global variables. Typical examples are two-dimensional elements defined in a global plane and the three-dimensional element in

Fig. 5.5. In these cases the Jacobian operator in (5.24) is a square matrix, which can be inverted as required in (5.25), and the element matrices correspond directly to the global displacement components.

In cases where the order of the global coordinate system is higher than the order of the natural coordinate system, it is usually most expedient to calculate first the element matrices in the local coordinate system and corresponding to local displacement components. Afterward, the matrices must be transformed in the usual manner to the global displacement system. Examples are the truss element or the plane stress element when they are oriented arbitrarily in three-dimensional space. However, alternatively, we may include the transformation to the global displacement components directly in the formulation. This is accomplished by introducing a transformation that expresses in the displacement interpolation the local nodal point displacements in terms of the global components.

EXAMPLE 5.22:   Evaluate the element stiffness matrix of the truss element in Fig. E5.22 using directly global nodal point displacements.

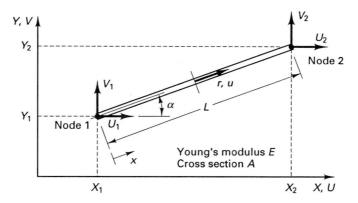

Figure E5.22   Truss element in global coordinate system

The stiffness matrix of the element is given in (5.27); i.e.,

$$\mathbf{K} = \int_V \mathbf{B}^T \mathbf{C} \mathbf{B} \, dV$$

where $\mathbf{B}$ is the strain-displacement matrix and $\mathbf{C}$ is the stress-strain matrix. For the truss element considered we have

$$u = [\cos \alpha \quad \sin \alpha] \begin{bmatrix} \frac{1}{2}(1 - r)U_1 + \frac{1}{2}(1 + r)U_2 \\ \frac{1}{2}(1 - r)V_1 + \frac{1}{2}(1 + r)V_2 \end{bmatrix}$$

Then, using $\epsilon = \partial u / \partial x$, expressed in the natural coordinate system as $\epsilon = (2/L) \, \partial u / \partial r$ (see Section 5.2), we can write the strain-displacement transformation corresponding to the displacement vector $\mathbf{U}^T = [U_1 \quad V_1 \quad U_2 \quad V_2]$ as

$$\mathbf{B} = \frac{1}{L}[\cos \alpha \quad \sin \alpha \quad \cos \alpha \quad \sin \alpha] \begin{bmatrix} -1 & & & \\ & -1 & & \text{zeros} \\ & & 1 & \\ \text{zeros} & & & 1 \end{bmatrix}$$

Also, as given in Section 5.2, we have

$$dV = \frac{AL}{2} dr \quad \text{and} \quad \mathbf{C} = E$$

Substituting the relations for **B**, **C**, and dV and evaluating the integral, we obtain

$$\mathbf{K} = \frac{AE}{L} \begin{bmatrix} \cos^2 \alpha & \cos \alpha \sin \alpha & -\cos^2 \alpha & -\cos \alpha \sin \alpha \\ \sin \alpha \cos \alpha & \sin^2 \alpha & -\sin \alpha \cos \alpha & -\sin^2 \alpha \\ -\cos^2 \alpha & -\cos \alpha \sin \alpha & \cos^2 \alpha & \cos \alpha \sin \alpha \\ -\sin \alpha \cos \alpha & -\sin^2 \alpha & \sin \alpha \cos \alpha & \sin^2 \alpha \end{bmatrix}$$

5.3.5 Displacement/Pressure Based Elements for Incompressible Media

We discussed in Section 4.4.3 the fact that pure displacement-based elements are not effective for the analysis of incompressible (or almost incompressible) media and introduced two displacement/pressure formulations. In the u/p formulation, the pressure is interpolated individually for each element and can (in the almost incompressible case) be statically condensed out prior to the element matrix assemblage, whereas in the u/p-c formulation the element pressures are defined by nodal variables which, as for the displacements, pertain to adjacent elements. Various effective elements of these formulations were given (see Tables 4.6 and 4.7) and discussed (see Section 4.5).

As for the pure displacement-based elements, we assumed in Chapter 4 that the displacement and pressure interpolation matrices are constructed using the generalized coordinate approach. However, it is now apparent that these matrices can be obtained directly using the isoparametric formulation.

In the u/p formulation, we use the same coordinate and displacement interpolations for an element as in the pure displacement formulation [see (5.18) and (5.19)], and we interpolate the pressure using

$$p = p_0 + p_1 r + p_2 s + p_3 t + \cdots \tag{5.54}$$

where $p_0, p_1, p_2, p_3, \ldots$ are the pressure parameters to be calculated and r, s, and t are the isoparametric coordinates. Of course, as an alternative, we could also interpolate the pressure using

$$p = p_0 + p_1 x + p_2 y + p_3 z + \cdots$$

where x, y, and z are the usual Cartesian coordinates.

In the u/p-c formulation we also use the displacement and coordinate interpolations as in the pure displacement formulation, and

$$p = \sum_{i=1}^{q_p} \tilde{h}_i \hat{p}_i \tag{5.55}$$

where the $\tilde{h}_i$, $i = 1, \ldots, q_p$ are the nodal point pressure interpolation functions and the $\hat{p}_i$ are the unknown nodal pressures. We note that the $\tilde{h}_i$ are different from the h_i which are used for the displacement and coordinate interpolations. For example, for the 9/4-c two-dimensional element, the displacement and coordinate interpolations are the functions corresponding to the nine element nodes in Table 5.4, whereas the $\tilde{h}_i$ are the functions corresponding to the four element corner nodes.

In practice, the isoparametric formulation of the u/p and u/p-c elements is effective because the generality of nonrectangular and curved elements is then also available (see Fig. 4.21 and T. Sussman and K. J. Bathe [A, B]).

5.3.6 Exercises

5.1. Use the procedure in Example 5.1 to prove that the functions in Fig. 5.3 for the four-node truss element are correct.

5.2. Use the procedure in Example 5.1 to prove that the functions in Fig. 5.4 for the two-dimensional element are correct.

5.3. Use the functions in Fig. 5.4 to construct the interpolation functions of the six-node element shown. Plot the interpolation functions in an oblique/aerial view (as in Example 5.4).

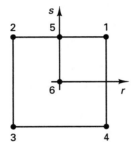

5.4. Prove that the construction of the interpolation functions in Fig. 5.5 gives the correct functions for the three-dimensional element.

5.5. Determine the interpolation function h_i for the element shown for use in a compatible finite element mesh.

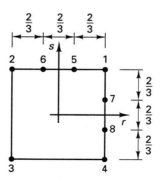

5.6. In the computation of isoparametric element matrices, the integration is performed over the natural coordinates r, s, t, which requires the transformation (5.28). Derive this transformation using the elementary volume $dV = (\mathbf{r}\, dr) \times (\mathbf{s}\, ds) \cdot (\mathbf{t}\, dt)$ shown.

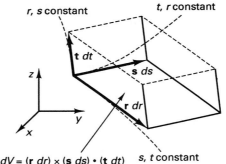

$$dV = (\mathbf{r}\ dr) \times (\mathbf{s}\ ds) \cdot (\mathbf{t}\ dt)$$

Here the vectors r, s, t are given by

$$\mathbf{r} = \begin{bmatrix} \dfrac{\partial x}{\partial r} \\[6pt] \dfrac{\partial y}{\partial r} \\[6pt] \dfrac{\partial z}{\partial r} \end{bmatrix}; \qquad \mathbf{s} = \begin{bmatrix} \dfrac{\partial x}{\partial s} \\[6pt] \dfrac{\partial y}{\partial s} \\[6pt] \dfrac{\partial z}{\partial s} \end{bmatrix}; \qquad \mathbf{t} = \begin{bmatrix} \dfrac{\partial x}{\partial t} \\[6pt] \dfrac{\partial y}{\partial t} \\[6pt] \dfrac{\partial z}{\partial t} \end{bmatrix}$$

5.7. Evaluate the Jacobian matrices for the following four-node elements.

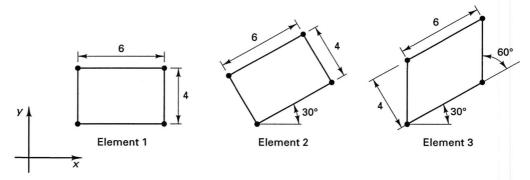

Show explicitly that the Jacobian matrices of elements 2 and 3 contain a rotation matrix representing a 30-degree rotation.

5.8. Calculate the Jacobian matrix of the element shown for all r, s. Identify the values of r, s for which the Jacobian matrix is singular.

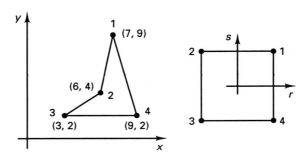

5.9. Evaluate the Jacobian matrices **J** for the following four-node elements.

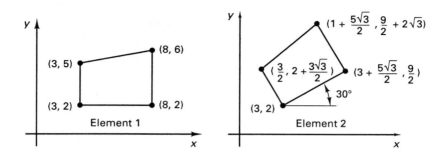

Show how the Jacobian matrix **J** of element 2 can be obtained by applying a rotation matrix to the Jacobian matrix **J** of element 1. Give this rotation matrix.

5.10. Consider the isoparametric elements given by

(a) **Case 1:**

$$x = \sum_{i=1}^{8} h_i x_i; \quad x_1 = 12, \, x_2 = 4, \, x_3 = 4, \, x_4 = 12, \, x_5 = 9, \, x_6 = 5, \, x_7 = 8, \, x_8 = 11$$

$$y = \sum_{i=1}^{8} h_i y_i; \quad y_1 = 12, \, y_2 = 8, \, y_3 = 2, \, y_4 = 2, \, y_5 = 8, \, y_6 = 5, \, y_7 = 1, \, y_8 = 7$$

(b) **Case 2:**

$$x = \sum_{i=1}^{6} h_i^* x_i; \quad x_1 = 8, \, x_2 = 2, \, x_3 = 1, \, x_4 = 9, \, x_5 = 5, \, x_6 = 5$$

$$y = \sum_{i=1}^{6} h_i^* y_i; \quad y_1 = 10, \, y_2 = 8, \, y_3 = 3, \, y_4 = 1, \, y_5 = 9, \, y_6 = 2$$

Draw the elements accurately on graph paper and show the physical locations of the lines $r = \frac{1}{2}$, $r = -\frac{1}{4}$, $s = \frac{3}{4}$, and $s = -\frac{1}{3}$ for each case. (You may also write a small program to perform this task.)

5.11. Consider the isoparametric finite elements shown. Sketch the following for each element.
 (a) The lines, s as the variable and constant $r = -\frac{2}{3}, -\frac{1}{3}, 0, \frac{1}{3}, \frac{2}{3}$.
 (b) The lines, r as the variable and constant $s = -\frac{2}{3}, -\frac{1}{3}, 0, \frac{1}{3}, \frac{2}{3}$.
 (c) The determinant of the Jacobian over element 1 (in an oblique aerial view).

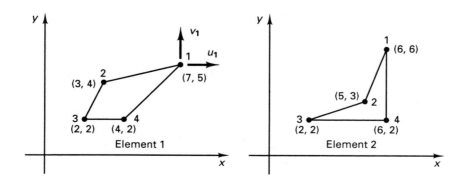

5.12. Prove that for any parallelogram-shaped isoparametric element the Jacobian determinant is constant. Also, prove that the Jacobian determinant always varies with r and/or s whenever the element is not square, rectangular, or parallelogram-shaped.

5.13. Consider the isoparametric element shown. Calculate the coordinates x, y of any point in the element as a function of r, s and establish the Jacobian matrix.

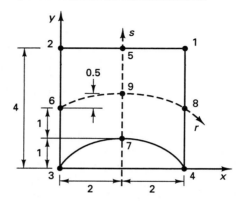

5.14. Calculate the nodal point forces corresponding to the surface loading on the axisymmetric element shown (consider 1 radian).

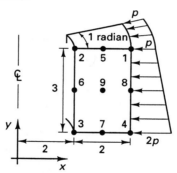

5.15. Consider the five-node plane strain isoparametric element shown.
  (a) Evaluate appropriate interpolation functions h_i, $i = 1$ to 5.
  (b) Evaluate the column in the strain-displacement matrix corresponding to the displacement u_1 at the point $x = 2.5$, $y = 2.5$.

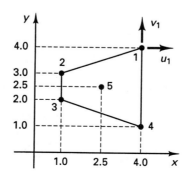

5.16. Consider the isoparametric axisymmetric two-dimensional finite element shown.
   (a) Construct the Jacobian matrix **J**.
   (b) Give an analytical expression of the column in the strain-displacement matrix $\mathbf{B}(r, s)$ that corresponds to the displacement u_1.

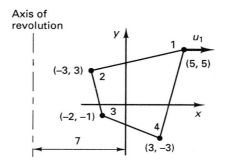

5.17. The eight-node isoparametric element shown has all its nodal point displacements constrained to zero except for u_1. The element is subjected to a concentrated load P into u_1.
   (a) Calculate and sketch the displacements corresponding to P.
   (b) Sketch all element stresses corresponding to the deformed configuration. Use an oblique/aerial view for your sketches.

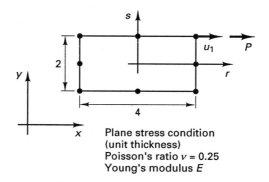

5.18. The eight-node element assemblage shown is used in a finite element analysis. Calculate the diagonal elements of the stiffness matrix and consistent mass matrix corresponding to the degree of freedom U_{100}.

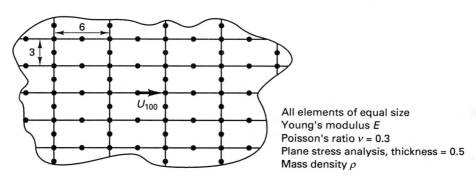

5.19. The problem in Example 5.13 is modeled by two five-node plane stress elements and one three-node bar element:

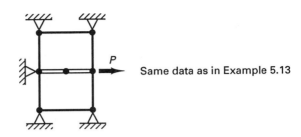

Same data as in Example 5.13

(a) Establish in detail all matrices used in the formulation of the governing equilibrium equations but do not perform any integrations.
(b) Assume that you have evaluated the unknown nodal point displacements. Present graphically in an oblique/aerial view all displacements and stresses in the elements.

5.20. The 20-node brick element shown is loaded by a concentrated load at the location indicated. Calculate the consistent nodal point loads.

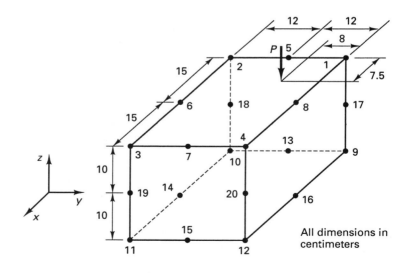

All dimensions in centimeters

5.21. The element in Exercise 5.20 is to be used in dynamic analysis. Construct a reasonable lumped mass matrix of the element; use $\rho = 7.8 \times 10^{-3}$ kg/cm^3.

5.22. The 12-node three-dimensional element shown is loaded with the pressure loading indicated. Calculate the nodal point consistent load vector for nodes 1, 2, 7, and 8.

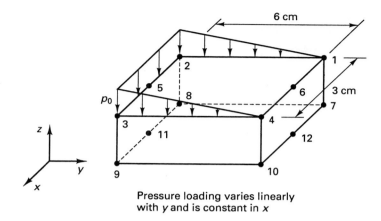

Pressure loading varies linearly
with *y* and is constant in *x*

5.23. Evaluate the Jacobian matrix **J** of the following element as a function of r, s and plot det **J** "over" the element (in our oblique/aerial view).

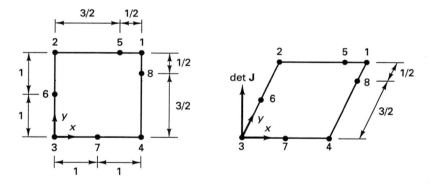

5.24. Plot, for node 9, the displacement interpolation functions and their *x*-derivatives for the nine-node element and the assemblage of two six-node triangles (formed using the interpolation functions in Fig. 5.11).

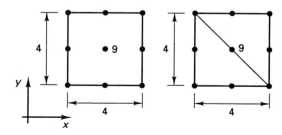

5.25. Prove that the interpolation functions in (5.36), with Δh defined in (5.37), define the same displacement assumptions as the functions in Fig. 5.11 (note that the origins of the coordinates used in the two formulations are different).

5.26. Collapse a 20-node brick element into a spatially isotropic 10-node tetrahedron (use the collapsing of sides in Fig. E5.16). Determine the correction that must be applied to the interpolation function h_{16} of the brick element in order to obtain the displacement assumption h_6 of the tetrahedron (given in Fig. 5.13).

5.27. Consider the six-node isoparametric plane strain finite element shown.

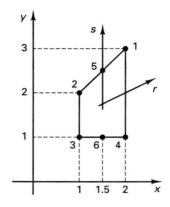

   (a) Construct the interpolation functions, $h_i(r, s)$, $i = 1, \ldots, 6$, of the element.

   (b) Prove in detail that this finite element does (or does not) satisfy all convergence requirements when used in a compatible finite element assemblage.

5.28. Consider a general isoparametric four-node element used in an assemblage of elements as shown.

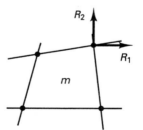

Either plane strain or plane stress condition

   (a) Prove that the nodal point forces defined as

$$\mathbf{F}^{(m)} = \int_{V^{(m)}} \mathbf{B}^{(m)^T} \boldsymbol{\tau}^{(m)} \, dV^{(m)}$$

       are in equilibrium for element m, where $\boldsymbol{\tau}^{(m)} = \mathbf{C}\mathbf{B}^{(m)}\mathbf{U}$ has been calculated.

   (b) Show that the sum of the nodal point forces at each node is in equilibrium with the applied external loads R_i (including the reactions). (*Hint:* Refer to Section 4.2.1, Fig. 4.2.)

5.29. Consider Table 5.1 and the case of angular distortion. Prove that the terms listed for the 12- and 16-node elements are indeed correct.

5.30. Consider Table 5.1 and the case of curved edge distortion. Prove that the terms listed in the column for the 8-, 9-, 12-, and 16-node elements are correct.

5.31. Consider the 4/1 isoparametric u/p element shown. Construct all matrices for the evaluation of the stiffness matrix of the element but do not perform any integrations.

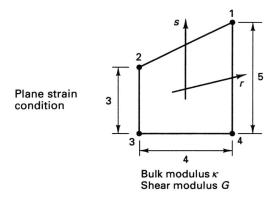

Plane strain
condition

Bulk modulus κ
Shear modulus G

5.4 FORMULATION OF STRUCTURAL ELEMENTS

The concepts of geometry and displacement interpolations that have been employed in the formulation of two- and three-dimensional continuum elements can also be employed in the evaluation of beam, plate, and shell structural element matrices. However, whereas in the formulation of the continuum elements the displacements u, v, w (whichever are applicable) are interpolated in terms of nodal point displacements of the same kind, in the formulation of structural elements, the displacements u, v, and w are interpolated in terms of midsurface displacements and rotations. We will show that this procedure corresponds in essence to a continuum isoparametric element formulation with displacement constraints. In addition, there is of course the major assumption that the stress normal to the midsurface is zero. The structural elements are for these reasons appropriately called *degenerate isoparametric elements*, but frequently we still refer to them simply as *isoparametric elements*.

Considering the formulation of structural elements, we have already discussed briefly in Section 4.2.3 how beam, plate, and shell elements can be formulated using the Bernoulli beam and Kirchhoff plate theory, in which shear deformations are neglected. Using the Kirchhoff theory it is difficult to satisfy interelement continuity on displacements and edge rotations because the plate (or shell) rotations are calculated from the transverse displacements. Furthermore, using an assemblage of flat elements to represent a shell structure, a relatively large number of elements may be required in order to represent the shell geometry to sufficient accuracy.

Our objective in this section is to discuss an alternative approach to formulating beam, plate, and shell elements. The basis of this method is a theory that includes the effects of shear deformations. In this theory the displacements and rotations of the midsurface normals are independent variables, and the interelement continuity conditions on these quantities can be satisfied directly, as in the analysis of continua. In addition, if the concepts of isoparametric interpolation are employed, the geometry of curved shell surfaces is interpolated and can be represented to a high degree of accuracy. In the following sections we discuss first the formulation of beam and axisymmetric shell elements, where we can demonstrate in detail the basic principles used, and we then present the formulation of general plate and shell elements.

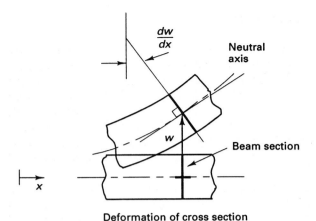

Deformation of cross section

(a) Beam deformations excluding shear effect

Boundary conditions between beam elements

$$\left. w \right|_{x^{-0}} = \left. w \right|_{x^{+0}} \quad ; \quad \left. \frac{dw}{dx} \right|_{x^{-0}} = \left. \frac{dw}{dx} \right|_{x^{+0}}$$

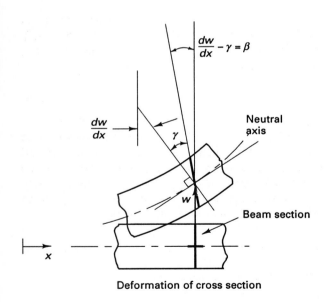

Deformation of cross section

(b) Beam deformations including shear effect

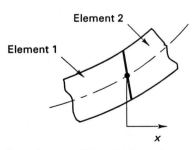

Boundary conditions between beam elements

$$\left. w \right|_{x^{-0}} = \left. w \right|_{x^{+0}}$$

$$\left. \beta \right|_{x^{-0}} = \left. \beta \right|_{x^{+0}}$$

Figure 5.18   Beam deformation assumptions

5.4.1 Beam and Axisymmetric Shell Elements

Let us discuss first some basic assumptions pertaining to the formulation of beam elements. The basic assumption in beam bending analysis excluding shear deformations is that a normal to the midsurface (neutral axis) of the beam remains straight during deformation and that its angular rotation is equal to the slope of the beam midsurface. This kinematic assumption, illustrated in Fig. 5.18(a), corresponds to the Bernoulli beam theory and leads to the well-known beam-bending governing differential equation in which the transverse displacement w is the only variable (see Example 3.20). Therefore, using beam elements formulated with this theory, displacement countinuity between elements requires that w and dw/dx be continuous.

Considering now beam bending analysis with the effect of shear deformations, we retain the assumption that a plane section orginally normal to the neutral axis remains plane, but because of shear deformations this section does not remain normal to the neutral axis. As illustrated in Fig. 5.18(b), the total rotation of the plane originally normal to the neutral axis of the beam is given by the rotation of the tangent to the neutral axis and the shear deformation,

$$\beta = \frac{dw}{dx} - \gamma \tag{5.56}$$

where γ is a constant shearing strain across the section. This kinematic assumption corresponds to Timoshenko beam theory (see S. H. Crandall, N. C. Dahl, and T. J. Lardner [A]). Since the actual shearing stress and strain vary over the section, the shearing strain γ in (5.56) is an equivalent constant strain on a corresponding shear area A_s,

$$\tau = \frac{V}{A_s}; \qquad \gamma = \frac{\tau}{G}; \qquad k = \frac{A_s}{A} \tag{5.57}$$

where V is the shear force at the section being considered. Different assumptions may be used to evaluate a reasonable factor k (see S. Timoshenko and J. N. Goodier [A] and K. Washizu [B]). One simple procedure is to evaluate the shear correction factor using the condition that when acting on A_s, the constant shear stress in (5.57) must yield the same shear strain energy as the actual shearing stress (evaluated from beam theory) acting on the actual cross-sectional area A of the beam. Consider the following example.

EXAMPLE 5.23:   Evaluate the shear correction factor k for a beam of rectangular cross section, width b, and depth h.

The shear strain energy $\mathcal{U}$ of the beam per unit length is

$$\mathcal{U} = \int_A \frac{1}{2G} \tau_a^2 \, dA \tag{a}$$

where τ_a is the actual shear stress, G is the shear modulus, and A is the cross-sectional area, $A = bh$.

In our finite element model, by assumption, the shear strain is constant over the cross-sectional area of the beam [see (5.56)]. Since in reality the shear strain varies over the beam cross section, we want to find an equivalent beam cross-sectional area A_s for our finite element model. This equivalency will be based on equating shear strain energies.

Hence using $\mathcal{U}$, given in (a), with the actual shear stress distribution, we can calculate A_s from

$$\int_A \frac{1}{2G} \tau_a{}^2 \, dA = \int_{A_s} \frac{1}{2G} \left(\frac{V}{A_s}\right)^2 dA_s \tag{b}$$

where V is the total shearing force at the section,

$$V = \int_A \tau_a \, dA \tag{c}$$

If we use $k = A_s/A$, we obtain from (b),

$$k = \frac{V^2}{A \int_A \tau_a{}^2 \, dA}$$

We now use (b) and (c) for the rectangular cross-section beam. Elementary beam theory gives (see S. H. Crandall, N. C. Dahl, and T. J. Lardner [A])

$$\tau_a = \frac{3}{2} \frac{V}{A} \left[\frac{(h/2)^2 - y^2}{(h/2)^2} \right]$$

which gives $k = \frac{5}{6}$.

The finite element formulation of a beam element with the assumption in (5.56) is obtained using the basic virtual work expressions in (4.19) to (4.22). In the following we consider first, for illustrative purposes, the specific formulation of the beam element matrices corresponding to the simple element in Fig. 5.19, and we discuss afterward the formulation of more general three-dimensional beam elements, and the formulation of axisymmetric shell elements.

Two-Dimensional Straight Beam Elements

Figure 5.19 shows the two-dimensional rectangular cross-section beam considered. Using the general expression of the principle of virtual work with the assumptions discussed above we have (see Exercise 5.32)

$$EI \int_0^L \left(\frac{d\beta}{dx}\right)\left(\frac{d\bar{\beta}}{dx}\right) dx + GAk \int_0^L \left(\frac{dw}{dx} - \beta\right)\left(\frac{d\bar{w}}{dx} - \bar{\beta}\right) dx = \int_0^L p\bar{w} \, dx + \int_0^L m\bar{\beta} \, dx \tag{5.58}$$

where p and m are the transverse and moment loadings per unit length. Using now the interpolations

$$w = \sum_{i=1}^q h_i w_i; \qquad \beta = \sum_{i=1}^q h_i \theta_i \tag{5.59}$$

where q is equal to the number of nodes used and the h_i are the one-dimensional interpolation functions listed in Fig. 5.3, we can directly employ the concepts of the isoparametric formulations discussed in Section 5.3 to establish all relevant element matrices. Let

$$w = \mathbf{H}_w \hat{\mathbf{u}}; \qquad \beta = \mathbf{H}_\beta \hat{\mathbf{u}}$$

$$\frac{\partial w}{\partial x} = \mathbf{B}_w \hat{\mathbf{u}}; \qquad \frac{\partial \beta}{\partial x} = \mathbf{B}_\beta \hat{\mathbf{u}} \tag{5.60}$$

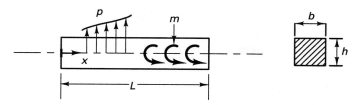

(a) Beam with applied loading
   E = Young's modulus; G = shear modulus;
   $k = \frac{5}{6}$; $A = hb$; $I = \frac{bh^3}{12}$

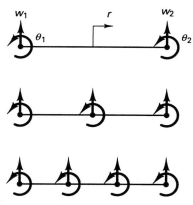

(b) 2-, 3-, and 4-node models; $\theta_i = \beta_i$, $i = 1, ..., q$
   (Interpolation functions are given in Fig. 5.3)

Figure 5.19   Formulation of two-dimensional beam element

where

$$\hat{\mathbf{u}}^T = [w_1 \ldots w_q \quad \theta_1 \ldots \theta_q]$$

$$\mathbf{H}_w = [h_1 \ldots h_q \quad 0 \ldots 0] \tag{5.61}$$

$$\mathbf{H}_\beta = [0 \cdots 0 \quad h_1 \cdots h_q]$$

and

$$\mathbf{B}_w = J^{-1} \left[\frac{\partial h_1}{\partial r} \quad \cdots \quad \frac{\partial h_q}{\partial r} \quad 0 \quad \cdots \quad 0 \right]$$

$$\mathbf{B}_\beta = J^{-1} \left[0 \quad \cdots \quad 0 \quad \frac{\partial h_1}{\partial r} \quad \cdots \quad \frac{\partial h_q}{\partial r} \right] \tag{5.62}$$

where $J = \partial x / \partial r$; then we have for a single element,

$$\mathbf{K} = EI \int_{-1}^{1} \mathbf{B}_\beta^T \mathbf{B}_\beta \det J \, dr + GAk \int_{-1}^{1} (\mathbf{B}_w - \mathbf{H}_\beta)^T (\mathbf{B}_w - \mathbf{H}_\beta) \det J \, dr$$

$$\mathbf{R} = \int_{-1}^{1} \mathbf{H}_w^T p \det J \, dr + \int_{1}^{-1} \mathbf{H}_\beta^T m \det J \, dr \tag{5.63}$$

Also, in dynamic analysis the mass matrix can be calculated using the d'Alembert principle [see (4.23)]; hence,

$$\mathbf{M} = \int_{-1}^{1} \begin{bmatrix} \mathbf{H}_w \\ \mathbf{H}_\beta \end{bmatrix}^T \begin{bmatrix} \rho bh & 0 \\ 0 & \dfrac{\rho bh^3}{12} \end{bmatrix} \begin{bmatrix} \mathbf{H}_w \\ \mathbf{H}_\beta \end{bmatrix} \det J \, dr \tag{5.64}$$

In these evaluations we are using the natural coordinate system of the beam because this is effective in the formulation of more general beam, plate, and shell elements. However, when considering a straight beam of constant cross section, the integrals can also be evaluated efficiently without using the natural coordinate system, as demonstrated in the following example.

EXAMPLE 5.24: Evaluate the detailed expressions for calculation of the stiffness matrix and the load vector of the three-node beam element shown in Fig. E5.24.

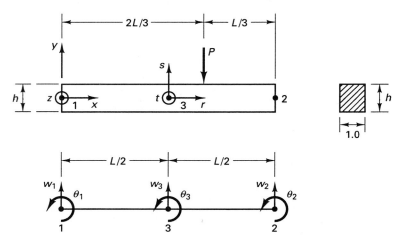

Figure E5.24   Three-node beam element

The interpolation functions to be used are listed in Fig. 5.3. These functions are given in terms of r and yield

$$x = \sum_{i=1}^{3} h_i x_i$$

Using $x_1 = 0$, $x_2 = L$, $x_3 = L/2$, we obtain

$$x = \frac{L}{2}(1 + r)$$

Hence, the interpolation functions in terms of x are

$$h_1 = \frac{2x^2}{L^2} - \frac{3x}{L} + 1$$

$$h_2 = \frac{2x^2}{L^2} - \frac{x}{L}$$

$$h_3 = \frac{4x}{L} - \frac{4x^2}{L^2}$$

Using the notation $(\ )' \equiv \partial/\partial x$ it follows that

$$h_1' = \frac{4x}{L^2} - \frac{3}{L}$$

$$h_2' = \frac{4x}{L^2} - \frac{1}{L}$$

$$h_3' = \frac{4}{L} - \frac{8x}{L^2}$$

Hence, with the degrees of freedom ordered as in (5.61), we have

$$\mathbf{K} = \frac{Eh^3}{12} \int_0^L \begin{bmatrix} 0 \\ 0 \\ 0 \\ h_1' \\ h_2' \\ h_3' \end{bmatrix} [0 \quad 0 \quad 0 \quad h_1' \quad h_2' \quad h_3'] \, dx$$

$$+ \frac{5Gh}{6} \int_0^L \begin{bmatrix} h_1' \\ h_2' \\ h_3' \\ -h_1 \\ -h_2 \\ -h_3 \end{bmatrix} [h_1' \quad h_2' \quad h_3' \quad -h_1 \quad -h_2 \quad -h_3] \, dx$$

and

$$\mathbf{R}^T = -P[-\tfrac{1}{9} \quad \tfrac{2}{9} \quad \tfrac{8}{9} \quad 0 \quad 0 \quad 0]$$

The element in Fig. 5.19 is a pure displacement-based element (assuming exact integration of all integrals) and can be employed provided three or four nodes are used (and the interior nodes are located at the midpoint and third-points, respectively). However, if the two-node element is employed or the interior nodes of the three- and four-node elements are not located at the midpoint and third-points, respectively, the use of the element cannot be recommended because the shearing deformations are not represented to sufficient accuracy. This deficiency is particularly pronounced when the element is thin.

In order to obtain some insight into the behavior of these elements when the beam becomes thin, we recall that the principle of virtual work is equivalent to the stationarity of the total potential (see Example 4.4). For the beam formulation the total potential is given by

$$\Pi = \frac{EI}{2} \int_0^L \left(\frac{d\beta}{dx}\right)^2 dx + \frac{GAk}{2} \int_0^L \left(\frac{dw}{dx} - \beta\right)^2 dx - \int_0^L pw \, dx - \int_0^L m\beta \, dx \qquad (5.65)$$

where the first two integrals represent, respectively, the bending and shearing strain energies and the last two integrals represent the potential of the loads.

Let us consider the total potential Π

$$\tilde{\Pi} = \int_0^L \left(\frac{d\beta}{dx}\right)^2 dx + \frac{GAk}{EI} \int_0^L \left(\frac{dw}{dx} - \beta\right)^2 dx \qquad (5.66)$$

which is obtained by neglecting the load contributions in (5.65) and dividing by $\frac{1}{2}EI$. The relation in (5.66) shows the relative importance of the bending and shearing contributions to the stiffness matrix of an element, where we note that the factor GAk/EI in the shearing term can be very large when a thin element is considered. This factor can be interpreted as a penalty number (see Section 3.4.1); i.e., we can write

$$\tilde{\Pi} = \int_0^L \left(\frac{d\beta}{dx}\right)^2 dx + \alpha \int_0^L \left(\frac{dw}{dx} - \beta\right)^2 dx; \qquad \alpha = \frac{GAk}{EI} \qquad (5.67)$$

where $\alpha \rightarrow \infty$ as $h \rightarrow 0$. However, this means that as the beam becomes thin, the constraint of zero shear deformations (i.e., $dw/dx = \beta$ with $\gamma = 0$) will be approached.

This argument holds for the actual continuous model which is governed by the stationarity condition of $\tilde{\Pi}$.

Considering now the finite element representation, it is important that the finite element displacement assumptions on β and w *admit* that for large values of α the shearing

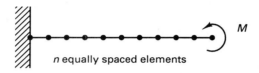

n equally spaced elements

$L = 10$ m
Square cross section; height = 0.1 m
2-node beam elements (full integration)
Young's modulus E

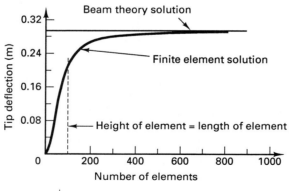

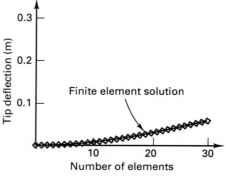

Figure 5.20   Solution of cantilever beam problem; tip deflection as a number of elements used, showing locking of elements

deformations can be small throughout the domain of the element. If by virtue of the assumptions used on w and β the shearing deformations cannot be small—and indeed zero—everywhere, then an erroneous shear strain energy (which can be large compared with the bending energy) is included in the analysis. This error results into much smaller displacements than the exact values when the beam structure analyzed is thin. Hence, in such cases, the finite element models are much too stiff.

This phenomenon is observed when the two-node beam element in Fig. 5.19 is used, which therefore should not be employed in the analysis of thin beam structures, and the conclusion is also applicable to the pure displacement-based low-order plate and shell elements discussed in Section 5.4.2. The very stiff behavior exhibited by the thin elements has been referred to as *element shear locking*. Figure 5.20 shows an example of locking using the two-node displacement-based element. We study the phenomenon of shear locking in the following example (see also Section 4.5.7).

EXAMPLE 5.25:   Consider a two-node isoparametric beam element modeling a cantilever beam that is subjected to only a moment end load (see Fig. E5.25). Determine what values of θ_2, w_2 would be obtained assuming that the shear strain is zero.

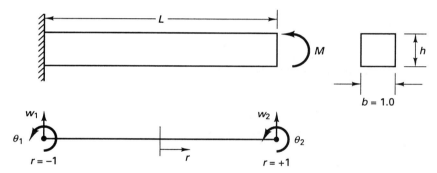

Figure E5.25   Two-node element representing a cantilever beam

The interpolations for w and β, for the given data, are

$$\beta = \frac{1+r}{2}\theta_2$$

$$w = \frac{1+r}{2}w_2$$

Hence, the shearing strain is

$$\gamma = \frac{w_2}{L} - \frac{1+r}{2}\theta_2$$

For an applied moment only, the shearing strain is to be zero. Imposing this condition gives

$$0 = \frac{w_2}{L} - \frac{1+r}{2}\theta_2 \tag{a}$$

However, for this expression to be zero all along the beam (i.e., for any value $-1 \leq r \leq +1$), we clearly must have $w_2 = \theta_2 = 0$. Hence, a zero shear strain in the beam can be reached only when there are no deformations!

Similarly, if we enforce (a) to hold at the two Gauss points $r = \pm 1/\sqrt{3}$, (i.e., if we use two-point Gauss integration), we obtain the two equations,

$$\begin{bmatrix} \dfrac{1}{L} & -\dfrac{1 + 1/\sqrt{3}}{2} \\[2mm] \dfrac{1}{L} & -\dfrac{1 - 1/\sqrt{3}}{2} \end{bmatrix} \begin{bmatrix} w_2 \\ \theta_2 \end{bmatrix} = \begin{bmatrix} 0 \\ 0 \end{bmatrix}$$

Since the coefficient matrix is nonsingular, the only solution is $w_2 = \theta_2 = 0$. This is of course the result obtained before, because setting the linearly varying shear strain equal to zero at two points means imposing a zero shear strain all along the element.

However, we can now also use (a) to investigate what happens when we enforce the shear strain to be zero only at the midpoint of the beam (i. e., at $r = 0$). In this case, (a) gives the relation

$$w_2 = \frac{\theta_2}{2} L \tag{b}$$

Hence, if we were to assume a constant shear strain of value

$$\gamma = \frac{w_2}{L} - \frac{\theta_2}{2}$$

a more attractive element might be obtained. We actually used this assumption in Example 4.30.

Various procedures may be proposed to modify this pure displacement-based beam element formulation—and the formulation of pure displacement-based isoparametric plate bending elements—in order to arrive at efficient nonlocking elements.

The key point of any such formulation is that the resulting element should be reliable and efficient; this means in particular that the element stiffness matrix must not contain any spurious zero energy mode and that the element should have a high predictive capability under general geometric and loading conditions. These requirements are considerably more easy to satisfy with beam elements than with general plate and shell elements.

An effective beam element is obtained by using a mixed interpolation of displacements and transverse shear strains. This mixed interpolation is an application of the more general procedure employed in the formulation of plate bending and shell elements (see Section 5.4.2).

The discussion in Example 5.25 suggests that to satisfy the possibility of a zero transverse shear strain in the element, we may assume for an element with q nodes the interpolations (see also Example 4.30)

$$\left. \begin{aligned} w &= \sum_{i=1}^{q} h_i w_i \\ \beta &= \sum_{i=1}^{q} h_i \theta_i \end{aligned} \right\} \tag{5.68}$$

$$\gamma = \sum_{i=1}^{q-1} h_i^* \gamma|_{G_i}^{\mathrm{DI}} \tag{5.69}$$

Here the h_i are the displacement and section rotation interpolation functions for q nodes and the h_i^* are the interpolation functions for the transverse shear strains. These functions are associated with the $(q - 1)$ discrete values $\gamma|_{G_i}^{\mathrm{DI}}$, where $\gamma|_{G_i}^{\mathrm{DI}}$ is the shear strain at the Gauss point i directly obtained from the displacement/section rotation interpolations (i.e., by *d*isplacement *i*nterpolation); hence,

$$\gamma\bigg|_{G_i}^{\mathrm{DI}} = \left(\frac{dw}{dx} - \beta\right)\bigg|_{G_i} \tag{5.70}$$

Figure 5.21 shows the shear strain interpolations used for the two-, three-, and four-node beam elements. These mixed interpolated beam elements are very reliable in that they do not lock, show excellent convergence behavior, and of course do not contain any spurious zero energy mode. For the solution of the problem in Fig. 5.20 only a single element needs to be employed to obtain the exact tip displacement and rotation. We can easily prove this result for the two-node element by continuing the analysis presented in Example 5.25, and the three- and four-node elements contain the interpolations of the two-node element and must therefore also give the exact solution. Hence, there is a drastic improvement in element behavior resulting from the use of mixed interpolation.

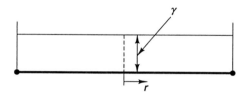

2-node element, constant γ; G_1 corresponds to $r = 0$

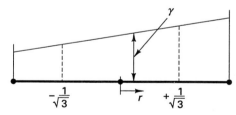

3-node element, linearly varying γ; G_1 and G_2 correspond to $r = \pm\sqrt{\dfrac{1}{3}}$

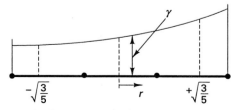

4-node element, parabolically varying γ;

G_1, G_2, and G_3 correspond to $r = \pm\sqrt{\dfrac{3}{5}}$ and $r = 0$

Figure 5.21   Shear strain interpolations for mixed interpolated beam elements

In addition, there is an attractive computational feature: the stiffness matrices of these elements can be evaluated efficiently by simply integrating the displacement-based model with one-point Gauss integration for the two-node element, two-point Gauss integration for the three-node element, and three-point Gauss integration for the four-node element. Namely, using one-point integration in the evaluation of the two-node element stiffness matrix, the transverse shear strain is assumed to be constant, and the contribution from the bending deformation is still evaluated exactly. A similar argument holds for the three- and four-node elements. This computational approach to evaluating the stiffness matrices of the elements may be called "reduced integration" of the displacement-based element but in fact is actually full integration of the mixed interpolated element. A mathematical analysis of the elements is presented in Section 4.5.7.

General Curved Beam Elements

In the preceding discussion we assumed that the elements considered were straight; hence the formulation was based on equation (5.58). To arrive at a general three-dimensional curved beam element formulation, we proceed in a similar way but now need to interpolate the curved geometry and corresponding beam displacements. With these interpolations a pure displacement-based element is derived that, as for the straight elements, is very stiff and not useful. In the case of straight beam elements only spurious shear strains are generated (always for the two-node element, and for the three- and four-node elements when the interior nodes are not at their natural positions; see Exercise 5.34), but for curved elements also spurious membrane strains are obtained. Hence, a curved element also displays *membrane locking* (see, for example, H. Stolarski and T. Belytschko [A]).

Efficient general beam elements are obtained by the mixed interpolation already introduced. However, now, in the case of general three-dimensional action, the transverse shear strains *and* the bending and membrane strains are interpolated using the functions in Fig. 5.21. These strain interpolations are tied to the nodal point displacements and rotations by evaluating the displacement-based strains and equating them to the assumed strains at the Gauss integration points.

It follows that the mixed interpolated element stiffness matrices can be numerically obtained by evaluating the displacement-based element matrices with Gauss point integration at the points given in Fig. 5.21.

Consider the three-dimensional beam of rectangular cross section in Fig. 5.22, and let us assume first that an accurate representation of the torsional rigidity is not required.

The basic kinematic assumption in the formulation of the element is the same as that employed in the formulation of the two-dimensional element in Fig. 5.19: namely that plane sections originally normal to the centerline axis remain plane and undistorted under deformation but not necessarily normal to this axis. This kinematic assumption does not allow for warping effects in torsion (which we can introduce by additional displacement functions; see Exercise 5.37).

Using the natural coordinates r, s, t, the Cartesian coordinates of a point in the element with q nodal points are then, before and after deformations,

$$^{\ell}x(r, s, t) = \sum_{k=1}^{q} h_k \, {}^{\ell}x_k + \frac{t}{2} \sum_{k=1}^{q} a_k h_k \, {}^{\ell}V_{tx}^k + \frac{s}{2} \sum_{k=1}^{q} b_k h_k \, {}^{\ell}V_{sx}^k$$

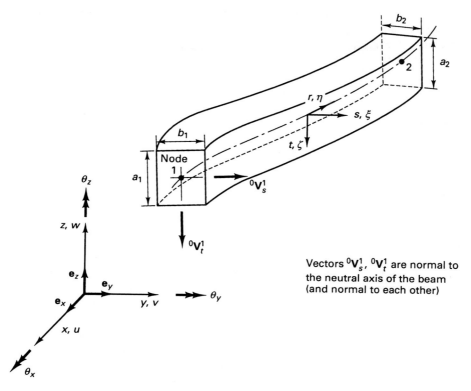

Figure 5.22   Three-dimensional beam element

$$\ell y(r, s, t) = \sum_{k=1}^{q} h_k\, \ell y_k + \frac{t}{2} \sum_{k=1}^{q} a_k h_k\, \ell V_{ty}^{k} + \frac{s}{2} \sum_{k=1}^{q} b_k h_k\, \ell V_{sy}^{k} \tag{5.71}$$

$$\ell z(r, s, t) = \sum_{k=1}^{q} h_k\, \ell z_k + \frac{t}{2} \sum_{k=1}^{q} a_k h_k\, \ell V_{tz}^{k} + \frac{s}{2} \sum_{k=1}^{q} b_k h_k\, \ell V_{sz}^{k}$$

where the $h_k(r)$ are the interpolation functions summarized in Fig. 5.3 and

$\ell x, \ell y, \ell z$ = Cartesian cordinates of any point in the element

$\ell x_k, \ell y_k, \ell z_k$ = Cartesian coordinates of nodal point k

a_k, b_k = cross-sectional dimensions of the beam at nodal point k

$\ell V_{tx}^{k}, \ell V_{ty}^{k}, \ell V_{tz}^{k}$ = components of unit vector ℓV_t^{k} in direction t at nodal point k

$\ell V_{sx}^{k}, \ell V_{sy}^{k}, \ell V_{sz}^{k}$ = components of unit vector ℓV_s^{k} in direction s at nodal point k; we call ℓV_t^{k} and ℓV_s^{k} the normal vectors or director vectors at nodal point k,

and the left superscript ℓ denotes the configuration of the element; i.e., $\ell = 0$ denotes the original configuration, whereas $\ell = 1$ corresponds to the configuration in the deformed position.

We assume here that the vectors $^0\mathbf{V}_s^k$, $^0\mathbf{V}_t^k$ are normal to the neutral axis of the beam and are normal to each other. However, this condition can be relaxed, as is done in the shell element formulation (see Section 5.4.2).

The displacement components at any point of the element are

$$u(r, s, t) = {}^1x - {}^0x$$

$$v(r, s, t) = {}^1y - {}^0y \tag{5.72}$$

$$w(r, s, t) = {}^1z - {}^0z$$

and substituting from (5.71), we obtain

$$u(r, s, t) = \sum_{k=1}^{q} h_k u_k + \frac{t}{2} \sum_{k=1}^{q} a_k h_k V_{tx}^k + \frac{s}{2} \sum_{k=1}^{q} b_k h_k V_{sx}^k$$

$$v(r, s, t) = \sum_{k=1}^{q} h_k v_k + \frac{t}{2} \sum_{k=1}^{q} a_k h_k V_{ty}^k + \frac{s}{2} \sum_{k=1}^{q} b_k h_k V_{sy}^k \tag{5.73}$$

$$w(r, s, t) = \sum_{k=1}^{q} h_k w_k + \frac{t}{2} \sum_{k=1}^{q} a_k h_k V_{tz}^k + \frac{s}{2} \sum_{k=1}^{q} b_k h_k V_{sz}^k$$

where

$$\mathbf{V}_t^k = {}^1\mathbf{V}_t^k - {}^0\mathbf{V}_t^k; \qquad \mathbf{V}_s^k = {}^1\mathbf{V}_s^k - {}^0\mathbf{V}_s^k \tag{5.74}$$

Finally, we express the vectors $\mathbf{V}_t^k$ and $\mathbf{V}_s^k$ in terms of rotations about the Cartesian axes x, y, z:

$$\mathbf{V}_t^k = \boldsymbol{\theta}_k \times {}^0\mathbf{V}_t^k$$

$$\mathbf{V}_s^k = \boldsymbol{\theta}_k \times {}^0\mathbf{V}_s^k \tag{5.75}$$

where $\boldsymbol{\theta}_k$ is a vector listing the nodal point rotations at nodal point k (see Fig. 5.22):

$$\boldsymbol{\theta}_k = \begin{bmatrix} \theta_x^k \\ \theta_y^k \\ \theta_z^k \end{bmatrix} \tag{5.76}$$

Using (5.71) to (5.76), we have all the basic equations necessary to establish the displacement and strain interpolation matrices employed in evaluating the beam element matrices.

The terms in the displacement interpolation matrix $\mathbf{H}$ are obtained by substituting (5.75) into (5.73). To evaluate the strain-displacement matrix, we recognize that for the beam the only strain components of interest are the longitudinal strain $\epsilon_{\eta\eta}$ and transverse shear strains $\gamma_{\eta\xi}$ and $\gamma_{\eta\zeta}$, where η, ξ, and ζ are convected (body-attached) coordinates axes (see Fig. 5.22). Thus, we seek a relation of the form

$$\begin{bmatrix} \epsilon_{\eta\eta} \\ \gamma_{\eta\xi} \\ \gamma_{\eta\zeta} \end{bmatrix} = \sum_{k=1}^{q} \mathbf{B}_k \hat{\mathbf{u}}_k \tag{5.77}$$

where

$$\hat{\mathbf{u}}_k^T = [u_k \; v_k \; w_k \quad \theta_x^k \; \theta_y^k \; \theta_z^k] \tag{5.78}$$

and the matrices $\mathbf{B}_k$, $k = 1, \ldots, q$, together constitute the matrix $\mathbf{B}$,

$$\mathbf{B} = [\mathbf{B}_1 \quad \cdots \quad \mathbf{B}_q] \tag{5.79}$$

Following the usual procedure of isoparametric finite element formulation, we have, using (5.73),

$$
\begin{bmatrix} \dfrac{\partial u}{\partial r} \\[2mm] \dfrac{\partial u}{\partial s} \\[2mm] \dfrac{\partial u}{\partial t} \end{bmatrix} = \sum_{k=1}^{q} \begin{bmatrix} \dfrac{\partial h_k}{\partial r} & [1 & (g)^k_{1i} & (g)^k_{2i} & (g)^k_{3i}] \\[2mm] h_k & [0 & (\hat{g})^k_{1i} & (\hat{g})^k_{2i} & (\hat{g})^k_{3i}] \\[2mm] h_k & [0 & (\bar{g})^k_{1i} & (\bar{g})^k_{2i} & (\bar{g})^k_{3i}] \end{bmatrix} \begin{bmatrix} u_k \\[1mm] \theta^k_x \\[1mm] \theta^k_y \\[1mm] \theta^k_z \end{bmatrix} \tag{5.80}
$$

and the derivatives of v and w are obtained by simply substituting v and w for u. In (5.80) we have $i = 1$ for u, $i = 2$ for v, and $i = 3$ for w, and we employ the notation

$$
(\hat{g})^k = \frac{b_k}{2} \begin{bmatrix} 0 & -{}^0V^k_{sz} & {}^0V^k_{sy} \\[1mm] {}^0V^k_{sz} & 0 & -{}^0V^k_{sx} \\[1mm] -{}^0V^k_{sy} & {}^0V^k_{sx} & 0 \end{bmatrix} \tag{5.81}
$$

$$
(\bar{g})^k = \frac{a_k}{2} \begin{bmatrix} 0 & -{}^0V^k_{tz} & {}^0V^k_{ty} \\[1mm] {}^0V^k_{tz} & 0 & -{}^0V^k_{tx} \\[1mm] -{}^0V^k_{ty} & {}^0V^k_{tx} & 0 \end{bmatrix} \tag{5.82}
$$

$$
(g)^k_{ij} = s(\hat{g})^k_{ij} + t(\bar{g})^k_{ij} \tag{5.83}
$$

To obtain the displacement derivatives corresponding to the coordinate axes x, y, and z, we employ the Jacobian transformation

$$
\frac{\partial}{\partial \mathbf{x}} = \mathbf{J}^{-1} \frac{\partial}{\partial \mathbf{r}} \tag{5.84}
$$

where the Jacobian matrix $\mathbf{J}$ contains the derivatives of the coordinates x, y, and z with respect to the natural coordinates r, s, and t. Substituting from (5.80) into (5.84), we obtain

$$
\begin{bmatrix} \dfrac{\partial u}{\partial x} \\[2mm] \dfrac{\partial u}{\partial y} \\[2mm] \dfrac{\partial u}{\partial z} \end{bmatrix} = \sum_{k=1}^{q} \begin{bmatrix} J^{-1}_{11} \dfrac{\partial h_k}{\partial r} & (G1)^k_{i1} & (G2)^k_{i1} & (G3)^k_{i1} \\[2mm] J^{-1}_{21} \dfrac{\partial h_k}{\partial r} & (G1)^k_{i2} & (G2)^k_{i2} & (G3)^k_{i2} \\[2mm] J^{-1}_{31} \dfrac{\partial h_k}{\partial r} & (G1)^k_{i3} & (G2)^k_{i3} & (G3)^k_{i3} \end{bmatrix} \begin{bmatrix} u_k \\[1mm] \theta^k_x \\[1mm] \theta^k_y \\[1mm] \theta^k_z \end{bmatrix} \tag{5.85}
$$

and again, the derivatives of v and w are obtained by simply substituting v and w for u. In (5.85) we employ the notation

$$
(Gm)^k_{in} = [J^{-1}_{n1}(g)^k_{mi}]\frac{\partial h_k}{\partial r} + [J^{-1}_{n2}(\hat{g})^k_{mi} + J^{-1}_{n3}(\bar{g})^k_{mi}]h_k \tag{5.86}
$$

Using the displacement derivatives in (5.85), we can now calculate the elements of the strain-displacement matrix at the element Gauss point by establishing the strain components corresponding to the x, y, z axes and transforming these components to the local strains $\epsilon_{\eta\eta}$, $\gamma_{\eta\xi}$, and $\gamma_{\eta\zeta}$.

The corresponding stress-strain law to be employed in the formulation is (using k as the shear correction factor)

TABLE 5.2 *Performance of isoparametric beam elements in the analysis of the problem in Fig. 5.23*

(a) $\theta_{\text{finite element}}/\theta_{\text{analytical}}$ at tip of beam, one three-node element solution

	Midnode at $\alpha = 22.5°$		Midnode at $\alpha = 20°$	
h/R	Displacement-based	Mixed interpolated	Displacement-based	Mixed interpolated
0.50	0.92	1.00	0.91	1.00
0.10	0.31	1.00	0.31	1.00
0.01	0.004	1.00	0.005	1.00
0.001	0.00004	1.00	0.00005	1.00

(b) $\theta_{\text{finite element}}/\theta_{\text{analytical}}$ at tip of beam, one four-node element solution

	Internal nodes at $\alpha_1 = 15°$, $\alpha_2 = 30°$		Internal nodes at $\alpha_1 = 10°$, $\alpha_2 = 25°$	
h/R	Displacement-based	Mixed interpolated	Displacement-based	Mixed interpolated
0.50	1.00	1.00	0.97	0.997
0.10	0.999	1.00	0.70	0.997
0.01	0.998	1.00	0.37	0.997
0.001	0.998	1.00	0.37	0.997

$$\begin{bmatrix} \tau_{\eta\eta} \\ \tau_{\eta\xi} \\ \tau_{\eta\zeta} \end{bmatrix} = \begin{bmatrix} E & 0 & 0 \\ 0 & Gk & 0 \\ 0 & 0 & Gk \end{bmatrix} \begin{bmatrix} \epsilon_{\eta\eta} \\ \gamma_{\eta\xi} \\ \gamma_{\eta\zeta} \end{bmatrix} \tag{5.87}$$

The stiffness matrix of the element is then obtained by numerical integration, using for the r-integration the Gauss points shown in Fig. 5.21 and for the s- and t-integrations either the Newton-Cotes or Gauss formulas (see Section 5.5).

Table 5.2 illustrates the performance of the mixed interpolated elements in the analysis of the curved cantilever in Fig. 5.23 and shows the efficiency of the elements.

As pointed out already, this element does not include warping effects, which can be significant for the rectangular cross-sectional beam elements and of course for beam ele-

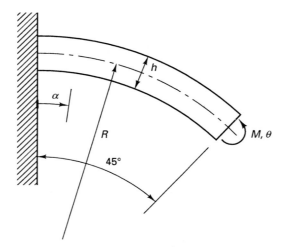

Figure 5.23 Curved cantilever problem to test isoparametric beam elements

ments of general cross sections. Warping displacements can be introduced by adding appropriate displacement interpolations to those given in (5.73). If additional degrees of freedom are also introduced, corresponding to the warping deformations, continuity of warping between elements can be imposed. However, it may be sufficient to allow for "free" warping in each element without enforcing continuity of warping between elements. This is achieved by adding warping deformations to the displacement interpolations and then statically condensing out the intensity of these deformations (see K. J. Bathe and A. B. Chaudhary [A] and Exercise 5.37).

In another application of the general curved beam formulation, the cross section is circular and hollow, that is, a pipe cross section is considered. In this case, ovalization and warping deformations can be important when the element is curved, and once again the displacement interpolations given in (5.73) must be amended. In this case it is important to impose continuity in the ovalization and warping deformations, and for this reason additional nodal degrees of freedom must be introduced (see K. J. Bathe and C. A. Almeida [A]).

Considering the basic formulation in (5.71) to (5.87), we recognize that the element can be arbitrarily curved and that the cross-sectional dimensions can change along its axis. The beam width and height and the location of the element axis are interpolated along the element. In the given formulation, the axis of the element coincides with the element geometric midline, but this is not necessary, and more general elements can be formulated directly (see Exercise 5.38).

In addition to representing a general formulation for linear analysis, this approach is particularly useful for the nonlinear large displacement analysis of beam structures. As discussed in Section 6.5.1, in such analyses initially straight beam elements become curved and distorted, and these deformations can be modeled accurately.

Of course, if linear analysis is pursued and the element is straight and has a constant cross-sectional area, the formulation reduces to the formulation given in (5.56) to (5.70). We illustrate this point in the following example.

EXAMPLE 5.26: Show that the application of the general formulation in (5.71) to (5.87) to the beam element in Fig. E5.24 reduces to the use of (5.58).

For the application of the general relations in (5.71) to (5.87), we refer to Figs. E5.24 and 5.22 and thus have

$$
{}^0\mathbf{V}_s = \begin{bmatrix} 0 \\ 1 \\ 0 \end{bmatrix}; \qquad {}^0\mathbf{V}_t = \begin{bmatrix} 0 \\ 0 \\ 1 \end{bmatrix}; \qquad a_k = 1; \quad b_k = h; \quad k = 1, 2, 3
$$

Hence, the relations in (5.71) reduce to

$$
{}^0x = \sum_{k=1}^{3} h_k \, {}^0x_k
$$

$$
{}^0y = \frac{s}{2} h
$$

$$
{}^0z = \frac{t}{2}
$$

We next evaluate (5.75) to obtain (see Section 2.4)

$$\mathbf{V}_t^k = \det \begin{bmatrix} \mathbf{e}_x & \mathbf{e}_y & \mathbf{e}_z \\ \theta_x^k & \theta_y^k & \theta_z^k \\ 0 & 0 & 1 \end{bmatrix}$$

or

$$\mathbf{V}_t^k = \theta_y^k \mathbf{e}_x - \theta_x^k \mathbf{e}_y \tag{a}$$

and

$$\mathbf{V}_s^k = \det \begin{bmatrix} \mathbf{e}_x & \mathbf{e}_y & \mathbf{e}_z \\ \theta_x^k & \theta_y^k & \theta_z^k \\ 0 & 1 & 0 \end{bmatrix}$$

or

$$\mathbf{V}_s^k = -\theta_z^k \mathbf{e}_x + \theta_x^k \mathbf{e}_z \tag{b}$$

The relations in (a) and (b) correspond to the three-dimensional action of the beam. We allow rotations only about the z-axis, in which case

$$\mathbf{V}_t^k = \mathbf{0}; \qquad \mathbf{V}_s^k = -\theta_z^k \mathbf{e}_x$$

Furthermore, we assume that the nodal points can displace only in the y direction. Hence, (5.73) yields the displacement assumptions

$$u(r, s) = -\frac{sh}{2} \sum_{k=1}^{3} h_k \theta_z^k \tag{c}$$

$$v(r) = \sum_{k=1}^{3} h_k v_k \tag{d}$$

where we note that u is only a function of r, s and v is only a function of r. These relations are identical to the displacement assumptions used before, but with the more conventional beam displacement notation we identified the transverse displacement and section rotation at a nodal point with w_k and θ_k instead of v_k and θ_z^k.

Now using (5.80), we obtain

$$\begin{bmatrix} \dfrac{\partial u}{\partial r} \\ \dfrac{\partial u}{\partial s} \end{bmatrix} = \sum_{k=1}^{3} \begin{bmatrix} -\dfrac{sh}{2}\dfrac{\partial h_k}{\partial r} \\ -\dfrac{h}{2}h_k \end{bmatrix} \theta_z^k$$

$$\begin{bmatrix} \dfrac{\partial v}{\partial r} \\ \dfrac{\partial v}{\partial s} \end{bmatrix} = \sum_{k=1}^{3} \begin{bmatrix} \dfrac{\partial h_k}{\partial r} \\ 0 \end{bmatrix} v_k$$

These relations could also be directly obtained by differentiating the displacements in (c) and (d). Since

$$\mathbf{J} = \begin{bmatrix} \dfrac{L}{2} & 0 \\ 0 & \dfrac{h}{2} \end{bmatrix}; \qquad \mathbf{J}^{-1} = \begin{bmatrix} \dfrac{2}{L} & 0 \\ 0 & \dfrac{2}{h} \end{bmatrix}$$

we obtain
$$\begin{bmatrix} \dfrac{\partial u}{\partial x} \\[3mm] \dfrac{\partial u}{\partial y} \end{bmatrix} = \sum_{k=1}^{3} \begin{bmatrix} -\dfrac{h}{2}\dfrac{2}{L}s\dfrac{\partial h_k}{\partial r} \\[3mm] -h_k \end{bmatrix} \theta_z^k \tag{e}$$

and
$$\begin{bmatrix} \dfrac{\partial v}{\partial x} \\[3mm] \dfrac{\partial v}{\partial y} \end{bmatrix} = \sum_{k=1}^{3} \begin{bmatrix} \dfrac{2}{L}\dfrac{\partial h_k}{\partial r} \\[3mm] 0 \end{bmatrix} v_k \tag{f}$$

To analyze the response of the beam in Fig E5.24 we now use the principle of virtual work [see (4.7)] with the appropriate strain measures:

$$\int_{-1}^{+1}\int_{-1}^{+1} \begin{bmatrix} \overline{\epsilon}_{xx} & \overline{\gamma}_{xy} \end{bmatrix} \begin{bmatrix} E & 0 \\ 0 & Gk \end{bmatrix} \begin{bmatrix} \epsilon_{xx} \\ \gamma_{xy} \end{bmatrix} \det \mathbf{J}\, ds\, dr = -P\overline{v}\,|_{r=1/3} \tag{g}$$

where
$$\epsilon_{xx} = \frac{\partial u}{\partial x}; \qquad \overline{\epsilon}_{xx} = \frac{\partial \overline{u}}{\partial x}$$

$$\gamma_{xy} = \frac{\partial u}{\partial y} + \frac{\partial v}{\partial x}; \qquad \overline{\gamma}_{xy} = \frac{\partial \overline{u}}{\partial y} + \frac{\partial \overline{v}}{\partial x}$$

Considering the relations in (e), (f), (g), and (5.58), we recognize that (g) corresponds to (5.58) if we use $\beta \equiv \theta_z$, and $w \equiv v$.

Transition Elements

In the preceding discussions, we considered continuum elements and beam elements separately. However, the very close relationship between these elements should be recognized; the only differences are the kinematic assumption that plane sections initially normal to the neutral axis remain plane and the stress assumption that stresses normal to the neutral axis are zero. In the beam formulation presented, the kinematic assumption was incorporated directly in the basic geometry and displacement interpolations and the stress assumption was used in the stress-strain law. Since these two assumptions are the only two basic differences between the beam and continuum elements, it is apparent that the structural element matrices can also be derived from the continuum element matrices by degeneration. Furthermore, elements can be devised that act as transition elements between continuum and structural elements. Consider the following example.

EXAMPLE 5.27: Assume that the strain-displacement matrix of a four-node plane stress element has been derived. Show how the strain-displacement matrix of a two-node beam element can be constructed.

Figure E5.27 shows the plane stress element with its degrees of freedom and the beam element for which we want to establish the strain-displacement matrix. Consider node 2 of the beam element and nodes 2 and 3 of the plane stress element. The entries in the strain-displacement matrix of the plane stress element are

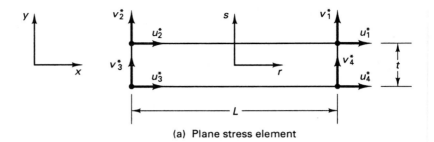

(a) Plane stress element

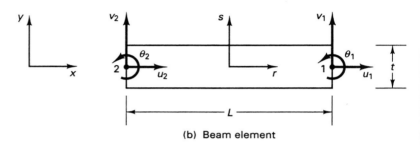

(b) Beam element

Figure E5.27   Derivation of beam element from plane stress element

$$
\mathbf{B}^* = \begin{bmatrix} \ddots & \begin{matrix} \overset{u_2^*}{\downarrow} \\ -\dfrac{1}{2L}(1+s) \\[2mm] 0 \\[2mm] \dfrac{1}{2t}(1-r) \end{matrix} & \begin{matrix} \overset{v_2^*}{\downarrow} \\ 0 \\[2mm] \dfrac{1}{2t}(1-r) \\[2mm] -\dfrac{1}{2L}(1+s) \end{matrix} & \begin{matrix} \overset{u_3^*}{\downarrow} \\ -\dfrac{1}{2L}(1-s) \\[2mm] 0 \\[2mm] -\dfrac{1}{2t}(1-r) \end{matrix} & \begin{matrix} \overset{v_3^*}{\downarrow} \\ 0 \\[2mm] -\dfrac{1}{2t}(1-r) \\[2mm] -\dfrac{1}{2L}(1-s) \end{matrix} & \ddots \end{bmatrix} \tag{a}
$$

Using now the beam deformation assumptions, we have the following kinematic constraints:

$$
u_2^* = u_2 - \frac{t}{2}\theta_2
$$

$$
u_3^* = u_2 + \frac{t}{2}\theta_2 \tag{b}
$$

$$
v_2^* = v_2; \qquad v_3^* = v_2
$$

These constraints are now substituted to obtain from the elements of $\mathbf{B}^*$ in (a) the elements of the strain-displacement matrix of the beam. Using the rows of $\mathbf{B}^*$, we have with (b),

$$
-\frac{1}{2L}(1+s)u_2^* - \frac{1}{2L}(1-s)u_3^* = -\frac{1}{2L}(1+s)\left(u_2 - \frac{t}{2}\theta_2\right)
$$

$$
-\frac{1}{2L}(1-s)\left(u_2 + \frac{t}{2}\theta_2\right) \tag{c}
$$

$$\frac{1}{2t}(1-r)v_2^* - \frac{1}{2t}(1-r)v_3^* = \frac{1}{2t}(1-r)v_2 - \frac{1}{2t}(1-r)v_2 \tag{d}$$

$$\frac{1}{2t}(1-r)u_2^* - \frac{1}{2L}(1+s)v_2^* - \frac{1}{2t}(1-r)u_3^* - \frac{1}{2L}(1-s)v_3^*$$

$$= \frac{1}{2t}(1-r)\left(u_2 - \frac{t}{2}\theta_2\right) - \frac{1}{2L}(1+s)v_2 - \frac{1}{2t}(1-r)\left(u_2 + \frac{t}{2}\theta_2\right) - \frac{1}{2L}(1-s)v_2 \tag{e}$$

The relations on the right-hand side of (c) to (e) comprise the entries of the beam strain-displacement matrix

$$\mathbf{B} = \begin{bmatrix} & \overset{\displaystyle u_2}{\downarrow} & \overset{\displaystyle v_2}{\downarrow} & \overset{\displaystyle \theta_2}{\downarrow} \\ & -\dfrac{1}{L} & 0 & \dfrac{t}{2L}s \\ \cdots & 0 & 0 & 0 \\ & 0 & -\dfrac{1}{L} & -\dfrac{1}{2}(1-r) \end{bmatrix}$$

However, the first- and third-row entries are those that are also obtained using the beam formulation of (5.71) to (5.86). We should note that the zeros in the second row of **B** only express the fact that the strain ϵ_{yy} is not included in the formulation. This strain is actually equal to $-\nu\epsilon_{xx}$ because the stress τ_{yy} is zero. As pointed out earlier, we would use the entries in **B** at $r = 0$.

The formulation of a structural element using the approach discussed in Example 5.27 is computationally inefficient and is certainly not recommended for general analysis. However, it is instructive to study this approach and recognize that the structural element matrices can in principle be obtained from continuum element matrices by imposing the appropriate static and kinematic assumptions. Moreover, this formulation directly suggests the construction of transition elements that can be used in an effective manner to couple structural and continuum elements without the use of constraint equations [see Fig. E5.28(a)]. To demonstrate the formulation of transition elements, we consider in the following example a simple transition beam element.

EXAMPLE 5.28: Construct the displacement and strain-displacement interpolation matrices of the transition element shown in Fig. E5.28.

We define the nodal point displacement vector of the element as

$$\hat{\mathbf{u}}^T = \begin{bmatrix} u_1 & v_1 & u_2 & v_2 & u_3 & v_3 & \theta_3 \end{bmatrix} \tag{a}$$

Since at $r = +1$ we have plane stress element degrees of freedom, the interpolation functions corresponding to nodes 1 and 2 are (see Fig. 5.4)

$$h_1 = \tfrac{1}{4}(1+r)(1+s); \qquad h_2 = \tfrac{1}{4}(1+r)(1-s)$$

Node 3 is a beam node, and the interpolation function is (see Fig. 5.3)

$$h_3 = \tfrac{1}{2}(1-r)$$

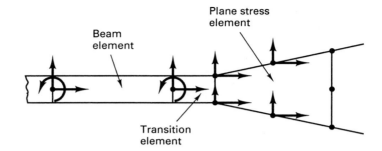

(a) Beam transition element connecting beam and plane stress elements

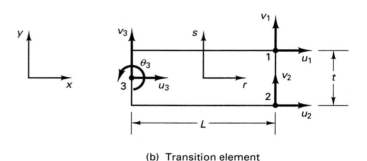

(b) Transition element

Figure E5.28   Two-dimensional displacement-based beam transition element

The displacements of the element are thus

$$u(r, s) = h_1 u_1 + h_2 u_2 + h_3 u_3 - \frac{t}{2} s h_3 \theta_3$$

Hence, corresponding to the displacement vector in (a) we have

$$\mathbf{H} = \begin{bmatrix} h_1 & 0 & h_2 & 0 & h_3 & 0 & -\dfrac{t}{2} s h_3 \\ 0 & h_1 & 0 & h_2 & 0 & h_3 & 0 \end{bmatrix}$$

The coordinate interpolation is the same as that of the four-node plane stress element:

$$x(r, s) = \frac{1}{2}(1 + r)L$$

$$y(r, s) = \frac{s}{2} t$$

Hence, $$\mathbf{J} = \begin{bmatrix} \dfrac{L}{2} & 0 \\ 0 & \dfrac{t}{2} \end{bmatrix} ; \quad \mathbf{J}^{-1} = \begin{bmatrix} \dfrac{2}{L} & 0 \\ 0 & \dfrac{2}{t} \end{bmatrix}$$

Using (5.25), we thus obtain

$$
\mathbf{B} = \begin{bmatrix}
\dfrac{1}{2L}(1+s) & 0 & \dfrac{1}{2L}(1-s) & 0 & -\dfrac{1}{L} & 0 & \dfrac{t}{2L}s \\[2ex]
0 & \dfrac{1}{2t}(1+r) & 0 & -\dfrac{1}{2t}(1+r) & 0 & 0 & 0 \\[2ex]
\dfrac{1}{2t}(1+r) & \dfrac{1}{2L}(1+s) & -\dfrac{1}{2t}(1+r) & \dfrac{1}{2L}(1-s) & 0 & -\dfrac{1}{L} & -\dfrac{1}{2}(1-r)
\end{bmatrix}
$$

We may finally note that the last three columns of the **B**-matrix could also have been derived as described in Example 5.27.

The isoparametric beam elements presented in this section are an alternative to the classical Hermitian beam elements (see Example 4.16), and we may ask how these types of beam elements compare in efficiency. There is no doubt that in linear analysis of straight, thin beams, the Hermitian elements are usually more effective, since for a cubic displacement description the isoparametric beam element requires twice as many degrees of freedom. However, the isoparametric beam element includes the effects of shear deformations and has the advantages that all displacements are interpolated to the same degree (which for the cubic element results in a cubic axial displacement variation) and that curved geometries can be represented accurately. The element is therefore used efficiently in the analysis of stiffened shells (because the element represents in a natural way the stiffeners for the shell elements discussed in the next section) and as a basis of formulating more complex elements, such as pipe and transition elements. Also, the generality of the formulation with all displacements interpolated to the same degree of variation renders the element efficient in geometric nonlinear analyses (see Section 6.5.1).

Further applications of the general beam formulation given here lie in the use for plane strain situations (see Exercise 5.40) and the development of axisymmetric shell elements.

Axisymmetric Shell Elements

The isoparametric beam element formulation presented above can be directly adapted to the analysis of axisymmetric shells. Figure 5.24 shows a typical three-node element.

In the formulation, the kinematics of the beam element is used as if it were employed in two-dimensional action (i.e., for motion in the x, y plane), but the effects of the hoop strain and stress are also included. Hence, the strain-displacement matrix of the element is the matrix of the beam amended by a row corresponding to the hoop strain u/x. This evaluation is quite analogous to the construction of the **B**-matrix of the two-dimensional axisymmetric element when compared with the two-dimensional plane stress element. In that case, also only a row corresponding to the hoop strain was added to the **B**-matrix of the plane stress element in order to obtain the **B**-matrix for the axisymmetric element. In addition of course the correct stress-strain law needs to be used (allowing for the Poisson effect coupling between the hoop and the r-direction and for the stress to be zero in the s-direction), and the integration is performed corresponding to axisymmetric conditions over 1 radian of the structure (see Example 5.9 and Exercise 5.41). Of course, using the procedures in Example 5.28, transition elements for axisymmetric shell conditions can also be designed (see Exercise 5.42).

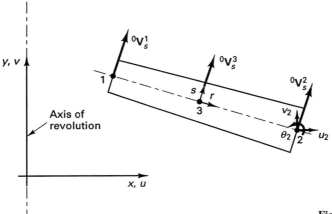

Figure 5.24   Axisymmetric shell element

5.4.2 Plate and General Shell Elements

The procedures we have employed in the previous section to formulate beam elements can also be directly used to establish effective plate and shell elements. In the following presentation we first discuss the formulation of plate elements, and then we proceed to summarize the formulation of general shell elements.

Plate Elements

The plate element formulation is a special case of the general shell element formulation presented later and is based on the theory of plates with transverse shear deformations included. This theory, due to E. Reissner [B] and R. D. Mindlin [A], uses the assumption that particles of the plate originally on a straight line that is normal to the undeformed middle surface remain on a straight line during deformation, but this line is not necessarily normal to the deformed middle surface. With this assumption, the displacement components of a point of coordinates x, y, and z are, in the small displacement bending theory,

$$u = -z\beta_x(x, y); \qquad v = -z\beta_y(x, y); \qquad w = w(x, y) \tag{5.88}$$

where w is the transverse displacement and β_x and β_y are the rotations of the normal to the undeformed middle surface in the x, z and y, z planes, respectively (see Fig. 5.25). It is instructive to note that in the Kirchhoff plate theory excluding shear deformations, $\beta_x = w_{,x}$ and $\beta_y = w_{,y}$ (and indeed we have selected the convention for β_x and β_y so as to have these Kirchhoff relations).

Considering the plate in Fig. 5.25 the bending strains ϵ_{xx}, ϵ_{yy}, γ_{xy} vary linearly through the plate thickness and are given by the curvatures of the plate using (5.88),

$$\begin{bmatrix} \epsilon_{xx} \\ \\ \epsilon_{yy} \\ \\ \gamma_{xy} \end{bmatrix} = -z \begin{bmatrix} \dfrac{\partial \beta_x}{\partial x} \\ \\ \dfrac{\partial \beta_y}{\partial y} \\ \\ \dfrac{\partial \beta_x}{\partial y} + \dfrac{\partial \beta_y}{\partial x} \end{bmatrix} \tag{5.89}$$

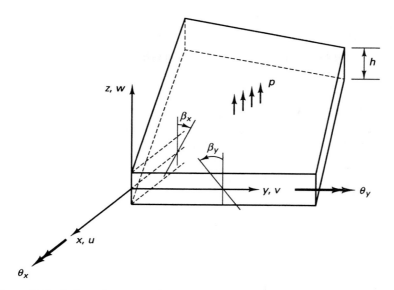

Figure 5.25 Deformation assumptions in analysis of plate including shear deformations

whereas the transverse shear strains are assumed to be constant through the thickness of the plate

$$
\begin{bmatrix} \gamma_{xz} \\ \gamma_{yz} \end{bmatrix} = \begin{bmatrix} \dfrac{\partial w}{\partial x} - \beta_x \\ \dfrac{\partial w}{\partial y} - \beta_y \end{bmatrix}
\tag{5.90}
$$

We may note that each transverse shear strain component is of the form (5.56) used in the description of the beam deformations. The state of stress in the plate corresponds to plane stress conditions (i.e., $\tau_{zz} = 0$). For an isotropic material, we can thus write

$$
\begin{bmatrix} \tau_{xx} \\ \tau_{yy} \\ \tau_{xy} \end{bmatrix} = -z \frac{E}{1 - \nu^2} \begin{bmatrix} 1 & \nu & 0 \\ \nu & 1 & 0 \\ 0 & 0 & \dfrac{1 - \nu}{2} \end{bmatrix} \begin{bmatrix} \dfrac{\partial \beta_x}{\partial x} \\ \dfrac{\partial \beta_y}{\partial y} \\ \dfrac{\partial \beta_x}{\partial y} + \dfrac{\partial \beta_y}{\partial x} \end{bmatrix}
\tag{5.91}
$$

$$
\begin{bmatrix} \tau_{xz} \\ \tau_{yz} \end{bmatrix} = \frac{E}{2(1 + \nu)} \begin{bmatrix} \dfrac{\partial w}{\partial x} - \beta_x \\ \dfrac{\partial w}{\partial y} - \beta_y \end{bmatrix}
\tag{5.92}
$$

To establish the element equilibrium equations we now proceed as in the formulation of the two-dimensional beam element of rectangular cross section [see (5.58) to (5.64)].

Considering the plate, the expression for the principle of virtual work is, with p equal to the transverse loading per unit of the midsurface area A,

$$\int_A \int_{-h/2}^{h/2} [\bar{\epsilon}_{xx} \quad \bar{\epsilon}_{yy} \quad \bar{\gamma}_{xy}] \begin{bmatrix} \tau_{xx} \\ \tau_{yy} \\ \tau_{xy} \end{bmatrix} dz \, dA + k \int_A \int_{-h/2}^{h/2} [\bar{\gamma}_{xz} \quad \bar{\gamma}_{yz}] \begin{bmatrix} \tau_{xz} \\ \tau_{yz} \end{bmatrix} dz \, dA = \int_A \bar{w} p \, dA \qquad (5.93)$$

where the overbar denotes virtual quantities and k is again a constant to account for the actual nonuniformity of the shearing stresses (the value usually used is $\frac{5}{6}$; see Example 5.23). Substituting from (5.89) to (5.92) into (5.93), we thus obtain

$$\int_A \boldsymbol{\kappa}^T \mathbf{C}_b \boldsymbol{\kappa} \, dA + \int_A \boldsymbol{\gamma}^T \mathbf{C}_s \boldsymbol{\gamma} \, dA = \int_A \bar{w} p \, dA \qquad (5.94)$$

where the internal bending moments and shear forces are $\mathbf{C}_b \boldsymbol{\kappa}$ and $\mathbf{C}_s \boldsymbol{\gamma}$, respectively, and

$$\boldsymbol{\kappa} = \begin{bmatrix} \dfrac{\partial \beta_x}{\partial x} \\[2mm] \dfrac{\partial \beta_y}{\partial y} \\[2mm] \dfrac{\partial \beta_x}{\partial y} + \dfrac{\partial \beta_y}{\partial x} \end{bmatrix}; \qquad \boldsymbol{\gamma} = \begin{bmatrix} \dfrac{\partial w}{\partial x} - \beta_x \\[2mm] \dfrac{\partial w}{\partial y} - \beta_y \end{bmatrix} \qquad \begin{matrix} (5.95) \\[4mm] (5.96) \end{matrix}$$

and

$$\mathbf{C}_b = \frac{Eh^3}{12(1 - \nu^2)} \begin{bmatrix} 1 & \nu & 0 \\ \nu & 1 & 0 \\ 0 & 0 & \dfrac{1-\nu}{2} \end{bmatrix}; \qquad \mathbf{C}_s = \frac{Ehk}{2(1 + \nu)} \begin{bmatrix} 1 & 0 \\ 0 & 1 \end{bmatrix} \qquad (5.97)$$

Let us note that the variational indicator corresponding to (5.93) is given by (see Example 4.4)

$$\Pi = \frac{1}{2} \int_A \int_{-h/2}^{h/2} [\epsilon_{xx} \quad \epsilon_{yy} \quad \gamma_{xy}] \frac{E}{1 - \nu^2} \begin{bmatrix} 1 & \nu & 0 \\ \nu & 1 & 0 \\ 0 & 0 & \dfrac{1-\nu}{2} \end{bmatrix} \begin{bmatrix} \epsilon_{xx} \\ \epsilon_{yy} \\ \gamma_{xy} \end{bmatrix} dz \, dA \qquad (5.98)$$

$$+ \frac{k}{2} \int_A \int_{-h/2}^{h/2} [\gamma_{xz} \quad \gamma_{yz}] \frac{E}{2(1 + \nu)} \begin{bmatrix} \gamma_{xz} \\ \gamma_{yz} \end{bmatrix} dz \, dA - \int_A w p \, dA$$

with the strains given by (5.89) and (5.90). The principle of virtual work corresponds to invoking $\delta \Pi = 0$ with respect to the transverse displacement w and section rotations β_x and β_y.

We emphasize that in this theory w, β_x, and β_y are independent variables. Hence, in the finite element discretization using the displacement method, we need to enforce inter-element continuity only on w, β_x, and β_y and not on any derivatives thereof, which can readily be achieved in the same way as in the isoparametric finite element analysis of solids.

Let us consider the pure displacement discretization first. As in the analysis of beams, the pure displacement discretization will not yield efficient lower-order elements but does provide the basis for the mixed interpolation that we shall discuss afterward.

In the pure displacement discretization we use

$$w = \sum_{i=1}^{q} h_i w_i; \qquad \beta_x = -\sum_{i=1}^{q} h_i \theta_y^i$$

$$\beta_y = \sum_{i=1}^{q} h_i \theta_x^i \qquad\qquad (5.99)$$

where the h_i are the interpolation functions and q is the number of nodes of the element. With these interpolations we can now proceed in the usual way, and all concepts pertaining to the isoparametric finite elements discussed earlier are directly applicable. For example, some interpolation functions applicable to the formulation of plate elements are listed in Fig. 5.4, and triangular elements can be established as discussed in Section 5.3.2. Since the interpolation functions are given in terms of the isoparametric coordinates r, s, we can also directly calculate the matrices of plate elements that are curved in their plane (to model, for example, a circular plate).

We demonstrate the formulation of a simple four-node element in the following example.

EXAMPLE 5.29: Derive the expressions used in the evaluation of the stiffness matrix of the four-node plate element shown in Fig. E5.29.

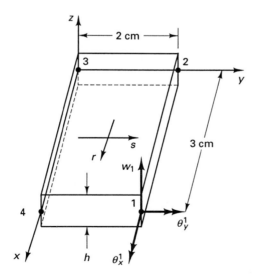

Figure E5.29   A four-node plate element

The calculations are very similar to those performed in the formulation of the two-dimensional plane stress element in Example 5.5.

For the element in Fig. E5.29 we have (see Example 5.3)

$$\mathbf{J} = \begin{bmatrix} \frac{3}{2} & 0 \\ 0 & 1 \end{bmatrix}$$

and then, using the interpolation functions defined in Fig. 5.4,

$$
\begin{bmatrix} \dfrac{\partial w}{\partial x} \\[2mm] \dfrac{\partial w}{\partial y} \end{bmatrix} = \frac{1}{4} \begin{bmatrix} \frac{2}{3} & 0 \\ 0 & 1 \end{bmatrix} \begin{bmatrix} (1+s) & -(1+s) & -(1-s) & (1-s) \\ (1+r) & (1-r) & -(1-r) & -(1+r) \end{bmatrix} \begin{bmatrix} w_1 \\ w_2 \\ w_3 \\ w_4 \end{bmatrix}
$$

with similar expressions for the derivatives of β_x and β_y. Thus, if we use the following notation,

$$\boldsymbol{\kappa}(r, s) = \mathbf{B}_\kappa \hat{\mathbf{u}}$$

$$\boldsymbol{\gamma}(r, s) = \mathbf{B}_\gamma \hat{\mathbf{u}}$$

$$w(r, s) = \mathbf{H}_w \hat{\mathbf{u}}$$

where

$$\hat{\mathbf{u}}^T = [w_1 \quad \theta_x^1 \quad \theta_y^1 ; w_2 \quad \dots \quad \theta_y^4]$$

we have

$$
\mathbf{B}_\kappa = \begin{bmatrix} 0 & 0 & -\frac{1}{6}(1+s) & | & & -\frac{1}{6}(1-s) \\ 0 & \frac{1}{4}(1+r) & 0 & | & \dots & 0 \\ 0 & \frac{1}{6}(1+s) & -\frac{1}{4}(1+r) & | & & \frac{1}{4}(1+r) \end{bmatrix}
$$

$$
\mathbf{B}_\gamma = \begin{bmatrix} \frac{1}{6}(1+s) & 0 & \frac{1}{4}(1+r)(1+s) & | & & \frac{1}{4}(1+r)(1-s) \\ \frac{1}{4}(1+r) & -\frac{1}{4}(1+r)(1+s) & 0 & | & \dots & 0 \end{bmatrix}
$$

$$\mathbf{H}_w = \frac{1}{4}[(1+r)(1+s) \quad 0 \quad 0 \quad | \quad \dots \quad 0]$$

The element stiffness matrix is then

$$\mathbf{K} = \frac{3}{2} \int_{-1}^{+1} \int_{-1}^{+1} (\mathbf{B}_\kappa^T \mathbf{C}_b \mathbf{B}_\kappa + \mathbf{B}_\gamma^T \mathbf{C}_s \mathbf{B}_\gamma) \, dr \, ds \qquad \text{(a)}$$

and the consistent load vector is

$$\mathbf{R}_s = \frac{3}{2} \int_{-1}^{+1} \int_{-1}^{+1} \mathbf{H}_w^T p \, dr \, ds \qquad \text{(b)}$$

where the integrals in (a) and (b) could be evaluated in closed form but are usually evaluated using numerical integration (see Section 5.5).

This pure displacement-based plate element formulation is of value only when higher-order elements are employed. Indeed, the least order of interpolation that should be used is a cubic interpolation, which results in a 16-node quadrilateral element and a 10-node triangular element. However, even these high-order elements still do not display a good predictive capability, particularly when the elements are geometrically distorted and used for stress predictions (see, for example, M. L. Bucalem and K. J. Bathe [A]).

As in the formulation of isoparametric beam elements, the basic difficulty is that spurious shear stresses are predicted with the displacement-based elements. These spurious shear stresses result in a strong artificial stiffening of the elements as the thickness/length ratio decreases. This effect of shear locking is more pronounced for a low-order element and when the elements are geometrically distorted because, simply, the error in the shear stresses is then larger.

To arrive at efficient and reliable plate bending elements, the pure displacement-based formulation must be extended, and a successful approach is to use a mixed interpolation of transverse displacement, section rotations, *and* transverse shear strains.

We should note here that in the above discussion, we assumed that the integrals for the computation of the element matrices (stiffness and mass matrices and load vectors) are evaluated accurately; hence, throughout our discussion we assumed and shall continue to assume that the error in the numerical integration (that usually is performed in practice; see Section 5.5) is small and certainly does not change the character of the element matrices. A number of authors have advocated the use of simple reduced integration to alleviate the shear locking problem. We discuss such techniques briefly in Section 5.5.6.

In the following we present a family of plate bending elements that have a good mathematical basis and are reliable and efficient. These elements are referred to as the MITCn elements, where n refers to the number of element nodes and $n = 4, 9, 16$ for the quadrilateral and $n = 7, 12$ for the triangular elements (here MITC stands for *mixed interpolation of tensorial components*), (see K. J. Bathe, M. L. Bucalem, and F. Brezzi [A]). Let us consider the MITC4 element in detail and give the basic interpolations for the other elements in tabular form.

An important feature of the MITC element formulation is the use of tensorial components of shear strains so as to render the resulting element relatively distortion-insensitive. Figure 5.26 shows a generic four-node element with the coordinate systems used.

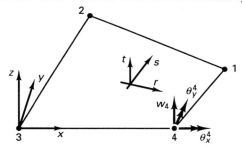

View of general element

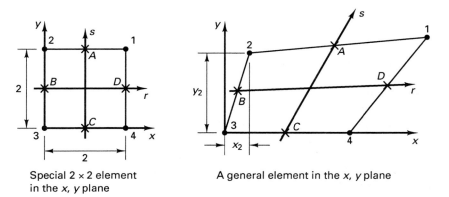

Special 2 × 2 element in the *x, y* plane   A general element in the *x, y* plane

Figure 5.26   Conventions used in formulation of four-node plate bending element

To circumvent the shear locking problem, we formulate the element stiffness matrix by including the bending and shear effects through different interpolations. For the section curvatures in (5.95) we use the same interpolation as in the displacement-based method, as evaluated using (5.99), but we proceed differently in evaluating the transverse shear strains.

Consider first the MITC4 element when it is of geometry 2×2 (for which the x, y coordinates could be taken to be equal to the r, s isoparametric coordinates). For this element we use the interpolation (see K. J. Bathe and E. N. Dvorkin [A])

$$\gamma_{rz} = \tfrac{1}{2}(1 + s)\gamma_{rz}^A + \tfrac{1}{2}(1 - s)\gamma_{rz}^C$$
$$\gamma_{sz} = \tfrac{1}{2}(1 + r)\gamma_{sz}^D + \tfrac{1}{2}(1 - r)\gamma_{sz}^B \tag{5.100}$$

where γ_{rz}^A, γ_{rz}^C, γ_{sz}^D, and γ_{sz}^B are the (physical) shear strains at points A, B, C, and D evaluated by the displacement and section rotations in (5.99). Hence,

$$\gamma_{rz} = \frac{1}{2}(1 + s)\left(\frac{w_1 - w_2}{2} + \frac{\theta_y^1 + \theta_y^2}{2}\right) + \frac{1}{2}(1 - s)\left(\frac{w_4 - w_3}{2} + \frac{\theta_y^4 + \theta_y^3}{2}\right)$$

$$\gamma_{sz} = \frac{1}{2}(1 + r)\left(\frac{w_1 - w_4}{2} - \frac{\theta_x^1 + \theta_x^4}{2}\right) + \frac{1}{2}(1 - r)\left(\frac{w_2 - w_3}{2} - \frac{\theta_x^2 + \theta_x^3}{2}\right) \tag{5.101}$$

With these interpolations given, all strain-displacement interpolation matrices can be directly constructed and the stiffness matrix is formulated in the standard manner. Of course, the same procedure can also be directly employed for any rectangular element.

Considering next the case of a general quadrilateral four-node element, we use the same basic idea of interpolating the transverse shear strains, but—using the interpolation in (5.100)—we interpolate the covariant tensor components measured in the r, s, z coordinate system. In this way we are directly taking account of the element distortion (from the 2×2 geometry). Proceeding in this way with the tensor shear strain components, we obtain (see Example 5.30) the following expressions for the γ_{xz} and γ_{yz} shear strains:

$$\gamma_{xz} = \gamma_{rz} \sin \beta - \gamma_{sz} \sin \alpha$$
$$\gamma_{yz} = -\gamma_{rz} \cos \beta + \gamma_{sz} \cos \alpha \tag{5.102}$$

where α and β are the angles between the r and x axes and s and x axes, respectively, and

$$\gamma_{rz} = \frac{\sqrt{(C_x + rB_x)^2 + (C_y + rB_y)^2}}{8 \det \mathbf{J}}$$

$$\left\{(1 + s)\left[\frac{w_1 - w_2}{2} + \frac{x_1 - x_2}{4}(\theta_y^1 + \theta_y^2) - \frac{y_1 - y_2}{4}(\theta_x^1 + \theta_x^2)\right]\right.$$

$$+ (1 - s)\left[\frac{w_4 - w_3}{2} + \frac{x_4 - x_3}{4}(\theta_y^4 + \theta_y^3) - \frac{y_4 - y_3}{4}(\theta_x^4 + \theta_x^3)\right]\right\} \tag{5.103}$$

$$\gamma_{sz} = \frac{\sqrt{(A_x + sB_x)^2 + (A_y + sB_y)^2}}{8 \det \mathbf{J}}$$

$$\left\{(1 + r)\left[\frac{w_1 - w_4}{2} + \frac{x_1 - x_4}{4}(\theta_y^1 + \theta_y^4) - \frac{y_1 - y_4}{4}(\theta_x^1 + \theta_x^4)\right]\right.$$

$$+ (1 - r)\left[\frac{w_2 - w_3}{2} + \frac{x_2 - x_3}{4}(\theta_y^2 + \theta_y^3) - \frac{y_2 - y_3}{4}(\theta_x^2 + \theta_x^3)\right]\right\}$$

In equations (5.103) we have

$$\det \mathbf{J} = \det \begin{bmatrix} \dfrac{\partial x}{\partial r} & \dfrac{\partial y}{\partial r} \\ \dfrac{\partial x}{\partial s} & \dfrac{\partial y}{\partial s} \end{bmatrix} \tag{5.104}$$

and

$$A_x = x_1 - x_2 - x_3 + x_4$$
$$B_x = x_1 - x_2 + x_3 - x_4$$
$$C_x = x_1 + x_2 - x_3 - x_4$$
$$A_y = y_1 - y_2 - y_3 + y_4 \qquad (5.105)$$
$$B_y = y_1 - y_2 + y_3 - y_4$$
$$C_y = y_1 + y_2 - y_3 - y_4$$

We further consider the above relationships in the following example.

EXAMPLE 5.30:   Derive the transverse shear strain interpolations of the general MITC4 plate bending element.

In the natural coordinate system of the plate bending element, the covariant base vectors are defined as

$$\mathbf{g}_r = \frac{\partial \mathbf{x}}{\partial r}; \qquad \mathbf{g}_s = \frac{\partial \mathbf{x}}{\partial s}$$

$$\mathbf{g}_z = \frac{h}{2}\mathbf{e}_z \qquad (a)$$

where $\mathbf{x}$ is the vector of coordinates, and $\mathbf{e}_x$, $\mathbf{e}_y$, $\mathbf{e}_z$ are the base vectors of the Cartesian system.

Let us recall that in the natural coordinate system, the strain tensor can be expressed using covariant tensor components and contravariant base vectors (see Section 2.4)

$$\boldsymbol{\epsilon} = \tilde{\epsilon}_{ij}\,\mathbf{g}^i\mathbf{g}^j; \qquad i, j \equiv r, s, z$$

where the tilde ($\sim$) indicates that the tensor components are measured in the natural coordinate system.

To obtain the shear tensor components we now use the equivalent of (5.100),

$$\tilde{\epsilon}_{rz} = \tfrac{1}{2}(1 + s)\tilde{\epsilon}_{rz}^A + \tfrac{1}{2}(1 - s)\tilde{\epsilon}_{rz}^C \qquad (b)$$

$$\tilde{\epsilon}_{sz} = \tfrac{1}{2}(1 + r)\tilde{\epsilon}_{sz}^D + \tfrac{1}{2}(1 - r)\tilde{\epsilon}_{sz}^B \qquad (c)$$

where $\tilde{\epsilon}_{rz}^A$, $\tilde{\epsilon}_{rz}^C$, $\tilde{\epsilon}_{sz}^D$, and $\tilde{\epsilon}_{sz}^B$ are the shear tensor components at points A, B, C, and D evaluated from the displacement interpolations. To obtain these components we use the linear terms of the general relation for the strain components in terms of the base vectors (see Example 2.28),

$$\tfrac{1}{0}\tilde{\epsilon}_{ij} = \tfrac{1}{2}[{}^1\mathbf{g}_i \cdot {}^1\mathbf{g}_j - {}^0\mathbf{g}_i \cdot {}^0\mathbf{g}_j]$$

where the left superscript of the base vectors is equal to 1 for the deformed configuration and equal to 0 for the initial configuration. Substituting from (5.99) and (a), we obtain

$$\tilde{\epsilon}_{rz}^A = \frac{1}{4}\left[\frac{h}{2}(w_1 - w_2) + \frac{h}{4}(x_1 - x_2)(\theta_y^1 + \theta_y^2) - \frac{h}{4}(y_1 - y_2)(\theta_x^1 + \theta_x^2)\right]$$

and

$$\tilde{\epsilon}_{rz}^C = \frac{1}{4}\left[\frac{h}{2}(w_4 - w_3) + \frac{h}{4}(x_4 - x_3)(\theta_y^4 + \theta_y^3) - \frac{h}{4}(y_4 - y_3)(\theta_x^4 + \theta_x^3)\right]$$

Therefore, using (b), we obtain

$$
\tilde{\epsilon}_{rz} = \frac{1}{8}(1 + s)\left[\frac{h}{2}(w_1 - w_2) + \frac{h}{4}(x_1 - x_2)(\theta_y^1 + \theta_y^2) - \frac{h}{4}(y_1 - y_2)(\theta_x^1 + \theta_x^2)\right]
$$

$$
+ \frac{1}{8}(1 - s)\left[\frac{h}{2}(w_4 - w_3) + \frac{h}{4}(x_4 - x_3)(\theta_y^4 + \theta_y^3) - \frac{h}{4}(y_4 - y_3)(\theta_x^4 + \theta_x^3)\right]
$$

and in the same way, using (c),

$$
\tilde{\epsilon}_{sz} = \frac{1}{8}(1 + r)\left[\frac{h}{2}(w_1 - w_4) + \frac{h}{4}(x_1 - x_4)(\theta_y^1 + \theta_y^4) - \frac{h}{4}(y_1 - y_4)(\theta_x^1 + \theta_x^4)\right]
$$

$$
+ \frac{1}{8}(1 - r)\left[\frac{h}{2}(w_2 - w_3) + \frac{h}{4}(x_2 - x_3)(\theta_y^2 + \theta_y^3) - \frac{h}{4}(y_2 - y_3)(\theta_x^2 + \theta_x^3)\right]
$$

Next we use

$$
\tilde{\epsilon}_{ij}\mathbf{g}^i\mathbf{g}^j = \epsilon_{kl}\mathbf{e}_k\mathbf{e}_l \tag{d}
$$

where the ϵ_{kl} are the components of the strain tensor measured in the Cartesian coordinate system. From (d) we obtain

$$
\gamma_{xz} = 2\tilde{\epsilon}_{rz}(\mathbf{g}^r \cdot \mathbf{e}_x)(\mathbf{g}^z \cdot \mathbf{e}_z) + 2\tilde{\epsilon}_{sz}(\mathbf{g}^s \cdot \mathbf{e}_x)(\mathbf{g}^z \cdot \mathbf{e}_z)
$$

$$
\gamma_{yz} = 2\tilde{\epsilon}_{rz}(\mathbf{g}^r \cdot \mathbf{e}_y)(\mathbf{g}^z \cdot \mathbf{e}_z) + 2\tilde{\epsilon}_{sz}(\mathbf{g}^s \cdot \mathbf{e}_y)(\mathbf{g}^z \cdot \mathbf{e}_z) \tag{e}
$$

However (using the standard procedure described in Section 2.4),

$$
\mathbf{g}^r = \sqrt{g^{rr}}\,(\sin \beta \mathbf{e}_x - \cos \beta \mathbf{e}_y)
$$

$$
\mathbf{g}^s = \sqrt{g^{ss}}\,(-\sin \alpha \mathbf{e}_x + \cos \alpha \mathbf{e}_y)
$$

$$
\mathbf{g}^z = \sqrt{g^{zz}}\,\mathbf{e}_z
$$

where α and β are the angles between the r and x axes and s and x axes, respectively, and

$$
g^{rr} = \frac{(C_x + rB_x)^2 + (C_y + rB_y)^2}{16(\det \mathbf{J})^2}
$$

$$
g^{ss} = \frac{(A_x + sB_x)^2 + (A_y + sB_y)^2}{16(\det \mathbf{J})^2}
$$

where A_x, B_x, C_x, A_y, B_y, and C_y are defined in (5.105) and

$$
g^{zz} = \frac{4}{h^2}
$$

Substituting into (e), the relations in (5.102) are obtained.

The MITC4 plate bending element is in rectangular or parallelogram geometric configurations identical or closely related to other four-node plate bending elements (see T. J. R. Hughes and T. E. Tezduyar [A] and R. H. MacNeal [A]). However, an important attribute of the MITC plate element is that it is a special case of a general shell element for linear and nonlinear analysis. Specifically, the use of covariant strain interpolations gives the element a relatively high predictive capability even when it is used with angular geometric distortions as shown in Fig. 5.31 (see also K. J. Bathe and E. N. Dvorkin [A]). In practice, elements with angular distortions are of course widely used.

Some observations pertaining to the MITC4 element are the following.

The element behaves like the two-node mixed interpolated isoparametric beam element (discussed in the previous section) when used in the analysis of two-dimensional beam action.

The element can be derived from the Hu-Washizu variational principle (see Example 4.30).

The element passes the patch test (for an analytical proof see K. J. Bathe and E. N. Dvorkin [B]).

A mathematical convergence analysis for the transverse displacement and section rotations has been provided by K. J. Bathe and F. Brezzi [A] (assuming uniform meshes, i.e., that the element assemblage consists of square elements of sides h). This analysis gives the results

$$\|\boldsymbol{\beta} - \boldsymbol{\beta}_h\|_1 \le c_1 h \quad ; \quad \|\boldsymbol{\nabla}w - \boldsymbol{\nabla}w_h\|_0 \le c_2 h \tag{5.106}$$

where $\boldsymbol{\beta}$ and w are the exact solutions, $\boldsymbol{\beta}_h$ and w_h are the finite element solutions corresponding to a mesh of elements with sides h, and c_1, c_2 are constants independent of h. A convergence analysis of the transverse shear strains gave the result that the L^2-norm of the error is not bounded independent of the plate thickness (see F. Brezzi, M. Fortin, and R. Stenberg [A]).

The essence of the results of these analytical convergence studies is also seen in practice for uniform and distorted meshes. The element predicts the transverse displacements and bending strains quite well, but the transverse shear strain predictions may not be satisfactory, particularly when very thin plates are analyzed.

A most important observation in the mathematical analysis of the MITC4 element was that this element, in its mathematical basis, is an analog of the 4/1 element of the u/p element family presented in Section 4.4.3: in the u/p formulation the displacements and pressure are interpolated to satisfy the constraint of (almost) incompressibility, $e_V \simeq 0$, whereas in the MITC4 element formulation the transverse displacement, section rotations and transverse shear strains are interpolated to satisfy the thin plate condition, $\boldsymbol{\gamma} \simeq \mathbf{0}$. This analogy between the incompressibility constraint in solid mechanics and the zero transverse shear strain constraint in the Reissner-Mindlin plate theory resulted in the development of a mathematical basis aimed at the construction of new plate bending elements (see K. J. Bathe and F. Brezzi [B]). Since these elements are all based on the mixed interpolation of the transverse displacement, section rotations and transverse shear strains and for general geometries use the tensorial components (as for the MITC4 element), we refer to these elements as MITC elements with n nodes (i.e., MITCn elements).

The basic difficulty is choosing the orders of interpolations of transverse displacement, section rotations, and transverse shear strains which *together* result in nonlocking behavior and optimal convergence of the element. The mathematical considerations for choosing the appropriate interpolations were summarized by K. J. Bathe and F. Brezzi [B], K. J. Bathe, M. L. Bucalem, and F. Brezzi [A], and F. Brezzi, K. J. Bathe, and M. Fortin [A], who presented the elements in Fig. 5.27 as well as additional ones, and also gave numerical results.

Figure 5.27 and Table 5.3 summarize the interpolations of 9- and 16-node quadrilateral elements and 7- and 12-node triangular elements and give the rates of convergence. In Fig. 5.27 the interpolations are given for the elements in geometrically nondistorted form, and we use tensorial components, as for the MITC4 element, to generalize the interpolations to geometrically distorted elements. Let us illustrate the use of the interpolations given in Fig. 5.27 in an example.

MITC4 element: 4 nodes for interpolation of section rotations and transverse displacement (2 × 2 Gauss integration)

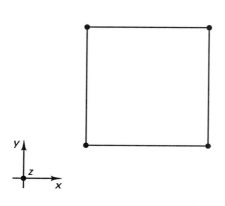

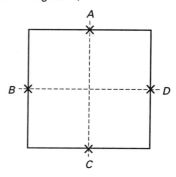

$\gamma_{xz} = a_1 + b_1 y$; tying at points A and C

$\gamma_{yz} = a_2 + b_2 x$; tying at points B and D

• Nodes for β_x, β_y, and w interpolation

MITC9 element: 9 nodes for interpolation of section rotations and 8 nodes for interpolation of transverse displacement (3 × 3 Gauss integration)

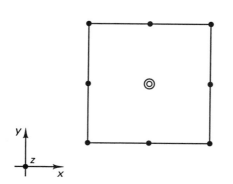

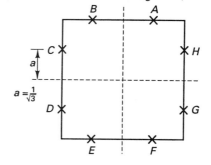

$a = \frac{1}{\sqrt{3}}$

• Nodes for β_x, β_y, and w interpolation

◎ Node for β_x, β_y interpolation

$\gamma_{xz} = a_1 + b_1 x + c_1 y + d_1 xy + e_1 y^2$; tying at points A, B, E, F

$\gamma_{yz} = a_2 + b_2 x + c_2 y + d_2 xy + e_2 x^2$; tying at points C, D, G, H

plus integral tying $\int_A (\nabla w - \boldsymbol{\beta} - \boldsymbol{\gamma}) \, dA = 0$

Figure 5.27   Plate bending elements; square and equilateral triangles of side lengths 2 units are considered.

MITC16 element: 16 nodes for interpolation of section rotations and 13 nodes for interpolation of transverse displacement (4 × 4 Gauss integration)

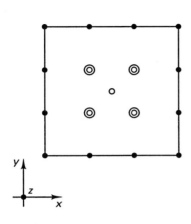

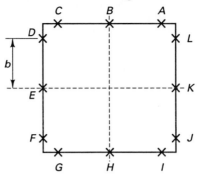

$b = \sqrt{\frac{3}{5}}$

- ● Nodes for β_x, β_y, and w interpolation
- ◎ Nodes for β_x, β_y interpolation
- ○ Node for w interpolation

$\gamma_{xz} = a_1 + b_1 x + c_1 y + d_1 x^2 + e_1 xy +$
$\quad f_1 y^2 + g_1 x^2 y + h_1 xy^2 + i_1 y^3;$
tying at points $A, B, C, G, H, I;$

$\gamma_{yz} = a_2 + b_2 x + c_2 y + d_2 x^2 + e_2 xy +$
$\quad f_2 y^2 + g_2 x^2 y + h_2 xy^2 + i_2 x^3;$
tying at points $D, E, F, J, K, L;$

plus integral tying $\int_A (\nabla w - \boldsymbol{\beta} - \boldsymbol{\gamma})\, dA =$
$\int_A (\nabla w - \boldsymbol{\beta} - \boldsymbol{\gamma}) x\, dA = \int_A (\nabla w - \boldsymbol{\beta} - \boldsymbol{\gamma}) y\, dA = 0$

MITC7 element: 7 nodes for interpolation of section rotations and 6 nodes for interpolation of transverse displacement (7-point Gauss integration)

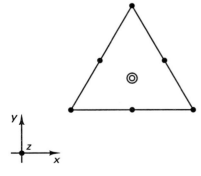

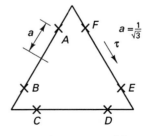

$a = \frac{1}{\sqrt{3}}$

$\gamma_{xz} = a_1 + b_1 x + c_1 y + y(dx + ey);$
$\gamma_{yz} = a_2 + b_2 x + c_2 y - x(dx + ey);$
tying of $\boldsymbol{\gamma} \cdot \boldsymbol{\tau}$ at A, B, C, D, E, F
plus integral tying $\int_A (\nabla w - \boldsymbol{\beta} - \boldsymbol{\gamma})\, dA = 0$

- ● Nodes for β_x, β_y, and w interpolation
- ◎ Node for β_x, β_y interpolation

Figure 5.27   (*continued*)

MITC12 element: 12 nodes for interpolation of section rotations and 10 nodes for interpolation of transverse displacement (13-point Gauss integration)

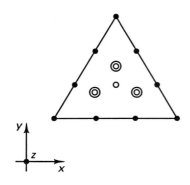

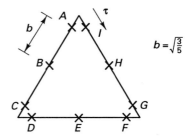

$$b = \sqrt{\tfrac{3}{5}}$$

- Nodes for β_x, β_y, and w interpolation
- Nodes for β_x, β_y interpolation
- Node for w interpolation

$$\gamma_{xz} = a_1 + b_1 x + c_1 y + d_1 x^2 + e_1 xy + f_1 y^2 + y(gx^2 + hxy + iy^2);$$

$$\gamma_{yz} = a_2 + b_2 x + c_2 y + d_2 x^2 + e_2 xy + f_2 y^2 - x(gx^2 + hxy + iy^2);$$

tying of $\boldsymbol{\gamma} \cdot \boldsymbol{\tau}$ at points $A, B, C, D, E, F, G, H, I$

plus integral tying $\int_A (\nabla w - \boldsymbol{\beta} - \boldsymbol{\gamma}) \, dA = \int_A (\nabla w - \boldsymbol{\beta} - \boldsymbol{\gamma}) x \, dA = \int_A (\nabla w - \boldsymbol{\beta} - \boldsymbol{\gamma}) y \, dA = 0$

Figure 5.27   *(continued)*

TABLE 5.3   *Interpolation spaces and theoretically predicted error estimates for plate bending elements*

Element	Spaces used for section rotations and transverse displacement[†]	Error estimates
MITC4	$\boldsymbol{\beta}_h \in Q_1 \times Q_1$ $w_h \in Q_1$	$\|\boldsymbol{\beta} - \boldsymbol{\beta}_h\|_1 \le ch$ $\|\nabla w - \nabla w_h\|_0 \le ch$
MITC9	$\boldsymbol{\beta}_h \in Q_2 \times Q_2$ $w_h \in Q_2 \cap P_3$	$\|\boldsymbol{\beta} - \boldsymbol{\beta}_h\|_1 \le ch^2$ $\|\nabla w - \nabla w_h\|_0 \le ch^2$
MITC16	$\boldsymbol{\beta}_h \in Q_3 \times Q_3$ $w_h \in Q_3 \cap P_4$	$\|\boldsymbol{\beta} - \boldsymbol{\beta}_h\|_1 \le ch^3$ $\|\nabla w - \nabla w_h\|_0 \le ch^3$
MITC7	$\boldsymbol{\beta}_h \in (P_2 \oplus \{L_1 L_2 L_3\}) \times (P_2 \oplus \{L_1 L_2 L_3\})$ $w_h \in P_2$	$\|\boldsymbol{\beta} - \boldsymbol{\beta}_h\|_1 \le ch^2$ $\|\nabla w - \nabla w_h\|_0 \le ch^2$
MITC12	$\boldsymbol{\beta}_h \in (P_3 \oplus \{L_1 L_2 L_3\} P_1) \times (P_3 \oplus \{L_1 L_2 L_3\} P_1)$ $w_h \in P_3$	$\|\boldsymbol{\beta} - \boldsymbol{\beta}_h\|_1 \le ch^3$ $\|\nabla w - \nabla w_h\|_0 \le ch^3$

[†] For notation used, see Section 4.3.

EXAMPLE 5.31: Show how to establish the strain interpolation matrices for the stiffness matrix of the MITC9 element shown in Fig. E5.31.

The geometry of the element is the same as for the four-node element considered in Fig. E5.29; hence the Jacobian matrix is the same.

Since the transverse displacements are determined by the eight-node interpolations, which are given in Fig. 5.4, we have

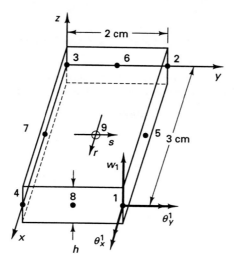

Figure E5.31 A nine-node plate bending element

$$
\begin{bmatrix} \dfrac{\partial w}{\partial x} \\[2ex] \dfrac{\partial w}{\partial y} \end{bmatrix} = \frac{1}{4}\begin{bmatrix} \frac{2}{3} & 0 \\ 0 & 1 \end{bmatrix}\begin{bmatrix} (1 + 2r)(1 + s) - (1 - s^2) & | & \\[2ex] & & \cdots \\[2ex] (1 + 2s)(1 + r) - (1 - r^2) & | & \end{bmatrix}\begin{bmatrix} w_1 \\ w_2 \\ \vdots \\ w_8 \end{bmatrix} \tag{a}
$$

The section rotations are determined by the nine-node interpolation functions, which are also given in Fig. 5.4, and we have

$$
\begin{bmatrix} \dfrac{\partial \beta_x}{\partial x} \\[2ex] \dfrac{\partial \beta_x}{\partial y} \end{bmatrix} = -\frac{1}{4}\begin{bmatrix} \frac{2}{3} & 0 \\ 0 & 1 \end{bmatrix}\begin{bmatrix} (1 + 2r)(1 + s) - (1 + 2r)(1 - s^2) & | & \\[2ex] & & \cdots \\[2ex] (1 + 2s)(1 + r) - (1 + 2s)(1 - r^2) & | & \end{bmatrix}\begin{bmatrix} \theta_y^1 \\ \theta_y^2 \\ \vdots \\ \theta_y^9 \end{bmatrix} \tag{b}
$$

$$
\begin{bmatrix} \dfrac{\partial \beta_y}{\partial x} \\[2ex] \dfrac{\partial \beta_y}{\partial y} \end{bmatrix} = \frac{1}{4}\begin{bmatrix} \frac{2}{3} & 0 \\ 0 & 1 \end{bmatrix}\begin{bmatrix} (1 + 2r)(1 + s) - (1 + 2r)(1 - s^2) & | & \\[2ex] & & \cdots \\[2ex] (1 + 2s)(1 + r) - (1 + 2s)(1 - r^2) & | & \end{bmatrix}\begin{bmatrix} \theta_x^1 \\ \theta_x^2 \\ \vdots \\ \theta_x^9 \end{bmatrix} \tag{c}
$$

Let us use the following ordering of nodal point displacements and rotations

$$
\hat{\mathbf{u}}^T = [w_1 \quad \theta_x^1 \quad \theta_y^1 \quad | \quad \cdots \quad | \quad w_8 \quad \theta_x^8 \quad \theta_y^8 \quad | \quad \theta_x^9 \quad \theta_y^9]
$$

The transverse displacement interpolation matrix $\mathbf{H}_w$ is then given by

$$
\mathbf{H}_w = [h_1 \quad 0 \quad 0 \quad | \quad h_2 \quad 0 \quad 0 \quad | \quad \cdots \quad | \quad h_8 \quad 0 \quad 0 \quad | \quad 0 \quad 0]
$$

where the h_1 to h_8 are given in Fig. 5.4 and correspond to an eight-node element.

The curvature interpolation matrix $\mathbf{B}_\kappa$ is obtained directly from the relations (b) and (c),

$$
\mathbf{B}_\kappa = \begin{bmatrix} 0 & 0 \\[1ex] 0 & \frac{1}{4}[(1 + 2s)(1 + r) - (1 + 2s)(1 - r^2)] \\[1ex] 0 & \frac{1}{6}[(1 + 2r)(1 + s) - (1 + 2r)(1 - s^2)] \end{bmatrix}
$$

$$
\begin{bmatrix} -\frac{1}{6}[(1 + 2r)(1 + s) - (1 + 2r)(1 - s^2)] & | \\ 0 & | & \cdots \\ -\frac{1}{4}[(1 + 2s)(1 + r) - (1 + 2s)(1 - r^2)] & | \end{bmatrix}
$$

433

The transverse shear strain interpolation matrix is obtained from the shear interpolation given in Fig. 5.27 and the tying procedure indicated in the same figure. Hence,

$$\mathbf{B}_\gamma = \begin{bmatrix} 1 & r & s & rs & s^2 & | & 0 & 0 & 0 & 0 & 0 \\ 0 & 0 & 0 & 0 & 0 & | & 1 & r & s & rs & r^2 \end{bmatrix} \boldsymbol{\alpha} \qquad \text{(e)}$$

where

$$\boldsymbol{\alpha}^T = \begin{bmatrix} a_1 & b_1 & c_1 & d_1 & e_1 & | & a_2 & b_2 & c_2 & d_2 & e_2 \end{bmatrix}$$

The values in the vector $\boldsymbol{\alpha}$ are expressed in terms of the nodal point displacements and rotations using the tying relations. For example, since point A is at $x = \frac{3}{2}[1 + 1/\sqrt{3}]$, $y = 2$, we have

$$\gamma_{xz}|_A = a_1 + b_1\left(\frac{3}{2}\right)\left(1 + \frac{1}{\sqrt{3}}\right) + c_1(2) + d_2(3)\left(1 + \frac{1}{\sqrt{3}}\right) + e_1(4)$$

$$= \left(\frac{\partial w}{\partial x} - \beta_x\right)\bigg|_{\text{at } r=1/\sqrt{3},\, s=1} \qquad \text{(f)}$$

Of course, $\partial w/\partial x$ is given by (a) and the section rotation β_x is given by (5.99) with the h_i corresponding to nine nodes.

Using all 10 tying relations in Fig. 5.27 as in (f), we can solve for the entries in (e) in terms of the nodal point displacements and rotations.

The numerical performance of the MITCn elements has been published by K. J. Bathe, M. L. Bucalem, and F. Brezzi [A]. However, let us briefly note that

The element matrices are all evaluated using full numerical Gauss integration (see Fig. 5.27).

The elements do not contain any spurious zero energy modes.

The elements pass the pure bending patch test (see Fig. 4.18).

To illustrate the performance of the elements and introduce a valuable test problem consider Figs. 5.28 to 5.32. In Fig. 5.28 the test problem is stated. We note that the transverse displacement and the section rotations are prescribed along the complete boundary of the square plate and that in this problem there are no boundary layers (as encountered in practical analyses; see B. Häggblad and K. J. Bathe [A]). Therefore, the numerically calculated orders of convergence should be close to the analytically predicted values. Figure 5.29 shows results obtained using uniform meshes, and these results compare well with the analytically predicted behavior (these predictions assume uniform meshes). Figures 5.30 and 5.31 show results obtained using a sequence of quasi-uniform[6] meshes, and we observe that the orders of convergence are not drastically affected by the element distortions. Finally, the convergence of the transverse shear strains, as predicted numerically, is shown in Fig. 5.32. In these specific finite element solutions the shear strains are predicted with surprisingly high orders of convergence (which in general of course cannot be expected).

---

[6] For the definition of a sequence of quasi-uniform meshes, see Section 5.3.3.

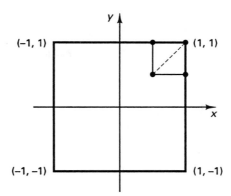

(a) Square plate considered in ad hoc plate bending problem; transverse loading $p = 0$, nonzero boundary conditions. A typical 4-node element is shown. The dashed line indicates the subdivision used for the triangular element meshes; $h = 2/N$, where N = number of elements per side.

(b) Exact transverse displacement and rotations: $w = \sin kx\, e^{ky} + \sin k\, e^{-k}$; $\theta_x = k \sin kx\, e^{ky}$; $\theta_y = -k \cos kx\, e^{ky}$

(c) Test problem: Prescribe the functional values of w, θ_x, and θ_y on the complete boundary and $p = 0$, calculate interior values; k is a chosen constant; we use $k = 5$

Figure 5.28   Ad-hoc test problem for plate bending elements

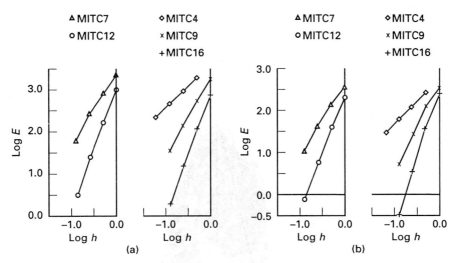

Figure 5.29 (a) Convergence of section rotations in analysis of ad-hoc problem using uniform meshes. The error measure is $E = \| \boldsymbol{\beta} - \boldsymbol{\beta}_h \|_1$. **(b)** Convergence of gradient of vertical displacement in analysis of ad-hoc problem using uniform meshes. The error measure is $E = \| \nabla w - \nabla w_h \|_0$.

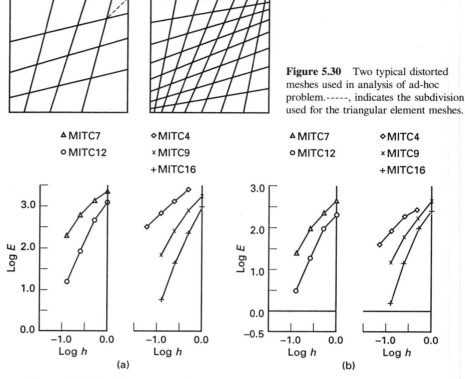

Figure 5.30 Two typical distorted meshes used in analysis of ad-hoc problem.-----, indicates the subdivision used for the triangular element meshes.

Figure 5.31 (a) Convergence of section rotations in analysis of ad-hoc problem using distorted meshes. The error measure is $E = \| \boldsymbol{\beta} - \boldsymbol{\beta}_h \|_1$. (b) Convergence of gradient of vertical displacement in analysis of ad-hoc problem using distorted meshes. The error measure is $E = \| \boldsymbol{\nabla} w - \boldsymbol{\nabla} w_h \|_0$.

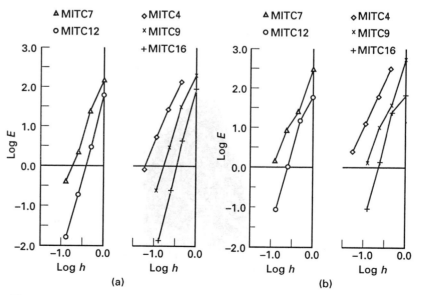

Figure 5.32 Convergence of transverse shear strains in analysis of ad-hoc problem. The error measure is $E = \| \boldsymbol{\gamma} - \boldsymbol{\gamma}_h \|_0$. (a) Uniform meshes. (b) Distorted meshes.

General Shell Elements

Let us consider next the formulation of general shell elements that can be used to analyze very complex shell geometries and stress distributions. For this objective we need to generalize the preceding plate element formulation approach, much in the same way as we generalized the isoparametric beam element formulation from straight two-dimensional to curved three-dimensional beams. As in the case of the formulation of beam elements (see Section 5.4.1), we consider the displacement interpolation which leads to a pure displacement-based element (see S. Ahmad, B. M. Irons, and O. C. Zienkiewicz [A]), and we then modify the formulation so as to not exhibit shear and membrane locking.

The displacement interpolation is obtained by considering the geometry interpolation. Consider a general shell element with a variable number of nodes, q. Figure 5.33 shows a nine-node element for which $q = 9$. Using the natural coordinates r, s, and t, the Cartesian coordinates of a point in the element with q nodal points are, before and after deformations,

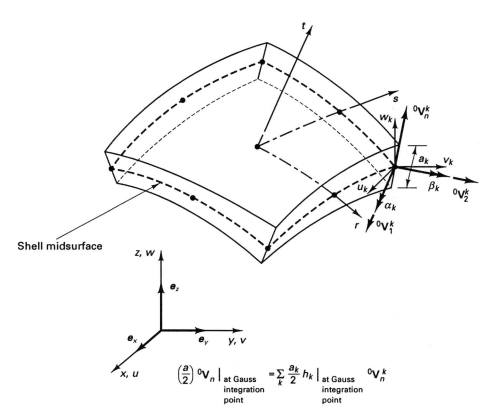

$$\left(\frac{a}{2}\right) {}^0\mathbf{V}_n \Big|_{\substack{\text{at Gauss} \\ \text{integration} \\ \text{point}}} = \sum_k \frac{a_k}{2} h_k \Big|_{\substack{\text{at Gauss} \\ \text{integration} \\ \text{point}}} {}^0\mathbf{V}_n^k$$

Figure 5.33   Nine-node shell element; also, definition of orthogonal $\bar{r}$, $\bar{s}$, t axes for constitutive relations

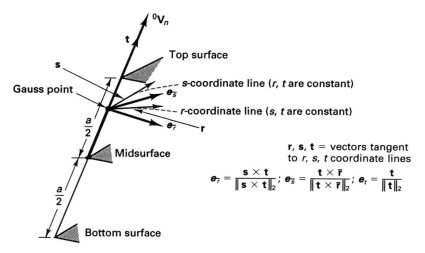

Figure 5.33   *(continued)*

$$
{}^{\ell}x(r, s, t) = \sum_{k=1}^{q} h_k \, {}^{\ell}x_k + \frac{t}{2} \sum_{k=1}^{q} a_k h_k \, {}^{\ell}V_{nx}^{k}
$$

$$
{}^{\ell}y(r, s, t) = \sum_{k=1}^{q} h_k \, {}^{\ell}y_k + \frac{t}{2} \sum_{k=1}^{q} a_k h_k \, {}^{\ell}V_{ny}^{k} \tag{5.107}
$$

$$
{}^{\ell}z(r, s, t) = \sum_{k=1}^{q} h_k \, {}^{\ell}z_k + \frac{t}{2} \sum_{k=1}^{q} a_k h_k \, {}^{\ell}V_{nz}^{k}
$$

where the $h_k(r, s)$ are the interpolation functions summarized in Fig. 5.4 and

$\quad {}^{\ell}x, {}^{\ell}y, {}^{\ell}z$ = Cartesian coordinates of any point in the element

$\quad {}^{\ell}x_k, {}^{\ell}y_k, {}^{\ell}z_k$ = Cartesian coordinates of nodal point k

$\quad a_k$ = thickness of shell in t direction at nodal point k

$\quad {}^{\ell}V_{nx}^{k}, {}^{\ell}V_{ny}^{k}, {}^{\ell}V_{nz}^{k}$ = components of unit vector ${}^{\ell}V_n^k$ "normal" to the shell midsurface in direction t at nodal point k; we call ${}^{\ell}V_n^k$ the normal vector[7] or, more appropriately, the director vector, at nodal point k

and the left superscript ℓ denotes, as in the general beam formulation, the configuration of the element; i.e., $\ell = 0$ and 1 denote the original and final configurations of the shell element. Hence, using (5.107), the displacement components are

$$
u(r, s, t) = \sum_{k=1}^{q} h_k u_k + \frac{t}{2} \sum_{k=1}^{q} a_k h_k V_{nx}^{k}
$$

$$
v(r, s, t) = \sum_{k=1}^{q} h_k v_k + \frac{t}{2} \sum_{k=1}^{q} a_k h_k V_{ny}^{k} \tag{5.108}
$$

$$
w(r, s, t) = \sum_{k=1}^{q} h_k w_k + \frac{t}{2} \sum_{k=1}^{q} a_k h_k V_{nz}^{k}
$$

[7] We call ${}^{\ell}V_n^k$ the *normal* vector although it may not be exactly normal to the midsurface of the shell in the original configuration (see Example 5.32), and in the final configuration (e.g., because of shear deformations).

where $\mathbf{V}_n^k$ stores the increments in the direction cosines of $^0\mathbf{V}_n^k$,

$$\mathbf{V}_n^k = {}^1\mathbf{V}_n^k - {}^0\mathbf{V}_n^k \tag{5.109}$$

The components of $\mathbf{V}_n^k$ can be expressed in terms of rotations at the nodal point k; however, there is no unique way of proceeding. An efficient way is to define two unit vectors $^0\mathbf{V}_1^k$ and $^0\mathbf{V}_2^k$ that are orthogonal to $^0\mathbf{V}_n^k$:

$$^0\mathbf{V}_1^k = \frac{\mathbf{e}_y \times {}^0\mathbf{V}_n^k}{\| \mathbf{e}_y \times {}^0\mathbf{V}_n^k \|_2} \tag{5.110a}$$

where $\mathbf{e}_y$ is a unit vector in the direction of the y-axis. (For the special case $^0\mathbf{V}_n^k$ parallel to $\mathbf{e}_y$, we may simply use $^0\mathbf{V}_1^k$ equal to $\mathbf{e}_z$.) We can now obtain $^0\mathbf{V}_2^k$,

$$^0\mathbf{V}_2^k = {}^0\mathbf{V}_n^k \times {}^0\mathbf{V}_1^k \tag{5.110b}$$

Let α_k and β_k be the rotations of the director vector $^0\mathbf{V}_n^k$ about the vectors $^0\mathbf{V}_1^k$ and $^0\mathbf{V}_2^k$. We then have, because α_k and β_k are small angles,

$$\mathbf{V}_n^k = -{}^0\mathbf{V}_2^k\,\alpha_k + {}^0\mathbf{V}_1^k\beta_k \tag{5.111}$$

This relationship can readily be proven when $^0\mathbf{V}_1 = \mathbf{e}_x$, $^0\mathbf{V}_2 = \mathbf{e}_y$ and $^0\mathbf{V}_n = \mathbf{e}_z$, but since these vectors are tensors, the relationship must also hold in general (see Section 2.4). Substituting from (5.111) into (5.108), we thus obtain

$$u(r, s, t) = \sum_{k=1}^{q} h_k\,u_k + \frac{t}{2}\sum_{k=1}^{q} a_k\,h_k(-{}^0V_{2x}^k\,\alpha_k + {}^0V_{1x}^k\,\beta_k)$$

$$v(r, s, t) = \sum_{k=1}^{q} h_k\,v_k + \frac{t}{2}\sum_{k=1}^{q} a_k\,h_k(-{}^0V_{2y}^k\,\alpha_k + {}^0V_{1y}^k\,\beta_k) \tag{5.112}$$

$$w(r, s, t) = \sum_{k=1}^{q} h_k\,w_k + \frac{t}{2}\sum_{k=1}^{q} a_k\,h_k(-{}^0V_{2z}^k\,\alpha_k + {}^0V_{1z}^k\,\beta_k)$$

With the element displacements and coordinates defined in (5.112) and (5.107) we can now proceed as usual to evaluate the element matrices of a pure displacement-based element. The entries in the displacement interpolation matrix $\mathbf{H}$ of the shell element are given in (5.112), and the entries in the strain-displacement interpolation matrix can be calculated using the procedures already described in the formulation of the beam element (see Section 5.4.1).

To evaluate the strain-displacement matrix, we obtain from (5.112),

$$\begin{bmatrix} \dfrac{\partial u}{\partial r} \\[2mm] \dfrac{\partial u}{\partial s} \\[2mm] \dfrac{\partial u}{\partial t} \end{bmatrix} = \sum_{k=1}^{q} \begin{bmatrix} \dfrac{\partial h_k}{\partial r}\begin{bmatrix} 1 & tg_{1x}^k & tg_{2x}^k \end{bmatrix} \\[3mm] \dfrac{\partial h_k}{\partial s}\begin{bmatrix} 1 & tg_{1x}^k & tg_{2x}^k \end{bmatrix} \\[3mm] h_k\begin{bmatrix} 0 & g_{1x}^k & g_{2x}^k \end{bmatrix} \end{bmatrix} \begin{bmatrix} u_k \\[2mm] \alpha_k \\[2mm] \beta_k \end{bmatrix} \tag{5.113}$$

and the derivatives of v and w are given by simply substituting for u and x the variables v, y and w, z, respectively. In (5.113) we use the notation

$$\mathbf{g}_1^k = -\tfrac{1}{2}a_k\,{}^0\mathbf{V}_2^k; \qquad \mathbf{g}_2^k = \tfrac{1}{2}a_k\,{}^0\mathbf{V}_1^k \tag{5.114}$$

To obtain the displacement derivatives corresponding to the Cartesian coordinates x, y, z, we use the standard transformation

$$\frac{\partial}{\partial \mathbf{x}} = \mathbf{J}^{-1} \frac{\partial}{\partial \mathbf{r}} \tag{5.115}$$

where the Jacobian matrix $\mathbf{J}$ contains the derivatives of the coordinates x, y, z with respect to the natural coordinates r, s, t. Substituting from (5.113) into (5.115), we obtain

$$\begin{bmatrix} \dfrac{\partial u}{\partial x} \\[2mm] \dfrac{\partial u}{\partial y} \\[2mm] \dfrac{\partial u}{\partial z} \end{bmatrix} = \sum_{k=1}^{q} \begin{bmatrix} \dfrac{\partial h_k}{\partial x} & g_{1x}^{k} G_x^{k} & g_{2x}^{k} G_x^{k} \\[2mm] \dfrac{\partial h_k}{\partial y} & g_{1x}^{k} G_y^{k} & g_{2x}^{k} G_y^{k} \\[2mm] \dfrac{\partial h_k}{\partial z} & g_{1x}^{k} G_z^{k} & g_{2x}^{k} G_z^{k} \end{bmatrix} \begin{bmatrix} u_k \\[2mm] \alpha_k \\[2mm] \beta_k \end{bmatrix} \tag{5.116}$$

and the derivatives of v and w are obtained in an analogous manner. In (5.116) we have

$$\frac{\partial h_k}{\partial x} = J_{11}^{-1} \frac{\partial h_k}{\partial r} + J_{12}^{-1} \frac{\partial h_k}{\partial s}$$

$$G_x^{k} = t\left(J_{11}^{-1} \frac{\partial h_k}{\partial r} + J_{12}^{-1} \frac{\partial h_k}{\partial s} \right) + J_{13}^{-1} h_k \tag{5.117}$$

where J_{ij}^{-1} is element (i, j) of $\mathbf{J}^{-1}$, and so on.

With the displacement derivatives defined in (5.116) we now directly assemble the strain-displacement matrix $\mathbf{B}$ of a shell element. Assuming that the rows in this matrix correspond to all six global Cartesian strain components, ϵ_{xx}, ϵ_{yy}, . . . , γ_{zx}, the entries in $\mathbf{B}$ are constructed in the usual way (see Section 5.3), but then the stress-strain law must contain the shell assumption that the stress normal to the shell surface is zero. We impose that the stress in the direction of the vector is zero. Thus, if $\boldsymbol{\tau}$ and $\boldsymbol{\epsilon}$ store the Cartesian stress and strain components, we use

$$\boldsymbol{\tau} = \mathbf{C}_{\text{sh}} \boldsymbol{\epsilon} \tag{5.118}$$

where

$$\boldsymbol{\tau}^T = \begin{bmatrix} \tau_{xx} & \tau_{yy} & \tau_{zz} & \tau_{xy} & \tau_{yz} & \tau_{zx} \end{bmatrix}$$

$$\boldsymbol{\epsilon}^T = \begin{bmatrix} \epsilon_{xx} & \epsilon_{yy} & \epsilon_{zz} & \gamma_{xy} & \gamma_{yz} & \gamma_{zx} \end{bmatrix}$$

$$\mathbf{C}_{\text{sh}} = \mathbf{Q}_{\text{sh}}^T \left(\frac{E}{1 - \nu^2} \begin{bmatrix} 1 & \nu & 0 & 0 & 0 & 0 \\ & 1 & 0 & 0 & 0 & 0 \\ & & 0 & 0 & 0 & 0 \\ & & & \dfrac{1-\nu}{2} & 0 & 0 \\ & \text{Symmetric} & & & k\dfrac{1-\nu}{2} & 0 \\ & & & & & k\dfrac{1-\nu}{2} \end{bmatrix} \right) \mathbf{Q}_{\text{sh}} \tag{5.119}$$

and $\mathbf{Q}_{\text{sh}}$ represents a matrix that transforms the stress-strain law from an $\bar{r}$, $\bar{s}$, t Cartesian shell-aligned coordinate system to the global Cartesian coordinate system. The elements of the matrix $\mathbf{Q}_{sh}$ are obtained from the direction cosines of the $\bar{r}, \bar{s}, t$ coordinate axes measured in the x, y, z coordinate directions,

$$\mathbf{Q}_{sh} = \begin{bmatrix} l_1^2 & m_1^2 & n_1^2 & l_1 m_1 & m_1 n_1 & n_1 l_1 \\ l_2^2 & m_2^2 & n_2^2 & l_2 m_2 & m_2 n_2 & n_2 l_2 \\ l_3^2 & m_3^2 & n_3^2 & l_3 m_3 & m_3 n_3 & n_3 l_3 \\ 2l_1 l_2 & 2m_1 m_2 & 2n_1 n_2 & l_1 m_2 + l_2 m_1 & m_1 n_2 + m_2 n_1 & n_1 l_2 + n_2 l_1 \\ 2l_2 l_3 & 2m_2 m_3 & 2n_2 n_3 & l_2 m_3 + l_3 m_2 & m_2 n_3 + m_3 n_2 & n_2 l_3 + n_3 l_2 \\ 2l_3 l_1 & 2m_3 m_1 & 2n_3 n_1 & l_3 m_1 + l_1 m_3 & m_3 n_1 + m_1 n_3 & n_3 l_1 + n_1 l_3 \end{bmatrix} \qquad (5.120)$$

where

$$l_1 = \cos(\mathbf{e}_x, \mathbf{e}_{\bar{r}}); \qquad m_1 = \cos(\mathbf{e}_y, \mathbf{e}_{\bar{r}}); \qquad n_1 = \cos(\mathbf{e}_z, \mathbf{e}_{\bar{r}})$$

$$l_2 = \cos(\mathbf{e}_x, \mathbf{e}_{\bar{s}}); \qquad m_2 = \cos(\mathbf{e}_y, \mathbf{e}_{\bar{s}}); \qquad n_2 = \cos(\mathbf{e}_z, \mathbf{e}_{\bar{s}}) \qquad (5.121)$$

$$l_3 = \cos(\mathbf{e}_x, \mathbf{e}_t); \qquad m_3 = \cos(\mathbf{e}_y, \mathbf{e}_t); \qquad n_3 = \cos(\mathbf{e}_z, \mathbf{e}_t)$$

and the relation in (5.119) corresponds to a fourth-order tensor transformation as described in Section 2.4.

It follows that in the analysis of a general shell the matrix $\mathbf{Q}_{sh}$ may have to be evaluated anew at each integration point that is employed in the numerical integration of the stiffness matrix (see Section 5.5). However, when special shells are considered and, in particular, when a plate is analyzed, the transformation matrix and the stress-strain matrix $\mathbf{C}_{sh}$ need only be evaluated at specific points and can then be employed repetitively. For example, in the analysis of an assemblage of flat plates, the stress-strain matrix $\mathbf{C}_{sh}$ needs to be calculated only once for each flat structural part.

In the above formulation the strain-displacement matrix is formulated corresponding to the Cartesian strain components, which can be directly established using the derivatives in (5.116). Alternatively, we could calculate the strain components corresponding to coordinate axes aligned with the shell element midsurface and establish a strain-displacement matrix for these strain components, as we did in the formulation of the general beam element in Section 5.4.1. The relative computational efficiency of these two approaches depends on whether it is more effective to transform the strain components (which always differ at the integration points) or to transform the stress-strain law.

It is instructive to compare this shell element formulation with a formulation in which flat elements with a superimposed plate bending and membrane stress behavior are employed (see Section 4.2.3). To identify the differences, assume that the general shell element is used as a flat element in the modeling of a shell; then the stiffness matrix of this element could also be obtained by superimposing the plate bending stiffness matrix derived in (5.94) to (5.99) (see Example 5.29) and the plane stress stiffness matrix discussed in Section 5.3.1. Thus, in this case, the general shell element reduces to a plate bending element *plus* a plane stress element, but a computational difference lies in the fact that these element matrices are calculated by integrating numerically only in the r-s element midplanes, whereas in the shell element stiffness calculation numerical integration is also performed in the t-direction (unless the general formulation is modified for this special case).

We illustrate some of the above relations in the following example.

EXAMPLE 5.32:   Consider the four-node shell element shown in Fig. E5.32.

(a) Develop the entries in the displacement interpolation matrix.
(b) Calculate the thickness at the midpoint of the element and give the direction in which this thickness is measured.

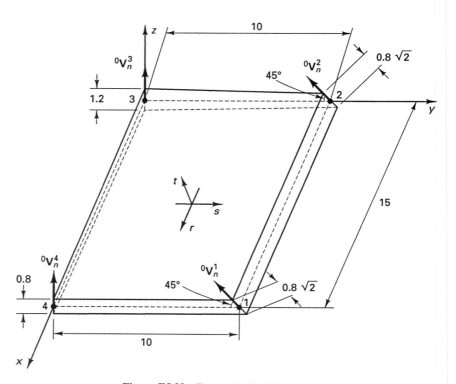

Figure E5.32   Four-node shell element

The shell element considered has varying thickness but in some respects can be compared with the plate element in Example 5.29.

The displacement interpolation matrix **H** is given by the relations in (5.112). The functions h_k are those of a four-node two-dimensional element (see Fig. 5.4 and Example 5.29). The director vectors ${}^0\mathbf{V}_n^k$ are given by the geometry of the element:

$$ {}^0\mathbf{V}_n^1 = \begin{bmatrix} 0 \\ -1/\sqrt{2} \\ 1/\sqrt{2} \end{bmatrix}; \qquad {}^0\mathbf{V}_n^2 = \begin{bmatrix} 0 \\ -1/\sqrt{2} \\ 1/\sqrt{2} \end{bmatrix}; \qquad {}^0\mathbf{V}_n^3 = \begin{bmatrix} 0 \\ 0 \\ 1 \end{bmatrix}; \qquad {}^0\mathbf{V}_n^4 = \begin{bmatrix} 0 \\ 0 \\ 1 \end{bmatrix} $$

Hence,
$$ {}^0\mathbf{V}_1^1 = {}^0\mathbf{V}_1^2 = {}^0\mathbf{V}_1^3 = {}^0\mathbf{V}_1^4 = \begin{bmatrix} 1 \\ 0 \\ 0 \end{bmatrix} $$

$$
{}^0\mathbf{V}_2^1 = {}^0\mathbf{V}_2^2 = \begin{bmatrix} 0 \\ 1/\sqrt{2} \\ 1/\sqrt{2} \end{bmatrix}; \qquad {}^0\mathbf{V}_2^3 = {}^0\mathbf{V}_2^4 = \begin{bmatrix} 0 \\ 1 \\ 0 \end{bmatrix}
$$

Also, $\qquad a_1 = a_2 = 0.8\sqrt{2}; \qquad a_3 = 1.2; \qquad a_4 = 0.8$

The above expressions give all entries in (5.112).

To evaluate the thickness at the element midpoint and the direction in which the thickness is measured, we use the relation

$$
\left(\frac{a}{2}\right){}^0\mathbf{V}_n \bigg|_{\text{midpoint}} = \sum_{k=1}^{4} \frac{a_k}{2} h_k \bigg|_{r=s=0} {}^0\mathbf{V}_n^k
$$

where a is the thickness and the director vector ${}^0\mathbf{V}_n$ gives the direction sought. This expression gives

$$
\frac{a}{2}{}^0\mathbf{V}_n = \frac{0.8\sqrt{2}}{4}\begin{bmatrix} 0 \\ -1/\sqrt{2} \\ 1/\sqrt{2} \end{bmatrix} + \frac{1.2}{8}\begin{bmatrix} 0 \\ 0 \\ 1 \end{bmatrix} + \frac{0.8}{8}\begin{bmatrix} 0 \\ 0 \\ 1 \end{bmatrix} = \begin{bmatrix} 0 \\ -0.2 \\ 0.45 \end{bmatrix}
$$

which gives $\qquad {}^0\mathbf{V}_n = \begin{bmatrix} 0.0 \\ -0.406 \\ 0.914 \end{bmatrix}; \qquad a = 0.985$

This shell element formulation clearly has an important attribute, namely, that any geometric shape of a shell can be directly represented. The generality is further increased if the formulation is extended to transition elements (similar to the extension for the isoparametric beam element discussed in Section 5.4.1). Figure 5.34 shows how shell transition

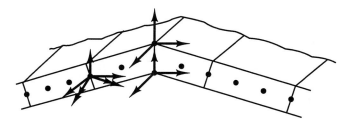

(a) Shell intersection

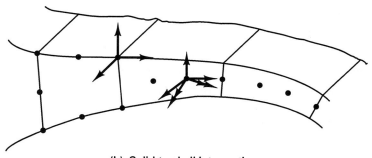

(b) Solid-to-shell intersection

Figure 5.34 Use of shell transition elements

elements can be used to model shell intersections and shell-to-solid transitions using compatible element idealizations without the use of special constraint equations. The features of generality and accuracy in the modeling of a shell structure can be especially important in the material and geometric nonlinear analysis of shell structures, since particularly in such analyses shell geometries must be accounted for accurately. We discuss the extension of the formulation to general nonlinear analysis in Section 6.5.2.

The pure displacement-based formulation has, as in the case of displacement-based isoparametric beam elements, the disadvantage that the lower-order elements lock as a result of spurious shear strains, and when the elements are curved, also because of spurious membrane strains. Indeed, the least order of interpolation that should be used is a cubic interpolation of displacements (and geometry) leading to 16-node quadrilateral and 10-node triangular shell elements. But even these elements, when geometrically distorted, show some shear and membrane locking (for these reasons the MITC16 and MITC12 plate bending elements are presented in Fig. 5.27). To circumvent the locking behavior, a mixed interpolation is used, and the use of tensorial components as proposed by E. N. Dvorkin and K. J. Bathe [A] and K. J. Bathe and E. N. Dvorkin [B] is particularly attractive.

The first step in the mixed interpolation is to write the complete strain tensor at an integration point as

$$\boldsymbol{\epsilon} = \underbrace{\tilde{\epsilon}_{rr}\mathbf{g}^r\mathbf{g}^r + \tilde{\epsilon}_{ss}\mathbf{g}^s\mathbf{g}^s + \tilde{\epsilon}_{rs}(\mathbf{g}^r\mathbf{g}^s + \mathbf{g}^s\mathbf{g}^r)}_{\text{in-layer strains}} + \underbrace{\tilde{\epsilon}_{rt}(\mathbf{g}^r\mathbf{g}^t + \mathbf{g}^t\mathbf{g}^r) + \tilde{\epsilon}_{st}(\mathbf{g}^s\mathbf{g}^t + \mathbf{g}^t\mathbf{g}^s)}_{\text{transverse shear strains}} \qquad (5.122)$$

where the $\tilde{\epsilon}_{rr}$, $\tilde{\epsilon}_{ss}$, . . . , are the covariant strain components corresponding to the base vectors

$$\mathbf{g}_r = \frac{\partial \mathbf{x}}{\partial r}; \qquad \mathbf{g}_s = \frac{\partial \mathbf{x}}{\partial s}; \qquad \mathbf{g}_t = \frac{\partial \mathbf{x}}{\partial t}$$

$$\mathbf{x} = \begin{bmatrix} x \\ y \\ z \end{bmatrix} \qquad (5.123)$$

and the $\mathbf{g}^r$, $\mathbf{g}^s$, $\mathbf{g}^t$ are the corresponding contravariant base vectors (see Section 2.4). We note that if we use indicial notation with $i = 1, 2, 3$ corresponding to r, s, and t, respectively, and $r_1 = r$, $r_2 = s$, $r_3 = t$, we can define

$${}^0\mathbf{g}_i = \frac{\partial \mathbf{x}}{\partial r_i}; \qquad {}^1\mathbf{g}_i = \frac{\partial (\mathbf{x} + \mathbf{u})}{\partial r_i} \qquad (5.124)$$

and then the covariant Green-Lagrange strain tensor components are

$${}^1_0\tilde{\epsilon}_{ij} = \tfrac{1}{2}({}^1\mathbf{g}_i \cdot {}^1\mathbf{g}_j - {}^0\mathbf{g}_i \cdot {}^0\mathbf{g}_j) \qquad (5.125)$$

The strain components in (5.118) are the linear Cartesian components of the strain tensor given by (5.125) (see Example 2.28).

In the mixed interpolation, the objective is to interpolate the in-layer and transverse shear strain components independently and tie these interpolations to the usual displacement interpolations. The result is that the stiffness matrix is then obtained corresponding to only the same nodal point variables (displacements and section rotations) as are used for the displacement-based elements. Of course, the key is to choose in-layer and transverse shear strain component interpolations, for the displacement interpolations used, such that the resulting element has an optimal predictive capability.

An attractive four-node element is the MITC4 shell element proposed by E. N. Dvorkin and K. J. Bathe [A] for which the in-layer strains are computed from the displacement interpolations (since the element is not curved and membrane locking is not present in the displacement-based element) and the covariant transverse shear strain components are interpolated and tied to the displacement interpolations as discussed for the plate element [see (5.101)]. The element performs quite well in out-of-plane bending (the plate bending) action, and also in in-plane (the membrane) action if the incompatible modes as discussed in Example 4.28 are added to the basic four-node element displacement interpolations.

A significantly better predictive capability is obtained with higher-order elements, and Fig. 5.35 shows the interpolations and tying points used for the 9-node and 16-node elements proposed by M. L. Bucalem and K. J. Bathe [A]. These elements are referred to as MITC9 and MITC16 *shell* elements.

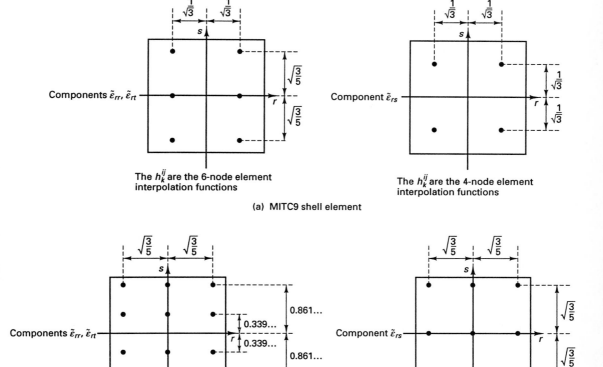

Figure 5.35 MITC shell elements; interpolations of strain components and tying points

Following our earlier discussion of the mixed interpolation of plate elements, in the formulation of these shell elements we use

$$\tilde{\varepsilon}_{ij} = \sum_{k=1}^{n_{ij}} h_k^{ij} \mathbf{B}_{ij}^{\mathrm{DI}}\big|_k \,\hat{\mathbf{u}} \qquad (5.126)$$

where n_{ij} denotes the number of tying points used for the strain component considered, h_k^{ij} is the interpolation function corresponding to the tying point k, and $\mathbf{B}_{ij}^{\mathrm{DI}}\big|_k \,\hat{\mathbf{u}}$ is the strain component evaluated at the tying point k by the displacement assumption (by *d*isplacement *i*nterpolation). Note that with (5.126) only point tying and no integral tying (as in the higher-order MITC plate elements) is performed.

Unfortunately, a mathematical analysis of the MITC9 and MITC16 shell elements, as achieved for the plate elements summarized in Fig. 5.27, is not yet available, although some valuable insight has been gained by the work of J. Pitkäranta [A]. Hence, the formulation of the shell elements is so far based on the mathematical and physical insight available from the formulations and analyses of beam and plate elements, intuition to represent shell behavior accurately, and well-chosen numerical tests.

Of course, the MITC shell elements presented here do not contain any spurious zero energy modes. Also, the membrane and pure bending patch tests are passed by these elements. A further valuable test is the analysis of the problem in Fig. 5.36. This test tells whether an element locks (as a result of spurious membrane or shear stresses) and indicates how sensitive the element predictive capability is when the curved element is geometrically distorted in the model of a curved shell. Table 5.4 gives the analysis results of the problem in Fig. 5.36 and shows the good performance of the MITC9 and MITC16 elements.

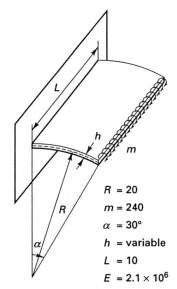

$R = 20$
$m = 240$
$\alpha = 30°$
$h = \text{variable}$
$L = 10$
$E = 2.1 \times 10^6$

Figure 5.36 Curved cantilever problem to test curved shell elements

Additional numerical results using the MITC9 and MITC16 shell elements are given by M. L. Bucalem and K. J. Bathe [A]; similarly formulated elements have been presented by H. C. Huang and E. Hinton [A], K. C. Park and G. M. Stanley [A], and J. Jang and P. M. Pinsky [A].

TABLE 5.4   *Performance of MITC9 and MITC16 shell elements in the analysis of the problem in Fig. 5.36*

Mesh	h/R	θ_{FE}/θ_{AN} MITC9 shell element (results at point A)[†]	MITC16 shell element (results at point B)[‡]
	1/100	0.9995	1.0001
	1/1000	0.9995	1.0001
	1/100000	0.9995	1.0001
	1/100	1.0000	1.0000
	1/1000	1.0000	1.0000
	1/100000	1.0000	0.9999
	1/100	0.9956	0.9975
	1/1000	0.9913	0.9796
	1/100000	0.9883	0.9318
	1/100	0.9995	1.0001
	1/1000	0.9995	1.0001
	1/100000	0.9995	1.0001
	1/100	0.9995	1.0000
	1/1000	0.9995	1.0001
	1/100000	0.9995	1.0001

[†] A is the middle of the edge.
[‡] B is the third point of the edge.

Boundary Conditions

The plate elements presented in this section are based on Reissner-Mindlin plate theory, in which the transverse displacement and section rotations are independent variables. This assumption is fundamentally different from the kinematic assumption used in Kirchhoff plate theory, in which the transverse displacement is the only independent variable. Hence, whereas in Kirchhoff plate theory all boundary conditions are written only in terms of the transverse displacement (and of course its derivatives), in the Reissner-Mindlin theory all boundary conditions are written in terms of the transverse displacement and the section rotations (and their derivatives). Since the section rotations are used as additional kinematic variables, the actual physical condition of a support can also be modeled more accurately.

As an example, consider the support conditions at the edge of the thin structure shown in Fig. 5.37. If this structure were modeled as a three-dimensional continuum, the element idealization might be as shown in Fig. 5.38(a), and then the boundary conditions would be

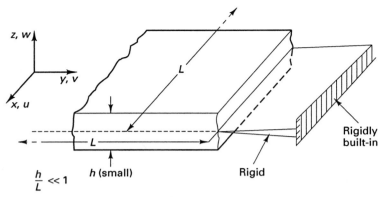

Figure 5.37   Knife-edge support for thin structure

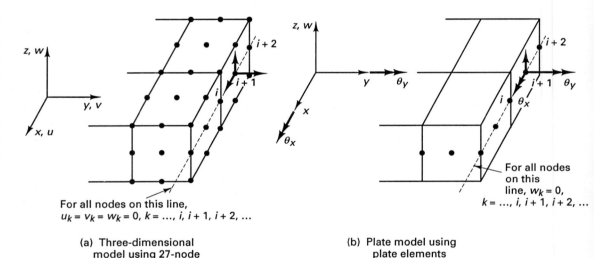

(a) Three-dimensional
      model using 27-node
      elements

(b) Plate model using
      plate elements

Figure 5.38   Three-dimensional and plate models for problem in Fig. 5.37

those given in the figure. Of course, such a model would be inefficient and impractical because the finite element discretization would have to be very fine for an accurate solution (recall that the three-dimensional elements would display the shear locking phenomenon).

Employing Reissner-Mindlin plate theory, the thin structure is represented using the assumptions given in (5.88) and Fig. 5.25. The boundary conditions are that the transverse displacement is restrained to zero but the section rotations are free; see Fig. 5.38(b). Surely, these conditions represent the physical situation as closely as possible consistent with the assumptions of the theory.

We note, on the other hand, that using Kirchhoff plate theory, the transverse displacement and edge rotation given by $\partial w/\partial x$ would both be zero, and therefore the finite element model would also have to impose $\theta_y = 0$. Hence, in summary, the edge conditions in Fig. 5.37 would be modeled as follows in a finite element solution.

Using three-dimensional elements:

$$\text{on the edge:} \quad u = v = w = 0 \tag{5.127}$$

Using Reissner-Mindlin plate theory-based elements (e.g., the MITC elements in Fig. 5.27):

$$\text{on the edge:} \quad w = 0; \qquad \theta_x \text{ and } \theta_y \text{ are left free} \tag{5.128}$$

Using Kirchhoff plate theory-based elements (e.g., the elements in Example 4.18):

$$\text{on the edge:} \quad w = \theta_y = 0; \qquad \theta_x \text{ is left free} \tag{5.129}$$

where in Kirchhoff plate theory,

$$\theta_y = -\frac{\partial w}{\partial x} \tag{5.130}$$

Of course, we could also visualize a physical support condition that, in addition to the rigid knife-edge support in Fig. 5.37, prevents the section rotation β_x. In this case we also would set θ_y to zero when using the Reissner-Mindlin plate theory-based elements, and we would set all u-displacements on the face of the plate equal to zero when using the three-dimensional elements.

The boundary condition in (5.128) is referred to as the "soft" boundary condition for a simple support, whereas when θ_y is also set to zero, the boundary condition is of the "hard" type. Similar possibilities also exist when the plate edge is "clamped", i.e., when the edge is also restrained against the rotation θ_x. In this case we clearly have $w = 0$ and $\theta_x = 0$ on the plate edge. However, again a choice exists regarding θ_y: in the soft boundary condition θ_y is left free, and in the hard boundary condition $\theta_y = 0$. In practice, we usually use the soft boundary conditions, but of course, depending on the actual physical situation, the hard boundary condition is also employed.

The important point is that when the Reissner-Mindlin plate theory-based elements are used, the boundary conditions on the transverse displacement and rotations are not necessarily the same as when Kirchhoff plate theory is being used and must be chosen to model appropriately the actual physical situation.

The same observations hold of course for the use of the shell elements presented earlier, for which the section rotations are also independent variables (and are not given by the derivatives of the transverse displacement).

Since the Reissner-Mindlin theory contains more variables for describing the plate behavior than the Kirchhoff theory, various interesting questions arise regarding a comparison of these theories and the convergence of results based on the Reissner-Mindlin theory to those based on the Kirchhoff theory. These questions have been addressed, for example, by K. O. Friedrichs and R. F. Dressler [A], E. Reissner [C], B. Häggblad and K. J. Bathe [A], and D. N. Arnold and R. S. Falk [A]. A main result is that when the Reissner-Mindlin theory is used, boundary layers along plate edges develop for specific boundary conditions when the thickness/length ratio of the plate becomes very small. These boundary layers represent the actual physical situation more realistically than the Kirchhoff plate theory does. Hence, the plate and shell elements presented in this section are not only attractive for computational reasons but can also be used to represent the actual situations in nature more accurately. Some numerical results and comparisons using the Kirchhoff and Reissner-Mindlin plate theories are given by B. Häggblad and K. J. Bathe [A] and K. J. Bathe, N. S. Lee, and M. L. Bucalem [A].

5.4.3 Exercises

5.32. Consider the beam of constant cross-sectional area in Fig. 5.19. Derive from (4.7), using the assumptions in Fig. 5.18, the virtual work expression in (5.58).

5.33. Consider the cubic displacement-based isoparametric beam element shown. Construct all matrices needed for the evaluation of the stiffness and mass matrices (but do not perform any integrations to evaluate these matrices).

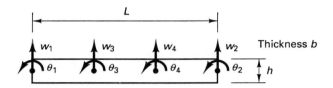

5.34. Consider the 3-node isoparametric displacement-based beam element used to model the cantilever beam problem in Fig. 5.20. Show analytically that excellent results are obtained when node 3 is placed exactly at the midlength of the beam, but that the results deteriorate when this node is shifted from that position.

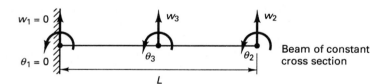

5.35. Consider the two-node beam element shown. Specialize the expressions (5.71) to (5.86) to this case.

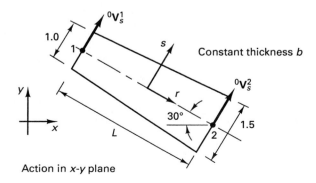

5.36. Consider the three-node beam element shown. Specialize the expressions (5.71) to (5.86) to this case.

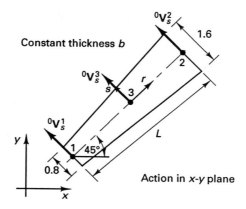

Constant thickness *b*

Action in *x-y* plane

5.37. Consider the cantilever beam shown. Idealize this structure by one two-node mixed interpolated beam element and analyze the response. First, neglect warping effects. Next, introduce warping displacements using the warping displacement function $w_w = xy(x^2 - y^2)$ and assuming a linear variation in warping along the element axis.

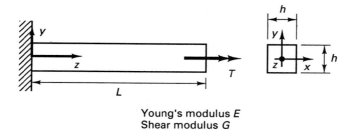

Young's modulus *E*
Shear modulus *G*

5.38. Consider the two-node mixed interpolated beam element shown. Derive all expressions needed to calculate the stiffness matrix, mass matrix, and nodal force vector for the degrees of freedom indicated. However, do not perform any integrations.

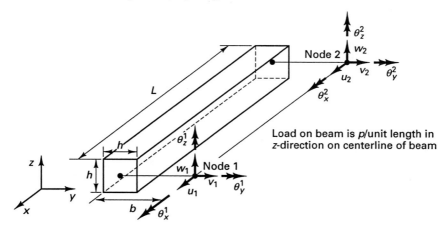

Load on beam is *p*/unit length in
z-direction on centerline of beam

5.39. Consider the plane stress element shown and evaluate the strain-displacement matrix of this element (called $\mathbf{B}_{pl}$).

Also consider the two-node displacement-based isoparametric beam element shown and evaluate the strain-displacement matrix (called $\mathbf{B}_b$).

Derive from $\mathbf{B}_{pl}$, using the appropriate kinematic constraints, the strain-displacement matrix of the degenerated plane stress element (called $\tilde{\mathbf{B}}_{pl}$) for the degrees of freedom used in the beam element. Show explicitly that

$$\int_V \mathbf{B}_b^T \mathbf{C}_b \mathbf{B}_b \, dV = \int_V \tilde{\mathbf{B}}_{pl}^T \tilde{\mathbf{C}} \tilde{\mathbf{B}}_{pl} \, dV$$

with $\mathbf{C}_b$ and $\tilde{\mathbf{C}}$ to be determined by you.

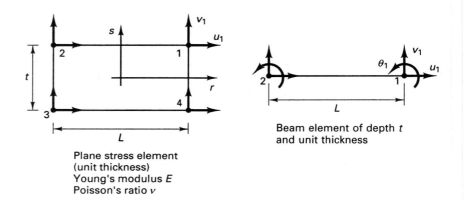

Plane stress element
(unit thickness)
Young's modulus E
Poisson's ratio ν

Beam element of depth t
and unit thickness

5.40. Consider the problem of an infinitely long, thin plate, rigidly clamped on two sides as shown. Calculate the stiffness matrix of a two-node plane strain beam element to be used to analyze the plate. [Use the mixed interpolation of (5.68) and (5.69).]

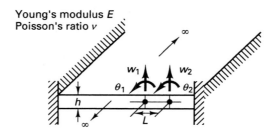

Young's modulus E
Poisson's ratio ν

5.41. Consider the axisymmetric shell element shown. Construct the strain-displacement matrix assuming mixed interpolation with a constant transverse shear strain. Also, establish the corresponding stress-strain matrix to be used in the evaluation of the stiffness matrix.

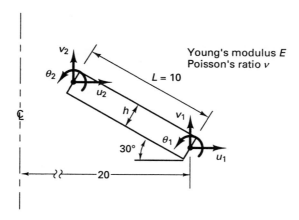

5.42. Assume that in Example 5.28 axisymmetric conditions are being considered. Construct the strain-displacement matrix of the transition element. Assume that the axis of revolution, i.e. the y axis, is at distance R from node 3.

5.43. Use a computer program to analyze the curved beam shown for the deformations and internal stresses.

    (a) Use displacement-based discretizations of, first, four-node plane stress elements, and then, eight-node plane stress elements.

    (b) Use discretizations of, first, two-node beam elements, and then, three-node beam elements.

        Compare the calculated solutions with the analytical solution and increase the fineness of your meshes until an accurate solution is obtained.

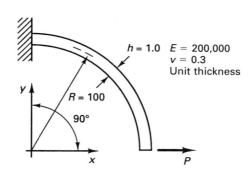

5.44. Perform the analysis in Exercise 5.43 but assume axisymmetric conditions; i.e., assume that the figure in Exercise 5.43 shows the cross section of an axisymmetric shell with the centerline at $x = 0$, and that P is a line load per unit length.

5.45. Consider the four-node plate bending element in Example 5.29. Assume that $w_1 = 0.1$ and $\theta_y^1 = 0.01$ and that all other nodal point displacements and rotations are zero. Plot the curvatures $\boldsymbol{\kappa}$ and transverse shear strains $\boldsymbol{\gamma}$ as a function of r, s over the midsurface of the element.

5.46. Consider the four-node plate bending element in Example 5.29. Assume that the element is loaded on its top surface with the constant traction shown. Calculate the consistent nodal point forces and moments.

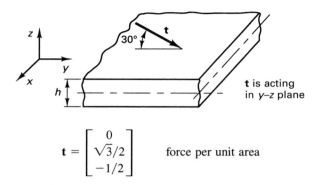

$$\mathbf{t} = \begin{bmatrix} 0 \\ \sqrt{3}/2 \\ -1/2 \end{bmatrix} \qquad \text{force per unit area}$$

5.47. Establish the transverse shear strain interpolation matrix $\mathbf{B}_\gamma$ of the parallelogram-shaped MITC4 element shown.

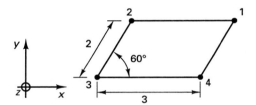

5.48. Consider the formulation of the MITC4 element and Example 4.30. Show that the MITC4 element formulation can be derived from the Hu-Washizu variational principle.

5.49. Consider the four-node shell element shown and develop the geometry and displacement interpolations (5.107) and (5.112).

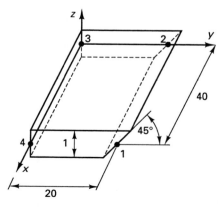

5.50. Show explicitly that using the general shell element formulation in (5.107) to (5.118) for a flat element is equivalent to the superposition of the Reissner-Mindlin plate element formulation in (5.88) to (5.99) and the plane stress membrane element formulation in Section 5.3.1.

5.51. Use a computer program to solve the problem shown in Fig. 5.36 with curved shell elements. First, use a single element, and then, use two geometrically distorted elements for the structure to study the element distortion sensitivity.

5.52. Consider the following Kirchhoff plate theory boundary conditions at the edge of a plate:

$$w = 0; \qquad \frac{\partial w}{\partial x} = \frac{\partial w}{\partial y} = 0 \tag{a}$$

Establish a corresponding reasonable choice of boundary conditions for the Reissner-Mindlin plate theory. Also, discuss and illustrate graphically that the boundary conditions in (a) do not uniquely determine the boundary conditions for the Reissner-Mindlin plate theory.

5.5 NUMERICAL INTEGRATION

An important aspect of isoparametric and related finite element analysis is the required numerical integration. The required matrix integrals in the finite element calculations have been written as

$$\int \mathbf{F}(r) \, dr; \quad \int \mathbf{F}(r, s) \, dr \, ds; \quad \int \mathbf{F}(r, s, t) \, dr \, ds \, dt \tag{5.131}$$

in the one-, two-, and three-dimensional cases, respectively. It was stated that these integrals are in practice evaluated numerically using

$$\left.\begin{aligned}
\int \mathbf{F}(r) \, dr &= \sum_i \alpha_i \mathbf{F}(r_i) + \mathbf{R}_n \\[2mm]
\int \mathbf{F}(r, s) \, dr \, ds &= \sum_{i,j} \alpha_{ij} \mathbf{F}(r_i, s_j) + \mathbf{R}_n \\[2mm]
\int \mathbf{F}(r, s, t) \, dr \, ds \, dt &= \sum_{i,j,k} \alpha_{ijk} \mathbf{F}(r_i, s_j, t_k) + \mathbf{R}_n
\end{aligned}\right\} \tag{5.132}$$

where the summations extend over all i, j, and k specified, the α_i, α_{ij}, and α_{ijk} are weighting factors, and $\mathbf{F}(r_i)$, $\mathbf{F}(r_i, s_j)$, and $\mathbf{F}(r_i, s_j, t_k)$ are the matrices $\mathbf{F}(r)$, $\mathbf{F}(r, s)$, and $\mathbf{F}(r, s, t)$ evaluated at the points specified in the arguments. The matrices $\mathbf{R}_n$ are error matrices, which in practice are usually not evaluated. Therefore, we use

$$\left.\begin{aligned}
\int \mathbf{F}(r) \, dr &= \sum_i \alpha_i \, \mathbf{F}(r_i) \\[2mm]
\int \mathbf{F}(r, s) \, dr \, ds &= \sum_{i,j} \alpha_{ij} \, \mathbf{F}(r_i, s_j) \\[2mm]
\int \mathbf{F}(r, s, t) \, dr \, ds \, dt &= \sum_{i,j,k} \alpha_{ijk} \, \mathbf{F}(r_i, s_j, t_k)
\end{aligned}\right\} \tag{5.133}$$

The purpose in this section is to present the theory and practical implications of numerical integrations. An important point is the integration accuracy that is needed, i.e., the number of integration points required in the element formation.

As presented above, in finite element analysis we integrate matrices, which means that each element of the matrix considered is integrated individually. Hence, for the derivation of the numerical integration formulas we can consider a typical element of a matrix, which we denote as F.

Consider the one-dimensional case first, i.e., the integration of $\int_a^b F(r)\,dr$. In an isoparametric element calculation we would actually have $a = -1$ and $b = +1$.

The numerical integration of $\int_a^b F(r)\,dr$ is essentially based on passing a polynomial $\psi(r)$ through given values of $F(r)$ and then using $\int_a^b \psi(r)\,dr$ as an approximation to $\int_a^b F(r)\,dr$. The number of evaluations of $F(r)$ and the positions of the sampling points in the interval from a to b determine how well $\psi(r)$ approximates $F(r)$ and hence the error of the numerical integration (see, for example, C. E. Fröberg [A]).

5.5.1 Interpolation Using a Polynomial

Assume that $F(r)$ has been evaluated at the $(n + 1)$ distinct points $r_0, r_1, \ldots, r_n$ to obtain $F_0, F_1, \ldots, F_n$, respectively, and that a polynomial $\psi(r)$ is to be passed through these data. Then there is a unique polynomial $\psi(r)$ given as

$$\psi(r) = a_0 + a_1 r + a_2 r^2 + \cdots + a_n r^n \tag{5.134}$$

Using the condition $\psi(r) = F(r)$ at the $(n + 1)$ interpolating points, we have

$$\mathbf{F} = \mathbf{Va} \tag{5.135}$$

where
$$\mathbf{F} = \begin{bmatrix} F_0 \\ F_1 \\ \cdot \\ \cdot \\ F_n \end{bmatrix}; \qquad \mathbf{a} = \begin{bmatrix} a_0 \\ a_1 \\ \cdot \\ \cdot \\ a_n \end{bmatrix} \tag{5.136}$$

and $\mathbf{V}$ is the *Vandermonde matrix*,

$$\mathbf{V} = \begin{bmatrix} 1 & r_0 & r_0^2 & \cdots & r_0^n \\ 1 & r_1 & r_1^2 & \cdots & r_1^n \\ \cdot & & \cdot & & \cdot \\ \cdot & & \cdot & & \cdot \\ 1 & r_n & r_n^2 & \cdots & r_n^n \end{bmatrix} \tag{5.137}$$

Since $\det \mathbf{V} \neq 0$, provided that the r_i are distinct points, we have a unique solution for $\mathbf{a}$.

However, a more convenient way to obtain $\psi(r)$ is to use *Lagrangian interpolation*. First, we recall that the $(n + 1)$ functions $1, r, r^2, \ldots, r^n$ form an $(n + 1)$-dimensional vector space, say V_n, in which $\psi(r)$ is an element (see Section 2.3). Since the coordinates $a_0, a_1, a_2, \ldots, a_n$ of $\psi(r)$ are relatively difficult to evaluate using (5.135), we seek a different basis for the space V_n in which the coordinates of $\psi(r)$ are more easily evaluated. This basis is provided by the fundamental polynomials of Lagrangian interpolation, given as

$$l_j(r) = \frac{(r - r_0)(r - r_1) \cdots (r - r_{j-1})(r - r_{j+1}) \cdots (r - r_n)}{(r_j - r_0)(r_j - r_1) \cdots (r_j - r_{j-1})(r_j - r_{j+1}) \cdots (r_j - r_n)} \tag{5.138}$$

where

$$l_j(r_i) = \delta_{ij} \tag{5.139}$$

where δ_{ij} is the Kronecker delta; i.e., $\delta_{ij} = 1$ for $i = j$, and $\delta_{ij} = 0$ for $i \neq j$. Using the property in (5.139), the coordinates of the base vectors are simply the values of $F(r)$, and the polynomial $\psi(r)$ is

$$\psi(r) = F_0 l_0(r) + F_1 l_1(r) + \cdots + F_n l_n(r) \tag{5.140}$$

EXAMPLE 5.33: Establish the interpolating polynomial $\psi(r)$ for the function $F(r) = 2^r - r$ when the data at the points $r = 0, 1,$ and 3 are used. In this case $r_0 = 0$, $r_1 = 1$, $r_2 = 3$, and $F_0 = 1$, $F_1 = 1$, $F_2 = 5$.

In the first approach we use the relation in (5.135) to calculate the unknown coefficients a_0, a_1, and a_2 of the polynomial $\psi(r) = a_0 + a_1 r + a_2 r^2$. In this case we have

$$\begin{bmatrix} 1 & 0 & 0 \\ 1 & 1 & 1 \\ 1 & 3 & 9 \end{bmatrix} \begin{bmatrix} a_0 \\ a_1 \\ a_2 \end{bmatrix} = \begin{bmatrix} 1 \\ 1 \\ 5 \end{bmatrix}$$

The solution gives $a_0 = 1$, $a_1 = -\frac{2}{3}$, $a_2 = \frac{2}{3}$, and therefore $\psi(r) = 1 - \frac{2}{3}r + \frac{2}{3}r^2$.

If Lagrangian interpolation is employed, we use the relation in (5.140) which in this case gives

$$\psi(r) = (1)\frac{(r-1)(r-3)}{(-1)(-3)} + (1)\frac{(r)(r-3)}{(1)(-2)} + (5)\frac{(r)(r-1)}{(3)(2)}$$

or, as before,

$$\psi(r) = 1 - \frac{2}{3}r + \frac{2}{3}r^2$$

5.5.2 The Newton-Cotes Formulas (One-Dimensional Integration)

Having established an interpolating polynomial $\psi(r)$, we can now obtain an approximation to the integral $\int_a^b F(r)\, dr$. In Newton-Cotes integration, it is assumed that the sampling points of F are spaced at equal distances, and we define

$$r_0 = a; \qquad r_n = b; \qquad h = \frac{b-a}{n} \tag{5.141}$$

Using Lagrangian interpolation to obtain $\psi(r)$ as an approximation to $F(r)$, we have

$$\int_a^b F(r)\, dr = \sum_{i=0}^{n} \left[\int_a^b l_i(r)\, dr \right] F_i + R_n \tag{5.142}$$

or, evaluated,

$$\int_a^b F(r)\, dr = (b - a) \sum_{i=0}^{n} C_i^n F_i + R_n \tag{5.143}$$

where R_n is the remainder and the C_i^n are the *Newton-Cotes constants* for numerical integration with n intervals.

The Newton-Cotes constants and corresponding remainder terms are summarized in Table 5.5 for $n = 1$ to 6. The cases $n = 1$ and $n = 2$ are the well-known *trapezoidal rule* and *Simpson formula*. We note that the formulas for $n = 3$ and $n = 5$ have the same order of accuracy as the formulas for $n = 2$ and $n = 4$, respectively. For this reason, the even formulas with $n = 2$ and $n = 4$ are used in practice.

TABLE 5.5 *Newton-Cotes numbers and error estimates*

Number of intervals n	C_0^n	C_1^n	C_2^n	C_3^n	C_4^n	C_5^n	C_6^n	Upper bound on error R_n as a function of the derivative of F
1	$\dfrac{1}{2}$	$\dfrac{1}{2}$						$10^{-1}(b-a)^3 F^{II}(r)$
2	$\dfrac{1}{6}$	$\dfrac{4}{6}$	$\dfrac{1}{6}$					$10^{-3}(b-a)^5 F^{IV}(r)$
3	$\dfrac{1}{8}$	$\dfrac{3}{8}$	$\dfrac{3}{8}$	$\dfrac{1}{8}$				$10^{-3}(b-a)^5 F^{IV}(r)$
4	$\dfrac{7}{90}$	$\dfrac{32}{90}$	$\dfrac{12}{90}$	$\dfrac{32}{90}$	$\dfrac{7}{90}$			$10^{-6}(b-a)^7 F^{VI}(r)$
5	$\dfrac{19}{288}$	$\dfrac{75}{288}$	$\dfrac{50}{288}$	$\dfrac{50}{288}$	$\dfrac{75}{288}$	$\dfrac{19}{288}$		$10^{-6}(b-a)^7 F^{VI}(r)$
6	$\dfrac{41}{840}$	$\dfrac{216}{840}$	$\dfrac{27}{840}$	$\dfrac{272}{840}$	$\dfrac{27}{840}$	$\dfrac{216}{840}$	$\dfrac{41}{840}$	$10^{-9}(b-a)^9 F^{VIII}(r)$

EXAMPLE 5.34:   Evaluate the Newton-Cotes constants when the interpolating polynomial is of order 2; i.e., $\psi(r)$ is a parabola.

In this case we have

$$\int_a^b F(r)\,dr \doteq \int_a^b \left[F_0 \frac{(r-r_1)(r-r_2)}{(r_0-r_1)(r_0-r_2)} + F_1 \frac{(r-r_0)(r-r_2)}{(r_1-r_0)(r_1-r_2)} + F_2 \frac{(r-r_0)(r-r_1)}{(r_2-r_0)(r_2-r_1)} \right] dr$$

Using $r_0 = a$, $r_1 = a + h$, $r_2 = a + 2h$, where $h = (b-a)/2$, the evaluation of the integral gives

$$\int_a^b F(r)\,dr \doteq \frac{b-a}{6}(F_0 + 4F_1 + F_2)$$

Hence the Newton-Cotes constants are as given in Table 5.5 for the case $n = 2$.

EXAMPLE 5.35:   Use Simpson's rule to integrate $\int_0^3 (2^r - r)\,dr$. $= \left[\frac{2^r}{\ln 2} - \frac{r^2}{2} \right]_0^3 = \frac{7}{\ln 2} - \frac{9}{2}$

In this case $n = 2$ and $h = \frac{3}{2}$. Therefore, $r_0 = 0$, $r_1 = \frac{3}{2}$, $r_2 = 3$, and $F_0 = 1$, $F_1 = 1.328427$, $F_2 = 5$, and we obtain

$$\int_0^3 (2^r - r)\,dr \doteq \frac{3}{6}[(1)(1) + (4)(1.328427) + (1)(5)]$$

or

$$\int_0^3 (2^r - r)\,dr \doteq 5.656854$$

The exact result is

$$\int_0^3 (2^r - r)\,dr = 5.598868$$

Hence the error is $R = 0.057986$

However, using the upper bound value on the error, we have

$$R < \frac{(3-0)^5}{1000}(\ln 2)^4 (2^r) = 0.448743$$

To obtain greater accuracy in the integration using the Newton-Cotes formulas we need to employ a smaller interval h, i.e., include more evaluations of the function to be integrated. Then we have the choice between two different strategies: we may use a higher-order Newton-Cotes formula or, alternatively, employ the lower-order formula in a repeated manner, in which case the integration procedure is referred to as a *composite formula*. Consider the following example.

EXAMPLE 5.36:   Increase the accuracy of the integration in Example 5.35 by using half the interval spacing.

In this case we have $h = \frac{3}{4}$, and the required function values are $F_0 = 1$, $F_1 = 0.931792$, $F_2 = 1.328427$, $F_3 = 2.506828$, and $F_4 = 5$. The choice now lies between using the higher-order Newton-Cotes formula with $n = 4$ or applying the Simpson's rule twice, i.e., to the first two intervals and then to the second two intervals. Using the Newton-Cotes formula with $n = 4$, we obtain

$$\int_0^3 (2^r - r)\, dr \doteq \frac{3}{90}(7F_0 + 32F_1 + 12F_2 + 32F_3 + 7F_4)$$

Hence,

$$\int_0^3 (2^r - r)\, dr \doteq 5.599232$$

On the other hand, using Simpson's rule twice, we have

$$\int_0^3 (2^r - r)\, dr = \int_0^{3/2} (2^r - r)\, dr + \int_{3/2}^3 (2^r - r)\, dr$$

The integration is performed using

$$\int_0^{3/2} (2^r - r)\, dr \doteq \frac{\frac{3}{2} - 0}{6}(F_0 + 4F_1 + F_2)$$

where F_0, F_1, and F_2 are the function values at $r = 0$, $r = \frac{3}{4}$, and $r = \frac{3}{2}$, respectively; i.e.,

$$F_0 = 1; \qquad F_1 = 0.931792; \qquad F_2 = 1.328427$$

Hence we use

$$\int_0^{3/2} (2^r - r)\, dr \doteq 1.513899 \tag{a}$$

Next we need to evaluate

$$\int_{3/2}^3 (2^r - r)\, dr \doteq \frac{3 - \frac{3}{2}}{6}(F_0 + 4F_1 + F_2)$$

where F_0, F_1, and F_2 are the function values at $r = \frac{3}{2}$, $r = \frac{9}{4}$, and $r = 3$, respectively,

$$F_0 = 1.328427; \qquad F_1 = 2.506828; \qquad F_2 = 5$$

Hence we have

$$\int_{3/2}^3 (2^r - r)\, dr \doteq 4.088935 \tag{b}$$

Adding the results in (a) and (b), we obtain

$$\int_0^3 (2^r - r)\, dr \doteq 5.602834$$

The use of a composite formula has a number of advantages over the application of high-order Newton-Cotes formulas. A composite formula, such as the repetitive use of Simpson's rule, is easy to employ. Convergence is ensured as the interval of sampling decreases, and, in practice, a sampling interval could be used that varies from one application of the basic formula to the next. This is particularly advantageous when there are discontinuities in the function to be integrated. For these reasons, in practice, composite formulas are commonly used.

EXAMPLE 5.37: Use a composite formula that employs Simpson's rule to evaluate the integral $\int_{-1}^{+13} F(r)\, dr$ of the function $F(r)$ in Fig. E5.37.

This function is best integrated by considering three intervals of integration, as follows:

$$\int_{-1}^{13} F\, dr = \int_{-1}^{2} (r^3 + 3)\, dr + \int_{2}^{9} [10 + (r - 1)^{1/3}]\, dr + \int_{9}^{13} \left[\frac{1}{128}(13 - r)^5 + 4\right] dr$$

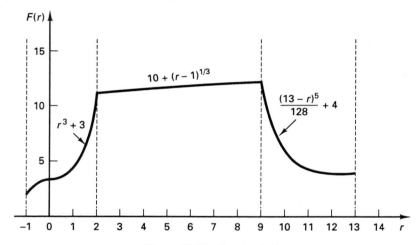

Figure E5.37   Function $F(r)$

We evaluate each of the three integrals using Simpson's rule and have

$$\int_{-1}^{2} (r^3 + 3)\, dr = \frac{2 - (-1)}{6}[(1)(2) + (4)(3.125) + (1)(11)]$$

or

$$\int_{-1}^{2} (r^3 + 3)\, dr = 12.75$$

$$\int_{2}^{9} [10 + (r - 1)^{1/3}]\, dr \doteq \frac{9 - 2}{6}[(1)(11) + (4)(11.650964) + (1)(12)]$$

or

$$\int_{2}^{9} [10 + (r - 1)^{1/3}]\, dr = 81.204498$$

$$\int_{9}^{13} \left[\frac{1}{128}(13 - r)^5 + 4\right] dr \doteq \frac{13 - 9}{6}[(1)(12) + (4)(4.25) + (1)(4)]$$

or

$$\int_{9}^{13} \left[\frac{1}{128}(13 - r)^5 + 4\right] dr \doteq 22$$

Hence,
$$\int_{-1}^{13} F \, dr \doteq 12.75 + 81.204498 + 22$$

or
$$\int_{-1}^{13} F \, dr \doteq 115.954498$$

5.5.3 The Gauss Formulas (One-Dimensional Integration)

The basic integration schemes that we have considered so far use equally spaced sampling points, although the basic methods could be employed to construct procedures that allow the interval of sampling to be varied; i.e., the composite formulas have been introduced. The methods discussed so far are effective when measurements of an unknown function to be integrated have been taken at certain intervals. However, in the integration of finite element matrices, a subroutine is called to evaluate the unknown function F at given points, and these points may be anywhere on the element. No additional difficulties arise if the sampling points are not equally spaced. Therefore, it seems natural to try to improve the accuracy that can be obtained for a given number of function evaluations by also optimizing the positions of the sampling points. A very important numerical intergration procedure in which both the positions of the sampling points and the weights have been optimized is *Gauss quadrature*. The basic assumption in Gauss numerical integration is that

$$\int_a^b F(r) \, dr = \alpha_1 F(r_1) + \alpha_2 F(r_2) + \cdots + \alpha_n F(r_n) + R_n \tag{5.144}$$

where both the weights $\alpha_1, \ldots, \alpha_n$ and the sampling points $r_1, \ldots, r_n$ are variables. It should be recalled that in the derivation of the Newton-Cotes formulas, only the weights were unknown, and they were determined from the integration of a polynomial $\psi(r)$ that passed through equally spaced sampling points of the function $F(r)$. We now also calculate the positions of the sampling points and therefore have $2n$ unknowns to determine a higher-order integration scheme.

In analogy with the derivation of the Newton-Cotes formulas, we use an interpolating polynomial $\psi(r)$ of the form given in (5.140),

$$\psi(r) = \sum_{j=1}^n F_j l_j(r) \tag{5.145}$$

where n samplings points are now considered, $r_1, \ldots, r_n$, which are still unknown. For the determination of the values $r_1, \ldots, r_n$, we define a function $P(r)$,

$$P(r) = (r - r_1)(r - r_2) \cdots (r - r_n) \tag{5.146}$$

which is a polynomial of order n. We note that $P(r) = 0$ at the sampling points $r_1, \ldots, r_n$. Therefore, we can write

$$F(r) = \psi(r) + P(r)(\beta_0 + \beta_1 r + \beta_2 r^2 + \cdots) \tag{5.147}$$

Integrating $F(r)$, we obtain

$$\int_a^b F(r) \, dr = \sum_{j=1}^n F_j \left[\int_a^b l_j(r) \, dr \right] + \sum_{j=0}^\infty \beta_j \left[\int_a^b r^j P(r) \, dr \right] \tag{5.148}$$

where it should be noted that in the first integral on the right in (5.148), functions of order $(n - 1)$ and lower are integrated, and in the second integral the functions that are integrated are of order n and higher. The unknown values $r_j, j = 1, 2, \ldots, n$, can now be determined using the conditions

$$\int_a^b P(r) r^k \, dr = 0 \qquad k = 0, 1, 2, \ldots, n - 1 \tag{5.149}$$

Then, since the polynomial $\psi(r)$ passes through n sampling points of $F(r)$, and $P(r)$ vanishes at these points, the conditions in (5.149) mean that the required integral $\int_a^b F(r) \, dr$ is approximated by integrating a polynomial of order $(2n - 1)$ instead of $F(r)$.

In summary, using the Newton-Cotes formulas, we use $(n + 1)$ equally spaced sampling points and integrate exactly a polynomial of order at most n. On the other hand, in Gauss quadrature we require n unequally spaced sampling points and integrate exactly a polynomial of order at most $(2n - 1)$. Polynomials of orders less than n and $(2n - 1)$, respectively, for the two cases are also integrated exactly.

To determine the sampling points and the integration weights, we realize that they depend on the interval a to b. However, to make the calculations general, we consider a natural interval from -1 to $+1$ and deduce the sampling points and weights for any interval. Namely, if r_i is a sampling point and α_i is the weight for the interval -1 to $+1$, the corresponding sampling point and weight in the integration from a to b are

$$\frac{a + b}{2} + \frac{b - a}{2} r_i \qquad \text{and} \qquad \frac{b - a}{2} \alpha_i$$

respectively.

Hence, consider an interval from -1 to $+1$. The sampling points are determined from (5.149) with $a = -1$ and $b = +1$. To calculate the integration weights we substitute for $F(r)$ in (5.144) the interpolating polynomial $\psi(r)$ from (5.145) and perform the integration. It should be noted that because the sampling points have been determined, the polynomial $\psi(r)$ is known, and hence

$$\alpha_j = \int_{-1}^{+1} l_j(r) \, dr; \qquad j = 1, 2, \ldots, n \tag{5.150}$$

TABLE 5.6 *Sampling points and weights in Gauss-Legendre numerical integration (interval -1 to $+1$)*

n	r_i			α_i		
1	0.	(15 zeros)		2.	(15 zeros)	
2	±0.57735	02691	89626	1.00000	00000	00000
3	±0.77459	66692	41483	0.55555	55555	55556
	0.00000	00000	00000	0.88888	88888	88889
4	±0.86113	63115	94053	0.34785	48451	37454
	±0.33998	10435	84856	0.65214	51548	62546
5	±0.90617	98459	38664	0.23692	68850	56189
	0.53846	93101	05683	0.47862	86704	99366
	0.00000	00000	00000	0.56888	88888	88889
6	±0.93246	95142	03152	0.17132	44923	79170
	±0.66120	93864	66265	0.36076	15730	48139
	±0.23861	91860	83197	0.46791	39345	72691

The sampling points and weights for the interval -1 to $+1$ have been published by A. N. Lowan, N. Davids, and A. Levenson [A] and are reproduced in Table 5.6 for $n = 1$ to 6.

The coefficients in Table 5.6 can be calculated directly using (5.149) and (5.150) (see Example 5.38). However, for larger n the solution becomes cumbersome, and it is expedient to use Legendre polynomials to solve for the coefficients, which are thus referred to as Gauss-Legendre coefficients.

EXAMPLE 5.38: Derive the sampling points and weights for two-point Gauss quadrature.

In this case $P(r) = (r - r_1)(r - r_2)$ and (5.149) gives the two equations

$$\int_{-1}^{+1} (r - r_1)(r - r_2)\, dr = 0$$

$$\int_{-1}^{+1} (r - r_1)(r - r_2)r\, dr = 0$$

Solving, we obtain $r_1 r_2 = -\tfrac{1}{3}$

and $r_1 + r_2 = 0$

Hence $r_1 = -\dfrac{1}{\sqrt{3}};\qquad r_2 = +\dfrac{1}{\sqrt{3}}$

The corresponding weights are obtained using (5.150), which in this case gives

$$\alpha_1 = \int_{-1}^{+1} \frac{r - r_2}{r_1 - r_2}\, dr$$

$$\alpha_2 = \int_{-1}^{+1} \frac{r - r_1}{r_2 - r_1}\, dr$$

Since $r_2 = -r_1$, we obtain $\alpha_1 = \alpha_2 = 1.0$.

EXAMPLE 5.39: Use two-point Gauss quadrature to evaluate the integral $\int_0^3 (2^r - r)\, dr$ considered in Examples 5.35 and 5.36.

Using two-point Gauss quadrature, we obtain from (5.144),

$$\int_0^3 (2^r - r)\, dr \doteq \alpha_1 F(r_1) + \alpha_2 F(r_2) \tag{a}$$

where α_1, α_2 and r_1, r_2 are weights and sampling points, respectively. Since the interval is from 0 to 3, we need to determine the values α_1, α_2, r_1, and r_2 from the values given in Table 5.6,

$$\alpha_1 = \tfrac{3}{2}(1);\qquad \alpha_2 = \tfrac{3}{2}(1)$$

$$r_1 = \frac{3}{2}\left(1 - \frac{1}{\sqrt{3}}\right);\qquad r_2 = \frac{3}{2}\left(1 + \frac{1}{\sqrt{3}}\right)$$

where $1/\sqrt{3} = 0.5773502692$. Thus,

$$F(r_1) = 0.91785978;\qquad F(r_2) = 2.78916389$$

and (a) gives $\displaystyle\int_0^3 (2^r - r)\, dr \doteq 5.56053551$

The Gauss-Legendre integration procedure is commonly used in isoparametric finite element analysis. However, it should be noted that other integration schemes, in which both the weights and sampling positions are varied to obtain maximum accuracy, have also been derived (see C. E. Fröberg [A] and A. H. Stroud and D. Secrest [A]).

5.5.4 Integrations in Two and Three Dimensions

So far we have considered the integration of a one-dimensional function $F(r)$. However, two- and three-dimensional integrals need to be evaluated in two- and three-dimensional finite element analyses. In the evaluation of rectangular elements, we can apply the above one-dimensional integration formulas successively in each direction.[8] As in the analytical evaluation of multidimensional integrals, in this procedure, successively, the innermost integral is evaluated by keeping the variables corresponding to the other integrals constant. Therefore, we have for a two-dimensional integral,

$$\int_{-1}^{+1} \int_{-1}^{+1} F(r, s) \, dr \, ds = \sum_i \alpha_i \int_{-1}^{+1} F(r_i, s) \, ds \tag{5.151}$$

or

$$\int_{-1}^{+1} \int_{-1}^{+1} F(r, s) \, dr \, ds = \sum_{i,j} \alpha_i \alpha_j \, F(r_i, s_j) \tag{5.152}$$

and corresponding to (5.133), $\alpha_{ij} = \alpha_i \alpha_j$, where α_i and α_j are the integration weights for one-dimensional integration. Similarly, for a three-dimensional integral,

$$\int_{-1}^{+1} \int_{-1}^{+1} \int_{-1}^{+1} F(r, s, t) \, dr \, ds \, dt = \sum_{i,j,k} \alpha_i \alpha_j \alpha_k F(r_i, s_j, t_k) \tag{5.153}$$

and $\alpha_{ijk} = \alpha_i \alpha_j \alpha_k$. We should note that it is not necessary in the numerical integration to use the same quadrature rule in the two or three dimensions; i.e., we can employ different numerical integration schemes in the r, s, and t directions.

> **EXAMPLE 5.40:**   Given that the (i, j)th element of a stiffness matrix $\mathbf{K}$ is $\int_{-1}^{+1} \int_{-1}^{+1} r^2 s^2 \, dr \, ds$. Evaluate the integral $\int_{-1}^{+1} \int_{-1}^{+1} r^2 s^2 \, dr \, ds$ using (1) Simpson's rule in both r and s, (2) Gauss quadrature in both r and s, and (3) Gauss quadrature in r and Simpson's rule in s.
>
> **1.** Using Simpson's rule, we have
>
> $$\int_{-1}^{+1} \int_{-1}^{+1} r^2 s^2 \, dr \, ds = \int_{-1}^{+1} \frac{1}{3}[(1)(1) + (4)(0) + (1)(1)]s^2 \, ds$$
>
> $$= \int_{-1}^{+1} \frac{2}{3} s^2 \, ds = \frac{1}{3}\left[(1)\left(\frac{2}{3}\right) + (4)(0) + (1)\left(\frac{2}{3}\right)\right] = \frac{4}{9}$$
>
> **2.** Using two-point Gauss quadrature, we have
>
> $$\int_{-1}^{+1} \int_{-1}^{+1} r^2 s^2 \, dr \, ds = \int_{-1}^{+1} \left[(1)\left(\frac{1}{\sqrt{3}}\right)^2 + (1)\left(\frac{1}{\sqrt{3}}\right)^2\right] s^2 \, ds$$
>
> $$= \int_{-1}^{+1} \frac{2}{3} s^2 \, ds = \frac{2}{3}\left[(1)\left(\frac{1}{\sqrt{3}}\right)^2 + (1)\left(\frac{1}{\sqrt{3}}\right)^2\right] = \frac{4}{9}$$

---

[8] This results in much generality of the integration, but for special cases somewhat less costly procedures can be designed (see B. M. Irons [C]).

3. Finally, using Gauss quadrature in r and Simpson's rule in s, we have

$$\int_{-1}^{+1} \int_{-1}^{+1} \left[(1)\left(\frac{1}{\sqrt{3}}\right)^2 + (1)\left(\frac{1}{\sqrt{3}}\right)^2 \right] s^2 \, ds$$

$$= \int_{-1}^{+1} \frac{2}{3} s^2 \, ds = \frac{1}{3}\left[(1)\left(\frac{2}{3}\right) + (4)(0) + (1)\left(\frac{2}{3}\right) \right] = \frac{4}{9}$$

We should note that these numerical integrations are exact because both integration schemes, i.e., Simpson's rule and two-point Gauss quadrature, integrate a parabola exactly.

The above procedure is directly applicable to the evaluation of matrices of quadrilateral elements in which all integration limits are -1 to $+1$. Hence, in the evaluation of a two-dimensional finite element, the integrations can be carried out for each entry of the stiffness and mass matrices and load vectors as illustrated in Example 5.40. Based on the information given in Table 5.6, some common Gauss quadrature rules for two-dimensional analysis are summarized in Table 5.7.

Considering next the evaluation of triangular and tetrahedral element matrices, however, the procedure given in Example 5.40 is not applicable directly because now the integration limits involve the variables themselves. A great deal of research has been spent on the development of suitable integration formulas for triangular domains, and here, too, formulas of the Newton-Cotes type (see P. Silvester [A]) and of the Gauss quadrature type are available (see P. C. Hammer, O. J. Marlowe, and A. H. Stroud [A] and G. R. Cowper [A]). As in the integration over quadrilateral domains, the Gauss quadrature rules are in general more efficient because they yield a higher integration accuracy for the same number of evaluations. Table 5.8 lists the integration stations and integration weights of the Gauss integration formulas published by G. R. Cowper [A].

5.5.5 Appropriate Order of Numerical Integration

In the practical use of the numerical integration procedures presented in the previous section, basically two questions arise, namely, what kind of integration scheme to use, and what order to select. We pointed out that in using the Newton-Cotes formulas, $(n + 1)$ function evaluations are required to integrate without error a polynomial of order n. On the other hand, if Gauss quadrature is used, a polynomial of order $(2n - 1)$ is integrated exactly with only n function evaluations. In each case of course any polynomial of lower order than n and $(2n - 1)$, respectively, is also integrated exactly.

In finite element analysis a large number of function evaluations directly increases the cost of analysis, and the use of Gauss quadrature is attractive. However, the Newton-Cotes formulas may be efficient in nonlinear analysis for the reasons discussed in Section 6.8.4.

Having selected a numerical integration scheme, the order of numerical integration to be used in the evaluation of the various finite element integrals needs to be determined. The choice of the order of numerical integration is important in practice because, first, the cost of analysis increases when a higher-order integration is employed, and second, using a different integration order, the results can be affected by a very large amount. These considerations are particularly important in three-dimensional analysis.

The matrices to be evaluated by numerical integration are the stiffness matrix $\mathbf{K}$, the mass matrix $\mathbf{M}$, the body force vector $\mathbf{R}_B$, the initial stress vector $\mathbf{R}_I$, and the surface load

TABLE 5.7 *Gauss numerical integrations over quadrilateral domains*

Integration order	Degree of precision	Location of integration points
2 × 2	3	y x s r $s = 0.577 \ldots$ $s = -0.577 \ldots$ $P^{(\dagger)}$ $r = 0.577 \ldots$ $r = -0.577 \ldots$
3 × 3	5	s r $s = 0.774 \ldots$ $s = 0$ $s = -0.774 \ldots$ $P^{(\dagger)}$ $r = -0.774 \ldots$ $r = 0$ $r = 0.774 \ldots$
4 × 4	7	s r $s = 0.861 \ldots$ $s = 0.339 \ldots$ $s = -0.339 \ldots$ $s = -0.861 \ldots$ $P^{(\dagger)}$ $r = -0.861 \ldots$ $r = -0.339 \ldots$ $r = 0.339 \ldots$ $r = 0.861 \ldots$

(†) The location of any integration point in the x, y coordinate system is given by: $x_p = \Sigma_i h_i(r_p, s_p)x_i$ and $y_p = \Sigma_i h_i(r_p, s_p)y_i$. The integration weights are given in Table 5.6 using (5.152).

vector $\mathbf{R}_S$. In general, the appropriate integration order depends on the matrix that is evaluated and the specific finite element being considered. To demonstrate the important aspects, consider the Gauss numerical integration order required to evaluate the matrices of the continuum and structural elements discussed in Sections 5.3 and 5.4.

A first observation in the selection of the order of numerical integration is that, in theory, if a high enough order is used, all matrices will be evaluated very accurately. On the other hand, using too low an order of integration, the matrices may be evaluated very inaccurately and, in fact, the problem solution may not be possible. For example, consider an element stiffness matrix. If the order of numerical integration is too low, the matrix can have a larger number of zero eigenvalues than the number of physical rigid body modes. Hence, for a successful solution of the equilibrium equations alone, it would be necessary

TABLE 5.8 *Gauss numerical integrations over triangular domains* $[\iint F\,dr\,ds = \frac{1}{2}\sum w_i F(r_i, s_i)]$

Integration order	Degree of precision	Integration points	r-coordinates	s-coordinates	Weights
3-point	2		$r_1 = 0.16666\ 66666\ 667$ $r_2 = 0.66666\ 66666\ 667$ $r_3 = r_1$	$s_1 = r_1$ $s_2 = r_1$ $s_3 = r_2$	$w_1 = 0.33333\ 33333\ 333$ $w_2 = w_1$ $w_3 = w_1$
7-point	5		$r_1 = 0.10128\ 65073\ 235$ $r_2 = 0.79742\ 69853\ 531$ $r_3 = r_1$ $r_4 = 0.47014\ 20641\ 051$ $r_5 = r_4$ $r_6 = 0.05971\ 58717\ 898$ $r_7 = 0.33333\ 33333\ 333$	$s_1 = r_1$ $s_2 = r_1$ $s_3 = r_2$ $s_4 = r_6$ $s_5 = r_4$ $s_6 = r_4$ $s_7 = r_7$	$w_1 = 0.12593\ 91805\ 448$ $w_2 = w_1$ $w_3 = w_1$ $w_4 = 0.13239\ 41527\ 885$ $w_5 = w_4$ $w_6 = w_4$ $w_7 = 0.225$
13-point	7		$r_1 = 0.06513\ 01029\ 022$ $r_2 = 0.86973\ 97941\ 956$ $r_3 = r_1$ $r_4 = 0.31286\ 54960\ 049$ $r_5 = 0.63844\ 41885\ 698$ $r_6 = 0.04869\ 03154\ 253$ $r_7 = r_5$ $r_8 = r_4$ $r_9 = r_6$ $r_{10} = 0.26034\ 59660\ 790$ $r_{11} = 0.47930\ 80678\ 419$ $r_{12} = r_{10}$ $r_{13} = 0.33333\ 33333\ 333$	$s_1 = r_1$ $s_2 = r_1$ $s_3 = r_2$ $s_4 = r_6$ $s_5 = r_4$ $s_6 = r_5$ $s_7 = r_6$ $s_8 = r_5$ $s_9 = r_4$ $s_{10} = r_{10}$ $s_{11} = r_{10}$ $s_{12} = r_{11}$ $s_{13} = r_{13}$	$w_1 = 0.05334\ 72356\ 088$ $w_2 = w_1$ $w_3 = w_1$ $w_4 = 0.07711\ 37608\ 903$ $w_5 = w_4$ $w_6 = w_4$ $w_7 = w_4$ $w_8 = w_4$ $w_9 = w_4$ $w_{10} = 0.17561\ 52574\ 332$ $w_{11} = w_{10}$ $w_{12} = w_{10}$ $w_{13} = -0.14957\ 00444\ 677$

that the deformation modes corresponding to all zero eigenvalues of the element be properly restrained in the assemblage of finite elements because otherwise the structure stiffness matrix would be singular. A simple example is the evaluation of the stiffness matrix of a three-node truss element. If one-point Gauss numerical integration is used, the row and column corresponding to the degree of freedom at the midnode of the element are null vectors, which may result in a structure stiffness matrix that is singular. Therefore, the integration order should in general be higher than a certain limit.

The integration order required to evaluate a specific element matrix accurately can be determined by studying the order of the function to be integrated. In the case of the stiffness matrix, we need to evaluate

$$\mathbf{K} = \int_V \mathbf{B}^T \mathbf{C} \mathbf{B} \det \mathbf{J} \, dV \tag{5.154}$$

where $\mathbf{C}$ is a constant material property matrix, $\mathbf{B}$ is the strain-displacement matrix in the natural coordinate system r, s, t, $\det \mathbf{J}$ is the determinant of the Jacobian transforming local (or global) to natural coordinates (see Section 5.3), and the integration is performed over the element volume in the natural coordinate system. The matrix function $\mathbf{F}$ to be integrated is, therefore,

$$\mathbf{F} = \mathbf{B}^T \mathbf{C} \mathbf{B} \det \mathbf{J} \tag{5.155}$$

The matrices $\mathbf{J}$ and $\mathbf{B}$ have been defined in Sections 5.3 and 5.4.

A case for which the order of the variables in $\mathbf{F}$ can be evaluated with relative ease arises when the four-node two-dimensional element studied in Example 5.5 is used as a rectangular or parallelogram element. It is instructive to consider this case in detail because the procedure of evaluating the required integration order is displayed clearly.

EXAMPLE 5.41: Evaluate the required Gauss numerical integration order for the calculation of the stiffness matrix of a four-node displacement-based rectangular element.

The integration order to be used depends on the order of the variables r and s in $\mathbf{F}$ defined in (5.155). For a rectangular element with sides $2a$ and $2b$, we can write

$$x = ar; \ y = bs$$

and consequently the Jacobian matrix $\mathbf{J}$ is

$$\mathbf{J} = \begin{bmatrix} a & 0 \\ 0 & b \end{bmatrix}$$

Since the elements of $\mathbf{J}$ are constant, referring to the information given in Example 5.5, the elements of the strain-displacement matrix $\mathbf{B}$ are therefore functions of r or s only. But the determinant of $\mathbf{J}$ is also constant; hence,

$$\mathbf{F} = f(r^2, rs, s^2)$$

where f denotes "function of."

Using two-point Gauss numerical integration in the r and s directions, all functions in r and s involving at most cubic terms are integrated without error; e.g., for integration order n, the order of r and s integrated exactly is $(2n - 1)$. Hence, two-point Gauss integration is adequate.

Note that the Jacobian matrix $\mathbf{J}$ is also constant for a four-node parallelogram element; hence, the same derivation and result are applicable.

In an analogous manner, the required integration order to evaluate exactly (or very accurately) the stiffness matrices, mass matrices, and element load vectors of other elements can be assessed. In this context it should be noted that the Jacobian matrix is not constant for nonrectangular and nonparallelogram element shapes, which may mean that a very high integration order might be required to evaluate the element matrices to high accuracy.

In the above example, a displacement-based element was considered, but we should emphasize that, of course, the same numerical integration schemes are also used in the evaluation of the element matrices of mixed formulations. Hence, in mixed formulations the required integration order must also be identified using the procedure just discussed (see Exercise 5.57).

In studying which integration order to use for geometrically distorted elements, we recognize that it is frequently not necessary to calculate the matrices to very high precision using a very high order of numerical integration. Namely, the change in the matrix entries (and their effects) due to using an order of l instead of $(l - 1)$ may be negligible. Hence, we need to ask what order of integration is generally sufficient, and we present the following guideline.

We recommend that *full numerical integration*[9] always be used for a displacement-based or mixed finite element formulation, where we define "full" numerical integration as the order that gives the exact matrices (i.e., the analytically integrated values) when the elements are geometrically undistorted. Table 5.9 lists this order for elements used in two-dimensional analyses.

Using this integration order for a geometrically distorted element will not yield the exactly integrated element matrices. The analysis is, however, reliable because the numerical integration errors are acceptably small assuming of course reasonable geometric distortions. Indeed, as shown by P. G. Ciarlet [A], if the geometric distortions are not excessive and are such that in exact integration the full order of convergence is still obtained (with the provisions discussed in Section 5.3.3), then that same order of convergence is also obtained using the full numerical integration recommended here. Hence, in that case, the order of numerical integration recommended in Table 5.9 does not result in a reduction of the order of convergence. On the other hand, if the element geometric distortions are very large, and in nonlinear analysis of course, a higher integration order may be appropriate (see Section 6.8.4).

Figure 5.39 shows some results obtained in the solution of the ad hoc test problem described in Fig. 4.12. These results were obtained using sequences of distorted, quasi-uniform meshes. Figure 5.39(a) describes the geometric distortions used, and Fig. 5.39(b) and (c) show the convergence results obtained with the eight-node and nine-node elements using the Gauss integration order in Table 5.9. These results show that the order of convergence (the slopes of the graphed curves when h is small) is approximately 4 in all cases (as is theoretically predicted). However, the actual value of the error for a given value of h is larger when the elements are distorted. That is, the constant c in (4.102) increases as the elements are distorted.

The reason for recommending the numerical integration orders in Table 5.9 is that the *reliability of the finite element procedures is of utmost concern* (see Section 1.3), and if an

---

[9] In Section 5.5.6 we briefly discuss "reduced" numerical integration, which is the counterpart of full numerical integration.

TABLE 5.9 *Recommended full Gauss numerical integration orders for the evaluation of isoparametric displacement-based element matrices (use of Table 5.7)*

Two-dimensional elements (plane stress, plane strain and axisymmetric conditions)	Integration order
4-node	2 × 2
4-node distorted	2 × 2
8-node	3 × 3
8-node distorted	3 × 3
9-node	3 × 3
9-node distorted	3 × 3
16-node	4 × 4
16-node distorted	4 × 4

(Note: In axisymmetric analysis, the hoop strain effect is in all cases not integrated exactly, but with sufficient accuracy.)

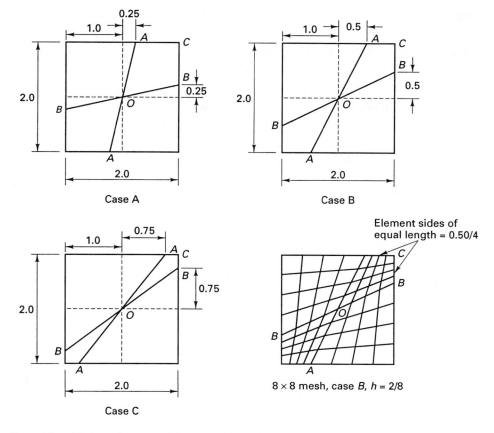

The lines *AA* and *BB* are drawn, and then the sides *AC*, *CB*, *BO*, *OA* are subdivided into equal lengths to form the elements in the domain *ACBO*. Similarly for the other three domains.

(a) Distortions used

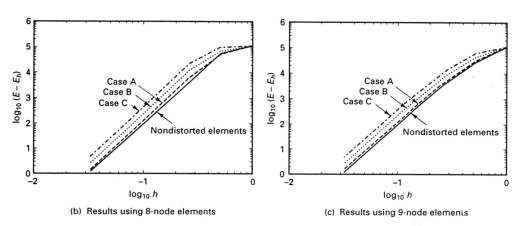

(b) Results using 8-node elements

(c) Results using 9-node elements

Figure 5.39 Solution of test problem of Fig. 4.12 with geometrically distorted elements, and the Gauss integration order of Table 5.9. $E = a(\mathbf{u}, \mathbf{u})$, $E_h = a(\mathbf{u}_h, \mathbf{u}_h)$

integration order lower than the "full" order is used (for a displacement-based or a mixed formulation), the analysis is in general unreliable.

An interesting case is the rectangular two-dimensional plane stress eight-node displacement-based isoparametric element evaluated with 2×2 Gauss integration. This integration order yields an element stiffness matrix with one spurious zero energy mode (see Exercise 5.56); that is, the element matrix not only has three zero eigenvalues (corresponding to the physical rigid body motions) but also has one additional zero eigenvalue that is purely a result of using too low an order of integration. Figure 5.40 shows a very simple analysis case using a single eight-node element with 2×2 Gauss integration in which the model is unstable; that is, if the solution is obtained, the calculated nodal point displacements are very large and have no resemblance to the correct solution.[10] In this simple analysis it is readily seen that the eight-node element using 2×2 Gauss integration is inadequate, and it can be argued that in more complex analysis the (single) spurious zero energy mode is usually adequately restrained in an assemblage of elements. However, in a large, complex model, in general, elements with spurious zero energy modes in an uncontrolled manner improve the overall solution results, introduce large errors, or result in an unstable solution.

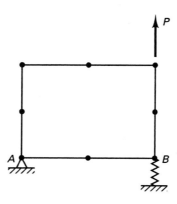

Figure 5.40 Eight-node plane stress element supported at B by a spring. Analysis unstable with 2×2 Gauss integration.

As an example, let us consider the dynamic analysis of the cantilever bracket shown in Fig. 5.41 and use the nine-node displacement-based element with 2×2 Gauss integration, in which case each element stiffness matrix has three spurious zero energy modes. We have considered this bracket already in Fig. 4.20, but with two pin supports instead of the fixed condition used now. (As noted there, the 16-element model of the pin-supported bracket using 2×2 Gauss integration for the element stiffness matrices was unstable). The frequency solution of the 16-element mesh of nine-node displacement-based elements representing the clamped cantilever bracket gives the results listed in Table 5.10. This table shows that the use of 2×2 Gauss integration (referred to as reduced integration; see Section 5.5.6) does not result in a spurious zero energy mode of the complete model (because the bracket is clamped at its left end) but in one *spurious nonzero* energy mode that is part of the predicted smallest six frequencies. Such modes of no physical reality—which we refer to also as "phantom" modes—can introduce uncontrolled errors into a

---

[10] In exact arithmetic the stiffness matrix is singular, but because of round-off errors in the computations a solution is usually obtained.

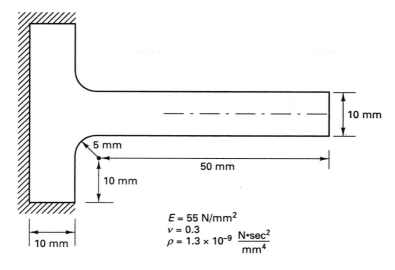

(a) Geometry and material data

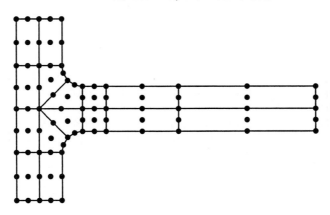

(b) Sixteen element mesh of 9-node elements

Figure 5.41   Frequency solution of clamped cantilever bracket

dynamic step-by-step solution[11] that may not be easily detectable, and even if these errors are detected, the analysis would require additional solution attempts all of which may result in extensive and undesirable numerical experimentation.

For these reasons any element with a spurious zero energy mode should not be used in engineering practice, in linear or in nonlinear analysis, and we therefore do not discuss such elements in this book. However, we should mention that to prevent the deleterious effects of spurious modes, significant research efforts have been conducted to control their

---

[11] The mode shapes of phantom frequencies may indicate that the response is not physical, but in a dynamic step-by-step solution, the frequencies and mode shapes are normally not calculated.

TABLE 5.10 *Smallest six frequencies (in Hz) of the 16-element mesh in Fig. 5.41(b) using a consistent mass matrix* [†]

Mode number	16-element model		16 × 64 element model,[‡]
	3 × 3 Gauss integration	2 × 2 Gauss integration	3 × 3 Gauss integration
1	112.4	110.5	110.6
2	634.5	617.8	606.4
3	906.9	905.5	905.2
4	1548	958.4[§]	1441
5	2654	1528	2345
6	2691	2602	2664

[†] The element consistent mass matrices are always integrated using 3 × 3 Gauss integration.

[‡] We include the results using a fine mesh (with 64 elements replacing each nine-node element of the 16-element mesh) for comparison purposes.

[§] Spurious i.e., phantom mode.

behavior (see, for example, T. Belytschko, W. K. Liu, J. S-J. Ong, and D. Lam [A] and T. J. R. Hughes [A]).

In the above discussion we focused attention on the evaluation of the element stiffness matrices. Considering the element force vectors, it is usually good practice to employ the same integration scheme and the same order of integration as for the stiffness matrices. For the evaluation of an element mass matrix, it should be recognized that for a lumped mass matrix only the volume of the element needs to be evaluated correctly and for the consistent mass matrix the order given in Table 5.9 is usually appropriate. However, special cases exist in which for the sufficiently accurate evaluation of a consistent mass matrix a higher-order integration may be necessary than in the calculation of the stiffness matrix.

EXAMPLE 5.42:   Evaluate the stiffness and mass matrices and the body force vector of element 2 in Example 4.5 using Gauss numerical integration.

The expressions to be integrated have been derived in Example 4.5,

$$\mathbf{K} = E \int_0^{80} \left(1 + \frac{x}{40}\right)^2 \begin{bmatrix} -\dfrac{1}{80} \\ \dfrac{1}{80} \end{bmatrix} \begin{bmatrix} -\dfrac{1}{80} & \dfrac{1}{80} \end{bmatrix} dx \tag{a}$$

$$\mathbf{M} = \rho \int_0^{80} \left(1 + \frac{x}{40}\right)^2 \begin{bmatrix} 1 - \dfrac{x}{80} \\ \dfrac{x}{80} \end{bmatrix} \begin{bmatrix} \left(1 - \dfrac{x}{80}\right) & \dfrac{x}{80} \end{bmatrix} dx \tag{b}$$

$$\mathbf{R}_B = \frac{1}{10} \int_0^{80} \left(1 + \frac{x}{40}\right)^2 \begin{bmatrix} 1 - \dfrac{x}{80} \\ \dfrac{x}{80} \end{bmatrix} dx \tag{c}$$

The expressions in (a) and (c) are integrated exactly with two-point integration, whereas the evaluation of the integral in (b) requires three-point integration. A higher-order integration is required in the evaluation of the mass matrix because this matrix is obtained from the displacement interpolation functions, whereas the stiffness matrix is calculated using derivatives of the displacement functions.

Using one-, two-, and three-point Gauss integration to evaluate (a), (b), and (c) we obtain

One-point integration:

$$\mathbf{K} = \frac{12E}{240}\begin{bmatrix} 1 & -1 \\ -1 & 1 \end{bmatrix}; \qquad \mathbf{M} = \frac{\rho}{6}\begin{bmatrix} 480 & 480 \\ 480 & 480 \end{bmatrix}; \qquad \mathbf{R}_B = \frac{1}{6}\begin{bmatrix} 96 \\ 96 \end{bmatrix}$$

Two-point integration:

$$\mathbf{K} = \frac{13E}{240}\begin{bmatrix} 1 & -1 \\ -1 & 1 \end{bmatrix}; \qquad \mathbf{M} = \frac{\rho}{6}\begin{bmatrix} 373.3 & 346.7 \\ 346.7 & 1013.3 \end{bmatrix}; \qquad \mathbf{R}_B = \frac{1}{6}\begin{bmatrix} 72 \\ 136 \end{bmatrix}$$

Three-point integration:

$$\mathbf{K} = \frac{13E}{240}\begin{bmatrix} 1 & -1 \\ -1 & 1 \end{bmatrix}; \qquad \mathbf{M} = \frac{\rho}{6}\begin{bmatrix} 384 & 336 \\ 336 & 1024 \end{bmatrix}; \qquad \mathbf{R}_B = \frac{1}{6}\begin{bmatrix} 72 \\ 136 \end{bmatrix}$$

It is interesting to note that with too low an order of integration the total mass of the element and the total load to which the element is subjected are not taken fully into account.

Table 5.9 summarizes the results of an analysis for the appropriate integration orders in the evaluation of the stiffness matrices of two-dimensional elements. Of course, the information given in the table is also valuable in deducing appropriate orders of integration for the calculation of the matrices of other elements.

EXAMPLE 5.43:   Discuss the required integration order for the evaluation of the MITC9 plate and isoparametric three-dimensional elements shown in Fig. E5.43.

Consider the plate element first. The integration in the r, s plane corresponds in essence to the evaluation of the nine-node element in Table 5.9. In general, this integration order of 3×3 will also be effective when the element is used in distorted form.

The required integration order for the evaluation of the stiffness matrix of the three-dimensional solid element can also be deduced from the information given in Table 5.9. The displacements vary linearly in the r direction; hence, two-point integration is sufficient. In the

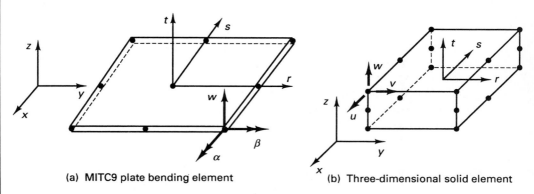

(a) MITC9 plate bending element   (b) Three-dimensional solid element

Figure E5.43   Elements considered in Example 5.43

t, s planes, i.e., at r equal to constants, the element displacements correspond to those of the eight-node element in Table 5.9. Hence, $2 \times 3 \times 3$ Gauss integration is required to evaluate the element stiffness matrix exactly.

5.5.6 Reduced and Selective Integration

Table 5.9 gives the recommended Gauss numerical integration orders for two-dimensional isoparametric displacement-based elements, and the recommended orders for other elements can be deduced (see Example 5.43). With these integration orders (referred to as "full" integration), the element matrices of geometrically undistorted elements are evaluated exactly, whereas for geometrically distorted elements a sufficiently accurate approximation is obtained (unless the geometric distortions are very large, in which case a higher integration order is recommended).

However, in view of our discussion in Section 4.3.4, we recall that the displacement formulation of finite element analysis yields a strain energy smaller than the exact strain energy of the mathematical/mechanical model being considered, and physically, a displacement formulation results in overestimating the system stiffness. Therefore, we may expect that by not evaluating the displacement-based element stiffness matrices accurately in the numerical integration, better overall solution results can be obtained. This should be the case if the error in the numerical integration compensates *appropriately* for the overestimation of structural stiffness due to the finite element discretization. In other words, a reduction in the order of the numerical integration from the order that is required to evaluate the element stiffness matrices exactly (for geometrically undistorted elements) may be expected to lead to improved results. When such a reduction in the order of numerical integration is used, we refer to the procedure as *reduced integration*. For example, the use of 2×2 Gauss integration (although not recommended for use in practice; see Section 5.5.5) for the nine-node isoparametric element stiffness matrix corresponds to a reduced integration. In addition to merely using a *reduced* integration order, *selective* integration may also be considered, in which case different strain terms are integrated with different orders of integration. In these cases of reduced and selective numerical integration the specific integration scheme should be regarded as an integral part of the element formulation.

The key question as to whether a reduced and/or selectively integrated element can be recommended for practical use is: Has the element formulation (using the specific integration procedure) been sufficiently tested and analyzed for its stability and convergence? If tractable, a mathematical stability and convergence analysis is of course most desirable.

A natural first step in such an analysis is to view the reduced and/or selectively integrated element as a mixed element (see D. S. Malkus and T. J. R. Hughes [A]). (An example is the two-node mixed interpolated beam element in Section 5.4.1 further mentioned below.) Once the exact equivalence between the reduced and/or selectively integrated element and a mixed formulation has been identified, the second step is to analyze the mixed formulation for stability and convergence and in this way obtain a deep understanding of the element based on the reduced/selective integration.

Since there are many possibilities for assumptions in mixed formulations, it is natural to assume that there exists *a* mixed formulation that is equivalent to the reduced/selectively integrated element and seek that formulation for analysis purposes. However, the mere fact that *in general* reduced/selectively integrated elements can be regarded as mixed formulations does not justify the use of reduced integration because of course not every mixed formulation represents a reliable and efficient finite element scheme. Rather, *this equivalence* (with the details to be identified in each specific case) *only points toward an approach for the analysis of reduced/selectively integrated elements.*

It also follows that *once a complete equivalence has been identified, we can consider the reduced/selective integration as merely an effective way to accurately calculate the finite element matrices of the mixed formulation,* and we adopt here this view and interpretation of reduced and selective integration.

A relatively simple example is the isoparametric two-node beam element based on one-point (r-direction) Gauss integration. In Example 4.30 and Section 5.4.1 we showed that this element is completely equivalent to the beam element obtained using the Hu-Washizu variational principle with linearly varying transverse displacement w, section rotation β, and a constant shear strain γ within each element. The stability and convergence of the element were considered in Section 4.5.7 where we showed that the ellipticity and inf-sup conditions are satisfied.

Let us consider the following additional example to emphasize these observations.

EXAMPLE 5.44:   A simple triangular plate bending element can be derived using the isoparametric displacement formulation in Section 5.4.2 but integrating the stiffness matrix terms with one-point integration. This integration evaluates the stiffness matrix terms corresponding to bending exactly, whereas the terms corresponding to the transverse shear are integrated approximately. Hence, the element stiffness matrix is based on reduced integration (or we may also say selective integration because only the shear terms are not integrated exactly).

Derive a variational formulation and the stiffness matrix for this element.

The element and its variational formulation have been presented by J.-L. Batoz, K. J. Bathe, and L. W. Ho [A]. We note that the element is a natural development when we are aware of the success of the one-point integrated isoparametric beam element (see Example 4.30 and Sections 4.5.7 and 5.4.1). This beam element has a strong variational basis, the mathematical analysis ensures good convergence properties, and computationally the element is simple and effective.

For the development of the variational basis of this plate element, we note that the one-point integration implicitly assumes a constant transverse shear strain (as in the isoparametric one-point integrated two-node beam element). Referring to Example 4.30, we can therefore directly establish the variational indicator for the plate element as

$$\tilde{\Pi}^*_{HR} = \int_A \left(\frac{1}{2} \boldsymbol{\kappa}^T \mathbf{C}_b \boldsymbol{\kappa} + \boldsymbol{\gamma}^T \mathbf{C}_s \boldsymbol{\gamma}^{AS} - \frac{1}{2} \boldsymbol{\gamma}^{AS^T} \mathbf{C}_s \boldsymbol{\gamma}^{AS} \right) dA - \int_A wp \, dA + \text{boundary terms} \qquad (a)$$

where $\boldsymbol{\kappa}, \mathbf{C}_b, \boldsymbol{\gamma}, \mathbf{C}_s$ have been defined in (5.95) to (5.97) and $\boldsymbol{\gamma}^{AS}$ contains the assumed transverse shear strains

$$\boldsymbol{\gamma}^{AS} = \begin{bmatrix} \gamma^{AS}_{xz} \\ \gamma^{AS}_{yz} \end{bmatrix} = \text{constant}$$

The relation in (a) is a modified Hellinger-Reissner functional. Substituting the interpolations for w, β_x, and β_y into $\boldsymbol{\kappa}$ and $\boldsymbol{\gamma}$, integrating over the element midsurface area A, and invoking the stationarity of $\tilde{\Pi}^*_{HR}$ with respect to the nodal point variables $\hat{\mathbf{u}}$,

$$\hat{\mathbf{u}} = \begin{bmatrix} w_1 \\ \theta_x^1 \\ \theta_y^1 \\ \cdot \\ \dot{\theta}_y^3 \end{bmatrix}$$

and $\boldsymbol{\gamma}^{AS}$, we obtain

$$\begin{bmatrix} \mathbf{K}_b & \mathbf{G}^T \\ \mathbf{G} & -\mathbf{D} \end{bmatrix} \begin{bmatrix} \hat{\mathbf{u}} \\ \boldsymbol{\gamma}^{AS} \end{bmatrix} = \begin{bmatrix} \mathbf{R} \\ \mathbf{0} \end{bmatrix}$$

where

$$\mathbf{K}_b = \int_A \mathbf{B}_b^T \mathbf{C}_b \mathbf{B}_b \, dA$$

$$\mathbf{D} = \int_A \mathbf{C}_s \, dA = A\mathbf{C}_s$$

$$\mathbf{G} = \mathbf{C}_s \int_A \mathbf{B}_s \, dA$$

and $\mathbf{B}_b$ and $\mathbf{B}_s$ are strain-displacement matrices,

$$\boldsymbol{\kappa} = \mathbf{B}_b \hat{\mathbf{u}}$$

$$\boldsymbol{\gamma} = \mathbf{B}_s \hat{\mathbf{u}}$$

Using static condensation, we obtain the stiffness matrix of the element with respect to the nodal point variables only,

$$\mathbf{K} = \mathbf{K}_b + \mathbf{G}^T \mathbf{D}^{-1} \mathbf{G}$$

As we discussed in Section 5.4.2, the pure displacement-based isoparametric plate element (i.e., using full numerical integration for the bending and transverse shear terms in the displacement-based stiffness matrix) is much too stiff (displays the shear locking phenomenon). The presentation in Example 5.44 shows that the one-point integrated element has a variational basis quite analogous to the basis of the one-point integrated isoparametric beam element. However, whereas the beam element is reliable and effective, the plate element stiffness matrix in Example 5.44 has a spurious zero eigenvalue and hence the element is unreliable and should not be used in practice (as was pointed out by J.-L. Batoz, K. J. Bathe, and L. W. Ho [A]).

The important point of this example is that a variational basis of an element might well exist, but whether the element is useful and effective can of course be determined only by a deeper analysis of the formulation.

The equivalence between a certain isoparametric reduced or selectively integrated displacement-based element and a mixed formulation may also hold only for specific geometric element shapes and may also no longer be valid when nonisotropic material laws (or geometric nonlinearities) are introduced. An analysis of the effects of each of these conditions should then be performed.

5.5.7 Exercises

5.53. Evaluate the Newton-Cotes constants when the interpolating polynomial is of order 3, i.e., $\psi(r)$ is a cubic.

5.54. Derive the sampling points and weights for three-point Gauss integration.

5.55. Show that 3×3 Gauss numerical integration is sufficient to calculate the stiffness and mass matrices of a nine-node geometrically undistorted displacement-based element for axisymmetric analysis.

5.56. Show that 2×2 Gauss integration of the stiffness matrix of the eight-node plane stress displacement-based square element results in the spurious zero energy mode shown. (*Hint:* You need to show that $\mathbf{B}\hat{\mathbf{u}} = \mathbf{0}$ for the given displacements.)

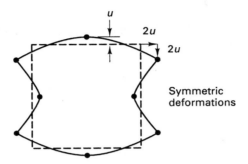

5.57. Consider the $9/3$ u/p element and show that 3×3 Gauss integration of a geometrically undistorted element gives the exact stiffness matrix. Also, show that 2×2 Gauss integration is not adequate.

5.58. Identify the required integration order for full integration of the stiffness matrix of the six-node displacement-based triangular element when using the Gauss integration in Table 5.8.

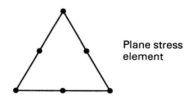

Plane stress element

5.59. Consider the nine-node plane stress element shown. All nodal point displacements are fixed except that u_1 is free. Calculate the displacement u_1 due to the load P.
 (a) Use analytical integration to evaluate the stiffness coefficient.
 (b) Use 1×1, 2×2, and 3×3 Gauss numerical integration to evaluate the stiffness coefficient. Compare your results.

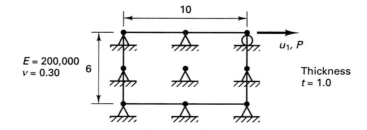

5.60. Consider the evaluation of lumped mass matrices for the elements shown in Table 5.9. Determine suitable Gauss integration orders for the evaluation of these matrices.

5.61. Consider the plate bending element formulation in Example 5.29. Assume that the element stiffness matrix is evaluated with one-point Gauss integration. Show that this element has spurious zero energy modes.[12]

5.62. Consider the plate bending element formulation in Example 5.29 and assume that the bending strain energy is evaluated with 2×2 Gauss integration and the shear strain energy is evaluated with one-point Gauss integration. Show that this element has spurious zero energy modes.[12]

5.6 COMPUTER PROGRAM IMPLEMENTATION OF ISOPARAMETRIC FINITE ELEMENTS

In Section 5.3 we discussed the isoparametric finite element formulation and gave the specific expressions needed in the calculation of four-node plane stress (or plane strain) elements (see Example 5.5). An important advantage of isoparametric element evaluations is the similarity between the calculations of different elements. For example, the calculation of three-dimensional elements is a relatively simple extension from the calculation of two-dimensional elements. Also, in one subroutine, elements with a variety of nodal point configurations can be calculated if an algorithm for selecting the appropriate interpolation functions is used (see Section 5.3).

The purpose of this section is to provide an actual computer program for the calculation of the stiffness matrix of four-node isoparametric elements. In essence, SUBROUTINE QUADS is the computer program implementation of the procedures presented in Example 5.5. In addition to plane stress and plane strain, axisymmetric conditions can be considered. It is believed that by showing the actual program implementation of the element, the relative ease of implementing isoparametric elements is best demonstrated. The input and output variables and the flow of the program are described by means of comment lines.

```
      SUBROUTINE QUADS (NEL,ITYPE,NINT,THIC,YM,PR,XX,S,IOUT)       QUA00001
C                                                                  QUA00002
C . . . . . . . . . . . . . . . . . . . . . . . . . . . . . . . .  QUA00003
C .                                                             .  QUA00004
C .   P R O G R A M                                             .  QUA00005
C .      TO CALCULATE ISOPARAMETRIC QUADRILATERAL ELEMENT STIFFNESS . QUA00006
C .      MATRIX FOR AXISYMMETRIC, PLANE STRESS, AND PLANE STRAIN . QUA00007
C .      CONDITIONS                                             .  QUA00008
C .                                                             .  QUA00009
C .   - - INPUT VARIABLES - -                                   .  QUA00010
C .      NEL      = NUMBER OF ELEMENT                           .  QUA00011
C .      ITYPE    = ELEMENT TYPE                                .  QUA00012
C .                   EQ.0 = AXISYMMETRIC                       .  QUA00013
C .                   EQ.1 = PLANE STRAIN                       .  QUA00014
C .                   EQ.2 = PLANE STRESS                       .  QUA00015
C .      NINT     = GAUSS NUMERICAL INTEGRATION ORDER           .  QUA00016
C .      THIC     = THICKNESS OF ELEMENT                        .  QUA00017
C .      YM       = YOUNG'S MODULUS                             .  QUA00018
C .      PR       = POISSON'S RATIO                             .  QUA00019
C .      XX(2,4)  = ELEMENT NODE COORDINATES                    .  QUA00020
C .      S(8,8)   = STORAGE FOR STIFFNESS MATRIX                .  QUA00021
C .      IOUT     = UNIT NUMBER USED FOR OUTPUT                 .  QUA00022
C .                                                             .  QUA00023
```

[12] Note that these elements should therefore not be used in practice (see Section 5.5.5).

```
C .  - - OUTPUT - -                                                . QUA00024
C .       S(8,8)    = CALCULATED STIFFNESS MATRIX                   . QUA00025
C .                                                                 . QUA00026
C . . . . . . . . . . . . . . . . . . . . . . . . . . . . . . . . .. QUA00027
      IMPLICIT DOUBLE PRECISION (A-H,O-Z)                             QUA00028
C . . . . . . . . . . . . . . . . . . . . . . . . . . . . . . . . .. QUA00029
C .  THIS PROGRAM IS USED IN SINGLE PRECISION ARITHMETIC ON CRAY    . QUA00030
C .  EQUIPMENT AND DOUBLE PRECISION ARITHMETIC ON IBM MACHINES,     . QUA00031
C .  ENGINEERING WORKSTATIONS AND PCS. DEACTIVATE ABOVE LINE FOR    . QUA00032
C .  SINGLE PRECISION ARITHMETIC.                                   . QUA00033
C . . . . . . . . . . . . . . . . . . . . . . . . . . . . . . . . .. QUA00034
      DIMENSION D(4,4),B(4,8),XX(2,4),S(8,8),XG(4,4),WGT(4,4),DB(4)   QUA00035
C                                                                    QUA00036
C     MATRIX XG STORES GAUSS - LEGENDRE SAMPLING POINTS              QUA00037
C                                                                    QUA00038
      DATA XG/   0.D0,    0.D0,    0.D0,    0.D0,   -.5773502691896D0, QUA00039
     1 .5773502691896D0,    0.D0,    0.D0,   -.7745966692415D0,   0.D0, QUA00040
     2 .7745966692415D0,    0.D0,   -.8611363115941D0,              QUA00041
     3 -.3399810435849D0,   .3399810435849D0,   .8611363115941D0 /  QUA00042
C                                                                    QUA00043
C     MATRIX WGT STORES GAUSS - LEGENDRE WEIGHTING FACTORS           QUA00044
C                                                                    QUA00045
      DATA WGT /  2.D0,    0.D0,    0.D0,    0.D0,    1.D0,    1.D0,  QUA00046
     1 0.D0,     0.D0,    .5555555555556D0,    .8888888888889D0,     QUA00047
     2 .5555555555556D0,    0.D0,    .3478548451375D0,    .6521451548625D0, QUA00048
     3 .6521451548625D0,    .3478548451375D0 /                      QUA00049
C                                                                    QUA00050
C     O B T A I N   S T R E S S - S T R A I N   L A W               QUA00051
C                                                                    QUA00052
      F=YM/(1.+PR)                                                   QUA00053
      G=F*PR/(1.-2.*PR)                                              QUA00054
      H=F + G                                                        QUA00055
C                                                                    QUA00056
C     PLANE STRAIN ANALYSIS                                          QUA00057
C                                                                    QUA00058
      D(1,1)=H                                                       QUA00059
      D(1,2)=G                                                       QUA00060
      D(1,3)=0.                                                      QUA00061
      D(2,1)=G                                                       QUA00062
      D(2,2)=H                                                       QUA00063
      D(2,3)=0.                                                      QUA00064
      D(3,1)=0.                                                      QUA00065
      D(3,2)=0.                                                      QUA00066
      D(3,3)=F/2.                                                    QUA00067
      IF (ITYPE.EQ.1) THEN                                           QUA00068
      THIC=1.                                                        QUA00069
      GO TO 20                                                       QUA00070
      ENDIF                                                          QUA00071
C                                                                    QUA00072
C     AXISYMMETRIC ANALYSIS                                          QUA00073
C                                                                    QUA00074
      D(1,4)=G                                                       QUA00075
      D(2,4)=G                                                       QUA00076
      D(3,4)=0.                                                      QUA00077
      D(4,1)=G                                                       QUA00078
      D(4,2)=G                                                       QUA00079
      D(4,3)=0.                                                      QUA00080
      D(4,4)=H                                                       QUA00081
      IF (ITYPE.EQ.0) GO TO 20                                       QUA00082
C                                                                    QUA00083
C     FOR PLANE STRESS ANALYSIS CONDENSE STRESS-STRAIN MATRIX        QUA00084
C                                                                    QUA00085
      DO 10 I=1,3                                                    QUA00086
      A=D(I,4)/D(4,4)                                                QUA00087
      DO 10 J=I,3                                                    QUA00088
      D(I,J)=D(I,J) - D(4,J)*A                                       QUA00089
   10 D(J,I)=D(I,J)                                                  QUA00090
C                                                                    QUA00091
```

```
C      C A L C U L A T E   E L E M E N T   S T I F F N E S S              QUA00092
C                                                                         QUA00093
   20 DO 30 I=1,8                                                         QUA00094
      DO 30 J=1,8                                                         QUA00095
   30 S(I,J)=0.                                                           QUA00096
      IST=3                                                               QUA00097
      IF (ITYPE.EQ.0) IST=4                                               QUA00098
      DO 80 LX=1,NINT                                                     QUA00099
      RI=XG(LX,NINT)                                                      QUA00100
      DO 80 LY=1,NINT                                                     QUA00101
      SI=XG(LY,NINT)                                                      QUA00102
C                                                                         QUA00103
C      EVALUATE DERIVATIVE OPERATOR B AND THE JACOBIAN DETERMINANT DET    QUA00104
C                                                                         QUA00105
      CALL STDM (XX,B,DET,RI,SI,XBAR,NEL,ITYPE,IOUT)                      QUA00106
C                                                                         QUA00107
C      ADD CONTRIBUTION TO ELEMENT STIFFNESS                             QUA00108
C                                                                         QUA00109
      IF (ITYPE.GT.0) XBAR=THIC                                           QUA00110
      WT=WGT(LX,NINT)*WGT(LY,NINT)*XBAR*DET                               QUA00111
      DO 70 J=1,8                                                         QUA00112
      DO 40 K=1,IST                                                       QUA00113
      DB(K)=0.0                                                           QUA00114
      DO 40 L=1,IST                                                       QUA00115
   40 DB(K)=DB(K) + D(K,L)*B(L,J)                                         QUA00116
      DO 60 I=J,8                                                         QUA00117
      STIFF=0.0                                                           QUA00118
      DO 50 L=1,IST                                                       QUA00119
   50 STIFF=STIFF + B(L,I)*DB(L)                                          QUA00120
   60 S(I,J)=S(I,J) + STIFF*WT                                            QUA00121
   70 CONTINUE                                                            QUA00122
   80 CONTINUE                                                            QUA00123
C                                                                         QUA00124
      DO 90 J=1,8                                                         QUA00125
      DO 90 I=J,8                                                         QUA00126
   90 S(J,I)=S(I,J)                                                       QUA00127
C                                                                         QUA00128
      RETURN                                                              QUA00129
C                                                                         QUA00130
      END                                                                 QUA00131
      SUBROUTINE STDM (XX,B,DET,R,S,XBAR,NEL,ITYPE,IOUT)                  QUA00132
C                                                                         QUA00133
C . . . . . . . . . . . . . . . . . . . . . . . . . . . . . . . . . .     QUA00134
C .                                                                   .   QUA00135
C .    P R O G R A M                                                  .   QUA00136
C .      TO EVALUATE THE STRAIN-DISPLACEMENT TRANSFORMATION MATRIX B  .   QUA00137
C .      AT POINT (R,S) FOR A QUADRILATERAL ELEMENT                   .   QUA00138
C .                                                                   .   QUA00139
C . . . . . . . . . . . . . . . . . . . . . . . . . . . . . . . . . .     QUA00140
      IMPLICIT DOUBLE PRECISION (A-H,O-Z)                                 QUA00141
      DIMENSION XX(2,4),B(4,8),H(4),P(2,4),XJ(2,2),XJI(2,2)              QUA00142
C                                                                         QUA00143
      RP = 1.0 + R                                                        QUA00144
      SP = 1.0 + S                                                        QUA00145
      RM = 1.0 - R                                                        QUA00146
      SM = 1.0 - S                                                        QUA00147
C                                                                         QUA00148
C      INTERPOLATION FUNCTIONS                                            QUA00149
C                                                                         QUA00150
      H(1) = 0.25* RP* SP                                                 QUA00151
      H(2) = 0.25* RM* SP                                                 QUA00152
      H(3) = 0.25* RM* SM                                                 QUA00153
      H(4) = 0.25* RP* SM                                                 QUA00154
C                                                                         QUA00155
C      NATURAL COORDINATE DERIVATIVES OF THE INTERPOLATION FUNCTIONS      QUA00156
C                                                                         QUA00157
C        1. WITH RESPECT TO R                                             QUA00158
C                                                                         QUA00159
      P(1,1) = 0.25* SP                                                   QUA00160
      P(1,2) = - P(1,1)                                                   QUA00161
      P(1,3) = - 0.25* SM                                                 QUA00162
      P(1,4) = - P(1,3)                                                   QUA00163
```

```
C                                                                    QUA00164
C              2. WITH RESPECT TO S                                  QUA00165
C                                                                    QUA00166
       P(2,1) = 0.25* RP                                             QUA00167
       P(2,2) = 0.25* RM                                             QUA00168
       P(2,3) = - P(2,2)                                             QUA00169
       P(2,4) = - P(2,1)                                             QUA00170
C                                                                    QUA00171
C       EVALUATE THE JACOBIAN MATRIX AT POINT (R,S)                  QUA00172
C                                                                    QUA00173
   10 DO 30 I=1,2                                                    QUA00174
       DO 30 J=1,2                                                   QUA00175
       DUM = 0.0                                                     QUA00176
       DO 20 K=1,4                                                   QUA00177
   20 DUM=DUM + P(I,K)*XX(J,K)                                       QUA00178
   30 XJ(I,J)=DUM                                                    QUA00179
C                                                                    QUA00180
C       COMPUTE THE DETERMINANT OF THE JACOBIAN MATRIX AT POINT (R,S) QUA00181
C                                                                    QUA00182
       DET = XJ(1,1)* XJ(2,2) - XJ(2,1)* XJ(1,2)                     QUA00183
       IF (DET.GT.0.00000001) GO TO 40                              QUA00184
       WRITE (IOUT,2000) NEL                                         QUA00185
       GO TO 800                                                     QUA00186
C                                                                    QUA00187
C       COMPUTE INVERSE OF THE JACOBIAN MATRIX                       QUA00188
C                                                                    QUA00189
   40 DUM=1./DET                                                     QUA00190
       XJI(1,1) = XJ(2,2)* DUM                                       QUA00191
       XJI(1,2) =-XJ(1,2)* DUM                                       QUA00192
       XJI(2,1) =-XJ(2,1)* DUM                                       QUA00193
       XJI(2,2) = XJ(1,1)* DUM                                       QUA00194
C                                                                    QUA00195
C       EVALUATE GLOBAL DERIVATIVE OPERATOR B                        QUA00196
C                                                                    QUA00197
       K2=0                                                          QUA00198
       DO 60 K=1,4                                                   QUA00199
       K2=K2 + 2                                                     QUA00200
       B(1,K2-1) = 0.                                                QUA00201
       B(1,K2  ) = 0.                                                QUA00202
       B(2,K2-1) = 0.                                                QUA00203
       B(2,K2  ) = 0.                                                QUA00204
       DO 50 I=1,2                                                   QUA00205
       B(1,K2-1) = B(1,K2-1) + XJI(1,I) * P(I,K)                     QUA00206
   50 B(2,K2  ) = B(2,K2  ) + XJI(2,I) * P(I,K)                     QUA00207
       B(3,K2  ) = B(1,K2-1)                                         QUA00208
   60 B(3,K2-1) = B(2,K2  )                                          QUA00209
C                                                                    QUA00210
C       IN CASE OF PLANE STRAIN OR PLANE STRESS ANALYSIS DO NOT INCLUDE QUA00211
C       THE NORMAL STRAIN COMPONENT                                  QUA00212
C                                                                    QUA00213
       IF (ITYPE.GT.0) GO TO 900                                     QUA00214
C                                                                    QUA00215
C       COMPUTE THE RADIUS AT POINT (R,S)                            QUA00216
C                                                                    QUA00217
       XBAR=0.0                                                      QUA00218
       DO 70 K=1,4                                                   QUA00219
   70 XBAR=XBAR + H(K)*XX(1,K)                                       QUA00220
C                                                                    QUA00221
C       EVALUATE THE HOOP STRAIN-DISPLACEMENT RELATION               QUA00222
C                                                                    QUA00223
       IF (XBAR.GT.0.00000001) GO TO 90                             QUA00224
C                                                                    QUA00225
C       FOR THE CASE OF ZERO RADIUS EQUATE RADIAL TO HOOP STRAIN     QUA00226
C                                                                    QUA00227
       DO 80 K=1,8                                                   QUA00228
   80 B(4,K)=B(1,K)                                                  QUA00229
       GO TO 900                                                     QUA00230
C                                                                    QUA00231
C       NON-ZERO RADIUS                                              QUA00232
C                                                                    QUA00233
```

```
   90 DUM=1./XBAR                                                     QUA00234
      K2=0                                                            QUA00235
      DO 100 K=1,4                                                    QUA00236
      K2=K2 + 2                                                       QUA00237
      B(4,K2  ) = 0.                                                  QUA00238
  100 B(4,K2-1) = H(K)*DUM                                            QUA00239
      GO TO 900                                                       QUA00240
C                                                                     QUA00241
  800 STOP                                                            QUA00242
  900 RETURN                                                          QUA00243
C                                                                     QUA00244
 2000 FORMAT (//,' *** ERROR *** ',                                   QUA00245
    1     ' ZERO OR NEGATIVE JACOBIAN DETERMINANT FOR ELEMENT (',I8,')')QUA00246
C                                                                     QUA00247
      END                                                             QUA00248
```

CHAPTER SIX

Finite Element Nonlinear Analysis in Solid and Structural Mechanics

6.1 INTRODUCTION TO NONLINEAR ANALYSIS

In the finite element formulation given in Section 4.2, we assumed that the displacements of the finite element assemblage are infinitesimally small and that the material is linearly elastic. In addition, we also assumed that the nature of the boundary conditions remains unchanged during the application of the loads on the finite element assemblage. With these assumptions, the finite element equilibrium equations derived were for static analysis

$$\mathbf{KU} = \mathbf{R} \tag{6.1}$$

These equations correspond to a *linear* analysis of a structural problem because the displacement response $\mathbf{U}$ is a linear function of the applied load vector $\mathbf{R}$; i.e., if the loads are $\alpha\mathbf{R}$ instead of $\mathbf{R}$, where α is a constant, the corresponding displacements are $\alpha\mathbf{U}$. When this is not the case, we perform a *nonlinear* analysis.

The linearity of a response prediction rests on the assumptions just stated, and it is instructive to identify in detail where these assumptions have entered the equilibrium equations in (6.1). The fact that the displacements must be small has entered into the evaluation of the matrix $\mathbf{K}$ and load vector $\mathbf{R}$ because all integrations have been performed over the original volume of the finite elements, and the strain-displacement matrix $\mathbf{B}$ of each element was assumed to be constant and independent of the element displacements. The assumption of a linear elastic material is implied in the use of a constant stress-strain matrix $\mathbf{C}$, and, finally, the assumption that the boundary conditions remain unchanged is reflected in the use of constant constraint relations [see (4.43) to (4.46)] for the complete response. If during loading a displacement boundary condition should change, e.g., a degree of freedom which was free becomes restrained at a certain load level, the response is linear only prior to the change in boundary condition. This situation arises, for example, in the analysis of a contact problem (see Example 6.2 and Section 6.7).

The above discussion of the basic assumptions used in a linear analysis defines what we mean by a nonlinear analysis and also suggests how to categorize different nonlinear analyses. Table 6.1 gives a classification that is used conveniently because it considers separately material nonlinear effects and kinematic nonlinear effects. The formulations listed in the table are those that we shall discuss in this chapter.

TABLE 6.1   *Classification of nonlinear analyses*

Type of analysis	Description	Typical formulation used	Stress and strain measures
Materially-nonlinear-only	Infinitesimal displacements and strains; the stress-strain relation is nonlinear	Materially-nonlinear -only (MNO)	Engineering stress and strain
Large displacements, large rotations, but small strains	Displacements and rotations of fibers are large, but fiber extensions and angle changes between fibers are small; the stress-strain relation may be linear or nonlinear	Total Lagrangian (TL) Updated Lagrangian (UL)	Second Piola-Kirchhoff stress, Green-Lagrange strain Cauchy stress, Almansi strain
Large displacements, large rotations, and large strains	Fiber extensions and angle changes between fibers are large, fiber displacements and rotations may also be large; the stress-strain relation may be linear or nonlinear	Total Lagrangian (TL) Updated Lagrangian (UL)	Second Piola-Kirchhoff stress, Green-Lagrange strain Cauchy stress, logarithmic strain

Figure 6.1 gives an illustration of the types of problems that are encountered, as listed in Table 6.1. We should note that in a materially-nonlinear-only analysis, the nonlinear effect lies only in the nonlinear stress-strain relation. The displacements and strains are infinitesimally small; therefore the usual engineering stress and strain measures can be employed in the response description. Considering the large displacement but small strain conditions, we note that in essence the material is subjected to infinitesimally small strains measured in a body-attached coordinate frame x', y' while this frame undergoes large rigid body displacements and rotations. The stress-strain relation of the material can be linear or nonlinear.

As shown in Fig. 6.1 and Table 6.1, the most general analysis case is the one in which the material is subjected to large displacements and large strains. In this case the stress-strain relation is also usually nonlinear.

In addition to the analysis categories listed in Table 6.1, Fig. 6.1 illustrates another type of nonlinear analysis, namely, the analysis of problems in which the boundary conditions change during the motion of the body under consideration. This situation arises in

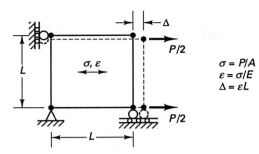

$$\sigma = P/A$$
$$\varepsilon = \sigma/E$$
$$\Delta = \varepsilon L$$

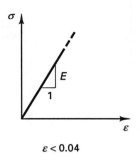

$$\varepsilon < 0.04$$

(a) Linear elastic (infinitesimal displacements)

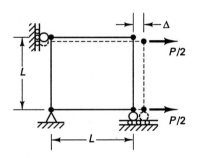

$$\sigma = P/A$$
$$\varepsilon = \frac{\sigma_Y}{E} + \frac{\sigma - \sigma_Y}{E_T}$$
$$\varepsilon < 0.04$$

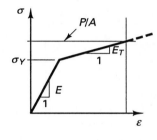

(b) Materially-nonlinear-only (infinitesimal displacements, but nonlinear stress-strain relation)

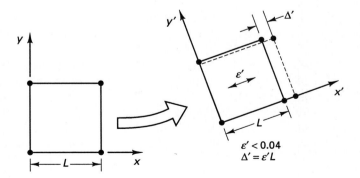

$$\varepsilon' < 0.04$$
$$\Delta' = \varepsilon' L$$

(c) Large displacements and large rotations but small strains. Linear or nonlinear material behavior

Figure 6.1   Classification of analyses

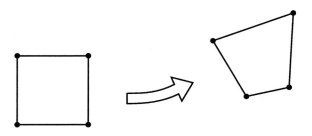

(d) Large displacements, large rotations, and large strains.
Linear or nonlinear material behavior

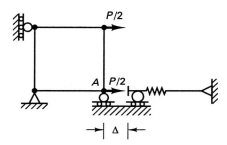

(e) Change in boundary condition at displacement Δ

Figure 6.1   *(continued)*

particular in the analysis of contact problems, of which a simple example is given in Fig. 6.1(e). In general, this change in boundary condition may be encountered in any one of the analyses summarized in Table 6.1.

In actual analysis, it is necessary to decide whether a problem falls into one or the other category of analysis, and this dictates which formulation will be used to describe the actual physical situation. Conversely, we may say that by the use of a specific formulation, a model of the actual physical situation is assumed, and the choice of formulation is part of the complete modeling process. Surely, the use of the most general large strain formulation "will always be correct"; however, the use of a more restrictive formulation may be computationally more effective and may also provide more insight into the response prediction.

Before we discuss the general formulations of nonlinear analyses, it would be instructive to consider first two simple examples that demonstrate some of the features listed in Table 6.1.

EXAMPLE 6.1:   A bar rigidly supported at both ends is subjected to an axial load as shown in Fig. E6.1(a). The stress-strain relation and the load-versus-time curve relation are given in Figs. E6.1(b) and (c), respectively. Assuming that the displacements and strains are small and that the load is applied slowly, calculate the displacement at the point of load application.

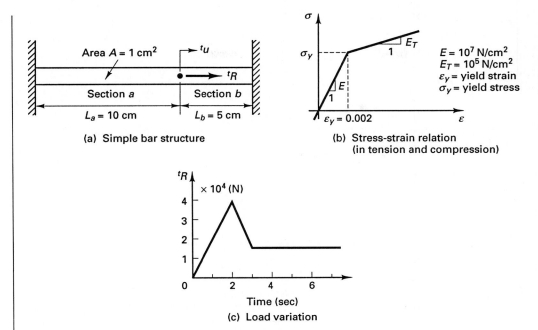

Figure E6.1   Analysis of simple bar structure

Since the load is applied slowly and the displacements and strains are small, we calculate the response of the bar using a static analysis with material nonlinearities only. Then we have for sections a and b, the strain relations

$$^t\epsilon_a = \frac{^tu}{L_a}; \qquad ^t\epsilon_b = -\frac{^tu}{L_b} \tag{a}$$

the equilibrium relations,

$$^tR + {}^t\sigma_b A = {}^t\sigma_a A \tag{b}$$

and the constitutive relations, under loading conditions,

$$^t\epsilon = \frac{^t\sigma}{E} \qquad \text{in the elastic region}$$

$$^t\epsilon = \epsilon_y + \frac{^t\sigma - \sigma_y}{E_T} \qquad \text{in the plastic region} \tag{c}$$

and in unloading,

$$\Delta\epsilon = \frac{\Delta\sigma}{E}$$

In these relations the superscript t denotes "at time t."

(i) *Both sections a and b are elastic*

During the initial phase of load application both sections a and b are elastic. Then we have, using (a) to (c),

$$^tR = EA {}^tu\left(\frac{1}{L_a} + \frac{1}{L_b}\right)$$

and substituting the values given in Fig. E6.1, we obtain

$$^t u = \frac{^t R}{3 \times 10^6}$$

with

$$^t \sigma_a = \frac{^t R}{3A}; \qquad ^t \sigma_b = -\frac{2}{3}\frac{^t R}{A} \tag{d}$$

(ii) *Section a is elastic while section b is plastic*
    Section *b* will become plastic at time *t** when, using (d),

$$^{t^*} R = \tfrac{3}{2}\sigma_y A$$

Afterward we therefore have

$$^t \sigma_a = E\frac{^t u}{L_a}$$

$$^t \sigma_b = -E_T\left(\frac{^t u}{L_b} - \epsilon_y\right) - \sigma_y \tag{e}$$

Using (e), we therefore have for $t \geq t^*$,

$$^t R = \frac{EA^t u}{L_a} + \frac{E_T A^t u}{L_b} - E_T \epsilon_y A + \sigma_y A$$

and thus

$$^t u = \frac{^t R/A + E_T \epsilon_y - \sigma_y}{(E/L_a) + (E_T/L_b)}$$

$$= \frac{^t R}{1.02 \times 10^6} - 1.9412 \times 10^{-2}$$

We may note that section *a* would become plastic when $^t \sigma_a = \sigma_y$ or $^t R = 4.02 \times 10^4$ N. Since the load does not reach this value [see Fig. E6.1(c)], section *a* remains elastic throughout the response history.

(iii) *In unloading both sections act elastically*

we have

$$\Delta u = \frac{\Delta R}{EA[(1/L_a) + (1/L_b)]}$$

The calculated response is depicted in Fig. E6.1(d).

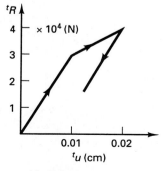

(d) Calculated response   **Figure E6.1**   *(continued)*

EXAMPLE 6.2: A pretensioned cable is subjected to a transverse load midway between the supports as shown in Fig. E6.2(a). A spring is placed below the load at a distance w_{gap}. Assume that the displacements are small so that the force in the cable remains constant, and that the load is applied slowly. Calculate the displacement under the load as a function of the load intensity.

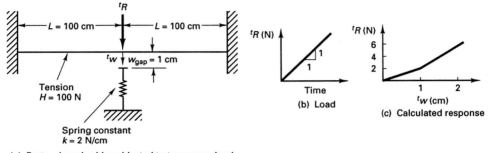

(a) **Pretensioned cable subjected to transverse load**

Figure E6.2   Analysis of pretensioned cable with a spring support

As in Example 6.1, we neglect inertia forces and assume small displacements. As long as the displacement $^t w$ under the load is smaller than w_{gap}, vertical equilibrium requires for small $^t w$,

$$^t R = 2H \frac{^t w}{L} \tag{a}$$

Once the displacement is larger than w_{gap}, the following equilibrium equation holds:

$$^t R = 2H \frac{^t w}{L} + k(^t w - w_{gap}) \tag{b}$$

Figure E6.2(c) shows graphically the force displacement relations given in (a) and (b).

We should note that in this analysis we neglected the elasticity of the cable; therefore the response is calculated using only the equilibrium equations in (a) and (b), and the only nonlinearity is due to the contact condition established when $^t w \geq w_{gap}$.

Although these examples represent two very simple problems, the given solutions display some important general features. The basic problem in a general nonlinear analysis is to find the state of equilibrium of a body corresponding to the applied loads. Assuming that the externally applied loads are described as a function of time, as in Examples 6.1 and 6.2, the equilibrium conditions of a system of finite elements representing the body under consideration can be expressed as

$$^t \mathbf{R} - {}^t \mathbf{F} = \mathbf{0} \tag{6.2}$$

where the vector $^t \mathbf{R}$ lists the externally applied nodal point forces in the configuration at time t and the vector $^t \mathbf{F}$ lists the nodal point forces that correspond to the element stresses in this configuration. Hence, using the notation in Chapter 4, relations (4.18) and (4.20) to (4.22), we have

$$^t \mathbf{R} = {}^t \mathbf{R}_B + {}^t \mathbf{R}_S + {}^t \mathbf{R}_C \tag{6.3}$$

and, identifying the current stresses as initial stresses, $\mathbf{R}_I = {}^t\mathbf{F}$,

$$
{}^t\mathbf{F} = \sum_m \int_{{}^t V^{(m)}} {}^t\mathbf{B}^{(m)T} \, {}^t\boldsymbol{\tau}^{(m)} \, {}^t dV^{(m)} \tag{6.4}
$$

where in a general large deformation analysis the stresses as well as the volume of the body at time t are unknown.

The relation in (6.2) must express the equilibrium of the system in the current deformed geometry taking due account of all nonlinearities. Also, in a dynamic analysis, the vector ${}^t\mathbf{R}$ would include the inertia and damping forces, as discussed in Section 4.2.1.

Considering the solution of the nonlinear response, we recognize that the equilibrium relation in (6.2) must be satisfied throughout the complete history of load application; i.e., the time variable t may take on any value from zero to the maximum time of interest (see Examples 6.1 and 6.2). In a static analysis without time effects other than the definition of the load level (e.g., without creep effects; see Section 6.6.3), time is only a convenient variable which denotes different intensities of load applications and correspondingly different configurations. However, in a dynamic analysis and in static analysis with material time effects, the time variable is an actual variable to be properly included in the modeling of the actual physical situation. Based on these considerations, we realize that the use of the time variable to describe the load application and history of solution represents a very general approach and corresponds to our earlier assertion that a "dynamic analysis is basically a static analysis including inertia effects."

As for the analysis results to be calculated, in many solutions only the stresses and displacements reached at specific load levels or at specific times are required. In some nonlinear static analyses the equilibrium configurations corresponding to these load levels can be calculated without also solving for other equilibrium configurations. However, when the analysis includes path-dependent nonlinear geometric or material conditions, or time-dependent phenomena, the equilibrium relations in (6.2) need to be solved for the complete time range of interest. This response calculation is effectively carried out using a step-by-step incremental solution, which reduces to a one-step analysis if in a static time-independent solution the total load is applied all together and only the configuration corresponding to that load is calculated. However, we shall see that for computational reasons, in practice, even the analysis of such a case frequently requires an incremental solution, performed automatically (see also Section 8.4), with a number of load steps to finally reach the total applied load.

The basic approach in an incremental step-by-step solution is to assume that the solution for the discrete time t is known and that the solution for the discrete time $t + \Delta t$ is required, where Δt is a suitably chosen time increment. Hence, considering (6.2) at time $t + \Delta t$ we have

$$
{}^{t+\Delta t}\mathbf{R} - {}^{t+\Delta t}\mathbf{F} = \mathbf{0} \tag{6.5}
$$

where the left superscript denotes "at time $t + \Delta t$." Assume that ${}^{t+\Delta t}\mathbf{R}$ is independent of the deformations. Since the solution is known at time t, we can write

$$
{}^{t+\Delta t}\mathbf{F} = {}^t\mathbf{F} + \mathbf{F} \tag{6.6}
$$

where $\mathbf{F}$ is the increment in nodal point forces corresponding to the increment in element displacements and stresses from time t to time $t + \Delta t$. This vector can be approximated using a tangent stiffness matrix ${}^{t}\mathbf{K}$ which corresponds to the geometric and material conditions at time t,

$$\mathbf{F} \doteq {}^{t}\mathbf{K}\mathbf{U} \tag{6.7}$$

where $\mathbf{U}$ is a vector of incremental nodal point displacements and

$$ {}^{t}\mathbf{K} = \frac{\partial {}^{t}\mathbf{F}}{\partial {}^{t}\mathbf{U}} \tag{6.8}$$

Hence, the tangent stiffness matrix corresponds to the derivative of the internal element nodal point forces ${}^{t}\mathbf{F}$ with respect to the nodal point displacements ${}^{t}\mathbf{U}$.

Substituting (6.7) and (6.6) into (6.5), we obtain

$$ {}^{t}\mathbf{K}\mathbf{U} = {}^{t+\Delta t}\mathbf{R} - {}^{t}\mathbf{F} \tag{6.9}$$

and solving for $\mathbf{U}$, we can calculate an approximation to the displacements at time $t + \Delta t$,

$$ {}^{t+\Delta t}\mathbf{U} \doteq {}^{t}\mathbf{U} + \mathbf{U} \tag{6.10}$$

The exact displacements at time $t + \Delta t$ are those that correspond to the applied loads ${}^{t+\Delta t}\mathbf{R}$. We calculate in (6.10) only an approximation to these displacements because (6.7) was used.

Much of our discussion in this chapter will focus on the proper and effective evaluation of ${}^{t}\mathbf{F}$ and ${}^{t}\mathbf{K}$.

Having evaluated an approximation to the displacements corresponding to time $t + \Delta t$, we could now solve for an approximation to the stresses and corresponding nodal point forces at time $t + \Delta t$, and then proceed to the next time increment calculations. However, because of the assumption in (6.7), such a solution may be subject to very significant errors and, depending on the time or load step sizes used, may indeed be unstable. In practice, it is therefore necessary to iterate until the solution of (6.5) is obtained to sufficient accuracy.

The widely used iteration methods in finite element analysis are based on the classical Newton-Raphson technique (see, for example, E. Kreyszig [A] and see N. Bićanić and K. H. Johnson [A]), which we formally derive in Section 8.4. This method is an extension of the simple incremental technique given in (6.9) and (6.10). That is, having calculated an *increment* in the nodal point displacements, which defines a *new total* displacement vector, we can repeat the incremental solution presented above using the currently known total displacements instead of the displacements at time t.

The equations used in the Newton-Raphson iteration are, for $i = 1, 2, 3, \ldots ,$

$$\boxed{\begin{array}{c} {}^{t+\Delta t}\mathbf{K}^{(i-1)}\Delta\mathbf{U}^{(i)} = {}^{t+\Delta t}\mathbf{R} - {}^{t+\Delta t}\mathbf{F}^{(i-1)} \\[4pt] {}^{t+\Delta t}\mathbf{U}^{(i)} = {}^{t+\Delta t}\mathbf{U}^{(i-1)} + \Delta\mathbf{U}^{(i)} \end{array}} \tag{6.11}$$

with the initial conditions

$$ {}^{t+\Delta t}\mathbf{U}^{(0)} = {}^{t}\mathbf{U}; \qquad {}^{t+\Delta t}\mathbf{K}^{(0)} = {}^{t}\mathbf{K}; \qquad {}^{t+\Delta t}\mathbf{F}^{(0)} = {}^{t}\mathbf{F} \tag{6.12}$$

Note that in the first iteration, the relations in (6.11) reduce to the equations (6.9) and (6.10). Then, in subsequent iterations, the latest estimates for the nodal point displacements are used to evaluate the corresponding element stresses and nodal point forces $^{t+\Delta t}\mathbf{F}^{(i-1)}$ and tangent stiffness matrix $^{t+\Delta t}\mathbf{K}^{(i-1)}$.

The out-of-balance load vector $^{t+\Delta t}\mathbf{R} - {}^{t+\Delta t}\mathbf{F}^{(i-1)}$ corresponds to a load vector that is not yet balanced by element stresses, and hence an increment in the nodal point displacements is required. This updating of the nodal point displacements in the iteration is continued until the out-of-balance loads and incremental displacements are small.

Let us summarize some important considerations regarding the Newton-Raphson iterative solution.

An important point is that the correct calculation of $^{t+\Delta t}\mathbf{F}^{(i-1)}$ from $^{t+\Delta t}\mathbf{U}^{(i-1)}$ is crucial. Any errors in this calculation will, in general, result in an incorrect response prediction.

The correct evaluation of the tangent stiffness matrix $^{t+\Delta t}\mathbf{K}^{(i-1)}$ is also important. The use of the proper tangent stiffness matrix may be necessary for convergence and, in general, will result in fewer iterations until convergence is reached.

However, because of the expense involved in evaluating and factoring a new tangent stiffness matrix, in practice, it can be more efficient, depending on the nonlinearities present in the analysis, to evaluate a new tangent stiffness matrix only at certain times. Specifically, in the modified Newton-Raphson method a new tangent stiffness matrix is established only at the beginning of each load step, and in quasi-Newton methods secant stiffness matrices are used instead of the tangent stiffness matrix (see Section 8.4). We note that, which scheme to use is only a matter of computational efficiency provided convergence is reached.

The use of the iterative solution requires appropriate convergence criteria. If inappropriate criteria are used, the iteration may be terminated before the necessary solution accuracy is reached or be continued after the required accuracy has been reached.

We discuss these numerical considerations in Section 8.4 but note here that whichever iterative technique is used, the basic requirements are (1) the evaluation of the (tangent) stiffness matrix corresponding to a given state and (2) the evaluation of the nodal force vector corresponding to the stresses in that state (the "state" being given by $^t\mathbf{U}$ or $^{t+\Delta t}\mathbf{U}^{(i-1)}$, $i = 1, 2, 3, \ldots$). Hence, our primary focus in this chapter is on explaining how, for a generic state, and we use the state at time t, the tangent stiffness matrices $^t\mathbf{K}$ and force vectors $^t\mathbf{F}$ for various elements and material stress-strain relations can be evaluated.

Let us now demonstrate these concepts in two examples.

EXAMPLE 6.3:   Idealize the simple arch structure shown in Fig. E6.3(a) as an assemblage of two bar elements. Assume that the force in one bar element is given by $^t F_{\text{bar}} = k\,^t\delta$, where k is a constant and $^t\delta$ is the elongation of the bar at time t. (The assumption that k is constant is likely to be valid only for small deformations in the bar, but we use this assumption in order to simplify the analysis.) Establish the equilibrium relation (6.5) for this problem.

(a) Bar assemblage subjected to apex load

(b) Simple model using one bar (truss) element, nodes 1 and 2

Figure E6.3   A simple arch structure

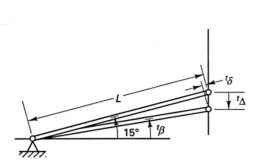

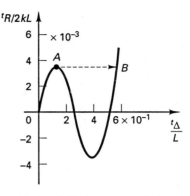

(c) Geometric variables in typical configuration   (d) Load-displacement relation

Figure E6.3 *(continued)*

This is a large displacement problem, and the response is calculated by focusing attention on the equilibrium of the bar assemblage in the configuration corresponding to a typical time t. Using symmetry as shown in Figs. E6.3(b) and (c), we have

$$(L - {}^t\delta) \cos {}^t\beta = L \cos 15°$$

$$(L - {}^t\delta) \sin {}^t\beta = L \sin 15° - {}^t\Delta$$

hence,

$${}^t\delta = L - \sqrt{L^2 - 2L\,{}^t\Delta \sin 15° + {}^t\Delta^2}$$

$$\sin {}^t\beta = \frac{L \sin 15° - {}^t\Delta}{L - {}^t\delta}$$

Equilibrium at time t requires that

$$2\,{}^tF_{\text{bar}} \sin {}^t\beta = {}^tR$$

hence, the relation in (6.5) is

$$\frac{{}^tR}{2kL} = \left\{ -1 + \frac{1}{\left[1 - 2\dfrac{{}^t\Delta}{L} \sin 15° + \left(\dfrac{{}^t\Delta}{L}\right)^2 \right]^{1/2}} \right\} \left(\sin 15° - \frac{{}^t\Delta}{L} \right) \tag{a}$$

Figure E6.3(d) shows the force-displacement relationship established in (a). It should be noted that between points A and B, for a given load level, we have two possible displacement configurations. If the structure is loaded with ${}^tR$ monotonically increasing, the displacement path with snap-through from A to B in Fig. E6.3(d) is likely to be followed in an actual physical situation.

EXAMPLE 6.4: Calculate the response of the bar assemblage considered in Example 6.1 using the modified Newton-Raphson iteration. Use two equal load steps to reach the maximum load application.

In the modified Newton-Raphson iteration, we use (6.11) and (6.12) but evaluate new tangent stiffness matrices only at the beginning of each step. Hence, the iterative equations are in this analysis

$$({}^tK_a + {}^tK_b)\,\Delta u^{(i)} = {}^{t+\Delta t}R - {}^{t+\Delta t}F_a^{(i-1)} - {}^{t+\Delta t}F_b^{(i-1)}$$

$${}^{t+\Delta t}u^{(i)} = {}^{t+\Delta t}u^{(i-1)} + \Delta u^{(i)} \tag{a}$$

with
$$^{t+\Delta t}u^{(0)} = {}^t u$$

$$^{t+\Delta t}F_a^{(0)} = {}^t F_a; \qquad ^{t+\Delta t}F_b^{(0)} = {}^t F_b \tag{b}$$

$$^t K_a = \frac{{}^t CA}{L_a}; \qquad {}^t K_b = \frac{{}^t CA}{L_b}$$

where
$$^t C \begin{cases} = E & \text{if section is elastic} \\ = E_T & \text{if section is plastic} \end{cases}$$

For an elastic section,
$$^{t+\Delta t}F^{(i-1)} = EA\,^{t+\Delta t}\epsilon^{(i-1)} \tag{c}$$

for a plastic section,
$$^{t+\Delta t}F^{(i-1)} = A[E_T({}^{t+\Delta t}\epsilon^{(i-1)} - \epsilon_y) + \sigma_y] \tag{d}$$

and the strains in the sections are
$$^{t+\Delta t}\epsilon_a^{(i-1)} = \frac{{}^{t+\Delta t}u^{(i-1)}}{L_a}$$

$$^{t+\Delta t}\epsilon_b^{(i-1)} = \frac{{}^{t+\Delta t}u^{(i-1)}}{L_b} \tag{e}$$

In the first load step, we have $t = 0$ and $\Delta t = 1$. Thus, the application of the relations in (a) to (e) gives

$t = 1$:

$$(^0 K_a + {}^0 K_b)\, \Delta u^{(1)} = {}^1 R - {}^1 F_a^{(0)} - {}^1 F_b^{(0)}$$

$$\Delta u^{(1)} = \frac{2 \times 10^4}{10^7(\frac{1}{10} + \frac{1}{5})} = 6.6667 \times 10^{-3} \text{ cm}$$

$(i = 1) \qquad {}^1 u^{(1)} = {}^1 u^{(0)} + \Delta u^{(1)} = 6.6667 \times 10^{-3} \text{ cm}$

$$^1\epsilon_a^{(1)} = \frac{{}^1 u^{(1)}}{L_a} = 6.6667 \times 10^{-4} < \epsilon_y \rightarrow \text{ section } a \text{ is elastic}$$

$$^1\epsilon_b^{(1)} = \frac{{}^1 u^{(1)}}{L_b} = 1.3333 \times 10^{-3} < \epsilon_y \rightarrow \text{ section } b \text{ is elastic}$$

$$^1 F_a^{(1)} = 6.6667 \times 10^3 \text{ N}$$

$$^1 F_b^{(1)} = 1.3333 \times 10^4 \text{ N}$$

$$(^0 K_a + {}^0 K_b)\, \Delta u^{(2)} = {}^1 R - {}^1 F_a^{(1)} - {}^1 F_b^{(1)}$$

$$= 0$$

$$\therefore \text{ Convergence is achieved in one iteration}$$

$$^1 u = 6.6667 \times 10^{-3} \text{ cm}$$

$t = 2$:

$$^1 K_a = \frac{EA}{L_a}; \qquad {}^1 K_b = \frac{EA}{L_b}$$

$$^2 F_a^{(0)} = {}^1 F_a; \qquad {}^2 F_b^{(0)} = {}^1 F_b$$

$$({}^1K_a + {}^1K_b) \Delta u^{(1)} = {}^2R - {}^2F_a^{(0)} - {}^2F_b^{(0)}$$

$$\Delta u^{(1)} = \frac{(4 \times 10^4) - (6.6667 \times 10^3) - (1.3333 \times 10^4)}{10^7(\frac{1}{10} + \frac{1}{5})}$$

$$= 6.6667 \times 10^{-3} \text{ cm}$$

$(i = 1)$ $\quad {}^2u^{(1)} = {}^2u^{(0)} + \Delta u^{(1)} = 1.3333 \times 10^{-2} \text{ cm}$

$\quad {}^2\epsilon_a^{(1)} = 1.3333 \times 10^{-3} < \epsilon_y \rightarrow$ section a is elastic

$\quad {}^2\epsilon_b^{(1)} = 2.6667 \times 10^{-3} > \epsilon_y \rightarrow$ section b is plastic

$\quad {}^2F_a^{(1)} = 1.3333 \times 10^4 \text{ N}$

$\quad {}^2F_b^{(1)} = [E_T({}^2\epsilon_b{}^{(1)} - \epsilon_y) + \sigma_y]A = 2.0067 \times 10^4 \text{ N}$

$$({}^1K_a + {}^1K_b) \Delta u^{(2)} = {}^2R - {}^2F_a^{(1)} - {}^2F_b^{(1)}$$
$$\Delta u^{(2)} = 2.2 \times 10^{-3} \text{ cm}$$

$(i = 2)$ $\quad {}^2u^{(2)} = {}^2u^{(1)} + \Delta u^{(2)} = 1.5533 \times 10^{-2} \text{ cm}$

$\quad {}^2\epsilon_a^{(2)} = 1.5533 \times 10^{-3} < \epsilon_y$

$\quad {}^2\epsilon_b^{(2)} = 3.1066 \times 10^{-3} > \epsilon_y$

$\quad \therefore {}^2F_a^{(2)} = 1.5533 \times 10^4 \text{ N}$

$\quad {}^2F_b^{(2)} = 2.0111 \times 10^4 \text{ N}$

$$({}^1K_a + {}^1K_b) \Delta u^{(3)} = {}^2R - {}^2F_a^{(2)} - {}^2F_b^{(2)}$$
$$\Delta u^{(3)} = 1.4521 \times 10^{-3} \text{ cm}$$

The procedure is repeated, and the results of successive iterations are tabulated in the accompanying table.

i	$\Delta u^{(i)}$ (cm)	${}^2u^{(i)}$ (cm)
3	1.4521×10^{-3}	1.6985×10^{-2}
4	9.5832×10^{-4}	1.7944×10^{-2}
5	6.3249×10^{-4}	1.8576×10^{-2}
6	4.1744×10^{-4}	1.8994×10^{-2}
7	2.7551×10^{-4}	1.9269×10^{-2}

After seven iterations, we have

$$ {}^2u \doteq {}^2u^{(7)} = 1.9269 \times 10^{-2} \text{ cm}$$

6.2 FORMULATION OF THE CONTINUUM MECHANICS INCREMENTAL EQUATIONS OF MOTION

The objective in the introductory discussion of nonlinear analysis in Section 6.1 was to describe various nonlinearities and the form of the basic finite element equations that are used to analyze the nonlinear response of a structural system. To show the procedure of analysis, we simply stated the finite element equations, discussed their solution, and gave a physical argument why the nonlinear response is appropriately predicted using these equations. We demonstrated the applicability of the approach in the solution of two very simple problems merely to give some insight into the steps of analysis used. In each of these analyses the applicable finite element matrices and vectors were developed using physical arguments.

The physical approach of analysis used in Examples 6.3 and 6.4 is very instructive and yields insight into the analysis; however, when considering a more complex solution, a consistent continuum-mechanics-based approach should be employed to develop the governing finite element equations. The objective in this section is to present the governing continuum mechanics equations for a displacement-based finite element solution. As in Section 4.2.1, we use the principle of virtual work but now include the possibility that the body considered undergoes large displacements and rotations and large strains and that the stress-strain relationship is nonlinear. The governing continuum mechanics equations to be presented can therefore be regarded as an extension of the basic equation given in (4.7). In the linear analysis of a general body, the equation in (4.7) was used as the basis for the development of the governing linear finite element equations [given in (4.17) to (4.27)]. Considering the nonlinear analysis of a general body, after having developed suitable continuum mechanics equations, we will proceed in a completely analogous manner to establish the nonlinear finite element equations that govern the nonlinear response of the body (see Section 6.3).

6.2.1 The Basic Problem

In Section 6.1 we underlined the fact that in a nonlinear analysis the equilibrium of the body considered must be established in the current configuration. We also pointed out that in general it is necessary to employ an incremental formulation and that a time variable is used to conveniently describe the loading and the motion of the body.

In the development to follow, we consider the motion of a general body in a stationary Cartesian coordinate system, as shown in Fig. 6.2, and assume that the body can experience large displacements, large strains, and a nonlinear constitutive response. The aim is to evaluate the equilibrium positions of the complete body at the discrete time points $0, \Delta t, 2\,\Delta t, 3\,\Delta t, \ldots$, where Δt is an increment in time. To develop the solution strategy, assume that the solutions for the static and kinematic variables for all time steps from time 0 to time t, inclusive, have been obtained. Then the solution process for the next required equilibrium position corresponding to time $t + \Delta t$ is typical and is applied repetitively until the complete solution path has been solved for. Hence, in the analysis we follow all particles of the body in their motion, from the original to the final configuration of the body, which means that we adopt a *Lagrangian* (or *material*) *formulation* of the problem. This approach stands in contrast to an *Eulerian formulation* which is usually used in the analysis of fluid mechanics problems, in which attention is focused on the motion of the material through a stationary control volume. Considering the analysis of solids and structures, a Lagrangian formulation usually represents a more natural and effective analysis approach than an Eulerian formulation. For example, using an Eulerian formulation of a structural problem with large displacements, new control volumes have to be created (because the boundaries of the solid change continuously), and the nonlinearities in the convective acceleration terms are difficult to deal with (see Section 7.4).

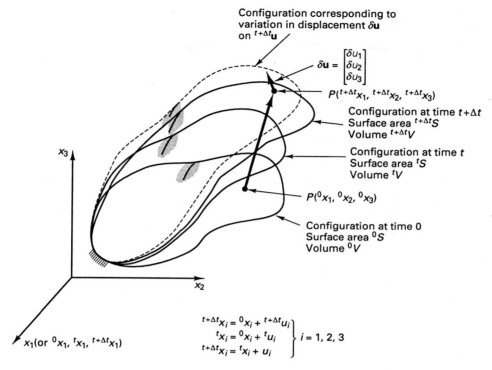

Figure 6.2   Motion of body in Cartesian coordinate frame

In our Lagrangian incremental analysis approach we express the equilibrium of the body at time $t + \Delta t$ using the principle of virtual displacements. Using tensor notation (see Section 2.4), this principle requires that

$$\int_{t+\Delta t_V} {}^{t+\Delta t}\tau_{ij}\, \delta_{t+\Delta t}e_{ij}\, d^{t+\Delta t}V = {}^{t+\Delta t}\mathscr{R} \qquad (6.13)$$

where

$\quad {}^{t+\Delta t}\tau_{ij} =$ Cartesian components of the *Cauchy stress* tensor (forces per unit areas in the deformed geometry)

$\quad \delta_{t+\Delta t}e_{ij} = \dfrac{1}{2}\left(\dfrac{\partial \delta u_i}{\partial^{t+\Delta t}x_j} + \dfrac{\partial \delta u_j}{\partial^{t+\Delta t}x_i}\right) =$ strain tensor corresponding to virtual displacements

$\quad \delta u_i =$ components of virtual displacement vector imposed on configuration at time $t + \Delta t$, a function of ${}^{t+\Delta t}x_j,\, j = 1, 2, 3$

$\quad {}^{t+\Delta t}x_i =$ Cartesian coordinates of material point at time $t + \Delta t$

$\quad {}^{t+\Delta t}V =$ volume at time $t + \Delta t$

and

$$
{}^{t+\Delta t}\mathcal{R} = \int_{{}^{t+\Delta t}V} {}^{t+\Delta t}f_i^B \, \delta u_i \, d^{t+\Delta t}V + \int_{{}^{t+\Delta t}S_f} {}^{t+\Delta t}f_i^S \, \delta u_i^S \, d^{t+\Delta t}S
\tag{6.14}
$$

where

${}^{t+\Delta t}f_i^B$ = components of externally applied forces per unit volume at time $t + \Delta t$
${}^{t+\Delta t}f_i^S$ = components of externally applied surface tractions per unit surface area at time $t + \Delta t$
${}^{t+\Delta t}S_f$ = surface at time $t + \Delta t$ on which external tractions are applied
δu_i^S = δu_i evaluated on the surface ${}^{t+\Delta t}S_f$ (the δu_i components are zero at and corresponding to the prescribed displacements on the surface ${}^{t+\Delta t}S_u$)

In (6.13), the left-hand side is the internal virtual work and the right-hand side is the external virtual work. The relation is derived as in linear infinitesimal displacement analysis (see Example 4.2), but the current configuration at time $t + \Delta t$ (with the stresses and forces at that time) is used. Hence, the derivation of (6.13) is based on the following equilibrium equations.

Within ${}^{t+\Delta t}V$ for $i = 1, 2, 3$,

$$
\frac{\partial^{t+\Delta t}\tau_{ij}}{\partial^{t+\Delta t}x_j} + {}^{t+\Delta t}f_i^B = 0 \qquad \text{sum over } j = 1, 2, 3
\tag{6.15a}
$$

and on the surface ${}^{t+\Delta t}S_f$, for $i = 1, 2, 3$,

$$
{}^{t+\Delta t}\tau_{ij} \, {}^{t+\Delta t}n_j = {}^{t+\Delta t}f_i^S \qquad \text{sum over } j = 1, 2, 3
\tag{6.15b}
$$

where the ${}^{t+\Delta t}n_j$ are the components of the unit normal to the surface ${}^{t+\Delta t}S_f$ at time $t + \Delta t$.

As shown in Example 4.2, the equation (6.15a) is multiplied by arbitrary continuous virtual displacements δu_i that are zero at and corresponding to the prescribed displacements. The integration of the expression obtained from (6.15a) over the volume at time $t+\Delta t$ and the use of the divergence theorem and (6.15b) then directly yield the relation in (6.13).

We note that the strain tensor components $\delta_{t+\Delta t}e_{ij}$ corresponding to the imposed virtual displacements are like the components of the infinitesimal strain tensor, but the derivatives are with respect to the current coordinates at time $t + \Delta t$. The use of the strain tensor $\delta_{t+\Delta t}e_{ij}$ in (6.13) is the *direct* result of the transformation by the divergence theorem used in the derivation of (6.13), and this strain tensor is obtained irrespective of the magnitude of the virtual displacements.

However, we now recognize that the virtual displacements δu_i may be thought of as a *variation* in the real displacements ${}^{t+\Delta t}u_i$ (subject to the constraint that these variations must be zero at and corresponding to the prescribed displacements). These displacement variations result in variations in the current strains of the body, and we shall later, in particular, use the variation in the Green-Lagrange strain components corresponding to δu_i (see Example 6.10).

It is most important to recognize that the virtual work principle stated in (6.13) is simply an application of the equation in (4.7) (used in linear analysis) to the body considered in the configuration at time $t + \Delta t$. Therefore, all previous discussions and results *pertaining to the use of the virtual work principle in linear analysis are now directly applicable, with the current configuration at time $t + \Delta t$ being considered.* [1]

A fundamental difficulty in the general application of (6.13) is that the configuration of the body at time $t + \Delta t$ is unknown. This is an important difference compared with linear analysis in which it is assumed that the displacements are infinitesimally small so that in (6.13) to (6.15) the original configuration is used. The continuous change in the configuration of the body entails some important consequences for the development of an incremental analysis procedure. For example, an important consideration must be that the Cauchy stresses at time $t + \Delta t$ cannot be obtained by simply adding to the Cauchy stresses at time t a stress increment that is due only to the straining of the material. Namely, the calculation of the Cauchy stresses at time $t + \Delta t$ must also take into account the rigid body rotation of the material because the components of the Cauchy stress tensor also change when the material is subjected to only a rigid body rotation.

The fact that the configuration of the body changes continuously in a large deformation analysis is dealt with in an elegant manner by using appropriate stress and strain measures and constitutive relations, as discussed in detail in the next sections.

Considering the discussions to follow, we recognize that a difficult point in the presentation of continuum mechanics relations for general large deformation analysis is the use of an effective notation because there are many different quantities that need to be dealt with. The symbols used should display all necessary information but should do so in a compact manner in order that the equations can be read with relative ease. For effective use of a notation, an understanding of the convention employed is most helpful, and for this purpose we summarize here briefly some basic facts and conventions used in our notation.

In our analysis we consider the motion of the body in a fixed (stationary) Cartesian coordinate system as displayed in Fig. 6.2. All kinematic and static variables are measured in this coordinate system, and throughout our description we use tensor notation.

The coordinates of a generic point P in the body at time 0 are ${}^{0}x_1$, ${}^{0}x_2$, ${}^{0}x_3$; at time t they are ${}^{t}x_1$, ${}^{t}x_2$, ${}^{t}x_3$; and at time $t + \Delta t$ they are ${}^{t+\Delta t}x_1$, ${}^{t+\Delta t}x_2$, ${}^{t+\Delta t}x_3$, where the left superscripts refer to the configuration of the body and the subscripts to the coordinate axes.

The notation for the displacements of the body is similar to the notation for the coordinates: at time t the displacements are ${}^{t}u_i$, $i = 1, 2, 3$, and at time $t + \Delta t$ the displacements are ${}^{t+\Delta t}u_i$, $i = 1, 2, 3$. Therefore, we have

$$\left.\begin{array}{c} {}^{t}x_i = {}^{0}x_i + {}^{t}u_i \\ {}^{t+\Delta t}x_i = {}^{0}x_i + {}^{t+\Delta t}u_i \end{array}\right\} \qquad i = 1, 2, 3 \qquad (6.16)$$

The increments in the displacements from time t to time $t + \Delta t$ are denoted as

$$u_i = {}^{t+\Delta t}u_i - {}^{t}u_i; \qquad i = 1, 2, 3 \qquad (6.17)$$

During motion of the body, its volume, surface area, mass density, stresses, and strains are changing continuously. We denote the specific mass, area, and volume of the body at times 0, t, and $t + \Delta t$ as ${}^{0}\rho$, ${}^{t}\rho$, ${}^{t+\Delta t}\rho$; ${}^{0}A$, ${}^{t}A$, ${}^{t+\Delta t}A$; and ${}^{0}V$, ${}^{t}V$, ${}^{t+\Delta t}V$, respectively.

Since the configuration of the body at time $t + \Delta t$ is not known, we will refer applied forces, stresses, and strains to a known equilibrium configuration. In analogy to the notation

[1] We may imagine that in considering the moving body, a picture is taken at time $t + \Delta t$ and then the principle of virtual displacements is applied to the state of the body in that picture.

used for coordinates and displacements, a left superscript indicates in which configuration the quantity (body force, surface traction, stress, etc.) occurs; in addition, a left subscript indicates the configuration with respect to which the quantity is measured. For example, the surface and body force components at time $t + \Delta t$, but measured in configuration 0, are $^{t+\Delta t}_{0}f_i^S$, $^{t+\Delta t}_{0}f_i^B$, $i = 1, 2, 3$. Here we have the exception that if the quantity under consideration occurs in the same configuration in which it is also measured, the left subscript may not be used; e.g., for the Cauchy stresses we have

$$^{t+\Delta t}\tau_{ij} \equiv \,^{t+\Delta t}_{t+\Delta t}\tau_{ij}$$

In the formulation of the governing equilibrium equations we also need to consider derivatives of displacements and coordinates. In our notation a comma denotes differentiation with respect to the coordinate following, and the left subscript denoting time indicates the configuration in which this coordinate is measured; thus we have, for example,

$$^{t+\Delta t}_{0}u_{i,j} = \frac{\partial^{t+\Delta t}u_i}{\partial^0 x_j}$$

and
$$^{\ \ 0}_{t+\Delta t}x_{m,n} = \frac{\partial^0 x_m}{\partial^{t+\Delta t}x_n} \tag{6.18}$$

Using these conventions, we shall define new symbols when they are first encountered.

6.2.2 The Deformation Gradient, Strain, and Stress Tensors

We mentioned in the previous section that in a large deformation analysis special attention must be given to the fact that the configuration of the body is changing continuously. This change in configuration can be dealt with in an elegant manner by defining auxiliary stress and strain measures. The objective in defining them is to express the internal virtual work in (6.13) in terms of an integral over a volume that is known and to be able to incrementally decompose the stresses and strains in an effective manner. There are various different stress and strain tensors that, in principle, could be used (see L. E. Malvern [A], Y. C. Fung [A], A. E. Green and W. Zerna [A], and R. Hill [A]). However, if the objective is to obtain an effective overall finite element solution procedure, only a few stress and strain measures need be considered. In the following we first consider the motion of a general body and define kinematic measures of this motion. We then introduce appropriate strain and the corresponding stress tensors. These are used later in the chapter to develop the incremental general finite element equations.

Consider the body in Fig. 6.2 at a generic time t. A fundamental measure of the deformation of the body is given by the *deformation gradient,* defined as[2]

---

[2] The deformation gradient is denoted as **F** in other books, but we use the notation $^t_0\mathbf{X}$ throughout this text because this symbol more naturally indicates that the differentiations of the coordinates $^t x_i$ with respect to the coordinates $^0 x_j$ are performed.

$$
{}_0^t\mathbf{X} = \begin{bmatrix}
\dfrac{\partial {}^tx_1}{\partial {}^0x_1} & \dfrac{\partial {}^tx_1}{\partial {}^0x_2} & \dfrac{\partial {}^tx_1}{\partial {}^0x_3} \\[2ex]
\dfrac{\partial {}^tx_2}{\partial {}^0x_1} & \dfrac{\partial {}^tx_2}{\partial {}^0x_2} & \dfrac{\partial {}^tx_2}{\partial {}^0x_3} \\[2ex]
\dfrac{\partial {}^tx_3}{\partial {}^0x_1} & \dfrac{\partial {}^tx_3}{\partial {}^0x_2} & \dfrac{\partial {}^tx_3}{\partial {}^0x_3}
\end{bmatrix}
\tag{6.19}
$$

or
$$
{}_0^t\mathbf{X} = ({}_0\boldsymbol{\nabla}{}^t\mathbf{x}^T)^T
\tag{6.20}
$$

where ${}_0\boldsymbol{\nabla}$ is the gradient operator

$$
{}_0\boldsymbol{\nabla} = \begin{bmatrix}
\dfrac{\partial}{\partial {}^0x_1} \\[2ex]
\dfrac{\partial}{\partial {}^0x_2} \\[2ex]
\dfrac{\partial}{\partial {}^0x_3}
\end{bmatrix}; \qquad {}^t\mathbf{x}^T = \begin{bmatrix} {}^tx_1 & {}^tx_2 & {}^tx_3 \end{bmatrix}
\tag{6.21}
$$

The deformation gradient describes the stretches and rotations that the material fibers have undergone from time 0 to time t. Namely, let $d^0\mathbf{x}$ be a differential material fiber at time 0; then, by the chain rule of differentiation, this material fiber at time t is given by

$$
d^t\mathbf{x} = {}_0^t\mathbf{X}\, d^0\mathbf{x}
\tag{6.22}
$$

Using chain differentiation, it also follows that

$$
d^0\mathbf{x} = {}_t^0\mathbf{X}\, d^t\mathbf{x}
\tag{6.23}
$$

where ${}_t^0\mathbf{X}$ is the inverse deformation gradient. From (6.22) and (6.23) we obtain

$$
d^0\mathbf{x} = ({}_t^0\mathbf{X})({}_0^t\mathbf{X})\, d^0\mathbf{x}
\tag{6.24}
$$

and hence [because (6.24) must hold for any differential length $d^0\mathbf{x}$], we have

$$
{}_t^0\mathbf{X} = ({}_0^t\mathbf{X})^{-1}
\tag{6.25}
$$

Therefore, the inverse deformation gradient ${}_t^0\mathbf{X}$ is actually the inverse of *the* deformation gradient ${}_0^t\mathbf{X}$.

An application of (6.18) is given by the evaluation of the mass density ${}^t\rho$ of the body at time t, namely,

$$
{}^t\rho = \frac{{}^0\rho}{\det ({}_0^t\mathbf{X})}
\tag{6.26}
$$

We prove and illustrate this relationship in the following examples.

EXAMPLE 6.5:   Consider the general motion of the body in Fig. 6.2 and establish that the mass density of the body changes as a function of the determinant of the deformation gradient,

$$ {}^t\rho = \frac{{}^0\rho}{\det({}_0^t\mathbf{X})} $$

Any infinitesimal volume of material at time 0 can be represented using (see Fig. E6.5)

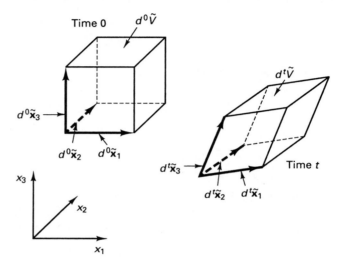

Figure E6.5   Infinitesimal volumes at times 0 and t

$$ d^0\tilde{\mathbf{x}}_1 = \begin{bmatrix} 1 \\ 0 \\ 0 \end{bmatrix} ds_1; \qquad d^0\tilde{\mathbf{x}}_2 = \begin{bmatrix} 0 \\ 1 \\ 0 \end{bmatrix} ds_2; \qquad d^0\tilde{\mathbf{x}}_3 = \begin{bmatrix} 0 \\ 0 \\ 1 \end{bmatrix} ds_3 $$

and
$$ d^0\tilde{V} = ds_1\, ds_2\, ds_3 $$

Using (6.22), we have after deformation,

$$ d^t\tilde{\mathbf{x}}_i = {}_0^t\mathbf{X}\, d^0\tilde{\mathbf{x}}_i \qquad i = 1, 2, 3 $$

where we note that of course the same deformation gradient applies to all material fibers of that infinitesimal volume, and we obtain

$$ d^t\tilde{V} = (d^t\tilde{\mathbf{x}}_1 \times d^t\tilde{\mathbf{x}}_2) \cdot d^t\tilde{\mathbf{x}}_3 $$
$$ = (\det {}_0^t\mathbf{X})\, ds_1\, ds_2\, ds_3 $$
$$ = \det {}_0^t\mathbf{X}\, d^0\tilde{V} $$

But if we assume that no mass is lost during the deformation, we have

$$ {}^t\rho\, d^t\tilde{V} = {}^0\rho\, d^0\tilde{V} $$

and hence,
$$ {}^t\rho = \frac{{}^0\rho}{\det {}_0^t\mathbf{X}} $$

EXAMPLE 6.6:   Consider the element in Fig. E6.6. Evaluate the deformation gradient and the mass density corresponding to the configuration at time t.

The displacement interpolation functions for this element were given in Fig. 5.4. Since the $^0x_1, ^0x_2$ axes correspond to the r, s axes, respectively, we have

$$h_1 = \tfrac{1}{4}(1 + {}^0x_1)(1 + {}^0x_2); \qquad h_2 = \tfrac{1}{4}(1 - {}^0x_1)(1 + {}^0x_2)$$

$$h_3 = \tfrac{1}{4}(1 - {}^0x_1)(1 - {}^0x_2); \qquad h_4 = \tfrac{1}{4}(1 + {}^0x_1)(1 - {}^0x_2)$$

and

$$\frac{\partial h_1}{\partial {}^0x_1} = \frac{1}{4}(1 + {}^0x_2); \qquad \frac{\partial h_2}{\partial {}^0x_1} = -\frac{1}{4}(1 + {}^0x_2)$$

$$\frac{\partial h_3}{\partial {}^0x_1} = -\frac{1}{4}(1 - {}^0x_2); \qquad \frac{\partial h_4}{\partial {}^0x_1} = \frac{1}{4}(1 - {}^0x_2)$$

$$\frac{\partial h_1}{\partial {}^0x_2} = \frac{1}{4}(1 + {}^0x_1); \qquad \frac{\partial h_2}{\partial {}^0x_2} = \frac{1}{4}(1 - {}^0x_1)$$

$$\frac{\partial h_3}{\partial {}^0x_2} = -\frac{1}{4}(1 - {}^0x_1); \qquad \frac{\partial h_4}{\partial {}^0x_2} = -\frac{1}{4}(1 + {}^0x_1)$$

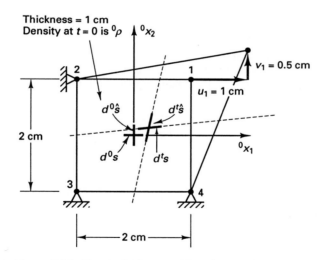

Figure E6.6   Four-node element subjected to large deformations

Now we use

$$^tx_i = \sum_{k=1}^{4} h_k \, {}^tx_i^k$$

and hence,

$$\frac{\partial {}^tx_i}{\partial {}^0x_j} = \sum_{k=1}^{4} \left(\frac{\partial h_k}{\partial {}^0x_j} \right) {}^tx_i^k$$

The nodal point coordinates at time t are

$$^tx_1^1 = 2; \qquad {}^tx_2^1 = 1.5; \qquad {}^tx_1^2 = -1; \qquad {}^tx_2^2 = 1$$

$$^tx_1^3 = -1; \qquad {}^tx_2^3 = -1; \qquad {}^tx_1^4 = 1; \qquad {}^tx_2^4 = -1$$

Hence,

$$\frac{\partial^t x_1}{\partial^0 x_1} = \frac{1}{4}[(1 + {}^0 x_2)(2) - (1 + {}^0 x_2)(-1) - (1 - {}^0 x_2)(-1) + (1 - {}^0 x_2)(1)]$$

$$= \frac{1}{4}(5 + {}^0 x_2)$$

and

$$\frac{\partial^t x_1}{\partial^0 x_2} = \frac{1}{4}(1 + {}^0 x_1); \qquad \frac{\partial^t x_2}{\partial^0 x_1} = \frac{1}{8}(1 + {}^0 x_2)$$

$$\frac{\partial^t x_2}{\partial^0 x_2} = \frac{1}{8}(9 + {}^0 x_1)$$

so that the deformation gradient is

$$_0^t \mathbf{X} = \frac{1}{4}\begin{bmatrix} (5 + {}^0 x_2) & (1 + {}^0 x_1) \\ \frac{1}{2}(1 + {}^0 x_2) & \frac{1}{2}(9 + {}^0 x_1) \end{bmatrix}$$

and using (6.26), the mass density in the deformed configuration is

$$^t\rho = \frac{32\,{}^0\rho}{(5 + {}^0 x_2)(9 + {}^0 x_1) - (1 + {}^0 x_1)(1 + {}^0 x_2)}$$

The deformation gradient is also used to measure the stretch of a material fiber and the change in angle between adjacent material fibers due to the deformation. In this calculation we use the *right Cauchy-Green deformation* tensor,

$$\boxed{{}_0^t \mathbf{C} = {}_0^t \mathbf{X}^T {}_0^t \mathbf{X}} \tag{6.27}$$

We note that ${}_0^t \mathbf{C}$ is, in general, not equal to the *left Cauchy-Green deformation* tensor,

$$_0^t \mathbf{B} = {}_0^t \mathbf{X} \, {}_0^t \mathbf{X}^T \tag{6.28}$$

EXAMPLE 6.7: The *stretch* ${}^t\lambda$ of a line element of a general body in motion is defined as ${}^t\lambda = d^t s / d^0 s$, where $d^0 s$ and $d^t s$ are the original and current lengths of the line element as shown in Fig. E6.7. Prove that

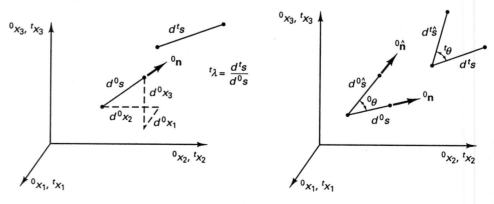

Figure E6.7 Stretch and rotation of line elements

$$'\lambda = ({}^0\mathbf{n}^T {}_0^t\mathbf{C} \, {}^0\mathbf{n})^{1/2} \tag{a}$$

where ${}^0\mathbf{n}$ is a vector of the direction cosines of the line element at time 0. Also, prove that considering two line elements emanating from the same material point, the angle $'\theta$ between the line elements at time t is given by

$$\cos '\theta = \frac{{}^0\mathbf{n}^T {}_0^t\mathbf{C} \, {}^0\hat{\mathbf{n}}}{'\lambda '\hat{\lambda}} \tag{b}$$

where the hat denotes the second line element (see Fig. E6.7).

As an example, apply the formulas in (a) and (b) to evaluate the stretches of the specific line elements d^0s and $d'\hat{s}$ shown in Fig. E6.6 and evaluate also the angular distortion between them.

To prove (a), we recognize that

$$(d's)^2 = d'\mathbf{x}^T \, d'\mathbf{x}; \qquad d'\mathbf{x} = {}_0^t\mathbf{X} \, d^0\mathbf{x}$$

so that using (6.27), $$(d's)^2 = d^0\mathbf{x}^T \, {}_0^t\mathbf{C} \, d^0\mathbf{x}$$

Hence, $$'\lambda^2 = \frac{d^0\mathbf{x}^T}{d^0s} \, {}_0^t\mathbf{C} \, \frac{d^0\mathbf{x}}{d^0s}$$

and since $${}^0\mathbf{n} = \frac{d^0\mathbf{x}}{d^0s}$$

we have $$'\lambda = ({}^0\mathbf{n}^T \, {}_0^t\mathbf{C} \, {}^0\mathbf{n})^{1/2}$$

To prove (b) we use (2.50)

$$d'\mathbf{x}^T \, d'\hat{\mathbf{x}} = (d's)(d'\hat{s}) \cos '\theta$$

Hence, $$\cos '\theta = \frac{d^0\mathbf{x}^T \, {}_0^t\mathbf{X}^T \, {}_0^t\hat{\mathbf{X}} \, d^0\hat{\mathbf{x}}}{(d's)(d'\hat{s})} \tag{c}$$

Since ${}_0^t\mathbf{X} \equiv {}_0^t\hat{\mathbf{X}}$ (it is the deformation gradient at the location of the differential line elements), we obtain from (c),

$$\cos '\theta = \frac{{}^0\mathbf{n}^T \, {}_0^t\mathbf{C} \, {}^0\hat{\mathbf{n}}}{'\lambda '\hat{\lambda}}$$

It should be noted that the relations in (a) and (b) show that when ${}_0^t\mathbf{C} = \mathbf{I}$, the stretches of the line elements are equal to 1 and the angle between line elements has not changed during the motion. Hence, when the Cauchy-Green deformation tensor is equal to the identity matrix, the motion could have been at most a rigid body motion.

If we apply (a) and (b) to the line elements depicted in Fig. E6.6, we obtain at ${}^0x_1 = 0$, ${}^0x_2 = 0$ (see Example 6.6)

$$ {}_0^t\mathbf{C} = \frac{1}{16}\begin{bmatrix} 25.25 & 7.25 \\ 7.25 & 21.25 \end{bmatrix}$$

$$ {}^0\mathbf{n} = \begin{bmatrix} 1 \\ 0 \end{bmatrix}; \qquad {}^0\hat{\mathbf{n}} = \begin{bmatrix} 0 \\ 1 \end{bmatrix}$$

Hence, using (a), $$'\lambda = 1.256; \qquad '\hat{\lambda} = 1.152$$

and using (b), $$\cos '\theta = 0.313; \qquad '\theta = 71.75°$$

Therefore, the angular distortion between the line elements d^0s and $d^0\hat{s}$ due to the motion from time 0 to time t is 18.25 degrees.

A most important property of the deformation gradient is that it can always be decomposed into a unique product of two matrices, a symmetric stretch matrix $_0^t\mathbf{U}$ and an orthogonal matrix $_0^t\mathbf{R}$ corresponding to a rotation such that

$$\boxed{\;_0^t\mathbf{X} = \;_0^t\mathbf{R}\;_0^t\mathbf{U}\;} \tag{6.29}$$

We can interpret (6.29), *conceptually*, to mean that the total deformation is obtained by first applying the stretch and then the rotation. That is, we could write (6.29) also as $_0^t\mathbf{X} = \;_\tau^t\mathbf{R}\;_0^t\mathbf{U}$, where τ corresponds to an intermediate (conceptual) time. Then we realize that the decomposition is really an application of the chain rule $_0^t\mathbf{X} = \;_\tau^t\mathbf{X}\;_0^\tau\mathbf{X}$, where $_\tau^t\mathbf{X} \equiv \;_\tau^t\mathbf{R}$ and $_0^\tau\mathbf{X} \equiv \;_0^\tau\mathbf{U}$. However, the state corresponding to τ is only conceptual, and we therefore usually use the notation in (6.29).

The relation in (6.29) is referred to as the *polar decomposition* of the deformation gradient, and we prove and demonstrate this property in the following examples.

To simplify the notation in the following discussion of continuum mechanics relations, we shall frequently not show the superscripts and subscripts t and 0 but always imply them, and when there is doubt, we shall also actually show them. For example, (6.29) is written as $\mathbf{X} = \mathbf{RU}$.

EXAMPLE 6.8:   Show that the deformation gradient $\mathbf{X}$ can always be decomposed as follows:

$$\mathbf{X} = \mathbf{RU} \tag{a}$$

where $\mathbf{R}$ is an orthogonal (rotation) matrix and $\mathbf{U}$ is a stretch (symmetric) matrix.

To prove the relationship in (a), we consider the Cauchy-Green deformation tensor $\mathbf{C}$ and represent this tensor in its principal coordinate axes. For this purpose we solve the eigenproblem

$$\mathbf{Cp} = \lambda\mathbf{p} \tag{b}$$

The complete solution of (b) can be written as (see Section 2.5)

$$\mathbf{CP} = \mathbf{PC'}$$

where the columns of $\mathbf{P}$ are the eigenvectors of $\mathbf{C}$, and $\mathbf{C'}$ is a diagonal matrix storing the corresponding eigenvalues. We also have

$$\mathbf{P}^T\mathbf{CP} = \mathbf{C'} \tag{c}$$

and $\mathbf{C'}$ is the representation of the Cauchy-Green deformation tensor in its principal coordinate axes. The representation of the deformation gradient in this coordinate system, denoted as $\mathbf{X'}$, is similarly obtained

$$\mathbf{X'} = \mathbf{P}^T\mathbf{XP} \tag{d}$$

where we note that (c) and (d) are really tensor transformations from the original to a new coordinate system (see Section 2.4).

Using these relations and $\mathbf{C} = \mathbf{X}^T\mathbf{X}$, we have

$$\mathbf{C'} = \mathbf{X'}^T\mathbf{X'}$$

and we note that the matrix

$$\mathbf{R'} = \mathbf{X'}(\mathbf{C'})^{-1/2}$$

is an orthogonal matrix; i.e., $\mathbf{R}'^T\mathbf{R}' = \mathbf{I}$. Hence, we can write

$$\mathbf{X}' = \mathbf{R}'\mathbf{U}' \qquad\qquad (e)$$

where

$$\mathbf{U}' = (\mathbf{C}')^{1/2}$$

and to evaluate $\mathbf{U}'$ we use the positive values of the square roots of the diagonal elements of $\mathbf{C}'$. The positive values must be used because the diagonal values in $\mathbf{U}'$ represent the stretches in the new coordinate system.

The relation in (e) is the decomposition of the deformation gradient $\mathbf{X}'$ into the product of the orthogonal matrix $\mathbf{R}'$ and the stretch matrix $\mathbf{U}'$. This decomposition has been accomplished in the principal axes of $\mathbf{C}$ but is also valid in any other (admissible) coordinate system because the deformation gradient is a tensor (see Section 2.4). Indeed, we can now obtain $\mathbf{R}$ and $\mathbf{U}$ directly corresponding to the decomposition in (a); i.e.,

$$\mathbf{R} = \mathbf{P}\mathbf{R}'\mathbf{P}^T$$

$$\mathbf{U} = \mathbf{P}\mathbf{U}'\mathbf{P}^T$$

where we used the inverse of the transformation employed in (d).

EXAMPLE 6.9: Consider the four-node element and its deformation shown in Fig. E6.9. (a) Evaluate the deformation gradient and its polar decomposition at time t. (b) Assume that the motion from time t to time $t + \Delta t$ consists only of a counterclockwise rigid body rotation of 45 degrees. Evaluate the new deformation gradient.

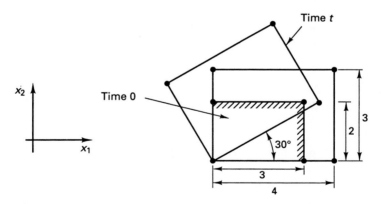

Figure E6.9   Four-node element subjected to stretching and rotation

To evaluate the deformation gradient at time t, we can here conveniently use ${}_0^t\mathbf{X} = {}_\tau^t\mathbf{R}\,{}_0^\tau\mathbf{U}$, where the hypothetical (or conceptual) configuration τ corresponds to the stretching of the fibers only. Hence,

$${}_\tau^t\mathbf{R} = \begin{bmatrix} \dfrac{\sqrt{3}}{2} & \dfrac{-1}{2} \\[2mm] \dfrac{1}{2} & \dfrac{\sqrt{3}}{2} \end{bmatrix}; \qquad {}_0^\tau\mathbf{U} = \begin{bmatrix} \dfrac{4}{3} & 0 \\[2mm] 0 & \dfrac{3}{2} \end{bmatrix}$$

and

$$ {}_0^t\mathbf{X} = \begin{bmatrix} \dfrac{2}{\sqrt{3}} & -\dfrac{3}{4} \\[2ex] \dfrac{2}{3} & \dfrac{3\sqrt{3}}{4} \end{bmatrix} $$

Of course, the same result is also obtained by writing ${}^t x_i$ in terms of ${}^0 x_j$, $i = 1, 2; j = 1, 2$, and using the definition of ${}_0^t\mathbf{X}$ given in (6.19).

Let us next subject the element to the counterclockwise rotation of 45 degrees. The deformation gradient is then

$$ {}_0^{t+\Delta t}\mathbf{X} = \begin{bmatrix} \cos 45° & -\sin 45° \\ \sin 45° & \cos 45° \end{bmatrix} \begin{bmatrix} \dfrac{2}{\sqrt{3}} & -\dfrac{3}{4} \\[2ex] \dfrac{2}{3} & \dfrac{3\sqrt{3}}{4} \end{bmatrix} $$

$$ = \frac{1}{\sqrt{2}} \begin{bmatrix} \dfrac{2\sqrt{3}-2}{3} & -\dfrac{3+3\sqrt{3}}{4} \\[2ex] \dfrac{2\sqrt{3}+2}{3} & \dfrac{-3+3\sqrt{3}}{4} \end{bmatrix} $$

The proof in Example 6.8 also indicates how any deformation gradient can be decomposed into the product in (6.29). Assume that $\mathbf{X}$ is given and we want to find $\mathbf{R}$ and $\mathbf{U}$; then we may calculate $\mathbf{C} = \mathbf{X}^T\mathbf{X} = \mathbf{U}^2$ and, using (2.109), we have (for $n = 2$ or 3), $\mathbf{U} = \sum_{i=1}^{n} \sqrt{\lambda_i}\, \mathbf{p}_i\mathbf{p}_i^T$ with $\mathbf{C}\mathbf{p}_i = \lambda_i\mathbf{p}_i$. With $\mathbf{U}$ given, we obtain $\mathbf{R}$ from $\mathbf{R} = \mathbf{X}\mathbf{U}^{-1}$.

The preceding relations can now be used to evaluate additional kinematic relations that describe the motion of the body. That is, it can be proven (see Exercise 6.7) that we also have

$$ \mathbf{X} = \mathbf{VR} \tag{6.30}^3 $$

where $\mathbf{V}$ is also a symmetric matrix

$$ \mathbf{V} = \mathbf{RUR}^T \tag{6.31} $$

We refer to $\mathbf{U}$ as the right stretch matrix and to $\mathbf{V}$ as the left stretch matrix.

Example 6.8 shows that we have the spectral decomposition of $\mathbf{U}$,

$$ \mathbf{U} = \mathbf{R}_L\mathbf{\Lambda}\mathbf{R}_L^T \tag{6.32} $$

Physically, $\mathbf{\Lambda}$ corresponds to the principal stretches and $\mathbf{R}_L$ stores the directions of these stretches, with the rigid body rotation removed since this rotation appears in $\mathbf{R}$. (In Example 6.8, the matrix $\mathbf{P}$ is equal to $\mathbf{R}_L$.) We also have

$$ \mathbf{V} = \mathbf{R}_E\mathbf{\Lambda}\mathbf{R}_E^T \tag{6.33} $$

where

$$ \mathbf{R}_E = \mathbf{RR}_L \tag{6.34} $$

We note that $\mathbf{R}_E$ stores the base vectors of the principal stretches in the stationary coordinate system x_i.

---

[3] Note that since we can write (6.30) as ${}_0^t\mathbf{X} = {}_t^t\mathbf{V}{}_0^t\mathbf{R}$, *conceptually*, the fibers can be thought of as being first rotated and then stretched [in contrast to the conceptual interpretation of (6.29)].

To proceed further with our description of the motion of the material particles in the body, we consider next the time rates of change of the quantities defined above. For this development we define

$$\dot{\mathbf{R}} = \mathbf{\Omega}_R \mathbf{R} \tag{6.35}$$

$$\dot{\mathbf{R}}_L = \mathbf{R}_L \mathbf{\Omega}_L \tag{6.36}$$

$$\dot{\mathbf{R}}_E = \mathbf{R}_E \mathbf{\Omega}_E \tag{6.37}$$

where $\mathbf{\Omega}_R$, $\mathbf{\Omega}_L$, and $\mathbf{\Omega}_E$ are skew-symmetric spin tensors, and clearly, using (6.34),

$$\mathbf{\Omega}_R = \mathbf{R}_E(\mathbf{\Omega}_E - \mathbf{\Omega}_L)\mathbf{R}_E^T \tag{6.38}$$

The *velocity gradient* $\mathbf{L}$ is defined as the gradient of the velocity field with respect to the *current* position ${}^t x_j$ of the material particles,

$$\mathbf{L} = \left[\frac{\partial {}^t \dot{u}_i}{\partial {}^t x_j} \right] \tag{6.39}$$

or

$$\mathbf{L} = \dot{\mathbf{X}} \mathbf{X}^{-1} \tag{6.40}$$

The symmetric part of $\mathbf{L}$ is the *velocity strain tensor* $\mathbf{D}$ (also called the rate-of-deformation tensor or stretching tensor), and the skew-symmetric part is the *spin tensor* $\mathbf{W}$ (also called the vorticity tensor). Hence,

$$\mathbf{L} = \mathbf{D} + \mathbf{W} \tag{6.41}$$

Using the polar decomposition of $\mathbf{X}$ we obtain from (6.40),

$$\mathbf{D} = \tfrac{1}{2}\mathbf{R}(\dot{\mathbf{U}}\mathbf{U}^{-1} + \mathbf{U}^{-1}\dot{\mathbf{U}})\mathbf{R}^T \tag{6.42}$$

$$\mathbf{W} = \mathbf{\Omega}_R + \tfrac{1}{2}\mathbf{R}(\dot{\mathbf{U}}\mathbf{U}^{-1} - \mathbf{U}^{-1}\dot{\mathbf{U}})\mathbf{R}^T \tag{6.43}$$

Substituting for $\mathbf{U}$ from (6.32), we can write

$$\mathbf{D} = \mathbf{R}_E \mathbf{D}_E \mathbf{R}_E^T \tag{6.44}$$

$$\mathbf{W} = \mathbf{R}_E \mathbf{W}_E \mathbf{R}_E^T \tag{6.45}$$

where

$$\mathbf{D}_E = \dot{\mathbf{\Lambda}}\mathbf{\Lambda}^{-1} + \tfrac{1}{2}(\mathbf{\Lambda}^{-1}\mathbf{\Omega}_L\mathbf{\Lambda} - \mathbf{\Lambda}\mathbf{\Omega}_L\mathbf{\Lambda}^{-1}) \tag{6.46}$$

$$\mathbf{W}_E = \mathbf{\Omega}_E - \tfrac{1}{2}(\mathbf{\Lambda}^{-1}\mathbf{\Omega}_L\mathbf{\Lambda} + \mathbf{\Lambda}\mathbf{\Omega}_L\mathbf{\Lambda}^{-1}) \tag{6.47}$$

Hence, we obtain for the elements of $\dot{\mathbf{\Lambda}}$,

$$[\dot{\mathbf{\Lambda}}]_{\alpha\alpha} = \lambda_\alpha[\mathbf{D}_E]_{\alpha\alpha} \qquad \text{no sum on } \alpha \tag{6.48}$$

where the λ_α are the stretches, and for the elements of $\mathbf{\Omega}_L$ and $\mathbf{\Omega}_E$, assuming that $\lambda_\alpha \neq \lambda_\beta$,

$$[\mathbf{\Omega}_L]_{\alpha\beta} = \frac{2\lambda_\beta\lambda_\alpha}{\lambda_\beta^2 - \lambda_\alpha^2}[\mathbf{D}_E]_{\alpha\beta} \tag{6.49}$$

$$[\mathbf{\Omega}_E]_{\alpha\beta} = [\mathbf{W}_E]_{\alpha\beta} + \frac{\lambda_\beta^2 + \lambda_\alpha^2}{\lambda_\beta^2 - \lambda_\alpha^2}[\mathbf{D}_E]_{\alpha\beta} \tag{6.50}$$

We note that $\mathbf{D}_E$ and $\mathbf{W}_E$ are the velocity strain and spin tensors referred to the principal axes of the deformation at time t. Hence, by representing the velocity strain and spin tensors in the basis given by $\mathbf{R}_E$, we obtain relationships that we can use directly to evaluate the components of $\dot{\mathbf{\Lambda}}$, $\mathbf{\Omega}_L$, and $\mathbf{\Omega}_E$.

We now want to define strain tensors that are valuable in finite element analysis. The *Green-Lagrange strain* tensor $_0^t\boldsymbol{\epsilon}$ is defined as

$$_0^t\boldsymbol{\epsilon} = {}_0^t\mathbf{R}_L[\tfrac{1}{2}(^t\boldsymbol{\Lambda}^2 - \mathbf{I})]_0^t\mathbf{R}_L^T \tag{6.51}$$

The *Hencky (or logarithmic) strain* tensor is defined as

$$_0^t\mathbf{E}^H = {}_0^t\mathbf{R}_L(\ln {}^t\boldsymbol{\Lambda})_0^t\mathbf{R}_L^T \tag{6.52}$$

We note that since $_0^t\mathbf{R}$ does not enter the definitions in (6.51) and (6.52), both strain tensors are independent of the rigid body motions of the particles.

The Green-Lagrange strain tensor is frequently written in terms of the right stretch tensor $_0^t\mathbf{U}$; that is, using (6.51), we obtain

$$\boxed{\begin{aligned}
_0^t\boldsymbol{\epsilon} &= \tfrac{1}{2}[(_0^t\mathbf{R}_L {}^t\boldsymbol{\Lambda} {}_0^t\mathbf{R}_L^T)(_0^t\mathbf{R}_L {}^t\boldsymbol{\Lambda} {}_0^t\mathbf{R}_L^T) - \mathbf{I}] \\
&= \tfrac{1}{2}(_0^t\mathbf{U} {}_0^t\mathbf{U} - \mathbf{I})
\end{aligned}} \tag{6.53}$$

Also, we can write the Green-Lagrange strain tensor in terms of the Cauchy-Green deformation tensor,

$$\begin{aligned}
_0^t\boldsymbol{\epsilon} &= \tfrac{1}{2}(_0^t\mathbf{U} {}_0^t\mathbf{R}^T {}_0^t\mathbf{R} {}_0^t\mathbf{U} - \mathbf{I}) \\
&= \tfrac{1}{2}(_0^t\mathbf{X}^T {}_0^t\mathbf{X} - \mathbf{I}) \\
&= \tfrac{1}{2}(_0^t\mathbf{C} - \mathbf{I})
\end{aligned} \tag{6.54}$$

Furthermore, evaluating the components in terms of displacements [i.e., using (6.16) and (6.19) in (6.54)], we have,

$$\boxed{_0^t\epsilon_{ij} = \tfrac{1}{2}(_0^t u_{i,j} + {}_0^t u_{j,i} + {}_0^t u_{k,i} {}_0^t u_{k,j})} \tag{6.55}$$

We should note that in the definition of the Green-Lagrange strain tensor, all derivatives are with respect to the *initial* coordinates of the material particles. For this reason, we say that the strain tensor is defined with respect to the initial coordinates of the body. Also note that, although only up to quadratic terms of displacement derivatives appear in (6.55), this is the complete strain tensor; i.e., we have not neglected any higher-order terms.

The Green-Lagrange and Hencky strain tensors are clearly of the general form

$$\mathbf{E}_g = \mathbf{R}_L g(\boldsymbol{\Lambda})\mathbf{R}_L^T \tag{6.56}$$

where $g(\boldsymbol{\Lambda}) = \mathrm{diag}\,[g(\lambda_i)]$. Hence, the rate of change of the strain tensors can be written as

$$\dot{\mathbf{E}}_g = \mathbf{R}_L \dot{\mathbf{E}}_L \mathbf{R}_L^T \tag{6.57}$$

where we have

$$\dot{\mathbf{E}}_L = \dot{\boldsymbol{\Lambda}} g'(\boldsymbol{\Lambda}) + \boldsymbol{\Omega}_L g(\boldsymbol{\Lambda}) - g(\boldsymbol{\Lambda})\boldsymbol{\Omega}_L \tag{6.58}$$

Expanding this equation, we can identify the components of $\dot{\mathbf{E}}_L$ as

$$[\dot{\mathbf{E}}_L]_{\alpha\beta} = \gamma_{\alpha\beta}[\mathbf{D}_E]_{\alpha\beta} \tag{6.59}$$

where for the Green-Lagrange strain tensor,

$$\gamma_{\alpha\beta} = \lambda_\alpha \lambda_\beta \tag{6.60}$$

and for the Hencky strain tensor,

$$\lambda_{\alpha\beta} = \begin{cases} 1 & \text{if } \lambda_\alpha = \lambda_\beta \\ \dfrac{2\lambda_\alpha \lambda_\beta}{\lambda_\beta^2 - \lambda_\alpha^2} \ln \dfrac{\lambda_\beta}{\lambda_\alpha} & \text{otherwise} \end{cases} \tag{6.61}$$

Using (6.57) and (6.59), we can now establish an important relationship between the time rate of change of the Green-Lagrange strain tensor ${}_0^t\dot{\boldsymbol{\epsilon}}$ and the velocity strain tensor ${}^t\mathbf{D}$. Using (6.57), (6.59), (6.60), and (6.44), we obtain

$$ {}_0^t\mathbf{R}_L^T \, {}_0^t\dot{\boldsymbol{\epsilon}} \, {}_0^t\mathbf{R}_L = {}^t\boldsymbol{\Lambda} \, {}_0^t\mathbf{R}_E^T \, {}^t\mathbf{D} \, {}_0^t\mathbf{R}_E \, {}^t\boldsymbol{\Lambda} \tag{6.62}$$

and hence, using (6.32) and (6.34),

$$\boxed{ {}_0^t\dot{\boldsymbol{\epsilon}} = {}_0^t\mathbf{X}^T \, {}^t\mathbf{D} \, {}_0^t\mathbf{X} }$$

$$\boxed{ {}^t\mathbf{D} = {}_t^0\mathbf{X}^T \, {}_0^t\dot{\boldsymbol{\epsilon}} \, {}_t^0\mathbf{X} } \tag{6.63}$$

or in component form (with super- and subscripts)

$$\boxed{ {}_0^t\dot{\epsilon}_{ij} = {}_0^t x_{m,i} \, {}_0^t x_{n,j} \, {}^t D_{mn} }$$

$$\boxed{ {}^t D_{mn} = {}_t^0 x_{i,m} \, {}_t^0 x_{j,n} \, {}_0^t\dot{\epsilon}_{ij} } \tag{6.64}$$

Of course, we can obtain the same result, but with less insight, by simply differentiating the Green-Lagrange strain tensor with respect to time,

$$ {}_0^t\dot{\boldsymbol{\epsilon}} = \tfrac{1}{2}({}_0^t\dot{\mathbf{X}}^T \, {}_0^t\mathbf{X} + {}_0^t\mathbf{X}^T \, {}_0^t\dot{\mathbf{X}}) \tag{6.65}$$

Using (6.40) and (6.41) to substitute into (6.65), we directly obtain (6.63). We demonstrate this derivation for virtual displacement increments, or variations in the current displacements, in the following example.

> **EXAMPLE 6.10:** Consider a body in its deformed configuration at time t (see Fig. E6.10). The current coordinates of the material particles of the body are ${}^t x_i$, $i = 1, 2, 3$, and the current displacements are ${}^t u_i = {}^t x_i - {}^0 x_i$.
>
> Assume that a virtual displacement field is applied, which we denote as δu_i (see Fig. E6.10). This virtual displacement field can be thought of as a variation on the current displacements; hence, we may write $\delta u_i \equiv \delta {}^t u_i$. However, the variation on the current displacements must correspond to a variation on the current Green-Lagrange strain components, $\delta {}_0^t\epsilon_{ij}$, and also to a small strain tensor $\delta_t e_{mn}$ referred to the current configuration. Evaluate the components $\delta {}_0^t\epsilon_{ij}$ and show that
>
> $$\delta {}_0^t\epsilon_{ij} = {}_0^t x_{m,i} \, {}_0^t x_{n,j} \, \delta_t e_{mn} \tag{a}$$

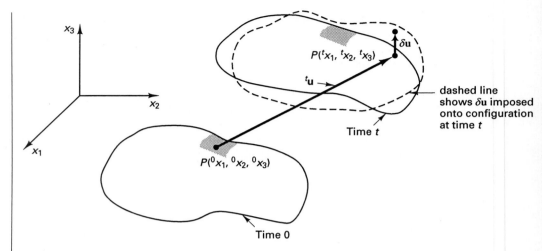

Figure E6.10 Body at time t subjected to virtual displacement field given by $\delta\mathbf{u}$. Note that $\delta\mathbf{u}$ is a function of ${}^t x_i$, $i = 1,2,3$, and we can think of δu_i as a variation on ${}^t u_i$.

where

$$\delta_t e_{mn} = \frac{1}{2}\left(\frac{\partial \delta u_m}{\partial {}^t x_n} + \frac{\partial \delta u_n}{\partial {}^t x_m}\right)$$

We use the definition of the Green-Lagrange strain in (6.54) to obtain

$$\delta{}_0^t\boldsymbol{\epsilon} = \tfrac{1}{2}[(\delta{}_0^t\mathbf{X}^T)({}_0^t\mathbf{X}) + ({}_0^t\mathbf{X}^T)(\delta{}_0^t\mathbf{X})] \qquad \text{(b)}$$

Let us define $\delta_t\mathbf{u}$ to be

$$\delta_t\mathbf{u} = \begin{bmatrix} \dfrac{\partial \delta u_1}{\partial {}^t x_1} & \dfrac{\partial \delta u_1}{\partial {}^t x_2} & \cdots \\[2ex] \dfrac{\partial \delta u_2}{\partial {}^t x_1} & \dfrac{\partial \delta u_2}{\partial {}^t x_2} & \cdots \\[1ex] & \cdots & \end{bmatrix}$$

then

$$\delta{}_0^t\mathbf{X} = \delta_t\mathbf{u}\ {}_0^t\mathbf{X}$$

and hence (b) can be written as

$$\begin{aligned}
\delta{}_0^t\boldsymbol{\epsilon} &= \tfrac{1}{2}[{}_0^t\mathbf{X}^T(\delta_t\mathbf{u})^T\ {}_0^t\mathbf{X} + {}_0^t\mathbf{X}^T(\delta_t\mathbf{u}){}_0^t\mathbf{X}] \\
&= {}_0^t\mathbf{X}^T\{\tfrac{1}{2}[(\delta_t\mathbf{u})^T + \delta_t\mathbf{u}]\}{}_0^t\mathbf{X} \\
&= {}_0^t\mathbf{X}^T\ \delta_t\mathbf{e}\ {}_0^t\mathbf{X}
\end{aligned}$$

which is (a) in matrix form.

Note that a simple closed-form relationship cannot be established between the time rate of change of the Hencky strain tensor and the velocity strain tensor [because of the complex expression in (6.61)]. We shall use the Hencky strain measure only later for large strain inelastic analysis, and the appropriate relationships will then be evaluated based on work conjugacy (see Section 6.6.4).

However, we shall use the Green-Lagrange strain tensor frequently and now want to define the appropriate stress tensor to use with this strain tensor. The stress measure to use is the *second Piola-Kirchhoff stress* tensor ${}_0^t\mathbf{S}$, which is work-conjugate with the Green-Lagrange strain tensor.[4]

Consider the stress power per unit reference volume ${}^t J \, {}^t\boldsymbol{\tau} \cdot {}^t\mathbf{D}$,[5] where ${}^t\boldsymbol{\tau}$ is the Cauchy stress tensor and ${}^t J = \det {}_0^t\mathbf{X}$. Then the second Piola-Kirchhoff stress tensor ${}_0^t\mathbf{S}$ is given by

$$
{}^t J \, {}^t\boldsymbol{\tau} \cdot {}^t\mathbf{D} = {}_0^t\mathbf{S} \cdot {}_0^t\dot{\boldsymbol{\epsilon}} \tag{6.66}
$$

To find the explicit expression for ${}_0^t\mathbf{S}$, we substitute from (6.63) to obtain

$$
{}^t J \, {}^t\boldsymbol{\tau} \cdot {}^t\mathbf{D} = {}_0^t\mathbf{S} \cdot ({}_0^t\mathbf{X}^T \, {}^t\mathbf{D} \, {}_0^t\mathbf{X}) \tag{6.67}
$$

Since this relationship must hold for any ${}^t\mathbf{D}$, we have[6]

$$
\boxed{{}_0^t\mathbf{S} = \frac{{}^0\rho}{{}^t\rho} {}_t^0\mathbf{X} \, {}^t\boldsymbol{\tau} \, {}_t^0\mathbf{X}^T}
$$

$$
\boxed{{}^t\boldsymbol{\tau} = \frac{{}^t\rho}{{}^0\rho} {}_0^t\mathbf{X} \, {}_0^t\mathbf{S} \, {}_0^t\mathbf{X}^T} \tag{6.68}
$$

or in component forms

$$
\boxed{{}_0^t S_{ij} = \frac{{}^0\rho}{{}^t\rho} {}_t^0 x_{i,m} \, {}_t^0 x_{j,n} \, {}^t\tau_{mn}}
$$

$$
\boxed{{}^t\tau_{mn} = \frac{{}^t\rho}{{}^0\rho} {}_0^t x_{m,i} \, {}_0^t x_{n,j} \, {}_0^t S_{ij}} \tag{6.69}
$$

There has been much discussion about the physical nature of the second Piola-Kirchhoff stress tensor. However, although it is possible to relate the transformation on the Cauchy stress tensor in (6.68) to some geometry arguments as discussed in the next example, it should be recognized that the second Piola-Kirchhoff stresses have little physical meaning and, in practice, Cauchy stresses must be calculated.

---

[4] We use extensively in this book the second Piola-Kirchhoff stress tensor ${}_0^t\mathbf{S}$ defined by (6.66) and (6.68). The first Piola-Kirchhoff stress tensor is given by ${}_0^t\mathbf{S} \, {}_0^t\mathbf{X}^T$ (or the transpose thereof). In addition, we also have the Kirchhoff stress tensor given by ${}^t J \, {}^t\boldsymbol{\tau}$ (see, for example, L. E. Malvern [A]).

[5] Note that here and in the following we use the notation that with **a** and **b** second-order tensors we have $\mathbf{a} \cdot \mathbf{b} = a_{ij} b_{ij}$ [sum over all i, j; see (2.79)].

[6] Here we use ${}_0^t\mathbf{S} \cdot ({}_0^t\mathbf{X}^T \, {}^t\mathbf{D} \, {}_0^t\mathbf{X}) = ({}_0^t\mathbf{X} \, {}_0^t\mathbf{S} \, {}_0^t\mathbf{X}^T) \cdot {}^t\mathbf{D}$, as can be easily proven by writing the matrices in component forms (see Exercise 2.14).

EXAMPLE 6.11: Figure E6.11 shows a generic body in the configurations at times 0 and t. Let $d'\mathbf{T}$ be the actual force on a surface area $d'S$ in the configuration at time t, and let us define a (fictitious) force

$$d^0\mathbf{T} = {}^0_t\mathbf{X}\, d'\mathbf{T}; \qquad {}^0_t\mathbf{X} = \left[\frac{\partial\, {}^0x_i}{\partial\, {}^tx_j}\right] \tag{a}$$

which acts on the surface area d^0S, where d^0S has become $d'S$ and ${}^0_t\mathbf{X}$ is the inverse of the deformation gradient, ${}^0_t\mathbf{X} = {}^t_0\mathbf{X}^{-1}$. Show that the second Piola-Kirchhoff stresses measured in the original configuration are the stress components corresponding to $d^0\mathbf{T}$.

Let the unit normals to the surface areas d^0S and $d'S$ be ${}^0\mathbf{n}$ and ${}'\mathbf{n}$, respectively. Force equilibrium (of the wedge ABC in Fig. E6.11) in the configuration at time t requires that

$$d'\mathbf{T} = {}^t\boldsymbol{\tau}^T\, {}'\mathbf{n}\, d'S \tag{b}$$

and similarly in the configuration at time 0

$$d^0\mathbf{T} = {}^t_0\mathbf{S}^T\, {}^0\mathbf{n}\, d^0S \tag{c}$$

The relations in (b) and (c) are referred to as *Cauchy's formula*. However, it can be shown that the following kinematic relationship exists:

$$ {}'\mathbf{n}\, d'S = \frac{{}^0\rho}{{}^t\rho}\, {}^0_t\mathbf{X}^T\, {}^0\mathbf{n}\, d^0S \tag{d}$$

This relation is referred to as *Nanson's formula*. Now using (a) to (d), we obtain

$$ {}^t_0\mathbf{S}^T\, {}^0\mathbf{n}\, d^0S = {}^0_t\mathbf{X}\, {}^t\boldsymbol{\tau}^T \frac{{}^0\rho}{{}^t\rho}\, {}^0_t\mathbf{X}^T\, {}^0\mathbf{n}\, d^0S $$

or

$$\left({}^t_0\mathbf{S}^T - \frac{{}^0\rho}{{}^t\rho}\, {}^0_t\mathbf{X}\, {}^t\boldsymbol{\tau}^T\, {}^0_t\mathbf{X}^T \right){}^0\mathbf{n}\, d^0S = \mathbf{0}$$

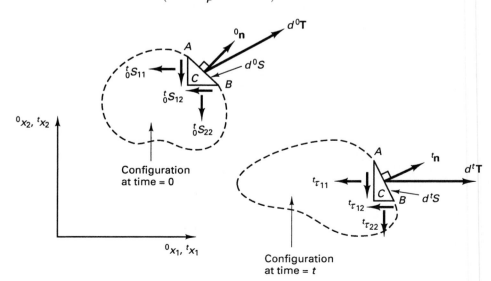

Figure E6.11   Second Piola-Kirchhoff and Cauchy stresses in two-dimensional action

However, this relationship must hold for any surface area and also any "interior surface area" that could be created by a cut in the body. Hence, the normal $^0\mathbf{n}$ is arbitrary and can be chosen to be in succession equal to the unit coordinate vectors. It follows that

$$_0^t\mathbf{S} = \frac{^0\rho}{^t\rho} {}_t^0\mathbf{X} \, {}^t\boldsymbol{\tau} \, {}_t^0\mathbf{X}^T$$

where we used the property that the matrices $^t\boldsymbol{\tau}$ and $_0^t\mathbf{S}$ are symmetric.

Finally, we may interpret the force defined in (a). We note that the force $d^0\mathbf{T}$, which is balanced by the second Piola-Kirchhoff stresses on the wedge ABC, is related to the actual force $d^t\mathbf{T}$ in the same way as an original fiber in d^0S is deformed

$$d^0\mathbf{x} = {}_t^0\mathbf{X} \, d^t\mathbf{x}$$

We may therefore say that in using (a) to obtain $d^0\mathbf{T}$, the force $d^t\mathbf{T}$ is "stretched and rotated" in the same way that $d^t\mathbf{x}$ is stretched and rotated to obtain $d^0\mathbf{x}$.

We note that the components of the Green-Lagrange strain tensor and second Piola-Kirchhoff stress tensor do not change when the material is subjected to only a rigid body translation because such motion does not change the deformation gradient.

The definition of the second Piola-Kirchhoff stress tensor also implies that the components do not change when the body being considered is undergoing a rigid body rotation. Since the invariance of the Green-Lagrange strain tensor components and second Piola-Kirchhoff stress tensor components in rigid body rotations is of great importance, we consider these properties in the following four examples.

Of course, the invariance of the Green-Lagrange strain tensor components with respect to rigid body rotations already follows from (6.53), since, as we pointed out earlier, the rigid body rotation of the fibers expressed in the matrix $_0^t\mathbf{R}$ does not enter the definition of (6.53). To gain further insight, let us consider the following example.

EXAMPLE 6.12:   Show that the components of the Green-Lagrange strain tensor are invariant under a rigid body rotation of the material.

Let the Green-Lagrange strain tensor components at time t be given by

$$_0^t\boldsymbol{\epsilon} = \tfrac{1}{2}({}_0^t\mathbf{X}^T {}_0^t\mathbf{X} - \mathbf{I}) \tag{a}$$

where $_0^t\mathbf{X}$ is the deformation gradient at time t corresponding to the *stationary* coordinate system x_i, $i = 1, 2, 3$.

Assume that the material is subjected to a rigid body rotation from time t to time $t + \Delta t$. Then corresponding to the stationary coordinate system x_i, we have

$$^{t+\Delta t}_{0}\mathbf{X} = \mathbf{R} \, {}_0^t\mathbf{X} \tag{b}$$

where $\mathbf{R}$ corresponds to the rotation, and then

$$^{t+\Delta t}_{0}\boldsymbol{\epsilon} = \tfrac{1}{2}({}^{t+\Delta t}_{0}\mathbf{X}^T \, {}^{t+\Delta t}_{0}\mathbf{X} - \mathbf{I}) \tag{c}$$

Substituting (b) into (c) and comparing the result with (a), we obtain

$$^{t+\Delta t}_{0}\boldsymbol{\epsilon} = {}_0^t\boldsymbol{\epsilon}$$

EXAMPLE 6.13:   A four-node element is stretched until time t and then undergoes without distortion a large rigid body rotation from time t to time $t + \Delta t$ as depicted in Fig. E6.13. Show explicitly that for the element the components of the Green-Lagrange strain tensor at time t and time $t + \Delta t$ are exactly equal.

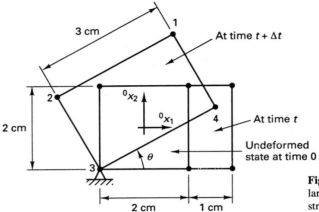

Figure E6.13   Element subjected to large rigid body rotation after initial stretch

The Green-Lagrange strain components at time t can be evaluated by inspection using (6.51),

$$_0^t\epsilon_{22} = 0; \qquad _0^t\epsilon_{12} = {}_0^t\epsilon_{21} = 0$$

and

$$_0^t\epsilon_{11} = \frac{1}{2}\left[\left(\frac{3}{2}\right)^2 - 1\right]$$

$$= \tfrac{5}{8}$$

Hence,

$$_0^t\boldsymbol{\epsilon} = \begin{bmatrix} \frac{5}{8} & 0 \\ 0 & 0 \end{bmatrix}$$

Alternatively, we can use (6.54), where we first evaluate the deformation gradient as in Example 6.6:

$$_0^t\mathbf{X} = \begin{bmatrix} \frac{3}{2} & 0 \\ 0 & 1 \end{bmatrix}$$

Hence,

$$_0^t\mathbf{C} = \begin{bmatrix} \frac{9}{4} & 0 \\ 0 & 1 \end{bmatrix}$$

and as before,

$$_0^t\boldsymbol{\epsilon} = \begin{bmatrix} \frac{5}{8} & 0 \\ 0 & 1 \end{bmatrix} \tag{a}$$

After the rigid body rotation the nodal point coordinates are

Node	$^{t+\Delta t}x_1$	$^{t+\Delta t}x_2$
1	$3\cos\theta - 1 - 2\sin\theta$	$3\sin\theta - 1 + 2\cos\theta$
2	$-1 - 2\sin\theta$	$2\cos\theta - 1$
3	-1	-1
4	$3\cos\theta - 1$	$3\sin\theta - 1$

Thus, using again the procedure in Example 6.6 to evaluate the deformation gradient, we obtain

$$
{}^{t+\Delta t}_{0}\mathbf{X} = \frac{1}{4}
\left[
\begin{array}{c|c}
\begin{array}{l}
(1 + {}^0x_2)(3\cos\theta - 1 - 2\sin\theta) \\
-(1 + {}^0x_2)(-1 - 2\sin\theta) \\
-(1 - {}^0x_2)(-1) \\
+(1 - {}^0x_2)(3\cos\theta - 1)
\end{array}
&
\begin{array}{l}
(1 + {}^0x_1)(3\cos\theta - 1 - 2\sin\theta) \\
+(1 - {}^0x_1)(-1 - 2\sin\theta) \\
-(1 - {}^0x_1)(-1) \\
-(1 + {}^0x_1)(3\cos\theta - 1)
\end{array}
\\ \hline
\begin{array}{l}
(1 + {}^0x_2)(3\sin\theta - 1 + 2\cos\theta) \\
-(1 + {}^0x_2)(2\cos\theta - 1) \\
-(1 - {}^0x_2)(-1) \\
+(1 - {}^0x_2)(3\sin\theta - 1)
\end{array}
&
\begin{array}{l}
(1 + {}^0x_1)(3\sin\theta - 1 + 2\cos\theta) \\
+(1 - {}^0x_1)(2\cos\theta - 1) \\
-(1 - {}^0x_1)(-1) \\
-(1 + {}^0x_1)(3\sin\theta - 1)
\end{array}
\end{array}
\right]
\quad\text{(b)}
$$

or

$$
{}^{t+\Delta t}_{0}\mathbf{X} =
\begin{bmatrix}
\frac{3}{2}\cos\theta & -\sin\theta \\
\frac{3}{2}\sin\theta & \cos\theta
\end{bmatrix}
\quad\text{(c)}
$$

In reference to (6.29) we note that this deformation gradient can be written as

$$
{}^{t+\Delta t}_{0}\mathbf{X} = {}^{t+\Delta t}_{t}\mathbf{R} \; {}^t_0\mathbf{U}
\quad\text{(d)}
$$

where

$$
{}^{t+\Delta t}_{t}\mathbf{R} =
\begin{bmatrix}
\cos\theta & -\sin\theta \\
\sin\theta & \cos\theta
\end{bmatrix};
\qquad
{}^t_0\mathbf{U} =
\begin{bmatrix}
\frac{3}{2} & 0 \\
0 & 1
\end{bmatrix}
$$

This decomposition certainly corresponds to the actual physical situation, in which we measured a stretch in the ${}^0x_1$ direction and then a rotation. Therefore, we could have established ${}^{t+\Delta t}_{0}\mathbf{X}$ using (d) instead of performing all the calculations leading to (b) and thus (c)!

Using (d) and (6.27), we obtain

$$
{}^{t+\Delta t}_{0}\mathbf{C} =
\begin{bmatrix}
\frac{9}{4} & 0 \\
0 & 1
\end{bmatrix}
$$

and thus using (6.54), we have

$$
{}^{t+\Delta t}_{0}\boldsymbol{\epsilon} =
\begin{bmatrix}
\frac{5}{8} & 0 \\
0 & 0
\end{bmatrix}
\quad\text{(e)}
$$

Hence ${}^t_0\boldsymbol{\epsilon}$ in (a) is equal to ${}^{t+\Delta t}_{0}\boldsymbol{\epsilon}$ in (e), which shows that the Green-Lagrange strain components did not change as a result of the rigid body rotation.

EXAMPLE 6.14: Show that the components of the second Piola-Kirchhoff stress tensor are invariant under a rigid body rotation of the material.

Here we consider a stationary coordinate system x_i, $i = 1, 2, 3$ and assume that the second Piola-Kirchhoff stress components are given in ${}^t_0\mathbf{S}$. Let the Cauchy stress, deformation gradient, and mass density at time t be ${}^t\boldsymbol{\tau}$, ${}^t_0\mathbf{X}$, and ${}^t\rho$. Hence,

$$
{}^t_0\mathbf{S} = \frac{{}^0\rho}{{}^t\rho} \, {}^t_0\mathbf{X} \, {}^t\boldsymbol{\tau} \, {}^t_0\mathbf{X}^T
\quad\text{(a)}
$$

where ${}^0_t\mathbf{X}$ is the inverse deformation gradient.

If a rigid body rotation is applied to the material from time t to time $t + \Delta t$, the deformation gradient changes to

$$
{}^{t+\Delta t}_{0}\mathbf{X} = \mathbf{R} \, {}^t_0\mathbf{X}
$$

where $\mathbf{R}$ is an orthogonal (rotation) matrix, and hence

$$
{}^0_{t+\Delta t}\mathbf{X} = {}^0_t\mathbf{X}\mathbf{R}^T
\quad\text{(b)}
$$

Equations (a) and (b) show that

$$^{t+\Delta t}_{0}\mathbf{S} = \frac{^{0}\rho}{^{t}\rho} {}^{0}_{t}\mathbf{X}\mathbf{R}^{T} \, {}^{t+\Delta t}\mathbf{\tau}\, \mathbf{R} \, {}^{0}_{t}\mathbf{X}^{T} \tag{c}$$

During the rigid body rotation of the material, the stress components remain constant in the rotating coordinate system. Hence the Cauchy stresses at time $t + \Delta t$ are in the fixed coordinate system,

$$^{t+\Delta t}\mathbf{\tau} = \mathbf{R} \, {}^{t}\mathbf{\tau}\mathbf{R}^{T} \tag{d}$$

Substituting from (d) into (c), we obtain

$$^{t+\Delta t}_{0}\mathbf{S} = \frac{^{0}\rho}{^{t}\rho} {}^{0}_{t}\mathbf{X}^{T} \, {}^{t}\mathbf{\tau} \, {}^{0}_{t}\mathbf{X}^{T}$$

which completes the proof. Note that the reason for the second Piola-Kirchhoff stress components not to change is that the same matrix $\mathbf{R}$ is used in equations (b) and (d).

EXAMPLE 6.15:   Figure E6.15 shows a four-node element in the configuration at time 0. The element is subjected to a stress (initial stress) of $^{0}\tau_{11}$. Assume that the element is rotated in time 0 to time Δt as a rigid body through a large angle θ and that the stress in a body-attached coordinate system does not change. Hence, the magnitude of $^{\Delta t}\bar{\tau}_{11}$ shown in Fig. E6.15 is equal to $^{0}\tau_{11}$. Show that the components of the second Piola-Kirchhoff stress tensor did not change as a result of the rigid body rotation.

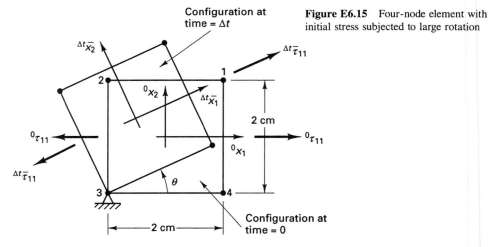

Figure E6.15   Four-node element with initial stress subjected to large rotation

The second Piola-Kirchhoff stress tensor at time 0 is equal to the Cauchy stress tensor because the element deformations are zero,

$$^{0}_{0}\mathbf{S} = \begin{bmatrix} ^{0}\tau_{11} & 0 \\ 0 & 0 \end{bmatrix} \tag{a}$$

The components of the Cauchy stress tensor at time Δt expressed in the coordinate axes $^{0}x_{1}$, $^{0}x_{2}$ are

$$^{\Delta t}\mathbf{\tau} = \begin{bmatrix} \cos\theta & -\sin\theta \\ \sin\theta & \cos\theta \end{bmatrix} \begin{bmatrix} ^{\Delta t}\bar{\tau}_{11} & 0 \\ 0 & 0 \end{bmatrix} \begin{bmatrix} \cos\theta & \sin\theta \\ -\sin\theta & \cos\theta \end{bmatrix} \tag{b}$$

This transformation corresponds to a second-order tensor transformation of the components $^{\Delta t}\bar{\tau}_{ij}$ from the body-attached coordinate frame $^{\Delta t}\bar{x}_1$, $^{\Delta t}\bar{x}_2$ to the stationary coordinate frame $^0x_1$, $^0x_2$ (see Section 2.4).

The relation between the Cauchy stresses and the second Piola-Kirchhoff stresses at time Δt is, according to (6.68),

$$^{\Delta t}\boldsymbol{\tau} = \frac{^{\Delta t}\rho}{^0\rho} \, {}^{\Delta t}_0\mathbf{X} \, {}^{\Delta t}_0\mathbf{S} \, {}^{\Delta t}_0\mathbf{X}^T \tag{c}$$

where in this case $^{\Delta t}\rho/^0\rho = 1$. The deformation gradient can be evaluated as in Example 6.6, where we note that the nodal point coordinates at time t are

$$^{\Delta t}x_1^1 = 2\cos\theta - 1 - 2\sin\theta; \qquad ^{\Delta t}x_2^1 = 2\sin\theta - 1 + 2\cos\theta$$

$$^{\Delta t}x_1^2 = -1 - 2\sin\theta; \qquad ^{\Delta t}x_2^2 = 2\cos\theta - 1$$

$$^{\Delta t}x_1^3 = -1; \qquad ^{\Delta t}x_2^3 = -1$$

$$^{\Delta t}x_1^4 = 2\cos\theta - 1; \qquad ^{\Delta t}x_2^4 = 2\sin\theta - 1$$

Hence, using the derivatives of the interpolation functions given in Example 6.6, we have

$$^{\Delta t}_0\mathbf{X} = \frac{1}{4}\begin{bmatrix} (1 + {}^0x_2)(2\cos\theta - 1 - 2\sin\theta) & (1 + {}^0x_1)(2\cos\theta - 1 - 2\sin\theta) \\ -(1 + {}^0x_2)(-1 - 2\sin\theta) & +(1 - {}^0x_1)(-1 - 2\sin\theta) \\ -(1 - {}^0x_2)(-1) & -(1 - {}^0x_1)(-1) \\ +(1 - {}^0x_2)(2\cos\theta - 1) & -(1 + {}^0x_1)(2\cos\theta - 1) \\ \hline (1 + {}^0x_2)(2\sin\theta - 1 + 2\cos\theta) & (1 + {}^0x_1)(2\sin\theta - 1 + 2\cos\theta) \\ -(1 + {}^0x_2)(2\cos\theta - 1) & +(1 - {}^0x_1)(2\cos\theta - 1) \\ -(1 - {}^0x_2)(-1) & -(1 - {}^0x_1)(-1) \\ +(1 - {}^0x_2)(2\sin\theta - 1) & -(1 + {}^0x_1)(2\sin\theta - 1) \end{bmatrix}$$

or

$$^{\Delta t}_0\mathbf{X} = \begin{bmatrix} \cos\theta & -\sin\theta \\ \sin\theta & \cos\theta \end{bmatrix} \tag{d}$$

Substituting now from (b) and (d) into (c), we obtain

$$^{\Delta t}_0\mathbf{S} = \begin{bmatrix} ^t\bar{\tau}_{11} & 0 \\ 0 & 0 \end{bmatrix} \tag{e}$$

But, since $^t\bar{\tau}_{11}$ is equal to $^0\tau_{11}$, the relations in (a) and (e) show that the components of the second Piola-Kirchhoff stress tensor did not change during the rigid body rotation. The reason there is no change in the second Piola-Kirchhoff stress tensor is that the deformation gradient corresponds in this case to the rotation matrix that is used in the transformation in (b).

It is important to note that in these examples we consider the coordinate system to remain stationary and the body of material to be moving in this coordinate system. This situation is of course quite different from expressing given stress and strain tensors in new coordinate systems.

The above relationships between the stresses and strains show that, using (6.69) for the stress transformation and (6.64) for the strain transformation (but, as in Example 6.10, using variations in strains rather than time derivatives), we obtain

$$\int_{t_V} {}^t\tau_{kl}\,\delta_t e_{kl}\,d^tV = \int_{t_V}\left(\frac{{}^t\rho}{{}^0\rho}\,{}^t_0S_{ij}\,{}^t_0x_{k,i}\,{}^t_0x_{l,j}\right)({}^0_tx_{m,k}\,{}^0_tx_{n,l}\,\delta^t_0\epsilon_{mn})\,d^tV$$

$$= \int_{t_V}\frac{{}^t\rho}{{}^0\rho}\,{}^t_0S_{ij}\,\delta_{mi}\,\delta_{nj}\,\delta^t_0\epsilon_{mn}\,d^tV = \int_{0_V}{}^t_0S_{ij}\,\delta^t_0\epsilon_{ij}\,d^0V \qquad (6.70)$$

where we have also used that ${}^t\rho\,d^tV = {}^0\rho\,d^0V$.

Of course, (6.70) follows from the definition of the second Piola-Kirchhoff stress tensor in (6.66), and indeed (6.70) is but (6.66) in integrated form over the volume of the body (and written for strain variations).

We have used in (6.70) a specific Cartesian coordinate system and should note that (6.70) is of course in component form a general tensor equation. Other suitable coordinate systems could also be chosen [see (6.178)].

Equation (6.70) is the basic expression of the total and updated Lagrangian formulations used in the incremental analysis of solids and structures, which we consider next. An important aspect of (6.70) is that in the final expression the integration is performed over the initial volume of the body. Instead of the initial configuration, any other previously calculated configuration could be used, with the second Piola-Kirchhoff stresses and Green-Lagrange strains then defined with respect to that configuration. More specifically, if the configuration at time τ is to be used, $\tau < t$, and we denote the coordinates at that time by ${}^\tau x_i$, then we would employ

$$\int_{t_V} {}^t\tau_{mn}\,\delta_t e_{mn}\,d^tV = \int_{\tau_V}{}^t_\tau S_{ij}\,\delta^t_\tau\epsilon_{ij}\,d^\tau V \qquad (6.71)$$

where the second Piola-Kirchhoff stresses ${}^t_\tau S_{ij}$ and Green-Lagrange strains ${}^t_\tau\epsilon_{ij}$ are defined as previously discussed, but instead of ${}^0x_i$, the coordinates ${}^\tau x_i$ corresponding to the configuration at time τ are used. We shall employ the relations in (6.70) and (6.71) often in the next sections.

Note that so far we have defined the stress and strain tensors that we shall employ; the use of appropriate constitutive relations is discussed in Section 6.6.

6.2.3 Continuum Mechanics Incremental Total and Updated Lagrangian Formulations, Materially-Nonlinear-Only Analysis

We discussed in Sections 6.1 and 6.2.1 the basic difficulties and the solution approach when a general nonlinear problem is analyzed, and we concluded that, for an effective incremental analysis, appropriate stress and strain measures need to be employed. This led in Section 6.2.2 to the presentation of some stress and strain tensors that are employed effectively in practice, and then to the principle of virtual displacements expressed in terms of second Piola-Kirchhoff stresses and Green-Lagrange strains. We now use this fundamental result in the development of two general continuum mechanics incremental formulations of nonlinear problems. We consider in this section only the continuum mechanics equations without reference to a particular finite element solution scheme. The use of the results and the generalization for incremental formulations with respect to general finite element solution variables are then discussed in Section 6.3.1 (and the sections thereafter).

The basic equation that we want to solve is relation (6.13), which expresses the equilibrium and compatibility requirements of the general body considered in the configuration corresponding to time $t + \Delta t$. [The constitutive equations also enter (6.13), namely, in the calculation of the stresses.] Since in general the body can undergo large displacements and large strains and the constitutive relations are nonlinear, the relation in (6.13) cannot be solved directly; however, an approximate solution can be obtained by referring all variables to a previously calculated known equilibrium configuration and linearizing the resulting equation. This solution can then be improved by iteration.

To develop a governing linearized equation, we recall that the solutions for times 0, Δt, $2\Delta t$, . . . , t have already been calculated and that we can employ (6.70) or (6.71) and refer the stresses and strains to one of these known equilibrium configurations. Hence, in principle, any one of the equilibrium configurations already calculated could be used. In practice, however, the choice lies essentially between two formulations which have been termed total Lagrangian (TL) and updated Lagrangian (UL) formulations (see K. J. Bathe, E. Ramm, and E. L. Wilson [A]). The TL formulation has also been referred to as the Lagrangian formulation. In this solution scheme all static and kinematic variables are referred to the initial configuration at time 0. The UL formulation is based on the same procedures that are used in the TL formulation, but in the solution all static and kinematic variables are referred to the last calculated configuration. *Both the TL and UL formulations include all kinematic nonlinear effects due to large displacements, large rotations, and large strains, but whether the large strain behavior is modeled appropriately depends on the constitutive relations specified (see Section 6.6).* The only advantage of using one formulation rather than the other lies in its greater numerical efficiency.

Using (6.70), in the TL formulation we consider the basic equation

$$\int_{0_V} {}^{t+\Delta t}_{0}S_{ij}\ \delta^{t+\Delta t}_{0}\epsilon_{ij}\ d^0V = {}^{t+\Delta t}\mathcal{R} \tag{6.72}$$

whereas in the UL formulation we consider

$$\int_{t_V} {}^{t+\Delta t}_{t}S_{ij}\ \delta^{t+\Delta t}_{t}\epsilon_{ij}\ d^tV = {}^{t+\Delta t}\mathcal{R} \tag{6.73}$$

in which ${}^{t+\Delta t}\mathcal{R}$ is the external virtual work given in (6.14). This expression also depends in general on the surface area and the volume of the body under consideration. However, for simplicity of discussion we assume for the moment that the loading is deformation-independent, a very important form of such loading being concentrated forces whose directions and intensities are independent of the structural response. Later we shall discuss how to include deformation-dependent loading in the analysis [see (6.83) and (6.84)].

Tables 6.2 and 6.3 summarize the relations used to arrive at the linearized equations of motion about the state at time t in the TL and UL formulations. The linearized equilibrium equations are, in the TL formulation,

$$\int_{0_V} {}_{0}C_{ijrs}\ {}_{0}e_{rs}\ \delta_0 e_{ij}\ d^0V + \int_{0_V} {}^{t}_{0}S_{ij}\ \delta_0\eta_{ij}\ d^0V = {}^{t+\Delta t}\mathcal{R} - \int_{0_V} {}^{t}_{0}S_{ij}\ \delta_0 e_{ij}\ d^0V \tag{6.74}$$

and in the UL formulation

$$\int_{t_V} {}_{t}C_{ijrs}\ {}_{t}e_{rs}\ \delta_t e_{ij}\ d^tV + \int_{t_V} {}^{t}\tau_{ij}\ \delta_t\eta_{ij}\ d^tV = {}^{t+\Delta t}\mathcal{R} - \int_{t_V} {}^{t}\tau_{ij}\ \delta_t e_{ij}\ d^tV \tag{6.75}$$

TABLE 6.2   *Continuum mechanics incremental decomposition: Total Lagrangian formulation*

1. *Equation of motion*

$$\int_{0_V} {}^{t+\Delta t}_0 S_{ij}\, \delta\, {}^{t+\Delta t}_0 \epsilon_{ij}\, d^0V = {}^{t+\Delta t}\mathcal{R}$$

where

$${}^{t+\Delta t}_0 S_{ij} = \frac{{}^0\rho}{{}^{t+\Delta t}\rho}\, {}_{t+\Delta t}^0 x_{i,m}\, {}^{t+\Delta t}\tau_{mn}\, {}_{t+\Delta t}^0 x_{j,n}; \qquad \delta\, {}^{t+\Delta t}_0 \epsilon_{ij} = \delta\tfrac{1}{2}\left({}^{t+\Delta t}_0 u_{i,j} + {}^{t+\Delta t}_0 u_{j,i} + {}^{t+\Delta t}_0 u_{k,i}\, {}^{t+\Delta t}_0 u_{k,j}\right)$$

2. *Incremental decompositions*
   (a) Stresses

$${}^{t+\Delta t}_0 S_{ij} = {}^t_0 S_{ij} + {}_0 S_{ij}$$

   (b) Strains

$${}^{t+\Delta t}_0 \epsilon_{ij} = {}^t_0 \epsilon_{ij} + {}_0 \epsilon_{ij}; \qquad {}_0 \epsilon_{ij} = {}_0 e_{ij} + {}_0 \eta_{ij}$$

$${}_0 e_{ij} = \tfrac{1}{2}\left({}_0 u_{i,j} + {}_0 u_{j,i} + \underbrace{{}^t_0 u_{k,i}\, {}_0 u_{k,j} + {}_0 u_{k,i}\, {}^t_0 u_{k,j}}_{\text{Initial displacement effect}}\right); \qquad {}_0 \eta_{ij} = \tfrac{1}{2}{}_0 u_{k,i}\, {}_0 u_{k,j}$$

3. *Equation of motion with incremental decompositions*
   Noting that $\delta^{t+\Delta t}_0 \epsilon_{ij} = \delta_0 \epsilon_{ij}$ the equation of motion is

$$\int_{0_V} {}_0 S_{ij}\, \delta_0 \epsilon_{ij}\, d^0V + \int_{0_V} {}^t_0 S_{ij}\, \delta_0 \eta_{ij}\, d^0V = {}^{t+\Delta t}\mathcal{R} - \int_{0_V} {}^t_0 S_{ij}\, \delta_0 e_{ij}\, d^0V$$

4. *Linearization of equation of motion*
   Using the approximations ${}_0 S_{ij} = {}_0 C_{ijrs}\, {}_0 e_{rs}$, $\delta_0 \epsilon_{ij} = \delta_0 e_{ij}$, we obtain as approximate equation of motion:

$$\int_{0_V} {}_0 C_{ijrs}\, {}_0 e_{rs}\, \delta_0 e_{ij}\, d^0V + \int_{0_V} {}^t_0 S_{ij}\, \delta_0 \eta_{ij}\, d^0V = {}^{t+\Delta t}\mathcal{R} - \int_{0_V} {}^t_0 S_{ij}\, \delta_0 e_{ij}\, d^0V$$

TABLE 6.3   *Continuum mechanics incremental decomposition: Updated Lagrangian formulation*

1. *Equation of motion*

$$\int_{t_V} {}^{t+\Delta t}_t S_{ij}\, \delta^{t+\Delta t}_t \epsilon_{ij}\, d^tV = {}^{t+\Delta t}\mathcal{R}$$

where

$${}^{t+\Delta t}_t S_{ij} = \frac{{}^t\rho}{{}^{t+\Delta t}\rho}\, {}_{t+\Delta t}^t x_{i,m}\, {}^{t+\Delta t}\tau_{mn}\, {}_{t+\Delta t}^t x_{j,n}; \qquad \delta^{t+\Delta t}_t \epsilon_{ij} = \delta\tfrac{1}{2}\left({}_t u_{i,j} + {}_t u_{j,i} + {}_t u_{k,i}\, {}_t u_{k,j}\right)$$

2. *Incremental decompositions*
   (a) Stresses

$${}^{t+\Delta t}_t S_{ij} = {}^t \tau_{ij} + {}_t S_{ij} \qquad \text{note that } {}^t_t S_{ij} \equiv {}^t \tau_{ij}$$

   (b) Strains

$${}^{t+\Delta t}_t \epsilon_{ij} = {}_t \epsilon_{ij}; \qquad {}_t \epsilon_{ij} = {}_t e_{ij} + {}_t \eta_{ij}$$

$${}_t e_{ij} = \tfrac{1}{2}\left({}_t u_{i,j} + {}_t u_{j,i}\right); \qquad {}_t \eta_{ij} = \tfrac{1}{2}{}_t u_{k,i}\, {}_t u_{k,j}$$

3. *Equation of motion with incremental decompositions*
   The equation of motion is

$$\int_{t_V} {}_t S_{ij}\, \delta_t \epsilon_{ij}\, d^tV + \int_{t_V} {}^t \tau_{ij}\, \delta_t \eta_{ij}\, d^tV = {}^{t+\Delta t}\mathcal{R} - \int_{t_V} {}^t \tau_{ij}\, \delta_t e_{ij}\, d^tV$$

4. *Linearization of equation of motion*
   Using the approximations ${}_t S_{ij} = {}_t C_{ijrs}\, {}_t e_{rs}$, $\delta_t \epsilon_{ij} = \delta_t e_{ij}$, we obtain as approximate equation of motion:

$$\int_{t_V} {}_t C_{ijrs}\, {}_t e_{rs}\, \delta_t e_{ij}\, d^tV + \int_{t_V} {}^t \tau_{ij}\, \delta_t \eta_{ij}\, d^tV = {}^{t+\Delta t}\mathcal{R} - \int_{t_V} {}^t \tau_{ij}\, \delta_t e_{ij}\, d^tV$$

where $_0C_{ijrs}$ and $_tC_{ijrs}$ are the incremental stress-strain tensors at time t referred to the configurations at times 0 and t, respectively. The derivation of $_0C_{ijrs}$ and $_tC_{ijrs}$ for various materials is discussed in Section 6.6. We also note that in (6.74) and (6.75) $_0^tS_{ij}$ and $^t\tau_{ij}$ are the known second Piola-Kirchhoff and Cauchy stresses at time t; and $_0e_{ij}$, $_0\eta_{ij}$ and $_te_{ij}$, $_t\eta_{ij}$ are the linear and nonlinear incremental strains which are referred to the configurations at times 0 and t, respectively.

Let us consider in more detail the steps performed in Table 6.2. The steps in Table 6.3 are performed analogously.

In step 2, we incrementally decompose the stresses and strains, which is allowed because all stresses and strains, including the increments, are referred to the original (same) configuration. Also note that we obtain the incremental Green-Lagrange strain components in Table 6.2 by simply using $_0\epsilon_{ij} = {}^{t+\Delta t}_0\epsilon_{ij} - {}^t_0\epsilon_{ij}$ and expressing ${}^{t+\Delta t}_0\epsilon_{ij}$ and ${}^t_0\epsilon_{ij}$ in terms of the displacements, where ${}^{t+\Delta t}u_i = {}^tu_i + u_i$.

In step 3, we use $\delta{}^{t+\Delta t}_0\epsilon_{ij} = \delta({}^t_0\epsilon_{ij} + {}_0\epsilon_{ij}) = \delta_0\epsilon_{ij}$; that is, here $\delta{}^t_0\epsilon_{ij} = 0$ because the variation is taken about the configuration at time $t + \Delta t$. We also bring all known quantities to the right-hand side in the principle of virtual work equation. Note that for a given displacement variation the expression $\int_{0_V} {}^t_0S_{ij}\,\delta_0e_{ij}\,d^0V$ is known. So far we have not made any assumption but have merely rewritten the original principle of virtual work equation.

In general, the left-hand side of the principle of virtual work equation given in step 3 is highly nonlinear in the incremental displacements u_i. In step 4, we now linearize the expression, and this linearization is achieved in the following manner.

First, we note that the term $\int_{0_V} {}^t_0S_{ij}\,\delta_0\eta_{ij}\,d^0V$ is already linear in the incremental displacements; hence, we keep this term without change. The nonlinear effects are due to the term $\int_{0_V} {}_0S_{ij}\,\delta_0\epsilon_{ij}\,d^0V$, which we linearize using a Taylor series expansion,

$$\int_{0_V} {}_0S_{ij}\,\delta_0\epsilon_{ij}\,d^0V = \int_{0_V}\left(\left.\frac{\partial {}^t_0S_{ij}}{\partial {}^t_0\epsilon_{rs}}\right|_t {}_0\epsilon_{rs} + \text{higher order terms}\right)\delta({}_0e_{ij} + {}_0\eta_{ij})\,d^0V$$

$$= \int_{0_V}\left(\underbrace{\left.\frac{\partial {}^t_0S_{ij}}{\partial {}^t_0\epsilon_{rs}}\right|_t}_{\downarrow}\,(\underbrace{{}_0e_{rs}}_{\downarrow} + \underbrace{{}_0\eta_{rs}}_{\downarrow}) + \underbrace{\text{higher order terms}}_{\downarrow}\right)\delta({}_0e_{ij} + \underbrace{{}_0\eta_{ij}}_{\downarrow})\,d^0V$$

$$\qquad\qquad {}_0C_{ijrs} \qquad\quad \text{Neglect} \qquad\quad \text{Neglect} \qquad\qquad \text{Neglect}$$

$$\doteq \int_{0_V} {}_0C_{ijrs}\,{}_0e_{rs}\,\delta_0e_{ij}\,d^0V$$

This term is now linear in the incremental displacements because δ_0e_{ij} is independent of the u_i.

Comparing the UL and TL formulations in Tables 6.2 and 6.3, we observe that they are quite analogous and that, in fact, the only theoretical difference between the two formulations lies in the choice of different reference configurations for the kinematic and static variables. Indeed, if in the numerical solution the appropriate constitutive tensors are employed, identical results are obtained (see Section 6.6).

The choice of using either the UL or the TL formulation in a finite element solution depends, in practice, on their relative numerical effectiveness, which in turn depends on the finite element and the constitutive law used. However, one general observation can be made considering Tables 6.2 and 6.3, namely, that the incremental linear strains $_0e_{ij}$ in the TL formulation contain an initial displacement effect that leads to a more complex strain-displacement matrix than in the UL formulation.

The relations in (6.74) and (6.75) can be employed to calculate an increment in the displacements, which then is used to evaluate approximations to the displacements, strains, and stresses corresponding to time $t + \Delta t$. The displacement approximations corresponding to $t + \Delta t$ are obtained simply by adding the calculated increments to the displacements at time t, and the strain approximations are evaluated from the displacements using the available kinematic relations [e.g., relation (6.54) in the TL formulation]. However, the evaluation of the stresses corresponding to time $t + \Delta t$ depends on the specific constitutive relations used and is discussed in detail in Section 6.6.

Assuming that the approximate displacements, strains, and thus stresses have been obtained, we can now check into how much difference there is between the internal virtual work when evaluated with the calculated static and kinematic variables for time $t + \Delta t$ and the external virtual work. Denoting the approximate values with a superscript (1) in anticipation that an iteration will in general be necessary, the error due to linearization is, in the TL formulation,

$$\text{Error} = {}^{t+\Delta t}\mathcal{R} - \int_{0_V} {}^{t+\Delta t}_{0}S^{(1)}_{ij} \; \delta^{t+\Delta t}_{0}\epsilon^{(1)}_{ij} \; d^0V \tag{6.76}$$

and in the UL formulation,

$$\text{Error} = {}^{t+\Delta t}\mathcal{R} - \int_{t+\Delta t_{V(1)}} {}^{t+\Delta t}\tau^{(1)}_{ij} \; \delta_{t+\Delta t}e^{(1)}_{ij} \; d^{t+\Delta t}V \tag{6.77}$$

We should note that the right-hand sides of (6.76) and (6.77) are equivalent to the right-hand sides of (6.74) and (6.75), respectively, but in each case the current configurations with the corresponding stress and strain variables are employed. The correspondence in the UL formulation can be seen directly, but when considering the TL formulation, it must be recognized that $\delta_0 e_{ij}$ is equivalent to $\delta^{t+\Delta t}_{0}\epsilon^{(1)}_{ij}$ when the same current displacements are used (see Exercise 6.29).

These considerations show that the right-hand sides in (6.74) and (6.75) represent an "out-of-balance virtual work" prior to the calculation of the increments in the displacements, whereas the right-hand sides of (6.76) and (6.77) represent the "out-of-balance virtual work" after the solution, as the result of the linearizations performed. In order to further reduce the "out-of-balance virtual work" we need to perform an iteration in which the above solution step is repeated until the difference between the external virtual work and the internal virtual work is negligible within a certain convergence measure. Using the TL formulation, the equation solved repetitively, for $k = 1, 2, 3, \ldots$, is

$$\int_{0_V} {}_0C^{(k-1)}_{ijrs} \, \Delta_0 e^{(k)}_{rs} \, \delta_0 e_{ij} \, d^0V + \int_{0_V} {}^{t+\Delta t}_{0}S^{(k-1)}_{ij} \, \delta\Delta_0 \eta^{(k)}_{ij} \, d^0V = {}^{t+\Delta t}\mathcal{R} - \int_{0_V} {}^{t+\Delta t}_{0}S^{(k-1)}_{ij} \, \delta^{t+\Delta t}_{0}\epsilon^{(k-1)}_{ij} \, d^0V \tag{6.78}$$

and using the UL formulation, the equation considered is

$$\int_{t+\Delta t_{V(k-1)}} {}^{t+\Delta t}C^{(k-1)}_{ijrs} \, \Delta_{t+\Delta t}e^{(k)}_{rs} \, \delta_{t+\Delta t}e_{ij} \, d^{t+\Delta t}V + \int_{t+\Delta t_{V(k-1)}} {}^{t+\Delta t}\tau^{(k-1)}_{ij} \, \delta\Delta_{t+\Delta t}\eta^{(k)}_{ij} \, d^{t+\Delta t}V$$

$$= {}^{t+\Delta t}\mathcal{R} - \int_{t+\Delta t_{V(k-1)}} {}^{t+\Delta t}\tau^{(k-1)}_{ij} \, \delta_{t+\Delta t}e^{(k-1)}_{ij} \, d^{t+\Delta t}V \tag{6.79}$$

where the case $k = 1$ corresponds to the relations in (6.74) and (6.75) and the displacements are updated as follows:

$$^{t+\Delta t}u_i^{(k)} = {}^{t+\Delta t}u_i^{(k-1)} + \Delta u_i^{(k)}; \qquad ^{t+\Delta t}u^{(0)} = {}^tu \tag{6.80}$$

The relations in (6.78) to (6.80) correspond to the Newton-Raphson iteration already introduced in Section 6.1. Therefore, the expressions in the integrals are all evaluated corresponding to the currently available displacements and corresponding stresses. Note that in (6.79) the Cauchy stresses, the tangent constitutive relation, and the incremental strains are all referred to the configuration and volume at time $t + \Delta t$, end of iteration $(k - 1)$; that is, the quantities are referred to $^{t+\Delta t}V^{(k-1)}$, where for $k = 1$, $^{t+\Delta t}V^{(0)} = {}^tV$.

In an overview of this section, we note once more a very important point. Our objective is to solve the equilibrium relation in (6.13), which can be regarded as an extension of the virtual work principle used in linear analysis. We saw that for a general incremental analysis, certain stress and strain measures can be employed effectively, and this led to a transformation of (6.13) into the updated and total Lagrangian forms. The linearization of these equations then resulted in the relations (6.78) and (6.79). It is most important to recognize that the solution of either (6.78) or (6.79) corresponds entirely to the solution of the relation in (6.13). Namely, provided that the appropriate constitutive relations are employed, identical numerical results are obtained using either (6.78) or (6.79) for solution, and, as mentioned earlier, whether to use the TL or the UL formulation depends in practice only on the relative numerical effectiveness of the two solution approaches.

So far we have assumed that the loading is deformation-independent and can be specified prior to the incremental analysis. Thus, we assumed that the expression in (6.14) can be evaluated using

$$^{t+\Delta t}\mathcal{R} = \int_{0_V} {}^{t+\Delta t}_0 f_i^B \, \delta u_i \, d^0V + \int_{0_{S_f}} {}^{t+\Delta t}_0 f_i^S \, \delta u_i^S \, d^0S \tag{6.81}$$

which is possible only for certain types of loading, such as concentrated loading that does not change direction as a function of the deformations. Using the displacement-based isoparametric elements, another important loading condition that can be modeled with (6.81) is the inertia force loading to be included in dynamic analysis. In this case we have

$$\int_{t+\Delta t_V} {}^{t+\Delta t}\rho \, {}^{t+\Delta t}\ddot{u}_i \, \delta u_i \, d^{t+\Delta t}V = \int_{0_V} {}^0\rho \, {}^{t+\Delta t}\ddot{u}_i \, \delta u_i \, d^0V \tag{6.82}$$

and hence, the mass matrix can be evaluated using the initial configuration of the body. The practical consequence is that in a dynamic analysis the mass matrices of isoparametric elements can be calculated prior to the step-by-step solution.

Assume now that the external virtual work is deformation-dependent and cannot be evaluated using (6.81). If in this case the load (or time) step is small enough, the external virtual work can frequently be approximated to sufficient accuracy using the intensity of loading corresponding to time $t + \Delta t$, but integrating over the volume and area last calculated in the iteration

$$\int_{t+\Delta t_V} {}^{t+\Delta t}f_i^B \, \delta u_i \, d^{t+\Delta t}V \doteq \int_{t+\Delta t_V^{(k-1)}} {}^{t+\Delta t}f_i^B \, \delta u_i \, d^{t+\Delta t}V \tag{6.83}$$

and

$$\int_{t+\Delta t_{S_f}} {}^{t+\Delta t}f_i^S \, \delta u_i^S \, d^{t+\Delta t}S \doteq \int_{t+\Delta t_{S_f}^{(k-1)}} {}^{t+\Delta t}f_i^S \, \delta u_i^S \, d^{t+\Delta t}S \qquad (6.84)$$

In order to obtain an iterative scheme that usually converges in fewer iterations, the effect of the unknown incremental displacements in the load terms needs to be included in the stiffness matrix. Depending on the loading considered, a nonsymmetric stiffness matrix is then obtained (see, for example, K. Schweizerhof and E. Ramm [A]), which may require substantially more computations per iteration.

The total and updated Lagrangian formulations are incremental continuum mechanics equations that include all nonlinear effects due to large displacements, large strains, and material nonlinearities; however, in practice, it is often sufficient to account for nonlinear material effects only. In this case, the nonlinear strain components and any updating of surface areas and volumes are neglected in the formulations. Therefore, (6.78) and (6.79) reduce to the same equation of motion, namely,

$$\int_V C_{ijrs}^{(k-1)} \, \Delta e_{rs}^{(k)} \, \delta e_{ij} \, dV = {}^{t+\Delta t}\mathcal{R} - \int_V {}^{t+\Delta t}\sigma_{ij}^{(k-1)} \, \delta e_{ij} \, dV \qquad (6.85)$$

where ${}^{t+\Delta t}\sigma_{ij}^{(k-1)}$ is the actual physical stress at time $t + \Delta t$ and end of iteration $(k - 1)$. In this analysis we assume that the volume of the body does not change and therefore ${}^{t+\Delta t}_0 S_{ij} \equiv {}^{t+\Delta t}\tau_{ij} \equiv {}^{t+\Delta t}\sigma_{ij}$, and there can be no deformation-dependent loading. Since no kinematic nonlinearities are considered in (6.85), it also follows that if the material is linear elastic, the relation in (6.85) is identical to the principle of virtual work discussed in Section 4.2.1 and would lead to a linear finite element solution.

In the above formulations we assumed that the proposed iteration does converge, so that the incremental analysis can actually be carried out. We discuss this question in detail in Section 8.4. Furthermore, we assumed in the formulation that a static analysis is performed or a dynamic analysis is sought with an implicit time integration scheme (see Section 9.5.2). If a dynamic analysis is to be performed using an explicit time integration method, the governing continuum mechanics equations are, using the TL formulation,

$$\int_{0_V} {}^t_0 S_{ij} \, \delta {}^t_0 \epsilon_{ij} \, d^0V = {}^t\mathcal{R} \qquad (6.86)$$

using the UL formulation,

$$\int_{t_V} {}^t\tau_{ij} \, \delta_t e_{ij} \, d^tV = {}^t\mathcal{R} \qquad (6.87)$$

and using the materially-nonlinear-only analysis,

$$\int_V {}^t\sigma_{ij} \, \delta e_{ij} \, dV = {}^t\mathcal{R} \qquad (6.88)$$

where the stress and strain tensors are as defined previously and equilibrium is considered at time t. In these analyses the external virtual work must include the inertia forces corresponding to time t, and the incremental solution corresponds to a marching-forward algorithm without equilibrium iterations. For this reason, deformation-dependent loading can be directly included by simply updating the load intensity and using the new geometry in the evaluation of ${}^t\mathcal{R}$. The details of the actual step-by-step solution are discussed in Section 9.5.1.

6.2.4 Exercises

6.1. A four-node plane strain finite element undergoes the deformation shown. The element is originally square, the density $^0\rho$ of the element is 0.05, and $d^0\mathbf{x}$ and $d^0\hat{\mathbf{x}}$ are infinitesimal fibers. For the deformed configuration at time t:

  (a) Calculate the displacements of the material points within the element as functions of $^0x_1$ and $^0x_2$.

  (b) Calculate the deformation gradient $^t_0\mathbf{X}$, the right Cauchy-Green deformation tensor $^t_0\mathbf{C}$, and the mass density $^t\rho$ as a function of $^0x_1$ and $^0x_2$.

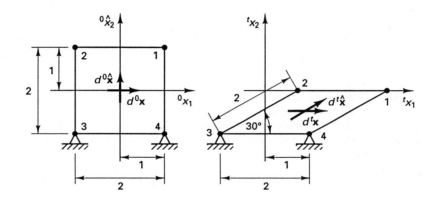

6.2. For the element in Exercise 6.1, calculate the stretches $^t\lambda$ and $^t\hat{\lambda}$ of the line segments $d^0\mathbf{x}$ and $d^0\hat{\mathbf{x}}$ and the angular distortion between these line segments.

6.3. Consider the four-node plane strain element shown. Calculate the deformation gradient for times Δt and $2\Delta t$. [*Hint:* Establish (by inspection) the matrices $^t_0\mathbf{R}$ and $^t_0\mathbf{U}$ such that $^t_0\mathbf{X} = {^t_0\mathbf{R}} \, {^t_0\mathbf{U}}$, where $^t_0\mathbf{R}$ is an orthogonal (rotation) matrix and $^t_0\mathbf{U}$ is a symmetric (stretch) matrix.]

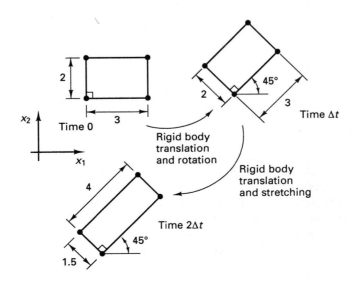

6.4. The four-node plane stress element of incompressible material shown is first stretched in the x_1 and x_2 directions and then rigidly rotated by 30 degrees.
   (a) Calculate the deformation gradient $^{2\Delta t}_0\mathbf{X}$ of the material points in the element.
   (b) Calculate the stretches of the line elements d^0s_1 and d^0s_2.

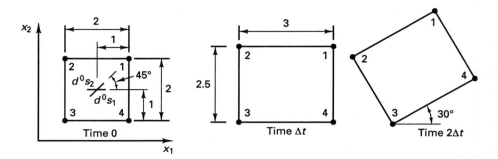

6.5. Consider the four-node element and its deformations to time Δt in Exercise 6.4. Assume that the deformation gradient at time Δt is now expressed in the coordinate axes $\bar{x}_1$, $\bar{x}_2$ shown. Calculate this deformation gradient $^{\Delta t}_0\overline{\mathbf{X}}$ and show that $^{\Delta t}_0\overline{\mathbf{X}}$ is not equal to $^{2\Delta t}_0\mathbf{X}$ calculated in Exercise 6.4. (In Exercise 6.4 the element was stretched *and* rotated, whereas here the element is *only* stretched.)

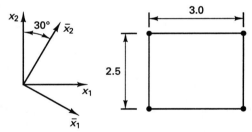

6.6. Consider the motions of two infinitesimal fibers in a two-dimensional continuum. At time 0, the fibers are

$$d^0\mathbf{x} = \frac{1}{\sqrt{2}}\begin{bmatrix}1\\1\end{bmatrix}d^0s; \qquad d^0\hat{\mathbf{x}} = \begin{bmatrix}0\\1\end{bmatrix}d^0\hat{s}$$

and at time t, the fibers are

$$d^t\mathbf{x} = \begin{bmatrix}2\\1\end{bmatrix}d^0s; \qquad d^t\hat{\mathbf{x}} = \begin{bmatrix}-1\\1\end{bmatrix}d^0\hat{s}$$

Both fibers emanate from the same material point.
   (a) Calculate the deformation gradient $^t_0\mathbf{X}$ at that material point.
   (b) Calculate the inverse deformation gradient $^0_t\mathbf{X}$ at that material point (i) by inverting $^t_0\mathbf{X}$ and (ii) without inverting $^t_0\mathbf{X}$.
   (c) Calculate the mass density ratio $^t\rho/^0\rho$ at the material point.

6.7. Prove that a deformation gradient $\mathbf{X}$ can always be decomposed into the form $\mathbf{X} = \mathbf{VR}$ where $\mathbf{V}$ is a symmetric matrix and $\mathbf{R}$ is an orthogonal matrix. Establish $\mathbf{V}$ and $\mathbf{R}$ for the deformation in Exercise 6.4.

6.8. A four-node plane strain element is subjected to the following deformations:

from time 0 to time Δt:

$$ {}_{0}^{\Delta t}\mathbf{U} = \begin{bmatrix} 2 & 0.5 \\ 0.5 & 0.5 \end{bmatrix} $$

from time Δt to time $2\Delta t$:

$$ {}_{\Delta t}^{2\Delta t}\mathbf{R} = \begin{bmatrix} \cos 30° & -\sin 30° \\ \sin 30° & \cos 30° \end{bmatrix} $$

(a) Sketch the element and its motions and establish the deformation gradient ${}_{0}^{2\Delta t}\mathbf{X}$.
(b) Calculate the spectral decomposition of ${}_{0}^{\Delta t}\mathbf{U}$ as per (6.32).
(c) Calculate the elements of the decomposition of $\mathbf{X} = \mathbf{VR}$ and interpret this decomposition conceptually.

6.9. Consider the four-node axisymmetric element shown. Evaluate the deformation gradient and the right and left stretch tensors $\mathbf{U}$, $\mathbf{V}$.

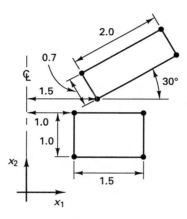

6.10. Consider the motion of the four-node finite element shown. Calculate for time t,
(a) The deformation gradient and the polar decompositions $\mathbf{X} = \mathbf{RU}$ and $\mathbf{X} = \mathbf{VR}$
(b) The spectral decompositions of $\mathbf{U}$ and $\mathbf{V}$ in (6.32) and (6.33)
(c) The velocity strain and spin tensors in (6.42) and (6.43).

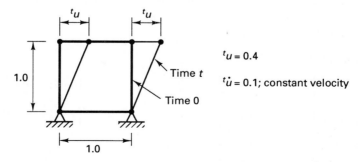

6.11. Prove the relations in (6.48) to (6.50).

6.12. Prove the relations in (6.56) to (6.61).

6.13. Consider the motion of the four-node element in Exercise 6.10. Calculate $[\dot{\boldsymbol{\Lambda}}]_{\alpha\alpha}$, $[\boldsymbol{\Omega}_L]_{\alpha\beta}$, and $[\boldsymbol{\Omega}_E]_{\alpha\beta}$ using the relations (6.48) to (6.50). Verify that (6.46) and (6.47) hold.

6.14. Calculate the components of the Green-Lagrange strain tensors of the elements and their deformations in Exercises 6.1, 6.3, and 6.4. In each case establish the relations in (6.51) and (6.53)
to (6.55).

6.15. Calculate the components of the Hencky strain tensor (6.52) for the elements and their deformations in Exercises 6.1, 6.3, and 6.4.

6.16. Consider the element and its motion in Exercise 6.10. For the Green-Lagrange strain and Hencky
strain tensors, calculate $\dot{\mathbf{E}}_g$ in (6.57) by direct differentiation of (6.56). Also, establish $\dot{\mathbf{E}}_g$ using
the detailed relations (6.59) to (6.61).

6.17. Consider the motion of a material fiber $d^0\mathbf{x}$ in a body.
  (a) Prove that for the material fiber the following relation holds using the Green-Lagrange strain
  tensor

$$ {}_0^t\epsilon_{ij}\, d^0x_i\, d^0x_j = \tfrac{1}{2}[(d^ts)^2 - (d^0s)^2] $$

  where $(d^ts)^2 = d^tx_i\, d^tx_i$, $(d^0s)^2 = d^0x_i\, d^0x_i$ and (6.22) is applicable.
  (b) At point A in a deformed body the Green-Lagrange strain tensor is known to be

$$ {}_0^t\boldsymbol{\epsilon} = \begin{bmatrix} 0.6 & 0.2 \\ 0.2 & -0.3 \end{bmatrix} $$

  Find the stretch ${}^t\lambda$ of the line element $d^0s = \| d^0\mathbf{x} \|_2$ shown. Can you calculate the rotation
  of the line element? Explain your answer.

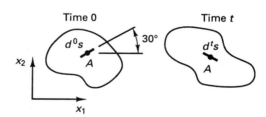

6.18. The nodal point velocities of a four-node element are as shown. Using the element interpolation
functions, evaluate the components of the velocity strain tensor and spin tensor of the element.
Physically explain why your answer is correct.

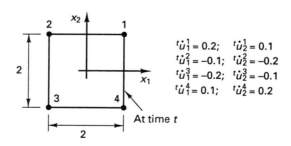

$$ {}^t\dot{u}_1^1 = 0.2; \quad {}^t\dot{u}_2^1 = 0.1 $$
$$ {}^t\dot{u}_1^2 = -0.1; \quad {}^t\dot{u}_2^2 = -0.2 $$
$$ {}^t\dot{u}_1^3 = -0.2; \quad {}^t\dot{u}_2^3 = -0.1 $$
$$ {}^t\dot{u}_1^4 = 0.1; \quad {}^t\dot{u}_2^4 = 0.2 $$

6.19. Consider the four-node plane strain element and its motion in Exercise 6.10. Evaluate the
components ${}^tD_{mn}$ using the relation (6.64).

6.20. Consider the four-node plane strain element shown. Evaluate the components of the tensor $\delta_t e_{mn}$ corresponding to the virtual displacement $\delta u_1^1 = \Delta$ at node 1 as a function of $^0x_1$ and $^0x_2$. (All other $\delta u_j^k = 0$.)

Evaluate all matrix expressions required but do not necessarily perform the matrix multiplications.

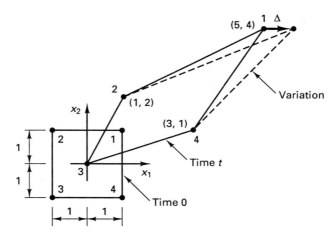

6.21. Consider the four-node element shown, subjected to an initial stress with components

$$\begin{array}{c}\text{Initial stress}\\ \text{(stress at time 0)}\end{array} = {}^0_0\mathbf{S} \equiv {}^0\boldsymbol{\tau} = \begin{bmatrix} 200 & 100 \\ 100 & 300 \end{bmatrix}$$

The element is undeformed in its initial configuration. Assume that the element is subjected to a counterclockwise rigid body rotation of 30 degrees from time 0 to time Δt.
(a) Calculate the Cauchy stresses $^{\Delta t}\boldsymbol{\tau}$ corresponding to the stationary coordinate system x_1, x_2.
(b) Calculate the second Piola-Kirchhoff stresses $^{\Delta t}_0\mathbf{S}$ corresponding to x_1, x_2.
(c) Calculate the deformation gradient $^{\Delta t}_0\mathbf{X}$.

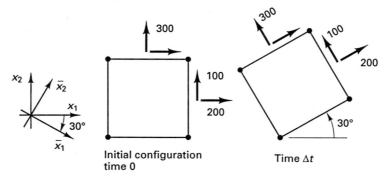

Next, assume that the element remains in its initial configuration but the coordinate system is rotated clockwise by 30 degrees.
(d) Calculate the Cauchy stresses $^0\bar{\boldsymbol{\tau}}$ corresponding to $\bar{x}_1, \bar{x}_2$.
(e) Calculate the second Piola-Kirchhoff stresses $^0_0\bar{\mathbf{S}}$ corresponding to $\bar{x}_1, \bar{x}_2$.
(f) Calculate the deformation gradient $^0_0\bar{\mathbf{X}}$ corresponding to $\bar{x}_1, \bar{x}_2$.

6.22. The four-node plane strain finite element shown carries at time t the second Piola-Kirchhoff stresses

$$_0^t S = \begin{bmatrix} 100 & 50 & 0 \\ 50 & 200 & 0 \\ 0 & 0 & 100 \end{bmatrix}$$

The deformation gradient at time t is

$$_0^t X = \begin{bmatrix} 2 & 1 & 0 \\ 0 & 2 & 0 \\ 0 & 0 & 1 \end{bmatrix}$$

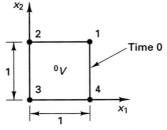

(a) Sketch the deformed configuration at time t.
(b) A rigid body rotation of 30 degrees counterclockwise is applied from time t to time $t + \Delta t$ to the element. Sketch the configuration at time $t + \Delta t$.
(c) Calculate corresponding to the stationary Cartesian coordinate system (i) the Cauchy stresses at time t, (ii) the Cauchy stresses at time $t + \Delta t$, and (iii) the second Piola-Kirchhoff stresses at time $t + \Delta t$.

6.23. The second Piola-Kirchhoff stresses $_0^t S$ are for the plane strain four-node element as shown.
(a) Calculate the Cauchy stresses at time t.
(b) Obtain the second Piola-Kirchhoff stresses at time $t + \Delta t$, $_0^{t+\Delta t} S$, and the Cauchy stresses at time $t + \Delta t$, $^{t+\Delta t} \tau$.

All stress components are measured in the stationary coordinate system x_1, x_2.

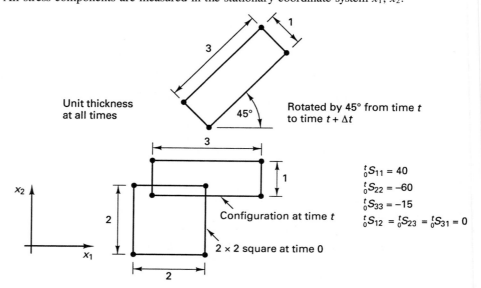

Unit thickness
at all times

Rotated by 45° from time t
to time $t + \Delta t$

Configuration at time t

2 × 2 square at time 0

$_0^t S_{11} = 40$
$_0^t S_{22} = -60$
$_0^t S_{33} = -15$
$_0^t S_{12} = _0^t S_{23} = _0^t S_{31} = 0$

6.24. We have used a computer program to perform the following finite element analysis.

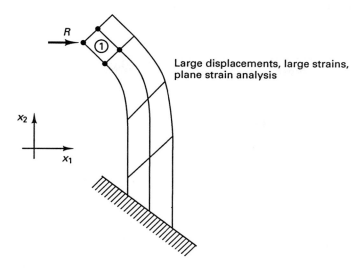

Large displacements, large strains, plane strain analysis

We would like to verify that the program is working properly. As part of this verification, we consider the displacements of element 1:

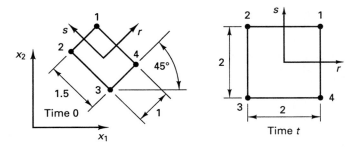

(a) Calculate the 2×2 deformation gradient $_0^t X$ at the centroid of the element. (*Hint:* Remember that $_0^t X = {}_t^0 X^{-1}$.)

(b) The program also prints out the Cauchy stresses at the centroid of the element:

$$\begin{bmatrix} {}^t\tau_{11} \\ {}^t\tau_{22} \\ {}^t\tau_{12} \end{bmatrix} = \begin{bmatrix} 20.50 \\ 20.50 \\ 12.50 \end{bmatrix}$$

The material law used in the analysis is given by

$$\begin{bmatrix} {}_0^t S_{11} \\ {}_0^t S_{22} \\ {}_0^t S_{12} \end{bmatrix} = \begin{bmatrix} 11 & 7 & 0 \\ 7 & 11 & 0 \\ 0 & 0 & 9 \end{bmatrix} \begin{bmatrix} {}_0^t \epsilon_{11} \\ {}_0^t \epsilon_{22} \\ {}_0^t \epsilon_{12} \end{bmatrix}$$

Show that the Cauchy stresses printed by the program are not correct and compute the correct Cauchy stresses based on the given element displacements.

Can you identify the program error?

6.25. Consider the sheet of material shown.
Here

$$' u_1 = -\tfrac{1}{2}\,{}^0 x_1 + 3; \qquad ' u_2 = \tfrac{1}{2}\,{}^0 x_2 + 2.5$$

Also, the stresses are

$$' \tau_{11} = -10 \text{ psi}$$
$$' \tau_{22} = 20 \text{ psi}$$
$$' \tau_{12} = 0$$

Identify six simple independent virtual displacement patterns and show that the principle of virtual work is satisfied for these patterns.

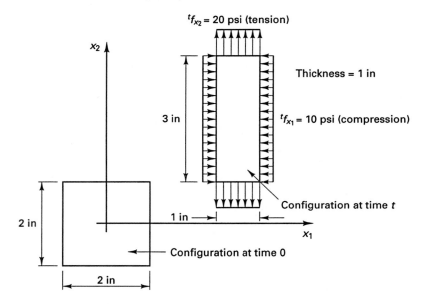

6.26. Consider the one-dimensional large strain analysis of the bar shown.

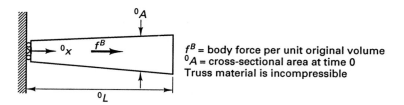

(a) For a cross section of the bar, derive an expression for the second Piola-Kirchhoff stress as a function of the Cauchy stress, the area ratio $' A /{}^0 A$, and the deformation gradient.

(b) Starting from the principle of virtual work, derive the governing differential equation of equilibrium in terms of quantities referred to the original configuration. Also, derive the boundary conditions.

(c) Now rewrite the governing differential equation in terms of quantities referred to the current configuration and compare this equation with the differential equation associated with small strain analysis.

6.27. Consider a thin disk spinning around its symmetry axis with constant angular velocity ω as shown. The disk is subjected to large displacements. Specialize the general equations of the principle of virtual work in Tables 6.2 and 6.3 to this case. In the analysis, only the displacements of the disk particles in the x_1 direction are considered.

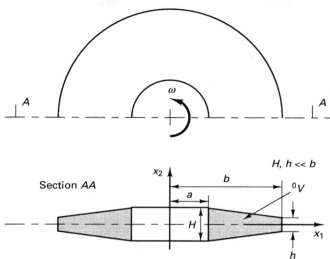

Section *AA*

6.28. Consider the four-node plane strain element shown. The nodal point displacements at time t and time $t + \Delta t$ are shown. Calculate the incremental Green-Lagrange strain tensor components $_0\epsilon$ from time t to time $t + \Delta t$.

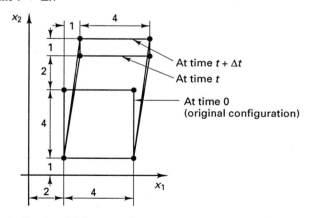

At time $t + \Delta t$
At time t
At time 0
(original configuration)

6.29. In the derivations in Section 6.2.3 we used

$$\int_{0_V} {}^{t+\Delta t}_0 S_{ij}\, \delta^{t+\Delta t}_0 \epsilon_{ij}\, d^0V = \int_{0_V} {}^{t+\Delta t}_0 S_{ij}\, \delta_0 \epsilon_{ij}\, d^0V$$

and hence, here $\delta {}^t_0\epsilon_{ij} = 0$. But we also used

$$\int_{0_V} {}^t_0 S_{ij}\, \delta_0 e_{ij}\, d^0V = \int_{0_V} {}^t_0 S_{ij}\, \delta^t_0 \epsilon_{ij}\, d^0V$$

and hence, here $\delta\,_0 e_{ij} = \delta {}^t_0 \epsilon_{ij}$ and clearly $\delta {}^t_0\epsilon_{ij} \neq 0$. Discuss briefly why all these equations are correct.

6.30. Establish the second Piola-Kirchhoff stresses $_0^t S_{ij}$ and the variations in the Green-Lagrange strains $\delta_0^t \epsilon_{ij}$ for the disk in Exercise 6.27 and show explicitly that for this case, $\int_{t_V} {}^t\tau_{ij} \, \delta_t e_{ij} \, d^t V = \int_{0_V} {}_0^t S_{ij} \, \delta_0^t \epsilon_{ij} \, d^0 V$ is indeed true.

6.3 DISPLACEMENT-BASED ISOPARAMETRIC CONTINUUM FINITE ELEMENTS

In the previous section we developed the linearized principle of virtual displacements (linearized about the state at time t) in *continuum* form. The only variables in the equations are the displacements of the material particles.

   If finite elements with only nodal point displacements as degrees of freedom are considered, then the governing finite element matrices corresponding to a full linearization of the principle of virtual displacements about the state at time t can be obtained directly by use of the equations given in the previous section. The key point to note is that in this case the element degrees of freedom, i.e., the element displacements, are exactly the variables with respect to which the general principle of virtual displacements has been linearized. Let us consider the following derivation to emphasize this point. This derivation will also show that if other than displacement degrees of freedom are used, such as rotations in structural elements or stresses in mixed formulations, the linearization with respect to such finite element degrees of freedom is more efficiently achieved by a direct Taylor series expansion with respect to such variables.

6.3.1 Linearization of the Principle of Virtual Work with Respect to Finite Element Variables

The principle of virtual displacements in the total Lagrangian formulation is given by

$$\int_{0_V} {}^{t+\Delta t}_0 S_{ij} \, \delta^{t+\Delta t}_0 \epsilon_{ij} \, d^0 V = {}^{t+\Delta t}\mathcal{R} \tag{6.89}$$

   Let us linearize this expression with respect to a general finite element nodal degree of freedom $^t a_k$, where $^t a_k$ may be a displacement or rotation. We assume that $^{t+\Delta t}\mathcal{R}$ is independent of the deformations. We then have, using a Taylor series expansion,

$$^{t+\Delta t}_0 S_{ij} \, \delta^{t+\Delta t}_0 \epsilon_{ij} \doteq {}_0^t S_{ij} \, \delta_0^t \epsilon_{ij} + \frac{\partial}{\partial^t a_k} \left({}_0^t S_{ij} \, \delta_0^t \epsilon_{ij} \right) da_k \tag{6.90}$$

where da_k is a differential increment in $^t a_k$. We note that

$$\delta_0^t \epsilon_{ij} = \frac{\partial_0^t \epsilon_{ij}}{\partial^t a_l} \delta a_l \tag{6.91}$$

where δa_l is a variation in $^t a_l$, and hence the variation is taken with respect to the nodal parameter $^t a_l$ about the configuration at time t.

The second term in (6.90) may be chain-differentiated to obtain

$$\frac{\partial}{\partial^t a_k}(_0^t S_{ij}\,\delta_0^t\epsilon_{ij})\,da_k = \frac{\partial_0^t S_{ij}}{\partial^t a_k}\delta_0^t\epsilon_{ij}\,da_k + {}_0^t S_{ij}\frac{\partial}{\partial^t a_k}(\delta_0^t\epsilon_{ij})\,da_k$$

$$= \left(\frac{\partial_0^t S_{ij}}{\partial_0^t\epsilon_{rs}}\frac{\partial_0^t\epsilon_{rs}}{\partial^t a_k}\right)\left(\frac{\partial_0^t\epsilon_{ij}}{\partial^t a_l}\delta a_l\right)da_k + {}_0^t S_{ij}\frac{\partial}{\partial^t a_k}\left(\frac{\partial_0^t\epsilon_{ij}}{\partial^t a_l}\delta a_l\right)da_k \qquad (6.92)$$

$$= {}_0 C_{ijrs}\frac{\partial_0^t\epsilon_{rs}}{\partial^t a_k}\frac{\partial_0^t\epsilon_{ij}}{\partial^t a_l}\delta a_l\,da_k + {}_0^t S_{ij}\frac{\partial^2\,_0^t\epsilon_{ij}}{\partial^t a_k\,\partial^t a_l}\delta a_l\,da_k$$

where in the last step we used

$$\frac{\partial_0^t S_{ij}}{\partial_0^t\epsilon_{rs}} = {}_0 C_{ijrs} \qquad (6.93)$$

Using the definition of the Green-Lagrange strain, we further have

$$\frac{\partial_0^t\epsilon_{ij}}{\partial^t a_k} = \frac{1}{2}\left(\frac{\partial_0^t u_{i,j}}{\partial^t a_k} + \frac{\partial_0^t u_{j,i}}{\partial^t a_k} + {}_0^t u_{m,i}\frac{\partial_0^t u_{m,j}}{\partial^t a_k} + {}_0^t u_{m,j}\frac{\partial_0^t u_{m,i}}{\partial^t a_k}\right) \qquad (6.94)$$

and

$$\frac{\partial^2\,_0^t\epsilon_{ij}}{\partial^t a_k\,\partial^t a_l} = \frac{1}{2}\left({}_0^t x_{m,i}\frac{\partial^2\,_0^t u_{m,j}}{\partial^t a_k\,\partial^t a_l} + {}_0^t x_{m,j}\frac{\partial^2\,_0^t u_{m,i}}{\partial^t a_k\,\partial^t a_l} + \frac{\partial_0^t u_{m,i}}{\partial^t a_k}\frac{\partial_0^t u_{m,j}}{\partial^t a_l} + \frac{\partial_0^t u_{m,i}}{\partial^t a_l}\frac{\partial_0^t u_{m,j}}{\partial^t a_k}\right) \qquad (6.95)$$

The substitution of (6.90) and (6.92) into the principle of virtual displacements (6.89) gives

$$\left\{\int_{0_V} {}_0 C_{ijrs}\frac{\partial_0^t\epsilon_{rs}}{\partial^t a_k}\frac{\partial_0^t\epsilon_{ij}}{\partial^t a_l}\,d^0V + \int_{0_V} {}_0^t S_{ij}\frac{\partial^2\,_0^t\epsilon_{ij}}{\partial^t a_k\,\partial^t a_l}\,d^0V\right\}da_k\,\delta a_l = {}^{t+\Delta t}\mathcal{R}_l - \left(\int_{0_V} {}_0^t S_{ij}\frac{\partial_0^t\epsilon_{ij}}{\partial^t a_l}\,d^0V\right)\delta a_l$$

$$(6.96)$$

where ${}^{t+\Delta t}\mathcal{R}_l$ denotes the external virtual work corresponding to δa_l.

If we now compare the expression in (6.96) [and using (6.94) and (6.95)] with the linearized principle of virtual displacement expression in Table 6.2, we recognize that for isoparametric displacement-based continuum elements with nodal displacement degrees of freedom only, both expressions can directly, and easily, be employed to obtain the same finite element equations. However, for elements with rotational degrees of freedom, the expression in (6.96) may be more direct for the derivation of the fully linearized finite element equations. Namely, the second derivatives of the displacement gradients with respect to the nodal point variables appearing in (6.95) are then not zero, and their effect also needs to be included. Consequently, if the continuum linearizations in Tables 6.2 and 6.3 are used, it must be recognized that the terms $_0^t S_{ij}\,\delta_0 e_{ij}$ and $^t\tau_{ij}\,\delta_t e_{ij}$, on the right-hand side of the equations, still contribute terms to the stiffness matrix when $_0 e_{ij}$ and $_t e_{ij}$ are not a linear function of the nodal point variables (see Section 6.5).

If, in addition, other than displacement and rotational element degrees of freedom are used, then certainly the above approach of linearization is very effective (see Section 6.4 for the derivation of the displacement/pressure formulations).

Here we have considered only a total Lagrangian formulation but should recognize that the same procedure of linearization is also applicable to updated Lagrangian formulations, and to all these formulations with all different material descriptions. The same procedure can also be employed to linearize the external virtual work term in (6.89) in case the loading is deformation dependent.

6.3.2 General Matrix Equations of Displacement-Based Continuum Elements

Let us now consider in more detail the matrices of isoparametric continuum finite elements with displacement degrees of freedom only.

The basic steps in the derivation of the governing finite element equations are the same as those used in linear analysis: the selection of the interpolation functions and the interpolation of the element coordinates and displacements with these functions in the governing continuum mechanics equations. By invoking the linearized principle of virtual displacements for each of the nodal point displacements in turn, the governing finite element equations are obtained. As in linear analysis, we need to consider only a single element of a specific type in this derivation because the governing equilibrium equations of an assemblage of elements can be constructed using the direct stiffness procedure.

In considering the element coordinate and displacement interpolations, we should recognize that it is important to employ the same interpolations for the coordinates and displacements at any and all times during the motion of the element. Since the new element coordinates are obtained by adding the element displacements to the original coordinates, it follows that the use of the same interpolations for the displacements and coordinates represents a consistent solution approach, and means that the discussions on convergence requirements in Sections 4.3 and 5.3.3 are directly applicable to the incremental analysis. In particular, it is then ensured that an assemblage of elements that are displacement-compatible across element boundaries in the original configuration will preserve this compatibility in all subsequent configurations.

In Sections 6.2.3 and 6.3.1 we derived the basic incremental equations used in our finite element formulations. While in practice an iteration is necessary, we also recognized that the equations in Tables 6.2 and 6.3 and Section 6.3.1 are the basic relations that are used in such iterations. Hence, in the following presentation we only need to focus on the basic incremental equations derived in Tables 6.2 and 6.3 (with the discussion in Section 6.3.1) and summarized in (6.74) and (6.75).

Substituting now the element coordinate and displacement interpolations into these equations as we did in linear analysis, we obtain—for a single element or for an assemblage of elements—

in materially-nonlinear-only analysis:
static analysis:

$$^t\mathbf{K}\mathbf{U} = {}^{t+\Delta t}\mathbf{R} - {}^t\mathbf{F} \tag{6.97}$$

dynamic analysis, implicit time integration:

$$\mathbf{M}\,{}^{t+\Delta t}\ddot{\mathbf{U}} + {}^t\mathbf{K}\mathbf{U} = {}^{t+\Delta t}\mathbf{R} - {}^t\mathbf{F} \tag{6.98}$$

dynamic analysis, explicit time integration:

$$\mathbf{M}\,{}^t\ddot{\mathbf{U}} = {}^t\mathbf{R} - {}^t\mathbf{F} \tag{6.99}$$

using the TL formulation:
static analysis:

$$({}_0^t\mathbf{K}_L + {}_0^t\mathbf{K}_{NL})\mathbf{U} = {}^{t+\Delta t}\mathbf{R} - {}_0^t\mathbf{F} \tag{6.100}$$

dynamic analysis, implicit time integration:

$$\mathbf{M}\,{}^{t+\Delta t}\ddot{\mathbf{U}} + ({}_0^t\mathbf{K}_L + {}_0^t\mathbf{K}_{NL})\mathbf{U} = {}^{t+\Delta t}\mathbf{R} - {}_0^t\mathbf{F} \qquad (6.101)$$

dynamic analysis, explicit time integration:

$$\mathbf{M}\,{}^t\ddot{\mathbf{U}} = {}^t\mathbf{R} - {}_0^t\mathbf{F} \qquad (6.102)$$

and using the UL formulation:
static analysis:

$$({}_t^t\mathbf{K}_L + {}_t^t\mathbf{K}_{NL})\mathbf{U} = {}^{t+\Delta t}\mathbf{R} - {}_t^t\mathbf{F} \qquad (6.103)$$

dynamic analysis, implicit time integration:

$$\mathbf{M}\,{}^{t+\Delta t}\ddot{\mathbf{U}} + ({}_t^t\mathbf{K}_L + {}_t^t\mathbf{K}_{NL})\mathbf{U} = {}^{t+\Delta t}\mathbf{R} - {}_t^t\mathbf{F} \qquad (6.104)$$

dynamic analysis, explicit time integration:

$$\mathbf{M}\,{}^t\ddot{\mathbf{U}} = {}^t\mathbf{R} - {}_t^t\mathbf{F} \qquad (6.105)$$

where $\mathbf{M}$ = time-independent mass matrix
$\quad\quad {}^t\mathbf{K}$ = linear strain incremental stiffness matrix, not including the initial displacement effect
$\quad {}_0^t\mathbf{K}_L, {}_t^t\mathbf{K}_L$ = linear strain incremental stiffness matrices
$\quad {}_0^t\mathbf{K}_{NL}, {}_t^t\mathbf{K}_{NL}$ = nonlinear strain (geometric or initial stress) incremental stiffness matrices
$\quad\quad {}^{t+\Delta t}\mathbf{R}$ = vector of externally applied nodal point loads at time $t + \Delta t$; this vector is also used at time t in explicit time integration
$\quad {}^t\mathbf{F}, {}_0^t\mathbf{F}, {}_t^t\mathbf{F}$ = vectors of nodal point forces equivalent to the element stresses at time t
$\quad\quad \mathbf{U}$ = vector of increments in the nodal point displacements
$\quad {}^t\ddot{\mathbf{U}}, {}^{t+\Delta t}\ddot{\mathbf{U}}$ = vectors of nodal point accelerations at times t and $t + \Delta t$

In the above finite element discretization we have assumed that damping effects are negligible or can be modeled in the nonlinear constitutive relationships (for example, by use of a strain-rate-dependent material law). We also assumed that the externally applied loads are deformation-independent, and thus the load vector corresponding to all load (or time) steps can be calculated prior to the incremental analysis. If the loads include deformation-dependent components, it is necessary to update and iterate on the load vector as briefly discussed in Section 6.2.3.

The above finite element matrices are evaluated as in linear analysis. Table 6.4 summarizes—for a single element—the basic integrals being considered and the corresponding matrix evaluations. The following notation is used for the calculation of the element matrices:

$\quad\quad \mathbf{H}^S, \mathbf{H}$ = surface- and volume-displacement interpolation matrices
$\quad {}^{t+\Delta t}_0\mathbf{f}^S, {}^{t+\Delta t}_0\mathbf{f}^B$ = vectors of surface and body forces defined per unit area and per unit volume of the element at time 0
$\quad \mathbf{B}_L, {}_0^t\mathbf{B}_L, {}_t^t\mathbf{B}_L$ = linear strain-displacement transformation matrices; $\mathbf{B}_L$ is equal to ${}_0^t\mathbf{B}_L$ when the initial displacement effect is neglected
$\quad {}_0^t\mathbf{B}_{NL}, {}_t^t\mathbf{B}_{NL}$ = nonlinear strain-displacement transformation matrices
$\quad\quad \mathbf{C}$ = stress-strain material property matrix (incremental or total)
$\quad {}_0\mathbf{C}, {}_t\mathbf{C}$ = incremental stress-strain material property matrices
$\quad {}^t\boldsymbol{\tau}, {}^t\hat{\boldsymbol{\tau}}$ = matrix and vector of Cauchy stresses
$\quad {}_0^t\mathbf{S}, {}_0^t\hat{\mathbf{S}}$ = matrix and vector of second Piola-Kirchhoff stresses
$\quad\quad {}^t\hat{\boldsymbol{\Sigma}}$ = vector of stresses in materially-nonlinear-only analysis

TABLE 6.4 *Finite element matrices*

Analysis type	Integral	Matrix evaluation
In all analyses	$\int_{0_V} {}^0\rho \, {}^{t+\Delta t}\ddot{u}_i \, \delta u_i \, d^0V$	$\mathbf{M} \, {}^{t+\Delta t}\ddot{\mathbf{u}} = \left(\int_{0_V} {}^0\rho \, \mathbf{H}^T\mathbf{H} \, d^0V \right) {}^{t+\Delta t}\ddot{\mathbf{u}}$
	${}^{t+\Delta t}\mathcal{R} = \int_{0_{S_f}} {}^{t+\Delta t}_0 f_i^S \, \delta u_i^S \, d^0S$	${}^{t+\Delta t}\mathbf{R} = \int_{0_{S_f}} \mathbf{H}^{S^T} \, {}^{t+\Delta t}_0 \mathbf{f}^S \, d^0S$
	$+ \int_{0_V} {}^{t+\Delta t}_0 f_i^B \, \delta u_i \, d^0V$	$+ \int_{0_V} \mathbf{H}^T \, {}^{t+\Delta t}_0 \mathbf{f}^B \, d^0V$
Materially-nonlinear-only	$\int_V C_{ijrs} \, e_{rs} \, \delta e_{ij} \, dV$	${}^t\mathbf{K}\hat{\mathbf{u}} = \left(\int_V \mathbf{B}_L^T \mathbf{C} \mathbf{B}_L \, dV \right) \hat{\mathbf{u}}$
	$\int_V {}^t\sigma_{ij} \, \delta e_{ij} \, dV$	${}^t\mathbf{F} = \int_V \mathbf{B}_L^T \, {}^t\hat{\boldsymbol{\Sigma}} \, dV$
Total Lagrangian formulation	$\int_{0_V} {}_0 C_{ijrs} \, {}_0e_{rs} \, \delta_0 e_{ij} \, d^0V$	${}_0^t\mathbf{K}_L\hat{\mathbf{u}} = \left(\int_{0_V} {}_0\mathbf{B}_L^T \, {}_0\mathbf{C} \, {}_0\mathbf{B}_L \, d^0V \right) \hat{\mathbf{u}}$
	$\int_{0_V} {}_0^t S_{ij} \, \delta_0 \eta_{ij} \, d^0V$	${}_0^t\mathbf{K}_{NL}\hat{\mathbf{u}} = \left(\int_{0_V} {}_0\mathbf{B}_{NL}^T \, {}_0^t\mathbf{S} \, {}_0\mathbf{B}_{NL} \, d^0V \right) \hat{\mathbf{u}}$
	$\int_{0_V} {}_0^t S_{ij} \, \delta_0 e_{ij} \, d^0V$	${}_0^t\mathbf{F} = \int_{0_V} {}_0\mathbf{B}_L^T \, {}_0^t\hat{\mathbf{S}} \, d^0V$
Updated Lagrangian formulation	$\int_{t_V} {}_t C_{ijrs} \, {}_te_{rs} \, \delta_t e_{ij} \, d^tV$	${}_t^t\mathbf{K}_L\hat{\mathbf{u}} \left(\int_{t_V} {}_t\mathbf{B}_L^T \, {}_t\mathbf{C} \, {}_t\mathbf{B}_L \, d^tV \right) \hat{\mathbf{u}}$
	$\int_{t_V} {}^t\tau_{ij} \, \delta_t \eta_{ij} \, d^tV$	${}_t^t\mathbf{K}_{NL}\hat{\mathbf{u}} = \left(\int_{t_V} {}_t\mathbf{B}_{NL}^T \, {}^t\boldsymbol{\tau} \, {}_t\mathbf{B}_{NL} \, d^tV \right) \hat{\mathbf{u}}$
	$\int_{t_V} {}^t\tau_{ij} \, \delta_t e_{ij} \, d^tV$	${}_t^t\mathbf{F} = \int_{t_V} {}_t\mathbf{B}_L^T \, {}^t\hat{\boldsymbol{\tau}} \, d^tV$

These matrices depend on the specific element considered. The displacement interpolation matrices are simply assembled as in linear analysis from the displacement interpolation functions. In the following sections we discuss the calculation of the strain-displacement and stress matrices and vectors pertaining to the continuum elements that we considered earlier for linear analysis in Chapter 5. The discussion is abbreviated because the basic numerical procedures employed in the calculation of the nonlinear finite matrices are those that we have already covered. For example, we consider again variable-number-nodes elements whose interpolation functions were previously given. As before, the displacement interpolations and strain-displacement matrices are expressed in terms of the isoparametric coordinates. Thus, the integrations indicated in Table 6.4 are performed as explained in Section 5.5.

In the following discussion we consider only the UL and TL formulations because the matrices of the materially-nonlinear-only analysis can be directly obtained from these formulations, and we are only concerned with the required kinematic expressions. The evaluation of the stresses and stress-strain matrices of the elements depends on the material model used. These considerations are discussed in Section 6.6.

6.3.3 Truss and Cable Elements

As discussed previously in Section 4.2.3, a truss element is a structural member capable of transmitting stresses only in the direction normal to the cross section. It is assumed that this normal stress is constant over the cross-sectional area.

In the following we consider a truss element that has an arbitrary orientation in space. The element is described by two to four nodes, as shown in Fig. 6.3, and is subjected to large displacements and large strains. The global coordinates of the nodal points of the element are at time 0, $^0x_1^k$, $^0x_2^k$, $^0x_3^k$ and at time t, $^tx_1^k$, $^tx_2^k$, $^tx_3^k$, where $k = 1, \ldots, N$, with N equal to the number of nodes ($2 \le N \le 4$). These nodal point coordinates are assumed to determine the spatial configuration of the truss at time 0 and time t using

$$^0x_1(r) = \sum_{k=1}^N h_k\,^0x_1^k; \qquad ^0x_2(r) = \sum_{k=1}^N h_k\,^0x_2^k; \qquad ^0x_3(r) = \sum_{k=1}^N h_k\,^0x_3^k \tag{6.106}$$

and

$$^tx_1(r) = \sum_{k=1}^N h_k\,^tx_1^k; \qquad ^tx_2(r) = \sum_{k=1}^N h_k\,^tx_2^k; \qquad ^tx_3(r) = \sum_{k=1}^N h_k\,^tx_3^k \tag{6.107}$$

where the interpolation functions $h_k(r)$ have been defined in Fig. 5.3. Using (6.106) and (6.107), it follows that

$$^tu_i(r) = \sum_{k=1}^N h_k\,^tu_i^k \tag{6.108}$$

and

$$u_i(r) = \sum_{k=1}^N h_k u_i^k, \qquad i = 1, 2, 3 \tag{6.109}$$

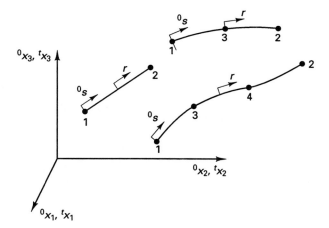

Figure 6.3   Two- to four-node truss element

Since for the truss element the only stress is the normal stress on its cross-sectional area, we consider only the corresponding longitudinal strain. Denoting the local element longitudinal strain by a curl, we have in the TL formulation,

$$_0^t\tilde{\epsilon}_{11} = \frac{d^0x_i}{d^0s}\frac{d^tu_i}{d^0s} + \frac{1}{2}\frac{d^tu_i}{d^0s}\frac{d^tu_i}{d^0s} \tag{6.110}$$

where $^0s(r)$ is the arc length at time 0 of the material point $^0x_1(r)$, $^0x_2(r)$, $^0x_3(r)$ given by

$$^0s(r) = \sum_{k=1}^{N} h_k \, ^0s_k \tag{6.111}$$

The increment in the strain component $^t_0\bar{\epsilon}_{11}$ is denoted as $_0\bar{\epsilon}_{11}$, where $_0\bar{\epsilon}_{11} = _0\tilde{e}_{11} + _0\tilde{\eta}_{11}$ and

$$_0\tilde{e}_{11} = \frac{d^0x_i}{d^0s}\frac{du_i}{d^0s} + \frac{d^tu_i}{d^0s}\frac{du_i}{d^0s} \tag{6.112}$$

$$_0\tilde{\eta}_{11} = \frac{1}{2}\frac{du_i}{d^0s}\frac{du_i}{d^0s} \tag{6.113}$$

For the strain-displacement matrices we define

$$^0\hat{\mathbf{x}}^T = [\,^0x_1^1 \quad ^0x_2^1 \quad ^0x_3^1 \quad \cdots \quad ^0x_1^N \quad ^0x_2^N \quad ^0x_3^N\,] \tag{6.114}$$

$$^t\hat{\mathbf{u}}^T = [\,^tu_1^1 \quad ^tu_2^1 \quad ^tu_3^1 \quad \cdots \quad ^tu_1^N \quad ^tu_2^N \quad ^tu_3^N\,]$$
$$\hat{\mathbf{u}}^T = [\,u_1^1 \quad u_2^1 \quad u_3^1 \quad \cdots \quad u_1^N \quad u_2^N \quad u_3^N\,] \tag{6.115}$$

$$\mathbf{H} = \left[h_1\mathbf{I}_3 \;\vdots\; \cdots \;\vdots\; h_N\mathbf{I}_3 \right]; \qquad \mathbf{I}_3 = \begin{bmatrix} 1 & 0 & 0 \\ 0 & 1 & 0 \\ 0 & 0 & 1 \end{bmatrix} \tag{6.116}$$

and hence, using (6.112) and (6.113),

$$^t_0\mathbf{B}_L = (^0J^{-1})^2 \, (^0\hat{\mathbf{x}}^T\mathbf{H}_{,r}^T\mathbf{H}_{,r} + {}^t\hat{\mathbf{u}}^T\mathbf{H}_{,r}^T\mathbf{H}_{,r}) \tag{6.117}$$

and
$$^t_0\mathbf{B}_{NL} = {}^0J^{-1}\mathbf{H}_{,r} \tag{6.118}$$

where $^0J^{-1} = dr/d^0s$. We note that since $^t_0\mathbf{B}_{NL}$ is independent of the orientation of the element, the matrix $^t_0\mathbf{K}_{NL}$ is so as well.

The only nonzero stress component is $^t_0\tilde{S}_{11}$, which we assume to be given as a function of the Green-Lagrange strain $^t_0\bar{\epsilon}_{11}$ at time t (see Section 6.6). The tangent stress-strain relationship is therefore

$$_0\tilde{C}_{1111} = \frac{\partial^t_0\tilde{S}_{11}}{\partial^t_0\bar{\epsilon}_{11}} \tag{6.119}$$

Using (6.114) to (6.119), the truss element matrices can be directly calculated as given in Table 6.4. Referring to Tables 6.2 to 6.4, the above relations can also be directly employed to develop the UL formulation, and of course the materially-nonlinear-only formulation. Consider the following examples.

EXAMPLE 6.16: For the two-node truss element shown in Fig. E6.16 develop the tangent stiffness matrix and force vector corresponding to the configuration at time t. Consider large displacement and large strain conditions.

We note that the element is straight and is at time 0 aligned with the $^0x_1$ axis. Hence, we need not use the curl on the stress and strain components, and the equations of the formulation are somewhat simpler than (6.110) to (6.119). In the following we use two formulation approaches to emphasize some important points.

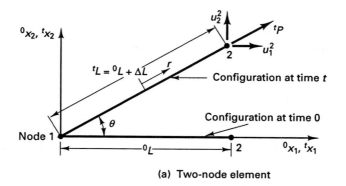

(a) Two-node element

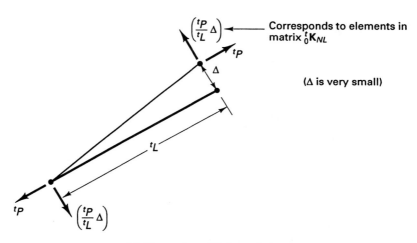

(b) Moment equilibrium of element

Figure E6.16   Formulation of two-node truss element

First Approach: Evaluation of Element Matrices Using Table 6.4: Using the TL formulation we need to express the strains $_0e_{11}$ and $_0\eta_{11}$ given in Table 6.2 [and (6.112) and (6.113)] in terms of the element displacement functions. Since the truss element undergoes displacements only in the $^0x_1$, $^0x_2$ plane, we have

$$_0e_{11} = \frac{\partial u_1}{\partial {}^0x_1} + \frac{\partial {}^tu_1}{\partial {}^0x_1}\frac{\partial u_1}{\partial {}^0x_1} + \frac{\partial {}^tu_2}{\partial {}^0x_1}\frac{\partial u_2}{\partial {}^0x_1}$$

$$_0\eta_{11} = \frac{1}{2}\left[\left(\frac{\partial u_1}{\partial {}^0x_1}\right)^2 + \left(\frac{\partial u_2}{\partial {}^0x_1}\right)^2\right]$$

But by geometry, or using $^tu_i = \Sigma_{k=1}^2 h_k\,{}^tu_i^k$ with $^tu_1^1 = 0$, $^tu_2^1 = 0$, $^tu_1^2 = ({}^0L + \Delta L)\cos\theta - {}^0L$, $^tu_2^2 = ({}^0L + \Delta L)\sin\theta$, $^0J = {}^0L/2$ and the interpolation functions given in Fig. 5.3, we obtain

$$\frac{\partial {}^tu_1}{\partial {}^0x_1} = \frac{({}^0L + \Delta L)\cos\theta}{{}^0L} - 1; \qquad \frac{\partial {}^tu_2}{\partial {}^0x_1} = \frac{({}^0L + \Delta L)\sin\theta}{{}^0L}$$

We therefore have

$$
_0e_{11} = \frac{1}{^0L}\left\{[-1 \quad 0 \quad 1 \quad 0] + \left(\frac{^0L + \Delta L}{^0L}\cos\theta - 1\right)[-1 \quad 0 \quad 1 \quad 0]\right.
$$

$$
\left. + \left(\frac{^0L + \Delta L}{^0L}\sin\theta\right)[0 \quad -1 \quad 0 \quad 1]\right\}
\begin{bmatrix} u_1^1 \\ u_2^1 \\ u_1^2 \\ u_2^2 \end{bmatrix}
$$

$$
= \frac{^0L + \Delta L}{(^0L)^2}[-\cos\theta \quad -\sin\theta \quad \cos\theta \quad \sin\theta]
\begin{bmatrix} u_1^1 \\ u_2^1 \\ u_1^2 \\ u_2^2 \end{bmatrix}
$$

and hence,

$$
_0^t\mathbf{B}_L = \frac{^0L + \Delta L}{(^0L)^2}[-\cos\theta \quad -\sin\theta \quad \cos\theta \quad \sin\theta]
$$

Of course, the same result for $_0^t\mathbf{B}_L$ is obtained using (6.117). The nonlinear strain displacement matrix is [from (6.118)]

$$
_0^t\mathbf{B}_{NL} = \frac{1}{^0L}\begin{bmatrix} -1 & 0 & 1 & 0 \\ 0 & -1 & 0 & 1 \end{bmatrix}
$$

In the total Lagrangian formulation we assume that $_0^tS_{11}$ is given in terms of $_0^t\epsilon_{11}$, and we have

$$
_0C_{1111} = \frac{\partial_0^tS_{11}}{\partial_0^t\epsilon_{11}}
$$

If we use $_0^tS_{11} = E_0^t\epsilon_{11}$, we have of course $_0C_{1111} = E$. The tangent stiffness matrix and force vector are therefore (see Table 6.4)

$$
_0^t\mathbf{K} = {_0C_{1111}}\frac{(^0L + \Delta L)^2}{(^0L)^3}{^0A}
\begin{bmatrix}
\cos^2\theta & \cos\theta\sin\theta & -\cos^2\theta & -\cos\theta\sin\theta \\
 & \sin^2\theta & -\sin\theta\cos\theta & -\sin^2\theta \\
 & & \cos^2\theta & \sin\theta\cos\theta \\
\text{Symmetric} & & & \sin^2\theta
\end{bmatrix}
$$

$$
+ \frac{^tP}{^0L + \Delta L}
\begin{bmatrix}
1 & 0 & -1 & 0 \\
0 & 1 & 0 & -1 \\
-1 & 0 & 1 & 0 \\
0 & -1 & 0 & 1
\end{bmatrix} \tag{a}
$$

$$
_0^t\mathbf{F} = {^tP}
\begin{bmatrix}
-\cos\theta \\
-\sin\theta \\
\cos\theta \\
\sin\theta
\end{bmatrix}
$$

where $'P$ is the current force carried in the truss element. Here we have used, with the Cauchy stress equal to $'P/'A$,

$$
{}_0^t S_{11} = \frac{{}^0\rho}{{}^t\rho}\left(\frac{{}^0 L}{{}^0 L + \Delta L}\right)^2 \frac{'P}{'A}; \qquad {}_0^t \epsilon_{11} = \frac{\Delta L}{{}^0 L} + \frac{1}{2}\left(\frac{\Delta L}{{}^0 L}\right)^2
$$

$$
{}^0\rho\, {}^0 L\, {}^0 A = {}^t\rho({}^0 L + \Delta L)\, 'A; \qquad {}_0^t S_{11} = \frac{{}^0 L}{{}^0 L + \Delta L}\frac{'P}{{}^0 A} \tag{b}
$$

$$
'P = {}_0^t S_{11}\, {}^0 A \frac{{}^0 L + \Delta L}{{}^0 L}
$$

The first term in (a) represents the linear strain stiffness matrix, and the second term is the nonlinear strain stiffness matrix, which, as noted earlier, is independent of the angle θ.

Second Approach: Taking the Derivative of the Force Vector ${}_0^t\mathbf{F}$:   The tangent stiffness matrix of any element can be obtained by direct differentiation of the force vector ${}_0^t\mathbf{F}$ (see Section 6.3.1); that is,

$$
{}_0^t\mathbf{K} = \frac{\partial {}_0^t\mathbf{F}}{\partial '\hat{\mathbf{u}}} \tag{c}
$$

where $'\hat{\mathbf{u}}$ is the vector of nodal point displacements corresponding to time t. Here we have for the general truss element formulation in (6.106) to (6.119), ${}_0^t\mathbf{F} = \int_{{}^0 V} {}_0^t\mathbf{B}_L^T\, {}_0^t\tilde{S}_{11}\, d^0 V$, so that

$$
\frac{\partial {}_0^t\mathbf{F}}{\partial '\hat{\mathbf{u}}} = \int_{{}^0 V} {}_0^t\mathbf{B}_L^T \frac{\partial {}_0^t\tilde{S}_{11}}{\partial {}_0^t\tilde{\epsilon}_{11}}\frac{\partial {}_0^t\tilde{\epsilon}_{11}}{\partial '\hat{\mathbf{u}}}\, d^0 V + \int_{{}^0 V} \frac{\partial {}_0^t\mathbf{B}_L^T}{\partial '\hat{\mathbf{u}}}\, {}_0^t\tilde{S}_{11}\, d^0 V \tag{d}
$$

Using (6.117) and (6.118), we have

$$
\frac{\partial {}_0^t\mathbf{B}_L^T}{\partial '\hat{\mathbf{u}}} = ({}^0 J^{-1})^2\, \mathbf{H}_{,r}^T\, \mathbf{H}_{,r} = {}_0^t\mathbf{B}_{NL}^T\, {}_0^t\mathbf{B}_{NL}
$$

so that the second term in (d) gives the ${}_0^t\mathbf{K}_{NL}$ matrix. Also, using (6.110) and (6.117), we directly see that

$$
\frac{\partial {}_0^t\tilde{\epsilon}_{11}}{\partial '\hat{\mathbf{u}}} = {}_0^t\mathbf{B}_L
$$

and hence, the first term in (d) gives the ${}_0^t\mathbf{K}_L$ matrix.

However, to gain more insight, let us consider the derivation of ${}_0^t\mathbf{K}$ in (c) specifically for the two-node truss element in Fig. E6.16 using the following details.

For the two-node element, ${}_0^t\mathbf{F}$ is given by simple equilibrium

$$
{}_0^t\mathbf{F} = {}'P \begin{bmatrix} -\cos\theta \\ -\sin\theta \\ \cos\theta \\ \sin\theta \end{bmatrix}
$$

where $'P$ is the current force (positive when a tensile force) carried by the element, and we have

$$
'\hat{\mathbf{u}}^T = [\,'u_1^1 \quad 'u_2^1 \quad 'u_1^2 \quad 'u_2^2\,]
$$

Let us consider the third and fourth columns of the stiffness matrix (from which the first and second columns can be derived). We have

$$'u_1^2 = ({}^0L + \Delta L) \cos \theta - {}^0L$$

$$'u_2^2 = ({}^0L + \Delta L) \sin \theta$$

and hence,

$$\begin{bmatrix} \dfrac{\partial}{\partial(\Delta L)} \\[2ex] \dfrac{\partial}{\partial \theta} \end{bmatrix} = \begin{bmatrix} \cos \theta & \sin \theta \\[1ex] -({}^0L + \Delta L) \sin \theta & ({}^0L + \Delta L) \cos \theta \end{bmatrix} \begin{bmatrix} \dfrac{\partial}{\partial \, 'u_1^2} \\[2ex] \dfrac{\partial}{\partial \, 'u_2^2} \end{bmatrix}$$

from which

$$\begin{bmatrix} \dfrac{\partial}{\partial \, 'u_1^2} \\[2ex] \dfrac{\partial}{\partial \, 'u_2^2} \end{bmatrix} = \begin{bmatrix} \cos \theta & -\dfrac{\sin \theta}{{}^0L + \Delta L} \\[2ex] \sin \theta & \dfrac{\cos \theta}{{}^0L + \Delta L} \end{bmatrix} \begin{bmatrix} \dfrac{\partial}{\partial(\Delta L)} \\[2ex] \dfrac{\partial}{\partial \theta} \end{bmatrix}$$

Therefore, the third column of ${}_0^t\mathbf{K}$ is given by[7]

$$\frac{\partial {}_0^t\mathbf{F}}{\partial \, 'u_1^2} = \frac{\partial {}_0^t\mathbf{F}}{\partial(\Delta L)} \frac{\partial(\Delta L)}{\partial \, 'u_1^2} + \frac{\partial {}_0^t\mathbf{F}}{\partial \theta} \frac{\partial \theta}{\partial \, 'u_1^2}$$

$$= \frac{\partial \, {}^tP}{\partial(\Delta L)} \begin{bmatrix} -\cos \theta \\ -\sin \theta \\ \cos \theta \\ \sin \theta \end{bmatrix} \cos \theta + {}^tP \begin{bmatrix} \sin \theta \\ -\cos \theta \\ -\sin \theta \\ \cos \theta \end{bmatrix} \left(\frac{-\sin \theta}{{}^0L + \Delta L} \right) \qquad (e)$$

$$= \frac{\partial \left(\dfrac{{}^tP}{{}^0L + \Delta L} \right)}{\partial(\Delta L)} ({}^0L + \Delta L) \begin{bmatrix} -\cos^2 \theta \\ -\sin \theta \cos \theta \\ \cos^2 \theta \\ \sin \theta \cos \theta \end{bmatrix} + \frac{{}^tP}{{}^0L + \Delta L} \begin{bmatrix} -1 \\ 0 \\ 1 \\ 0 \end{bmatrix}$$

Similarly, for the fourth column of ${}_0^t\mathbf{K}$,

$$\frac{\partial {}_0^t\mathbf{F}}{\partial \, 'u_2^2} = \frac{\partial {}_0^t\mathbf{F}}{\partial(\Delta L)} \frac{\partial(\Delta L)}{\partial \, 'u_2^2} + \frac{\partial {}_0^t\mathbf{F}}{\partial \theta} \frac{\partial \theta}{\partial \, 'u_2^2}$$

$$= \frac{\partial \left(\dfrac{{}^tP}{{}^0L + \Delta L} \right)}{\partial(\Delta L)} ({}^0L + \Delta L) \begin{bmatrix} -\cos \theta \sin \theta \\ -\sin^2 \theta \\ \sin \theta \cos \theta \\ \sin^2 \theta \end{bmatrix} + \frac{{}^tP}{{}^0L + \Delta L} \begin{bmatrix} 0 \\ -1 \\ 0 \\ 1 \end{bmatrix} \qquad (f)$$

However, using (b),

$$\frac{\partial \left(\dfrac{{}^tP}{{}^0L + \Delta L} \right)}{\partial(\Delta L)} ({}^0L + \Delta L) = \frac{\partial \, {}_0^tS_{11}}{\partial(\Delta L)} \frac{{}^0L + \Delta L}{{}^0L} \, {}^0A$$

$$= \frac{\partial \, {}_0^tS_{11}}{\partial \, {}_0^t\epsilon_{11}} \frac{\partial \, {}_0^t\epsilon_{11}}{\partial(\Delta L)} \frac{{}^0L + \Delta L}{{}^0L} \, {}^0A = \frac{\partial \, {}_0^tS_{11}}{\partial \, {}_0^t\epsilon_{11}} \frac{({}^0L + \Delta L)^2}{{}^0L^3} \, {}^0A$$

$$= {}_0C_{1111} \frac{({}^0L + \Delta L)^2}{{}^0L^3} \, {}^0A$$

[7] Note that if the material stress-strain relationship is such that ${}^tP$ is constant with changes in ΔL, only the second term in the second line of this equation is nonzero.

Hence, the results in (e) and (f) are those already given in (a).

We note that the entries in the nonlinear strain stiffness matrix can also be directly obtained from equilibrium considerations as shown in Fig. E6.16(b).

Also, the updated Lagrangian formulation could be obtained from the result in (a) by using the relation (see Example 6.23)

$$ {}_0C_{1111} = \frac{{}^0\rho}{{}^t\rho}\left(\frac{{}^0L}{{}^0L + \Delta L}\right)^4 {}_tC_{1111} $$

so that in (a)
$$ {}_0C_{1111}\frac{({}^0L + \Delta L)^2}{({}^0L)^3}\,{}^0A = {}_tC_{1111}\frac{{}^tA}{{}^0L + \Delta L} \tag{g} $$

If we also note that for infinitesimally small displacements the linear strain stiffness matrix reduces to the well-known truss element matrix (see Example 4.1), we recognize that with the result of (g) substituted in (a), the updated Lagrangian stiffness matrix is in fact what we would expect it to be from physical considerations.

EXAMPLE 6.17:   Establish the equilibrium equations used in the nonlinear analysis of the simple arch structure considered in Example 6.3 when the modified Newton-Raphson iteration is used for solution.

In the modified Newton-Raphson iteration, we use (6.11) and (6.12) but evaluate new tangent stiffness matrices only at the beginning of each step.

As in Example 6.3, we idealize the structure using one truss element [see Fig. E6.3(b)]. Since the displacements at node 1 are zero, we need to consider only the displacements at node 2. Using the derivations given in Example 6.16, with $\theta = {}^t\beta$ we have

$$ {}_0^t\mathbf{K}_L = \frac{EA}{L}\begin{bmatrix} (\cos{}^t\beta)^2 & \sin{}^t\beta\cos{}^t\beta \\ \sin{}^t\beta\cos{}^t\beta & (\sin{}^t\beta)^2 \end{bmatrix} $$

$$ {}_0^t\mathbf{K}_{NL} = \frac{{}^tP}{L}\begin{bmatrix} 1 & 0 \\ 0 & 1 \end{bmatrix} $$

$$ {}_0^t\mathbf{F} = {}^tP\begin{bmatrix} \cos{}^t\beta \\ \sin{}^t\beta \end{bmatrix} $$

where we assumed in the stiffness expressions that L and EA/L are constant throughout the response.

The matrices correspond to the global displacements ${}^tu_1^2$ and ${}^tu_2^2$ at node 2. However, ${}^tu_1^2$ is zero, hence the governing equilibrium equation is

$$ \left[\frac{EA}{L}(\sin{}^t\beta)^2 + \frac{{}^tP}{L}\right]\Delta u_2^{2(i)} = -\frac{{}^{t+\Delta t}R}{2} - {}^{t+\Delta t}P^{(i-1)}\sin({}^{t+\Delta t}\beta^{(i-1)}) $$

where ${}^{t+\Delta t}R/2$ is positive as shown in Fig. E6.3(b) and ${}^{t+\Delta t}P^{(i-1)}$ is the force in the bar (tensile force being positive) corresponding to the displacements at time $t + \Delta t$ and end of iteration $(i - 1)$.

6.3.4 Two-Dimensional Axisymmetric, Plane Strain, and Plane Stress Elements

For the derivation of the required matrices and vectors, we consider a typical two-dimensional element in its configuration at time 0 and at time t, as illustrated for a nine-node element in Fig. 6.4. The global coordinates of the nodal points of the element are

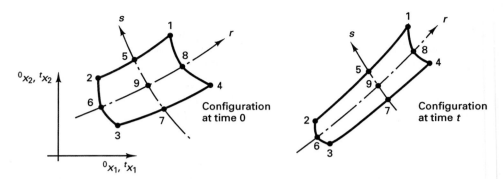

Figure 6.4   Two-dimensional element shown in the global $'x_1, 'x_2$ plane

at time 0, $^0x_1^k$, $^0x_2^k$, and at time t, $'x_1^k$, $'x_2^k$, where $k = 1, 2, \ldots, N$, and N denotes the total number of element nodes.

Using the interpolation concepts discussed in Section 5.3, we have at time 0,

$$^0x_1 = \sum_{k=1}^{N} h_k \,{}^0x_1^k; \qquad {}^0x_2 = \sum_{k=1}^{N} h_k \,{}^0x_2^k \tag{6.120}$$

and at time t

$$'x_1 = \sum_{k=1}^{N} h_k \,'x_1^k; \qquad 'x_2 = \sum_{k=1}^{N} h_k \,'x_2^k \tag{6.121}$$

where the h_k are the interpolation functions presented in Fig. 5.4.

Since we use the isoparametric finite element discretization, the element displacements are interpolated in the same way as the geometry; i.e.,

$$'u_1 = \sum_{k=1}^{N} h_k \,'u_1^k; \qquad 'u_2 = \sum_{k=1}^{N} h_k \,'u_2^k \tag{6.122}$$

$$u_1 = \sum_{k=1}^{N} h_k \, u_1^k; \qquad u_2 = \sum_{k=1}^{N} h_k \, u_2^k \tag{6.123}$$

The evaluation of strains requires the following derivatives:

$$\frac{\partial 'u_i}{\partial ^0x_j} = \sum_{k=1}^{N} \left(\frac{\partial h_k}{\partial ^0x_j} \right) 'u_i^k \tag{6.124}$$

$$\frac{\partial u_i}{\partial ^0x_j} = \sum_{k=1}^{N} \left(\frac{\partial h_k}{\partial ^0x_j} \right) u_i^k \qquad \begin{matrix} i = 1, 2 \\ j = 1, 2 \end{matrix} \tag{6.125}$$

$$\frac{\partial u_i}{\partial 'x_j} = \sum_{k=1}^{N} \left(\frac{\partial h_k}{\partial 'x_j} \right) u_i^k \tag{6.126}$$

These derivatives are calculated in the same way as in linear analysis, i.e., using a Jacobian transformation. As an example, consider briefly the evaluation of the derivatives in (6.126). The other derivatives are obtained in an analogous manner.

The chain rule relating $'x_1$, $'x_2$, to r, s derivatives is written as

$$
\begin{bmatrix} \dfrac{\partial}{\partial r} \\[2ex] \dfrac{\partial}{\partial s} \end{bmatrix} = {}^t\mathbf{J} \begin{bmatrix} \dfrac{\partial}{\partial {}^t x_1} \\[2ex] \dfrac{\partial}{\partial {}^t x_2} \end{bmatrix}
$$

in which

$$
{}^t\mathbf{J} = \begin{bmatrix} \dfrac{\partial {}^t x_1}{\partial r} & \dfrac{\partial {}^t x_2}{\partial r} \\[2ex] \dfrac{\partial {}^t x_1}{\partial s} & \dfrac{\partial {}^t x_2}{\partial s} \end{bmatrix}
$$

Inverting the Jacobian operator $\mathbf{J}$, we obtain

$$
\begin{bmatrix} \dfrac{\partial}{\partial {}^t x_1} \\[2ex] \dfrac{\partial}{\partial {}^t x_2} \end{bmatrix} = \frac{1}{\det {}^t\mathbf{J}} \begin{bmatrix} \dfrac{\partial {}^t x_2}{\partial s} & -\dfrac{\partial {}^t x_2}{\partial r} \\[2ex] -\dfrac{\partial {}^t x_1}{\partial s} & \dfrac{\partial {}^t x_1}{\partial r} \end{bmatrix} \begin{bmatrix} \dfrac{\partial}{\partial r} \\[2ex] \dfrac{\partial}{\partial s} \end{bmatrix}
$$

where the Jacobian determinant is

$$
\det {}^t\mathbf{J} = \frac{\partial {}^t x_1}{\partial r}\frac{\partial {}^t x_2}{\partial s} - \frac{\partial {}^t x_1}{\partial s}\frac{\partial {}^t x_2}{\partial r}
$$

and the derivatives of the coordinates with respect to r and s are obtained as usual using (6.121); e.g.,

$$
\frac{\partial {}^t x_1}{\partial r} = \sum_{k=1}^{N} \frac{\partial h_k}{\partial r} {}^t x_1^k
$$

With all required derivatives defined, it is now possible to establish the strain-displacement transformation matrices for the elements. Table 6.5 gives the required matrices for the UL and TL formulations. In the numerical integration these matrices are evaluated at the Gauss integration points (see Section 5.5).

As we pointed out earlier, the choice between the TL and UL formulations essentially depends on their relative numerical effectiveness. Table 6.5 shows that all matrices of the two formulations have corresponding patterns of zero elements, except that ${}_0^t\mathbf{B}_L$ is a full matrix whereas ${}_t^t\mathbf{B}_L$ is sparse. The strain-displacement transformation matrix ${}_0^t\mathbf{B}_L$ is full because of the initial displacement effect in the linear strain terms (see Tables 6.2 and 6.3). Therefore, the calculation of the matrix product ${}_t^t\mathbf{B}_L^T\,{}_t\mathbf{C}\,{}_t^t\mathbf{B}_L$ in the UL formulation requires less time than the calculation of the matrix product ${}_0^t\mathbf{B}_L^T\,{}_0\mathbf{C}\,{}_0^t\mathbf{B}_L$ in the TL formulation.

The second numerical difference between the two formulations is that in the TL formulation all derivatives of interpolation functions are with respect to the initial coordinates, whereas in the UL formulation all derivatives are with respect to the coordinates at time t. Therefore, in the TL formulation the derivatives could be calculated only once in the first load step and stored on back-up storage for use in all subsequent load steps. However, in practice, such storage can be expensive and in a computer implementation the derivatives of the interpolation functions are in general best recalculated in each time step.

TABLE 6.5 *Matrices used in the two-dimensional element formulation*

A. *Total Lagrangian formulation*
  1. *Incremental strains*

$$_0\epsilon_{11} = {_0u_{1,1}} + {_0^tu_{1,1}}\,{_0u_{1,1}} + {_0^tu_{2,1}}\,{_0u_{2,1}} + \tfrac{1}{2}(({_0u_{1,1}})^2 + ({_0u_{2,1}})^2)$$

$$_0\epsilon_{22} = {_0u_{2,2}} + {_0^tu_{1,2}}\,{_0u_{1,2}} + {_0^tu_{2,2}}\,{_0u_{2,2}} + \tfrac{1}{2}(({_0u_{1,2}})^2 + ({_0u_{2,2}})^2)$$

$$_0\epsilon_{12} = \tfrac{1}{2}({_0u_{1,2}} + {_0u_{2,1}}) + \tfrac{1}{2}({_0^tu_{1,1}}\,{_0u_{1,2}} + {_0^tu_{2,1}}\,{_0u_{2,2}} + {_0^tu_{1,2}}\,{_0u_{1,1}} + {_0^tu_{2,2}}\,{_0u_{2,1}}) + \tfrac{1}{2}({_0u_{1,1}}\,{_0u_{1,2}} + {_0u_{2,1}}\,{_0u_{2,2}})$$

$$_0\epsilon_{33} = \frac{u_1}{^0x_1} + \frac{^tu_1u_1}{(^0x_1)^2} + \frac{1}{2}\left(\frac{u_1}{^0x_1}\right)^2 \qquad \text{for axisymmetric analysis}$$

where $\; _0u_{i,j} = \dfrac{\partial u_i}{\partial\,^0x_j}; \qquad _0^tu_{i,j} = \dfrac{\partial\,^tu_i}{\partial\,^0x_j}$

  2. *Linear strain-displacement transformation matrix*
   Using $\;_0\mathbf{e} = {_0^t\mathbf{B}_L}\hat{\mathbf{u}}$
   where $_0\mathbf{e}^T = [{_0e_{11}}\quad {_0e_{22}}\quad 2{_0e_{12}}\quad {_0e_{33}}]; \qquad \hat{\mathbf{u}}^T = [u_1^1\quad u_2^1\quad u_1^2\quad u_2^2 \cdots u_1^N\quad u_2^N]$
   and $\quad {_0^t\mathbf{B}_L} = {_0^t\mathbf{B}_{L0}} + {_0^t\mathbf{B}_{L1}}$

$$_0^t\mathbf{B}_{L0} = \begin{bmatrix} {_0h_{1,1}} & 0 & {_0h_{2,1}} & 0 & {_0h_{3,1}} & 0 & \cdots & {_0h_{N,1}} & 0 \\ 0 & {_0h_{1,2}} & 0 & {_0h_{2,2}} & 0 & {_0h_{3,2}} & \cdots & 0 & {_0h_{N,2}} \\ {_0h_{1,2}} & {_0h_{1,1}} & {_0h_{2,2}} & {_0h_{2,1}} & {_0h_{3,2}} & {_0h_{3,1}} & \cdots & {_0h_{N,2}} & {_0h_{N,1}} \\ \dfrac{h_1}{^0\overline{x_1}} & 0 & \dfrac{h_2}{^0\overline{x_1}} & 0 & \dfrac{h_3}{^0\overline{x_1}} & 0 & \cdots & \dfrac{h_N}{^0\overline{x_1}} & 0 \end{bmatrix}$$

   where $\; _0h_{k,j} = \dfrac{\partial h_k}{\partial\,^0x_j}; \qquad u_j^k = {^{t+\Delta t}u_j^k} - {^tu_j^k}; \qquad {^0\overline{x_1}} = \sum\limits_{k=1}^{N} h_k\,{^0x_1^k}; \qquad N = \text{number of nodes}$

and

$$_0^t\mathbf{B}_{L1} = \begin{bmatrix} l_{11}\,{_0h_{1,1}} & l_{21}\,{_0h_{1,1}} & l_{11}\,{_0h_{2,1}} & l_{21}\,{_0h_{2,1}} \\ l_{12}\,{_0h_{1,2}} & l_{22}\,{_0h_{1,2}} & l_{12}\,{_0h_{2,2}} & l_{22}\,{_0h_{2,2}} \\ (l_{11}\,{_0h_{1,2}} + l_{12}\,{_0h_{1,1}}) & (l_{21}\,{_0h_{1,2}} + l_{22}\,{_0h_{1,1}}) & (l_{11}\,{_0h_{2,2}} + l_{12}\,{_0h_{2,1}}) & (l_{21}\,{_0h_{2,2}} + l_{22}\,{_0h_{2,1}}) \\ l_{33}\dfrac{h_1}{^0\overline{x_1}} & 0 & l_{33}\dfrac{h_2}{^0\overline{x_1}} & 0 \end{bmatrix}$$

$$\begin{matrix} \cdots & l_{11}\,{_0h_{N,1}} & l_{21}\,{_0h_{N,1}} \\ \cdots & l_{12}\,{_0h_{N,2}} & l_{22}\,{_0h_{N,2}} \\ \cdots & (l_{11}\,{_0h_{N,2}} + l_{12}\,{_0h_{N,1}}) & (l_{21}\,{_0h_{N,2}} + l_{22}\,{_0h_{N,1}}) \\ \cdots & l_{33}\dfrac{h_N}{^0\overline{x_1}} & 0 \end{matrix}$$

   where $\; l_{11} = \sum\limits_{k=1}^{N} {_0h_{k,1}}\,{^tu_1^k}; \qquad l_{22} = \sum\limits_{k=1}^{N} {_0h_{k,2}}\,{^tu_2^k}; \qquad l_{21} = \sum\limits_{k=1}^{N} {_0h_{k,1}}\,{^tu_2^k}; \qquad l_{12} = \sum\limits_{k=1}^{N} {_0h_{k,2}}\,{^tu_1^k};$

$$l_{33} = \frac{\sum\limits_{k=1}^{N} h_k\,{^tu_1^k}}{^0\overline{x_1}}$$

  3. *Nonlinear strain-displacement transformation matrix*

$$_0^t\mathbf{B}_{NL} = \begin{bmatrix} {_0h_{1,1}} & 0 & {_0h_{2,1}} & 0 & {_0h_{3,1}} & 0 & \cdots & {_0h_{N,1}} & 0 \\ {_0h_{1,2}} & 0 & {_0h_{2,2}} & 0 & {_0h_{3,2}} & 0 & \cdots & {_0h_{N,2}} & 0 \\ 0 & {_0h_{1,1}} & 0 & {_0h_{2,1}} & 0 & {_0h_{3,1}} & \cdots & 0 & {_0h_{N,1}} \\ 0 & {_0h_{1,2}} & 0 & {_0h_{2,2}} & 0 & {_0h_{3,2}} & \cdots & 0 & {_0h_{N,2}} \\ \dfrac{h_1}{^0\overline{x_1}} & 0 & \dfrac{h_2}{^0\overline{x_1}} & 0 & \dfrac{h_3}{^0\overline{x_1}} & 0 & \cdots & \dfrac{h_N}{^0\overline{x_1}} & 0 \end{bmatrix}$$

TABLE 6.5   *(cont.)*

4. *Second Piola-Kirchhoff stress matrix and vector*

$$
{}_0^t\mathbf{S} = \begin{bmatrix} {}_0^t S_{11} & {}_0^t S_{12} & 0 & 0 & 0 \\ {}_0^t S_{21} & {}_0^t S_{22} & 0 & 0 & 0 \\ 0 & 0 & {}_0^t S_{11} & {}_0^t S_{12} & 0 \\ 0 & 0 & {}_0^t S_{21} & {}_0^t S_{22} & 0 \\ 0 & 0 & 0 & 0 & {}_0^t S_{33} \end{bmatrix} ; \qquad {}_0^t\hat{\mathbf{S}} = \begin{bmatrix} {}_0^t S_{11} \\ {}_0^t S_{22} \\ {}_0^t S_{12} \\ {}_0^t S_{33} \end{bmatrix}
$$

B. *Updated Lagrangian formulation*

1. *Incremental strains*

$$
{}_t\epsilon_{11} = {}_t u_{1,1} + \tfrac{1}{2}(({}_t u_{1,1})^2 + ({}_t u_{2,1})^2)
$$

$$
{}_t\epsilon_{22} = {}_t u_{2,2} + \tfrac{1}{2}(({}_t u_{1,2})^2 + ({}_t u_{2,2})^2)
$$

$$
{}_t\epsilon_{12} = \tfrac{1}{2}({}_t u_{1,2} + {}_t u_{2,1}) + \tfrac{1}{2}({}_t u_{1,1}\,{}_t u_{1,2} + {}_t u_{2,1}\,{}_t u_{2,2})
$$

$$
{}_t\epsilon_{33} = \frac{u_1}{{}^t x_1} + \frac{1}{2}\left(\frac{u_1}{{}^t x_1}\right)^2 \qquad \text{for axisymmetric analysis}
$$

where $\,{}_t u_{i,j} = \dfrac{\partial u_i}{\partial\,{}^t x_j}$

2. *Linear strain-displacement transformation matrix*

Using ${}_t\mathbf{e} = {}_t^t\mathbf{B}_L\hat{\mathbf{u}}$

where ${}_t\mathbf{e}^T = [{}_t e_{11} \quad {}_t e_{22} \quad 2{}_t e_{12} \quad {}_t e_{33}]; \qquad \hat{\mathbf{u}}^T = [u_1^1 \quad u_2^1 \quad u_1^2 \quad u_2^2 \quad \cdots \quad u_1^N \quad u_2^N]$

$$
{}_t^t\mathbf{B}_L = \begin{bmatrix} {}_t h_{1,1} & 0 & {}_t h_{2,1} & 0 & {}_t h_{3,1} & 0 & \cdots & {}_t h_{N,1} & 0 \\ 0 & {}_t h_{1,2} & 0 & {}_t h_{2,2} & 0 & {}_t h_{3,2} & \cdots & 0 & {}_t h_{N,2} \\ {}_t h_{1,2} & {}_t h_{1,1} & {}_t h_{2,2} & {}_t h_{2,1} & {}_t h_{3,2} & {}_t h_{3,1} & \cdots & {}_t h_{N,2} & {}_t h_{N,1} \\ \dfrac{h_1}{{}^t x_1} & 0 & \dfrac{h_2}{{}^t x_1} & 0 & \dfrac{h_3}{{}^t x_1} & 0 & \cdots & \dfrac{h_N}{{}^t x_1} & 0 \end{bmatrix}
$$

where $\,{}_t h_{k,j} = \dfrac{\partial h_k}{\partial\,{}^t x_j}; \qquad u_j^k = {}^{t+\Delta t}u_j^k - {}^t u_j^k; \qquad \bar{x}_1 = \displaystyle\sum_{k=1}^{N} h_k\,{}^t x_1^k; \qquad N = \text{number of nodes}$

3. *Nonlinear strain-displacement transformation matrix*

$$
{}_t^t\mathbf{B}_{NL} = \begin{bmatrix} {}_t h_{1,1} & 0 & {}_t h_{2,1} & 0 & {}_t h_{3,1} & 0 & \cdots & {}_t h_{N,1} & 0 \\ {}_t h_{1,2} & 0 & {}_t h_{2,2} & 0 & {}_t h_{3,2} & 0 & \cdots & {}_t h_{N,2} & 0 \\ 0 & {}_t h_{1,1} & 0 & {}_t h_{2,1} & 0 & {}_t h_{3,1} & \cdots & 0 & {}_t h_{N,1} \\ 0 & {}_t h_{1,2} & 0 & {}_t h_{2,2} & 0 & {}_t h_{3,2} & \cdots & 0 & {}_t h_{N,2} \\ \dfrac{h_1}{{}^t x_1} & 0 & \dfrac{h_2}{{}^t x_1} & 0 & \dfrac{h_3}{{}^t x_1} & 0 & \cdots & \dfrac{h_N}{{}^t x_1} & 0 \end{bmatrix}
$$

4. *Cauchy stress matrix and stress vector*

$$
{}^t\boldsymbol{\tau} = \begin{bmatrix} {}^t\tau_{11} & {}^t\tau_{12} & 0 & 0 & 0 \\ {}^t\tau_{21} & {}^t\tau_{22} & 0 & 0 & 0 \\ 0 & 0 & {}^t\tau_{11} & {}^t\tau_{12} & 0 \\ 0 & 0 & {}^t\tau_{21} & {}^t\tau_{22} & 0 \\ 0 & 0 & 0 & 0 & {}^t\tau_{33} \end{bmatrix} ; \qquad {}^t\hat{\boldsymbol{\tau}} = \begin{bmatrix} {}^t\tau_{11} \\ {}^t\tau_{22} \\ {}^t\tau_{12} \\ {}^t\tau_{33} \end{bmatrix}
$$

EXAMPLE 6.18: Establish the matrices $_0^t\mathbf{B}_{L0}$, $_0^t\mathbf{B}_{L1}$, and $_0^t\mathbf{B}_{NL}$ corresponding to the TL formulation for the two-dimensional plane strain element shown in Fig. E6.18.

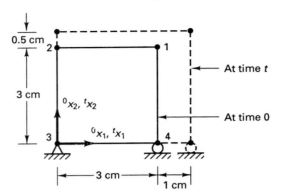

Figure E6.18 Four-node plane strain element in large displacement/large strain conditions

In this case we can directly use the information given in Table 6.5 with

$$^tu_1^1 = 1; \qquad ^tu_2^1 = 0.5$$
$$^tu_1^2 = 0; \qquad ^tu_2^2 = 0.5 \qquad ^0\mathbf{J} = \begin{bmatrix} \frac{3}{2} & 0 \\ 0 & \frac{3}{2} \end{bmatrix}$$
$$^tu_1^3 = 0; \qquad ^tu_2^3 = 0$$
$$^tu_1^4 = 1; \qquad ^tu_2^4 = 0$$

The interpolation functions of the four-node element are given in Fig. 5.4 (and the required derivatives have been given in Example 5.5), so that we obtain

$$_0^t\mathbf{B}_{L0} =$$

$$\frac{1}{6}\begin{bmatrix} (1+s) & 0 & -(1+s) & 0 & -(1-s) & 0 & (1-s) & 0 \\ 0 & (1+r) & 0 & (1-r) & 0 & -(1-r) & 0 & -(1+r) \\ (1+r) & (1+s) & (1-r) & -(1+s) & -(1-r) & -(1-s) & -(1+r) & (1-s) \end{bmatrix}$$

To evaluate $_0^t\mathbf{B}_{L1}$ we also need the l_{ij} values, where

$$l_{11} = \sum_{k=1}^{4} {_0}h_{k,1}\, {^tu_1^k} = \tfrac{2}{3}\{h_{1,r}\, {^tu_1^1} + h_{4,r}\, {^tu_1^4}\} = \tfrac{1}{3}$$

$$l_{12} = \sum_{k=1}^{4} {_0}h_{k,2}\, {^tu_1^k} = \tfrac{2}{3}\{h_{1,s}\, {^tu_1^1} + h_{4,s}\, {^tu_1^4}\} = 0$$

$$l_{21} = \sum_{k=1}^{4} {_0}h_{k,1}\, {^tu_2^k} = \tfrac{2}{3}\{h_{1,r}\, {^tu_2^1} + h_{2,r}\, {^tu_2^2}\} = 0$$

$$l_{22} = \sum_{k=1}^{4} {_0}h_{k,2}\, {^tu_2^k} = \tfrac{2}{3}\{h_{1,s}\, {^tu_2^1} + h_{2,s}\, {^tu_2^2}\} = \tfrac{1}{6}$$

Hence, we have

$$_0^t\mathbf{B}_{L1} =$$

$$\frac{1}{36}\begin{bmatrix} 2(1+s) & 0 & -2(1+s) & 0 & -2(1-s) & 0 & 2(1-s) & 0 \\ 0 & (1+r) & 0 & (1-r) & 0 & -(1-r) & 0 & -(1+r) \\ 2(1+r) & (1+s) & 2(1-r) & -(1+s) & -2(1-r) & -(1-s) & -2(1+r) & (1-s) \end{bmatrix}$$

The nonlinear strain-displacement matrix can also directly be constructed using the derivatives of the interpolation functions and the Jacobian matrix:

$$
{}_0^t\mathbf{B}_{NL} =
$$

$$
\frac{1}{6}
\begin{bmatrix}
(1+s) & 0 & -(1+s) & 0 & -(1-s) & 0 & (1-s) & 0 \\
(1+r) & 0 & (1-r) & 0 & -(1-r) & 0 & -(1+r) & 0 \\
0 & (1+s) & 0 & -(1+s) & 0 & -(1-s) & 0 & (1-s) \\
0 & (1+r) & 0 & (1-r) & 0 & -(1-r) & 0 & -(1+r)
\end{bmatrix}
$$

6.3.5 Three-Dimensional Solid Elements

The evaluation of the matrices required in three-dimensional isoparametric finite element analysis is accomplished using the same procedures as in two-dimensional analysis. Thus, referring to Section 6.3.4, we simply note that for a typical element we now use the coordinate and displacement interpolations,

$$
{}^0x_i = \sum_{k=1}^{N} h_k \, {}^0x_i^k; \qquad {}^tx_i = \sum_{k=1}^{N} h_k \, {}^tx_i^k; \qquad i = 1, 2, 3 \tag{6.127}
$$

$$
{}^tu_i = \sum_{k=1}^{N} h_k \, {}^tu_i^k; \qquad u_i = \sum_{k=1}^{N} h_k \, u_i^k; \qquad i = 1, 2, 3 \tag{6.128}
$$

where the element interpolation functions h_k have been given in Fig. 5.5. Using (6.127) and (6.128) in the same way as in two-dimensional analysis, we can develop the relevant element matrices used in the TL and UL formulations for three-dimensional analysis (see Table 6.6).

TABLE 6.6   *Matrices used in the three-dimensional element formulation*

A. *Total Lagrangian formulation*

1. *Incremental strains*

$$
{}_0\epsilon_{ij} = \tfrac{1}{2}\left({}_0u_{i,j} + {}_0u_{j,i}\right) + \tfrac{1}{2}\left({}_0^tu_{k,i}\,{}_0u_{k,j} + {}_0u_{k,i}\,{}_0^tu_{k,j}\right) + \tfrac{1}{2}\left({}_0u_{k,i}\,{}_0u_{k,j}\right) \qquad i = 1, 2, 3; j = 1, 2, 3; k = 1, 2, 3
$$

where ${}_0u_{i,j} = \dfrac{\partial u_i}{\partial {}^0x_j}$

2. *Linear strain-displacement transformation matrix*

Using ${}_0\mathbf{e} = {}_0^t\mathbf{B}_L\hat{\mathbf{u}}$

where ${}_0\mathbf{e}^T = \begin{bmatrix} {}_0e_{11} & {}_0e_{22} & {}_0e_{33} & 2{}_0e_{12} & 2{}_0e_{23} & 2{}_0e_{31} \end{bmatrix}$;

$\hat{\mathbf{u}}^T = \begin{bmatrix} u_1^1 & u_2^1 & u_3^1 & u_1^2 & u_2^2 & u_3^2 & \cdots & u_1^N & u_2^N & u_3^N \end{bmatrix}$

${}_0^t\mathbf{B}_L = {}_0^t\mathbf{B}_{L0} + {}_0^t\mathbf{B}_{L1}$

$$
{}_0^t\mathbf{B}_{L0} =
\begin{bmatrix}
{}_0h_{1,1} & 0 & 0 & {}_0h_{2,1} & \cdots & 0 \\
0 & {}_0h_{1,2} & 0 & 0 & \cdots & 0 \\
0 & 0 & {}_0h_{1,3} & 0 & \cdots & {}_0h_{N,3} \\
{}_0h_{1,2} & {}_0h_{1,1} & 0 & {}_0h_{2,2} & \cdots & 0 \\
0 & {}_0h_{1,3} & {}_0h_{1,2} & 0 & \cdots & {}_0h_{N,2} \\
{}_0h_{1,3} & 0 & {}_0h_{1,1} & {}_0h_{2,3} & \cdots & {}_0h_{N,1}
\end{bmatrix}
$$

where ${}_0h_{k,j} = \dfrac{\partial h_k}{\partial {}^0x_j}$; $u_j^k = {}^{t+\Delta t}u_j^k - {}^tu_j^k$

TABLE 6.6   (*cont.*)

$$
{}_0^t\mathbf{B}_{L1} = \begin{bmatrix}
l_{11}\,{}_0h_{1,1} & l_{21}\,{}_0h_{1,1} & l_{31}\,{}_0h_{1,1} & l_{11}\,{}_0h_{2,1} & \cdots & l_{31}\,{}_0h_{N,1} \\
l_{12}\,{}_0h_{1,2} & l_{22}\,{}_0h_{1,2} & l_{32}\,{}_0h_{1,2} & l_{12}\,{}_0h_{2,2} & \cdots & l_{32}\,{}_0h_{N,2} \\
l_{13}\,{}_0h_{1,3} & l_{23}\,{}_0h_{1,3} & l_{33}\,{}_0h_{1,3} & l_{13}\,{}_0h_{2,3} & \cdots & l_{33}\,{}_0h_{N,3} \\
(l_{11}\,{}_0h_{1,2} + l_{12}\,{}_0h_{1,1}) & (l_{21}\,{}_0h_{1,2} + l_{22}\,{}_0h_{1,1}) & (l_{31}\,{}_0h_{1,2} + l_{32}\,{}_0h_{1,1}) & (l_{11}\,{}_0h_{2,2} + l_{12}\,{}_0h_{2,1}) & \cdots & (l_{31}\,{}_0h_{N,2} + l_{32}\,{}_0h_{N,1}) \\
(l_{12}\,{}_0h_{1,3} + l_{13}\,{}_0h_{1,2}) & (l_{22}\,{}_0h_{1,3} + l_{23}\,{}_0h_{1,2}) & (l_{32}\,{}_0h_{1,3} + l_{33}\,{}_0h_{1,2}) & (l_{12}\,{}_0h_{2,3} + l_{13}\,{}_0h_{2,2}) & \cdots & (l_{32}\,{}_0h_{N,3} + l_{33}\,{}_0h_{N,2}) \\
(l_{11}\,{}_0h_{1,3} + l_{13}\,{}_0h_{1,1}) & (l_{21}\,{}_0h_{1,3} + l_{23}\,{}_0h_{1,1}) & (l_{31}\,{}_0h_{1,3} + l_{33}\,{}_0h_{1,1}) & (l_{11}\,{}_0h_{2,3} + l_{13}\,{}_0h_{2,1}) & \cdots & (l_{31}\,{}_0h_{N,3} + l_{33}\,{}_0h_{N,1})
\end{bmatrix}
$$

where $l_{ij} = \displaystyle\sum_{k=1}^{N} {}_0h_{k,j}\,{}^t u_i^k$

3. *Nonlinear strain-displacement transformation matrix*

$$
{}_0^t\mathbf{B}_{NL} = \begin{bmatrix}
{}_0^t\tilde{\mathbf{B}}_{NL} & \tilde{\mathbf{0}} & \tilde{\mathbf{0}} \\
\tilde{\mathbf{0}} & {}_0^t\tilde{\mathbf{B}}_{NL} & \tilde{\mathbf{0}} \\
\tilde{\mathbf{0}} & \tilde{\mathbf{0}} & {}_0^t\tilde{\mathbf{B}}_{NL}
\end{bmatrix}; \qquad
\tilde{\mathbf{0}} = \begin{bmatrix} 0 \\ 0 \\ 0 \end{bmatrix}
$$

where
$$
{}_0^t\tilde{\mathbf{B}}_{NL} = \begin{bmatrix}
{}_0h_{1,1} & 0 & 0 & {}_0h_{2,1} & \cdots & {}_0h_{N,1} \\
{}_0h_{1,2} & 0 & 0 & {}_0h_{2,2} & \cdots & {}_0h_{N,2} \\
{}_0h_{1,3} & 0 & 0 & {}_0h_{2,3} & \cdots & {}_0h_{N,3}
\end{bmatrix}
$$

4. *Second Piola-Kirchhoff stress matrix and vector*

$$
{}_0^t\mathbf{S} = \begin{bmatrix}
{}_0^t\tilde{\mathbf{S}} & \bar{\mathbf{0}} & \bar{\mathbf{0}} \\
\bar{\mathbf{0}} & {}_0^t\tilde{\mathbf{S}} & \bar{\mathbf{0}} \\
\bar{\mathbf{0}} & \bar{\mathbf{0}} & {}_0^t\tilde{\mathbf{S}}
\end{bmatrix}; \qquad
\bar{\mathbf{0}} = \begin{bmatrix} 0 & 0 & 0 \\ 0 & 0 & 0 \\ 0 & 0 & 0 \end{bmatrix}
$$

$$
{}_0^t\hat{\mathbf{S}}^T = \begin{bmatrix} {}_0^t S_{11} & {}_0^t S_{22} & {}_0^t S_{33} & {}_0^t S_{12} & {}_0^t S_{23} & {}_0^t S_{31} \end{bmatrix}
$$

where
$$
{}_0^t\tilde{\mathbf{S}} = \begin{bmatrix}
{}_0^t S_{11} & {}_0^t S_{12} & {}_0^t S_{13} \\
{}_0^t S_{21} & {}_0^t S_{22} & {}_0^t S_{23} \\
{}_0^t S_{31} & {}_0^t S_{32} & {}_0^t S_{33}
\end{bmatrix}
$$

B. *Updated Lagrangian formulation*

1. *Incremental strains*

$$
{}_t\epsilon_{ij} = \tfrac{1}{2}({}_tu_{i,j} + {}_tu_{j,i}) + \tfrac{1}{2}({}_tu_{k,i}\,{}_tu_{k,j}) \qquad i = 1, 2, 3;\, j = 1, 2, 3;\, k = 1, 2, 3
$$

where ${}_tu_{i,j} = \dfrac{\partial u_i}{\partial^t x_j}$

2. *Linear strain-displacement transformation matrix*

Using ${}_t\mathbf{e} = {}_t^t\mathbf{B}_L\hat{\mathbf{u}}$

where ${}_t\mathbf{e}^T = \begin{bmatrix} {}_te_{11} & {}_te_{22} & {}_te_{33} & 2{}_te_{12} & 2{}_te_{23} & 2{}_te_{31} \end{bmatrix}$

$\hat{\mathbf{u}}^T = \begin{bmatrix} u_1^1 & u_2^1 & u_3^1 & u_1^2 & u_2^2 & u_3^2 & \cdots & u_1^N & u_2^N & u_3^N \end{bmatrix}$

$$
{}_t^t\mathbf{B}_L = \begin{bmatrix}
{}_th_{1,1} & 0 & 0 & {}_th_{2,1} & \cdots & 0 \\
0 & {}_th_{1,2} & 0 & 0 & \cdots & 0 \\
0 & 0 & {}_th_{1,3} & 0 & \cdots & {}_th_{N,3} \\
{}_th_{1,2} & {}_th_{1,1} & 0 & {}_th_{2,2} & \cdots & 0 \\
0 & {}_th_{1,3} & {}_th_{1,2} & 0 & \cdots & {}_th_{N,2} \\
{}_th_{1,3} & 0 & {}_th_{1,1} & {}_th_{2,3} & \cdots & {}_th_{N,1}
\end{bmatrix}
$$

where ${}_th_{k,j} = \dfrac{\partial h_k}{\partial^t x_j}$; $u_j^k = {}^{t+\Delta t}u_j^k - {}^t u_j^k$; $N =$ number of nodes

3. *Nonlinear strain-displacement transformation matrix*

$$
{}_t^t\mathbf{B}_{NL} = \begin{bmatrix}
{}_t^t\tilde{\mathbf{B}}_{NL} & \tilde{\mathbf{0}} & \tilde{\mathbf{0}} \\
\tilde{\mathbf{0}} & {}_t^t\tilde{\mathbf{B}}_{NL} & \tilde{\mathbf{0}} \\
\tilde{\mathbf{0}} & \tilde{\mathbf{0}} & {}_t^t\tilde{\mathbf{B}}_{NL}
\end{bmatrix}; \qquad
\tilde{\mathbf{0}} = \begin{bmatrix} 0 \\ 0 \\ 0 \end{bmatrix}
$$

TABLE 6.6 (*cont.*)

where
$$
{}_t^t\tilde{\mathbf{B}}_{NL} = \begin{bmatrix} {}_t h_{1,1} & 0 & 0 & {}_t h_{2,1} & \cdots & {}_t h_{N,1} \\ {}_t h_{1,2} & 0 & 0 & {}_t h_{2,2} & \cdots & {}_t h_{N,2} \\ {}_t h_{1,3} & 0 & 0 & {}_t h_{2,3} & \cdots & {}_t h_{N,3} \end{bmatrix}
$$

4. *Cauchy stress matrix and stress vector*

$$
{}^t\boldsymbol{\tau} = \begin{bmatrix} {}^t\hat{\boldsymbol{\tau}} & \bar{\mathbf{0}} & \bar{\mathbf{0}} \\ \bar{\mathbf{0}} & {}^t\hat{\boldsymbol{\tau}} & \bar{\mathbf{0}} \\ \bar{\mathbf{0}} & \bar{\mathbf{0}} & {}^t\hat{\boldsymbol{\tau}} \end{bmatrix}; \qquad
{}^t\hat{\boldsymbol{\tau}} = \begin{bmatrix} {}^t\tau_{11} \\ {}^t\tau_{22} \\ {}^t\tau_{33} \\ {}^t\tau_{12} \\ {}^t\tau_{23} \\ {}^t\tau_{31} \end{bmatrix} \qquad
\bar{\mathbf{0}} = \begin{bmatrix} 0 & 0 & 0 \\ 0 & 0 & 0 \\ 0 & 0 & 0 \end{bmatrix}
$$

where
$$
{}^t\tilde{\boldsymbol{\tau}} = \begin{bmatrix} {}^t\tau_{11} & {}^t\tau_{12} & {}^t\tau_{13} \\ {}^t\tau_{21} & {}^t\tau_{22} & {}^t\tau_{23} \\ {}^t\tau_{31} & {}^t\tau_{32} & {}^t\tau_{33} \end{bmatrix}
$$

6.3.6 Exercises

6.31. Consider the problem shown and evaluate the following quantities in terms of the given data: ${}_0 e_{ij}$, ${}_0\eta_{ij}$, ${}_0^t u_{k,i}$, ${}_0^t u_{k,j}$, ${}_0^t x_{i,k}$.

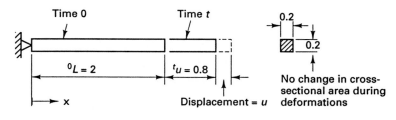

6.32. Consider the truss element shown. The truss has a cross-sectional area A and a Young's modulus E. We assume small strain conditions, i.e., $\Delta/{}^0L \ll 1$.

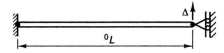

(a) Evaluate the total stiffness matrix as a function of Δ and plot the linear strain stiffness matrix element ${}_0^t K_L$ and nonlinear strain stiffness matrix element ${}_0^t K_{NL}$ as a function of Δ.

(b) Let R be the external load applied to obtain the displacement Δ. Plot the force R as a function of Δ.

6.33. Consider the snap-action toggle shown in its initial configuration. Assume small strain conditions and that each element has a cross-sectional area A and Young's modulus E.

(a) For each element, calculate the linear and nonlinear strain stiffness matrices ${}_0^t\mathbf{K}_L$ and ${}_0^t\mathbf{K}_{NL}$ and the force vector ${}_0^t\mathbf{F}$.

(b) Calculate the linear and nonlinear strain stiffness matrices ${}_0^t\mathbf{K}_L$ and ${}_0^t\mathbf{K}_{NL}$ and the force vector ${}_0^t\mathbf{F}$ of the complete toggle.

Eliminate prescribed degrees of freedom.

(c) Using your results from part (b), establish the force-deflection curve P versus Δ.

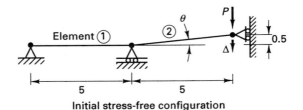

Initial stress-free configuration

6.34. Consider the three-element truss structure shown. Derive the tangent stiffness matrix ${}_0^t\mathbf{K}$ and force vector ${}_0^t\mathbf{F}$ corresponding to the configuration at time t allowing for large displacements, large rotations, and large strains. Assume that the constitutive relationship is ${}_0^t S_{11} = C \, {}_0^t \epsilon_{11}$, with C given as some function of the strain.

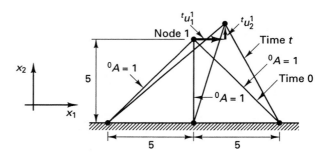

6.35. Consider the evaluation of the stiffness matrix of the four-node element shown when calculated with the information given in Table 6.5. Let the two-dimensional element be loaded with a deformation-dependent pressure between nodes 1 and 2. Establish the terms that should be added to the stiffness matrix if the effect of the pressure is included in the linearization to obtain the exact tangent stiffness matrix. Consider plane stress, plane strain, and axisymmetric conditions.

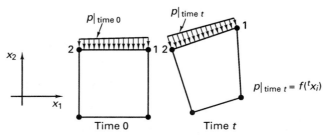

6.36. The initial configuration and configuration at time t of a four-node plane strain element are as shown. The material law is linear, $_0^t S_{ij} = {}_0^t C_{ijrs}\, {}_0^t \epsilon_{rs}$, with $E = 20,000$ N/m² and $\nu = 0.3$.

(a) Calculate the nodal point forces required to hold the element in equilibrium at time t. Use an appropriate finite element formulation.

(b) If the element now rotates rigidly from time t to time $t + \Delta t$ by an angle of 90 degrees counterclockwise, calculate the new nodal point forces corresponding to the configuration at time $t + \Delta t$.

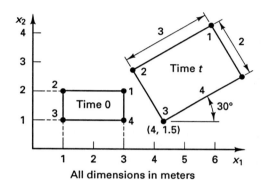

All dimensions in meters

6.37. During a TL analysis, we find that a plane strain element is deformed as shown.

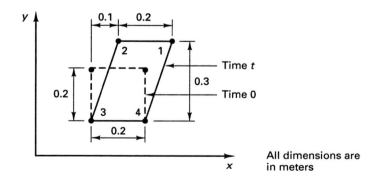

All dimensions are in meters

The stress state, not including $^t\tau_{zz}$, is

$$^t\boldsymbol{\tau} = \begin{bmatrix} 5.849 \times 10^7 & 6.971 \times 10^7 \\ 6.971 \times 10^7 & 1.514 \times 10^8 \end{bmatrix} \text{Pa}$$

The Poisson's ratio $\nu = 0.3$ and the tangent Young's modulus is E. Compute $_0^t K_{11}$.

6.38. The two-dimensional four-node isoparametric finite element shown is used in an axisymmetric analysis. Evaluate the last row in the $_0^t\mathbf{B}_L$, $_0^t\mathbf{B}_{NL}$ and $_t^t\mathbf{B}_L$, $_t^t\mathbf{B}_{NL}$ matrices at the material particle P corresponding to the TL and UL formulations. The last row in the strain-displacement matrices corresponds to the circumferential strain.

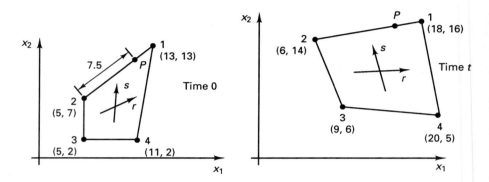

6.39. Consider the four-node plane stress element shown. Using the total Lagrangian formulation calculate the following.

(a) The element of the tangent stiffness matrix corresponding to the incremental displacement u_1^1; i.e., evaluate element $(1, 1)$ of the matrix $(_0^t\mathbf{K}_L + _0^t\mathbf{K}_{NL})$.

(b) The element of the force vector $_0^t\mathbf{F}$ corresponding to u_1^1; i.e., evaluate element (1) of $_0^t\mathbf{F}$, where $_0^t\mathbf{F}$ is the force vector corresponding to the current element stresses.

Assume that Young's modulus E and Poisson's ratio $\nu = 0.3$ relate the incremental second Piola-Kirchhoff stresses to the incremental Green-Lagrange strains and assume thickness h at time 0.

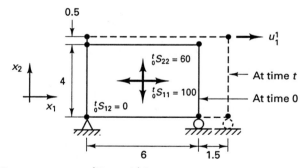

Constant stresses $_0^t S_{11}$ and $_0^t S_{22}$ and all other stresses are zero

6.40. A two-node finite element for modeling large strain torsion problems is to be constructed. The element has a circular cross section and is straight, and all cross sections are parallel to the x_1, x_2 plane as shown.

The kinematic assumption to be employed in the element is that each cross section rotates rigidly about its center. This is illustrated in the figure. Notice that the total rotation of fiber AA is fully described by $^t\theta_3$ and that the fiber rotation can be large. Also, note that the fiber AA does not stretch or shrink and that the center of the fiber (point C) remains fixed.

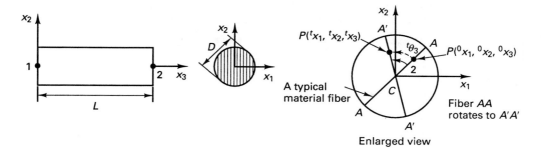

Enlarged view

(a) Calculate the deformation gradient $_0^t\mathbf{X}$ in terms of the initial coordinates and $^t\theta_3$.
(b) Calculate the Green-Lagrange strain tensor $_0^t\boldsymbol{\epsilon}$. Clearly identify any terms that are associated with large strain effects.
(c) Calculate the mass density ratio $^t\rho/^0\rho$ in terms of the initial coordinates and $^t\theta_3$.
(d) Establish the strain-displacement matrix of the element.

6.4 DISPLACEMENT/PRESSURE FORMULATIONS FOR LARGE DEFORMATIONS

As discussed in Section 4.4.3, for (almost) incompressible analysis, a pure displacement-based procedure is, in general, not effective and instead, a displacement/pressure formulation is attractive. Materials in large deformations frequently behave as almost incompressible, and it is therefore important to extend the total and updated Lagrangian formulations of the previous sections to incompressible analysis. Typical applications are in the large strain analysis of rubberlike materials and in the large strain inelastic analysis of metals.

The formulations we present here are a direct and natural extension of the pure displacement-based large deformation formulations given in the previous section and of the pressure/displacement formulations that we discussed for linear analysis in Sections 4.4.3 and 5.3.5.

6.4.1 Total Lagrangian Formulation

We make the fundamental assumption that the material description used has an incremental potential $d_0^t\overline{W}$ such that

$$d_0^t\overline{W} = {}_0^t\overline{S}_{ij}\, d_0^t\epsilon_{ij} \tag{6.129}$$

and hence

$${}_0^t\overline{S}_{ij} = \frac{\partial d_0^t\overline{W}}{\partial d_0^t\epsilon_{ij}} \tag{6.130}$$

where the overbar in $d_0^t\overline{W}$ and on the second Piola-Kirchhoff stress (and other quantities in the following discussion) denotes that the quantity is computed only from the displacement fields. Since we shall interpolate the displacements and the pressure independently, the actual stress $_0^t S_{ij}$ will also contain the interpolated pressure.

We note that such incremental potential is given for elastic materials and also for inelastic materials provided the normality rule holds. A consequence of (6.129) is that the tensor

$$_0\overline{C}_{ijrs} = \frac{\partial_0^t \overline{S}_{ij}}{\partial_0^t \epsilon_{rs}} = \frac{\partial^2 \, {}_0^t\overline{W}}{\partial_0^t \epsilon_{rs} \, \partial_0^t \epsilon_{ij}} \tag{6.131}$$

has the symmetry property $_0\overline{C}_{ijrs} = {}_0\overline{C}_{rsij}$

and the pure displacement and displacement/pressure formulations produce symmetric coefficient matrices.

Using (6.130), the principle of virtual displacements at time t in total Lagrangian form with displacements as the only variables can be written as

$$\int_{0_V} \frac{\partial_0^t \overline{W}}{\partial_0^t \epsilon_{ij}} \, \delta_0^t \epsilon_{ij} \, d^0V = \int_{0_V} \delta_0^t \overline{W} \, d^0V$$

$$= \delta\left(\int_{0_V} {}_0^t\overline{W} \, d^0V\right) = {}^t\mathcal{R} \tag{6.132}$$

The linearization and finite element discretization of (6.132) was presented in Section 6.3. We now use (6.132) as the starting equation to develop the displacement/pressure formulation for large deformations.

The basic element interpolations that we shall use are

$$^t u_i = \sum_{k=1}^{N} h_k \, {}^t u_i^k; \qquad {}^t\tilde{p} = \sum_{i=1}^{q} g_i \, {}^t\hat{p}_i \tag{6.133}$$

where the h_k are the displacement interpolation functions and the g_i are the pressure interpolation functions, with ${}^t\tilde{p}$ as the *total* element pressure at time t. Note that the interpolation of the pressure may correspond to the u/p or to the u/p-c formulation (see Section 5.3.5).

The key step in the construction of the displacement/pressure formulation is to properly modify the potential to include the effect of the interpolated pressure. For this purpose we add to the potential ${}_0^t\overline{W}$ a properly chosen potential ${}_0^t Q$, which is a function of the displacements and the separately interpolated pressure ${}^t\tilde{p}$ (see T. Sussman and K. J. Bathe [B]). The principle of virtual work is then given by

$$\delta\left(\int_{0_V} {}_0^t W \, d^0V\right) = {}^t\mathcal{R} \tag{6.134}$$

where $${}_0^t W = {}_0^t\overline{W} + {}_0^t Q \tag{6.135}$$

and we now consider the variation with respect to the interpolated displacements and the interpolated pressure.

The modified potential ${}_0^t W$ must fulfill the requirements that use of (6.134) gives ${}^t\tilde{p}$ as the actual solution for the pressure and also yields a physically reasonable constraint between the interpolated pressure and the pressure computed only from the displacements.

A potential that fulfills these requirements for the isotropic materials considered later is given by

$${}_0^t W = {}_0^t\overline{W} - \frac{1}{2\kappa}({}^t\overline{p} - {}^t\tilde{p})^2 \tag{6.136}$$

where κ is the constant bulk modulus of the material. Using (6.136), the governing finite element equations can be derived with the approach for linearization presented in Section 6.3.1. Hence, we obtain for a typical element,

$$\begin{pmatrix} {}^t\mathbf{KUU} & {}^t\mathbf{KUP} \\ {}^t\mathbf{KPU} & {}^t\mathbf{KPP} \end{pmatrix} \begin{pmatrix} \hat{\mathbf{u}} \\ \hat{\mathbf{p}} \end{pmatrix} = \begin{pmatrix} {}^{t+\Delta t}\mathbf{R} \\ \mathbf{0} \end{pmatrix} - \begin{pmatrix} {}^t\mathbf{FU} \\ {}^t\mathbf{FP} \end{pmatrix} \tag{6.137}$$

where $\hat{\mathbf{u}}$ and $\hat{\mathbf{p}}$ are vectors of the increments in the nodal point displacements ${}^t\hat{u}_i$ and nodal point or element internal pressure variables ${}^t\hat{p}_i$ [note that here ${}^t\hat{u}_i$ is any one of the components ${}^tu_i^k$ in (6.122), (6.128), and (6.133)]. The vectors ${}^t\mathbf{FU}$ and ${}^t\mathbf{FP}$ contain the entries

$$\begin{aligned} {}^tFU_i &= \frac{\partial}{\partial {}^t\hat{u}_i}\left(\int_{0_V} {}_0^t W \, d^0V \right) \\ {}^tFP_i &= \frac{\partial}{\partial {}^t\hat{p}_i}\left(\int_{0_V} {}_0^t W \, d^0V \right) \end{aligned} \tag{6.138}$$

and the matrices ${}^t\mathbf{KUU}$, ${}^t\mathbf{KUP}$, ${}^t\mathbf{KPU}$, and ${}^t\mathbf{KPP}$ contain the elements

$$\begin{aligned} {}^tKUU_{ij} &= \frac{\partial {}^tFU_i}{\partial {}^t\hat{u}_j} \\[2mm] {}^tKUP_{ij} &= \frac{\partial {}^tFU_i}{\partial {}^t\hat{p}_j} = \frac{\partial {}^tFP_j}{\partial {}^t\hat{u}_i} = {}^tKPU_{ji} \\[2mm] {}^tKPP_{ij} &= \frac{\partial {}^tFP_i}{\partial {}^t\hat{p}_j} \end{aligned} \tag{6.139}$$

Using chain differentiation, we obtain

$$\begin{aligned} {}^tFU_i &= \int_{0_V} {}_0^t S_{kl} \frac{\partial {}_0^t \epsilon_{kl}}{\partial {}^t\hat{u}_i} \, d^0V \\[2mm] {}^tFP_i &= \int_{0_V} \frac{1}{\kappa}({}^t\bar{p} - {}^t\tilde{p}) \frac{\partial {}^t\tilde{p}}{\partial {}^t\hat{p}_i} \, d^0V \\[2mm] {}^tKUU_{ij} &= \int_{0_V} {}_0CUU_{klrs} \frac{\partial {}_0^t\epsilon_{kl}}{\partial {}^t\hat{u}_i} \frac{\partial {}_0^t\epsilon_{rs}}{\partial {}^t\hat{u}_j} \, d^0V + \int_{0_V} {}_0^t S_{kl} \frac{\partial^2 \, {}_0^t\epsilon_{kl}}{\partial {}^t\hat{u}_i \, \partial {}^t\hat{u}_j} \, d^0V \\[2mm] {}^tKUP_{ij} &= \int_{0_V} {}_0CUP_{kl} \frac{\partial {}_0^t\epsilon_{kl}}{\partial {}^t\hat{u}_i} \frac{\partial {}^t\tilde{p}}{\partial {}^t\hat{p}_j} \, d^0V \\[2mm] {}^tKPP_{ij} &= \int_{0_V} -\frac{1}{\kappa} \frac{\partial {}^t\tilde{p}}{\partial {}^t\hat{p}_i} \frac{\partial {}^t\tilde{p}}{\partial {}^t\hat{p}_j} \, d^0V \end{aligned} \tag{6.140}$$

where

$$\begin{aligned} {}_0^t S_{kl} &= {}_0^t\bar{S}_{kl} - \frac{1}{\kappa}({}^t\bar{p} - {}^t\tilde{p})\frac{\partial {}^t\bar{p}}{\partial {}_0^t\epsilon_{kl}} \\[2mm] {}_0CUU_{klrs} &= {}_0\bar{C}_{klrs} - \frac{1}{\kappa}\frac{\partial {}^t\bar{p}}{\partial {}_0^t\epsilon_{kl}} \frac{\partial {}^t\bar{p}}{\partial {}_0^t\epsilon_{rs}} - \frac{1}{\kappa}({}^t\bar{p} - {}^t\tilde{p})\frac{\partial^2 \, {}^t\bar{p}}{\partial {}_0^t\epsilon_{kl} \, \partial {}_0^t\epsilon_{rs}} \\[2mm] {}_0CUP_{kl} &= \frac{1}{\kappa}\frac{\partial {}^t\bar{p}}{\partial {}_0^t\epsilon_{kl}} \end{aligned} \tag{6.141}$$

Note that in (6.141) we have

$$\overset{t}{_0}\overline{S}_{kl} = \frac{1}{2}\left(\frac{\partial \overset{t}{_0}\overline{W}}{\partial \overset{t}{_0}\epsilon_{kl}} + \frac{\partial \overset{t}{_0}\overline{W}}{\partial \overset{t}{_0}\epsilon_{lk}}\right)$$

$$\overset{t}{_0}\overline{C}_{klrs} = \frac{1}{2}\left(\frac{\partial \overset{t}{_0}\overline{S}_{kl}}{\partial \overset{t}{_0}\epsilon_{rs}} + \frac{\partial \overset{t}{_0}\overline{S}_{kl}}{\partial \overset{t}{_0}\epsilon_{sr}}\right) \tag{6.142}$$

Furthermore, we note that with the interpolations of (6.133) we have

$$\frac{\partial^t\bar{p}}{\partial^t\hat{p}_i} = g_i \tag{6.143}$$

and (see Exercise 6.42) $$\frac{\partial \overset{t}{_0}\epsilon_{kl}}{\partial^t u_n^L} = \frac{1}{2}\left(\overset{t}{_0}x_{n,k}\,_0h_{L,l} + \overset{t}{_0}x_{n,l}\,_0h_{L,k}\right) \tag{6.144}$$

$$\frac{\partial^2 \overset{t}{_0}\epsilon_{kl}}{\partial^t u_n^L\,\partial^t u_m^M} = \frac{1}{2}\left(_0h_{L,k}\,_0h_{M,l} + \,_0h_{L,l}\,_0h_{M,k}\right)\delta_{nm} \tag{6.145}$$

where a typical nodal point displacement is denoted as $^tu_n^L$ (with the appropriate indices n and L). These strain derivatives give the same contributions as do the quantities $_0e_{ij}$ and $_0\eta_{ij}$ used in Table 6.2.

A study of the above relations shows that if the pressure interpolation is not included, the equations reduce to the total Lagrangian formulation already presented in Section 6.2.3 (see Exercise 6.43).

The displacement/pressure formulation is effective for the analysis of rubberlike materials in large strains. In this case, the Mooney-Rivlin or Ogden material laws may be used, for which the strain energy density per unit volume $_0^t\overline{W}$ is explicity defined (see Section 6.6.2).

Let us demonstrate that this formulation, when used in small strain elastic analysis, reduces to the formulation already discussed in Section 5.3.5.

> **EXAMPLE 6.19:** Show how the displacement/pressure formulation discussed above reduces to the formulation presented in Section 5.3.5 when isotropic linear elasticity with small displacements and small strains is considered.
>
> Considering the general equations (6.137) to (6.145), we note that in this case:
>
> The second Piola-Kirchhoff stress $_0^t S_{kl}$ reduces to the engineering stress measure $^t\sigma_{kl}$.
>
> The Green-Lagrange strains $_0^t\epsilon_{kl}$ reduce to the infinitesimally small engineering strains $^te_{kl}$.
>
> The nonlinear strain stiffness matrix in (6.140) is neglected.
>
> The integration is over the volume V (which is equal to ^0V) and the subscript 0 on the constitutive tensors is also not needed.
>
> In this case we have
>
> $$\overline{C}_{klrs} = \lambda\delta_{kl}\delta_{rs} + \mu(\delta_{kr}\delta_{ls} + \delta_{ks}\delta_{lr})$$
>
> where λ and μ are the Lamé constants,
>
> $$\lambda = \frac{E\nu}{(1+\nu)(1-2\nu)}; \qquad \mu = \frac{E}{2(1+\nu)}$$

with E and ν the Young's modulus and the Poisson's ratio. The bulk modulus κ is

$$\kappa = \frac{E}{3(1 - 2\nu)}$$

We have

$${}^t\overline{p} = -\kappa \, {}^t e_{mm}$$

$$\frac{\partial {}^t \overline{p}}{\partial {}^t e_{kl}} = -\kappa \, \delta_{kl}$$

$$\frac{\partial^2 \, {}^t \overline{p}}{\partial {}^t e_{kl} \, \partial {}^t e_{rs}} = 0$$

so that

$${}^t \sigma_{kl} = {}^t S_{kl} - {}^t \overline{p} \, \delta_{kl}$$

$$CUU_{klrs} = \overline{C}_{klrs} - \kappa \, \delta_{kl} \, \delta_{rs}$$

$$CUP_{kl} = -\delta_{kl}$$

On substituting these quantities into (6.137), we note that the general formulation reduces, in this case, to the formulation already presented in Sections 4.4.3 and 5.3.5.

6.4.2 Updated Lagrangian Formulation

As we discussed in Section 6.2.3, the updated Lagrangian formulation is conceptually identical to the total Lagrangian formulation but uses the configuration at time t as reference configuration. In this case $\frac{t}{T}S_{ij} = {}^t\tau_{ij}$ and $d\frac{t}{T}\epsilon_{ij} = d_t e_{ij}$, with the subscript T denoting the configuration[8] that is fixed and used as reference, and

$$d_t e_{ij} = \frac{1}{2}\left(\frac{\partial du_i}{\partial {}^t x_j} + \frac{\partial du_j}{\partial {}^t x_i}\right) \tag{6.146}$$

Following the presentation of the previous section, we thus obtain

$$d\frac{t}{T}\overline{W} = {}^t\overline{\tau}_{ij} \, d_t e_{ij} \tag{6.147}$$

and note that

$$\frac{t}{T}\overline{W} \, d^T V = \frac{t}{0}\overline{W} \, d^0 V \tag{6.148}$$

If in addition we use

$$\frac{t}{T}Q \, d^T V = \frac{t}{0}Q \, d^0 V; \qquad \frac{d^T V}{d^0 V} = \det \frac{T}{0}\mathbf{X} \tag{6.149}$$

we can write the principle of virtual work (6.134) as

$$\delta \int_{{}^T V} \left(\frac{t}{T}\overline{W} + \frac{t}{T}Q\right) d^T V = {}^t\mathcal{R} \tag{6.150}$$

Note that if we use the modification to the total potential $\frac{t}{0}\overline{W}$ in the previous section,

$$\frac{t}{0}Q = -\frac{1}{2\kappa}({}^t\overline{p} - {}^t\tilde{p})^2 \tag{6.151}$$

---

[8] We use the capital letter T to denote the reference configuration considered fixed at time t, so that when differentiations are performed, it is realized that no variation of this configuration is allowed.

then
$$\overset{t}{_f}Q = -\frac{1}{2\kappa^*}(^t\bar{p} - {}^t\tilde{p})^2 \tag{6.152}$$

with
$$\kappa^* = \kappa \det {}^t_0\mathbf{X} \tag{6.153}$$

The governing finite element equations can now be derived by chain differentiation, and provided the same physical material descriptions are used, the same finite element equations are obtained as in the total Lagrangian formulation. The details of the derivation are given by T. Sussman and K. J. Bathe [B].

6.4.3 Exercises

6.41. Show that using (6.136), the actual solution for the pressure is given by the independently interpolated value $^t\tilde{p}$.

6.42. Let $^tu_n = \Sigma_L\, h_L\, {}^tu_n^L$ and prove that (6.144) and (6.145) hold. Here you may want to recall that

$$\frac{\partial(A_{M,i}\,{}^tu_i^M)}{\partial{}^tu_k^L} = A_{M,i}\,\delta_{ik}\,\delta_{ML} = A_{L,k}$$

where δ_{ik} is the Kronecker delta.

6.43. Show explicitly that the pressure/displacement mixed formulation reduces to the pure displacement-based formulation if the pressure interpolation is not included.

6.44. Prove the relations in (6.140) and (6.141).

6.45. Consider the 4/1 plane strain element shown. Develop in detail all expressions for the calculation of the matrices in (6.137) assuming large strain analysis but do not perform any integrations. (*Hint:* See Example 4.32.)

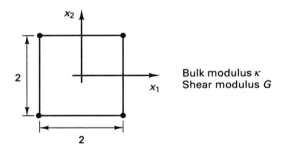

6.46. Consider the 4/1 element in Exercise 6.45 and develop in detail all expressions for the calculation of the matrices in (6.137) but corresponding to the updated Lagrangian formulation. However, do not perform any integrations.

6.47. You want to obtain some insight into whether the computer program you use employs the tangent stiffness matrix in plane strain analysis. Consider a single nine-node element in the deformed state shown. Assuming that the calculation of the stresses and the force vector $^t\mathbf{F}$ is correct, design a test to determine whether the stiffness matrix calculation for node 1 is probably also correct. For this analysis case the u/p formulation (9/3 element) would be efficient. (*Hint:* Note that $^t\mathbf{K} = \partial{}^t\mathbf{F}/\partial{}^t\mathbf{U}$.)

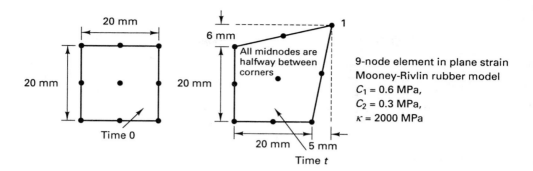

6.48. Perform the numerical experiment in Exercise 6.47 for the case of the axisymmetric element shown.

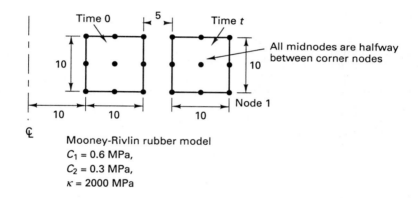

6.49. Use a computer program to analyze the thick disk shown. The applied pressure increases uniformly, and the analysis is required up to a maximum displacement of 3 in.

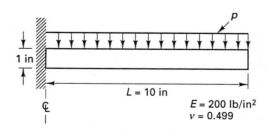

6.50. Use a computer program to analyze the plate with a hole shown on the following page. The plate is stretched by imposing a uniform horizontal displacement at the right end.

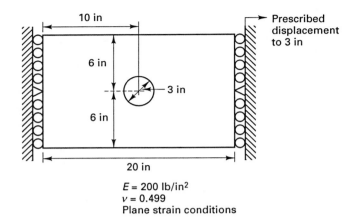

$E = 200$ lb/in^2
$v = 0.499$
Plane strain conditions

6.5 STRUCTURAL ELEMENTS

A large number of beam, plate, and shell elements have been proposed for nonlinear analysis (see, for example, A. K. Noor [A]). Our objective here is not to survey the various formulations proposed in the literature but to present briefly those elements that we already have discussed for linear analysis in Section 5.4. These beam, plate, and shell elements have evolved from the isoparametric formulation and are particularly attractive because of the consistent formulation, the generality of the elements, and the computational efficiency.

In the following discussion, we first consider beam and axisymmetric shell elements and then discuss plate and general shell elements.

6.5.1 Beam and Axisymmetric Shell Elements

In this section we consider the one-dimensional bending elements that we discussed in Section 5.4.1 for linear analysis; there we considered the plane stress and plane strain planar beam elements, an axisymmetric shell element, and a general three-dimensional beam element. We observed that the planar beam and the axisymmetric shell element formulations are actually cases easily derivable from the general three-dimensional beam element formulation. Hence, we consider here the calculation of the element matrices pertaining to the large displacement–large rotation behavior of a general beam of rectangular cross-sectional area. The relations given can be directly used to also obtain the matrices corresponding to the planar beam elements and axisymmetric shell elements (see Examples 6.20 and 6.21).

Figure 6.5 shows a typical element in the original configuration and the position at time t. To describe the element behavior we use the same assumptions that we employed in linear analysis (namely, that plane sections initially normal to the neutral axis remain plane and that only the longitudinal stress and two shear stresses are nonzero), but the displacements and rotations of the element can now be arbitrarily large. The element strains are still

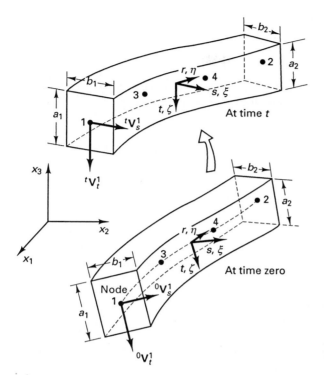

Figure 6.5   Beam element undergoing large displacements and rotations

assumed to be small, which means that the cross-sectional area does not change.[9] This is an appropriate assumption for most geometrically nonlinear analyses of beam-type structures.

Using the general continuum mechanics equations for nonlinear analysis presented in Section 6.2, the beam element matrices for nonlinear analysis are evaluated by a direct extension of the formulation given in Section 5.4.1. The calculations are performed as in the evaluation of the matrices of the finite elements with displacement degrees of freedom only (see Sections 5.4.1 and 6.3).

With the same notation as in Section 5.4.1, the geometry of the beam element at time t is given by

$$^{t}x_i = \sum_{k=1}^{q} h_k \, ^{t}x_i^k + \frac{t}{2} \sum_{k=1}^{q} a_k h_k \, ^{t}V_{ti}^k + \frac{s}{2} \sum_{k=1}^{q} b_k h_k \, ^{t}V_{si}^k \qquad i = 1, 2, 3 \qquad (6.154)$$

where the coordinates of a typical point in the beam are $^{t}x_1$, $^{t}x_2$, $^{t}x_3$. Considering the

---

[9] To have the element formulation applicable to large strains, the changes in thickness and width varying along the length of the element would need to be calculated. These changes depend on the stress-strain material relationship of the element.

configurations at times 0, t, and $t + \Delta t$, the displacement components are

$$^t u_i = {}^t x_i - {}^0 x_i \tag{6.155}$$

and

$$u_i = {}^{t+\Delta t} x_i - {}^t x_i \tag{6.156}$$

Substituting (6.154) into (6.155) and (6.156), we obtain expressions for the displacement components in terms of the nodal point displacements and changes in the direction cosines of the nodal point director vectors; i.e.,

$$^t u_i = \sum_{k=1}^{q} h_k \, {}^t u_i^k + \frac{t}{2} \sum_{k=1}^{q} a_k h_k ({}^t V_{ti}^k - {}^0 V_{ti}^k) + \frac{s}{2} \sum_{k=1}^{q} b_k h_k ({}^t V_{si}^k - {}^0 V_{si}^k) \tag{6.157}$$

and

$$u_i = \sum_{k=1}^{q} h_k u_i^k + \frac{t}{2} \sum_{k=1}^{q} a_k h_k V_{ti}^k + \frac{s}{2} \sum_{k=1}^{q} b_k h_k V_{si}^k \tag{6.158}$$

where

$$V_{ti}^k = {}^{t+\Delta t} V_{ti}^k - {}^t V_{ti}^k \tag{6.159}$$

$$V_{si}^k = {}^{t+\Delta t} V_{si}^k - {}^t V_{si}^k \tag{6.160}$$

The relation in (6.157) is directly employed to evaluate the total displacements and total strains (hence also total stresses) for both the UL and TL formulations and holds for any magnitude of displacement components.

We use the relation in (6.158) in the linearization of the principle of virtual work and need to express the components V_{ti}^k and V_{si}^k of the vectors $\mathbf{V}_t^k$, $\mathbf{V}_s^k$ in terms of nodal rotational degrees of freedom. Depending on the size of the incremental step, the actual rotation corresponding to the vectors $\mathbf{V}_t^k$ and $\mathbf{V}_s^k$ may be a large rotation, and therefore cannot be represented by vector component rotations about the Cartesian axes. However, we recall that our objective is to express the continuum linear and nonlinear strain increments in Tables 6.2 and 6.3 by finite element degrees of freedom and corresponding interpolations so as to achieve a full linearization of the principle of virtual work (see Section 6.3.1). For this purpose we define the vector of nodal rotational degrees of freedom $\boldsymbol{\theta}_k$ with components measured about the Cartesian axes and use the second-order approximations (see Exercise 6.55),

$$\mathbf{V}_t^k = \boldsymbol{\theta}_k \times {}^t\mathbf{V}_t^k + \frac{1}{2} \boldsymbol{\theta}_k \times (\boldsymbol{\theta}_k \times {}^t\mathbf{V}_t^k) \tag{6.161}$$

$$\mathbf{V}_s^k = \boldsymbol{\theta}_k \times {}^t\mathbf{V}_s^k + \frac{1}{2} \boldsymbol{\theta}_k \times (\boldsymbol{\theta}_k \times {}^t\mathbf{V}_s^k) \tag{6.162}$$

The only purpose of using $\boldsymbol{\theta}_k$ is to evaluate (approximations to) the new director vectors, and $\boldsymbol{\theta}_k$ is discarded thereafter.

Substituting from (6.161) and (6.162) into (6.158) we obtain the expression for u_i to evaluate the continuum linear and nonlinear incremental strain tensors in Tables 6.2 and 6.3. Since the relations in (6.161) and (6.162) involve quadratic expressions, we neglect all higher-order terms in the solution variables to obtain the fully linearized form of the principle of virtual work equation—linearized about the state at time t with respect to the solution variables (the nodal point displacements and rotations). With this process, the exact tangent stiffness matrix is arrived at and employed in the incremental finite element solution. However, we should note that the continuum *linear* strain increments in Tables 6.2 and 6.3 now include *quadratic* terms in rotations, and hence the right-hand-side terms

$$\int_{^0V} {}_0^t S_{ij}\, \delta_0 e_{ij}\, d^0V \qquad \text{and} \qquad \int_{^tV} {}^t\tau_{ij}\, \delta_t e_{ij}\, d^tV$$

in (6.74) and (6.75) contribute, in this case, to the tangent stiffness matrices of the TL and UL formulations. The same incremental equations are of course also obtained if we use the procedure in Section 6.3.1 to develop these equations.

A kinematic assumption in this interpolation is that "plane sections remain plane," and hence warping is not included. However, warping displacement behavior can be added to the assumed deformations as discussed in Section 5.4.1.

The linear and nonlinear strain displacement matrices of the beam element corresponding to the UL formulation can now be evaluated using the approach employed in linear analysis. That is, using (6.158), the strain components are calculated corresponding to the global axes and are then transformed to obtain the strain components corresponding to the local beam axes, η, ξ, ζ. Since the element stiffness matrix is evaluated using numerical integration, the transformation from global to local strain components must be performed during the numerical integration at each integration point.

Considering the TL formulation, we recognize that, first, derivatives analogous to those used in the UL formulation are required, but the derivatives are taken with respect to the coordinates at time 0. In addition, however, in order to include the initial displacement effect, the derivatives of the displacements at time t with respect to the original coordinates are needed. These derivatives are evaluated using (6.157).

The above interpolations lead to the displacement-based finite element formulation which, as discussed in Section 5.4.1, yields a very slowly converging discretization. In order to obtain an effective scheme a mixed interpolation should be used which, for the beam formulation, is equivalent to employing an appropriate Gauss integration order for the r-direction integration: namely one-point integration for the two-node element, two-point integration for the three-node element, and three-point integration for the four-node element.

The finite element equations thus arrived at are

$$ {}^t\mathbf{K} \begin{bmatrix} \vdots \\ \mathbf{u}_k \\ \boldsymbol{\theta}_k \\ \vdots \end{bmatrix} = {}^{t+\Delta t}\mathbf{R} - {}^t\mathbf{F} \tag{6.163}$$

Having solved (6.163) for $\mathbf{u}_k$ and $\boldsymbol{\theta}_k$, we obtain approximations for the nodal point displacements and director vectors at time $t + \Delta t$ using

$$ {}^{t+\Delta t}\mathbf{u}_k = {}^t\mathbf{u}_k + \mathbf{u}_k \tag{6.164}$$

and

$$ {}^{t+\Delta t}\mathbf{V}_t^k = {}^t\mathbf{V}_t^k + \int_{\boldsymbol{\theta}_k} d\boldsymbol{\theta}_k \times {}^\tau\mathbf{V}_t^k \tag{6.165}$$

$$ {}^{t+\Delta t}\mathbf{V}_s^k = {}^t\mathbf{V}_s^k + \int_{\boldsymbol{\theta}_k} d\boldsymbol{\theta}_k \times {}^\tau\mathbf{V}_s^k \tag{6.166}$$

The integrations in (6.165) and (6.166) can be performed in one step using an orthogonal matrix for finite rotations (see, for example, J. H. Argyris [B] and Exercise 6.55) or in a number of steps using a simple Euler forward method (see Section 9.6). Of course, $\boldsymbol{\theta}_k$ (and $\mathbf{u}_k$) are approximations to the actual required increments (because of the linearization of the principle of virtual work), but with the integrations in (6.165) and (6.166) we intend to arrive at a more accurate evaluation of the new director vectors than by simply substituting into (6.161) and (6.162).

The above presentation corresponds of course to the first iteration of the usual Newton-Raphson iterative solution process or to a typical iteration when the last calculated values of coordinates and director vectors are used.

It should be noted that this beam element formulation admits very large displacements and rotations and has an important advantage when compared with the formulation of a straight beam element based on Hermitian displacement interpolations: all individual displacement components are expressed using the same functions because the displacement expressions are derived from the geometry interpolation. Thus there is no directionality in the displacement interpolations, and the change in the geometry of the beam structure with increasing deformations is modeled more accurately than by using straight beam elements based on Hermitian functions, as for example presented by K. J. Bathe and S. Bolourchi [A].

We mentioned earlier that this general beam formulation can be used to derive the matrices pertaining to the formulations of planar beam elements for plane stress or plane strain conditions or axisymmetric shell elements. We demonstrate such derivations in the following examples.

EXAMPLE 6.20: Consider the two-node beam element shown in Fig. E6.20. Evaluate the coordinate and displacement interpolations and derivatives that are required for the calculation of the strain-displacement matrices of the UL and TL formulations.

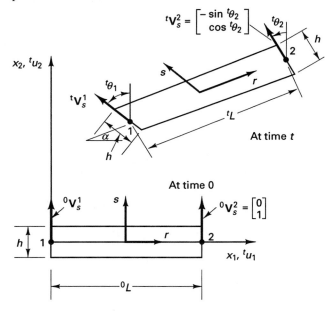

Figure E6.20   Two-node beam element in large displacements and rotations

Using the variables in Fig. E6.20, we have corresponding to (6.154),

$$^tx_1 = \left(\frac{1-r}{2}\right){}^tx_1^1 + \left(\frac{1+r}{2}\right){}^tx_1^2 - \frac{sh}{2}\left(\frac{1-r}{2}\right)\sin\,{}^t\theta_1 - \frac{sh}{2}\left(\frac{1+r}{2}\right)\sin\,{}^t\theta_2$$

$$^tx_2 = \left(\frac{1-r}{2}\right){}^tx_2^1 + \left(\frac{1+r}{2}\right){}^tx_2^2 + \frac{sh}{2}\left(\frac{1-r}{2}\right)\cos\,{}^t\theta_1 + \frac{sh}{2}\left(\frac{1+r}{2}\right)\cos\,{}^t\theta_2$$

$$^0x_1 = \left(\frac{1+r}{2}\right){}^0L$$

$$^0x_2 = \frac{sh}{2}$$

Hence, the displacement components are at any point at time t,

$$^tu_1 = \left(\frac{{}^tx_1^1 + {}^tx_1^2 - {}^0L}{2}\right) + \left(\frac{{}^tx_1^2 - {}^tx_1^1 - {}^0L}{2}\right)r - \frac{sh}{2}\left[\left(\frac{1-r}{2}\right)\sin\,{}^t\theta_1 + \left(\frac{1+r}{2}\right)\sin\,{}^t\theta_2\right]$$

$$^tu_2 = \left(\frac{{}^tx_2^1 + {}^tx_2^2}{2}\right) + \left(\frac{{}^tx_2^2 - {}^tx_2^1}{2}\right)r + \frac{sh}{2}\left[\left(\frac{1-r}{2}\right)\cos\,{}^t\theta_1 + \left(\frac{1+r}{2}\right)\cos\,{}^t\theta_2 - 1\right]$$

The incremental displacements are given by (6.158); hence,

$$u_1 = \frac{1-r}{2}u_1^1 + \frac{1+r}{2}u_1^2 + \frac{sh}{2}\left(\frac{1-r}{2}\right)\left[(-\cos\,{}^t\theta_1)\theta_1 + \frac{1}{2}\sin\,{}^t\theta_1(\theta_1)^2\right]$$

$$+ \frac{sh}{2}\left(\frac{1+r}{2}\right)\left[(-\cos\,{}^t\theta_2)\theta_2 + \frac{1}{2}\sin\,{}^t\theta_2(\theta_2)^2\right] \tag{a}$$

$$u_2 = \frac{1-r}{2}u_2^1 + \frac{1+r}{2}u_2^2 + \frac{sh}{2}\left(\frac{1-r}{2}\right)\left[(-\sin\,{}^t\theta_1)\theta_1 - \frac{1}{2}\cos\,{}^t\theta_1(\theta_1)^2\right]$$

$$+ \frac{sh}{2}\left(\frac{1+r}{2}\right)\left[(-\sin\,{}^t\theta_2)\theta_2 - \frac{1}{2}\cos\,{}^t\theta_2(\theta_2)^2\right] \tag{b}$$

We note the quadratic terms in nodal rotations, which are underlined with a dashed line. Using (a) and (b) to evaluate the continuum incremental strain terms $_0e_{ij}$, $_te_{ij}$, $_0\eta_{ij}$, and $_t\eta_{ij}$ in Tables 6.2 and 6.3, we recognize that the fully linearized finite element equations are obtained by including the underlined terms in the evaluation of $\int_{0V}{}_0^tS_{ij}\,\delta_0e_{ij}\,d^0V$ and $\int_{tV}{}^t\tau_{ij}\,\delta_te_{ij}\,d^tV$. These terms add for the structural elements a contribution to the nonlinear strain stiffness matrices. However, these quadratic terms in rotation do not contribute in the linearized form of the other integrals because they result in those integrals in higher-order terms that are neglected in the linearization.

In considering the UL formulation, the required derivatives for the Jacobian are

$$\frac{\partial^tx_1}{\partial r} = \frac{L\cos\alpha}{2} - \frac{sh}{4}(\sin\,{}^t\theta_2 - \sin\,{}^t\theta_1)$$

$$\frac{\partial^tx_1}{\partial s} = \left(-\frac{h}{2}\right)\left[\left(\frac{1-r}{2}\right)\sin\,{}^t\theta_1 + \left(\frac{1+r}{2}\right)\sin\,{}^t\theta_2\right]$$

$$\frac{\partial^tx_2}{\partial r} = \frac{L\sin\alpha}{2} + \frac{sh}{4}(\cos\,{}^t\theta_2 - \cos\,{}^t\theta_1)$$

$$\frac{\partial^t x_2}{\partial s} = \frac{h}{2}\left[\left(\frac{1-r}{2}\right)\cos{^t\theta_1} + \left(\frac{1+r}{2}\right)\cos{^t\theta_2}\right]$$

where we assumed $^tL = {^0L} = L$.

Next we consider the TL formulation. Here we use

$$^0\mathbf{J} = \begin{bmatrix} \dfrac{^0L}{2} & 0 \\ 0 & \dfrac{h}{2} \end{bmatrix}$$

Also, the initial displacement effect is taken into account using the derivatives

$$^t_0 u_{1,1} = (\cos\alpha - 1) - \frac{sh}{2L}(\sin{^t\theta_2} - \sin{^t\theta_1})$$

$$^t_0 u_{1,2} = -\left(\frac{1-r}{2}\right)\sin{^t\theta_1} - \left(\frac{1+r}{2}\right)\sin{^t\theta_2}$$

$$^t_0 u_{2,1} = \sin\alpha + \frac{sh}{2L}(\cos{^t\theta_2} - \cos{^t\theta_1})$$

$$^t_0 u_{2,2} = \left(\frac{1-r}{2}\right)\cos{^t\theta_1} + \left(\frac{1+r}{2}\right)\cos{^t\theta_2} - 1$$

where we again assumed $^tL = {^0L} = L$.

In each case, we note that these expressions lead to the strain terms corresponding to the global stationary coordinate system. These terms must be transformed to the local η, ξ axes for construction of the strain-displacement matrix of the element.

Finally, we should note that the element can be employed in plane stress or plane strain conditions, depending on the stress-strain relation used (see Section 4.2.3). In plane stress analysis the thickness of the element (normal to the x_1, x_2 plane) must of course be given (this thickness is assumed to be unity in plane strain analysis).

EXAMPLE 6.21:   The two-node element in Example 6.20 is to be used as a shell element in axisymmetric conditions. Discuss what terms in addition to those given in Example 6.20 need to be included in the construction of the strain-displacement matrices for the TL formulation.

In axisymmetric analysis the integration is performed over 1 radian and the hoop strain effect must be included (see Example 5.9). Table 6.5 gives the incremental hoop strain $_0\epsilon_{33}$, which must be evaluated using the interpolations stated in Example 6.20 to give a third row in the strain-displacement matrices $^t_0\mathbf{B}_{L0}$ and $^t_0\mathbf{B}_{L1}$. The third row of the matrix $^t_0\mathbf{B}_{L0}$ corresponds to the term $u_1/{^0x_1}$, hence,

$$^t_0\mathbf{B}_{L0} = \begin{bmatrix} \cdots & | & \cdots & | & \cdots & | & \cdots & | & \cdots & | & \cdots \\ \cdots & | & \cdots & | & \cdots & | & \cdots & | & \cdots & | & \cdots \\ \dfrac{1-r}{2\,^0x_1} & | & 0 & | & \dfrac{-sh}{2}\left(\dfrac{1-r}{2}\right)\dfrac{\cos{^t\theta_1}}{^0x_1} & | & \dfrac{1+r}{2\,^0x_1} & | & 0 & | & \dfrac{-sh}{2}\left(\dfrac{1+r}{2}\right)\dfrac{\cos{^t\theta_2}}{^0x_1} \end{bmatrix}$$

where we have used the following ordering of nodal variables in the solution vector

$$\hat{\mathbf{u}}^T = [u_1^1 \quad u_2^1 \quad \theta_1 \quad u_1^2 \quad u_2^2 \quad \theta_2]$$

and $^0x_1 = [(1 + r)/2]L$. The third row of the matrix $^t_0\mathbf{B}_{L1}$ corresponds to the strain term $^tu_1 u_1/({^0x_1})^2$ and for its evaluation the interpolations of $^tu_1$, $^0x_1$, and u_1 are similarly used.

The terms in the nonlinear strain stiffness matrix corresponding to $_0^t S_{33}$ are evaluated from the expression

$$_0^t S_{33} \left\{ \delta\theta_1 \left[\frac{sh}{2}\left(\frac{1-r}{2}\right) \frac{\sin\ {}^t\theta_1}{{}^0x_1}\left(1 + \frac{{}^t u_1}{{}^0x_1}\right)\right]\theta_1 + \delta\theta_2 \left[\frac{sh}{2}\left(\frac{1+r}{2}\right) \frac{\sin\ {}^t\theta_2}{{}^0x_1}\left(1 + \frac{{}^t u_1}{{}^0x_1}\right)\right]\theta_2 \right.$$

$$+ \left(\frac{1-r}{2\ {}^0x_1} \delta u_1^1 - \left[\frac{sh}{2}\left(\frac{1-r}{2}\right)\frac{\cos\ {}^t\theta_1}{{}^0x_1}\right]\delta\theta_1 + \frac{1+r}{2\ {}^0x_1}\delta u_1^2 - \left[\frac{sh}{2}\left(\frac{1+r}{2}\right)\frac{\cos\ {}^t\theta_2}{{}^0x_1}\right]\delta\theta_2\right)$$

$$\left. \times \left(\frac{1-r}{2\ {}^0x_1} u_1^1 - \left[\frac{sh}{2}\left(\frac{1-r}{2}\right)\frac{\cos\ {}^t\theta_1}{{}^0x_1}\right]\theta_1 + \frac{1+r}{2\ {}^0x_1} u_1^2 - \left[\frac{sh}{2}\left(\frac{1+r}{2}\right)\frac{\cos\ {}^t\theta_2}{{}^0x_1}\right]\theta_2\right)\right\}$$

This expression is of the form $\delta\hat{\mathbf{u}}^T(_0^t\mathbf{K}_{NL}^*)\hat{\mathbf{u}}$, where $\mathbf{K}_{NL}^*$ represents a contribution to the element nonlinear strain stiffness matrix.

6.5.2 Plate and General Shell Elements

Many plate and shell elements have been proposed for the nonlinear analysis of plates, specific shells, and general shell structures. However, as with the beam element discussed in the previous section, the isoparametric formulations of plate and shell elements for nonlinear analysis are very attractive because these formulations are both consistent and general, and the elements can be employed in an effective manner for the analysis of a variety of plates and shells. As in linear analysis, in essence a very general shell theory is employed in the formulation so that the shell elements are applicable, in principle, to the analysis of any plate and shell structure.

Considering a plate undergoing large deflections, we recognize that as soon as the plate has deflected significantly, the action of the structure is really that of a shell; i.e., the structure is now curved, and both membrane and bending stresses are significant. Therefore, in the discussion below we consider only general shell elements, where we imply that if a specific element is initially flat, it represents a plate.

In the following presentation we consider the nonlinear formulation of the MITC shell elements discussed for linear analysis in Section 5.4.2. Figure 6.6 shows a typical nine-node

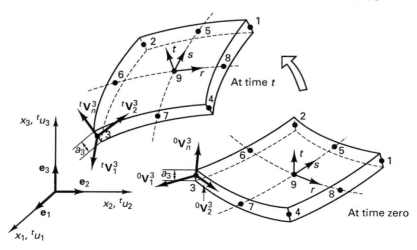

Figure 6.6   Shell element undergoing large displacements and rotations

element in its original position and its configuration at time t. The element behavior is based on the same assumptions that are employed in linear analysis, namely, that straight lines defined by the nodal director vectors (which, usually, give lines that in the original configuration are close to normal to the midsurface of the shell) remain straight during the element deformations and that no transverse normal stress is developed in the directions of the director vectors. However, the nonlinear formulation given here does admit arbitrarily large displacements and rotations of the shell element.[10]

The UL and TL formulations of the shell element are based on the general continuum mechanics equations presented in Section 6.2.3 and are a direct extension of the formulation for linear analysis. Also, the calculation of the element matrices follows closely the calculations used for the beam elements (see Section 6.5.1).

Using the same notation as in Section 5.4.2, the coordinates of a generic point in the shell element now undergoing very large displacements and rotations are (see K. J. Bathe and S. Bolourchi [B])

$$^t x_i = \sum_{k=1}^{q} h_k \, ^t x_i^k + \frac{t}{2} \sum_{k=1}^{q} a_k h_k \, ^t V_{ni}^k \tag{6.167}$$

Using (6.167) at times 0, t, and $t + \Delta t$, we thus have

$$^t u_i = \, ^t x_i - \, ^0 x_i \tag{6.168}$$

and

$$u_i = \, ^{t+\Delta t} x_i - \, ^t x_i \tag{6.169}$$

Substituting from (6.167) into (6.168) and (6.169), we obtain

$$^t u_i = \sum_{k=1}^{q} h_k \, ^t u_i^k + \frac{t}{2} \sum_{k=1}^{q} a_k h_k \, (^t V_{ni}^k - \, ^0 V_{ni}^k) \tag{6.170}$$

and

$$u_i = \sum_{k=1}^{q} h_k u_i^k + \frac{t}{2} \sum_{k=1}^{q} a_k h_k \, V_{ni}^k \tag{6.171}$$

where

$$V_{ni}^k = \, ^{t+\Delta t} V_{ni}^k - \, ^t V_{ni}^k \tag{6.172}$$

The relation in (6.170) is employed to evaluate the total displacements and total strains (hence also total stresses for both the UL and TL formulations) of the particles in the element. To apply (6.171) the same thoughts as in the beam element formulation for use of (6.158), (6.161), and (6.162) are applicable. Now we express the vector components V_{ni}^k in terms of rotations about two vectors that are orthogonal to $^t \mathbf{V}_n^k$. These two vectors $^t \mathbf{V}_1^k$ and $^t \mathbf{V}_2^k$ are defined at time 0 (as in linear analysis) using

$$^0 \mathbf{V}_1^k = \frac{\mathbf{e}_2 \times \, ^0 \mathbf{V}_n^k}{\| \mathbf{e}_2 \times \, ^0 \mathbf{V}_n^k \|_2} \tag{6.173}$$

$$^0 \mathbf{V}_2^k = \, ^0 \mathbf{V}_n^k \times \, ^0 \mathbf{V}_1^k \tag{6.174}$$

where we set $^0 \mathbf{V}_1^k$ equal to $\mathbf{e}_3$ if $^0 \mathbf{V}_n^k$ is parallel to $\mathbf{e}_2$. The vectors for time t are then obtained by an integration process briefly described for the director vector in (6.177).

---

[10] As in the beam formulation in Section 6.5.1, to have the element formulation applicable to large strains, the change in thickness varying over the surface of the element would need to be calculated. The change in thickness depends on the material stress-strain relationship of the element.

Let α_k and β_k be the rotations of the director vector ${}^t\mathbf{V}_n^k$ about the vectors ${}^t\mathbf{V}_1^k$ and ${}^t\mathbf{V}_2^k$ in the configuration at time t. Then we have approximately for small angles α_k and β_k, but including second-order rotation effects (see Exercise 6.57),

$$\mathbf{V}_n^k = -{}^t\mathbf{V}_2^k\,\alpha_k + {}^t\mathbf{V}_1^k\,\beta_k - \tfrac{1}{2}(\alpha_k^2 + \beta_k^2)\,{}^t\mathbf{V}_n^k \tag{6.175}$$

We include the quadratic terms in rotations because we want to arrive at the consistent tangent stiffness matrix, and these terms contribute to the nonlinear strain stiffness effects. Namely, substituting from (6.175) into (6.171), we obtain

$$u_i = \sum_{k=1}^q h_k u_i^k + \frac{t}{2}\sum_{k=1}^q a_k h_k\left[-{}^t V_{2i}^k\,\alpha_k + {}^t V_{1i}^k\,\beta_k - \frac{1}{2}(\alpha_k^2 + \beta_k^2)\,{}^t V_{ni}^k\right] \tag{6.176}$$

Using this expression to evaluate the continuum terms in Tables 6.2 and 6.3, we notice that the terms $\int_{{}^tV}{}^t\tau_{ij}\,\delta_t e_{ij}\,d{}^tV$ and $\int_{{}^0V}{}^t_0 S_{ij}\,\delta_0 e_{ij}\,d^0V$ result in a stiffness contribution due to the quadratic terms in (6.176) that we naturally add to the other terms of the nonlinear strain stiffness matrix.

We arrived at a similar result in the formulation of the isoparametric beam elements discussed in the previous section [see (6.161) and (6.162) and the ensuing discussion].

The finite element solution will yield the nodal point variables u_i^k, α_k, and β_k, which can then be employed to evaluate ${}^{t+\Delta t}\mathbf{V}_n^k$,

$$ {}^{t+\Delta t}\mathbf{V}_n^k = {}^t\mathbf{V}_n^k + \int_{\alpha_k,\beta_k} -{}^\tau\mathbf{V}_2^k\,d\alpha_k + {}^\tau\mathbf{V}_1^k\,d\beta_k \tag{6.177}$$

This integration can be performed in one step using an orthogonal matrix for finite rotations (see, for example, J. H. Argyris [B] and Exercise 6.57) or using the Euler forward method and a number of steps (see Section 9.6).

The relations in (6.167) to (6.176) can be directly employed to establish the strain-displacement matrices of displacement-based shell elements. However, as discussed in Section 5.4.2, these elements are not efficient because of the phenomena of shear and membrane locking. In Section 5.4.2, we introduced the mixed interpolated elements for linear analysis, and an important feature of these elements is that they can be directly extended to nonlinear analysis. (In fact, the elements were formulated originally for nonlinear analysis, and the linear analysis elements are obtained simply by neglecting all nonlinear terms.)

The starting point of the formulation is the principle of virtual work written in terms of covariant strain components and contravariant stress components. In the total Lagrangian formulation we use

$$ \int_{0_V} {}^{t+\Delta t}_0\tilde{S}^{ij}\,\delta{}^{t+\Delta t}_0\tilde{\epsilon}_{ij}\,d^0V = {}^{t+\Delta t}\mathcal{R} \tag{6.178}$$

and in the updated Lagrangian formulation we use

$$ \int_{{}^tV} {}^{t+\Delta t}_t\tilde{S}^{ij}\,\delta{}^{t+\Delta t}_t\tilde{\epsilon}_{ij}\,d{}^tV = {}^{t+\Delta t}\mathcal{R} \tag{6.179}$$

The incremental forms are of course given in Tables 6.2 and 6.3, but here covariant strain and contravariant stress components are employed.

As discussed in Section 5.4.2, the basic step in the MITC shell element formulation is to assume strain interpolations and to tie these to the strains obtained from the displacement interpolations.

The strain interpolations are as detailed in Section 5.4.2, but of course the interpolations are now used for the Green-Lagrange strain components $^{t+\Delta t}_{0}\tilde{\epsilon}^{AS}_{ij}$ and $^{t+\Delta t}_{t}\tilde{\epsilon}^{AS}_{ij}$, where the superscript AS denotes *assumed strain*. These assumed strain components are tied to the strain components $^{t+\Delta t}_{0}\tilde{\epsilon}^{DI}_{ij}$ and $^{t+\Delta t}_{t}\tilde{\epsilon}^{DI}_{ij}$, obtained from the displacement interpolations (6.170) and (6.171).

The covariant strain components $^{t+\Delta t}_{0}\tilde{\epsilon}^{DI}_{ij}$ and $^{t+\Delta t}_{t}\tilde{\epsilon}^{DI}_{ij}$ are calculated from the fundamental expressions using base vectors,

$$^{t+\Delta t}_{0}\tilde{\epsilon}^{DI}_{ij} = \tfrac{1}{2}(^{t+\Delta t}\mathbf{g}_i \cdot {}^{t+\Delta t}\mathbf{g}_j - {}^{0}\mathbf{g}_i \cdot {}^{0}\mathbf{g}_j) \tag{6.180}$$

and

$$^{t+\Delta t}_{t}\tilde{\epsilon}^{DI}_{ij} = \tfrac{1}{2}(^{t+\Delta t}\mathbf{g}_i \cdot {}^{t+\Delta t}\mathbf{g}_j - {}^{t}\mathbf{g}_i \cdot {}^{t}\mathbf{g}_j) \tag{6.181}$$

where

$$^{t+\Delta t}\mathbf{g}_i = \frac{\partial^{t+\Delta t}\mathbf{x}}{\partial r_i}; \qquad {}^{t}\mathbf{g}_i = \frac{\partial^{t}\mathbf{x}}{\partial r_i}; \qquad {}^{0}\mathbf{g}_i = \frac{\partial^{0}\mathbf{x}}{\partial r_i} \tag{6.182}$$

and we use $r_1 \equiv r$, $r_2 \equiv s$, $r_3 \equiv t$, and of course,

$$^{t+\Delta t}\mathbf{x} = {}^{0}\mathbf{x} + {}^{t+\Delta t}\mathbf{u}; \qquad {}^{t}\mathbf{x} = {}^{0}\mathbf{x} + {}^{t}\mathbf{u} \tag{6.183}$$

Using the interpolations discussed in Section 5.4.2, with the above strain components, the MITC shell elements already presented for linear analysis in Section 5.4.2 are now obtained, including large displacement and large rotation effects. These elements satisfy the criteria of reliability and effectiveness that we enumerated in Section 5.4.2.

It may be noted once more that the shell elements discussed above are general elements since no specific shell theory has been employed in their formulation. In fact, the use of the general incremental virtual work equation with only the two basic shell assumptions—that lines originally normal to the shell midsurface remain straight and that the transverse normal stress remains zero (more accurately, actually the directions of the director vectors are used)—is equivalent to using a general nonlinear shell theory. This generality in the formulation is preserved by employing the above interpolations of the shell geometry, displacements, and strains. An important feature is the use of the director vector of the shell midsurface which makes it possible for the elements to undergo arbitrary large displacements and rotations.

6.5.3 Exercises

6.51. Consider the two-node beam element shown.
  (a) Plot the displacements of the material particles corresponding to $^{t}u^2_1$, $^{t}u^2_2$, and $^{t}\theta_2$, and evaluate the Green-Lagrange strain components corresponding to these displacements at $r = s = 0$.

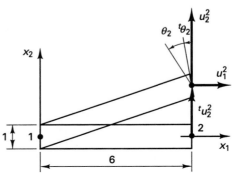

(b) Establish the derivatives $_0u_{i,j}$ (i.e., $\partial u_i/\partial^0 x_j$), $i = 1, 2; j = 1, 2$, corresponding to the nodal incremental displacement and rotation variables u_1^2, u_2^2, and θ_2.

At node 1 displacements and rotations are zero; at node 2 $'u_1^2 = 0$, $'u_2^2 = 2$, $'\theta_2 = 10°$.

6.52. Consider the two-node beam element shown. Calculate for the degrees of freedom u_1^2, u_2^2, and θ_2 the stiffness matrix $'\mathbf{K}$ and nodal force vector $'\mathbf{F}$ using the total Lagrangian formulation.
(a) Use the displacement method and analytical integration.
(b) Use one-point Gauss integration for the r direction.

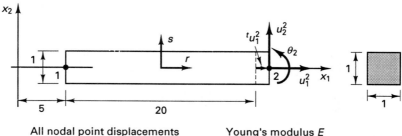

All nodal point displacements   Young's modulus E
and rotations are zero at time t,   Shear modulus G
except $'u_1^2 = 0.1$

6.53. Perform the same calculations as in Exercise 6.52 but now assume that the element is an axisymmetric shell element, with the x_2 axis the axis of revolution.

6.54. Consider the beam element in Exercise 6.52. Calculate the stiffness matrix $'\mathbf{K}$ and force vector $'\mathbf{F}$ for the degrees of freedom at node 2 using the mixed interpolation of linear displacements and rotations and constant transverse shear strain (see Section 5.4.1).

6.55. Consider the four-node shell element shown. Evaluate the displacements of the particles in the element for the given nodal point displacements and director vectors at time t. Draw these displacements over the original geometry of the element.

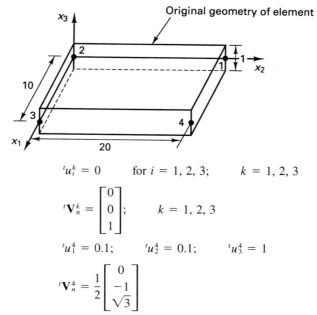

Original geometry of element

$'u_i^k = 0$ for $i = 1, 2, 3$; $k = 1, 2, 3$

$'\mathbf{V}_n^k = \begin{bmatrix} 0 \\ 0 \\ 1 \end{bmatrix}$; $k = 1, 2, 3$

$'u_1^4 = 0.1$; $'u_2^4 = 0.1$; $'u_3^4 = 1$

$'\mathbf{V}_n^4 = \frac{1}{2}\begin{bmatrix} 0 \\ -1 \\ \sqrt{3} \end{bmatrix}$

6.56. Show that the expressions in (6.161) and (6.162) contain all second-order terms in $\boldsymbol{\theta}_k$ to obtain the increments in the director vectors. Obtain the result by a simple geometric argument and by the fact that the rotation can be expressed through the rotation matrix $\mathbf{Q}$, see, for example, J. H. Argyris [B], where

$$\mathbf{Q} = \mathbf{I} + \frac{\sin \gamma_k}{\gamma_k}\mathbf{S}_k + \frac{1}{2}\left(\frac{\sin \dfrac{\gamma_k}{2}}{\dfrac{\gamma_k}{2}}\right)^2 \mathbf{S}_k^2; \qquad \gamma_k = (\theta_{k1}^2 + \theta_{k2}^2 + \theta_{k3}^2)^{\frac{1}{2}}$$

and

$$\mathbf{S}_k = \begin{bmatrix} 0 & -\theta_{k3} & \theta_{k2} \\ \theta_{k3} & 0 & -\theta_{k1} \\ -\theta_{k2} & \theta_{k1} & 0 \end{bmatrix}$$

6.57. Show that the expression in (6.175) includes all second-order terms in α_k and β_k to obtain the increment in the director vector $'\mathbf{V}_n^k$. Obtain the result by a simple geometric argument and by use of the matrix $\mathbf{Q}$ of Exercise 6.55 but with

$$\gamma_k = (\alpha_k^2 + \beta_k^2)^{\frac{1}{2}} \qquad \mathbf{S}_k = \begin{bmatrix} 0 & 0 & \beta_k \\ 0 & 0 & -\alpha_k \\ -\beta_k & \alpha_k & 0 \end{bmatrix}$$

6.58. Calculate the covariant strain terms $'_0\tilde{\epsilon}_{ij}^{DI}$ for the element and its deformation given in Exercise 6.56.

6.59. Use a computer program to solve for the large displacement response of the cantilever shown. Analyze the structure for a tip rotation of π (180 degrees) and compare your displacement and stress results with the analytical solution. (*Hint*: The four-node isoparametric mixed interpolated beam element performs particularly well in this analysis.)

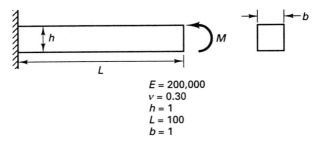

$E = 200{,}000$
$\nu = 0.30$
$h = 1$
$L = 100$
$b = 1$

6.60. Use a computer program to solve for the response of the spherical shell structure shown. Calculate the displacements and stresses accurately. (The solution of this structure has been extensively used in the evaluation of shell elements; see, for example, E. N. Dvorkin and K. J. Bathe [A]).

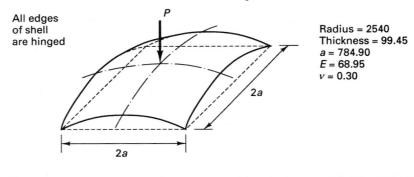

All edges
of shell
are hinged

Radius = 2540
Thickness = 99.45
$a = 784.90$
$E = 68.95$
$\nu = 0.30$

6.6 USE OF CONSTITUTIVE RELATIONS

In Sections 6.3 to 6.5 we discussed the evaluation of the displacement and strain-displacement relations for various elements. We pointed out that these kinematic relations yield an accurate representation of large deformations (including large strains in the case of two- and three-dimensional continuum elements).

The kinematic descriptions in the element formulations are therefore very general. However, it must be noted that in order for a formulation of an element to be applicable to a specific response prediction, *it is also necessary to use appropriate constitutive descriptions.* Clearly, the finite element equilibrium equations contain the displacement and strain-displacement matrices plus the constitutive matrix of the material (see Table 6.4). Therefore, *in order for a formulation to be applicable to a certain response prediction, it is imperative that both the kinematic and the constitutive descriptions be appropriate.* For example, assume that the TL formulation is employed to describe the kinematic behavior of a two-dimensional element and a material law is used which is formulated only for small strain conditions. In this case the analysis can model only small strains although the TL kinematic formulation does admit large strains.

The objective in this section is to present some fundamental observations pertaining to the use of material laws in nonlinear finite element analysis. Many different material laws are employed in practice, and we shall not attempt to survey and summarize these models. Instead, our only objectives are to discuss the stress and strain tensors that are used effectively with certain classes of material models and to present some important general observations pertaining to material models, their implementations, and their use.

The three classes of models that we consider in the following sections are those with which we are widely concerned in practice, namely, elastic, elastoplastic, and creep material models. Some basic properties of these material descriptions are given in Table 6.7, which provides a very brief overview of the major classes of material behavior.

In our discussion of the use of the material models, we need to keep in mind how the complete nonlinear analysis is performed incrementally. Referring to the previous sections, and specifically to relations (6.11), (6.78), and (6.79) and Section 6.2.3, we can summarize the complete process as given in Table 6.8.

This table shows that the material relationships are used at two points of the solution process: the evaluation of the stresses and the evaluation of the tangent stress-strain matrices. The stresses are used in the calculation of the nodal point force vectors and the nonlinear strain stiffness matrices, and the tangent stress-strain matrices are used in the calculation of the linear strain stiffness matrices. As we pointed out earlier (see Section 6.1), it is imperative that the stresses be evaluated with high accuracy since otherwise the solution result is not correct, and it is important that the stiffness matrices be truly tangent matrices since otherwise, in general, more iterations to convergence are needed than necessary.

Table 6.8 shows that the basic task in the evaluation of the stresses and the tangent stress-strain matrix is the following:

Given all stress components $^t\boldsymbol{\sigma}$ and strain components $^t\mathbf{e}$ and any internal material variables that we call here $^t\kappa_i$, all corresponding to time t,

$$\{^t\boldsymbol{\sigma}, \,^t\mathbf{e}, \,^t\kappa_1, \,^t\kappa_2, \ldots\}$$

TABLE 6.7   *Overview of some material descriptions*

Material model	Characteristics	Examples
Elastic, linear or nonlinear	Stress is a function of strain only; same stress path on unloading as on loading. $${}^{t}\sigma_{ij} = {}^{t}C_{ijrs}\,{}^{t}e_{rs}$$ linear elastic: ${}^{t}C_{ijrs}$ is constant nonlinear elastic: ${}^{t}C_{ijrs}$ varies as a function of strain	Almost all materials provided the stresses are small enough: steels, cast iron, glass, rock, wood, and so on, before yielding or fracture
Hyperelastic	Stress is calculated from a strain energy functional W, $${}_{0}^{t}S_{ij} = \frac{\partial W}{\partial {}_{0}^{t}\epsilon_{ij}}$$	Rubberlike materials, e.g., Mooney-Rivlin and Ogden models
Hypoelastic	Stress increments are calculated from strain increments $$d\sigma_{ij} = C_{ijrs}\,de_{rs}$$ The material moduli C_{ijrs} are defined as functions of stress, strain, fracture criteria, loading and unloading parameters, maximum strains reached, and so on.	Concrete models (see, for example, K. J. Bathe, J. Walczak, A. Welch, and N. Mistry [A])
Elastoplastic	Linear elastic behavior until yield, use of yield condition, flow rule, and hardening rule to calculate stress and plastic strain increments; plastic strain increments are instantaneous.	Metals, soils, rocks, when subjected to high stresses
Creep	Time effect of increasing strains under constant load, or decreasing stress under constant deformations; creep strain increments are noninstantaneous.	Metals at high temperatures
Viscoplasticity	Time-dependent inelastic strains; rate effects are included.	Polymers, metals

and also given all strain components corresponding to time $t + \Delta t$ and end of iteration $(i - 1)$, denoted as ${}^{t+\Delta t}\mathbf{e}^{(i-1)}$

Calculate all stress components, internal material variables, and the tangent stress-strain matrix, corresponding to ${}^{t+\Delta t}\mathbf{e}^{(i-1)}$,

$$\{{}^{t+\Delta t}\boldsymbol{\sigma}^{(i-1)}, \mathbf{C}^{(i-1)}, {}^{t+\Delta t}\kappa_1^{(i-1)}, {}^{t+\Delta t}\kappa_2^{(i-1)}, \ldots]$$

Hence we shall assume in the following discussion that the strains are known corresponding to the state for which the stresses and the stress-strain tangent relationship are required. For ease of writing, we shall frequently also not include the superscript $(i - 1)$ but simply denote the current strain state as ${}^{t+\Delta t}\mathbf{e}$. This convention shall not imply that no equilibrium iterations are performed. However, since the solution process for the stresses

TABLE 6.8 *Solution process in incremental nonlinear finite element analysis*

Accepted and known solution at time t: stresses $^t\boldsymbol{\sigma}$

   strains $^t\mathbf{e}$

   internal material parameters $^t\kappa_1$, $^t\kappa_2$, . . .

1. *Known*:   nodal point variables $^{t+\Delta t}\mathbf{U}^{(i-1)}$ and hence element strains $^{t+\Delta t}\mathbf{e}^{(i-1)}$

2. *Calculate*:   stresses $^{t+\Delta t}\boldsymbol{\sigma}^{(i-1)}$

   tangent stress-strain matrix corresponding to $^{t+\Delta t}\boldsymbol{\sigma}^{(i-1)}$, denoted as $\mathbf{C}^{(i-1)}$

   internal material parameters $^{t+\Delta t}\kappa_1^{(i-1)}$, $^{t+\Delta t}\kappa_2^{(i-1)}$, . . .

   a. In elastic analysis: the strains $^{t+\Delta t}\mathbf{e}^{(i-1)}$ directly give the stresses $^{t+\Delta t}\boldsymbol{\sigma}^{(i-1)}$ and the stress-strain matrix $\mathbf{C}^{(i-1)}$

   b. In inelastic analysis: an integration process is performed for the stresses

$$^{t+\Delta t}\boldsymbol{\sigma}^{(i-1)} = \,^t\boldsymbol{\sigma} + \int_t^{t+\Delta t^{(i-1)}} d\boldsymbol{\sigma}$$

   and the tangent stress-strain matrix $\mathbf{C}^{(i-1)}$ corresponding to the state $t + \Delta t$, end of iteration $(i - 1)$, is evaluated *consistent* with this integration process.

   In isoparametric finite element analysis these stress and strain computations are performed at all integration points of the mesh in order to establish the equations used in step 3.

3. *Calculate*:   nodal point variables $\Delta\mathbf{U}^{(i)}$ using $^{t+\Delta t}\mathbf{K}^{(i-1)}\,\Delta\mathbf{U}^{(i)} = \,^{t+\Delta t}\mathbf{R} - \,^{t+\Delta t}\mathbf{F}^{(i-1)}$, and then $^{t+\Delta t}\mathbf{U}^{(i)} = \,^{t+\Delta t}\mathbf{U}^{(i-1)} + \Delta\mathbf{U}^{(i)}$

   Repeat Steps 1 to 3 until convergence.

---

and the tangent stress-strain matrix is identical whether or not equilibrium iterations are used, we need not show the iteration superscript. All that matters is that the conditions are completely known at time t and a new strain state has been calculated for which the new stresses, internal material parameters, and the new tangent stress-strain matrix shall be evaluated.

We should note that the evaluation of the stresses and the tangent stress-strain matrix is, in our numerical evaluation of the element stiffness matrix and force vector, performed at each element integration point. Hence, it is imperative that these computations be performed as efficiently as possible.

In inelastic analysis, an integration process is needed from the state at time t to the current strain state, but in elastic analysis no integration of the stresses is required (as we employ a total strain formulation and not a rate-type formulation; see Example 6.24). In elastic analysis, the stresses and the tangent stress-strain matrix can be directly evaluated for a given strain state. Hence, in the following discussion when considering elastic conditions (Sections 6.6.1 and 6.6.2), we shall also, for further ease of writing, simply consider the strain state at time t and evaluate the corresponding stresses and tangent stress-strain matrix at that time [the same procedure is used for any time, including time $t + \Delta t$].

6.6.1 Elastic Material Behavior—Generalization of Hooke's Law

A simple and widely used elastic material description for large deformation analysis is obtained by generalizing the linear elastic relations summarized in Chapter 4 (see Table 4.3) to the TL formulation:

$$^t_0 S_{ij} = \,^t_0 C_{ijrs}\,^t_0\epsilon_{rs} \tag{6.184}$$

where the ${}_0^t S_{ij}$ and ${}_0^t \epsilon_{rs}$ are the components of the second Piola-Kirchhoff stress and Green-Lagrange strain tensors and the ${}_0^t C_{ijrs}$ are the components of the constant elasticity tensor. Considering three-dimensional stress conditions, we have

$$ {}_0^t C_{ijrs} = \lambda \delta_{ij} \delta_{rs} + \mu(\delta_{ir}\delta_{js} + \delta_{is}\delta_{jr}) \tag{6.185} $$

where λ and μ are the Lamé constants and δ_{ij} is the Kronecker delta,

$$ \lambda = \frac{E\nu}{(1 + \nu)(1 - 2\nu)}; \qquad \mu = \frac{E}{2(1 + \nu)} $$

$$ \delta_{ij} = \begin{cases} 0; & i \neq j \\ 1; & i = j \end{cases} $$

The components of the elasticity tensor given in (6.185) are identical to the values given in Table 4.3 (see Exercise 2.10).

Considering this material description we can make a number of important observations. We recognize that in infinitesimal displacement analysis, the relation in (6.184) reduces to the description used in linear elastic analysis because under these conditions the stress and strain variables reduce to the engineering stress and strain measures. However, an important observation is that *in large displacement and large rotation but small strain analysis,* the relation in (6.184) provides a natural material description because the components of the second Piola-Kirchhoff stress and Green-Lagrange strain tensors do not change under rigid body rotations (see Section 6.2.2 and Examples 6.12 to 6.15). Thus, only the actual straining of material will yield an increase in the components of the stress tensor, and as long as this material straining (accompanied by large rotations and displacements) is small, the use of the relation (6.184) is completely equivalent to using Hooke's law in infinitesimal displacement conditions.

The fundamental observation that "the second Piola-Kirchhoff stress and Green-Lagrange strain components do not change measured in a fixed coordinate system when the material is subjected to rigid body motions" is important not only for elastic analysis. Indeed, this observation implies that any material description which has been developed for infinitesimal displacement analysis using engineering stress and strain measures can directly be employed in large displacement and large rotation but small strain analysis, provided second Piola-Kirchhoff stresses and Green-Lagrange strains are used. Figure 6.7 illustrates this fundamental fact. A practical consequence is, for example, that elastoplastic and creep material models (see Section 6.6.3) can be directly employed for large displacement, large rotation, and small strain analysis by simply substituting second Piola-Kirchhoff stresses and Green-Lagrange strains for the engineering stress and strain measures.

The preceding observations are of special importance because, in practice, Hooke's law is applicable only to small strains and because there are many engineering problems in which large displacements, large rotations, but only small strain conditions are encountered. This is, for example, frequently the case in the elastic or elastoplastic buckling or collapse analysis of slender (beam or shell) structures.

The stress-strain description given in (6.184) implicitly assumes that a TL formulation is used to analyze the physical problem. Let us now assume that we want to employ a UL formulation but that we are given the constitutive relationship in (6.184). In this case we can write, substituting (6.184) into (6.72),

$$ \int_{{}^0V} {}_0^t C_{ijrs} \, {}_0^t \epsilon_{rs} \, \delta {}_0^t \epsilon_{ij} \, d^0V = {}^t\mathcal{R} \tag{6.186} $$

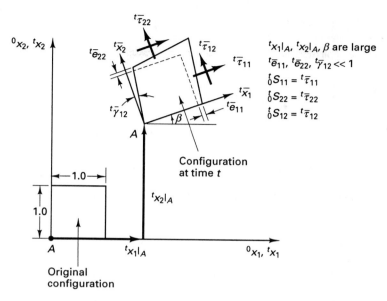

Figure 6.7   Large displacement/large rotation but small strain conditions

Thus, if we define a new constitutive tensor,

$$_t^t C_{mnpq} = \frac{^t\rho}{^0\rho}\, _0^t x_{m,i}\, _0^t x_{n,j}\, _0^t C_{ijrs}\, _0^t x_{p,r}\, _0^t x_{q,s} \tag{6.187}$$

meaning that

$$_0^t C_{ijrs} = \frac{^0\rho}{^t\rho}\, _t^0 x_{i,m}\, _t^0 x_{j,n}\, _t^t C_{mnpq}\, _t^0 x_{r,p}\, _t^0 x_{s,q} \tag{6.188}$$

and if we use (see Example 6.10)

$$\delta_t e_{mn} = \, _t^0 x_{i,m}\, _t^0 x_{j,n}\, \delta_0^t \epsilon_{ij} \tag{6.189}$$

we recognize that (6.186) can be written as

$$\int_{t_V} \, _t^t C_{mnpq}\, _t^t \epsilon_{pq}^A\, \delta_t e_{mn}\, d^t V = \, ^t\mathcal{R} \tag{6.190}$$

where

$$^t\tau_{mn} = \, _t^t C_{mnpq}\, _t^t \epsilon_{pq}^A \tag{6.191}$$

and the $_t^t \epsilon_{pq}^A$ are the components of the *Almansi strain tensor*,

$$_t^t \epsilon_{pq}^A = \, _t^0 x_{r,p}\, _t^0 x_{s,q}\, _0^t \epsilon_{rs} \tag{6.192}$$

Like the Green-Lagrange strain tensor, the Almansi strain tensor can also be defined in a number of different but completely equivalent ways,[11] namely,

$$_t^t \epsilon_{ij}^A = \tfrac{1}{2}\left(_t^t u_{i,j} + _t^t u_{j,i} - _t^t u_{k,i}\, _t^t u_{k,j} \right) \tag{6.193}$$

and we have

$$_t^t \epsilon_{ij}^A\, d^t x_i\, d^t x_j = \tfrac{1}{2}\{ (d^t s)^2 - (d^0 s)^2 \} \tag{6.194}$$

---

[11] However, in contrast to the Green-Lagrange strain tensor, the components of the Almansi strain tensor are not invariant under a rigid body rotation of the material.

EXAMPLE 6.22: Prove that the definitions of the Almansi strain tensor given in (6.192) to (6.194) are all equivalent.

The relation in (6.192) can be written in matrix form as

$$\,_t^t\boldsymbol{\epsilon}^A = \,_t^0\mathbf{X}^T \,_0^t\boldsymbol{\epsilon} \,_t^0\mathbf{X} \tag{a}$$

But using (6.54) to substitute for $\,_0^t\boldsymbol{\epsilon}$ in (a) and recognizing that

$$\,_t^0\mathbf{X} \,_0^t\mathbf{X} = \mathbf{I}$$

we obtain

$$\,_t^t\boldsymbol{\epsilon}^A = \tfrac{1}{2}(\mathbf{I} - \,_t^0\mathbf{X}^T \,_t^0\mathbf{X}) \tag{b}$$

However, we have

$$\,_t^0\mathbf{X} = [\,_t\boldsymbol{\nabla} \,^0\mathbf{x}^T]^T$$

where, in accordance with (6.21),

$$\,_t\boldsymbol{\nabla} = \begin{bmatrix} \dfrac{\partial}{\partial \,^t x_1} \\[1.5ex] \dfrac{\partial}{\partial \,^t x_2} \\[1.5ex] \dfrac{\partial}{\partial \,^t x_3} \end{bmatrix}; \qquad \,^0\mathbf{x}^T = \begin{bmatrix} \,^0x_1 & \,^0x_2 & \,^0x_3 \end{bmatrix}$$

Substituting into (b), we obtain

$$\,_t^t\boldsymbol{\epsilon}^A = \tfrac{1}{2}\{\mathbf{I} - [\,_t\boldsymbol{\nabla}(\,^t\mathbf{x}^T - \,^t\mathbf{u}^T)][\,_t\boldsymbol{\nabla}(\,^t\mathbf{x}^T - \,^t\mathbf{u}^T)]^T\}$$

Since

$$\,_t\boldsymbol{\nabla} \,^t\mathbf{x}^T = \mathbf{I}$$

we thus obtain

$$\,_t^t\boldsymbol{\epsilon}^A = \tfrac{1}{2}[\mathbf{I} - (\mathbf{I} - \,_t\boldsymbol{\nabla} \,^t\mathbf{u}^T)(\mathbf{I} - \,_t\boldsymbol{\nabla} \,^t\mathbf{u}^T)^T]$$

or

$$\,_t^t\boldsymbol{\epsilon}^A = \tfrac{1}{2}[\,_t\boldsymbol{\nabla} \,^t\mathbf{u}^T + (\,_t\boldsymbol{\nabla} \,^t\mathbf{u}^T)^T - (\,_t\boldsymbol{\nabla} \,^t\mathbf{u}^T)(\,_t\boldsymbol{\nabla} \,^t\mathbf{u}^T)^T] \tag{c}$$

and the components of $\,_t^t\boldsymbol{\epsilon}^A$ in (c) are the relations in (6.193).

To show that (6.194) also holds, we use the relation in (b) to obtain

$$d^t\mathbf{x}^T \,_t^t\boldsymbol{\epsilon}^A \, d^t\mathbf{x} = \tfrac{1}{2}(d^t\mathbf{x}^T \, d^t\mathbf{x} - d^0\mathbf{x}^T \, d^0\mathbf{x}) \tag{d}$$

because

$$d^0\mathbf{x} = \,_t^0\mathbf{X} \, d^t\mathbf{x}$$

But (d) can also be written as

$$d^t\mathbf{x}^T \,_t^t\boldsymbol{\epsilon}^A \, d^t\mathbf{x} = \tfrac{1}{2}[(d^t s)^2 - (d^0 s)^2] \tag{e}$$

because

$$d^t\mathbf{x}^T \, d^t\mathbf{x} = (d^t s)^2; \qquad d^0\mathbf{x}^T \, d^0\mathbf{x} = (d^0 s)^2$$

and (e) is equivalent to (6.194).

Of course, using (6.190) with the Almansi strain and the constitutive tensor $\,_t^t C_{mnpq}$ is quite equivalent to transforming the second Piola-Kirchhoff stress $\,_0^t S_{ij}$ (obtained using $\,_0^t S_{ij} = \,_0^t C_{ijrs} \,_0^t \epsilon_{rs}$) to the Cauchy stress and then using (6.13) to evaluate $\,^t\mathcal{R}$. Indeed, if $\,_0^t C_{ijrs}$ is known, this procedure is computationally more efficient, and the definition and use of the Almansi strain with (6.190) may be regarded as only of theoretical interest.

However, in the following example we prove an important result, which can be stated in summary as follows.

Consider the TL and UL formulations in Tables 6.2 and 6.3,

$$\int_{\,^0V} \,_0 C_{ijrs} \,_0 e_{rs} \, \delta\,_0 e_{ij} \, d^0V + \int_{\,^0V} \,_0^t S_{ij} \, \delta\,_0 \eta_{ij} \, d^0V = \,^{t+\Delta t}\mathcal{R} - \int_{\,^0V} \,_0^t S_{ij} \, \delta\,_0 e_{ij} \, d^0V \tag{6.195}$$

$$\int_{t_V} {}_tC_{ijrs}\,{}_te_{rs}\,\delta_t e_{ij}\,d^tV + \int_{t_V} {}^t\tau_{ij}\,\delta_t\eta_{ij}\,d^tV = {}^{t+\Delta t}\mathcal{R} - \int_{t_V} {}^t\tau_{ij}\,\delta_t e_{ij}\,d^tV \qquad (6.196)$$

The corresponding integral terms in the formulations are identical provided the transformations for the stresses given in (6.69) and for the constitutive tensors given in (6.187) are used. Hence, whether we choose the TL or the UL continuum formulation is decided merely by considerations of numerical efficiency.

EXAMPLE 6.23:   Consider the total and updated Lagrangian formulations in incremental form (see Tables 6.2 and 6.3).

(a) Derive the relationship that should be satisfied between the tensors ${}_0C_{ijrs}$ and ${}_tC_{ijrs}$ so that the incremental relations

$$_0S_{ij} = {}_0C_{ijrs}\,{}_0\epsilon_{rs} \qquad (a)$$

and

$$_tS_{ij} = {}_tC_{ijrs}\,{}_t\epsilon_{rs} \qquad (b)$$

refer to the *same* physical material response.

(b) Show that when the relationship derived in part (a) is satisfied, each integral term in the linearized TL formulation is identical to its corresponding term in the UL formulation.

A constitutive law relates a stress measure to a strain measure. Since there are different stress and corresponding strain measures, the constitutive law for a given material may take different forms, but these forms are related by the fact that they all describe the same given material. Hence, if equations (a) and (b) describe the same material, ${}_0C_{ijrs}$ and ${}_tC_{ijrs}$ must be related by purely kinematic transformations.

To derive the kinematic transformations we express ${}_tS_{ij}$ in terms of ${}_0S_{ij}$, and ${}_t\epsilon_{rs}$ in terms of ${}_0\epsilon_{rs}$.

We have

$$_tS_{ij} = {}^{t+\Delta t}_tS_{ij} - {}^t\tau_{ij} \qquad (c)$$

Using

$$^t\tau_{ij} = \frac{{}^t\rho}{{}^0\rho}\,{}^t_0x_{i,r}\,{}^t_0S_{rs}\,{}^t_0x_{j,s} \qquad (d)$$

and

$$^{t+\Delta t}_tS_{ij} = \frac{{}^t\rho}{{}^0\rho}\,{}^t_0x_{i,r}\,{}^{t+\Delta t}_0S_{rs}\,{}^t_0x_{j,s}$$

and (c), we obtain

$$_tS_{ij} = \frac{{}^t\rho}{{}^0\rho}\,{}^t_0x_{i,r}\,{}^t_0x_{j,s}\,{}_0S_{rs} \qquad (e)$$

We also have for the strain terms

$$_0\epsilon_{ij} = {}^{t+\Delta t}_0\epsilon_{ij} - {}^t_0\epsilon_{ij}$$

and

$$_t\epsilon_{ij} = {}^{t+\Delta t}_t\epsilon_{ij}$$

Hence,

$$_0\epsilon_{ij} = \tfrac{1}{2}\left({}^{t+\Delta t}_0x_{k,i}\,{}^{t+\Delta t}_0x_{k,j} - {}^t_0x_{k,i}\,{}^t_0x_{k,j}\right) \qquad (f)$$

and

$$_t\epsilon_{ij} = \tfrac{1}{2}\left({}^{t+\Delta t}_tx_{k,i}\,{}^{t+\Delta t}_tx_{k,j} - \delta_{ij}\right) \qquad (g)$$

We should note here that ${}_t\epsilon_{ij}$ is the Green-Lagrange strain based on the displacements from time t to time $t + \Delta t$, with the reference configuration at time t.[12]

---

[12] For example, ${}^t_t\epsilon_{ij} = 0$, and this strain measure should not be confused with the Almansi strain ${}^t_t\epsilon^A_{ij}$ defined in (6.192).

Using (f) and (g), we obtain

$$
{}_0\epsilon_{ij} = \tfrac{1}{2}{}_0^t x_{p,i}\,{}_0^t x_{q,j}\left({}_t^{t+\Delta t}x_{k,p}\,{}_t^{t+\Delta t}x_{k,q} - \delta_{pq}\right)
$$

$$
= {}_0^t x_{p,i}\,{}_0^t x_{q,j}\,{}_t\epsilon_{pq} \tag{h}
$$

We may now use (e) and (h) in the material law (b), which gives

$$
\frac{{}^t\rho}{{}^0\rho}\,{}_0^t x_{i,a}\,{}_0^t x_{j,b}\,{}_0 S_{ab} = {}_t C_{ijrs}\,{}_t^0 x_{p,r}\,{}_t^0 x_{q,s}\,{}_0\epsilon_{pq}
$$

or

$$
{}_0 S_{ij} = \left(\frac{{}^0\rho}{{}^t\rho}\,{}_t^0 x_{i,m}\,{}_t^0 x_{j,n}\,{}_t C_{mnpq}\,{}_t^0 x_{r,p}\,{}_t^0 x_{s,q}\right){}_0\epsilon_{rs}
$$

Hence, for the same material to be described, the relation between the constitutive tensors is

$$
{}_0 C_{ijrs} = \frac{{}^0\rho}{{}^t\rho}\,{}_t^0 x_{i,m}\,{}_t^0 x_{j,n}\,{}_t C_{mnpq}\,{}_t^0 x_{r,p}\,{}_t^0 x_{s,q} \tag{i}
$$

We note that the same material law transformation as earlier stated in (6.188) must be used if ${}_t C_{ijrs}$ is known and the TL formulation with (a) is to be employed. Of course, the transformation in (6.187) would be applicable if ${}_0 C_{ijrs}$ were known and the UL formulation were to be used.

Next, we want to show that each term in the TL formulation is identical to its corresponding term in the UL formulation. Considering the right-hand sides, ${}^{t+\Delta t}\mathcal{R}$ is of course the same in both formulations, and

$$
\int_{{}^0 V} {}_0^t S_{ij}\,\delta\,{}_0 e_{ij}\,d^0 V = \int_{{}^t V} {}^t\tau_{ij}\,\delta_t e_{ij}\,d^t V
$$

because $\delta\,{}_0 e_{ij} = \delta\,{}_0^t\epsilon_{ij}$.

The fact that $\delta\,{}_0 e_{ij} = \delta\,{}_0^t\epsilon_{ij}$ needs some explanation. In this evaluation of $\delta\,{}_0^t\epsilon_{ij}$ we calculate the variation in the Green-Lagrange strain corresponding to the configuration at time t, and the equation says that this value is equal to the linear strain increment corresponding to the virtual displacement δu_i. Let us recall that when taking the variation about the configuration at time $t + \Delta t$, we used $\delta\,{}^{t+\Delta t}_0\epsilon_{ij} = \delta\,{}_0 e_{ij} + \delta\,{}_0\eta_{ij}$ (see Table 6.2). If the incremental displacements are zero, i.e., $u_i = 0$, then the configuration at time $t + \Delta t$ is identical to the configuration at time t. Hence,

$$
\delta\,{}^{t+\Delta t}_0\epsilon_{ij}\big|_{u_i=0} = \delta\,{}_0^t\epsilon_{ij}
$$

It follows that, considering δu_i as a variation on u_i,

$$
\delta\,{}^{t+\Delta t}_0\epsilon_{ij}\big|_{u_i=0} = \delta\,{}_0^t\epsilon_{ij} + \delta\,{}_0\epsilon_{ij}\big|_{u_i=0}
$$

$$
= \delta\,{}_0 e_{ij}\big|_{u_i=0} \qquad \text{here } \delta\,{}_0^t\epsilon_{ij} = 0 \text{ because } {}_0^t\epsilon_{ij} \text{ is independent of } u_i.
$$

$$
= \delta\,{}_0 e_{ij}\big|_{u_i=0} + \delta\,{}_0\eta_{ij}\big|_{u_i=0}
$$

$$
= \delta\,{}_0 e_{ij}
$$

because $\delta\,{}_0\eta_{ij}$ is a linear function in u_i and therefore $\delta\,{}_0\eta_{ij}\big|_{u_i=0} = 0$.

Next, we prove that

$$
\int_{{}^0 V} {}_0^t S_{ij}\,\delta\,{}_0\eta_{ij}\,d^0 V = \int_{{}^t V} {}^t\tau_{ij}\,\delta_t\eta_{ij}\,d^t V \tag{j}
$$

However, from (h) it also follows that, grouping the terms nonlinear in the incremental displacements u_i,

$$
{}_0\eta_{ij} = {}_0^t x_{p,i}\,{}_0^t x_{q,j}\,{}_t\eta_{pq}
$$

and hence,
$$\delta_0 \eta_{ij} = {}_0^t x_{p,i} \, {}_0^t x_{q,j} \, \delta_t \eta_{pq} \tag{k}$$

Substituting from (d) and (k) into (j), with appropriate changes on indices, directly verifies (j).

Finally, we prove that

$$\int_{0_V} {}_0 C_{ijrs} \, {}_0 e_{rs} \, \delta_0 e_{ij} \, d^0V = \int_{t_V} {}_t C_{ijrs} \, {}_t e_{rs} \, \delta_t e_{ij} \, d^tV \tag{l}$$

Here we again use (h), which also gives

$${}_0 e_{ij} = {}_0^t x_{p,i} \, {}_0^t x_{q,j} \, {}_t e_{ij} \tag{m}$$

and hence,
$$\delta_0 e_{ij} = {}_0^t x_{p,i} \, {}_0^t x_{q,j} \, \delta_t e_{ij} \tag{n}$$

Substituting from (i), (m), and (n) with appropriate changes on indices, into (l) also directly verifies (l).

In summary, we note that if $_0 C_{ijrs}$ and $_t C_{ijrs}$ in the incremental stress-strain relations (a) and (b) are *for any material* related in such a way as to represent the same physical material response, then the TL and UL incremental continuum mechanics formulations are identical. This observation pertains not only to elastic materials but is general and holds for any material.

The preceding discussion shows that the UL formulation may be used if the constitutive relationship corresponding to the TL formulation is known (and this observation holds for any material law that can be written in the form used in the TL formulation), and vice versa. This equivalence between the UL and TL formulations of course holds for any level of strain, but in most practical analyses, the linear elastic material behavior (Hooke's law) is valid only for small strain conditions. In that case, for an isotropic elastic material, the results using either (6.184) and (6.185), or directly

$${}^t \tau_{ij} = {}_t^t C_{ijrs} \, {}_t^t \epsilon_{rs}^A \tag{6.197}$$

$${}_t^t C_{ijrs} = \lambda \delta_{ij} \delta_{rs} + \mu(\delta_{ir}\delta_{js} + \delta_{is}\delta_{jr}) \tag{6.198}$$

$$\lambda = \frac{E\nu}{(1 + \nu)(1 - 2\nu)}; \qquad \mu = \frac{E}{2(1 + \nu)}$$

where λ and μ are the same constants as in (6.185), are practically the same. Hence, the same constants can be used to define the material law for the total and updated Lagrangian formulations, and only small differences would be observed in the solution results for large displacements and rotations as long as the strains are small. The reason is that considering large displacements and rotations but small strains, the transformations on the constitutive tensors given in (6.187) and (6.188) reduce to mere rotations. Therefore, since the material is assumed to be isotropic, the transformations do not change the components of the constitutive tensors and the use of either (6.184) and (6.185) or (6.197) and (6.198) to characterize the material response is quite equivalent.

However, when large strains are modeled using (6.184) and (6.197) with the same elastic material constants, completely different response predictions must be expected. Figure 6.8 shows the results obtained in a simple analysis of this kind. We note that the force-displacement response is totally different when using the two descriptions and that an instability is observed in the TL formulation at the displacement $(-2 + 2/\sqrt{3})$.

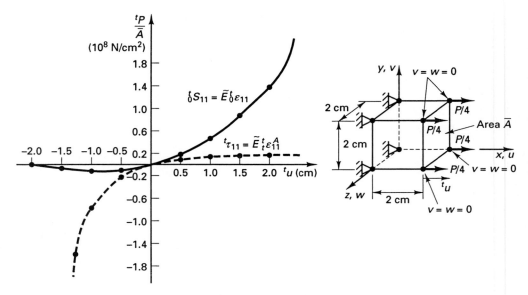

(a) P-Δ response of 8-node element under uniform loading
($E = 10^7$ N/cm², $v = 0.30$), $\bar{A}$ is restrained to be constant.

$$\tilde{E} = \frac{E(1 - v)}{(1 + v)(1 - 2v)}$$

(i) Using $_0^t S_{11} = \tilde{E}\,_0^t\varepsilon_{11}$

$$^tP = \frac{\tilde{E}\,\bar{A}}{2}\left(1 + \frac{^tu}{^0L}\right)\left(\left(1 + \frac{^tu}{^0L}\right)^2 - 1\right)$$

(ii) Using $^t\tau_{11} = \tilde{E}\,_t^t\varepsilon_{11}^A$

$$^tP = \frac{\tilde{E}\,\bar{A}}{2}\left(1 - \left(\frac{^0L}{^0L + {}^tu}\right)^2\right)$$

(b) Basic relations

Figure 6.8   One-dimensional response analysis

Of course, if the transformations of (6.187) or (6.188), whichever are applicable, were performed, the same force-displacement curves would be obtained using either the total or the updated Lagrangian formulations (see Exercise 6.62).

Let us further demonstrate in the following example the differences in response that are observed when using different stress-strain measures with the same material constants.

EXAMPLE 6.24:   Consider the four-node element shown in Fig. E6.24. The displacements of the element are given as a function of time.

Calculate the Cauchy stresses using the following two stress measures:

(i) Use the *total formulation* of the second Piola-Kirchhoff stress and Green-Lagrange strain tensors,

$$_0^t S_{ij} = {}_0^t C_{ijrs}\,_0^t\epsilon_{rs} \qquad\qquad (a)$$

(ii) Use the *rate formulation* of the Jaumann stress rate and the velocity strain tensors (see L. E. Malvern [A]),

$$\overset{t}{\underset{}{}}\overset{\triangledown}{\tau}_{ij} = {}_t C_{ijrs}\, {}^t D_{rs} \tag{b}$$

and let the constitutive tensors ${}_0^t C_{ijrs}$ and ${}_t C_{ijrs}$ be given by the same matrix in Table 4.2.

We note that the components of the Jaumann stress rate tensor are given by (see L. E. Malvern [A])

$$\overset{t}{\overset{\triangledown}{\tau}}_{ij} = {}^t \dot{\tau}_{ij} + {}^t \tau_{ip}\, {}^t W_{pj} + {}^t \tau_{jp}\, {}^t W_{pi} \tag{c}$$

where the ${}^t W_{ij}$ are the components of the spin tensor [see (6.43)]. The relation (c) expresses that the rate of change of the Cauchy stress, ${}^t \tau_{ij}$, is equal to the Jaumann stress rate (which gives the rate of change in Cauchy stress due to material straining) plus the effect of rate of rigid body rotation of the material (and hence, rate of rotation of stress). The Jaumann stress rate is used in practice, although the rate formulation results in numerical integration errors and a nonphysical behavior (see Section 6.6 and M. Kojić and K. J. Bathe [A]).

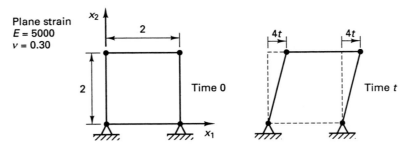

Figure E6.24   Four-node element subjected to motion

Consider case (i). The deformation gradient is

$$\overset{t}{\underset{0}{}}\mathbf{X} = \begin{bmatrix} 1 & 2t \\ 0 & 1 \end{bmatrix}$$

and hence,

$$\overset{t}{\underset{0}{}}\boldsymbol{\epsilon} = \begin{bmatrix} 0 & t \\ t & 2t^2 \end{bmatrix}$$

Using Table 4.2 with the given values of E and ν, we obtain as nonzero values $C_{1111} = 6731$, $C_{2211} = C_{1122} = 2885$, $C_{2222} = 6731$, $C_{1212} = 1923$.

Hence, using the total Lagrangian description, we have

$$\overset{t}{\underset{0}{}}S_{11} = 5770t^2; \qquad \overset{t}{\underset{0}{}}S_{22} = 13{,}462t^2; \qquad \overset{t}{\underset{0}{}}S_{12} = 3846t$$

and using the standard transformations between the second Piola-Kirchhoff and Cauchy stresses (to two significant figures),

$$\begin{bmatrix} {}^t \tau_{11} \\ {}^t \tau_{22} \\ {}^t \tau_{12} \end{bmatrix} = \begin{bmatrix} 21{,}000t^2 + 54{,}000t^4 \\ 13{,}000t^2 \\ 3800t + 27{,}000t^3 \end{bmatrix} \tag{c}$$

Next consider case (ii). The velocity strain tensor $^t\mathbf{D}$ is computed as given in (6.42). Hence,

$$^t\mathbf{L} = \begin{bmatrix} 0 & 2 \\ 0 & 0 \end{bmatrix}; \qquad ^t\mathbf{D} = \begin{bmatrix} 0 & 1 \\ 1 & 0 \end{bmatrix}; \qquad ^t\mathbf{W} = \begin{bmatrix} 0 & +1 \\ -1 & 0 \end{bmatrix}$$

Now we use the same constitutive matrix $\mathbf{C}$ to obtain

$$\begin{bmatrix} ^t\overset{\triangledown}{\tau}_{11} \\ ^t\overset{\triangledown}{\tau}_{22} \\ ^t\overset{\triangledown}{\tau}_{12} \end{bmatrix} = \begin{bmatrix} 0 \\ 0 \\ 3846 \end{bmatrix}$$

We note that the Jaumann stress rate is independent of time. However, the material also rotates as expressed in $^t\mathbf{W}$ and the time rates of the Cauchy stress components are given by

$$\begin{bmatrix} ^t\dot{\tau}_{11} \\ ^t\dot{\tau}_{22} \\ ^t\dot{\tau}_{12} \end{bmatrix} = \begin{bmatrix} 2\,^t\tau_{12} \\ -2\,^t\tau_{12} \\ 3846 + {}^t\tau_{22} - {}^t\tau_{11} \end{bmatrix}$$

These differential equations can be solved to obtain (again to two significant figures and hence using $G = \dfrac{E}{2(1 + \nu)} \doteq 1900$)

$$\begin{bmatrix} ^t\tau_{11} \\ ^t\tau_{22} \\ ^t\tau_{12} \end{bmatrix} = \begin{bmatrix} 1900(1 - \cos 2t) \\ -1900(1 - \cos 2t) \\ 1900 \sin 2t \end{bmatrix} \qquad \text{(d)}$$

We note that the results given in (c) and (d) are quite different when t is larger than about 0.1 and that in each material description normal stresses are generated (that are zero when infinitesimally small strains are assumed). Also, the oscillatory behavior of the Cauchy stresses in (d) with period π is peculiar.

6.6.2 Rubberlike Material Behavior

We introduced in Section 6.4 the displacement/pressure formulations that are much suited for the analysis of rubberlike materials because such materials exhibit an almost incompressible response. The basic ingredient in these formulations is the strain energy density $_0^t\bar{W}$, which is defined by the specific material model used.

Various definitions of $_0^t\bar{W}$ are available, but two commonly used models are the Mooney-Rivlin and Ogden models (see R. S. Rivlin [A] and R. W. Ogden [A]).

The conventional Mooney-Rivlin material model is described by the strain energy density per unit original volume

$$_0^t\tilde{W} = C_1(_0^t I_1 - 3) + C_2(_0^t I_2 - 3); \qquad _0^t I_3 = 1 \qquad (6.199)$$

where C_1 and C_2 are material constants and the invariants $_0^t I_i$ are given in terms of the components of the Cauchy-Green deformation tensor (see 6.27)

$$_0^t I_1 = {}_0^t C_{kk}$$

$$_0^t I_2 = \frac{1}{2}[(_0^t I_1)^2 - {}_0^t C_{ij}\,{}_0^t C_{ij}] \qquad (6.200)$$

$$_0^t I_3 = \det {}_0^t\mathbf{C}$$

Note that the value $_0^t \tilde{W}$ in (6.199) is not yet a strain energy density $_0^t \overline{W}$ that we use in our formulation, as we discuss below.

We note that a so-called neo-Hookean material description is obtained with $C_2 = 0$, and if small strains are considered $2(C_1 + C_2)$ is the shear modulus and $6(C_1 + C_2)$ is the Young's modulus.

EXAMPLE 6.25:   Consider the one-dimensional response of the bar shown in Fig. E6.25. Plot the force-displacement relationship for the following two cases: (i) $C_1 = 100$, $C_2 = 0$ and (ii) $C_1 = 75$, $C_2 = 25$.

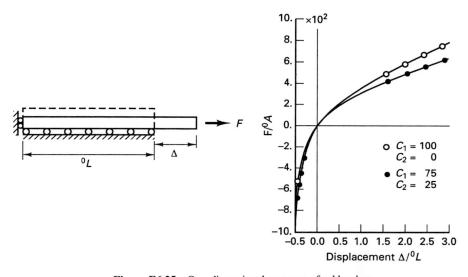

Figure E6.25   One-dimensional response of rubber bar

Using $_0^t S_{ij} = \partial_0^t \tilde{W}/\partial_0^t \epsilon_{ij}$ (see 6.129) with the Mooney-Rivlin material model in (6.199) specialized to the case considered, we obtain

$$F = 2\ {}^0 A[C_1(\lambda - \lambda^{-2}) + C_2(1 - \lambda^{-3})]$$

$$\lambda = 1 + \frac{\Delta}{{}^0 L}$$

Substituting the values for C_1 and C_2, we obtain the curves shown in the figure.

The description in (6.199) assumes that the material is totally incompressible (since $_0^t I_3 = 1$). A better assumption is that the bulk modulus is several thousand times as large as the shear modulus, which then means that the material is almost incompressible. This assumption is incorporated by dropping the restriction that $_0^t I_3 = 1$ and including a hydrostatic work term in the strain energy function to obtain

$$_0^t \tilde{\overline{W}} = C_1(_0^t I_1 - 3) + C_2(_0^t I_2 - 3) + W_H(_0^t I_3) \tag{6.201}$$

However, this expression cannot be used directly in the displacement/pressure formulations because all three terms contribute to the pressure. To obtain an appropriate expression, we define the reduced invariants

$$_0^t J_1 = {}_0^t I_1 ({}_0^t I_3)^{-1/3}$$

$$_0^t J_2 = {}_0^t I_2 ({}_0^t I_3)^{-2/3} \tag{6.202}$$

$$_0^t J_3 = ({}_0^t I_3)^{1/2}$$

and we then use

$$_0^t \overline{W} = C_1({}_0^t J_1 - 3) + C_2({}_0^t J_2 - 3) + \tfrac{1}{2}\kappa({}_0^t J_3 - 1)^2 \tag{6.203}$$

where κ is the bulk modulus. We note that in this description

$$^t\overline{p} = -\kappa({}_0^t J_3 - 1) \tag{6.204}$$

The relations in (6.203) and (6.204) are used to calculate, by chain differentiation, all required derivatives in the displacement/pressure formulation in Section 6.4.

The basic (three-term) Ogden material description uses the form

$$_0^t \tilde{W} = \sum_{n=1}^3 \frac{\mu_n}{\alpha_n}(\lambda_1^{\alpha_n} + \lambda_2^{\alpha_n} + \lambda_3^{\alpha_n} - 3); \qquad \lambda_1\lambda_2\lambda_3 = 1 \tag{6.205}$$

where the λ_i are the principal values of the stretch tensor $_0^t\mathbf{U}$ and the μ_i and α_i are material constants. We note that $\tfrac{1}{2}\sum_{n=1}^3 \alpha_n\mu_n$ is the small strain shear modulus.

The material description is more effectively used with the principal values L_i *of* $_0^t\mathbf{C}$ [instead of the principal values of $_0^t\mathbf{U}$, where $_0^t\mathbf{C} = ({}_0^t\mathbf{U})^2$]. Then we have

$$_0^t \tilde{W} = \sum_{n=1}^3 \frac{\mu_n}{\alpha_n}(L_1^{\alpha_n/2} + L_2^{\alpha_n/2} + L_3^{\alpha_n/2} - 3); \qquad L_1L_2L_3 = 1 \tag{6.206}$$

As for the Mooney-Rivlin material model, we now assume that the rubberlike material is only almost incompressible and also replace the L_i with the terms $L_i(L_1L_2L_3)^{-1/3}$ so as to render the three terms under the summation sign unaffected by volumetric deformations. The modified Ogden material description is then given by

$$_0^t \overline{W} = \sum_{n=1}^3 \left\{ \frac{\mu_n}{\alpha_n}[(L_1^{\alpha_n/2} + L_2^{\alpha_n/2} + L_3^{\alpha_n/2})(L_1 L_2 L_3)^{-\alpha_n/6} - 3] \right\} + \frac{1}{2}\kappa({}_0^t J_3 - 1)^2 \tag{6.207}$$

Using (6.207) and (6.204), we can now directly obtain, by differentiation, all terms of the displacement/pressure formulation given in Section 6.4 (see T. Sussman and K. J. Bathe [B]).

In the foregoing presentation we implicitly assumed that the total Lagrangian formulation is used for the analysis. Since the strain energy densities with the material constants are defined for this formulation, it is most natural and effective to use a total Lagrangian solution. However, an updated Lagrangian solution, given the values of $_0^t\overline{W}$ above, could also be pursued and identical numerical results would be obtained if the transformation rules in Section 6.4.2 (or 6.6.1) are followed.

Finally, we should also note that the basic Mooney-Rivlin and Ogden material models can be generalized in a straightforward manner to higher-order models with more terms in the expressions for $^t\tilde{W}$ (see Exercise 6.69).

6.6.3 Inelastic Material Behavior; Elastoplasticity, Creep, and Viscoplasticity

A fundamental observation comparing elastic and inelastic analysis is that in elastic solutions the total stress can be evaluated from the total strain alone [as given in (6.184) and (6.191)], whereas in an inelastic response calculation the total stress at time t also depends on the stress and strain history. Typical inelastic phenomena are elastoplasticity, creep, and viscoplasticity, and a very large number of material models have been developed in order to characterize such a material response. Our objective is again not to summarize or survey the models available but rather to present some of the basic finite element procedures that are employed in inelastic response calculations. We are mainly concerned with the general approach followed in inelastic finite element analysis and some formulations and numerical procedures that are used efficiently.

In the incremental analysis of inelastic response, basically three kinematic conditions are encountered.

Small displacement and small strain conditions:
In this case a materially-nonlinear-only formulation is used that assumes infinitesimally small displacements and rotations and considers only material nonlinearities. As long as the material is elastic, the solution using this formulation is identical to the linear elastic solution discussed in Section 4.2.

Large displacements and rotations but small strains:
In this case the total Lagrangian formulation is employed effectively. As discussed in Section 6.2.3, the kinematic assumptions permit large displacements, large rotations, and large strains. However, assuming small strains, the material model used for materially-nonlinear-only analysis can be directly employed in the TL formulation for large displacement and large rotation analysis by simply substituting in the material characterization the second Piola-Kirchhoff stresses and Green-Lagrange strains for the small displacement engineering stress and strain measures (see Section 6.6.1, Fig. 6.7). The use of the TL formulation in inelastic analysis is therefore a direct extension of using the TL formulation in small strain but large displacement and large rotation elastic conditions.

Large displacements and large strains:
In this case a total or updated Lagrangian formulation can be employed efficiently. However, the underlying constitutive formulations are more complex—although they are direct extensions of the materially-nonlinear-only and large displacement–small strain cases. There are various issues that need to be discussed specifically for the large strain analysis case, and for this reason we defer the presentation to Section 6.6.4.

Since the large displacement–small strain case represents, from the computational view, a simple extension of the materially-nonlinear-only case, we consider in this section only inelastic conditions in small displacements and small strains. However, Table 6.9 shows how in elastoplastic analysis some of the major equations, further discussed below, are simply used with second Piola-Kirchhoff stresses and Green-Lagrange strains to include large displacement effects.

TABLE 6.9   *Continuum elastoplasticity formulations*

Materially-nonlinear-only formulation (infinitesimally small displacements):

$$\int_V C_{ijrs}^{EP} e_{rs} \delta e_{ij}\, dV = {}^{t+\Delta t}\mathcal{R} - \int_V {}^t\sigma_{ij}\, \delta e_{ij}\, dV$$

$${}^tF({}^t\sigma_{ij}, {}^t\kappa, \ldots) = 0; \qquad de_{ij}^P = d\lambda\, \frac{\partial^t F}{\partial^t \sigma_{ij}}; \qquad d\sigma_{ij} = C_{ijrs}^E(de_{rs} - de_{rs}^P); \qquad {}^{t+dt}\sigma_{ij} = {}^t\sigma_{ij} + d\sigma_{ij}$$

Total Lagrangian formulation (large displacements and large rotations, but small strains),

$${}_0\bar{\epsilon}^P = \int_0^t [2/3\, d_0\epsilon_{ij}^P\, d_0\epsilon_{ij}^P]^{1/2} < 2\%:$$

$$\int_{0_V} {}_0C_{ijrs}^{EP}\, {}_0e_{rs}\, \delta_0 e_{ij}\, d^0V + \int_{0_V} {}_0^t S_{ij}\, \delta_0 \eta_{ij}\, d^0V = {}^{t+\Delta t}\mathcal{R} - \int_{0_V} {}_0^t S_{ij}\, \delta_0 e_{ij}\, d^0V$$

$${}^tF({}_0^t S_{ij}, {}^t\kappa, \ldots) = 0; \qquad d_0\epsilon_{ij}^P = d\lambda\, \frac{\partial^t F}{\partial_0^t S_{ij}}; \qquad d_0 S_{ij} = {}_0C_{ijrs}^E(d_0\epsilon_{rs} - d_0\epsilon_{rs}^P); \qquad {}_0^{t+dt} S_{ij} = {}_0^t S_{ij} + d_0 S_{ij}$$

Referring to the summary of computations in Table 6.8, let us assume that the solution has been obtained accurately to time t and that the total strains ${}^{t+\Delta t}e_{rs}$ corresponding to time $t + \Delta t$ have been computed (we now omit any iteration superscript). Hence, we assume that all stresses, inelastic strains, and state variables for time t are known accurately. We then have two basic requirements for our solution scheme:

The computation of the stresses, inelastic strains, and state variables corresponding to the total strains at time $t + \Delta t$.

The computation of the tangent constitutive relation corresponding to the state evaluated above, which in materially-nonlinear-only analysis can be written as

$$C_{ijrs}^{IN} = \frac{\partial^{t+\Delta t}\sigma_{ij}}{\partial^{t+\Delta t}e_{rs}} \tag{6.208}$$

The tangent stress-strain law is employed in the evaluation of the tangent stiffness matrix. If the stress-strain relationship used in the evaluation of the stiffness matrix is not a true tangent relation, then the next calculated displacement (and hence strain) increment will, in general, not give as accurate an approximation to the solution sought as possible (and this will decrease the rate of convergence of the equilibrium iterations; see Section 8.4).

A crucial requirement is that the stresses for the new state be accurately calculated. If we denote the calculated total strains as ${}^{t+\Delta t}\mathbf{e}$, then our requirement is to obtain the stresses ${}^{t+\Delta t}\boldsymbol{\sigma}$ accurately. We should note that, in general, any error introduced in the evaluation of ${}^{t+\Delta t}\boldsymbol{\sigma}$ is an error that cannot be compensated for later in the solution by some corrective iterative scheme. Instead, errors present in the stresses and plastic strains, and the state variables for time $t + \Delta t$ will, in general, irreversibly deteriorate the subsequent response prediction.

Let us point out here that of course in an equilibrium iteration, the tangent constitutive relation in (6.10) needs to be calculated corresponding to the current state, and also, the stresses to be calculated are ${}^{t+\Delta t}\boldsymbol{\sigma}^{(i-1)}$ for the given strains ${}^{t+\Delta t}\mathbf{e}^{(i-1)}$ (see Section 8.4).

In the following presentation, we first consider the basic computational scheme for the case of elastoplasticity, and then we briefly consider the cases of creep and viscoplasticity.

Elastoplasticity

We assume that the elastoplastic response is governed by the classical incremental theory of plasticity based on the Prandtl-Reuss equations (see, for example, L. E. Malvern [A], R. Hill [B], A. Mendelson [A], and M. Życzkowski [A]).

Using the additive decomposition of strains, $de_{ij} = de_{ij}^E + de_{ij}^P$, the stress increment is given by the basic relationship

$$d\sigma_{ij} = C_{ijrs}^E (de_{rs} - de_{rs}^P) \tag{6.209}$$

where the C_{ijrs}^E are the components of the elastic constitutive tensor and the de_{ij}, de_{ij}^E, de_{ij}^P are the components of the total strain increment, the elastic strain increment, and the plastic strain increment, respectively. This incremental relationship holds throughout the inelastic response. To calculate the plastic strains, we use three properties to characterize the material behavior:

A *yield function*, which gives the yield condition that specifies the state of multiaxial stress corresponding to start of plastic flow

A *flow rule*, which relates the plastic strain increments to the current stresses and the stress increments

A *hardening rule*, which specifies how the yield function is modified during plastic flow.

The yield function has the general form at time t,

$$^t f_y(^t \sigma_{ij}, \, ^t e_{ij}^P, \ldots) \tag{6.210}$$

where " . . . " denotes state variables that depend on the material characterization. The instantaneous material response is elastic if

$$^t f_y < 0 \tag{6.211}$$

and elastic or plastic depending on the loading condition if

$$^t f_y = 0 \tag{6.212}$$

whereas $^t f_y > 0$ is inadmissible. Hence the relation (6.212) represents the yield condition, which must hold throughout the plastic response.

Assuming that for the material the associated flow rule is applicable during plastic response we use the function $^t f_y$ in the flow rule to obtain the plastic strain increments

$$de_{ij}^P = d\lambda \, \frac{\partial \, ^t f_y}{\partial \, ^t \sigma_{ij}} \tag{6.213}$$

where $d\lambda$ is a scalar to be determined [and depending on the state variables additional quantities appear in (6.213)]. The hardening rule—which also depends on the particular material model used—changes the state variables in ^tf_y as a consequence of plastic flow and therefore changes the yield condition during the response.

Let us consider von Mises plasticity with isotropic hardening, and a general three-dimensional stress state. In the following we present a simple solution procedure that is widely used and referred to as the *radial return method* (see M. L. Wilkins [A] and R. D. Krieg and D. B. Krieg [A]). Our objective is to present the procedure such that it can be seen to be the basis of a general approach toward the solution of inelastic stress conditions.

Since in von Mises plasticity the plastic volumetric strains are zero (as we shall see later), it is effective to write the general stress-strain relationship at time $t + \Delta t$ in the form [see also (4.125) to (4.133)]

$$^{t+\Delta t}\mathbf{S} = \frac{E}{1 + \nu}(^{t+\Delta t}\mathbf{e}' - {}^{t+\Delta t}\mathbf{e}^P) \tag{6.214}$$

$$^{t+\Delta t}\sigma_m = \frac{E}{1 - 2\nu}\,^{t+\Delta t}e_m \tag{6.215}$$

where $^{t+\Delta t}\mathbf{S}$ is the deviatoric stress tensor with components[13]

$$^{t+\Delta t}S_{ij} = {}^{t+\Delta t}\sigma_{ij} - {}^{t+\Delta t}\sigma_m\delta_{ij} \tag{6.216}$$

$^{t+\Delta t}\sigma_m$ is the mean stress

$$^{t+\Delta t}\sigma_m = \frac{^{t+\Delta t}\sigma_{ii}}{3} \tag{6.217}$$

$^{t+\Delta t}\mathbf{e}'$ is the deviatoric strain tensor with components

$$^{t+\Delta t}e'_{ij} = {}^{t+\Delta t}e_{ij} - {}^{t+\Delta t}e_m\delta_{ij} \tag{6.218}$$

$^{t+\Delta t}e_m$ is the mean strain

$$^{t+\Delta t}e_m = \frac{^{t+\Delta t}e_{ii}}{3} \tag{6.219}$$

and $^{t+\Delta t}\mathbf{e}^P$ is the plastic strain tensor with components $^{t+\Delta t}e^P_{ij}$. Note that in (6.214) we have 3×3 matrices on each side of the equal sign, with the components of the tensors. We should recall that the total strain at time $t + \Delta t$ is known (see Table 6.8), and hence, $^{t+\Delta t}\mathbf{e}'$ and $^{t+\Delta t}e_m$ are known.

The relations (6.214) and (6.215) represent the integrated forms of (6.209), where we note that the deviatoric stresses depend on the plastic strains, which are in general highly dependent on the stress history, and that the mean stress is independent of the plastic strains (because the plastic mean strain is zero; i.e., the plastic deformation is isochoric). Hence, $^{t+\Delta t}\sigma_m$ is given directly by (6.215), and our task is now to calculate $^{t+\Delta t}\mathbf{e}^P$ and $^{t+\Delta t}\mathbf{S}$.

Since we assume that the complete stress and strain conditions are known at time t, we can write (6.214) in the form

$$^{t+\Delta t}\mathbf{S} = \frac{E}{1 + \nu}(^{t+\Delta t}\mathbf{e}'' - \Delta\mathbf{e}^P) \tag{6.220}$$

where

$$^{t+\Delta t}\mathbf{e}'' = {}^{t+\Delta t}\mathbf{e}' - {}^t\mathbf{e}^P \tag{6.221}$$

is a known quantity.

---

[13] Note that the deviatoric stress does not carry a subscript 0 as does the second Piola-Kirchhoff stress.

Hence, the task of integrating the constitutive relations is now reduced to determining in (6.220) the stresses $^{t+\Delta t}\mathbf{S}$ and the plastic incremental strains $\Delta\mathbf{e}^P$ subject to the yield condition, flow rule, and hardening rule.

In von Mises plasticity, the yield condition is at time $t + \Delta t$,

$$^{t+\Delta t}f_y^{vM} = \tfrac{1}{2}\,^{t+\Delta t}\mathbf{S}\cdot{}^{t+\Delta t}\mathbf{S} - \tfrac{1}{3}(^{t+\Delta t}\sigma_y)^2 = 0 \qquad (6.222)^{14}$$

where $^{t+\Delta t}\sigma_y$ is the yield stress at time $t + \Delta t$. This stress is a function of the effective plastic strain, which defines the hardening of the material,

$$^{t+\Delta t}\sigma_y = f_e(^{t+\Delta t}\overline{e}^P) \qquad (6.223)$$

with

$$^{t+\Delta t}\overline{e}^P = \int_0^{t+\Delta t}\sqrt{\tfrac{2}{3}de^P\cdot de^P} \qquad (6.224)$$

Figure 6.9 shows a yield curve schematically.

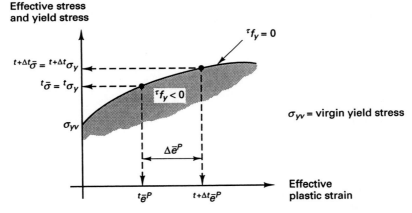

Figure 6.9 General generic yield curve. Yielding is assumed at times t and $t + \Delta t$. Let, at time τ, $^\tau f_y = {}^\tau\overline{\sigma} - {}^\tau\sigma_y$; then the response must satisfy $^\tau f_y \leq 0$, $\dot{\overline{e}}^P \geq 0$, $\dot{\overline{e}}^P\,{}^\tau f_y = 0$.

The flow rule gives for the finite step

$$\Delta\mathbf{e}^P = \lambda\frac{\partial^{t+\Delta t}f_y^{vM}}{\partial^{t+\Delta t}\boldsymbol{\sigma}} = \lambda^{t+\Delta t}\mathbf{S} \qquad (6.225)$$

Geometrically, this equation means that $\Delta\mathbf{e}^P$ is in the direction of $^{t+\Delta t}\mathbf{S}$, and the equation shows that the volumetric plastic strains are zero (the trace of $^{t+\Delta t}\mathbf{S}$ is zero).

To determine λ we take the dot products of the tensor components on each side of (6.225) to obtain[15]

$$\Delta\overline{e}^P = \tfrac{2}{3}\lambda^{t+\Delta t}\overline{\sigma} \qquad (6.226)$$

where $\Delta\overline{e}^P$ is the increment in the effective plastic strain and $^{t+\Delta t}\overline{\sigma}$ is the effective stress

$$\Delta\overline{e}^P = \sqrt{\tfrac{2}{3}\Delta\mathbf{e}^P\cdot\Delta\mathbf{e}^P}; \qquad {}^{t+\Delta t}\overline{\sigma} = \sqrt{\tfrac{3}{2}\,{}^{t+\Delta t}\mathbf{S}\cdot{}^{t+\Delta t}\mathbf{S}} \qquad (6.227)$$

---

[14] Note that here and in the following we use the notation that for second-order tensors **a** and **b** we have $\mathbf{a}\cdot\mathbf{b} = a_{ij}b_{ij}$ [sum over all i, j; see (2.79)].

[15] Note that geometrically λ simply gives the difference in the "lengths" of $\Delta\mathbf{e}^P$ and $^{t+\Delta t}\mathbf{S}$.

The relations in (6.227) correspond to the plastic strain and the stress in a uniaxial stress condition (see Exercise 6.73), and using (6.225) we have that in general three-dimensional analysis the plastic work ${}^t\sigma_{ij}de_{ij}^P$ is given by ${}^t\overline{\sigma}\,d\overline{e}^P$. From (6.226)

$$\lambda = \frac{3}{2}\frac{\Delta\overline{e}^P}{{}^{t+\Delta t}\overline{\sigma}} \tag{6.228}$$

However, using the requirement that during yielding the yield stress is equal to the effective stress (because the yield condition is satisfied), we can relate $\Delta\overline{e}^P$ to the effective stress at time $t + \Delta t$ (and other known variables). This relation is obtained from the effective stress–effective plastic strain curve shown schematically in Fig. 6.9.

We next substitute from (6.225) into (6.220) to obtain

$$^{t+\Delta t}\mathbf{S} = \frac{1}{a_E + \lambda}\,{}^{t+\Delta t}\mathbf{e}'' \tag{6.229}$$

and so ${}^{t+\Delta t}\mathbf{e}''$ is also in the direction of ${}^{t+\Delta t}\mathbf{S}$. To evaluate the scalar multiplier in (6.229) we can again simply take the dot product of the tensor components on each side of (6.229). We obtain

$$a^2\,{}^{t+\Delta t}\overline{\sigma}^2 - d^2 = 0 \tag{6.230}$$

where

$$a = a_E + \lambda; \qquad a_E = \frac{1+\nu}{E} \tag{6.231}$$

$$d^2 = \tfrac{3}{2}\,{}^{t+\Delta t}\mathbf{e}'' \cdot {}^{t+\Delta t}\mathbf{e}'' \tag{6.232}$$

We note that the coefficient d is constant, whereas the coefficient a varies with λ, and hence with ${}^{t+\Delta t}\overline{\sigma}$.

Let us define the function

$$f(\overline{\sigma}^*) = a^2(\overline{\sigma}^*)^2 - d^2 \tag{6.233}$$

and call $f(\overline{\sigma}^*)$ the *effective stress function*. Considering (6.230) we recognize that $f = 0$ at $\overline{\sigma}^* = {}^{t+\Delta t}\overline{\sigma}$. Hence, solving for the zero value of the effective stress function provides the solution for ${}^{t+\Delta t}\overline{\sigma}$ and λ, and hence, the solution for the current stress state ${}^{t+\Delta t}\mathbf{S}$ [see (6.229)] and the incremental plastic strains $\Delta\mathbf{e}^P$ [see (6.225)]. Since the key step in the solution—here and in more complex inelastic analysis—is the calculation of the zero of a function $f(\overline{\sigma}^*)$, the complete solution algorithm has been termed the effective-stress-function (ESF) algorithm (see K. J. Bathe, A. B. Chaudhary, E. N. Dvorkin, and M. Kojić [A], where the method is introduced for more complex thermoelastoplastic and creep solutions).

The attractiveness of the ESF algorithm lies in the general applicability of the method. The effective stress function can be quite complicated (because of a complicated effective stress–effective plastic strain relationship) or because of thermal and creep effects (as considered later). The zero of the function is in general efficiently found by a numerical bisection scheme, which can be made very stable because the function contains only one unknown, the effective stress.

However, if the material is modeled as bilinear (see Fig. 6.10), the effective stress–effective strain relationship is a straight line with slope E_P and we can solve directly for the effective stress at time $t + \Delta t$. Namely,

$$\Delta\overline{e}^P = \frac{{}^{t+\Delta t}\overline{\sigma} - {}^t\sigma_y}{E_P} \tag{6.234}$$

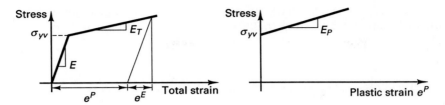

Figure 6.10   Bilinear elastoplastic material model

with
$$E_P = \frac{EE_T}{E - E_T} \tag{6.235}$$

where E_T is the tangent modulus, and hence,

$$^{t+\Delta t}\overline{\sigma} = \frac{2E_P \, d + 3\,^{t}\sigma_y}{2E_P \, a_E + 3} \tag{6.236}$$

In case of perfect plasticity $E_P = 0$ and $^{t+\Delta t}\overline{\sigma} = \sigma_{yv}$, so that from (6.230),

$$\lambda = \frac{d}{\sigma_{yv}} - a_E \tag{6.237}$$

The elastoplasticity computations are of course started by first testing whether the material is yielding from time t to time $t + \Delta t$. Yielding is assumed to be present throughout the time interval if $^{t+\Delta t}\overline{\sigma}^E > {}^{t}\sigma_y$, where $^{t+\Delta t}\overline{\sigma}^E$ is the elastic stress solution

$$^{t+\Delta t}\overline{\sigma}^E = \frac{d}{a_E} \tag{6.238}$$

The above solution process can be interpreted to consist of, first, an elastic prediction of stress (in which $\Delta \mathbf{e}^P$ is assumed to be zero) and then, if this stress prediction lies outside the yield surface corresponding to time t, a stress correction. Figure 6.11 illustrates geometrically the solution process.

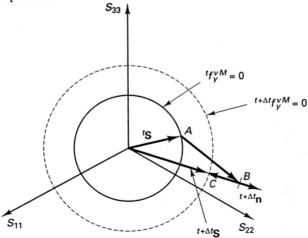

Figure 6.11   Geometric representation of stress solution in elastoplastic analysis principal stress directions)

Point A corresponds to the stress solution at time t. Point B corresponds to the elastic stress prediction, which from (6.220) is

$$^{t+\Delta t}\mathbf{S}^E = \frac{E}{1 + \nu}(^{t+\Delta t}\mathbf{e}'') \tag{6.239}$$

The stress correction corresponds to the vector BC and is

$$^{t+\Delta t}\mathbf{S}^c = \frac{E}{1 + \nu}(-\Delta \mathbf{e}^P) \tag{6.240}$$

where $\Delta \mathbf{e}^P$ is given by (6.225).

Since $^{t+\Delta t}\mathbf{S}$ and $^{t+\Delta t}\mathbf{S}^c$ are in the same direction and $^{t+\Delta t}\mathbf{S} = {}^{t+\Delta t}\mathbf{S}^E + {}^{t+\Delta t}\mathbf{S}^c$, we note that the normal $^{t+\Delta t}\mathbf{n}$ is in the direction of $^{t+\Delta t}\mathbf{S}^E$ (and $^{t+\Delta t}\mathbf{S}$, $\Delta \mathbf{e}^P$, and $^{t+\Delta t}\mathbf{e}''$) and is given by

$$^{t+\Delta t}\mathbf{n} = \frac{^{t+\Delta t}\mathbf{e}''}{\| \, ^{t+\Delta t}\mathbf{e}'' \, \|_2} \tag{6.241}$$

Since the stress correction along this vector returns the stress state to the yield surface radially, the method has been called the radial return method (see R. D. Krieg and D. B. Krieg [A]).

This interpretation of the solution scheme gives some indication of the numerical error in the solution process. We see that the yield condition and hardening law are accurately satisfied at the discrete solution times, but the magnitude of the plastic strains is obtained in (6.225) by an estimate based on the Euler backward integration for the flow rule. If the direction of the deviatoric stress vector does not change (hence $^\tau \mathbf{n}$ is constant for all τ), the solution is exact, but any change in the direction of this vector will introduce numerical integration errors. Some studies on solution errors are presented by R. D. Krieg and D. B. Krieg [A], H. L. Schreyer, R. F. Kulak, and J. M. Kramer [A], M. Ortiz and E. P. Popov [A], and N. S. Lee and K. J. Bathe [B]. These investigations indicate the high accuracy that is achieved in using the solution algorithm.

As we have pointed out, the second important requirement of the computational scheme is the evaluation of an accurate tangent stress-strain relation for the stiffness matrix. This tangent stress-strain matrix must be *consistent* with the numerical stress integration scheme used in order to have the full convergence benefits of the Newton-Raphson iteration (see Section 8.4.1). Let us consider that we require the tangent material matrix corresponding to time $t + \Delta t$. We assume the schematic yield curve in Fig. 6.9 is applicable.

For ease of writing let us define the stress and strain vectors

$$\begin{aligned} ^{t+\Delta t}\boldsymbol{\sigma}^T &= [^{t+\Delta t}\sigma_{11} \quad ^{t+\Delta t}\sigma_{22} \quad ^{t+\Delta t}\sigma_{33} \quad ^{t+\Delta t}\sigma_{12} \quad ^{t+\Delta t}\sigma_{23} \quad ^{t+\Delta t}\sigma_{31}] \\ &= [^{t+\Delta t}\sigma_1 \quad ^{t+\Delta t}\sigma_2 \quad ^{t+\Delta t}\sigma_3 \quad ^{t+\Delta t}\sigma_4 \quad ^{t+\Delta t}\sigma_5 \quad ^{t+\Delta t}\sigma_6] \end{aligned} \tag{6.242}$$

$$\begin{aligned} ^{t+\Delta t}\mathbf{e}^T &= [^{t+\Delta t}e_{11} \quad ^{t+\Delta t}e_{22} \quad ^{t+\Delta t}e_{33} \quad ^{t+\Delta t}\gamma_{12} \quad ^{t+\Delta t}\gamma_{23} \quad ^{t+\Delta t}\gamma_{31}] \\ &= [^{t+\Delta t}e_1 \quad ^{t+\Delta t}e_2 \quad ^{t+\Delta t}e_3 \quad ^{t+\Delta t}e_4 \quad ^{t+\Delta t}e_5 \quad ^{t+\Delta t}e_6] \end{aligned} \tag{6.243}$$

where we use the engineering shear strains $^{t+\Delta t}\gamma_{ij} = {}^{t+\Delta t}e_{ij} + {}^{t+\Delta t}e_{ji}$. Then the tangent stress-strain matrix at time $t + \Delta t$ is given by the derivative of the stresses with respect to the strains, evaluated at time $t + \Delta t$, which we write as

$$\mathbf{C}^{EP} = \frac{\partial \, ^{t+\Delta t}\boldsymbol{\sigma}}{\partial \, ^{t+\Delta t}\mathbf{e}} \tag{6.244}$$

We now need to establish the derivative in (6.244) *using the assumptions of the above stress integration,* and in particular the fact that the effective stress alone (or effective plastic strain alone) determines the current stress state. Hence, using the stress integration assumption, we may think of (6.244) as

$$\mathbf{C}^{EP} = \frac{\partial^{t+\Delta t}\boldsymbol{\sigma}}{\partial^{t+\Delta t}\overline{\sigma}} \frac{\partial^{t+\Delta t}\overline{\sigma}}{\partial^{t+\Delta t}\mathbf{e}} \tag{6.245}$$

or instead of the effective stress we can use the effective strain.

The derivation is achieved by careful differentiations. Let us present the first steps using for all stresses and strains the conventions in (6.242) and (6.243).

With the earlier established relations, we have

$$\left.\begin{aligned}{}^{t+\Delta t}\sigma_i &= {}^{t+\Delta t}S_i + {}^{t+\Delta t}\sigma_m; \qquad i = 1, 2, 3 \\ {}^{t+\Delta t}\sigma_i &= {}^{t+\Delta t}S_i; \qquad\qquad i = 4, 5, 6 \end{aligned}\right\} \tag{6.246}$$

and

Using (6.244), we obtain for the elements of the tangent stress-strain matrix,

$$\left.\begin{aligned} C_{ij}^{EP} &= C_{ij}' + \frac{E}{3(1 - 2\nu)}\,\delta_{ij}; \qquad 1 \le i, j \le 3 \\ C_{ij}^{EP} &= C_{ij}'; \qquad\qquad \text{otherwise} \end{aligned}\right\} \tag{6.247}$$

where

$$C_{ij}' = \frac{\partial^{\;t+\Delta t}S_i}{\partial^{\;t+\Delta t}e_j} \tag{6.248}$$

However, ${}^{t+\Delta t}S_i$ is given by (6.229), in which λ is given by (6.228) and a_E is a constant. Therefore, (6.248) will ultimately involve a differentiation of λ (and hence, of $\Delta\overline{e}^P$ and ${}^{t+\Delta t}\overline{\sigma}$) with respect to the strain components. Using the chain rule, we obtain

$$\frac{\partial^{\;t+\Delta t}S_i}{\partial^{\;t+\Delta t}e_j} = \frac{\partial^{\;t+\Delta t}S_i}{\partial^{\;t+\Delta t}e_k''}\frac{\partial^{\;t+\Delta t}e_k''}{\partial^{\;t+\Delta t}e_l'}\frac{\partial^{\;t+\Delta t}e_l'}{\partial^{\;t+\Delta t}e_j} \tag{6.249}$$

where from (6.221),

$$\frac{\partial^{\;t+\Delta t}e_k''}{\partial^{\;t+\Delta t}e_l'} = \delta_{kl} \tag{6.250}$$

and from (6.218),

$$\left.\begin{aligned} \left[\frac{\partial^{\;t+\Delta t}e_l'}{\partial^{\;t+\Delta t}e_j}\right] &= \frac{1}{3}\begin{bmatrix} 2 & -1 & -1 \\ -1 & 2 & -1 \\ -1 & -1 & 2 \end{bmatrix}; \qquad 1 \le l, j \le 3 \\ \frac{\partial^{\;t+\Delta t}e_l'}{\partial^{\;t+\Delta t}e_j} &= \delta_{lj}; \qquad\qquad\qquad \text{otherwise} \end{aligned}\right\} \tag{6.251}$$

Also, using (6.229), we obtain

$$\frac{\partial^{t+\Delta t}S_i}{\partial^{t+\Delta t}e_k''} = \frac{1}{a_E + \lambda}\,\delta_{ik} - \frac{1}{(a_E + \lambda)^2}\frac{\partial\lambda}{\partial^{t+\Delta t}e_k''}\,{}^{t+\Delta t}e_i'' \tag{6.252}$$

To conclude the derivation, in the evaluation of $\partial\lambda/\partial^{\,t+\Delta t}e_k''$ we use the relation (6.228), the given material relationship of effective stress versus effective plastic strain, and the condition that the effective stress function must be zero.

Of course, we considered in the preceding discussion a very special but commonly used elastoplastic material assumption. We also considered the general three-dimensional stress state. However, the stress integrations and tangent stress-strain relationships for other stress and strain conditions can be derived directly using the above procedures. For example, in axisymmetric and plane strain conditions, the appropriate strain variables would simply be set to zero. For plane stress conditions, the stress throughout the thickness is assumed zero, and so on (see Fig. 4.5).

We have presented the solution procedure for von Mises plasticity with isotropic hardening, but the algorithm can also be developed directly for the conditions of kinematic hardening and combined isotropic-kinematic (i.e., mixed) hardening (see M. Kojić and K. J. Bathe [B] and A. L. Eterovic and K. J. Bathe [A]).

The salient feature of the plasticity model used here is that only a single state variable (the effective stress) needs to be solved from a governing equation (the effective stress function equation) to obtain the complete stress state. The solution procedure can of course also be employed for more complex plasticity models, in which a number of internal state variables or governing parameters define the stress state. In this case, we need to establish and solve the appropriate state variable equations in an analogous manner as for the effective stress function equation discussed above.

To illustrate the application of the solution procedure to another easily tractable material law, we consider in the following example the Drucker-Prager material model, which is widely used to characterize soil and rock structures.

EXAMPLE 6.26: Consider the Drucker-Prager material model for which the yield function at time $t + \Delta t$ is given by (see D. C. Drucker and W. Prager [A], C. S. Desai and H. J. Siriwardane [A]),

$$^{t+\Delta t}f_y^{DP} = \alpha\,^{t+\Delta t}I_1 + \sqrt{^{t+\Delta t}J_2} - k \tag{a}$$

where $^{t+\Delta t}I_1 = {}^{t+\Delta t}\sigma_{ii}$ and $^{t+\Delta t}J_2 = \frac{1}{2}\,^{t+\Delta t}S_{ij}\,^{t+\Delta t}S_{ij}$ and α, k are material property parameters, see Fig. E6.26. For example, if the cohesion c and angle of friction θ of the material are measured in a triaxial compression test, we have

$$\alpha = \frac{2\sin\theta}{\sqrt{3}(3-\sin\theta)}$$

$$k = \frac{6c\cos\theta}{\sqrt{3}(3-\sin\theta)}$$

Consider the case of perfect plasticity, i.e., c and θ constant, and derive the relations for the stress integration.

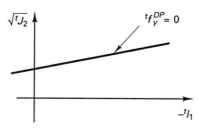

Figure E6.26 Drucker-Prager yield function

Comparing the yield function of the Drucker-Prager material model with the von Mises yield function, we recognize that the mean stress is present in (a). Hence, volumetric plastic strains are present in the response when the Drucker-Prager material model is used.

The constitutive relation for the material is

$$^{t+\Delta t}S_{ij} = \frac{1}{a_E}(^{t+\Delta t}e'_{ij} - {}^{t}e_{ij}^{P'} - \Delta e_{ij}^{P'}) \tag{b}$$

$$^{t+\Delta t}\sigma_m = \frac{1}{a_m}(^{t+\Delta t}e_m - {}^{t}e_m^P - \Delta e_m^P) \tag{c}$$

where ${}^{t}e_{ij}^{P'}$ and $\Delta e_{ij}^{P'}$ are the deviatoric plastic strains at time t and their increments, ${}^{t}e_m^P$ and Δe_m^P are the mean plastic strain at time t and its increment, and $a_m = (1 - 2\nu)/E$.

The flow rule (6.213) gives

$$\Delta e_{ij}^P = \lambda \alpha \delta_{ij} + \lambda \frac{^{t+\Delta t}S_{ij}}{2\sqrt{^{t+\Delta t}J_2}}$$

Hence
$$\Delta e_m^P = \tfrac{1}{3}\Delta e_{ii}^P = \lambda \alpha \tag{d}$$

and
$$\Delta e_{ij}^{P'} = \Delta e_{ij}^P - \Delta e_m^P \delta_{ij} = \lambda \frac{^{t+\Delta t}S_{ij}}{2\sqrt{^{t+\Delta t}J_2}} \tag{e}$$

Our objective is now to evaluate λ. Since the material is nonhardening, this evaluation can be achieved analytically in terms of known quantities, and once λ is known, the stresses for time $t + \Delta t$ can be evaluated directly.

Using the constitutive relation and the flow rule, we use (e) in (b), solve for $^{t+\Delta t}S_{ij}$, and take the scalar product of both sides of the resulting equation to obtain

$$\lambda = \sqrt{2}\ ^{t+\Delta t}d - 2a_E\sqrt{^{t+\Delta t}J_2} \tag{f}$$

where
$$^{t+\Delta t}d^2 = {}^{t+\Delta t}e_{ij}'' \cdot {}^{t+\Delta t}e_{ij}''$$
and
$$^{t+\Delta t}e_{ij}'' = {}^{t+\Delta t}e_{ij}' - {}^{t}e_{ij}^{P'}$$

We also use (d) in (c) to obtain

$$^{t+\Delta t}\sigma_m = \frac{1}{a_m}(^{t+\Delta t}e_m'' - \lambda\alpha) \tag{g}$$

where
$$^{t+\Delta t}e_m'' = {}^{t+\Delta t}e_m - {}^{t}e_m^P$$

Finally, we use the yield condition $^{t+\Delta t}f_y^{\mathrm{DP}} = 0$ and substitute for $^{t+\Delta t}I_1$ and $\sqrt{^{t+\Delta t}J_2}$ from (f) and (g) to obtain

$$\lambda = \frac{\dfrac{3\alpha}{a_m}\,^{t+\Delta t}e_m'' + \dfrac{^{t+\Delta t}d}{\sqrt{2}\ a_E} - k}{3\dfrac{\alpha^2}{a_m} + \dfrac{1}{2a_E}}$$

With λ known we can now evaluate directly the plastic strain increments from (b), (d), and (e) [where we use (f) to substitute in (e) for $\sqrt{^{t+\Delta t}J_2}$]. The stresses at time $t + \Delta t$ are then obtained from (b) and (c).

Thermoelastoplasticity and Creep

The effective-stress-function algorithm presented above was originally designed for the complex case of thermoelastoplasticity and creep (see K. J. Bathe, A. B. Chaudhary, E. N. Dvorkin, and M. Kojić [A]). In this case the relations presented earlier need to be generalized, and we obtain

$$^{t+\Delta t}\mathbf{S} = \frac{^{t+\Delta t}E}{1 + {}^{t+\Delta t}\nu}({}^{t+\Delta t}\mathbf{e}' - {}^{t+\Delta t}\mathbf{e}^{P} - {}^{t+\Delta t}\mathbf{e}^{C}) \tag{6.253}$$

$$^{t+\Delta t}\sigma_m = \frac{^{t+\Delta t}E}{1 - 2{}^{t+\Delta t}\nu}({}^{t+\Delta t}e_m - {}^{t+\Delta t}e^{TH}) \tag{6.254}$$

where the Young's modulus and Poisson's ratio are now considered temperature-dependent (which we model as time-dependent, with the temperature prescribed at each time step) and $^{t+\Delta t}\mathbf{e}^{C}$, $^{t+\Delta t}e^{TH}$ represent the creep and thermal strains, respectively. The thermal strain is calculated from

$$^{t+\Delta t}e^{TH} = {}^{t+\Delta t}\alpha_m({}^{t+\Delta t}\theta - \theta_{\text{ref}}) \tag{6.255}$$

where $^{t+\Delta t}\alpha_m$ is the mean coefficient of thermal expansion and θ_{ref} is the reference temperature.

The relation (6.220) now becomes

$$^{t+\Delta t}\mathbf{S} = \frac{^{t+\Delta t}E}{1 + {}^{t+\Delta t}\nu}({}^{t+\Delta t}\mathbf{e}'' - \Delta\mathbf{e}^{P} - \Delta\mathbf{e}^{C}) \tag{6.256}$$

where the known strains are

$$^{t+\Delta t}\mathbf{e}'' = {}^{t+\Delta t}\mathbf{e}' - {}^{t}\mathbf{e}^{P} - {}^{t}\mathbf{e}^{C} \tag{6.257}$$

Let us again consider the von Mises yield condition and isotropic hardening. The plastic strain increment $\Delta\mathbf{e}^{P}$ is calculated in the same way as enumerated above except that now the effective stress–effective plastic strain curves are temperature-dependent (see Fig. 6.12). Hence, all relations derived are directly applicable, but the material constants are a function of temperature.

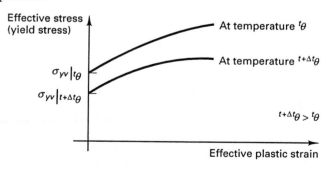

Figure 6.12 Effective stress–effective plastic strain curves at different temperatures (schematic representation)

The incremental creep strain $\Delta\mathbf{e}^{C}$ is calculated quite analogously to the incremental plastic strain (see, for example, H. Kraus [A]). Using the α-method of time integration (see

M. D. Snyder and K. J. Bathe [A] and Section 9.6), we have

$$\Delta \mathbf{e}^C = \Delta t \, {}^{\tau}\gamma \, {}^{\tau}\mathbf{S} \tag{6.258}$$

where
$$^{\tau}\mathbf{S} = (1 - \alpha) \, {}^{t}\mathbf{S} + \alpha \, {}^{t+\Delta t}\mathbf{S} \tag{6.259}$$

and α is the integration parameter ($0 \leq \alpha \leq 1$).

The function ${}^{\tau}\gamma$ is given by

$$^{\tau}\gamma = \frac{3}{2} \frac{{}^{\tau}\dot{\bar{e}}^C}{{}^{\tau}\bar{\sigma}} \tag{6.260}$$

where the effective creep strain increment is

$$\Delta \bar{e}^C = \sqrt{\tfrac{2}{3} \Delta \mathbf{e}^C \cdot \Delta \mathbf{e}^C} \tag{6.261}$$

and the weighted effective stress is

$$^{\tau}\bar{\sigma} = (1 - \alpha) \, {}^{t}\bar{\sigma} + \alpha \, {}^{t+\Delta t}\bar{\sigma} \tag{6.262}$$

Since the material is assumed incompressible in creep, we have in uniaxial stress conditions ${}^{t}\bar{\sigma} = {}^{t}\sigma_{11}$ and ${}^{t}\bar{e}^C = {}^{t}e^C_{11}$.

These relations are like those used for the calculation of the plastic strain increment, but in that case we performed the integration with $\alpha = 1$ (the Euler backward method).

The evaluation of the scalar function ${}^{\tau}\gamma$ is based on a creep law. A typical uniaxial creep law used in practice is

$$^{t}e^C = a_0 \, {}^{t}\sigma^{a_1} \, t^{a_2} \, e^{-a_3/({}^{t}\theta + 273.16)} \tag{6.263}$$

where ${}^{t}e^C$ and ${}^{t}\sigma$ are the creep strain and the stress, respectively, ${}^{t}\theta$ is the temperature in degrees Celsius, and a_0, a_1, a_2, a_3 are constants. The generalization of (6.263) to multiaxial conditions is achieved by substitution of the effective stress and effective creep strain for the uniaxial variables,

$$^{t}\bar{e}^C = a_0 \, {}^{t}\bar{\sigma}^{a_1} \, t^{a_2} \, e^{-a_3/({}^{t}\theta + 273.16)} \tag{6.264}$$

This equation and other creep laws are of the form

$$^{t}\bar{e}^C = f_1({}^{t}\bar{\sigma}) f_2(t) f_3({}^{t}\theta) \tag{6.265}$$

and we use

$$\Delta \bar{e}^C = \Delta t \, f_1({}^{\tau}\bar{\sigma}) \dot{f}_2(\tau) f_3({}^{\tau}\theta) \tag{6.266}$$

where
$$^{\tau}\theta = (1 - \alpha) \, {}^{t}\theta + \alpha \, {}^{t+\Delta t}\theta \tag{6.267}$$

and $\tau = t + \alpha \Delta t$. The incremental creep law in (6.266) is based on experimental evidence and corresponds to a time differentiation of the function f_2 only.

Using equations (6.266) and (6.262), the function ${}^{\tau}\gamma$ can be determined for a given value of ${}^{\tau}\bar{\sigma}$, and the creep strain increment can be calculated. This approach corresponds to the so-called *time hardening procedure*. Physical observations, however, show that the use of the *strain hardening procedure* gives better results for variable stress conditions. In the strain hardening method, the creep strain rate is expressed in terms of the effective creep strain ${}^{t}\bar{e}^C$ instead of the time τ. This is achieved by evaluating from (6.265) and (6.266) the pseudotime τ_p,

$$^{t}\bar{e}^C + f_1({}^{\tau}\bar{\sigma}) f_3({}^{\tau}\theta)[\alpha \, \Delta t \dot{f}_2(\tau_p) - f_2(\tau_p)] = 0 \tag{6.268}$$

In general, this equation needs to be solved numerically for τ_p. The creep strain increment $\Delta\bar{e}^C$ can then be computed from (6.266) with τ replaced by τ_p. Figure 6.13 illustrates schematically the difference between the assumptions of time and strain hardening in creep strain calculations.

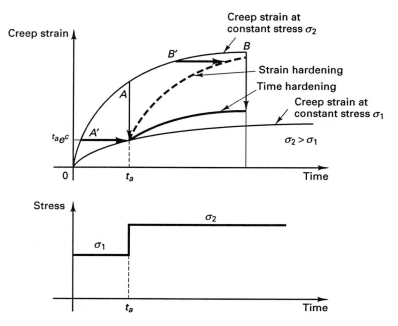

Figure 6.13 Creep strain in time hardening and strain hardening assumptions. In the time hardening assumption, curve A-B defines the incremental creep strain from time t_a onward. In the strain hardening assumption, curve A'-B' defines the incremental creep strain from time t_a onward.

We should note that for cyclic loading conditions, additional considerations are necessary to account for the reversal of stress (see H. Kraus [A]).

The key observation regarding the above computation is that the inelastic strain increments are a function of the unknown effective stress $^{t+\Delta t}\bar{\sigma}$ only. To solve for this stress value, we use the effective stress function for the problem.

Let us substitute into (6.256) for $\Delta\mathbf{e}^P$ from (6.225) and for $\Delta\mathbf{e}^C$ from (6.258). Since all material properties are now a function of temperature, we obtain

$$^{t+\Delta t}\mathbf{S} = \frac{1}{{}^{t+\Delta t}a_E + \alpha\,\Delta t\,{}^{\tau}\gamma + \lambda}\left[{}^{t+\Delta t}\mathbf{e}'' - (1-\alpha)\Delta t\,{}^{\tau}\gamma\,{}^{t}\mathbf{S}\right] \tag{6.269}$$

where

$$^{t+\Delta t}a_E = \frac{1 + {}^{t+\Delta t}\nu}{{}^{t+\Delta t}E} \tag{6.270}$$

Taking the scalar product of both sides in (6.269), we find that the unknown effective stress satisfies

$$a^2\,{}^{t+\Delta t}\bar{\sigma}^2 + b\,{}^{\tau}\gamma - c^2\,{}^{\tau}\gamma^2 - d^2 = 0 \tag{6.271}$$

where
$$a = {}^{t+\Delta t}a_E + \alpha \Delta t \, {}^\tau \gamma + \lambda$$
$$b = 3(1 - \alpha) \, \Delta t \, {}^{t+\Delta t}\mathbf{e}'' \cdot {}^t\mathbf{S}$$
$$c = (1 - \alpha) \, \Delta t \, {}^t\overline{\sigma} \tag{6.272}$$
$$d^2 = \tfrac{3}{2} \, {}^{t+\Delta t}\mathbf{e}'' \cdot {}^{t+\Delta t}\mathbf{e}''$$

The coefficients b, c, and d are constants that depend only on known values, whereas the coefficient a is a function of ${}^{t+\Delta t}\overline{\sigma}$. Since ${}^{t+\Delta t}\overline{\sigma}$ is the variable to be solved for, we define the *effective stress function,*

$$f(\overline{\sigma}^*) = a^2(\overline{\sigma}^*)^2 + b \, {}^\tau \gamma - c^2 \, {}^\tau \gamma^2 - d^2 \tag{6.273}$$

The function $f(\overline{\sigma}^*)$ is zero at ${}^{t+\Delta t}\overline{\sigma}$ (see Fig. 6.14). Hence, the value of ${}^{t+\Delta t}\overline{\sigma}$ can, in general, be evaluated by any numerical iterative scheme that calculates the zero of a function, for example, a stable and efficient bisection technique. Once ${}^{t+\Delta t}\overline{\sigma}$ is known, we can use the above equations to evaluate the inelastic strains and stresses at time $t + \Delta t$.

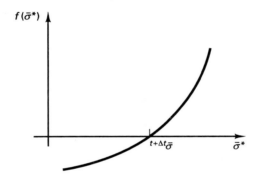

Figure 6.14 Effective stress function, schematically shown, with zero value at ${}^{t+\Delta t}\overline{\sigma}$

This solution scheme for the thermoplastic and creep inelastic response is clearly an extension of the method presented for the isothermal plastic strain calculations. Therefore, the considerations given earlier regarding the accuracy of the solution scheme are applicable here also. However, for the creep strain calculations the α-method with $0 \le \alpha \le 1$ is used in the incremental relations. In practice, stability considerations usually require that $\alpha \ge \tfrac{1}{2}$ (the α-integration scheme is unconditionally stable in linear analysis provided $\alpha \ge \tfrac{1}{2}$), and frequently we use $\alpha = 1$. We consider the α-integration scheme in some detail in Section 9.6.

In the foregoing presentation we discussed how the stresses at time $t + \Delta t$ are calculated but did not present the evaluation of the tangent stress-strain relationship. This evaluation requires the derivative of the stresses with respect to the strains [see (6.244)], and we refer to the remarks given at the end of the next section in which we consider viscoplastic strains.

Viscoplasticity

The plasticity model considered above does not model time effects that physically occur in the material. Such effects may be important and a viscoplastic material model may be more appropriate to characterize the material response. Let us consider a quite widely used viscoplastic model proposed by P. Perzyna [A]. The model uses the concepts of the von Mises plasticity model but introduces time-rate effects. An important aspect of the theory of viscoplasticity is that there is no yield condition but instead the rate of the inelastic response is determined by the instantaneous difference between the effective stress and the "material" effective stress.

The implementation of the model is representative of that of viscoplastic models and can be achieved using the methods already presented.

Let us consider the Perzyna model without temperature effects. In this case the model postulates that the increments in strain are at any time

$$de_{ij} = de_{ij}^E + de_{ij}^{VP} \tag{6.274}$$

where the superscripts E and VP denote elastic and viscoplastic strain increments. The elastic strain increments are calculated as usual, and the viscoplastic strain increments at time t are

$$de_{ij}^{VP} = \begin{cases} \beta\phi(^t\overline{\sigma})\dfrac{3}{2\,^t\overline{\sigma}}\,^tS_{ij}\,dt & \text{if } ^t\overline{\sigma} > {}^t\overline{\sigma}_0 \\ 0 & \text{if } ^t\overline{\sigma} \leq {}^t\overline{\sigma}_0 \end{cases} \tag{6.275}$$

In this relation β is a material constant, $^t\overline{\sigma}$ is the current effective stress, and

$$\phi(^t\overline{\sigma}) = \left(\frac{^t\overline{\sigma} - {}^t\overline{\sigma}_0}{^t\overline{\sigma}_0}\right)^N \tag{6.276}$$

where $^t\overline{\sigma}_0$ is the material effective stress, that is, the effective stress corresponding to the accumulated effective viscoplastic strain $^t\overline{e}^{VP}$ (see Fig. 6.15), and N is another material constant. The relations for calculating deviatoric stresses, the effective stress, and the effective inelastic strain were given earlier [see (6.216), (6.227), and (6.224)]. We note that the expression for the viscoplastic strains in (6.275) is of the form of the expression for the creep strains [see (6.258)] and the plastic strains [see (6.225)] because the underlying physical phenomena of all these strain components are similar (but different time scales are applicable). A consequence is that the viscoplastic strains also correspond to an incompressible response [as do the plastic and creep strain components in (6.225) and (6.258)].

The model requires the elastic constants E (Young's modulus) and ν (Poisson's ratio), the material constants β, N, and the curve in Fig. 6.15. We note that β (with unit $1/\text{time}$) and N determine the rate behavior of the material. That is, viscoplastic strains are accumulated as long as the effective stress is larger than the material effective stress, and the rate of such accumulation is determined by β and N.

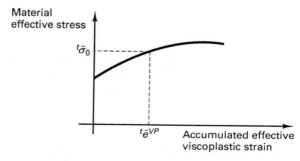

Figure 6.15 Schematic representation of material effective stress versus accumulated effective viscoplastic strain

Let us now consider the calculation of the stresses at time $t + \Delta t$. We proceed as in the case of plasticity and creep. Assuming that the total strains corresponding to time $t + \Delta t$ and all stress and strain variables corresponding to time t are known, we have (as in the case of plasticity and creep)

$$^{t+\Delta t}\sigma_m = \frac{E}{1 - 2\nu} \, ^{t+\Delta t}e_m \tag{6.277}$$

$$^{t+\Delta t}\mathbf{S} = \frac{E}{1 + \nu}(^{t+\Delta t}\mathbf{e}'' - \Delta \mathbf{e}^{VP}) \tag{6.278}$$

$$^{t+\Delta t}\mathbf{e}'' = \,^{t+\Delta t}\mathbf{e}' - \,^{t}\mathbf{e}^{VP} \tag{6.279}$$

where the variables are as in (6.214) to (6.221) but we consider viscoplastic strains instead of plastic strains.

The viscoplastic strain increment is given by [compare (6.258)]

$$\Delta \mathbf{e}^{VP} = \Delta t \, ^{\tau}\gamma \, ^{\tau}\mathbf{S} \tag{6.280}$$

where using the α-method of integration,

$$^{\tau}\mathbf{S} = (1 - \alpha) \, ^{t}\mathbf{S} + \alpha \, ^{t+\Delta t}\mathbf{S} \tag{6.281}$$

and the scalar $^{\tau}\gamma$ is given by

$$^{\tau}\gamma = \begin{cases} \beta \, ^{\tau}\phi \, \dfrac{3}{2 \, ^{\tau}\overline{\sigma}} & \text{if } ^{\tau}\overline{\sigma} > \,^{\tau}\overline{\sigma}_0 \\ 0 & \text{if } ^{\tau}\overline{\sigma} \leq \,^{\tau}\overline{\sigma}_0 \end{cases} \tag{6.282}$$

We note that $^{\tau}\gamma$ depends on $^{\tau}\overline{\sigma}$ and $^{\tau}\overline{\sigma}_0$, where $^{\tau}\overline{\sigma}_0$ depends on the accumulated effective viscoplastic strain (see Fig. 6.15). Hence, as in the analysis of creep response, the above relations represent a one-parameter system of equations in the effective stress $^{t+\Delta t}\overline{\sigma}$, which is obtained as the zero of the effective stress function,

$$f(\overline{\sigma}^*) = a^2(\overline{\sigma}^*)^2 + b \, ^{\tau}\gamma - c^2 \, ^{\tau}\gamma^2 - d^2 \tag{6.283}$$

where

$$a = a_E + \alpha \, \Delta t \, ^{\tau}\gamma$$

$$b = 3(1 - \alpha) \, \Delta t \, ^{t+\Delta t}\mathbf{e}'' \cdot \,^{t}\mathbf{S} \tag{6.284}$$

$$c = (1 - \alpha) \, \Delta t \, ^{t}\overline{\sigma}$$

$$d^2 = \tfrac{3}{2} \, ^{t+\Delta t}\mathbf{e}'' \cdot \,^{t+\Delta t}\mathbf{e}''$$

$$a_E = \frac{1 + \nu}{E}$$

This function is obtained as in the case of thermoplasticity and creep [see (6.271) and (6.272)] but neglecting all temperature dependency and the plastic parameter λ (since the viscoplastic strains are calculated by the procedure used for the creep strains). Of course, a dependence on temperature for the material properties could be included directly. Indeed, an important consideration in the use of viscoplastic models is that various functional dependencies can be directly, and with relative ease, included in the calculations. The basic reason for this ease in use is that there is no explicit yield condition. Instead, the solution is obtained by integrating the inelastic strains until the effective stress is equal to the material effective stress (given by the effective viscoplastic strain). This integration is efficiently performed with the α-method because with $\alpha \geq \frac{1}{2}$ the integration can proceed with relatively large time steps (see Section 9.6).

We considered in the above discussions of thermoelastoplasticity and creep and viscoplasticity only the evaluation of the stresses corresponding to given total strains. The consistent tangent constitutive matrices would be calculated as discussed for the case of plasticity but, in general, can be obtained only in analytical form provided tractable functional relationships for the inelastic strains are used. If the analytical derivation is not possible, a numerical evaluation of the tangent constitutive relation can be achieved by use of a finite difference scheme to calculate the required differentiations in (6.208) (see, for example, M. Kojić and K. J. Bathe [B]).

6.6.4 Large Strain Elastoplasticity

The formulations for inelastic response discussed in the previous section have been presented for small or large displacement response with small strains. Additional considerations are important when large strains are modeled.

The extension of the infinitesimal small strain theory of plasticity to large strains can be achieved by a number of alternative formulations (see, for example, A. E. Green and P. M. Naghdi [A], E. H. Lee [A], J. Lubliner [A], and J. C. Simo [A]). However, our purpose here is to merely introduce the basic considerations, and hence we briefly discuss only one formulation, namely, a total strain formulation based on Cauchy stresses and logarithmic strains. This approach is also very attractive for a number of reasons as enumerated below.

The basic considerations in any formulation relate to the choice of adequate stress and strain measures, the characterization of the elastic behavior, and the proper characterization of plastic flow.

An effective large strain procedure should surely reduce to the formulations presented in the previous section when the strains are small. However, an important feature of the materially-nonlinear-only and large displacement–small strain analysis procedures presented is that these formulations are *total strain* and not rate-type formulations. That is, the equations of equilibrium are written for time $t + \Delta t$ and the total strain for that time is calculated. Hence, numerical integration is used only in the calculation of the inelastic strain from time t to time $t + \Delta t$. In contrast, using a rate-type formulation, rates of stress, strain, and rotational effects are integrated, which leads to additional numerical errors and, for an accurate solution, requires significantly smaller solution steps than are needed in a total strain formulation.

For large deformation analysis, rate-type formulations are frequently based on the Jaumann stress rate–velocity strain description (see Example 6.24). In addition to the numerical integration errors, such a hypoelastic stress-strain description also leads to nonconservative and therefore nonphysical response predictions in purely *elastic* cyclic motions (see M. Kojić and K. J. Bathe [A]). This nonphysical behavior may be judged to be small, but is not due to numerical integration error.

A natural approach based on micromechanical observations for large strain elastoplasticity is based on the hyperelastic material description with the product decomposition of the deformation gradient into elastic and plastic parts (see E. H. Lee [A], J. R. Rice [A], and R. J. Asaro [A]). Such an approach also lends itself to a total formulation that is a natural extension of the infinitesimal strain formulation discussed in the previous section.

One important feature of the large strain elastoplastic analysis is that the uniaxial stress-strain law used to characterize the response is given by the Cauchy stress–logarithmic strain relationship (see Fig. 6.16). The yield condition, flow rule, and hardening rule are used for the Cauchy stresses.

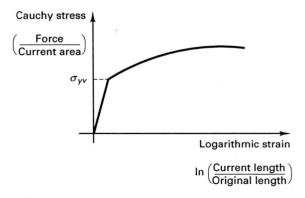

Figure 6.16   Large strain elastoplastic one-dimensional response model

Using the multiplicative decomposition of the deformation gradient (to characterize the large strain elastoplastic deformation of a body), we have

$$\mathbf{X} = \mathbf{X}^E \mathbf{X}^P \tag{6.285}$$

where $\mathbf{X}^E$ and $\mathbf{X}^P$ represent, respectively, the elastic and plastic deformation gradients. The relation (6.285) is assumed to hold throughout the response, but for ease of writing we do not include the left superscripts and subscripts (until we present the actual computational procedure); hence for example, we have $\mathbf{X} \equiv {}_0^t\mathbf{X}$.

Relation (6.285) is a key equation in our large strain elastoplasticity formulation. At time t the relation (6.285) reads ${}_0^t\mathbf{X} = {}_0^t\mathbf{X}^E\,{}_0^t\mathbf{X}^P$, or we may—as mentioned following (6.29) and used in Example 6.9—also write ${}_0^t\mathbf{X} = {}_\tau^t\mathbf{X}^E\,{}_0^\tau\mathbf{X}^P$ for conceptual understanding. Hence, the approach used is *conceptually* based on a relaxed hypothetical configuration (corresponding to τ) which for each particle is obtained by unloading the material from the current configuration to a state of zero stress in such a way that no inelastic process takes place. The plastic deformation gradient $\mathbf{X}^P$ corresponds to the deformation from the original to this hypothetical configuration. The elastic deformations and therefore stresses are measured using $\mathbf{X}^E$, which is thought of as a deformation gradient measured from the relaxed configuration τ.

Let us, as in Section 6.6.3, characterize the material with the von Mises yield condition and isotropic hardening. Hence, our only aim in the following discussion is to extend the plasticity formulation of Section 6.6.3 to large strains.

As in small strain plasticity, we assume that the plastic deformation is incompressible; hence,

$$\det \mathbf{X}^P = 1 \tag{6.286}$$

and $J = \det \mathbf{X} = \det \mathbf{X}^E = {}^0\rho/{}^t\rho$. If we assume, for the moment, that $\mathbf{X}^P$ is known, we have

$$\mathbf{X}^E = \mathbf{X}(\mathbf{X}^P)^{-1} \qquad (6.287)$$

Also, since the velocity gradient $\mathbf{L} = \dot{\mathbf{X}}\mathbf{X}^{-1}$ [see (6.40)], we may write

$$\mathbf{L} = \mathbf{L}^E + \mathbf{L}^P \qquad (6.288)$$

where by substituting from (6.285), the elastic and plastic parts of the velocity gradient are, respectively,

$$\mathbf{L}^E = \dot{\mathbf{X}}^E(\mathbf{X}^E)^{-1}; \qquad \mathbf{L}^P = \mathbf{X}^E\dot{\mathbf{X}}^P(\mathbf{X}^P)^{-1}(\mathbf{X}^E)^{-1} \qquad (6.289)$$

The variables that characterize the large strain elastoplastic response are therefore $\mathbf{X}$, $\mathbf{X}^P$, $\boldsymbol{\tau}$, and σ_y, where $\boldsymbol{\tau}$ are the Cauchy stresses and σ_y is the current yield stress (including the effect of hardening). The evaluation of $\boldsymbol{\tau}$ must be based on evolution equations for $\mathbf{X}^P$ and σ_y (where in comparison to small strain plasticity $\mathbf{X}^P$ is used instead of $\mathbf{e}^P$). Since the Cauchy stresses are calculated throughout the solution, the constitutive description is used efficiently in an updated Lagrangian formulation.

Since $\det \mathbf{X}^P = 1$, we have $J = \det \mathbf{X}^E > 0$ and we can calculate the polar decomposition

$$\mathbf{X}^E = \mathbf{R}^E\mathbf{U}^E \qquad (6.290)$$

The logarithmic strain is used in the large strain one-dimensional response characterization (see Fig. 6.16), hence it is natural to use the elastic Hencky or logarithmic strain,

$$\mathbf{E}^E = \ln \mathbf{U}^E \qquad (6.291)$$

in the multidimensional characterization of the Cauchy stress. We note that the evaluation of $\mathbf{E}^E$ requires a spectral decomposition of $\mathbf{U}^E$ [see (6.32) and (6.52)].

Since $\mathbf{E}^E$ is associated with the (conceptual) intermediate configuration τ, we next define a stress measure, $\bar{\boldsymbol{\tau}}$, corresponding to that configuration,

$$\bar{\boldsymbol{\tau}} = J(\mathbf{R}^E)^T\boldsymbol{\tau}\mathbf{R}^E \qquad (6.292)$$

With these stress and strain measures we have the elastic work conjugacy (see S. N. Atluri [A] and Exercise 6.86),

$$\bar{\boldsymbol{\tau}} \cdot \dot{\mathbf{E}}^E = J\boldsymbol{\tau} \cdot \mathbf{D}^E \qquad (6.293)$$

where $\mathbf{D}^E = \text{sym} (\mathbf{L}^E)$. The appropriate plastic velocity gradient to use is then[16]

$$\begin{aligned}\bar{\mathbf{L}}^P &= (\mathbf{X}^E)^{-1}\mathbf{L}^P\mathbf{X}^E \\ &= \dot{\mathbf{X}}^P(\mathbf{X}^P)^{-1}\end{aligned} \qquad (6.294)$$

---

[16] We can prove that with the definitions of $\bar{\boldsymbol{\tau}}$ in (6.292) and $\bar{\mathbf{L}}^P$ in (6.294), we have

$$J\boldsymbol{\tau} \cdot \mathbf{D} = \bar{\boldsymbol{\tau}} \cdot \dot{\mathbf{E}}^E + \bar{\boldsymbol{\tau}} \cdot \bar{\mathbf{D}}^P$$

where $\mathbf{D}$ is the (total) velocity strain [see (6.41)] and $\bar{\mathbf{D}}^P$ is given in (6.298) (see Exercise 6.87).

The stress $\bar{\tau}$ is given by the usual stress-strain relationship of isotropic elasticity. Let $\bar{\mathbf{S}}$ be the deviatoric stress components and $\bar{\sigma}_m$ be the mean stress, then

$$\bar{\mathbf{S}} = 2\mu\mathbf{E}^{E'}; \qquad \bar{\sigma}_m = 3\kappa E_m^E \qquad (6.295)$$

where the elastic deviatoric strain components are given in $\mathbf{E}^{E'}$ and E_m^E is the elastic mean strain component. This choice of (hyperelastic) stress-strain law uses the *total* elastic strain and has the advantage of providing an excellent description of the stress even when the elastic strains are of moderate size (see L. Anand [A]).

The yield condition is as in (6.222), but using the deviatoric Cauchy stresses $\mathbf{S}$, hence we have[17]

$$\bar{\sigma} = \sqrt{\tfrac{3}{2}\mathbf{S}\cdot\mathbf{S}} \qquad (6.296)$$
$$= J^{-1}\sqrt{\tfrac{3}{2}\bar{\mathbf{S}}\cdot\bar{\mathbf{S}}}$$

where $\bar{\mathbf{S}}$ is the deviatoric stress corresponding to the relaxed configuration, $\bar{\mathbf{S}} = J(\mathbf{R}^E)^T\mathbf{S}\mathbf{R}^E$. We also note that the unit normal to the yield surface in the relaxed hypothetical configuration is

$$\bar{\mathbf{n}} = \sqrt{\frac{3}{2}}\frac{\bar{\mathbf{S}}}{J\bar{\sigma}} \qquad (6.297)$$

To obtain the evolution equation of the plastic deformation gradient, we use (6.293) and the plastic velocity strain tensor,

$$\bar{\mathbf{D}}^P = \operatorname{sym}(\bar{\mathbf{L}}^P) \qquad (6.298)$$

This strain tensor is obtained from the flow rule, in analogy to (6.225), from[18]

$$\bar{\mathbf{D}}^P = \sqrt{\tfrac{3}{2}}\,\dot{\bar{e}}^P\,\bar{\mathbf{n}} \qquad (6.299)$$

where

$$\dot{\bar{e}}^P = \sqrt{\tfrac{2}{3}\bar{\mathbf{D}}^P\cdot\bar{\mathbf{D}}^P} \qquad (6.300)$$

Substituting from (6.297) into (6.299) corresponds to (6.225) in the small strain case. Of course, the relation $\dot{\bar{\sigma}} = f(\dot{\bar{e}}^P)$ is obtained from the uniaxial stress-strain relationship in Fig. 6.16. Consistent with the other assumptions used, the modified plastic spin tensor $\bar{\mathbf{W}}^P = \operatorname{skw}(\bar{\mathbf{L}}^P)$ is assumed to be zero.

Hence, we notice that the basic equations used for the solution of infinitesimal strain problems have been generalized to large strains by use of the Cauchy stress–logarithmic strain relationship in Fig. 6.16, the corresponding elastic stress-strain law for the Cauchy stress and logarithmic (Hencky) strain, and a plastic deformation gradient that represents the inelastic response and conceptually a deformation from which the elastic response is measured. Since the large strain formulation is a direct extension of the formulation used for small strains (see also Exercise 6.84), the computational procedures discussed earlier are also directly applicable and Table 6.10 summarizes the sequence of solution steps (see also A. L. Eterovic and K. J. Bathe [A]).

In the preceding discussion we assumed a general three-dimensional response, but the equations can also be used directly for two-dimensional analyses, that is, plane stress, plane strain, and axisymmetric situations, by imposing the fundamental conditions of the specific

---

[17] Note that the effective stress carries the overbar defined in (6.227).

[18] This flow rule relation can be derived from the principle of maximum plastic dissipation (see J. Lubliner [A] and A. L. Eterovic and K. J. Bathe [B]).

TABLE 6.10 *Large strain elastoplastic updated Lagrangian Hencky formulation*

The trial elastic state:
Obtain the trial elastic deformation gradient

$$\mathbf{X}_*^E = {}_{0}^{t+\Delta t}\mathbf{X}({}_{0}^{t}\mathbf{X}^P)^{-1}$$

Perform the polar decomposition

$$\mathbf{X}_*^E = \mathbf{R}_*^E \mathbf{U}_*^E$$

Obtain the trial elastic strain tensor

$$\mathbf{E}_*^E = \ln \mathbf{U}_*^E$$

Obtain the trial elastic stress tensor $\overline{\boldsymbol{\tau}}_*$ using the equation for the mean stress and the deviatoric stress

$$\text{tr}\,(\overline{\boldsymbol{\tau}}_*) = 3\kappa\,\text{tr}\,(\mathbf{E}_*^E)$$

$$\overline{\mathbf{S}}_* = 2\mu\mathbf{E}_*^{E'}$$

Obtain the trial equivalent tensile stress

$$\overline{\sigma}_* = J^{-1}\sqrt{\tfrac{3}{2}\,\overline{\mathbf{S}}_* \cdot \overline{\mathbf{S}}_*}$$

Check whether the solution step corresponds to elastic conditions:
If $\overline{\sigma}_* < {}^{t}\sigma_y$, then the solution step was elastic and we conclude the solution step by setting

$${}^{t+\Delta t}\overline{\sigma} = \overline{\sigma}_*; \qquad {}^{t+\Delta t}\sigma_y = {}^{t}\sigma_y; \qquad {}^{t+\Delta t}\mathbf{E}^E = \mathbf{E}_*^E; \qquad {}^{t+\Delta t}\overline{\boldsymbol{\tau}} = \overline{\boldsymbol{\tau}}_*; \qquad {}^{t+\Delta t}\boldsymbol{\tau} = ({}^{t+\Delta t}J)^{-1}\mathbf{R}_*^E\overline{\boldsymbol{\tau}}_*(\mathbf{R}_*^E)^T$$

Otherwise we continue as follows.
Plastic solution step:
Use the effective-stress-function algorithm to calculate ${}^{t+\Delta t}\overline{\sigma}$ and ${}^{t+\Delta t}\overline{e}^P$ (see 6.233)
Calculate the stress deviator of ${}^{t+\Delta t}\overline{\boldsymbol{\tau}}$,

$$\lambda = \frac{3}{2}\frac{{}^{t+\Delta t}\overline{e}^P - {}^{t}\overline{e}^P}{{}^{t+\Delta t}J\,{}^{t+\Delta t}\overline{\sigma}}$$

$${}^{t+\Delta t}\overline{\mathbf{S}} = \frac{\overline{\mathbf{S}}_*}{1 + 2\mu\lambda}$$

Calculate ${}^{t+\Delta t}\overline{\boldsymbol{\tau}}$,

$${}^{t+\Delta t}\overline{\boldsymbol{\tau}} = {}^{t+\Delta t}\overline{\mathbf{S}} + \tfrac{1}{3}\,\text{tr}\,(\overline{\boldsymbol{\tau}}_*)\mathbf{I}$$

Calculate the Cauchy stresses,

$${}^{t+\Delta t}\boldsymbol{\tau} = ({}^{t+\Delta t}J)^{-1}\mathbf{R}_*^E\,{}^{t+\Delta t}\overline{\boldsymbol{\tau}}(\mathbf{R}_*^E)^T$$

Update the plastic deformation gradient by integration of (6.294),

$${}^{t+\Delta t}_{0}\mathbf{X}^P = \exp\,(\lambda\,{}^{t+\Delta t}\overline{\mathbf{S}})\,{}_{0}^{t}\mathbf{X}^P$$

---

two-dimensional response being considered (see Fig. 4.5). In beam and shell analyses, these equations can also be employed, but the kinematic relations in Sections 6.5 must then include the effects of the change in thickness of the elements.

The large strain formulation has been presented above for elastoplastic response, but we note that the same approach can also be employed for creep and viscoplastic response— because of the analogies mentioned in Section 6.6.3—if the appropriate substitutions of variables and experimentally obtained formulas are made (see Exercise 6.90).

Finally, we should note that because of the incompressibility constraint on the inelastic strains (6.286), it is important to employ the displacement/pressure formulations discussed in Section 6.4 when analyzing two-dimensional plane strain, axisymmetric, or fully three-dimensional response situations. This observation holds in elastoplasticity for small strain but particularly large strain conditions. Even in small strain analysis, the plastic strains are usually much larger than the elastic strains, and this is certainly the case in large strain conditions.

6.6.5 Exercises

6.61. Consider the eight-node brick element in Fig. 6.8. Plot the force-displacement responses assuming plane stress conditions in the y and z directions.

6.62. Consider the eight-node brick element in Fig. 6.8. Show explicitly that using (6.188) to transform $\tilde{E}(\equiv {}_t^t C_{ijrs})$ in the total Lagrangian formulation (i) for the figure, the force-displacement response is as calculated in (ii) in the figure. Also, show that using (6.187) to transform $\tilde{E}(\equiv {}_0^t C_{ijrs})$ in the updated Lagrangian formulation (ii) in the figure, the force-displacement response is as calculated in (i) in the figure.

6.63. A four-node element spins without deformation about its center at a constant angular velocity ω, as shown. Use that the Jaumann stress rate is zero to calculate the Cauchy stresses (corresponding to the axes x_1, x_2) at any time t.

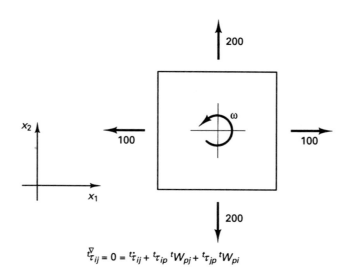

$${}^t_{\ }\overset{\triangledown}{\tau}_{ij} = 0 = {}^t_{\ }\dot{\tau}_{ij} + {}^t\tau_{ip}\,{}^tW_{pj} + {}^t\tau_{jp}\,{}^tW_{pi}$$

6.64. Consider the Mooney-Rivlin material description in (6.199). Show that this formula results in a pressure, the value of which depends on ${}_0^t I_1$ and ${}_0^t I_2$. Then show that in the description (6.203) only the last term with the bulk modulus results in a pressure.

6.65. Consider the three-term Ogden material description in (6.205). Show that this formula results in a pressure as a function of the stretches, whereas in expression (6.207) the terms under the summation sign do not affect the pressure.

6.66. Show that for the two-term Mooney-Rivlin model (6.199), in small strains, the Young's modulus is given by $6(C_1 + C_2)$ and the shear modulus is given by $2(C_1 + C_2)$. Also, show that these moduli are given in the Ogden model (6.205) by the values $\frac{3}{2}\sum_{n=1}^{3} \alpha_n \mu_n$ and $\frac{1}{2}\sum_{n=1}^{3} \alpha_n \mu_n$, respectively.

6.67. Consider the four-node element in plane strain conditions shown. Calculate the force-displacement response for case 1 and case 2. Assume the bulk modulus κ to be very large.

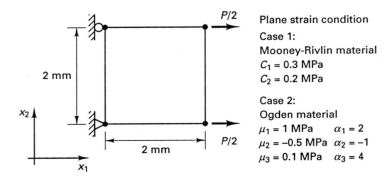

Plane strain condition

Case 1:
Mooney-Rivlin material
$C_1 = 0.3$ MPa
$C_2 = 0.2$ MPa

Case 2:
Ogden material
$\mu_1 = 1$ MPa $\alpha_1 = 2$
$\mu_2 = -0.5$ MPa $\alpha_2 = -1$
$\mu_3 = 0.1$ MPa $\alpha_3 = 4$

6.68. Consider the deformation of the four-node element shown. Calculate the force-displacement response. Assume the bulk modulus κ to be very large.

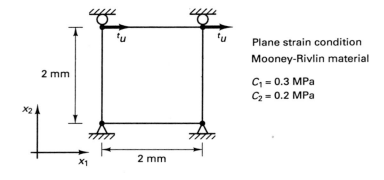

Plane strain condition

Mooney-Rivlin material

$C_1 = 0.3$ MPa
$C_2 = 0.2$ MPa

6.69. Assume that instead of (6.199) the following higher-order Mooney-Rivlin material model is used:

$$_0^t \tilde{W} = C_1(_0^t I_1 - 3) + C_2(_0^t I_2 - 3) + C_3(_0^t I_1 - 3)^2 + C_4(_0^t I_1 - 3)(_0^t I_2 - 3) + C_5(_0^t I_2 - 3)^2$$

with

$$C_1 = 75; \qquad C_2 = 25; \qquad C_3 = 10; \qquad C_4 = 10; \qquad C_5 = 10$$

Plot the force-displacement relationship for the one-dimensional bar problem in Fig. E6.25.

6.70. In *plane stress* solutions of incompressible response, we can use the pure displacement method of finite element analysis and adjust the element thickness to always fulfill the incompressibility constraint. Use this approach and derive for the Mooney-Rivlin law in (6.199) the stress-strain relationship $_0^t S_{ij} = _0^t C_{ijrs} \, _0^t \epsilon_{rs}$ and the tangent constitutive tensor $_0 C_{ijrs}$.

6.71. Use a computer program to analyze the thick cylinder shown. The constitutive behavior is given by the Mooney-Rivlin law (6.203) with $C_1 = 0.6$ MPa, $C_2 = 0.3$ MPa, and $\kappa = 2000$ MPa.

The internal pressure increases uniformly until a maximum displacement of 10 mm is reached.

Use a sufficiently fine mesh to obtain an accurate solution. (*Hint:* The 9/3 element is a much more effective element than the 4/1 element.)

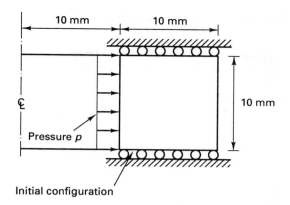

Initial configuration

6.72. Use a computer program to solve for the response of the elastic circular thick plate due to a concentrated load at its center. Increase the load P until the deflection under the load is 2 cm. (*Hint:* Here axisymmetric elements of the u/p formulation are effective.)

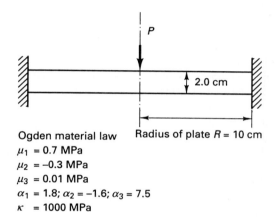

Ogden material law   Radius of plate $R = 10$ cm
$\mu_1 = 0.7$ MPa
$\mu_2 = -0.3$ MPa
$\mu_3 = 0.01$ MPa
$\alpha_1 = 1.8;\ \alpha_2 = -1.6;\ \alpha_3 = 7.5$
$\kappa = 1000$ MPa

6.73. Show that in the uniaxial stress condition the effective stress $^t\bar{\sigma}$ and effective plastic strain $^t\bar{e}^P$ reduce to the uniaxial (nonzero) stress and corresponding plastic strain. Then assume that in a uniaxial stress experiment the stress varies as shown by the points 1 to 6. Plot the stress–effective *plastic* strain relation for the stress path.

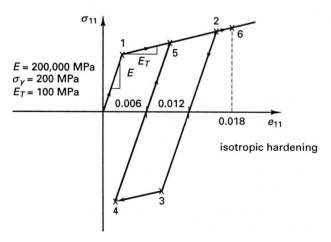

$E = 200,000$ MPa
$\sigma_y = 200$ MPa
$E_T = 100$ MPa

isotropic hardening

619

6.74. Prove that for a bilinear elastoplastic material described by the von Mises yield condition and flow rule, the effective stress function method gives the solution (6.236). State how the stress state at time $t + \Delta t$ can therefore be computed if the complete state at time t is known and the strains at time $t + \Delta t$ have been computed.

6.75. Show that the effective stress function in (6.233) can also be written in terms of the equivalent plastic strain as

$$\tilde{f}(e_*^P) = 3\mu(e_*^P - {}^te^P) + \sigma_y(e_*^P) - \bar{\sigma}_*$$

where the solution $\tilde{f}(e_*^P) = 0$ corresponds to $e_* = {}^{t+\Delta t}e^P$. Here $\sigma_y(.)$ denotes the yield stress function and $\bar{\sigma}_*$ is the effective stress corresponding to the elastic stress prediction [see (6.239)].

6.76. Consider isothermal von Mises plasticity with kinematic hardening in three-dimensional stress conditions in which case the yield condition is

$${}^{t+\Delta t}f_y^{vM} = \tfrac{1}{2}\,{}^{t+\Delta t}\tilde{\mathbf{S}} \cdot {}^{t+\Delta t}\tilde{\mathbf{S}} - \tfrac{1}{3}(\sigma_{yv})^2 = 0$$

where ${}^{t+\Delta t}\tilde{\mathbf{S}}$ is the shifted deviatoric stress due to the back stress ${}^{t+\Delta t}\boldsymbol{\alpha}$

$${}^{t+\Delta t}\tilde{\mathbf{S}} = {}^{t+\Delta t}\mathbf{S} - {}^{t+\Delta t}\boldsymbol{\alpha}$$

and σ_{yv} is the constant (virgin) yield stress. Assume small strain conditions and derive the effective-stress-function algorithm for this case.

6.77. Assume that the bilinear elastoplastic von Mises material in Fig. 6.10 with isotropic hardening is considered. Derive the tangent stress-strain matrix consistent with the effective-stress-function algorithm as indicated in (6.245) to (6.252).

6.78. Consider the creep law (6.263) with $a_0 = 6.4 \times 10^{-18}$, $a_1 = 4.4$, $a_2 = 2.0$, and $a_3 = 0.0$. The stress states are $\sigma = 100$ MPa for $0 \leq t < 4$ hr and $\sigma = 200$ MPa for $t \geq 4$ hr. For $0 \leq t \leq 10$ hr draw the creep strain response as calculated by the time hardening and the strain hardening methods.

6.79. Derive the relation (6.268).

6.80. Derive the effective stress function given in (6.273) and show that near the solution this function has the curvature shown in Fig. 6.14.

6.81. A one-dimensional viscoplastic response is defined by $\dot{\epsilon}^{VP} = \hat{\gamma}[\sigma - (\sigma_{yv} + E_{VP}\epsilon^{VP})]$. The elastic strain response is given as usual by $e^E = \sigma/E$.

Calculate analytically the total strain response when the applied stress $\sigma_{\text{applied}} > \sigma_{yv}$. Consider the cases of $E_{VP} > 0$ and $E_{VP} = 0$; $\hat{\gamma} = $ constant.

6.82. The constitutive behavior of a four-node plane stress element is given by the viscoplastic material model in (6.275) with the constants $\beta = 10^{-4}$ (1/sec), $N = 1$. Also, $E = 20,000$ MPa, $\nu = 0.3$, and the material effective stress-viscoplastic strain curve is given in the figure.

Assume a one-dimensional stress situation, that the stress at time 0 is zero, and that a constant load is applied as shown. Calculate the viscoplastic strain and displacement response of the element.

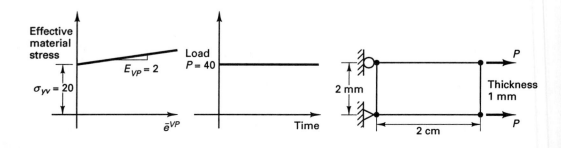

6.83. Consider the general large strain elastoplastic formulation in Section 6.6.4. Derive from these general equations all equations for the one-dimensional response of the bar in Fig. 6.16.

6.84. Show explicitly for each equation in Table 6.10 that the large strain elastoplasticity formulation reduces to the formulation for materially-nonlinear-only analysis if the displacements and strains are small.

6.85. Consider the 8-node brick element in Fig. 6.8. Assume elastic conditions with $E = 10^7$ N/cm² and $\nu = 0.30$ and plot the force-displacement response using the updated Lagrangian Hencky formulation of Section 6.6.4. Also plot this response for plane stress conditions in the y and z directions.

6.86. Consider an elastic material and show that (6.293) holds with the stress and strain quantities defined in Section 6.6.4. (Refer to the general continuum mechanics relations given in Section 6.2.2.)

6.87. Show that using the definitions in Section 6.6.4, we have $J\boldsymbol{\tau} \cdot \mathbf{D} = \overline{\boldsymbol{\tau}} \cdot \dot{\mathbf{E}}^E + \overline{\boldsymbol{\tau}} \cdot \overline{\mathbf{D}}^P$, where $\mathbf{D} = \frac{1}{2}(\mathbf{L} + \mathbf{L}^T)$ [see (6.41)].

6.88. Use the large strain elastoplasticity options in a computer program to calculate for a four-node plane stress element the stress response corresponding to the following strain path: In (a) the element is pulled out, in (b) the element is sheared over, in (c) the sheared element is pushed down, in (d) the element is brought to its original configuration. Explain whether your results make physical sense.

Assume $\Delta = \frac{1}{100}$, $E = 200,000$, $\nu = 0.3$, $\sigma_{yv} = 4000$.

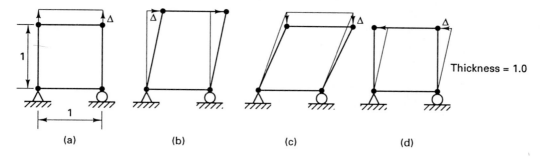

    (a)   (b)   (c)   (d)

6.89. Use a computer program to calculate the elastoplastic large strain response of the plane strain cantilever shown.

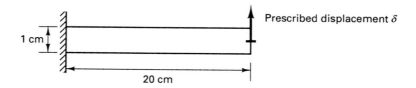

Let $E = 200,000$ MPa, $\nu = 0.3$, $E_T = 200$ MPa, $\sigma_y = 200$ MPa and increase δ to the value $\frac{1}{2}L$. Plot the force-displacement relationship and the stresses at $\delta = L/1000$, $\delta = L/10$, $\delta = L/2$. Refine the finite element model to obtain a reasonably accurate stress prediction. (*Hint:* The 9/3 element performs well in large strain analysis.)

6.90. Assume that the large strain creep response of a material can be described by the theory in Section 6.6.4 with $\mathbf{X}^P$ replaced by the inelastic deformation gradient $\mathbf{X}^{IN}$ given by the creep deformations. Modify the entries in Table 6.10 to correspond to the creep solution.

Then use a computer program to calculate the large strain creep response of the thick cylinder shown. Obtain an accurate stress prediction for various values of internal pressure p.

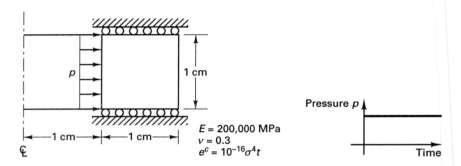

6.7 CONTACT CONDITIONS

A particularly difficult nonlinear behavior to analyze is contact between two or more bodies. Contact problems range from frictionless contact in small displacements to contact with friction in general large strain inelastic conditions. Although the formulation of the contact conditions is the same in all these cases, the solution of the nonlinear problems can in some analyses be much more difficult than in other cases. The nonlinearity of the analysis problem is now decided not only by the geometric and material nonlinearities considered so far but also by the contact conditions.

The objective in this section is to briefly state the contact conditions in the context of a finite element analysis and present a general approach for solution.

6.7.1 Continuum Mechanics Equations

Let us consider N bodies that are in contact at time t. Let ^tS_c be the complete area of contact for each body L, $L = 1, \ldots, N$; then the principle of virtual work for the N bodies at time t gives

$$\sum_{L=1}^{N} \left\{ \int_{^tV} {}^t\tau_{ij}\,\delta_t e_{ij}\,d'V \right\} = \sum_{L=1}^{N} \left\{ \int_{^tV} \delta u_i\,{}^tf_i^B\,d'V + \int_{^tS_f} \delta u_i^S\,{}^tf_i^S\,d'S \right\} + \sum_{L=1}^{N} \int_{^tS_c} \delta u_i^c\,{}^tf_i^c\,d'S \qquad (6.301)$$

where the part given in the braces corresponds to the usual terms (see Section 6.2.3) and the last summation sign gives the contribution of the contact forces. We note that the contact force effect is included as a contribution in the externally applied tractions. The components of the contact tractions are denoted as $^tf_i^c$ and act over the areas ^tS_c, and the components of the known externally applied tractions are denoted as $^tf_i^S$ and act over the areas ^tS_f. We might assume that the areas ^tS_f are not part of the areas ^tS_c, although such assumption is not necessary.

Figure 6.17 illustrates schematically the case of two bodies, which we now consider in more detail. The concepts given below can be directly generalized to multiple-body contact.

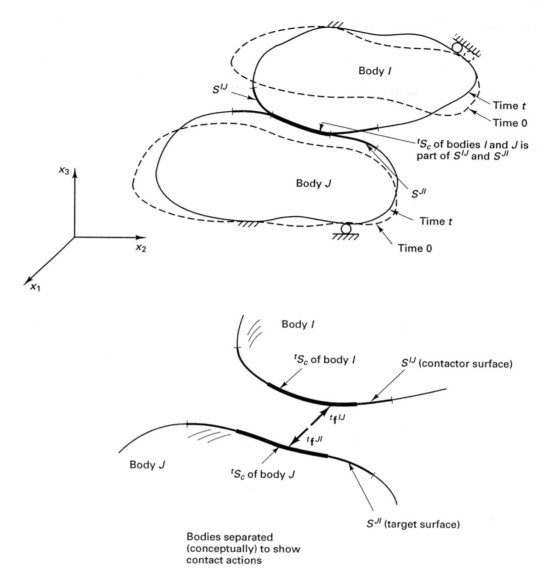

Figure 6.17 Bodies in contact at time t

In Fig. 6.17 we denote the two bodies as body I and body J. Note that each body is supported such that without contact no rigid body motion is possible. Let ${}^t\mathbf{f}^{IJ}$ be the vector of contact surface tractions on body I due to contact with body J, then ${}^t\mathbf{f}^{IJ} = -{}^t\mathbf{f}^{JI}$. Hence, the virtual work due to the contact tractions in (6.301) can be written as

$$\int_{S^{IJ}} \delta u_i^I \, {}^t f_i^{IJ} \, dS^{IJ} + \int_{S^{JI}} \delta u_i^J \, {}^t f_i^{JI} \, dS^{JI} = \int_{S^{IJ}} \delta u_i^{IJ} \, {}^t f_i^{IJ} \, dS^{IJ} \tag{6.302}$$

where δu_i^I and δu_i^J are the components of the virtual displacements on the contact surfaces of bodies I and J, respectively, and

$$\delta u_i^{IJ} = \delta u_i^I - \delta u_i^J \tag{6.303}$$

623

We call the pair of surfaces S^{IJ} and S^{JI} a "contact surface pair" and note that these surfaces are not necessarily of equal size. However, the actual area of contact at time t for body I is ^tS_c of body I, and for body J is ^tS_c of body J, and in each case this area is part of S^{IJ} and S^{JI} (see Fig. 6.17). It is convenient to call S^{IJ} the "contactor surface" and S^{JI} the "target surface." Hence, the right-hand side of (6.302) can be interpreted as the virtual work that the contact tractions produce over the virtual relative displacements on the contact surface pair.

In the following we analyze the right-hand side of (6.302).

Let $\mathbf{n}$ be the unit outward normal to S^{JI} and let $\mathbf{s}$ be a vector such that $\mathbf{n}$, $\mathbf{s}$ form a right-hand basis (see Fig. 6.18). We can decompose the contact tractions $^t\mathbf{f}^{IJ}$ acting on S^{IJ} into normal and tangential components corresponding to $\mathbf{n}$ and $\mathbf{s}$ on S^{JI},

$$^t\mathbf{f}^{IJ} = \lambda\mathbf{n} + t\mathbf{s} \tag{6.304}$$

where λ and t are the normal and tangential traction components (for brevity of notation we do not use a superscript). Hence,

$$\lambda = (^t\mathbf{f}^{IJ})^T\mathbf{n}; \qquad t = (^t\mathbf{f}^{IJ})^T\mathbf{s} \tag{6.305}$$

To define the actual values of $\mathbf{n}$, $\mathbf{s}$ that we use in our contact calculations, consider a generic point $\mathbf{x}$ on S^{IJ} and let $\mathbf{y}^*(\mathbf{x}, t)$ be the point on S^{JI} satisfying

$$\| \mathbf{x} - \mathbf{y}^*(\mathbf{x}, t)\|_2 = \min_{\mathbf{y}\in S^{JI}} \{\| \mathbf{x} - \mathbf{y}\|_2\} \tag{6.306}$$

The (signed) distance from $\mathbf{x}$ to S^{JI} is then given by

$$g(\mathbf{x}, t) = (\mathbf{x} - \mathbf{y}^*)^T\mathbf{n}^* \tag{6.307}$$

where $\mathbf{n}^*$ is the unit "normal vector" that we use at $\mathbf{y}^*(\mathbf{x}, t)$ (see Fig. 6.18) and $\mathbf{n}^*$, $\mathbf{s}^*$ are used in (6.304) corresponding to the point $\mathbf{x}$. The function g is the gap function for the contact surface pair.

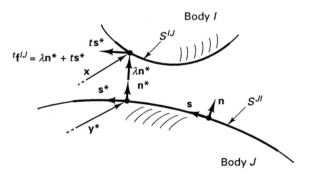

Figure 6.18   Definitions used in contact analysis

With these definitions, the conditions for normal contact can now be written as

$$g \geq 0; \qquad \lambda \geq 0; \qquad g\lambda = 0 \tag{6.308}$$

where the last equation expresses the fact that if $g > 0$, then we must have $\lambda = 0$, and vice versa.

To include frictional conditions, let us assume that Coulomb's law of friction holds pointwise on the contact surface and that μ is the coefficient of friction. This assumption means of course that frictional effects are included in a very simplified manner (for more details see, for example, E. Rabinowicz [A] and J. T. Oden and J. A. C. Martins [A]).

Let us define the nondimensional variable τ given by

$$\tau = \frac{t}{\mu\lambda} \tag{6.309}$$

where $\mu\lambda$ is the "frictional resistance," and the magnitude of the relative tangential velocity

$$\dot{u}(\mathbf{x}, t) = (\dot{\mathbf{u}}{}^{J}|_{\mathbf{y}^*(\mathbf{x}, t)} - \dot{\mathbf{u}}{}^{I}|_{(\mathbf{x}, t)}) \cdot \mathbf{s}^* \tag{6.310}$$

corresponding to the unit tangential vector $\mathbf{s}$ at $\mathbf{y}^*(\mathbf{x}, t)$. Hence, $\dot{u}(\mathbf{x}, t)\mathbf{s}^*$ is the tangential velocity at time t of the material point at $\mathbf{y}^*$ relative to the material point at $\mathbf{x}$. With these definitions Coulomb's law of friction states

and

while

$$\left. \begin{array}{l} |\tau| \le 1 \\[4pt] |\tau| < 1 \text{ implies } \dot{u} = 0 \\[4pt] |\tau| = 1 \text{ implies sign } (\dot{u}) = \text{sign } (\tau) \end{array} \right\} \tag{6.311}$$

Figure 6.19 illustrates these interface conditions.

The solution of the contact problem in Fig. 6.17 therefore entails the solution of the virtual work equation (6.301) (specialized for bodies I and J) subject to the conditions (6.308) and (6.311).

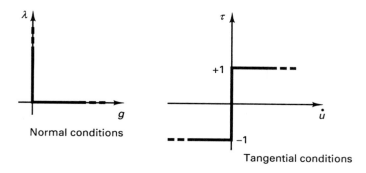

Figure 6.19   Interface conditions in contact analysis

In the preceding equations, we considered in essence static (or pseudo-static) contact conditions. In dynamic analysis, the distributed body force includes the inertia force effects, and the kinematic interface conditions must be satisfied at all instances of time, requiring displacement, velocity, and acceleration compatibility between the contacting bodies. The time integration scheme, e.g., the trapezoidal rule, see Section 9.5.2, in general does not automatically satisfy that the time derivatives of the displacements are also compatible in the contact area and this compatibility must be separately imposed on the step-by-step solution (see, for example, T. J. R. Hughes, R. L. Taylor, J. L. Sackman, A. Curnier, and W. Kanoknukulchai [A]).

Various algorithmic procedures have been proposed to solve contact problems in finite element analysis. Most of these procedures are based on penalty and Lagrange multiplier techniques (see Section 3.4) for enforcing the contact constraints (see, for example, the works of T. J. R. Hughes, R. L. Taylor, J. L. Sackman, A. Curnier, and W. Kanoknukulchai

[A], J. T. Oden and E. B. Pires [A], J. C. Simo, P. Wriggers, and R. L. Taylor [A], K. J. Bathe and A. B. Chaudhary [B] and the references therein).

To exemplify the solution of contact problems, let us consider in the next section how the contact constraints are imposed in one solution approach (see also A. L. Eterovic and K. J. Bathe [C]).

6.7.2 A Solution Approach for Contact Problems: The Constraint Function Method

Let w be a function of g and λ such that the solutions of $w(g, \lambda) = 0$ satisfy the conditions (6.308), and similarly, let v be a function of τ and $\dot{u}$ such that the solutions of $v(\dot{u}, \tau) = 0$ satisfy the conditions (6.311). Then the contact conditions are given by

$$w(g, \lambda) = 0 \tag{6.312}$$

and

$$v(\dot{u}, \tau) = 0 \tag{6.313}$$

These conditions can now be imposed on the principle of virtual work equation using either a penalty approach or a Lagrange multiplier method (see Section 3.4). The variables λ and τ can be considered Lagrange multipliers, and so we let $\delta\lambda$ and $\delta\tau$ be variations in these quantities (see Section 4.4.2).

Multiplying (6.312) by $\delta\lambda$ and (6.313) by $\delta\tau$ and integrating over S^{IJ}, we obtain the constraint equation

$$\int_{S^{IJ}} [\delta\lambda \, w(g, \lambda) + \delta\tau \, v(\dot{u}, \tau)] \, dS^{IJ} = 0 \tag{6.314}$$

In summary, the governing equations to be solved for the two-body contact problem in Fig. 6.17 are the usual principle of virtual work equation, with the effect of the contact tractions included through externally applied (but unknown) forces, plus the constraint equation (6.314). Of course, the principle of virtual work (6.301) is in the two-body contact problem specialized to bodies I and J only, and the contact force term is given by (6.302) and (6.303).

The finite element solution of the governing continuum mechanics equations is obtained by using the discretization procedures for the principle of virtual work, and in addition now discretizing the contact conditions also.

To exemplify the formulation of the governing finite element equations, let us consider the two-dimensional case of contactor and target bodies shown schematically in Fig. 6.20. We notice that node k_1 and node k_2 define a straight boundary but are not necessarily the corner nodes of an element. Instead they are any adjacent nodes on the target body.

The discretization of the continuum mechanics equations (6.301) and (6.314) corresponding to the conditions at time $t + \Delta t$ gives

$${}^{t+\Delta t}\mathbf{F}({}^{t+\Delta t}\mathbf{U}) = {}^{t+\Delta t}\mathbf{R} - {}^{t+\Delta t}\mathbf{R}_c({}^{t+\Delta t}\mathbf{U}, {}^{t+\Delta t}\boldsymbol{\tau}) \tag{6.315}$$

and

$${}^{t+\Delta t}\mathbf{F}_c({}^{t+\Delta t}\mathbf{U}, {}^{t+\Delta t}\boldsymbol{\tau}) = \mathbf{0} \tag{6.316}$$

where with m contactor nodes,

$${}^{t+\Delta t}\boldsymbol{\tau}^T = [\lambda_1, \tau_1, \ldots, \lambda_k, \tau_k, \ldots, \lambda_m, \tau_m] \tag{6.317}$$

Note that the relative velocity and gap functions are of course expressed in terms of the nodal point displacements.

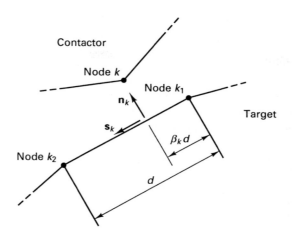

Figure 6.20   Two-dimensional case of contact

The vector $^{t+\Delta t}\mathbf{R}_c$ is obtained by assembling for all m contactor nodes, $k = 1, \ldots, m$, the nodal point force vectors due to contact. For the contactor node k and the corresponding target nodes, the nodal force vector is

$$^{t+\Delta t}\mathbf{R}_k^c = \begin{bmatrix} -\lambda_k(\mathbf{n}_k + \mu\tau_k\mathbf{s}_k) \\ (1-\beta_k)\lambda_k(\mathbf{n}_k + \mu\tau_k\mathbf{s}_k) \\ \beta_k\lambda_k(\mathbf{n}_k + \mu\tau_k\mathbf{s}_k)] \end{bmatrix} \qquad (6.318)$$

where β_k, $\mathbf{n}_k$, $\mathbf{s}_k$ are defined in Fig. 6.20.
The vector $^{t+\Delta t}\mathbf{F}_c$ can be written as

$$^{t+\Delta t}\mathbf{F}_c^T = [^{t+\Delta t}\mathbf{F}_1^{c^T}, \ldots, {}^{t+\Delta t}\mathbf{F}_m^{c^T}] \qquad (6.319)$$

where

$$^{t+\Delta t}\mathbf{F}_k^c = \begin{bmatrix} w(g_k, \lambda_k) \\ v(\dot{u}_k, \tau_k) \end{bmatrix} \qquad (6.320)$$

The incremental equations for solution of (6.315) and (6.316) are obtained by linearization about the last calculated state. Following the procedures discussed in Section 6.3.1, the resulting equations corresponding to the linearization about the state at time t are

$$\begin{bmatrix} (^t\mathbf{K} + {}^t\mathbf{K}_{uu}^c) & {}^t\mathbf{K}_{u\tau}^c \\ {}^t\mathbf{K}_{\tau u}^c & {}^t\mathbf{K}_{\tau\tau}^c \end{bmatrix} \begin{bmatrix} \Delta\mathbf{U} \\ \Delta\boldsymbol{\tau} \end{bmatrix} = \begin{bmatrix} {}^{t+\Delta t}\mathbf{R} - {}^t\mathbf{F} - {}^t\mathbf{R}_c \\ -{}^t\mathbf{F}_c \end{bmatrix} \qquad (6.321)$$

where $\Delta\mathbf{U}$ and $\Delta\boldsymbol{\tau}$ are the increments in the solution variables $^t\mathbf{U}$ and $^t\boldsymbol{\tau}$, and $^t\mathbf{K}_{uu}^c$, $^t\mathbf{K}_{u\tau}^c$, $^t\mathbf{K}_{\tau u}^c$, and $^t\mathbf{K}_{\tau\tau}^c$ are contact stiffness matrices,

$$\left. \begin{aligned} {}^t\mathbf{K}_{uu}^c = \frac{\partial^t\mathbf{R}_c}{\partial^t\mathbf{U}}; \qquad {}^t\mathbf{K}_{u\tau}^c = \frac{\partial^t\mathbf{R}_c}{\partial^t\boldsymbol{\tau}} \\ {}^t\mathbf{K}_{\tau u}^c = \frac{\partial^t\mathbf{F}_c}{\partial^t\mathbf{U}}; \qquad {}^t\mathbf{K}_{\tau\tau}^c = \frac{\partial^t\mathbf{F}_c}{\partial^t\boldsymbol{\tau}} \end{aligned} \right\} \qquad (6.322)$$

The detailed expressions of these matrices depend on the actual constraint functions used. In practice, we use functions that very closely approximate the constraints shown in

Fig. 6.19 but that are differentiable as required by the expressions in (6.322) (see Exercise 6.93).

The continuum mechanics formulation in Section 6.7.1 has been given for very general conditions of deformations and constitutive relations (but Coulomb's law of friction was assumed). Of course, the formulation is also applicable to frictionless contact. In this case, only the constraint (6.308) needs to be imposed, and the finite element equations have only the normal forces at the contactor nodes as unknowns. Note that the coefficient matrix in (6.321) including frictional conditions is in general nonsymmetric, but a symmetric matrix can be obtained when friction is neglected.

Of particular concern in the solution of contact problems is the capacity of the algorithm to converge when complex geometries, deformations, and contact conditions are analyzed. It should be noted here that although the incremental equations (6.321) correspond to a full linearization, the use of too large incremental steps may lead to convergence difficulties in the equilibrium iterations because the predicted intermediate state is too far from the solution. Also, full quadratic convergence when near the solution may not be observed when the change in the tangent coefficient matrix is not sufficiently smooth, for example, as a result of geometric kinks on the target surface.

6.7.3 Exercises

6.91. Show that with the sign conventions used in (6.303) to (6.310) the statements of frictional contact in (6.308) and (6.311) are correct.

6.92. Consider frictionless contact between two bodies. Develop the general governing finite element equations with the imposition of the constraint function (6.312) using a penalty method (see Section 3.4.1).

6.93. The following constraint function $w(g, \lambda)$ for the constraint function algorithm is proposed

$$w(g, \lambda) = \frac{g + \lambda}{2} - \sqrt{\left(\frac{g - \lambda}{2}\right)^2 + \epsilon}$$

where ϵ is very small but larger than zero. Plot this function for various values of ϵ and show that this $w(g, \lambda)$ is indeed a suitable function.

6.94. Design a function $v(\dot{u}, \tau)$, as used in (6.313), to impose the frictional constraint given in (6.311).

6.8 SOME PRACTICAL CONSIDERATIONS

The establishment of an appropriate mathematical model for the analysis of an engineering problem is to a large degree based on sufficient understanding of the problem under consideration and a reasonable knowledge of the finite element procedures available for solution (see Section 1.2). This observation is particularly applicable in nonlinear analysis because the appropriate nonlinear kinematic formulations, material models, and solution strategies need to be selected.

The objective in this section is to discuss briefly some important practical aspects pertaining to the selection of appropriate models and solution methods for nonlinear analysis.

6.8.1 The General Approach to Nonlinear Analysis

In an actual engineering analysis, it is good practice that a nonlinear analysis of a problem is always preceded by a linear analysis, so that the nonlinear analysis is considered an extension of the complete analysis process beyond the assumptions of linear analysis. Based on the linear response solution, the analyst is able to predict which nonlinearities will be significant and how to account for these nonlinearities most appropriately. Namely, the linear analysis results indicate the regions where geometric nonlinearities may be significant and where the material exceeds its elastic limit.

Unfortunately, when performing a nonlinear analysis, there is frequently a tendency to select immediately a large number of elements and the most general nonlinear formulations available for modeling the problem. The engineering time used to prepare the model is large, the computer time that is needed for the analysis of the model is also very significant, and usually a voluminous amount of information is generated that cannot be fully absorbed and interpreted. If there are significant modeling or program input errors, it may also happen that the analyst "gives up in despair" during the course of the analysis because a relatively large amount of money has already been spent on the analysis, no significant results are as yet available, and the analyst is unable to realistically estimate how much further expense there would be until significant results could be produced.

The important point is that such an approach to nonlinear analysis cannot be recommended. Instead, a linear model should first be established that contains important characteristics of the analysis problem. After some linear analyses have been performed that provide insight into the problem under consideration, the allowance for some nonlinearities—and not necessarily immediately for all nonlinearities that can be anticipated—should be made by choosing appropriate nonlinear formulations and material models. Here it should be noted that by employing the formulations discussed in Chapter 5 and this chapter, finite elements formulated using the linear analysis assumptions, the materially-nonlinear-only formulation, and the TL and UL formulations can all be used together in one finite element idealization. If this finite element mesh is a compatible mesh in linear analysis, the elements will also remain displacement-compatible in nonlinear analysis. The subdivision of the complete finite element idealization into elements governed by different nonlinear formulations merely means that in the analysis different nonlinearities are being accounted for in different parts of the structure. An effective procedure for introducing different kinds of nonlinearities into the analysis is the use of linear and nonlinear element groups.

> The complete process of analysis can be likened to a series of laboratory experiments in which different assumptions are made in each experiment—in the finite element analysis these experiments are performed on the computer with a finite element program.

The advantages of starting with a linear analysis after which judiciously selected nonlinear analyses are performed are that, first, the effect of each nonlinearity introduced can more easily be explained, second, confidence in the analysis results can be established and, third, useful information is accumulated throughout the period of analysis.

In addition to the general recommendations for an appropriate approach to nonlinear analysis given above, some practical aspects can be important and are briefly discussed in the following sections.

6.8.2 Collapse and Buckling Analyses

The objective of a nonlinear analysis is in many cases to estimate the maximum load that a structure can support prior to structural instability or collapse. In the analysis the load distribution on the structure is known, but the load magnitude that the structure can sustain is unknown.

Figure 6.21 illustrates schematically the response of some structures that collapse or buckle. In each case, only the kinematic nonlinearities are considered, and the response would be different if material nonlinearities were also present.

A thin plate does not have a collapse point; indeed because of membrane action, the plate increases its stiffness as the displacements grow. An arch, however, for specific geometric parameters, will collapse if the load increases. As shown in Fig. 6.21(a), the response beyond the collapse point A is referred to as the postbuckling behavior. In actuality, the response beyond point A, when induced by a load increase, is a dynamic response. However, the prediction of the (idealized) static postbuckling response can be important because, if the points A and A' are very close to each other, then the collapse load corresponding to point A may not be as serious a restriction in the design as when the points A and A' are far apart.

The response of the column depicted in Fig. 6.21(b) depends on the value of β. This parameter represents the imperfection in the geometry and material properties of the column or the load application (from being exactly vertical). We note that the bifurcation buckling response of a perfectly straight column with only an end compressive load is approached as β becomes very small.

In all the analyses cases, however, the response can be calculated by an incremental analysis, provided the load can also decrease as the structural response dictates in the postbuckling regime. Hence, we should consider the following generic problem statement.

Let $^{\Delta t}\mathbf{R}$ be the vector which defines the *load distribution*. This vector corresponds to the first load step. Also, let $^{\tau}\beta$ be the *load multiplier* for any time τ to the load vector $^{\Delta t}\mathbf{R}$ such that the load at time τ is $^{\tau}\beta \, ^{\Delta t}\mathbf{R}$. In practice, we are frequently interested in calculating the response of the structure as τ increases. As illustrated in Fig. 6.21(a), this task requires that the load multiplier $^{\tau}\beta$ increase and decrease with τ as the structural response is calculated.

We present a specific algorithm for the solution of the load multiplier $^{\tau}\beta$ and the structural response in Section 8.4.3. With this solution method, the response of structures such as those shown in Fig. 6.21 is evaluated.

However, the complete incremental nonlinear solution of a structure up to collapse and beyond can be expensive, and a linearized buckling analysis for the lowest buckling loads may be of value (see Section 3.2.3). The lowest calculated buckling load may be a reasonably good estimate of the actual collapse load (but only when the prebuckling displacements are small), and it may be important to use the buckling modes to define geometric imperfections of the structure. That is, if imperfections that correspond to the lowest buckling modes are imposed on the "perfect" geometry of the structural model, the load-carrying capacity may be significantly reduced and be much more representative of

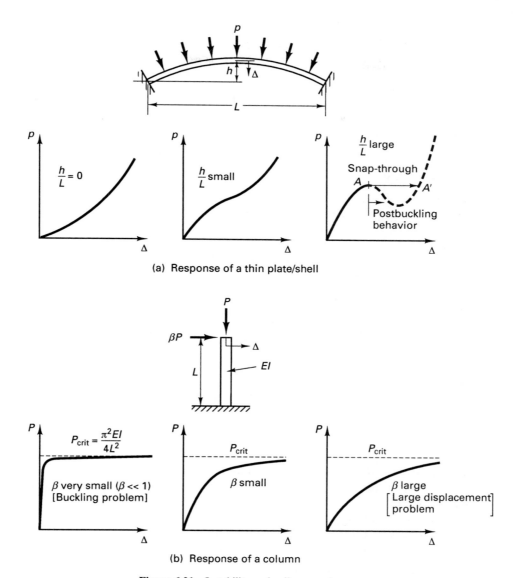

Figure 6.21   Instability and collapse analyses

the load-carrying capacity of the actual physical structure (see the discussion of the analysis in Fig. 6.23).

Let us consider the calculation of the linearized buckling load. The stiffness matrices at times $t - \Delta t$ and t are $^{t-\Delta t}\mathbf{K}$ and $^{t}\mathbf{K}$, and the corresponding vectors of externally applied loads are $^{t-\Delta t}\mathbf{R}$ and $^{t}\mathbf{R}$. In the linearized buckling analysis, we assume that at any time τ,

$$\boxed{{}^{\tau}\mathbf{K} = {}^{t-\Delta t}\mathbf{K} + \lambda({}^{t}\mathbf{K} - {}^{t-\Delta t}\mathbf{K})} \qquad (6.323)$$

and

$$\boxed{ {}^{\tau}\mathbf{R} = {}^{t-\Delta t}\mathbf{R} + \lambda({}^{t}\mathbf{R} - {}^{t-\Delta t}\mathbf{R}) } \qquad (6.324)$$

where λ is a scaling factor, and we are interested in those values of λ that are greater than 1.

At collapse or buckling the tangent stiffness matrix is singular, and hence, the condition for calculating λ is

$$\det {}^{\tau}\mathbf{K} = 0 \qquad (6.325)$$

or, equivalently (see Section 10.2),

$${}^{\tau}\mathbf{K}\boldsymbol{\phi} = \mathbf{0} \qquad (6.326)$$

where $\boldsymbol{\phi}$ is a nonzero vector. Substituting from (6.323) into (6.326), we obtain the eigenproblem

$${}^{t-\Delta t}\mathbf{K}\boldsymbol{\phi} = \lambda({}^{t-\Delta t}\mathbf{K} - {}^{t}\mathbf{K})\boldsymbol{\phi} \qquad (6.327)$$

The eigenvalues λ_i, $i = 1, \ldots, n$ give the buckling loads [by using (6.324)], and the eigenvectors $\boldsymbol{\phi}_i$ represent the corresponding buckling modes. We assume that the matrices ${}^{t}\mathbf{K}$ and ${}^{t-\Delta t}\mathbf{K}$ are both positive definite but note that in general ${}^{t-\Delta t}\mathbf{K} - {}^{t}\mathbf{K}$ is indefinite; hence, the eigenproblem will have both positive and negative solutions (i.e., some eigenvalues will be negative). We are interested in only the smallest positive eigenvalues and therefore rewrite (6.327) as

$$\boxed{ {}^{t}\mathbf{K}\boldsymbol{\phi} = \gamma\,{}^{t-\Delta t}\mathbf{K}\boldsymbol{\phi} } \qquad (6.328)$$

where

$$\gamma = \frac{\lambda - 1}{\lambda} \qquad (6.329)$$

The eigenvalues γ_i in (6.328) are all positive, and usually only the smallest values γ_1, $\gamma_2, \ldots$, are of interest. Namely, γ_1 corresponds to the smallest positive value of λ in the problem (6.327).

An important consideration is that the standard eigensolution techniques presented in Chapter 11 can be employed directly to solve for the smallest eigenvalues and corresponding vectors in (6.328) because both matrices in (6.328) are assumed to be positive definite. However, (6.329) shows that the eigenvalues γ_i may be very closely spaced so that an effective shifting strategy may be important (see Sections 10.2.3 and 11.2.3).

Having evaluated γ_1, we obtain λ_1 from (6.329), and then the buckling (or collapse) load is given by (6.324),

$$\boxed{ \mathbf{R}_{\text{buckling}} = {}^{t-\Delta t}\mathbf{R} + \lambda_1({}^{t}\mathbf{R} - {}^{t-\Delta t}\mathbf{R}) } \qquad (6.330)$$

Similarly, we can evaluate the linearized buckling loads corresponding to γ_i, $i > 1$.

In practice, most frequently, the times $t - \Delta t$ and t correspond to the times 0 (initial configuration with ${}^{0}\mathbf{R} = \mathbf{0}$) and Δt (the first load step with ${}^{\Delta t}\mathbf{R}$). However, the above equations are applicable to any load step prior to collapse. Also, the relations (6.323) and

(6.324) show that this analysis can be performed equally well when geometric or material nonlinearities are considered.

The assumptions used in the linearized buckling analysis are displayed in (6.323) and (6.324); namely, we assume that the elements in the stiffness matrix vary linearly from time $t - \Delta t$ onward, the slope of the change being given by the difference from time $t - \Delta t$ to time t. The linearized buckling analysis therefore gives a reasonable estimate of the collapse load only if the precollapse displacements are relatively small (and any changes in the material properties are not significantly violating the assumption of linearity). Figure 6.22 gives the results of two analyses that illustrate this observation. In the analysis of the column, the prebuckling displacements are negligible and excellent results are obtained. On

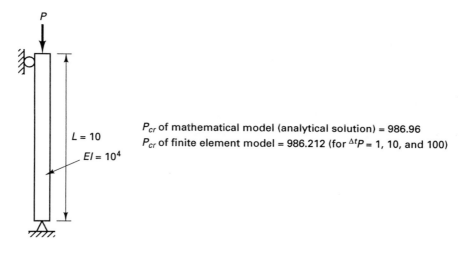

P_{cr} of mathematical model (analytical solution) = 986.96
P_{cr} of finite element model = 986.212 (for $^{\Delta t}P$ = 1, 10, and 100)

$L = 10$
$EI = 10^4$

(a) Linearized buckling analysis of column; two Hermitian beam elements discussed in K. J. Bathe and S. Bolourchi [A] are used to model the column

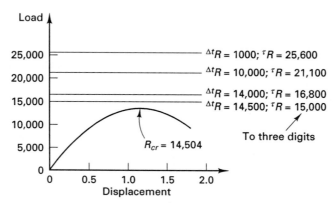

$^{\Delta t}R = 1000$; $^{r}R = 25{,}600$

$^{\Delta t}R = 10{,}000$; $^{r}R = 21{,}100$

$^{\Delta t}R = 14{,}000$; $^{r}R = 16{,}800$
$^{\Delta t}R = 14{,}500$; $^{r}R = 15{,}000$

To three digits

$R_{cr} = 14{,}504$

(b) Linearized buckling analysis of arch in Fig. E6.3; $L = 10$; $EA = 2.1 \times 10^6$

Figure 6.22 Linearized buckling analyses of two structures; in each case time t-Δt corresponds to time 0 (the unstressed state).

the other hand, in the analysis of the arch, the precollapse displacements are large and the linearized buckling analysis very much overestimates the collapse load unless the state of loading corresponding to Δt is already close to that load. In general, a linearized buckling analysis will give good results if the structure displays a column type of buckling behavior.

However, as mentioned already, even if the linearized buckling load cannot be used as an estimate of the actual collapse load of the structure, it may be important to impose the buckling mode as an imperfection on the structural model. This imperfection may well be present in the actual physical structure and, if the effect is significant, should be included in the analysis.

To illustrate these thoughts, consider the analysis of the arch in Fig. 6.23. The complete structure is modeled using ten two-node isoparametric beam elements. In the analysis,

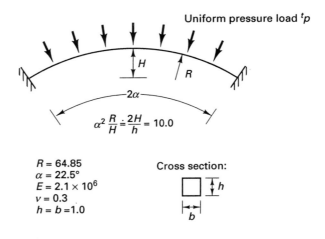

(a) Arch considered; ten 2-node isoparametric beam
     elements are used to model the complete structure

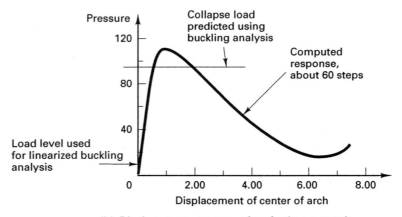

(b) Displacement response of perfectly symmetric
     structure

Figure 6.23   Collapse analysis of arch

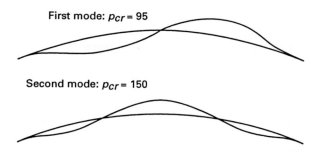

First mode: p_{cr} = 95

Second mode: p_{cr} = 150

(c) Collapse loads and buckling modes using a linearized buckling analysis ($^{\Delta t}p$ = 10)

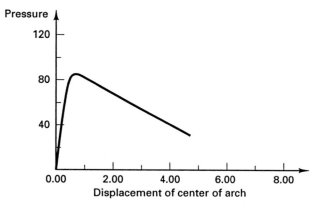

(d) Response of arch with antisymmetric imperfection

Figure 6.23   (*continued*)

symmetry conditions were not used so as to allow antisymmetric behavior of the model. The objective was to predict the collapse and postcollapse response.

Figure 6.23(b) shows the response calculated using a load-displacement-constraint method as described in Section 8.4.3. Also, a linearized buckling analysis was performed using as state $t - \Delta t$ the unstressed configuration and as state Δt the configuration corresponding to a pressure of 10. The two smallest critical pressures and corresponding buckling modes are shown in Fig. 6.23(c). We note that the smallest critical pressure corresponds to an antisymmetric buckling displacement. However, the response in Fig. 6.23(b) was obtained assuming a perfectly symmetric arch, and hence symmetric deformations were calculated in each solution step.

The antisymmetric linearized buckling deformations indicate that the structure is sensitive to antisymmetric imperfections. Hence, we introduced a geometric imperfection into the model of the arch by adding a multiple of the first buckling mode, $\boldsymbol{\phi}_1$, to the geometry of the undeformed arch. In this addition the mode is scaled so that the magnitude of the imperfection is less than 0.01 (one-hundredth of the cross-sectional depth).

Figure 6.23(d) shows the calculated response—again using a load-displacement-constraint method as discussed in Section 8.4.3—of the arch with this geometric imperfection. We notice that the collapse load now predicted is significantly smaller than the value given in Fig. 6.23(b). This reduction in the collapse load is associated with a nonsymmetric behavior of the structural model which is made possible because of the imposed geometric imperfection.

The collapse analysis of a structure requires, in general, an incremental load analysis, which should include the geometric and material nonlinearities. The preceding discussion indicates that structural imperfections can also have a major effect on the predicted load-carrying capacity of a structure. Hence, when such a situation is anticipated, imperfections should be introduced in the structural model. Here we considered geometric imperfections and a simple example. In the analysis of a complex structure, multiples of the 2nd, 3rd, . . . buckling modes would also be added to the geometry, but it may also be appropriate to introduce perturbations in the material properties or the applied loading, all of which should serve to excite the structure to embark on the deformation path that corresponds to the smallest load-carrying capacity.

While we have presented in this chapter the formulation of the incremental equations, the solution of these equations and the solution of the buckling eigenproblem are discussed in Chapters 8 and 11, respectively.

Finally, we should mention that in addition to the static buckling analyses, dynamic solutions also may need to be considered. A dynamic buckling or collapse analysis requires that complete dynamic incremental analyses be performed for given different load levels (including of course the possible effects of imperfections). Figure 6.24 illustrates a sequence of such analyses. The structural model is stable for the pressure levels $p^{(1)}$ and $p^{(2)}$ but is unstable for the load level $p^{(3)}$. If the difference between $p^{(2)}$ and $p^{(3)}$ is small, a good estimate of the collapse load is given by $p^{(2)}$, otherwise further analyses are needed to decrease the difference between the load level at which the structure is still stable and the level at which it is unstable. Such dynamic solutions are obtained using the procedures described in Chapter 9.

6.8.3 The Effects of Element Distortions

We mentioned in Sections 5.3.3 and 5.5.5 that finite elements are in general most effective in the prediction of displacements and stresses when they are undistorted. However, in practice, elements must largely be of general straight-sided shapes with angular distortions

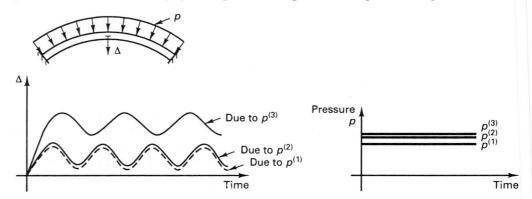

Figure 6.24   Dynamic buckling of arch; the structure shows a stable dynamic response due to load levels $p^{(1)}$ and $p^{(2)}$ and a much larger response due to $p^{(3)}$.

(for example, we use general quadrilateral elements in two-dimensional analysis) in order to provide mesh gradings and to mesh complex geometries effectively. To model curved boundaries, curved element sides or faces also need to be used. In addition, in geometric nonlinear analysis, significant angular and curved edge distortions and distortions due to movement of noncorner element nodes may arise as a consequence of the deformations. While the actual solution error increases as a result of all these element distortions, as long as the distortions are "small" (as discussed in Section 5.3.3), the order of convergence is not affected. We also noted that frequently the Lagrangian elements are more effective than the elements lacking the interior nodes.

Using the large displacement formulations, the principle of virtual displacements is applied to each individual element corresponding to the current configuration instead of the initial configuration used in linear analysis. Thus, element distortions must be expected to affect the accuracy of the nonlinear response prediction in a manner similar to that in linear analysis, but now the considerations concerning the element distortions in linear analysis summarized in Section 5.3.3 are applicable throughout the response history of the mesh. In an analysis it is therefore necessary to monitor the changing shape of each element, and if element distortions adversely affect the response prediction, a different and finer mesh may be required for the geometrically nonlinear analysis. Also, mesh rezoning can be used at certain critical times with the objective to keep closely to an element layout in which only the angular distortions are present. In these mesh constructions Lagrangian elements are used very effectively (see N. S. Lee and K. J. Bathe [A, B]).

We should also point out that these considerations are equally applicable to the TL and the UL formulations because, except for certain constitutive assumptions, both formulations are completely equivalent (see Example 6.23).

6.8.4 The Effects of Order of Numerical Integration

To select the appropriate numerical integration scheme and order of integration in nonlinear analysis, some specific considerations beyond those already discussed in Section 5.5.5 are important.

Based on the information given above and in Section 5.5.5 on the required integration order for undistorted and distorted elements, we can directly conclude that in geometric nonlinear analysis, at least the same integration order should be employed as in linear analysis.

However, a higher integration order than that used in linear analysis may be required in the analysis of materially nonlinear response simply in order for the analysis to capture the onset and spread of the materially nonlinear conditions accurately enough. Specifically, since the material nonlinearities are measured only at the integration points of the elements, the use of a relatively low integration order may mean that the spread of the materially nonlinear conditions through the elements is not represented accurately. This consideration is particularly important in the materially nonlinear analysis of beam, plate, and shell structures and also leads to the conclusion that the Newton-Cotes methods may be effective (say for integration in certain directions) because then integration points for stiffness and stress evaluations are on the boundaries of the elements (e.g., on the top and bottom surfaces of a shell).

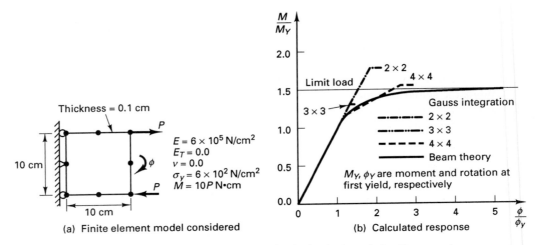

Thickness = 0.1 cm

$E = 6 \times 10^5$ N/cm^2
$E_T = 0.0$
$v = 0.0$
$\sigma_y = 6 \times 10^2$ N/cm^2
$M = 10P$ N·cm

(a) Finite element model considered

(b) Calculated response

Figure 6.25   Effect of integration order in elastic-plastic analysis of beam section

Figure 6.25 gives the results of using different orders of Gauss integration for an eight-node plane stress element representing the section of a beam. The element is subjected to an increasing bending moment, and the numerically predicted response is compared with the response calculated using beam theory. This analysis illustrates that to predict the materially nonlinear response accurately a higher integration order in the thickness direction of the beam is required than in linear analysis. Another example that demonstrates the effect of using different integration orders in materially nonlinear analysis follows.

EXAMPLE 6.27: Consider element 2 in Example 4.5 and assume that in an elastoplastic analysis the stresses at time t in the element are such that the tangent moduli of the material are equal to $E/100$ for $0 \leq x \leq 40$ and equal to E for $40 < x \leq 80$ as illustrated in Fig. E6.27. Evaluate the tangent stiffness matrix $^t\mathbf{K}$ using one-, two-, three-, and four-point Gauss integration and compare these results with the exact stiffness matrix. Consider only material nonlinearities.

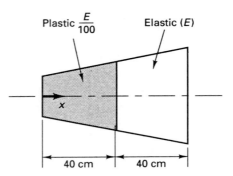

Plastic $\dfrac{E}{100}$ Elastic (E)

x

40 cm   40 cm

Figure E6.27   Element 2 of Example 4.5 in elastic-plastic conditions

For the evaluation of the matrix $'\mathbf{K}$ we use the information given in Example 4.5 and in Table 5.6. Thus, we obtain the following results:

One-point integration:

$$'\mathbf{K} = 2 \times 40 \begin{bmatrix} -\frac{1}{80} \\ \frac{1}{80} \end{bmatrix} \frac{E}{100} \begin{bmatrix} -\frac{1}{80} & \frac{1}{80} \end{bmatrix} (1 + 1)^2 = 0.0005E \begin{bmatrix} 1 & -1 \\ -1 & 1 \end{bmatrix}$$

Two-point integration:

$$'\mathbf{K} = 1 \times 40 \begin{bmatrix} -\frac{1}{80} \\ \frac{1}{80} \end{bmatrix} \frac{E}{100} \begin{bmatrix} -\frac{1}{80} & \frac{1}{80} \end{bmatrix} \left(1 + 1 - \frac{1}{\sqrt{3}}\right)^2$$

$$+ 1 \times 40 \begin{bmatrix} -\frac{1}{80} \\ \frac{1}{80} \end{bmatrix} E \begin{bmatrix} -\frac{1}{80} & \frac{1}{80} \end{bmatrix} \left(1 + 1 + \frac{1}{\sqrt{3}}\right)^2$$

$$= 0.04164E \begin{bmatrix} 1 & -1 \\ -1 & 1 \end{bmatrix}$$

Three-point integration:

$$'\mathbf{K} = \frac{5}{9} 40 \begin{bmatrix} -\frac{1}{80} \\ \frac{1}{80} \end{bmatrix} \frac{E}{100} \begin{bmatrix} -\frac{1}{80} & \frac{1}{80} \end{bmatrix} \left(1 + 1 - \frac{\sqrt{3}}{5}\right)^2$$

$$+ \frac{8}{9} 40 \begin{bmatrix} -\frac{1}{80} \\ \frac{1}{80} \end{bmatrix} \frac{E}{100} \begin{bmatrix} -\frac{1}{80} & \frac{1}{80} \end{bmatrix} (1 + 1)^2$$

$$+ \frac{5}{9} 40 \begin{bmatrix} -\frac{1}{80} \\ \frac{1}{80} \end{bmatrix} E \begin{bmatrix} -\frac{1}{80} & \frac{1}{80} \end{bmatrix} (1 + 1 + \sqrt{3}/5)^2$$

$$'\mathbf{K} = 0.02700E \begin{bmatrix} 1 & -1 \\ -1 & 1 \end{bmatrix}$$

Four-point integration:

	r_i	α_i
$n = 4$	$\pm 0.8611 \ldots$	$0.3478 \ldots$
	$\pm 0.3399 \ldots$	$0.6521 \ldots$

$$'\mathbf{K} = 0.3478 \ldots (40) \begin{bmatrix} -\frac{1}{80} \\ \frac{1}{80} \end{bmatrix} \frac{E}{100} \begin{bmatrix} -\frac{1}{80} & \frac{1}{80} \end{bmatrix} (1 + 1 - 0.8611 \ldots)^2$$

$$+ \cdots$$

$$'\mathbf{K} = 0.04026E \begin{bmatrix} 1 & -1 \\ -1 & 1 \end{bmatrix}$$

The exact stiffness matrix is

$$
{}^{t}\mathbf{K} = \begin{bmatrix} -\frac{1}{80} \\ \frac{1}{80} \end{bmatrix} \frac{E}{100} \begin{bmatrix} -\frac{1}{80} & \frac{1}{80} \end{bmatrix} \left\{ \int_{0}^{40} \left(1 + \frac{y}{40} \right)^{2} dy + \int_{40}^{80} 100 \left(1 + \frac{y}{40} \right)^{2} dy \right\}
$$

$$
= \begin{bmatrix} -\frac{1}{80} \\ \frac{1}{80} \end{bmatrix} E \begin{bmatrix} -\frac{1}{80} & \frac{1}{80} \end{bmatrix} \left\{ \frac{40}{300} \left(1 + \frac{y}{40} \right)^{3} \Big|_{0}^{40} + \frac{40}{3} \left(1 + \frac{y}{40} \right)^{3} \Big|_{40}^{80} \right\}
$$

$$
{}^{t}\mathbf{K} = 0.03973 E \begin{bmatrix} 1 & -1 \\ -1 & 1 \end{bmatrix}
$$

It is interesting to note that in this case the two-point integration yields more accurate results than the three-point integration and that a good approximation to the exact stiffness matrix is obtained using four-point integration.

The above remarks show that in nonlinear analysis the use of a higher integration order than in linear analysis may be appropriate. Such higher integration order, when needed, should of course be used for displacement-based and mixed finite elements. Hence, referring to Section 5.5.6, where we briefly mentioned the use of reduced and selective integration, our recommendations given in that section also pertain to, and are at least equally important in, nonlinear analysis. In short, the recommendations were that only well-formulated displacement-based and mixed elements should be used. To calculate the element matrices of a mixed formulation effectively, in some special cases a displacement-based formulation with a special integration scheme can be used. We should, however, note that this correspondence may hold only in linear analysis, and it is important that the correspondence be studied for nonlinear analysis in each individual case.

6.8.5 Exercises

6.95. Use a computer program to calculate the linearized buckling load of the column structure shown. Compare your calculated results with an analytical solution. (*Hint:* Here you can use Hermitian beam elements, isoparametric beam elements, or plane stress elements to model the column.)

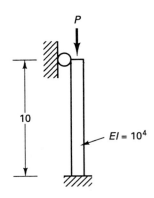

P

10

$EI = 10^{4}$

6.96. Use a computer program to calculate the large displacement response of the cantilever beam shown. Compare your results with an analytical solution (see, for example, J. T. Holden [A]).

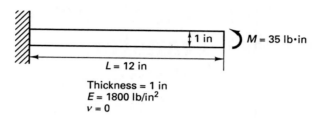

Thickness = 1 in
$E = 1800$ lb/in^2
$v = 0$

6.97. Use a computer program to analyze the arch shown in Fig. 6.23.
    (a) Perform the analysis described in Fig. 6.23.
    (b) Then change the geometry to consider that $2H/h = 20.0$ and repeat the analysis.
6.98. Verify the results given in Fig. 6.25.

CHAPTER SEVEN

Finite Element Analysis of Heat Transfer, Field Problems, and Incompressible Fluid Flows

7.1 INTRODUCTION

In the preceding chapters we considered the finite element formulation and solution of problems in stress analysis of solids and structural systems. However, finite element analysis procedures are now also widely used in the solution of nonstructural problems, in particular, for heat transfer, field, and fluid flow problems.

Our objective in the following sections is to discuss the application of the finite element method to the solution of such problems. Since many of the finite element procedures presented in the earlier chapters are directly applicable, we can frequently be brief. In addition to concentrating on some practical solution procedures, emphasis is directed to the general techniques that are employed and to demonstrating the commonality among the various problem formulations. In this way we also hope that the applicability of finite element procedures to the solution of problems not discussed here becomes apparent (e.g., coupled fluid flow–structural problems, general non-Newtonian flow conditions).

7.2 HEAT TRANSFER ANALYSIS

In the study of finite element analysis of heat transfer problems it is instructive to first recall the differential and variational equations that govern the heat transfer conditions to be analyzed. These equations provide the basis for the finite element formulation and solution of heat transfer problems as we shall then discuss.

7.2.1 Governing Heat Transfer Equations

Consider a three-dimensional body in heat transfer conditions as shown in Fig. 7.1 and consider first steady-state conditions. For the heat transfer analysis we assume that the material obeys Fourier's law of heat conduction (see, for example, J. H. Lienhard [A])

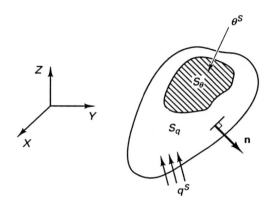

Prescribed temperature θ^S on S_θ
Prescribed heat flow input q^S on S_q

Figure 7.1   Body subjected to heat transfer

$$q_x = -k_x \frac{\partial \theta}{\partial x}; \qquad qy = -k_y \frac{\partial \theta}{\partial y}; \qquad q_z = -k_z \frac{\partial \theta}{\partial z}$$

where q_x, q_y, and q_z are the heat flows conducted per unit area, θ is the temperature of the body, and k_x, k_y, k_z are the thermal conductivities corresponding to the principal axes x, y, and z. Considering the heat flow equilibrium in the interior of the body, we thus obtain

$$\frac{\partial}{\partial x}\left(k_x \frac{\partial \theta}{\partial x}\right) + \frac{\partial}{\partial y}\left(k_y \frac{\partial \theta}{\partial y}\right) + \frac{\partial}{\partial z}\left(k_z \frac{\partial \theta}{\partial z}\right) = -q^B \tag{7.1}$$

where q^B is the rate of heat generated per unit volume. On the surfaces of the body the following conditions must be satisfied:

$$\theta|_{S_\theta} = \theta^S \tag{7.2}$$

$$k_n \frac{\partial \theta}{\partial n}\bigg|_{S_q} = q^S \tag{7.3}$$

where θ^S is the known surface temperature on S_θ, k_n is the body thermal conductivity, n denotes the coordinate axis in the direction of the unit normal vector **n** (pointing outward) to the surface, q^S is the prescribed heat flux input on the surface S_q of the body, and $S_\theta \cup S_q = S$, $S_\theta \cap S_q = 0$.

A number of important assumptions apply to the use of (7.1) to (7.3). A primary assumption is that the material particles of the body are at rest, and thus we consider the heat conduction conditions in solids and structures. If the heat transfer in a moving fluid is to be analyzed, it is necessary to include in (7.1) a term allowing for the convective heat transfer through the medium (see Section 7.4). Another assumption is that the heat transfer conditions can be analyzed decoupled from the stress conditions. This assumption is valid in many structural analyses, but may not be appropriate, for example, in the analysis of metal forming processes where the deformations may generate heat and change the temperature field. Such a change in turn may affect the material properties and result in further deformations. Another assumption is that there are no phase changes and latent heat effects (see Example 7.5 on how to incorporate such effects). However, we will assume in the following formulation that the material parameters are temperature-dependent.

A variety of boundary conditions are encountered in heat transfer analysis:

Temperature conditions
The temperature may be prescribed at specific points and surfaces of the body, denoted by S_θ in (7.2).

Heat flow conditions
The heat flow input may be prescribed at specific points and surfaces of the body. These heat flow boundary conditions are specified in (7.3).

Convection boundary conditions
Included in (7.3) are convection boundary conditions where

$$q^S = h(\theta_e - \theta^S) \tag{7.4}$$

and h is the convection coefficient, which may be temperature-dependent. Here the environmental temperature θ_e is known, but the surface temperature θ^S is unknown.

Radiation boundary conditions
Radiation boundary conditions are also specified in (7.3) with

$$q^S = \kappa(\theta_r - \theta^S) \tag{7.5}$$

where θ_r is the known temperature of the external radiative source and κ is a coefficient, evaluated using absolute temperatures,

$$\kappa = h_r[(\theta_r)^2 + (\theta^S)^2](\theta_r + \theta^S) \tag{7.6}$$

The variable h_r is determined from the Stefan-Boltzmann constant, the emissivity of the radiant and absorbing materials, and the geometric view factors.

We assume here that θ_r is known. If, on the other hand, the situation of two bodies radiating heat to each other is considered, the analysis is considerably more complicated (see Example 7.6 for such a case).

In addition to these boundary conditions the temperature initial conditions must also be specified in a transient analysis.

For the finite element solution of the heat transfer problem we use the *principle of virtual temperatures* given as

$$\boxed{\int_V \bar{\boldsymbol{\theta}}'^T \mathbf{k} \boldsymbol{\theta}' \, dV = \int_V \bar{\theta} q^B \, dV + \int_{S_q} \bar{\theta}^S q^S \, dS + \sum_i \bar{\theta}^i Q^i} \tag{7.7}$$

where

$$\boldsymbol{\theta}'^T = \begin{bmatrix} \dfrac{\partial \theta}{\partial x} & \dfrac{\partial \theta}{\partial y} & \dfrac{\partial \theta}{\partial z} \end{bmatrix} \tag{7.8}$$

$$\mathbf{k} = \begin{bmatrix} k_x & 0 & 0 \\ 0 & k_y & 0 \\ 0 & 0 & k_z \end{bmatrix} \tag{7.9}$$

and the Q^i are concentrated heat flow inputs. Each Q^i is equivalent to a surface heat flow input over a very small area. The bar over the temperature θ indicates that a virtual temperature distribution is being considered.

The principle of virtual temperatures is an equation of heat flow equilibrium: for θ to be the solution of the temperature in the body under consideration, (7.7) must hold for arbitrary virtual (continuous) temperature distributions that are zero on S_θ.

We note that the principle of virtual temperatures is an expression like the principle of virtual displacements used in stress analysis (see Section 4.2). We use the principle of virtual temperatures in the same way as the principle of virtual displacements, and indeed all procedures discussed in Chapters 4 and 5 are directly applicable, except that we now only have the scalar of unknown temperature, whereas in the previous discussion we solved for the vector of unknown displacements.

To further deepen our understanding of the principle of virtual temperatures, we derive the expression in (7.7) in the following example (this derivation is analogous to the presentation in Example 4.2).

EXAMPLE 7.1:   Derive the principle of virtual temperatures from the basic differential equations (7.1) to (7.3).

Here we follow the procedure in Example 4.2 (see also Section 3.3.4).

Let us write the governing heat transfer equations in indicial notation. Using $x_1 \equiv x$, $x_2 \equiv y$, $x_3 \equiv z$, and the earlier definitions, we obtain the following.

The differential heat flow equilibrium equation to be satisfied throughout the body

$$(k_i \theta_{,i})_{,i} + q^B = 0 \qquad \text{no sum on } i \text{ in parentheses} \tag{a}$$

The essential boundary condition

$$\theta = \theta^S \qquad \text{on } S_\theta \tag{b}$$

The natural boundary condition

$$k_n \theta_{,n} = q^S \qquad \text{on } S_q \tag{c}$$

where $S = S_\theta \cup S_q$, $S_\theta \cap S_q = 0$.

Let us consider any arbitrarily chosen continuous temperature distribution $\bar{\theta}$, with $\bar{\theta} = 0$ on S_θ. Then we have

$$\int_V [(k_i \theta_{,i})_{,i} + q^B] \bar{\theta} \, dV = 0 \tag{d}$$

We call $\bar{\theta}$ the "virtual temperature distribution." Since $\bar{\theta}$ is arbitrary, (d) can be satisfied if and only if the quantity in the brackets vanishes. Hence, (d) is equivalent to (a).

Our objective is to now transform (d) such that we lower the order of derivatives in the integral (from second to first order), and we can introduce the natural boundary condition (c). For this purpose we use the mathematical identity

$$[\bar{\theta}(k_i \theta_{,i})]_{,i} = \bar{\theta}_{,i}(k_i \theta_{,i}) + \bar{\theta}(k_i \theta_{,i})_{,i}$$

to transform the relation in (d), to obtain

$$\int_V \{[\bar{\theta}(k_i \theta_{,i})]_{,i} - \bar{\theta}_{,i}(k_i \theta_{,i}) + q^B \bar{\theta}\} \, dV = 0 \tag{e}$$

Our objective is now achieved by using the divergence theorem (see also Example 4.2). We have

$$\int_V [\bar{\theta}(k_i \theta_{,i})]_{,i} \, dV = \int_S [\bar{\theta}(k_i \theta_{,i})] n_i \, dS = \int_S \bar{\theta}(k_n \theta_{,n}) \, dS$$

We thus obtain from (e)

$$\int_V [-\bar{\theta}_{,i}(k_i \theta_{,i}) + q^B \bar{\theta}] \, dV + \int_S \bar{\theta}(k_n \theta_{,n}) \, dS = 0$$

In light of (c) and the condition that $\bar{\theta} = 0$ on S_θ, we therefore have the required result

$$\int_V \bar{\theta}_{,i}(k_i \theta_{,i}) \, dV = \int_V \bar{\theta} q^B \, dV + \int_{S_q} \bar{\theta}^S q^S \, dS$$

where we note that the prescribed heat flux condition (the natural boundary condition) now appears as a forcing term on the right-hand side of the equation.

It is also of value to recognize that the principle of virtual temperatures corresponds to the condition of stationarity of the following functional

$$\Pi = \int_V \frac{1}{2} \left[k_x \left(\frac{\partial \theta}{\partial x} \right)^2 + k_y \left(\frac{\partial \theta}{\partial y} \right)^2 + k_z \left(\frac{\partial \theta}{\partial z} \right)^2 \right] dV - \int_V \theta q^B \, dV - \int_{S_q} \theta^S q^S \, dS - \sum_i \theta^i Q^i \quad (7.10)$$

Namely, invoking $\delta \Pi = 0$, we obtain

$$\int_V \delta\boldsymbol{\theta}'^T \, \mathbf{k}\boldsymbol{\theta}' \, dV = \int_V \delta\theta q^B \, dV + \int_{S_q} \delta\theta^S q^S \, dS + \sum_i \delta\theta^i Q^i \quad (7.11)$$

where $\delta\theta$ can be arbitrary but must be zero on S_θ. Using integration by parts (i.e., the divergence theorem) on (7.11) we can of course extract the governing differential equation of equilibrium (7.1) and the heat flow boundary condition (7.3) (which in essence corresponds to reversing the process used in Example 7.1; see Example 3.18). However, on comparing (7.11) with (7.7), we recognize that (7.11) is the principle of virtual temperatures with $\delta\theta \equiv \bar{\theta}$.

In the heat transfer problem considered above, we assumed steady-state conditions. However, when significant heat flow input changes are specified over a "short" time period (due to a change of any of the boundary conditions or the heat generation in the body), this period being short measured on the natural time constants of the system (given by the thermal eigenvalues; see Chapter 9), it is important to include a term that takes account of the rate at which heat is stored within the material. This rate of heat absorption is

$$q^c = \rho c \dot{\theta} \quad (7.12)$$

where c is the material specific heat capacity. The variable q^c can be understood to be part of the heat generated—of course, q^c must be subtracted from the otherwise generated heat q^B in (7.7) because it is heat stored—and the effect leads to a transient response solution.

7.2.2 Incremental Equations

The principle of virtual temperatures expresses the heat flow equilibrium at all times of interest. For a general solution scheme of both linear and nonlinear, steady-state and transient problems we aim to develop incremental equilibrium equations. As in an incremental finite element stress analysis (see Section 6.1), assume that the conditions at time t have been calculated and that the temperatures are to be determined for time $t + \Delta t$, where Δt is the time increment.

Steady-State Conditions

Considering first steady-state conditions, in which the time stepping is merely used to describe the heat flow loading, the principle of virtual temperatures applied at time $t + \Delta t$ gives

$$\int_V \overline{\boldsymbol{\theta}}'^T {}^{t+\Delta t}\mathbf{k}\, {}^{t+\Delta t}\boldsymbol{\theta}'\, dV$$

$$= {}^{t+\Delta t}\mathcal{Q} + \int_{S_c} \overline{\theta}^S\, {}^{t+\Delta t}h({}^{t+\Delta t}\theta_e - {}^{t+\Delta t}\theta^S)\, dS + \int_{S_r} \overline{\theta}^S\, {}^{t+\Delta t}\kappa({}^{t+\Delta t}\theta_r - {}^{t+\Delta t}\theta^S)\, dS \tag{7.13}$$

where the superscript $t + \Delta t$ denotes "at time $t + \Delta t$," S_c and S_r are the surface areas with convection and radiation boundary conditions, respectively, and ${}^{t+\Delta t}\mathcal{Q}$ corresponds to further external heat flow input to the system at time $t + \Delta t$. Note that in (7.13) the temperatures ${}^{t+\Delta t}\theta_e$ and ${}^{t+\Delta t}\theta_r$ are known, whereas ${}^{t+\Delta t}\theta^S$ is the unknown surface temperature on S_c and S_r. The quantity ${}^{t+\Delta t}\mathcal{Q}$ includes the effects of the internal heat generation ${}^{t+\Delta t}q^B$, the surface heat flux inputs ${}^{t+\Delta t}q^S$ that are not included in the convection and radiation boundary conditions, and the concentrated heat flow inputs ${}^{t+\Delta t}Q^i$,

$$ {}^{t+\Delta t}\mathcal{Q} = \int_V \overline{\theta}\, {}^{t+\Delta t}q^B\, dV + \int_{S_q} \overline{\theta}^S\, {}^{t+\Delta t}q^S\, dS + \sum_i \overline{\theta}^i\, {}^{t+\Delta t}Q^i \tag{7.14}$$

Considering the general heat flow equilibrium relation in (7.13), we note that in linear analysis ${}^{t+\Delta t}\mathbf{k}$ and ${}^{t+\Delta t}h$ are constant and radiation boundary conditions are not included. Hence, the relation in (7.13) can be rearranged to obtain in linear analysis,

$$\int_V \overline{\boldsymbol{\theta}}'^T\mathbf{k}\, {}^{t+\Delta t}\boldsymbol{\theta}'\, dV + \int_{S_c} \overline{\theta}^S h\, {}^{t+\Delta t}\theta^S\, dS = {}^{t+\Delta t}\mathcal{Q} + \int_{S_c} \overline{\theta}^S h\, {}^{t+\Delta t}\theta_e\, dS \tag{7.15}$$

and it is possible to solve directly for the unknown temperature ${}^{t+\Delta t}\theta$.

In general nonlinear heat transfer analysis the relation in (7.13) is a nonlinear equation in the unknown temperature at time $t + \Delta t$. An approximate solution for this temperature can be obtained by incrementally decomposing (7.13) as summarized in Table 7.1. As in stress analysis (see Section 6.1), this decomposition can be understood to be the first step of a Newton-Raphson iteration for heat flow equilibrium in which

$$ {}^{t+\Delta t}\theta^{(i)} = {}^{t+\Delta t}\theta^{(i-1)} + \Delta\theta^{(i)} \tag{7.16}$$

where ${}^{t+\Delta t}\theta^{(i-1)}$ is the temperature distribution at the end of iteration $(i - 1)$ and $\Delta\theta^{(i)}$ is the temperature increment in iteration (i); also, ${}^{t+\Delta t}\theta^{(0)} = {}^t\theta$. In Table 7.1 we use θ to describe $\Delta\theta^{(1)}$ and consider the equation for the first iteration.

In a full Newton-Raphson iteration the accurate solution of (7.13) would be obtained by using (7.16) and updating all variables in the incremental equation of Table 7.1. in each

TABLE 7.1 *Incremental nonlinear heat flow equilibrium equation*

1. *Equilibrium equation at time $t + \Delta t$*

$$\int_V \bar{\boldsymbol{\theta}}'^T \, {}^{t+\Delta t}\mathbf{k} \, {}^{t+\Delta t}\boldsymbol{\theta}' \, dV = {}^{t+\Delta t}\mathcal{Q} + \int_{S_c} \bar{\theta}^S \, {}^{t+\Delta t}h({}^{t+\Delta t}\theta_e - {}^{t+\Delta t}\theta^S) \, dS + \int_{S_r} \bar{\theta}^S \, {}^{t+\Delta t}\kappa({}^{t+\Delta t}\theta_r - {}^{t+\Delta t}\theta^S) \, dS$$

2. *Linearization of equation*

We use: ${}^{t+\Delta t}\theta = {}^t\theta + \theta$; ${}^{t+\Delta t}\boldsymbol{\theta}' = {}^t\boldsymbol{\theta}' + \boldsymbol{\theta}'$; ${}^t\tilde{\kappa} = 4 \, {}^t h_r({}^t\theta^S)^3$

$$ {}^t\kappa = {}^t h_r(({}^{t+\Delta t}\theta_r)^2 + ({}^t\theta^S)^2)({}^{t+\Delta t}\theta_r + {}^t\theta^S) $$

Substituting into the equation of heat flow equilibrium, we obtain

$$\int_V \bar{\boldsymbol{\theta}}'^T \, {}^t\mathbf{k}\boldsymbol{\theta}' \, dV + \int_{S_c} \bar{\theta}^S \, {}^t h\theta^S \, dS + \int_{S_r} \bar{\theta}^S \, {}^t\tilde{\kappa}\theta^S \, dS = {}^{t+\Delta t}\mathcal{Q} + \int_{S_c} \bar{\theta}^S \, {}^t h({}^{t+\Delta t}\theta_e - {}^t\theta^S) \, dS$$

$$+ \int_{S_r} \bar{\theta}^S \, {}^t\kappa({}^{t+\Delta t}\theta_r - {}^t\theta^S) \, dS - \int_V \bar{\boldsymbol{\theta}}'^T \, {}^t\mathbf{k} \, {}^t\boldsymbol{\theta}' \, dV$$

iteration. Hence, we solve for $i = 1, 2, \ldots,$

$$\int_V \bar{\boldsymbol{\theta}}'^T \, {}^{t+\Delta t}\mathbf{k}^{(i-1)} \, \Delta\boldsymbol{\theta}'^{(i)} \, dV + \int_{S_c} \bar{\theta}^S \, {}^{t+\Delta t}h^{(i-1)} \, \Delta\theta^{S(i)} \, dS + \int_{S_r} \bar{\theta}^S \, {}^{t+\Delta t}\tilde{\kappa}^{(i-1)} \, \Delta\theta^{S(i)} \, dS$$

$$= {}^{t+\Delta t}\mathcal{Q} + \int_{S_c} \bar{\theta}^S \, {}^{t+\Delta t}h^{(i-1)}({}^{t+\Delta t}\theta_e - {}^{t+\Delta t}\theta^{S(i-1)}) \, dS \qquad (7.17)$$

$$+ \int_{S_r} \bar{\theta}^S \, {}^{t+\Delta t}\kappa^{(i-1)}({}^{t+\Delta t}\theta_r - {}^{t+\Delta t}\theta^{S(i-1)}) \, dS - \int_V \bar{\boldsymbol{\theta}}'^T \, {}^{t+\Delta t}\mathbf{k}^{(i-1)} \, {}^{t+\Delta t}\boldsymbol{\theta}'^{(i-1)} \, dV$$

where ${}^{t+\Delta t}h^{(i-1)}$, ${}^{t+\Delta t}\kappa^{(i-1)}$, and ${}^{t+\Delta t}\mathbf{k}^{(i-1)}$ are the convection and radiation coefficients and the conductivity constitutive matrix that correspond to the temperature ${}^{t+\Delta t}\theta^{(i-1)}$.

Frequently, in practice, the modified Newton-Raphson iteration is employed, in which case the left-hand side of (7.17) is evaluated only at the beginning of the time step and not updated until the next time increment (see Section 8.4.1).

Although it might appear that an actual linearization of the heat flow equilibrium equation is achieved in Table 7.1, a closer study shows that the equations in the table correspond to only an approximate linearization. Consequently, (7.17) is, in general, also not a full linearization about the state of the last iteration. The difficulty lies in that the tangent relations of the material constants, that is, of the conduction, convection, and radiation coefficients when temperature-dependent, need to be included in the linearization, and this can be achieved only when the functional relationship between the material property and temperature is given in analytical form. We demonstrate this observation in the following example.

> **EXAMPLE 7.2:** Consider the analysis of the slab shown in Fig. E7.2. Establish the incremental form of the principle of virtual temperatures for the modified Newton-Raphson iteration and for the full Newton-Raphson iteration.

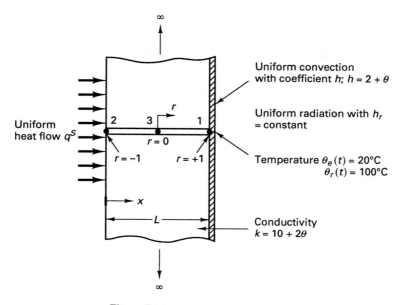

Figure E7.2   Analysis of an infinite slab

The principle of virtual temperatures for the one-dimensional problem, considering a unit cross-sectional area of the slab, is

$$\int_0^L \bar{\theta}' \,^{t+\Delta t}k \,^{t+\Delta t}\theta' \, dx$$

$$= [\bar{\theta}^S q^S]|_{x=0} + [\bar{\theta}^S \,^{t+\Delta t}h(^{t+\Delta t}\theta_e - \,^{t+\delta t}\theta^S)]|_{x=L} + [\bar{\theta}^S \,^{t+\Delta t}\kappa(^{t+\Delta t}\theta_r - \,^{t+\Delta t}\theta^S)]|_{x=L} \qquad (a)$$

where $^{t+\Delta t}\theta' = \partial^{t+\Delta t}\theta/\partial x$, $\bar{\theta}' = \partial\bar{\theta}/\partial x$, and $^{t+\Delta t}\kappa$ is evaluated using degrees Kelvin.

The incremental form in the modified Newton-Raphson iteration is based on the decomposition given (for the first iteration) in Table 7.1,

$$\int_0^L \bar{\theta}'(10 + 2^t\theta) \, \Delta\theta'^{(i)} \, dx + [\bar{\theta}^S 2(2 + \,^t\theta^S) \, \Delta\theta^{S(i)}]|_{x=L} + [\bar{\theta}^S 4h_r(^t\theta^S)^3 \, \Delta\theta^{S(i)}]|_{x=L}$$

$$= [\bar{\theta}^S q^S]|_{x=0} + [\bar{\theta}^S(2 + \,^{t+\Delta t}\theta^{S(i-1)})(20 - \,^{t+\Delta t}\theta^{S(i-1)})]|_{x=L} \qquad (b)$$

$$+ \{\bar{\theta}^S \,^{t+\Delta t}\kappa^{i-1}[100 - \,^{t+\Delta t}\theta^{S(i-1)}]\}|_{x=L} - \int_0^L \bar{\theta}'(10 + 2^{t+\Delta t}\theta^{(i-1)})^{t+\Delta t}\theta'^{(i-1)} \, dx$$

In the full Newton-Raphson iteration the same right-hand side is used, but the left-hand side is given by

$$\text{Left-hand side} = \int_0^L \bar{\theta}'(10 + 2 \,^{t+\Delta t}\theta^{(i-1)}) \, \Delta\theta'^{(i)} \, dx + [\bar{\theta}^S 2(2 + \,^{t+\Delta t}\theta^{S(i-1)}) \, \Delta\theta^{S(i)}]|_{x=L}$$

$$+ [\bar{\theta}^S 4h_r(^{t+\Delta t}\theta^{S(i-1)})^3 \, \Delta\theta^{S(i)}]|_{x=L} \qquad (c)$$

The *actual* linearization, however, is obtained by differentiating the equation of the principle of virtual temperatures about the last calculated state and using the analytical expressions.

Let us consider as an example the conduction term in (a) and use the procedure of linearization about the state at time t that we employed in Section 6.3.1. Hence, we use the Taylor series expansion

$$\bar{\theta}'\,^{t+\Delta t}q \doteq \bar{\theta}'\,^{t}q + \frac{\partial}{\partial\theta}(\bar{\theta}'\,^{t}q)\,d\theta$$

However, since $(\partial\bar{\theta}'/\partial\theta) = 0$, we have

$$\frac{\partial}{\partial\theta}(\bar{\theta}'\,^{t}q)\,d\theta = \left[\bar{\theta}'\frac{\partial}{\partial\theta}(^{t}q)\right]d\theta$$

Now substituting for $^{t}q = -(10 + 2^{t}\theta)(\partial^{t}\theta/\partial x)$, we obtain

$$\bar{\theta}'\,^{t+\Delta t}q \doteq -\bar{\theta}'\left(\underbrace{[10 + 2^{t}\theta]\frac{\partial^{t}\theta}{\partial x}}_{\text{Term 1}} + \underbrace{2\frac{\partial^{t}\theta}{\partial x}\,d\theta}_{\text{Term 2}} + \underbrace{(10 + 2^{t}\theta)\,d\theta'}_{\text{Term 3}}\right) \qquad \text{(d)}$$

We note that the term 1 and term 3 on the right-hand side of (d) are included in the incremental principle of virtual temperatures given in (b) [and in (c)] but that term 2 is an extra expression not accounted for in (b), (c), and Table 7.1. In the finite element solution to the slab, this term would lead to a nonsymmetric tangent conductivity matrix.

Also, in a similar manner, the actual linearization of the convection and radiation terms can be obtained. This development shows that for the convection part a temperature-dependent term is also neglected, whereas the linearization of the radiation part is complete because in this example the h_r-coefficient is temperature-independent (see Exercise 7.2).

As shown above in a specific example, (7.17) does not, in general, correspond to the exact linearization of the principle of virtual temperatures about the last calculated temperature state. However, (7.17) represents a general iterative solution scheme which, in particular, can be applied when the material relationships are given piecewise linear as a function of temperature (such a definition can be convenient in the use of a general program implementation that is not based on specific analytical expressions of material properties). If iteration convergence is obtained, the correct solution of the principle of virtual temperatures (7.7) has been calculated [since the equation (7.7) is satisfied when the right-hand side in (7.17) is zero], and frequently in practice only a few iterations are needed for reasonable time (load) step magnitudes.

Of course, if specific analytical relationships of the material constants are to be used and convergence difficulties are encountered with (7.17), it may be advantageous to use the exact linearization of the principle of virtual temperatures in the iterative solution (see Exercise 7.3).

Transient Conditions

In transient analysis, the heat capacity effect is included in much the same way as we introduced the inertia forces in stress analysis (see Sections 4.2.1 and 6.2.3).

The principle of virtual temperatures at time $t + \Delta t$ is now

$$\int_{V}\bar{\theta}^{T\,t+\Delta t}(\rho c)^{t+\Delta t}\dot{\theta}\,dV + \int_{V}\bar{\theta}'^{T\,t+\Delta t}\mathbf{k}\,^{t+\Delta t}\boldsymbol{\theta}'\,dV$$

$$= {}^{t+\Delta t}\mathcal{Q} + \int_{S_c}\bar{\theta}^{S\,t+\Delta t}h(^{t+\Delta t}\theta_e - {}^{t+\Delta t}\theta^S)\,dS + \int_{S_r}\bar{\theta}^{S\,t+\Delta t}\kappa(^{t+\Delta t}\theta_r - {}^{t+\Delta t}\theta^S)\,dS \qquad (7.18)$$

where $^{t+\Delta t}\mathfrak{Q}$ is defined as in (7.14), but $^{t+\Delta t}q^B$ is now the rate of heat generation excluding the heat capacity effect.

The relation in (7.18) is used to calculate the temperature at time $t + \Delta t$ when an implicit time integration method is employed (such as the Euler backward method). On the other hand, in an explicit time integration scheme, the principle of virtual temperatures is applied at time t to calculate the unknown temperature at time $t + \Delta t$ (see Sections 7.2.3 and 9.6). Whereas a Newton-Raphson iterative method including the heat capacity effects is used in implicit integration (when nonlinearities are present), a simple forward integration without iteration is employed with an explicit method.

7.2.3 Finite Element Discretization of Heat Transfer Equations

The finite element solution of the heat transfer governing equations is obtained using procedures analogous to those employed in stress analysis. We consider first the analysis of steady-state conditions. Assume that the complete body under consideration has been idealized as an assemblage of finite elements; then, in analogy to stress analysis we have at time $t + \Delta t$ for element m,

$$^{t+\Delta t}\theta^{(m)} = \mathbf{H}^{(m)}\,{}^{t+\Delta t}\mathbf{\theta}$$

$$^{t+\Delta t}\theta^{S(m)} = \mathbf{H}^{S(m)}\,{}^{t+\Delta t}\mathbf{\theta} \tag{7.19}$$

$$^{t+\Delta t}\mathbf{\theta}'^{(m)} = \mathbf{B}^{(m)}\,{}^{t+\Delta t}\mathbf{\theta}$$

where the superscript (m) denotes element m and $^{t+\Delta t}\mathbf{\theta}$ is a vector of all nodal point temperatures at time $t + \Delta t$,

$$^{t+\Delta t}\mathbf{\theta}^T = [^{t+\Delta t}\theta_1 \;\; {}^{t+\Delta t}\theta_2 \cdots {}^{t+\Delta t}\theta_n] \tag{7.20}$$

The matrices $\mathbf{H}^{(m)}$ and $\mathbf{B}^{(m)}$ are the element temperature and temperature-gradient interpolation matrices, respectively, and the matrix $\mathbf{H}^{S(m)}$ is the surface temperature interpolation matrix. We evaluate in (7.19) the element temperatures and temperature gradients at time $t + \Delta t$, but the same interpolation matrices are also employed to calculate the element temperature conditions at any other time, and hence for incremental temperatures and incremental temperature gradients.

Linear Steady-State Conditions

Using the relations in (7.19) and substituting into (7.15), we obtain the finite element governing equations in linear heat transfer analysis:

$$(\mathbf{K}^k + \mathbf{K}^c)^{t+\Delta t}\mathbf{\theta} = {}^{t+\Delta t}\mathbf{Q} + {}^{t+\Delta t}\mathbf{Q}^e \tag{7.21}$$

where $\mathbf{K}^k$ is the conductivity matrix,

$$\mathbf{K}^k = \sum_m \int_{V^{(m)}} \mathbf{B}^{(m)T}\,\mathbf{k}^{(m)}\,\mathbf{B}^{(m)}\,dV^{(m)} \tag{7.22}$$

and $\mathbf{K}^c$ is the convection matrix,

$$\mathbf{K}^c = \sum_m \int_{S_c^{(m)}} h^{(m)}\,\mathbf{H}^{S(m)T}\,\mathbf{H}^{S(m)}\,dS^{(m)} \tag{7.23}$$

The nodal point heat flow input vector $^{t+\Delta t}\mathbf{Q}$ is given by

$$^{t+\Delta t}\mathbf{Q} = {}^{t+\Delta t}\mathbf{Q}_B + {}^{t+\Delta t}\mathbf{Q}_S + {}^{t+\Delta t}\mathbf{Q}_C \tag{7.24}$$

where

$$^{t+\Delta t}\mathbf{Q}_B = \sum_m \int_{V^{(m)}} \mathbf{H}^{(m)T} \, {}^{t+\Delta t}q^{B(m)} \, dV^{(m)} \tag{7.25}$$

$$^{t+\Delta t}\mathbf{Q}_S = \sum_m \int_{S_q^{(m)}} \mathbf{H}^{S(m)T} \, {}^{t+\Delta t}q^{S(m)} \, dS^{(m)} \tag{7.26}$$

and $^{t+\Delta t}\mathbf{Q}_C$ is a vector of concentrated nodal point heat flow input. The nodal point heat flow contribution $^{t+\Delta t}\mathbf{Q}^e$ is due to the convection boundary conditions. Using the element surface temperature interpolations to define the environmental temperature $^{t+\Delta t}\theta_e$ on the element surfaces in terms of the given nodal point environmental temperatures $^{t+\Delta t}\boldsymbol{\theta}_e$, we have

$$^{t+\Delta t}\mathbf{Q}^e = \sum_m \int_{S_c^{(m)}} h^{(m)} \mathbf{H}^{S(m)T} \, \mathbf{H}^{S(m)} \, {}^{t+\Delta t}\boldsymbol{\theta}_e \, dS^{(m)} \tag{7.27}$$

The above formulation is effectively used with the variable-number-nodes isoparametric finite elements discussed in Chapter 5. We demonstrate the calculation of the element matrices in the following example.

EXAMPLE 7.3:   Consider the four-node isoparametric element in Fig. E7.3. Discuss the calculation of the conductivity matrix $\mathbf{K}^k$, convection matrix $\mathbf{K}^c$, and heat flow input vectors $^{t+\Delta t}\mathbf{Q}_B$ and $^{t+\Delta t}\mathbf{Q}^e$.

For the evalution of these matrices we need the matrices $\mathbf{H}$, $\mathbf{B}$, $\mathbf{H}^S$, and $\mathbf{k}$. The temperature interpolation matrix $\mathbf{H}$ is composed of the interpolation functions defined in Fig. 5.4,

$$\mathbf{H} = \tfrac{1}{4}[(1 + r)(1 + s) \quad (1 - r)(1 + s) \quad (1 - r)(1 - s) \quad (1 + r)(1 - s)]$$

We obtain $\mathbf{H}^S$ by evaluating $\mathbf{H}$ at $r = 1$, so that

$$\mathbf{H}^S = \tfrac{1}{2}[(1 + s) \quad 0 \quad 0 \quad (1 - s)]$$

To evaluate $\mathbf{B}$ we first evaluate the Jacobian operator $\mathbf{J}$ (see Example 5.3):

$$\mathbf{J} = \begin{bmatrix} 1 & \dfrac{1 + s}{4} \\ 0 & \dfrac{3 + r}{4} \end{bmatrix}$$

Hence

$$\mathbf{B} = \frac{1}{4} \begin{bmatrix} 1 & -\left(\dfrac{1 + s}{3 + r}\right) \\ 0 & \dfrac{4}{(3 + r)} \end{bmatrix} \begin{bmatrix} (1 + s) & -(1 + s) & -(1 - s) & (1 - s) \\ (1 + r) & (1 - r) & -(1 - r) & -(1 + r) \end{bmatrix}$$

$$= \frac{1}{4(3 + r)} \begin{bmatrix} 2(1 + s) & -4(1 + s) & 2(2s - r - 1) & 2(2 + r - s) \\ 4(1 + r) & 4(1 - r) & -4(1 - r) & -4(1 + r) \end{bmatrix}$$

Finally, we have

$$\mathbf{k} = \begin{bmatrix} k & 0 \\ 0 & k \end{bmatrix}$$

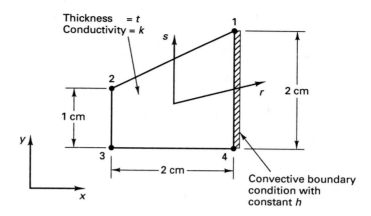

Figure E7.3   Four-node element in heat transfer conditions

The element matrices can now be evaluated using numerical integration as in the analysis of solids and structures (see Chapter 5).

Nonlinear Steady-State Conditions

For general nonlinear analysis the temperature and temperature gradient interpolations of (7.19) are substituted into the heat flow equilibrium relation (7.17) to obtain

$$({}^{t+\Delta t}\mathbf{K}^{k(i-1)} + {}^{t+\Delta t}\mathbf{K}^{c(i-1)} + {}^{t+\Delta t}\mathbf{K}^{r(i-1)})\,\Delta\boldsymbol{\theta}^{(i)} = {}^{t+\Delta t}\mathbf{Q} + {}^{t+\Delta t}\mathbf{Q}^{c(i-1)} + {}^{t+\Delta t}\mathbf{Q}^{r(i-1)} - {}^{t+\Delta t}\mathbf{Q}^{k(i-1)}$$

$$(7.28)$$

where the nodal point temperatures at the end of iteration (i) are

$$^{t+\Delta t}\boldsymbol{\theta}^{(i)} = {}^{t+\Delta t}\boldsymbol{\theta}^{(i-1)} + \Delta\boldsymbol{\theta}^{(i)} \tag{7.29}$$

The matrices and vectors used in (7.28) are directly obtained from the individual terms used in (7.17) and are defined in Table 7.2. The nodal point heat flow input vector $^{t+\Delta t}\mathbf{Q}$ was already defined in (7.24).

TABLE 7.2   *Finite element matrices in nonlinear heat transfer analysis*

Integral	Finite element evaluation
$\displaystyle\int_V \bar{\boldsymbol{\theta}}'^T\,{}^{t+\Delta t}\mathbf{k}^{(i-1)}\,\Delta\boldsymbol{\theta}'^{(i)}\,dV$	$\displaystyle {}^{t+\Delta t}\mathbf{K}^{k(i-1)}\,\Delta\boldsymbol{\theta}^{(i)} = \left(\sum_m \int_{V^{(m)}} \mathbf{B}^{(m)^T}\,{}^{t+\Delta t}\mathbf{k}^{(m)(i-1)}\,\mathbf{B}^{(m)}\,dV^{(m)}\right)\Delta\boldsymbol{\theta}^{(i)}$
$\displaystyle\int_{S_c} \bar{\boldsymbol{\theta}}^S\,{}^{t+\Delta t}h^{(i-1)}\,\Delta\boldsymbol{\theta}^{S(i)}\,dS$	$\displaystyle {}^{t+\Delta t}\mathbf{K}^{c(i-1)}\,\Delta\boldsymbol{\theta}^{(i)} = \left(\sum_m \int_{S_c^{(m)}} {}^{t+\Delta t}h^{(m)(i-1)}\,\mathbf{H}^{S(m)^T}\mathbf{H}^{S(m)}\,dS^{(m)}\right)\Delta\boldsymbol{\theta}^{(i)}$
$\displaystyle\int_{S_r} \bar{\boldsymbol{\theta}}^S\,{}^{t+\Delta t}\bar{\kappa}^{(i-1)}\,\Delta\boldsymbol{\theta}^{S(i)}\,dS$	$\displaystyle {}^{t+\Delta t}\mathbf{K}^{r(i-1)}\,\Delta\boldsymbol{\theta}^{(i)} = \left(\sum_m \int_{S_r^{(m)}} {}^{t+\Delta t}\bar{\kappa}^{(m)(i-1)}\,\mathbf{H}^{S(m)^T}\mathbf{H}^{S(m)}\,dS^{(m)}\right)\Delta\boldsymbol{\theta}^{(i)}$
$\displaystyle\int_{S_c} \bar{\boldsymbol{\theta}}^S\,{}^{t+\Delta t}h^{(i-1)}\big({}^{t+\Delta t}\theta_e - {}^{t+\Delta t}\theta^{S(i-1)}\big)\,dS$	$\displaystyle {}^{t+\Delta t}\mathbf{Q}^{c(i-1)} = \sum_m \int_{S_c^{(m)}} {}^{t+\Delta t}h^{(m)(i-1)}\,\mathbf{H}^{S(m)T}\big[\mathbf{H}^{S(m)}\big({}^{t+\Delta t}\boldsymbol{\theta}_e - {}^{t+\Delta t}\boldsymbol{\theta}^{(i-1)}\big)\big]\,dS^{(m)}$
$\displaystyle\int_{S_r} \bar{\boldsymbol{\theta}}^S\,{}^{t+\Delta t}\kappa^{(i-1)}\big({}^{t+\Delta t}\theta_r - {}^{t+\Delta t}\theta^{S(i-1)}\big)\,dS$	$\displaystyle {}^{t+\Delta t}\mathbf{Q}^{r(i-1)} = \sum_m \int_{S_r^{(m)}} {}^{t+\Delta t}\kappa^{(m)(i-1)}\,\mathbf{H}^{S(m)T}\big[\mathbf{H}^{S(m)}\big({}^{t+\Delta t}\boldsymbol{\theta}_r - {}^{t+\Delta t}\boldsymbol{\theta}^{(i-1)}\big)\big]\,dS^{(m)}$
$\displaystyle\int_V \bar{\boldsymbol{\theta}}'^T\,{}^{t+\Delta t}\mathbf{k}^{(i-1)}\,{}^{t+\Delta t}\boldsymbol{\theta}'^{(i-1)}\,dV$	$\displaystyle {}^{t+\Delta t}\mathbf{Q}^{k(i-1)} = \sum_m \int_{V^{(m)}} \mathbf{B}^{(m)^T}\big[{}^{t+\Delta t}\mathbf{k}^{(m)(i-1)}\,\mathbf{B}^{(m)}\,{}^{t+\Delta t}\boldsymbol{\theta}^{(i-1)}\big]\,dV^{(m)}$

Specified Temperatures

In addition to convection and radiation boundary conditions, nodal point temperature conditions may also be specified. These boundary conditions can be incorporated in the same way as known nodal point displacements are prescribed in stress analysis.

A common procedure is to substitute the known nodal point temperatures in the heat flow equilibrium equations (7.21) and (7.28) and delete the corresponding equations from those to be solved (see Section 4.2.2). However, an effective way to impose nodal point temperatures can be the procedure that is employed to impose convection boundary conditions. Namely, by assigning a very large value of convection coefficient h, where h is much larger than the conductivity of the material, the surface nodal point temperature will be equal to the prescribed environmental nodal point temperature.

EXAMPLE 7.4: Establish the governing finite element equations for the analysis of the infinite parallel-sided slab shown in Fig. E7.2 but neglect the radiation effects. Use the modifed Newton-Raphson solution and only one parabolic one-dimensional element to model the slab. (In practice, depending on the temperature gradient to be predicted by the analysis, many more elements may be needed.)

The governing equations for this problem are obtained from (7.28),

$$({}^{t}\mathbf{K}^{k} + {}^{t}\mathbf{K}^{c}) \, \Delta\boldsymbol{\theta}^{(i)} = {}^{t+\Delta t}\mathbf{Q} + {}^{t+\Delta t}\mathbf{Q}^{c(i-1)} - {}^{t+\Delta t}\mathbf{Q}^{k(i-1)} \tag{a}$$

where

$$ {}^{t}\mathbf{K}^{k} = \int_{V} \mathbf{B}^{T} \, {}^{t}k\mathbf{B} \, dV $$

$$ {}^{t}\mathbf{K}^{c} = \int_{S_c} {}^{t}h \, \mathbf{H}^{S^T} \mathbf{H}^{S} \, dS $$

$$ {}^{t+\Delta t}\mathbf{Q}^{c(i-1)} = \int_{S_c} {}^{t+\Delta t}h^{(i-1)}\mathbf{H}^{S^T}[\mathbf{H}^{S}({}^{t+\Delta t}\boldsymbol{\theta}_{e} - {}^{t+\Delta t}\boldsymbol{\theta}^{(i-1)})] \, dS $$

$$ {}^{t+\Delta t}\mathbf{Q}^{k(i-1)} = \int_{V} \mathbf{B}^{T}[{}^{t+\Delta t}k^{(i-1)}\mathbf{B} \, {}^{t+\Delta t}\boldsymbol{\theta}^{(i-1)}] \, dV $$

$$ {}^{t+\Delta t}\mathbf{Q}^{T} = \begin{bmatrix} 0 & q^{S} & 0 \end{bmatrix} $$

and

$$ \Delta\boldsymbol{\theta}^{(i)T} = \begin{bmatrix} \Delta\theta_1^{(i)} & \Delta\theta_2^{(i)} & \Delta\theta_3^{(i)} \end{bmatrix} $$

$$ {}^{t+\Delta t}\boldsymbol{\theta}^{(i-1)T} = \begin{bmatrix} {}^{t+\Delta t}\theta_1^{(i-1)} & {}^{t+\Delta t}\theta_2^{(i-1)} & {}^{t+\Delta t}\theta_3^{(i-1)} \end{bmatrix} $$

$$ {}^{t+\Delta t}\boldsymbol{\theta}_{e}^{T} = \begin{bmatrix} 20 & 0 & 0 \end{bmatrix} $$

For the one-dimensional parabolic element, we use the interpolation functions h_1, h_2, and h_3 in Fig. 5.3 to construct $\mathbf{H}$,

$$ \mathbf{H} = \begin{bmatrix} \frac{1}{2}r(1+r) & -\frac{1}{2}r(1-r) & (1-r^2) \end{bmatrix} $$

and $\mathbf{H}^S$ corresponding to node 1 is equal to $\mathbf{H}$ evaluated at $r = +1$,

$$ \mathbf{H}^{S} = \begin{bmatrix} 1 & 0 & 0 \end{bmatrix} $$

We also have $J = L/2$; hence,

$$\mathbf{B} = \frac{2}{L} \left[\frac{1}{2}(1 + 2r) \quad -\frac{1}{2}(1 - 2r) \quad -2r \right]$$

Also, the conductivity of the material is given by, for example, for time t,

$$^t k = 10 + 2 \sum_{i=1}^{3} h_i \, {}^t \theta_i$$

and similarly for the convection coefficient we have

$$^t h \big|_{r=+1} = 2 + {}^t \theta_1$$

With these quantities defined we can now evaluate all matrices in (a) and perform the temperature analysis. Note that we are using $S_c = 1$ and $V = 1 \times L$.

See Exercise 7.6 for the analysis including the radiation effects.

Transient Analysis

As mentioned earlier, in transient heat transfer analysis the heat capacity effects are included in the analysis as part of the rate of heat generated. The equations considered in the solution depend, however, on whether implicit or explicit time integration is used, just as in structural analysis (see Chapter 9 and, for example, K. J. Bathe and M. R. Khoshgoftaar [A]).

If the *Euler backward implicit time integration is employed,* the heat flow equilibrium equations used are obtained directly from the equations governing steady-state conditions [see (7.18)]. Namely, using for element m,

$$\dot{\boldsymbol{\theta}}^{(m)}(x, y, z, t) = \mathbf{H}^{(m)}(x, y, z)\dot{\boldsymbol{\theta}}(t) \tag{7.30}$$

and now using (7.12), we have in (7.28),

$$^{t+\Delta t}\mathbf{Q}_B = \sum_m \int_{V^{(m)}} \mathbf{H}^{(m)T}({}^{t+\Delta t}q^{B(m)} - {}^{t+\Delta t}(\rho c)^{(m)} \, \mathbf{H}^{(m)} \, {}^{t+\Delta t}\dot{\boldsymbol{\theta}}) \, dV^{(m)} \tag{7.31}$$

where $^{t+\Delta t}q^{B(m)}$ no longer includes the rate at which heat is stored within the material. Hence, the finite element heat flow equilibrium equations considered in transient conditions are, in linear analysis,

$$\mathbf{C} \, {}^{t+\Delta t}\dot{\boldsymbol{\theta}} + (\mathbf{K}^k + \mathbf{K}^c)^{t+\Delta t}\boldsymbol{\theta} = {}^{t+\Delta t}\mathbf{Q} + {}^{t+\Delta t}\mathbf{Q}^e \tag{7.32}$$

and in nonlinear analysis (using the full Newton-Raphson iteration but without linearizing the heat capacity effect, see Section 9.6),

$$^{t+\Delta t}\mathbf{C}^{(i)} \, {}^{t+\Delta t}\dot{\boldsymbol{\theta}}^{(i)} + ({}^{t+\Delta t}\mathbf{K}^{k(i-1)} + {}^{t+\Delta t}\mathbf{K}^{c(i-1)} + {}^{t+\Delta t}\mathbf{K}^{r(i-1)}) \, \Delta\boldsymbol{\theta}^{(i)}$$
$$= {}^{t+\Delta t}\mathbf{Q} + {}^{t+\Delta t}\mathbf{Q}^{c(i-1)} + {}^{t+\Delta t}\mathbf{Q}^{r(i-1)} - {}^{t+\Delta t}\mathbf{Q}^{k(i-1)} \tag{7.33}$$

where $\mathbf{C}$, $^{t+\Delta t}\mathbf{C}^{(i)}$ are the heat capacity matrices,

$$\mathbf{C} = \sum_m \int_{V^{(m)}} \mathbf{H}^{(m)T} \rho c^{(m)} \, \mathbf{H}^{(m)} \, dV^{(m)}$$

$$^{t+\Delta t}\mathbf{C}^{(i)} = \sum_m \int_{V^{(m)}} \mathbf{H}^{(m)T} \, {}^{t+\Delta t}(\rho c)^{(m)(i)} \, \mathbf{H}^{(m)} \, dV^{(m)} \tag{7.34}$$

The matrices defined in (7.34) are consistent heat capacity matrices because the same element interpolations are employed for the temperatures as for the time derivatives of temperatures. Following the concepts of displacement analysis, it is also possible to use a lumped heat capacity matrix and lumped heat flow input vector, which are evaluated by simply lumping heat capacities and heat flow inputs, using appropriate contributory areas, to the element nodes (see Section 4.2.4).

If, on the other hand, the *Euler forward explicit time integration is used,* the solution for the unknown temperatures at time $t + \Delta t$ is obtained by considering heat flow equilibrium at time t. Applying the relation in (7.7) at time t and substituting the finite element interpolations for temperatures, temperature gradients, and time derivatives of temperatures, we obtain in linear and nonlinear analysis, respectively,

$$\mathbf{C}\,{}^{t}\dot{\boldsymbol{\theta}} = {}^{t}\mathbf{Q} + {}^{t}\mathbf{Q}^{c} - {}^{t}\mathbf{Q}^{k} \tag{7.35}$$

$$\mathbf{C}\,{}^{t}\dot{\boldsymbol{\theta}} = {}^{t}\mathbf{Q} + {}^{t}\mathbf{Q}^{c} + {}^{t}\mathbf{Q}^{r} - {}^{t}\mathbf{Q}^{k} \tag{7.36}$$

where the nodal point heat flow input vectors on the right of (7.35) and (7.36) are defined in Table 7.2 [but the superscript $(i - 1)$ is not used and $t + \Delta t$ is replaced by t). The solution using explicit time integration is effective only when a lumped heat capacity matrix is employed.

In closing this section we recall that we did not include in the above formulations the effects of phase changes and latent heat generation and of bodies radiating onto each other. These effects can be included in the analysis as briefly described in the following examples. We discuss the solution of the governing equations as a function of time in Section 9.6.

EXAMPLE 7.5: Consider that the slab shown in Fig. E7.2 is initially at a temperature θ_i and that θ_i is below the phase change temperature θ_{ph}. The heating of the slab will result in traversing θ_{ph} and hence in a phase change. Assume that the slab is a pure substance with latent heat l per unit mass and a constant mass density of ρ and specific heat capacity c. Show how the latent heat effect can be included in the transient analysis of the slab.

In this problem solution, the following boundary conditions must be satisfied at the phase transition interface S_{ph},

$$\left.\begin{array}{c} \theta = \theta_{ph} \\[10pt] \Delta q^{S}\,dS = -\rho l\,\dfrac{dV}{dt} \end{array}\right\} \quad \text{on } S_{ph} \tag{a}$$

where dV/dt is the rate of volume currently converted on S_{ph}. The relations in (a) state that at the interface separating the two phases heat is absorbed at a rate proportional to the volumetric rate of conversion of the material.

In this case a transient analysis is required. We use the simple three-node element idealization with a lumped heat capacity matrix (for a unit cross section),

$$\mathbf{C} = \begin{bmatrix} \rho c\,\dfrac{L}{4} & & \\ & \rho c\,\dfrac{L}{2} & \\ & & \rho c\,\dfrac{L}{4} \end{bmatrix} \tag{b}$$

We also choose to use the Euler backward time integration scheme (see Section 9.6 for details), with a constant time step Δt, in which

$$^{t+\Delta t}\dot{\boldsymbol{\theta}}^{(i)} = \frac{^{t+\Delta t}\boldsymbol{\theta}^{(i)} - {}^{t}\boldsymbol{\theta}}{\Delta t} = \frac{\boldsymbol{\theta}^{(i)}}{\Delta t} \tag{c}$$

Using (b) and (c) with the given initial condition and the matrices defined in Example 7.4, a transient analysis not including latent heat effects can be performed directly.

However, to introduce the interface conditions in (a), we calculate for each nodal point a "latent heat contribution." This results in the vector $\mathbf{H}_l$,

$$\mathbf{H}_l = \begin{bmatrix} \rho l \dfrac{L}{4} \\[2ex] \rho l \dfrac{L}{2} \\[2ex] \rho l \dfrac{L}{4} \end{bmatrix} \tag{d}$$

Let us call $H_{l,\text{total},k}$ the entry in $\mathbf{H}_l$ corresponding to nodal point k. The transient analysis including the latent heat effects can then be performed as follows.

As long as $^{t+\Delta t}\theta_k^{(i)}$ as calculated by the usual step-by-step solution is smaller than θ_{ph}, no considerations for latent heat enter the solution.

However, consider that at the start of a new step $^{t}\theta_k + \Delta\theta_k^{(1)} = {}^{t+\Delta t}\theta_k^{(1)} \geq \theta_{\text{ph}}$ and that with the adjustment for latent heat given below, the "projected" (but not accepted) increments in nodal temperatures are $\Delta\theta_k^{(i)} > 0$. Then we calculate for the first step traversing the phase change:

$$\tilde{\theta}_k = \theta_{\text{ph}} - {}^{t}\theta_k \tag{e}$$

$$\Delta Q_{l,k}^{(1)} = \int_{V_k} \frac{1}{\Delta t} \rho c (\Delta\theta_k^{(1)} - \tilde{\theta}_k)\, dV$$

$$\Delta Q_{l,k}^{(i)} = \int_{V_k} \frac{1}{\Delta t} \rho c\, \Delta\theta_k^{(i)}\, dV; \qquad i = 2, 3, \ldots$$

for all subsequent steps and iterations transversing the phase change:

$$\Delta Q_{l,k}^{(i)} = \int_{V_k} \frac{1}{\Delta t} \rho c\, \Delta\theta_k^{(i)}\, dV; \qquad i = 1, 2, 3, \ldots$$

where the volume integration is peformed over the volume V_k associated with the finite element node k, until

$$\sum_{\substack{\text{steps,} \\ \text{iterations}}} \Delta Q_{l,k}^{(i)}\, \Delta t = H_{l,\text{total},k} \tag{f}$$

In the last iteration only a portion of the value of $\Delta Q_{l,k}^{(i)}\, \Delta t$ may be used to reach $H_{l,\text{total},k}$.

The solution procedure is based on the condition that as long as a value $\Delta Q_{l,k}^{(i)}$ is applicable, the temperature increment at node k is given only by the $\tilde{\theta}_k$ defined in (e) rather than by the usual sum of all $\Delta\theta_k^{(i)}$. These temperature increments are added as usual to the current temperatures only after condition (f) has been fulfilled. Hence, in essence the temperature increase at a node is constrained to the phase change temperature θ_{ph} until $H_{l,\text{total},k}$ has been supplied to the node. The same concept is used when the phase change occurs during cooling and when a nonpure substance is being considered (in which case the temperature during the phase change is not constant). More details on this solution approach are given by W. D. Rolph, III, and K. J. Bathe [A].

EXAMPLE 7.6: Consider the two slabs shown in Fig. E7.6 radiating on each other. Assume gray diffuse surface radiation. Formulate the problem of heat flow between the slabs.

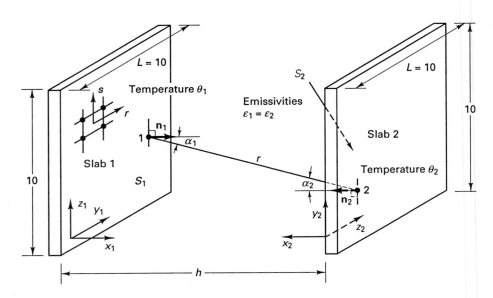

Figure E7.6   Two slabs radiating upon each other

In this example, we assume that the temperatures of the two slabs are given quantities. Of course, in an actual analysis the temperatures of the slab surfaces would also have to be calculated. To obtain the heat flow between the two slabs due to radiation, we introduce an additional variable to the temperature, namely, radiosity. The radiosity equations between two radiating surfaces, called surface 1 and surface 2, are based on Lambert's cosine law (see E. M. Sparrow and R. D. Cess [A]).

$$R_1(y_1, z_1) = \epsilon_1 \sigma \theta_1^4(y_1, z_1) + \rho_1 \int_{S_2} R_2(y_2, z_2) \frac{\cos \alpha_1(y_1, z_1) \cos \alpha_2(y_2, z_2)}{\pi r^2(y_1, z_1, y_2, z_2)} \, dy_2 \, dz_2 \qquad (a)$$

$$R_2(y_2, z_2) = \epsilon_2 \sigma \theta_2^4(y_2, z_2) + \rho_2 \int_{S_1} R_1(y_1, z_1) \frac{\cos \alpha_1(y_1, z_1) \cos \alpha_2(y_2, z_2)}{\pi r^2(y_1, z_1, y_2, z_2)} \, dy_1 \, dz_1 \qquad (b)$$

where for the two surfaces ϵ_1, ϵ_2 are the emissivities, σ is the Stefan-Boltzman constant, ρ_1, ρ_2 are the reflectivities (for gray diffuse radiation $\rho_1 = 1 - \epsilon_1$, $\rho_2 = 1 - \epsilon_2$), and α_1, α_2 are the angles between the normals and the ray of radiation between the points considered. The length of that ray is r. Once the radiosities over the slab surfaces are known, the radiative heat flux leaving surface i at point (y_i, z_i) is given by

$$q_i(y_i, z_i) = \frac{\epsilon_i}{\rho_i} (\sigma \theta_i^4 - R_i)\big|_{y_i, z_i} \qquad (c)$$

For the finite element solution of the radiosities, we use the Galerkin method to weigh (a) with δR_1 and (b) with δR_2 [see (3.14)]. We then discretize the two surfaces in the usual way; e.g., using four-node elements, we have for each element on surface 1

$$y_1 = \sum_{k=1}^{4} h_k(r, s) y_1^k$$

$$z_1 = \sum_{k=1}^{4} h_k(r, s) z_1^k$$

$$R_1 = \sum_{k=1}^{4} h_k(r, s) R_1^k$$

where the R_1^k are the unknown nodal radiosities for the element on surface 1.

The Galerkin procedure with the finite element expansions then gives the equation

$$\mathbf{K}_R \mathbf{R} = \mathbf{Q}^\epsilon \qquad\qquad (d)$$

where the vector $\mathbf{R}$ lists all nodal variables of radiosities (of both surfaces) and $\mathbf{Q}^\epsilon$ is a forcing vector corresponding to the emitted energies $(\epsilon_1/\rho_1)\sigma\theta_1^4$ and $(\epsilon_2/\rho_2)\sigma\theta_2^4$ over the surfaces. The solution of (d) gives the radiosities of the surfaces, and then the heat flow into the surfaces is calculated using (c). Note that the evaluation of the elements in $\mathbf{K}_R$ is performed by numerical integration which includes the evaluation of the term $(\cos \alpha_1 \cos \alpha_2)/\pi r^2$.

In a practical analysis, this procedure can include general curved surfaces and also obstructions, in which case a test must be included that identifies whether two differential surfaces (such as the contributory areas of integration points) can "see each other." Of course, as pointed out already, in practice the temperature of the surfaces is usually unknown and also needs to be calculated.

7.2.4 Exercises

7.1. Consider the square column shown. Assume planar heat flow conditions (in the x, y plane) and state the principle of virtual temperatures (7.7) for this case. Then derive from the principle of virtual temperatures the governing differential equations of heat flow within the column and on its surface.

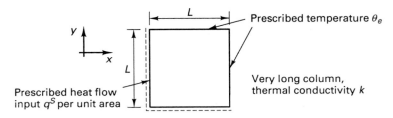

7.2. Consider Example 7.2 and establish the actual linearization of the principle of virtual temperatures about the state $t + \Delta t$, iteration $(i - 1)$. (The actual linearization of the conduction term was achieved in Example 7.2.)

7.3. Assume that the slab shown, in steady-state conditions, is to be anlayzed using the full Newton-Raphson iteration. Establish the incremental equation of the principle of virtual temperatures corresponding to the general equation in Table 7.1 and then determine any additional terms that should be added to achieve a full linearization in the full Newton-Raphson solution.

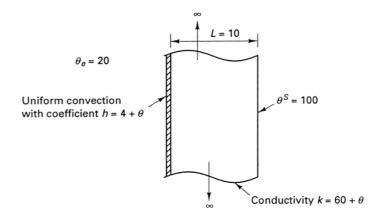

7.4. The four-node isoparametric element shown is to be used in a linear transient heat transfer analysis. Establish all expressions/matrices needed to calculate the heat capacity, conductivity and convection matrices, and heat flow load vectors but do not perform any integrations. (Consider 1 radian for the axisymmetric analysis.)

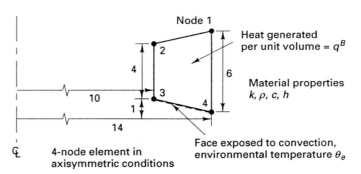

7.5. Consider the nine-node isoparametric element used in a heat transfer analysis as shown. Calculate the entries $K(1, 1)$ and $C(1, 1)$ corresponding to θ_1 of the conductivity and heat capacity matrices.

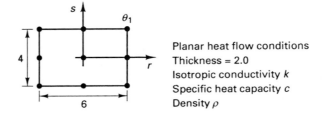

7.6. Consider Example 7.4 and evaluate all additional matrices needed to include the radiation effects shown in Fig. E7.2.

7.7. Use a computer program to solve for the steady-state temperature and heat flow distributions in the square column shown. Verify that an accurate solution has been obtained. (*Hint*: The isobands of heat flow can be used to indicate the solution error; see Section 4.3.6.)

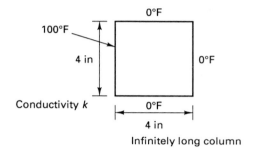

Infinitely long column

7.8 Use a computer program to solve for the solidification of the semi-infinite slab of liquid shown (see Example 7.5 and use a one-dimensional model).

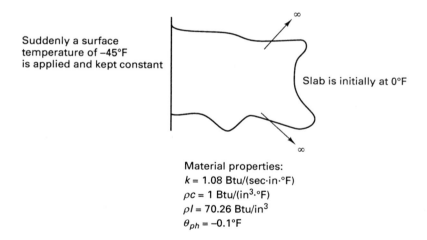

Suddenly a surface temperature of –45°F is applied and kept constant

Slab is initially at 0°F

Material properties:
$k = 1.08$ Btu/(sec·in·°F)
$\rho c = 1$ Btu/(in^3·°F)
$\rho l = 70.26$ Btu/in^3
$\theta_{ph} = -0.1$°F

7.3 ANALYSIS OF FIELD PROBLEMS

The heat transfer governing equations described in Section 7.2 using finite element procedures are directly applicable to a number of field problems. This analogy is summarized in Table 7.3. Hence, it follows that, in practice, if a finite element program is available for heat transfer analysis, the same program can also be employed directly for a variety of other analyses by simply operating on the appropriate field variables. We consider in the following a few field problems in more detail.

TABLE 7.3 *Analogies in analysis of field problems*

Problem	Variable θ	Constants k_x, k_y, k_z	Input q^B	Input q^S
Heat transfer	Temperature	Thermal conductivity	Internal heat generation	Prescribed heat flow
Seepage	Total head	Permeability	Internal flow generation	Prescribed flow condition
Torsion	Stress function	(Shear modulus)$^{-1}$	2 × (Angle of twist)	—
Inviscid incompressible irrotational flow	Potential function	1	Source or sink	Prescribed velocity
Electric conduction	Voltage	Electric conductivity	Internal current source	Prescribed current
Electrostatic field analysis	Field potential	Permittivity	Charge density	Prescribed field

7.3.1 Seepage

The equations discussed in Section 7.2.1 are directly applicable in seepage analysis provided confined flow conditions are considered. In this case the boundary surfaces and boundary conditions are all known. To solve for unconfined flow conditions the position of the free surface must also be calculated, for which a special solution procedure needs to be employed (see C. S. Desai [A] and K. J. Bathe and M. R. Khoshgoftaar [B]).

The basic seepage law used in the analysis is Darcy's law, which gives the flow through the porous medium in terms of the gradient of the total potential ϕ (see, for example, A. Verruijt [A]),

$$q_x = -k_x \frac{\partial \phi}{\partial x}; \qquad q_y = -k_y \frac{\partial \phi}{\partial y}; \qquad q_z = -k_z \frac{\partial \phi}{\partial z} \tag{7.37}$$

Continuity of flow conditions then results in the equation

$$\frac{\partial}{\partial x}\left(k_x \frac{\partial \phi}{\partial x}\right) + \frac{\partial}{\partial y}\left(k_y \frac{\partial \phi}{\partial y}\right) + \frac{\partial}{\partial z}\left(k_z \frac{\partial \phi}{\partial z}\right) = -q^B \tag{7.38}$$

where k_x, k_y, and k_z are the permeabilities of the medium and q^B is the flow generated per unit volume. The boundary conditions are those of a prescribed total potential ϕ on the surface S_ϕ,

$$\phi|_{S_\phi} = \phi^S \tag{7.39}$$

and of a prescribed flow condition along the surface S_q,

$$k_n \frac{\partial \phi}{\partial n}\bigg|_{S_q} = q^S \tag{7.40}$$

where n denotes the coordinate axis in the direction of the unit normal vector **n** (pointing outward) to the surface. In (7.38) to (7.40) we are employing the same notation as in (7.1) to (7.3), and on comparing these sets of equations we find a complete analogy between the

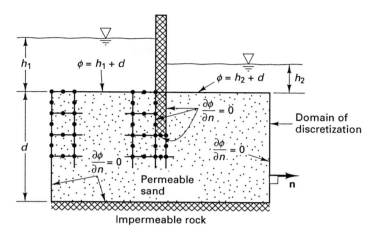

Figure 7.2   Analysis of seepage conditions under a dam

heat transfer conditions considered in Section 7.2 and the seepage conditions considered here. Figure 7.2 illustrates a finite element analysis of a seepage problem.

7.3.2 Incompressible Inviscid Flow

Consider an incompressible fluid in irrotational two-dimensional flow conditions. In this case the vorticity vanishes, so that (see, for example, F. M. White [A])

$$\frac{\partial v_x}{\partial y} - \frac{\partial v_y}{\partial x} = 0 \tag{7.41}$$

where v_x and v_y are the fluid velocities in the x and y directions, respectively. The continuity condition is given by

$$\frac{\partial v_x}{\partial x} + \frac{\partial v_y}{\partial y} = 0 \tag{7.42}$$

To solve (7.41) and (7.42) we define a potential function $\phi(x, y)$ such that

$$v_x = \frac{\partial \phi}{\partial x}; \qquad v_y = \frac{\partial \phi}{\partial y} \tag{7.43}$$

The relation in (7.41) is then identically satisfied, and (7.42) reduces to

$$\frac{\partial^2 \phi}{\partial x^2} + \frac{\partial^2 \phi}{\partial y^2} = 0 \tag{7.44}$$

Using (7.43), we impose all boundary normal velocities, v_n^S using

$$\left.\frac{\partial \phi}{\partial n}\right|_s = v_n^S \tag{7.45}$$

where $\partial \phi / \partial n$ denotes the derivative of ϕ in the direction of the unit normal vector (pointing outward) to the boundary. In addition, we need to prescribe an arbitrary value ϕ at an arbitrary point because the solution of (7.44) and (7.45) can be determined only after one value of ϕ is fixed.

The solution of (7.44) with the boundary conditions is analogous to the solution of a heat transfer problem. Once the potential function ϕ has been evaluated, we can use Bernoulli's equation to calculate the pressure distribution in the fluid. Figure 7.3 illustrates a finite element analysis of the flow around an object in a channel.

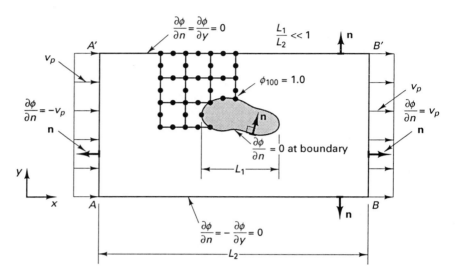

Figure 7.3 Analysis of flow in a channel with an island, v_p is the prescribed velocity. Note that on the boundary A-A' the inflow condition requires that a negative gradient of ϕ be imposed, whereas on the boundary B-B' a positive gradient is prescribed. (However, using a heat transfer program, the boundary conditions would be $q^S = v_p$ on A-A' and $q^S = -v_p$ on B-B' for a flow to the right because the flow is calculated as proportional to minus the gradient of the potential.)

7.3.3 Torsion

With the introduction of a stress function ϕ, the elastic torsional behavior of a shaft is governed by the equation (see, for example, Y. C. Fung [A])

$$\frac{\partial^2 \phi}{\partial x^2} + \frac{\partial^2 \phi}{\partial y^2} + 2G\theta = 0 \tag{7.46}$$

where θ is the angle of twist per unit length and G is the shear modulus of the shaft material. The shear stress components at any point can be calculated using

$$\tau_{zx} = \frac{\partial \phi}{\partial y}; \qquad \tau_{zy} = -\frac{\partial \phi}{\partial x} \tag{7.47}$$

and the applied torque is given by

$$T = 2 \int_A \phi \, dA \tag{7.48}$$

where A is the cross-sectional area of the shaft. The boundary condition on ϕ is that ϕ is zero on the boundary of the shaft. Hence, the heat transfer equations in (7.1) and (7.2) also govern the torsional behavior of a shaft provided the appropriate field variables are used.

EXAMPLE 7.7:   Evaluate the torsional rigidity of a square shaft using the two different finite element meshes shown in Fig. E7.7.

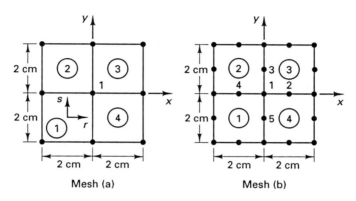

Figure E7.7   Finite element meshes used in calculation of torsional rigidity of a square shaft

Using the analogy between this torsional problem and a heat transfer problem for which the governing finite element equations have been stated in Section 7.2.3, we now want to solve

$$\left[\sum_m \int_{V^{(m)}} \mathbf{B}^{(m)^T} \mathbf{k}^{*(m)} \mathbf{B}^{(m)} \, dV^{(m)} \right] \boldsymbol{\phi} = \sum_m \int_{V^{(m)}} \mathbf{H}^{(m)^T} \theta \, dV^{(m)} \qquad \text{(a)}$$

where
$$\phi^{(m)} = \mathbf{H}^{(m)} \boldsymbol{\phi}$$

$$\boldsymbol{\phi}'^{(m)} = \mathbf{B}^{(m)} \boldsymbol{\phi}$$

$$\boldsymbol{\phi}^T = [\phi_1 \quad \phi_2 \quad \cdots \quad \phi_n]$$

$$\mathbf{k}^{*(m)} = \begin{bmatrix} \dfrac{1}{2G} & 0 \\ 0 & \dfrac{1}{2G} \end{bmatrix}$$

$$\boldsymbol{\phi}'^{(m)} = \begin{bmatrix} -\tau_{zy} \\ \tau_{zx} \end{bmatrix}$$

$$= \mathbf{B}^{(m)} \boldsymbol{\phi}$$

and
$$T = \sum_m \int_{A^{(m)}} 2\phi^{(m)} \, dA^{(m)} \qquad \text{(b)}$$

In each of the analysis cases we need to consider only one element because of symmetry conditions. Using mesh (a), we have for element 1,

$$\phi = \tfrac{1}{4}(1 + r)(1 + s)\phi_1$$

and
$$\begin{bmatrix} \dfrac{\partial \phi}{\partial r} \\[2mm] \dfrac{\partial \phi}{\partial s} \end{bmatrix} = \frac{1}{4} \begin{bmatrix} (1+s) \\[2mm] (1+r) \end{bmatrix} \phi_1$$

Hence the equations in (a) reduce to (considering a unit length of shaft)

$$\left\{ 4 \int_{-1}^{+1} \int_{-1}^{+1} \frac{1}{4} [(1+s) \quad (1+r)] \frac{1}{2G} \frac{1}{4} \begin{bmatrix} (1+s) \\ (1+r) \end{bmatrix} \det \mathbf{J} \; dr \; ds \right\} \phi_1$$

$$= 4\theta \int_{-1}^{+1} \int_{-1}^{+1} \frac{1}{4} (1+r)(1+s) \det \mathbf{J} \; dr \; ds; \qquad \det \mathbf{J} = 1$$

or
$$\frac{1}{3G} \phi_1 = \theta$$

Hence,
$$\phi_1 = 3G\theta$$

Using (b), we thus obtain

$$T = 4 \int_{-1}^{+1} \int_{-1}^{+1} \tfrac{1}{2} (1+r)(1+s)(3G\theta) \; dr \; ds = 24G\theta$$

so that
$$\frac{T}{\theta} = 24G$$

Considering next mesh (b), we recognize that the ϕ values on the boundary are zero and that for element 1 we have $\phi_4 = \phi_5$. Hence, we have only two unknowns ϕ_1 and ϕ_4 to be calculated. The interpolation functions for the eight-node element are given in Fig. 5.5. Proceeding in the same way as in the analysis with mesh (a), we obtain

$$\phi_1 = 2.157G\theta$$

$$\phi_4 = 1.921G\theta$$

$$T = 35.2G\theta$$

so that
$$\frac{T}{\theta} = 35.2G$$

The exact solution of (7.46) for T/θ is $36.1G$. Hence, the analysis with mesh (a) gives an error of 33.5 percent, whereas the analysis with mesh (b) yields a result of only 2.5 percent error.[1]

7.3.4 Acoustic Fluid

Consider an inviscid isentropic fluid with the fluid particles undergoing only small displacements. Not including body force effects, the equations governing the response of the fluid are the momentum equations (see, for example, F. M. White [A]),

$$\rho \dot{\mathbf{v}} + \nabla p = \mathbf{0} \tag{7.49}$$

---

[1] Note that this finite element analysis underestimates the stress function values ϕ (for an imposed value of twist θ) and thus yields a lower bound on the torsional rigidity, whereas a displacement and stress analysis using the procedures in Chapter 4 would yield an upper bound on T/θ (provided the monotonic convergence requirements of Section 4.3.2 are fulfilled).

and the constitutive equation

$$\beta \mathbf{\nabla} \cdot \mathbf{v} + \dot{p} = 0 \tag{7.50}$$

where $\mathbf{v}$ is the velocity of the fluid particles, p is the pressure, and β is the bulk modulus. The boundary conditions are as follows.

On the boundary S_v a prescribed velocity v_n^S in the direction of the unit normal vector $\mathbf{n}$ (pointing outward) to the fluid boundary,

$$\mathbf{v} \cdot \mathbf{n}\big|_{S_v} = v_n^S \tag{7.51}$$

On the boundary S_f a prescribed pressure p^S,

$$p\big|_{S_f} = p^S \tag{7.52}$$

To solve for the fluid motion, it is convenient to introduce the velocity potential ϕ, where

$$\mathbf{v} = \mathbf{\nabla}\phi; \qquad p = -\rho\dot{\phi} \tag{7.53}$$

With this definition (7.49) is identically satisfied [neglecting changes in density in (7.49)], and (7.50) becomes the acoustic equation

$$\nabla^2 \phi = \frac{1}{c^2}\ddot{\phi} \tag{7.54}$$

with the wave speed $c = \sqrt{\beta/\rho}$. The boundary conditions are now of course

$$\frac{\partial \phi}{\partial n}\bigg|_{S_v} = v_n^S \tag{7.55}$$

and

$$-\rho\dot{\phi}\big|_{S_f} = p^S \tag{7.56}$$

On comparing the governing equations (7.54) to (7.56) with the heat transfer governing equations, we recognize that a strong analogy exists. However, in the analysis of the fluid, the second time derivative of the solution variable is taken instead of the first time derivative in heat transfer analysis. Hence, for example, when using a heat transfer program to calculate the frequencies of an acoustic fluid, the frequencies sought are obtained by taking the square roots of the calculated frequencies. We demonstrate this observation in the following example.

EXAMPLE 7.8:   Consider an acoustic fluid in a closed rigid cavity (see Fig. E7.8). Use a 2×2 mesh of eight-node elements to model the fluid and estimate the lowest frequency of vibration of the fluid.

We use the governing fluid equation (7.54) with the boundary condition (7.55). Hence, by analogy to the development of the principle of virtual temperatures (see Example 7.1), the appropriate variational equation is

$$\int_V \delta\phi \frac{1}{c^2}\ddot{\phi}\, dV + \int_V (\mathbf{\nabla}\delta\phi) \cdot (\mathbf{\nabla}\phi)\, dV = 0 \tag{a}$$

Substituting the finite element interpolations into (a), we obtain

$$\mathbf{M}\ddot{\boldsymbol{\phi}} + \mathbf{K}\boldsymbol{\phi} = \mathbf{0} \tag{b}$$

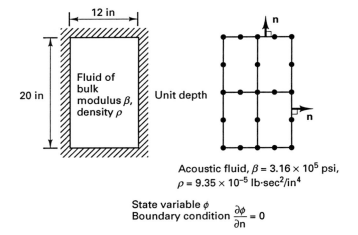

Figure E7.8 Problem and finite element discretization of fluid in rigid cavity

where the $\mathbf{M}\ddot{\boldsymbol{\phi}}$ term corresponds to the strain energy and the $\mathbf{K}\boldsymbol{\phi}$ term to the kinetic energy. The corresponding eigenvalue problem is

$$\mathbf{K}\boldsymbol{\phi} = \omega^2 \mathbf{M}\boldsymbol{\phi} \tag{c}$$

The matrices $\mathbf{K}$ and $\mathbf{M}$ are calculated as in heat transfer analysis [the heat conduction matrix $\mathbf{K}$ (with unit material conductivities in all directions) corresponds to the matrix $\mathbf{K}$ in (b), and the heat capacity matrix $\mathbf{C}$ (with $\rho c|_{\text{heat transfer}}$ replaced by $1/c^2|_{\text{acoustic fluid}}$) corresponds to the matrix $\mathbf{M}$ in (b)].

The problem (c) can therefore be solved directly with a heat transfer program that calculates the eigenvalues of the problem $\mathbf{K}\boldsymbol{\theta} = \lambda \mathbf{C}\boldsymbol{\theta}$ (see Section 9.6). For a 2×2 finite element discretization of eight-node elements, the results are $\lambda_1 = 0$, $\lambda_2 = (9166)^2$, $\lambda_3 = (15,277)^2$, and hence, the lowest nonzero calculated frequency of the problem in (c) is $\omega_2 = 9166$. We should note that the zero frequency corresponds to $\phi = $ constant in the cavity. The analytical solution to the problem gives $\omega_2 = 9132$.

Equations (7.54) to (7.56) have been used to develop an efficient finite element formulation to model the interaction between acoustic fluids and structures (see G. C. Everstine [A], L. G. Olson and K. J. Bathe [A], and Example 7.9). Also, the analysis procedure has been generalized to consider the fluid to undergo very large particle motions (see C. Nitikitpaiboon and K. J. Bathe [B]).

EXAMPLE 7.9:   Consider the problem shown in Fig. E7.9 and the model indicated. Evaluate the matrices for the fluid-structure interaction problem and calculate the lowest frequency of vibration.

The analysis of the problem requires the coupling of the fluid response with the response of the spring.

The principle of virtual work for the piston/spring gives

$$\bar{u}m\ddot{u} + \bar{u}ku = \bar{u}f^F + \bar{u}R(t) \tag{a}$$

where f^F corresponds to the force exerted by the fluid on the piston/spring. The "principle of

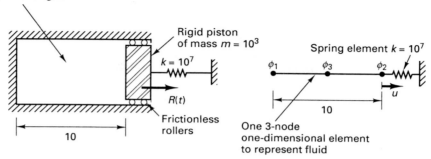

Unit cross-sectional area
Bulk modulus $\beta = 2.1 \times 10^9$ Pa
Mass density $\rho = 1000$ kg/m^3

Rigid piston
of mass $m = 10^3$

Spring element $k = 10^7$

$k = 10^7$

$R(t)$

Frictionless
rollers

One 3-node
one-dimensional element
to represent fluid

Figure E7.9 Acoustic fluid in a cavity with piston

virtual potentials" of the fluid is

$$\int_{V_f} \overline{\phi} \frac{1}{c^2} \ddot{\phi} \, dV_f + \int_{V_f} \nabla \overline{\phi} \cdot \nabla \phi \, dV_f = \int_I \overline{\phi}^I \dot{u}_n \, dI \tag{b}$$

where I denotes the (wetted) fluid-structure interface and $\dot{u}_n$ is the velocity of that interface (of the piston). We note that (b) is derived from (7.54) as we have shown (for the principle of virtual temperatures) in Example 7.1. Also, we have $\partial \phi / \partial n \,|_I = \dot{u}_n$, with n denoting the direction of the unit normal vector on the fluid domain (pointing outward to this domain).

We now represent the fluid domain by one three-node element. Using the developments of Chapter 5 (see specifically Section 5.3), we have corresponding to (b),

$$\mathbf{M}_F \ddot{\boldsymbol{\phi}} + \mathbf{K}_F \boldsymbol{\phi} = \mathbf{R}_{\dot{u}}$$

with $\mathbf{M}_F$, $\mathbf{K}_F$, and $\mathbf{R}_{\dot{u}}$ defined by

$$\frac{1}{c^2}\begin{bmatrix} \frac{4}{3} & -\frac{1}{3} & \frac{2}{3} \\ & \frac{4}{3} & \frac{2}{3} \\ \text{Sym.} & & \frac{16}{3} \end{bmatrix}\begin{bmatrix} \ddot{\phi}_1 \\ \ddot{\phi}_2 \\ \ddot{\phi}_3 \end{bmatrix} + \begin{bmatrix} \frac{7}{30} & \frac{1}{30} & \frac{-8}{30} \\ & \frac{7}{30} & \frac{-8}{30} \\ \text{Sym.} & & \frac{16}{30} \end{bmatrix}\begin{bmatrix} \phi_1 \\ \phi_2 \\ \phi_3 \end{bmatrix} = \begin{bmatrix} 0 \\ \dot{u}_n \\ 0 \end{bmatrix} \tag{c}$$

Next we can couple (a) and (c) by noting that $\dot{u}_n$ in (c) is equal to the time derivative of the displacement u in (a) and that f^F in (a) is given by the pressure in the fluid,

$$f^F = -\rho_F \dot{\phi} \,|_I = -\rho_F \dot{\phi}_2$$

since the cavity has unit cross-sectional area.

The coupled fluid-structure equations are

$$\begin{bmatrix} m & 0 & 0 & 0 \\ \hline 0 & & & \\ 0 & & -\rho_F \mathbf{M}_F & \\ 0 & & & \end{bmatrix}\begin{bmatrix} \ddot{u} \\ \ddot{\phi}_1 \\ \ddot{\phi}_2 \\ \ddot{\phi}_3 \end{bmatrix} + \begin{bmatrix} 0 & 0 & \rho_F & 0 \\ 0 & 0 & 0 & 0 \\ \rho_F & 0 & 0 & 0 \\ 0 & 0 & 0 & 0 \end{bmatrix}\begin{bmatrix} \dot{u} \\ \dot{\phi}_1 \\ \dot{\phi}_2 \\ \dot{\phi}_3 \end{bmatrix}$$

$$+ \begin{bmatrix} k & 0 & 0 & 0 \\ \hline 0 & & & \\ 0 & & -\rho_F \mathbf{K}_F & \\ 0 & & & \end{bmatrix}\begin{bmatrix} u \\ \phi_1 \\ \phi_2 \\ \phi_3 \end{bmatrix} = \begin{bmatrix} R(t) \\ 0 \\ 0 \\ 0 \end{bmatrix} \tag{d}$$

669

TABLE E7.9   *Frequencies of fluid-structure model in Fig. E7.9*

Coupled system	Piston without fluid	Fluid without piston, open cavity	Fluid with stationary piston, $k = \infty$
$\omega_1 = 0$		0	0
$\omega_2 = 212$	$\omega = \sqrt{k/m} = 100$	229	502
$\omega_3 = 744$		822	1122

We note that to obtain symmetric coefficient matrices in (d) we have multiplied both sides of (c) by $-\rho_F$. Also, note that in (d) the coefficient matrix to the first time derivatives of the nodal variables is not a damping matrix but simply a matrix that couples the fluid and structural response. There is no physical damping in this problem.

The solution to the problem would be obtained by the time integration of the dynamic response using for example the trapezoidal rule (see Section 9.2.4). However, it is also interesting to evaluate the free-vibration frequencies of the fluid-structure system and compare them with the frequencies of the fluid and the structure when acting alone. Table E7.9 lists these frequencies. We notice that in the fluid-structure system, because of the fluid, the (lowest frequency) structural vibration occurs at a 112 percent higher frequency. This frequency can be expressed as $\omega_2 = \sqrt{(k + k')/(m + m')}$, where k' and m' are an increase in stiffness and mass due to the fluid. Note also that the first frequency $\omega_1 = 0$ corresponds to a "rigid body mode" with $u = 0$ and $\phi_1 = \phi_2 = \phi_3 = $ constant.

Further details of this formulation are given by L. G. Olson and K. J. Bathe [A] and C. Nitikitpaiboon and K. J. Bathe [B].

7.3.5 Exercises

7.9. Use a computer program to solve for the seepage flow in the problem shown. Assume a very long dam. Verify that an accurate solution of the response has been obtained.

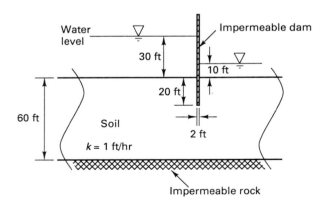

7.10. Use a computer program to solve for the flow of a fluid around the circular object shown. Assume an inviscid fluid and planar flow conditions.

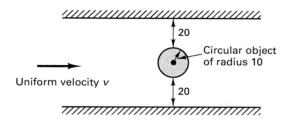

7.11. Use a computer program to solve for the torsional rigidity of the shaft considered in Example 7.7.

7.12. Calculate the steady-state distribution of voltage in the specimen shown. The solution of this kind of problem is of interest in monitoring crack growth (see, for example, R. O. Ritchie and K. J. Bathe [A]).

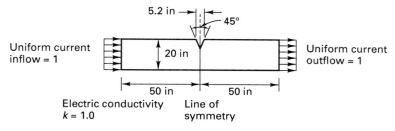

7.13. Use a computer program to solve for the three lowest frequencies of the fluid-spring system considered in Example 7.9. Use a coarse and a fine finite element discretization and compare your results with those given in Example 7.9.

7.14. Use a computer program to solve for the frequency of the cylinder shown oscillating in a cavity of water. (*Hint:* Here the ϕ formulation in Section 7.3.4 is effective.)

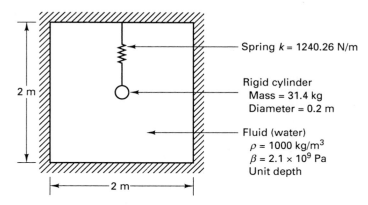

7.4 ANALYSIS OF VISCOUS INCOMPRESSIBLE FLUID FLOWS

A frequently followed approach in the analysis of fluid mechanics problems is to develop the governing differential equations for the specific flow, geometry, and boundary conditions under consideration and then solve these equations using finite difference procedures.

However, during the last decade, much progress has been made toward the analysis of *general* fluid flow problems using finite element procedures, and at present very complex fluid flows are solved. Inviscid and viscous, compressible and incompressible fluid flows with or without heat transfer are analyzed and also the coupling between structural and fluid response is considered (see, for example, K. J. Bathe, H. Zhang, and M. H. Wang [A]).

The objective in this section is to discuss briefly how the finite element procedures presented earlier can also be employed in the analysis of fluid flow problems and to present some important additional techniques that are required if practical problems of fluid flows are to be solved. We consider the large application area of incompressible viscous fluid flow with or without heat transfer. The methods applicable in this field of analysis are also directly used for compressible flow solutions, although additional complex analysis phenomena (notably the calculation of shock fronts) need to be addressed when compressible fluid flow is analyzed.

In order to identify the similarities and differences in the basic finite element formulations of problems in solid (see Chapter 6) and fluid mechanics, consider the summary of the governing continuum mechanics equations given in Table 7.4. In this table and in the discussion to follow we use the indicial notation employed in Chapter 6. Considering the kinematics of a viscous fluid, the fluid particles can undergo very large motions and, for a general description, it is effective to use an Eulerian formulation. The essence of this formulation is that we focus attention on a stationary control volume and that we use this volume to measure the equilibrium and mass continuity of the fluid particles. This means that in the Eulerian formulation a separate equation is written to express the mass conservation relation—a condition that is embodied in the determinant of the deformation gradient when using a Lagrangian formulation. It further means that the inertia forces involve convective terms that, in the numerical solution, result in a nonsymmetric coefficient matrix that depends on the velocities to be calculated.

An advantage of an Eulerian formulation lies in the use of simple stress and strain rate measures, namely, measures that we use in infinitesimal displacement analysis, except that velocities must be calculated instead of displacements. However, if the domain of solution changes, such as in free surface problems, a pure Eulerian formulation would require the creation of new control volumes, and it is more effective to use an arbitrary Lagrangian-Eulerian formulation, as briefly enumerated below.

In the Lagrangian formulations (as discussed in Chapter 6), the mesh moves with (is "attached to") the material particles. Hence, the same material particle is always at the same element mesh point (given in an isoparametric element by the r, s, t coordinates). In the finite element pure Eulerian formulation the mesh points are stationary and the material particles move through the finite element mesh in whichever way the flow conditions govern such movements. In an arbitrary Lagrangian-Eulerian formulation, the mesh points move but not necessarily with the material particles. In fact, the mesh movement corresponds to the nature of the problem and is imposed by the solution algorithm. While the finite element mesh spans the complete analysis domain throughout the solution and its boundaries move with the movements of free surfaces and structural (or solid) boundaries, the fluid particles move relatively to the mesh points. This approach allows the modeling of general free surfaces and interactions between fluid flows and structures (see, for example, A. Huerta and W. K. Liu [A], C. Nitikitpaiboon and K. J. Bathe [B] and K. J. Bathe, H. Zhang, and M. H. Wang [A]).

TABLE 7.4 *Basic continuum mechanics equations used in Lagrangian and Eulerian formulations*

Lagrangian formulation	Eulerian formulation
Geometric representation	**Geometric representation**
${}^tV,\ {}^tS$ ${}^0V,\ {}^0S$ ${}^tx_i = {}^0x_i + {}^tu_i$	Control volume ${}^tx_i \equiv x_i$ $\dfrac{D}{Dt}(\ ) = \dfrac{\partial}{\partial t}(\ ) + {}^tv_j\,\dfrac{\partial}{\partial x_j}(\ )$
Conservation of mass	**Conservation of mass**
$$m = \int_{{}^0V} {}^0\rho\, d^0V = \int_{{}^tV} {}^t\rho\, d^tV \Rightarrow \frac{{}^0\rho}{{}^t\rho} = \det({}_0^t\mathbf{X})$$	$$m = \int_{{}^0V} {}^0\rho\, d^0V = \int_{{}^tV} {}^t\rho\, d^tV \Rightarrow \frac{D}{Dt}({}^t\rho) + {}^t\rho\,\frac{\partial {}^tv_i}{\partial x_i} = 0$$
	Incompressible flow: ${}^tv_{i,i} = 0$
Equations of motion	**Equations of motion**
$$\frac{\partial}{\partial^t x_j}({}^t\tau_{ij}) + {}^t\tilde{f}_i^B = 0;\quad {}^t\tilde{f}_i^B = {}^tf_i^B - {}^t\rho\,{}^t\ddot{u}_i$$	$$\frac{\partial}{\partial x_j}({}^t\tau_{ij}) + {}^t\tilde{f}_i^B = 0;\quad {}^t\tilde{f}_i^B = {}^tf_i^B - {}^t\rho\,\frac{D}{Dt}({}^tv_i)$$
Principle of virtual displacements	**Principle of virtual velocities**
$$\int_{{}^tV} {}^t\tau_{ij}\,\delta_t e_{ij}\, d^tV = \int_{{}^tV} {}^t\tilde{f}_i^B\,\delta u_i\, d^tV + \int_{{}^tS} {}^tf_i^S\,\delta u_i^S\, d^tS$$	$$\int_{{}^tV} {}^t\tau_{ij}\,\delta e_{ij}\, dV = \int_V {}^t\tilde{f}_i^B\,\delta v_i\, dV + \int_S {}^tf_i^S\,\delta v_i^S\, dS$$
Total Lagrangian formulation:	$${}^t\tau_{ij} = -{}^tp\,\delta_{ij} + 2\mu\,{}^te_{ij};\quad {}^te_{ij} = \tfrac{1}{2}({}^tv_{i,j} + {}^tv_{j,i})$$
$$\int_{{}^0V} {}_0^t S_{ij}\,\delta_0\epsilon_{ij}\, d^0V = {}^t\mathcal{R}$$	

To demonstrate the differences in the Lagrangian and Eulerian formulations consider the following example.

> **EXAMPLE 7.10:**   The motions of fluid particles in a duct are given by
>
> $$'x_1 = -5 + \sqrt{25 + 10\,{}^0x_1 + ({}^0x_1)^2 + 4t} \tag{a}$$
>
> (i) Calculate the velocities and accelerations of the particles. Express your results in the Lagrangian form $'\dot{u}_1 = f_1({}^0x_1, t)$, $'\ddot{u}_1 = f_2({}^0x_1, t)$.
>
> (ii) Eliminate ${}^0x_1$ from your expressions in (i) to obtain the spatial expressions for the velocities and accelerations.
>
> (iii) Show that your expression for the acceleration in (ii) may also be obtained by combining the local acceleration and convective acceleration (i.e., by use of the usual Eulerian expression).
> To obtain the result requested in (i) we simply differentiate the expression in (a) with respect to time and note that $d'x_1/dt = d'u_1/dt$ (because $d^0x_1/dt = 0$)
>
> $$\frac{d'u_1}{dt} = \frac{2}{[25 + 10\,{}^0x_1 + ({}^0x_1)^2 + 4t]^{1/2}} \tag{b}$$
>
> Similarly,
> $$\frac{d^2\,'u_1}{dt^2} = \frac{-4}{[25 + 10\,{}^0x_1 + ({}^0x_1)^2 + 4t]^{3/2}} \tag{c}$$
>
> To express (b) and (c) in terms of $'x_1$ we might solve from (a) for ${}^0x_1$ in terms of $'x_1$ and t. However, in this simple example we note
>
> $$'x_1 + 5 = \sqrt{25 + 10\,{}^0x_1 + ({}^0x_1)^2 + 4t}$$
>
> and hence
>
> $$\frac{d'u_1}{dt} = \frac{2}{'x_1 + 5}; \qquad \frac{d^2\,'u_1}{dt^2} = \frac{-4}{('x_1 + 5)^3} \tag{d}$$
>
> In the Eulerian formulation, we simply write $x_1 \equiv\, 'x_1$, and it is implied that x_1 can be any coordinate value. Of course, the expressions in (d) are also valid for any time. We should recognize that in (d) we focus our attention on the coordinate x_1 and measure the velocity and acceleration of the particles as they pass that coordinate. In this calculation we do not use (and generally do not care to know) the initial positions of the particles.
> On the other hand, if we use (b) and (c), we focus our attention on the particles given by their initial positions and we measure the velocities and accelerations of these particles at a particular given time.
> We may also obtain the acceleration in (d) from the general Eulerian expression of acceleration (see Table 7.4). Here we employ (without using the superscript)
>
> $$\frac{Dv}{Dt} = \frac{\partial v}{\partial t} + \frac{\partial v}{\partial x}v; \qquad v \equiv \frac{d'u_1}{dx_1}; \qquad x_1 \equiv x$$
>
> which gives
>
> $$\frac{Dv}{Dt} = \frac{\partial}{\partial t}\left(\frac{2}{x+5}\right) + \left[\frac{\partial}{\partial x}\left(\frac{2}{x+5}\right)\right]\left(\frac{2}{x+5}\right) = 0 - \frac{4}{(x+5)^3}$$
>
> Hence, the local derivative of the velocity is zero and the convective part of the acceleration is $-4/(x+5)^3$.

7.4.1 Continuum Mechanics Equations

Let us summarize the continuum mechanics equations for incompressible fluid flow including heat transfer. These equations are of course developed in detail in standard textbooks on fluid mechanics (see, for example, F. M. White [A] or H. Schlichting [A]), but we summarize the equations here to state the notation and provide the basis for the derivation of the governing finite element equations. We will note that in some respects the notation below is different from the notation we used in the analysis of solid mechanics problems (see Chapter 6) because, for example, the velocity v_i is now the basic kinematic variable to be calculated instead of the displacement solved for in the analysis of solids.

Using a stationary Cartesian reference frame $(x_i, i = 1, 2, 3)$, the governing equations of incompressible fluid flow within the domain V are, using index notation, the usual summation convention, and implying that the conditions at time t are considered without use of a superscript t (which is used in Table 7.4),

momentum:
$$\rho\left(\frac{\partial v_i}{\partial t} + v_{i,j}v_j\right) = \tau_{ij,j} + f_i^B \tag{7.57}$$

constitutive:
$$\tau_{ij} = -p\delta_{ij} + 2\mu e_{ij} \tag{7.58}$$

continuity:
$$v_{i,i} = 0 \tag{7.59}$$

heat transfer:
$$\rho c_p\left[\frac{\partial \theta}{\partial t} + \theta_{,i}v_i\right] = (k\theta_{,i})_{,i} + q^B \tag{7.60}$$

Here we have

v_i = velocity of fluid flow in direction x_i

ρ = mass density

τ_{ij} = components of stress tensor

f_i^B = components of body force vector

p = pressure

δ_{ij} = Kronecker delta

μ = fluid (laminar) viscosity

e_{ij} = components of velocity strain tensor $= \frac{1}{2}(v_{i,j} + v_{j,i})$

c_p = specific heat at constant pressure

θ = temperature

k = thermal conductivity

q^B = rate of heat generated per unit volume [this term also includes the rate of heat dissipated $(=2\mu e_{ij}e_{ij})$]

The boundary conditions corresponding to (7.57) to (7.60) are

Prescribed fluid velocities v_i^S on the surface S_v

$$v_i\big|_{S_v} = v_i^S \tag{7.61}$$

Prescribed tractions f_i^S on the surface S_f,

$$\tau_{ij} n_j \big|_{S_f} = f_i^S \tag{7.62}$$

where the n_j are the components of the unit normal vector **n** (pointing outward) to the fluid surface and the f_i^S are the components of the (physical) traction vector.

Prescribed temperatures θ^S on the surface S_θ,

$$\theta \big|_{S_\theta} = \theta^S \tag{7.63}$$

Prescribed heat flux into the surface S_q,

$$k \frac{\partial \theta}{\partial n} \bigg|_{S_q} = q^S \tag{7.64}$$

where q^S is the heat flux input to the body. We note that for (7.61) to (7.64) the discussions in Sections 4.2.1 and 7.2.1 are directly applicable.

The heat flux input in (7.64) comprises the effect of actually applied distributed heat flow, and the effect of convection and radiation heat transfer. These applied heat fluxes are included in the analysis as discussed in Section 7.2.

Another form of (7.57) is obtained if these momentum equations are written to also include the continuity condition, see Example 7.12. This form is referred to as the conservative form (because momentum conservation is explicitly imposed) and is largely used in finite volume discretization methods, see S. V. Patankar [A].

Equations (7.57) to (7.60) are the standard Navier-Stokes equations governing the motion of a viscous, incompressible fluid in laminar flow with heat transfer. Inherent nonlinearities are due to the convective terms in (7.57) and (7.60) and the radiation boundary condition in (7.64). Additional nonlinearities arise if the viscosity coefficient depends on the temperature or on the velocity strain, if the specific heat c_p, conductivity k, and convection and radiation coefficients depend on temperature, and of course if turbulence descriptions are included (see, for example, W. Rodi [A]).

Before proceeding to develop the finite element equations, let us assume that μ, c_p, and k are constant and rewrite (7.57) to (7.60) into standard forms that reflect some important characteristics of fluid flows. If we substitute (7.58) and (7.59) into (7.57), we obtain

$$\rho(\dot{v}_i + v_{i,j} v_j) = -p_{,i} + f_i^B + \mu v_{i,jj} \tag{7.65}$$

Hence (7.65) is the momentum equation containing the incompressibility condition.

Let us now define the nondimensionalized variables

$$x_i^* = \frac{x_i}{L}; \qquad v_i^* = \frac{v_i}{v}; \qquad t^* = \frac{tv}{L}$$

$$p^* = \frac{p}{\rho v^2}; \qquad f_i^{B*} = \frac{f_i^B L}{\rho v^2} \tag{7.66}$$

$$\theta^* = \frac{\theta - \theta_0}{\Delta \theta}; \qquad q^{B*} = \frac{q^B L}{\rho c_p \Delta \theta v}$$

where L, v, θ_0, and $\Delta\theta$ are chosen characteristic values for length, velocity, temperature, and temperature difference of the problem considered. Using these nondimensionalized variables, we can rewrite the momentum and energy equations in the following forms.

$$\dot{v}_i^* + v_{i,j}^* v_j^* = -p_{,i}^* + f_i^{B*} + \underbrace{\frac{1}{\text{Re}} v_{i,jj}^*}_{} \tag{7.67}$$

$$\underbrace{\phantom{v_{i,j}^* v_j^*}}_{\text{convection}} \qquad \underbrace{\phantom{\frac{1}{\text{Re}} v_{i,jj}^*}}_{\text{diffusion}}$$

and

$$\dot{\theta}^* + \theta_{,i}^* v_i^* = q^{B*} + \underbrace{\frac{1}{\text{Pe}} \theta_{,ii}^*}_{} \tag{7.68}$$

$$\underbrace{\phantom{\theta_{,i}^* v_i^*}}_{\text{convection}} \qquad \underbrace{\phantom{\frac{1}{\text{Pe}} \theta_{,ii}^*}}_{\text{diffusion}}$$

where Re is the Reynolds number

$$\text{Re} = \frac{vL}{\nu}; \qquad \nu = \frac{\mu}{\rho} \tag{7.69}$$

and Pe is the Peclet number

$$\text{Pe} = \frac{vL}{\alpha}; \qquad \alpha = \frac{k}{\rho c_p} \tag{7.70}$$

in which ν and α are the kinematic viscosity and diffusivity of the fluid. Note that using the Prandtl number $\text{Pr} = \nu/\alpha$, we have $\text{Pe} = (\text{Pr})(\text{Re})$.

The relations (7.67) and (7.68) demonstrate a fundamental difficulty in the solution of fluid flow problems: as the Reynolds number increases, the fluid flow is dominated by the convection term in (7.67), and similarly, as the Peclet number increases, the heat transfer in the fluid is dominated by the convection term in (7.68). General analysis procedures must therefore be able to solve for the response governed primarily by diffusion at low Reynolds and Peclet numbers and primarily by convection at high Reynolds and Peclet numbers. We will refer to this observation again in Section 7.4.3.

7.4.2 Finite Element Governing Equations

The finite element solution of the continuum mechanics equations governing the fluid flow is obtained by establishing a weak form of the equations using the Galerkin procedure (see Section 3.3.4 and Examples 4.2 and 7.1). The momentum equations are weighted with the velocities, the continuity equation is weighted with pressure, and the heat transfer equation is weighted with temperature. Integrating over the domain of interest V and using the divergence theorem—to lower the order of the derivatives in the expressions and to incorporate the natural boundary conditions as forcing terms—gives the variational equations to be discretized by finite element interpolations:
momentum:

$$\int_V \bar{v}_i \rho(\dot{v}_i + v_{i,j} v_j) \, dV + \int_V \bar{e}_{ij} \tau_{ij} \, dV = \int_V \bar{v}_i f_i^B \, dV + \int_{S_f} \bar{v}_i^S f_i^s \, dS \tag{7.71}$$

continuity:

$$\int_V \bar{p} v_{i,i} \, dV = 0 \tag{7.72}$$

heat transfer:

$$\int_V \overline{\theta}\rho c_p(\dot{\theta} + \theta_{,i}v_i)\,dV + \int_V k\overline{\theta}_{,i}\theta_{,i}\,dV = \int_V \overline{\theta}q^B\,dV + \int_{S_q} \overline{\theta}^S q^S\,dS \qquad (7.73)$$

where the overbar denotes a virtual quantity.

We may refer to the relation in (7.71) as the principle of virtual velocities, and of course (7.73) represents the principle of virtual temperatures [see (7.7)]. The relations in (7.71) to (7.73) are very similar to the equations we used in Sections 4.2 and 7.2 for the stress and temperature analysis of solids, but the Eulerian formulations in (7.71) and (7.73) include the convective terms. Also, incompressible conditions are considered, and therefore, the finite element formulations and discussions in Sections 4.4.3 and 4.5 are now important. Indeed, we can now directly apply the mixed formulations in Section 4.4.3 but using velocity (instead of displacement) and pressure as variables.

Assume that the finite element discretization of (7.71) to (7.73) is performed with any one of the elements presented in Section 4.4.3, with velocity and pressure as variables and temperature as an additional variable at all velocity nodes (in practice, we would of course use the isoparametric generalizations; see Section 5.3.5). The governing matrix equations for a single element are then

$$\mathbf{M}_v\dot{\hat{\mathbf{v}}} + (\mathbf{K}_{\mu vv} + \mathbf{K}_{vv})\hat{\mathbf{v}} + \mathbf{K}_{vp}\hat{\mathbf{p}} = \mathbf{R}_B + \mathbf{R}_S \qquad (7.74)$$

$$\mathbf{K}_{vp}^T\hat{\mathbf{v}} = \mathbf{0} \qquad (7.75)$$

$$\mathbf{C}\dot{\hat{\boldsymbol{\theta}}} + (\mathbf{K}_{v\theta} + \mathbf{K}_{\theta\theta})\hat{\boldsymbol{\theta}} = \mathbf{Q}_B + \mathbf{Q}_S \qquad (7.76)$$

where $\hat{\mathbf{v}}$, $\hat{\boldsymbol{\theta}}$, and $\hat{\mathbf{p}}$ are, respectively, the unknown nodal point velocities and temperatures, and nodal point or element internal pressure variables.

For example, in two-dimensional planar flow analysis, we have for an element in the x_2, x_3 plane,

$$\begin{bmatrix} \mathbf{M}_{v_2} & & & \\ & \mathbf{M}_{v_3} & & \text{Zeros} \\ & & 0 & \\ \text{Sym.} & & & \mathbf{C} \end{bmatrix} \begin{bmatrix} \dot{\hat{\mathbf{v}}}_2 \\ \dot{\hat{\mathbf{v}}}_3 \\ \dot{\hat{\mathbf{p}}} \\ \dot{\hat{\boldsymbol{\theta}}} \end{bmatrix} + \begin{bmatrix} \mathbf{K}_{\mu v_2 v_2} + \mathbf{K}_{vv_2} & \mathbf{K}_{\mu v_2 v_3} & \mathbf{K}_{v_2 p} & 0 \\ \mathbf{K}_{\mu v_2 v_3}^T & \mathbf{K}_{\mu v_3 v_3} + \mathbf{K}_{vv_3} & \mathbf{K}_{v_3 p} & 0 \\ \mathbf{K}_{v_2 p}^T & \mathbf{K}_{v_3 p}^T & 0 & 0 \\ 0 & 0 & 0 & \mathbf{K}_{v\theta} + \mathbf{K}_{\theta\theta} \end{bmatrix} \begin{bmatrix} \hat{\mathbf{v}}_2 \\ \hat{\mathbf{v}}_3 \\ \hat{\mathbf{p}} \\ \hat{\boldsymbol{\theta}} \end{bmatrix}$$

$$= \begin{bmatrix} \mathbf{R}_{B_2} + \mathbf{R}_{S_2} \\ \mathbf{R}_{B_3} + \mathbf{R}_{S_3} \\ 0 \\ \mathbf{Q}_B + \mathbf{Q}_S \end{bmatrix} \qquad (7.77)$$

Let $\mathbf{H}$ and $\tilde{\mathbf{H}}$ contain the interpolation functions corresponding to the velocities and temperature, and pressure, respectively; then

$$\mathbf{M}_{v_2} = \mathbf{M}_{v_3} = \rho \int_V \mathbf{H}^T\mathbf{H}\,dV \qquad (7.78)$$

$$\mathbf{K}_{\mu v_2 v_2} = \int_V (2\mu\mathbf{H}_{,x_2}^T\mathbf{H}_{,x_2} + \mu\mathbf{H}_{,x_3}^T\mathbf{H}_{,x_3})\,dV$$

$$\mathbf{K}_{\mu v_2 v_3} = \int_V (\mu\mathbf{H}_{,x_3}^T\mathbf{H}_{,x_2})\,dV \qquad (7.79)$$

$$\mathbf{K}_{\mu v_3 v_3} = \int_V (2\mu \mathbf{H}^T_{,x_3} \mathbf{H}_{,x_3} + \mu \mathbf{H}^T_{,x_2} \mathbf{H}_{,x_2})\, dV$$

$$\mathbf{K}_{v v_2} = \mathbf{K}_{v v_3} = \rho \int_V (\mathbf{H}^T \mathbf{H} \hat{v}_2\, \mathbf{H}_{,x_2} + \mathbf{H}^T \mathbf{H} \hat{v}_3\, \mathbf{H}_{,x_3})\, dV \tag{7.80}$$

$$\mathbf{K}_{v_2 p} = - \int_V \mathbf{H}^T_{,x_2} \tilde{\mathbf{H}}\, dV \tag{7.81}$$

$$\mathbf{K}_{v_3 p} = - \int_V \mathbf{H}^T_{,x_3} \tilde{\mathbf{H}}\, dV \tag{7.82}$$

$$\mathbf{R}_B = \int_V \mathbf{H}^T \mathbf{f}^B\, dV \tag{7.83}$$

$$\mathbf{R}_S = \int_{S_f} \mathbf{H}^{ST} \mathbf{f}^S\, dS \tag{7.84}$$

$$\mathbf{C} = \rho \int_V c_p \mathbf{H}^T \mathbf{H}\, dV \tag{7.85}$$

$$\mathbf{K}_{\theta\theta} = \int_V k(\mathbf{H}^T_{,x_2} \mathbf{H}_{,x_2} + \mathbf{H}^T_{,x_3} \mathbf{H}_{,x_3})\, dV \tag{7.86}$$

$$\mathbf{K}_{v\theta} = \rho \int_V c_p \mathbf{H}^T \mathbf{H} \hat{v}_2 \mathbf{H}_{,x_2}\, dV + \rho \int_V c_p \mathbf{H}^T \mathbf{H} \hat{v}_3 \mathbf{H}_{,x_3}\, dV \tag{7.87}$$

$$\mathbf{Q}_B = \int_V \mathbf{H}^T q^B\, dV \tag{7.88}$$

$$\mathbf{Q}_S = \int_{S_q} \mathbf{H}^{ST} q^S\, dS \tag{7.89}$$

Here we should note that in considering a straight boundary the components of $\mathbf{f}^S$ are

$$f_n = -p + 2\mu \frac{\partial v_n}{\partial n} \tag{7.90}$$

$$f_t = \mu \left(\frac{\partial v_t}{\partial n} + \frac{\partial v_n}{\partial t} \right) \tag{7.91}$$

where n and t denote the coordinate axes in the normal and tangential directions on the boundary and v_n and v_t are the normal and tangential boundary velocities.

We note that since totally incompressible conditions are considered, the diagonal elements corresponding to the pressure variables are zero. Hence, even if the pressure variables stored in $\hat{\mathbf{p}}$ correspond to element internal variables and not nodal point variables (as in the u/p formulation; see Section 4.4.3), the pressure variables cannot be statically condensed out at the element level. For such a procedure to be used, we must consider an almost incompressible condition, meaning that (7.72) would need to be replaced by (see Sections 4.4.3 and 4.5)

$$\int_V \bar{p} \left(\frac{p}{\kappa} + v_{i,i} \right) dV = 0 \tag{7.92}$$

in which κ (being very large) is the bulk modulus.

We can now refer to all the procedures discussed in Chapters 4 (notably Sections 4.4 and 4.5) and 5. They are directly applicable to obtain appropriate finite element discretizations of the governing fluid flow equations (see also the exercises at the end of this section). Of course, we note that the resulting finite element equations are in general highly nonlinear equations [see (7.77)] because of the convective terms and boundary radiation conditions and because in general the material properties are not constant (e.g., the viscosity μ depends significantly on the temperature θ).

The finite element governing fluid flow equations—given for a two-dimensional element in (7.77)—can be written in the form

$$\mathbf{R} - \mathbf{F} = \mathbf{0} \tag{7.93}$$

This relation must hold for all times considered, and the solution can be obtained incrementally for times Δt, $2\Delta t$, ..., as discussed in Chapters 6 and 9. In steady-state analysis, the terms $\mathbf{M\dot{v}}$ and $\mathbf{C\dot{\theta}}$ are neglected, and the incremental analysis can be pursued using a form of Newton-Raphson iteration for each time $t + \Delta t$ considered, time then denoting merely the load levels (see Chapter 6). In transient analysis, using implicit integration, a form of Newton-Raphson iteration should also be used for each time step. Alternatively, explicit integration can be performed on the velocity and temperature variables, while the incompressibility constraint demands implicit integration of the pressure equations.

A major difficulty in the solution of fluid flow problems is that the number of solution variables is generally very large (to obtain a realistic resolution of the fluid response, very fine finite element discretizations need to be employed) and that the coefficient matrices are nonsymmetric. Hence, explicit schemes that do not require the solution of a set of equations (see Sections 9.5.1 and 9.6.1) and iterative methods for the solution of equations are very attractive (see Section 8.3).

Finally, we may ask why the relations (7.57) and (7.60) were used to develop the finite element equations instead of (7.67) and (7.68). One reason is that (7.57) and (7.60) are directly applicable to flow with nonconstant material conditions. Another reason is that the momentum equation (7.57) when used in the Galerkin method leads to a surface force vector that contains the *physical* tractions given in (7.90) and (7.91), whereas if (7.67) is used, the resulting surface "force" vector contains nonphysical components (see Example 7.11). Therefore, the formulation based on (7.57) is frequently more general and natural, in particular when arbitrary Lagrangian-Eulerian formulations are developed that are used for the analysis of free surface flows and interactions between fluid flows and structures. Of course, the finite element matrix equations (7.74) to (7.76) are applicable to the solution of fluid flow and heat transfer problems in any set of consistent units, including the use of nondimensionalized variables.

In the following examples we consider two additional forms of the Navier-Stokes equations that can be used for finite element solutions.

EXAMPLE 7.11: Consider the solution of the Navier-Stokes equations [see (7.67)],

$$v_{i,j}v_j = -p_{,i} + \frac{1}{\text{Re}}\, v_{i,jj} \qquad i, j = 1, 2$$

Use the Galerkin procedure by weighting this equation with velocity and derive the naturally arising boundary terms. Consider two-dimensional analysis and compare these terms with the expressions of the physical tractions.

Using the Galerkin procedure, we obtain

$$\int_V \bar{v}_i \left(v_{i,j} v_j + p_{,i} - \frac{1}{\text{Re}} v_{i,jj} \right) dV = 0 \tag{a}$$

The boundary terms are established as in Examples 4.2 and 7.1. Here we use the identities

$$\bar{v}_i p_{,j} \delta_{ij} = (\bar{v}_i p \delta_{ij})_{,j} - \bar{v}_{i,j} p \delta_{ij}$$

and

$$\bar{v}_i v_{i,jj} = (\bar{v}_i v_{i,j})_{,j} - \bar{v}_{i,j} v_{i,j}$$

Hence, using the divergence theorem, we obtain from (a) the boundary term

$$\int_S \bar{v}_i (-p\delta_{ij} + \frac{1}{\text{Re}} v_{i,j}) n_j \, dS$$

However, this relation can be interpreted as

$$\int_S \bar{v}_i \tilde{f}_i \, dS$$

where

$$\tilde{f}_i = (-p\delta_{ij} + \frac{1}{\text{Re}} v_{i,j}) n_j$$

Considering a straight boundary, we have

$$\tilde{f}_n = -p + \frac{1}{\text{Re}} \frac{\partial v_n}{\partial n}$$

$$\tilde{f}_t = \frac{1}{\text{Re}} \frac{\partial v_t}{\partial n} \tag{b}$$

where n and t denote the coordinate axes in the directions normal and tangential to the surface boundary.

The relation (7.67) was obtained using nondimensionalized variables, and for given characteristic velocity and length we have $1/\text{Re} \sim \nu$. Hence, we see that the expressions in (b) are not equal to the actual force expressions in (7.90) and (7.91).

EXAMPLE 7.12:   Show that the momentum equations (7.57) can also be written as

$$\rho \frac{\partial v_i}{\partial t} + F_{ij,j} = f_i^B \tag{a}$$

where

$$F_{ij} = \rho v_j v_i - \tau_{ij} \tag{b}$$

Then identify the difference that will arise when (a) is used instead of (7.57) in the Galerkin procedure to obtain the governing finite element equations.

Using (b), we obtain

$$F_{ij,j} = (\rho v_j v_i - \tau_{ij})_{,j} = \rho v_{j,j} v_i + \rho v_j v_{i,j} - \tau_{ij,j} = \rho v_{i,j} v_j - \tau_{ij,j} \tag{c}$$

Hence, by inspection we see that (c) used in (a) gives (7.57).

The form (a) is referred to as the conservative form of the momentum equations because, by the divergence theorem, for *any* subdomain V_{SD} of the fluid

$$\int_{V_{SD}} F_{ij,j} \, dV = \int_{S_{SD}} F_{ij} n_j \, dS$$

where S_{SD} is the surface area of the volume V_{SD} and the n_j are the components of the unit normal vector to S_{SD}. Similarly, the energy equation can also be written in conservative form.

To identify the difference in the finite element discretization, we only need to compare the terms $\int_V \overline{v}_i(v_j v_i)_{,j}\, dV$ and $\int_V \overline{v}_i(v_{i,j}v_j)\, dV$ because the other terms are identical, and the difference is the term $\int_V \overline{v}_i(v_i v_{j,j})\, dV$. The form of the momentum equations in (a) is typically used in finite volume methods (see S. V. Patankar [A]). Note, however, that if (a) is used in a finite element (Galerkin) formulation, the use of the divergence theorem gives on the surface S_f the usual traction term (see Example 4.2) and an additional term involving the unknown velocities.

7.4.3 High Reynolds and High Peclet Number Flows

The finite element formulation of fluid flows presented in the previous section is a natural development when we consider the formulations presented earlier for the analysis of solids. The standard Galerkin procedure was used on the differential equations of motion and heat transfer, resulting in the "principle of virtual velocities" and the "principle of virtual temperatures." The finite element discretization is appropriately obtained with finite elements that are stable and convergent with the incompressibility constraint. Hence, we used elements that satisfy the inf-sup condition, as discussed in Sections 4.4.3 and 4.5. With such elements, excellent results are obtained for low-Reynolds-number flows (in particular Stokes flows).

However, as we pointed out in Section 7.4.2, a major difference between the formulations for the analysis of fluid flows and of solids is the convective terms arising in the Eulerian fluid flow formulation. These convective terms give rise to the nonsymmetry in the finite element coefficient matrix, and when the convection is strong (as defined by the Reynolds and Peclet numbers; see discussion below), the system of equations is strongly nonsymmetric and then an additional numerical difficulty arises.

However, before we discuss this difficulty, let us recall that of course depending on the flow considered, as the Reynolds number increases and when a certain range is reached, the flow condition turns from laminar to turbulent. In theory, the turbulent flow could still be calculated by solving the general Navier-Stokes equations presented in the previous section, but such solution would require extremely fine discretization to model the details of turbulence. For practical flow conditions, the resulting finite element systems would be too large, by far, for present software and hardware capabilities. For this reason, it is common practice to solve the Navier-Stokes equations for the mean flow and express the turbulence effects by means of turbulent viscosity and heat conductivity coefficients and use wall functions to describe the near-wall behaviors.

The modeling of turbulence is a very large and important field (see W. Rodi [A]), and the finite element procedures we presented earlier for solution are in many regards directly applicable. However, one important factor in the finite element scheme must then also be that the Navier-Stokes equations corresponding to laminar flow at high Reynolds and Peclet numbers can be solved (with reasonably sized meshes). Namely, it is this solution that provides the basis for obtaining the solution of the turbulent flow.

Hence, in the following we briefly address the difficulty of solving high Reynolds (or Peclet) number conditions assuming laminar flow. For this purpose let us consider the simplest possible case that displays the difficulties that we encounter in general flow conditions. These difficulties arise from the magnitude of the convective terms when compared to the diffusive terms in (7.67) and (7.68). Hence, we consider a model problem of one-dimensional flow with prescribed velocity v (see Fig. 7.4). The temperature is prescribed

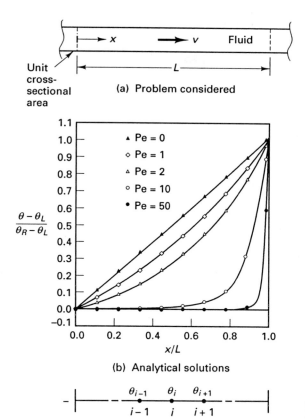

(a) Problem considered

(b) Analytical solutions

(c) Finite element nodes (and finite difference stations)

Figure 7.4   Heat transfer in one-dimensional flow condition; prescribed velocity v; $q^B = 0$; $\text{Pe} = \dfrac{vL}{\alpha}$, $\alpha = k/\rho c_p$

at two points, which we label $x = 0$ and $x = L$, and we want to calculate the temperature for $0 < x < L$.

The governing differential equation obtained from (7.60) is

$$\rho c_p \frac{d\theta}{dx} v = k \frac{d^2\theta}{dx^2} \tag{7.94}$$

with the boundary conditions

$$\begin{aligned} \theta &= \theta_L && \text{at } x = 0 \\ \theta &= \theta_R && \text{at } x = L \end{aligned} \tag{7.95}$$

and the left-hand side in (7.94) represents the convective terms and the right-hand side the diffusive terms.

Of course, the convective and diffusive terms appear in a similar form in the Navier-Stokes equations [see (7.67)], which can also be considered in a one-dimensional analogously simple form. However, the resulting differential equation is nonlinear in v, whereas (7.94) is linear in θ. Since the solution of (7.94) already displays the basic solution difficulties, we prefer to consider (7.94) but recognize that the basic observations are also applicable to the solution of the Navier-Stokes equations.

Figure 7.4 shows for various Peclet numbers, $\mathrm{Pe} = vL/\alpha$, the exact solution to the problem in (7.94), given by

$$\frac{\theta - \theta_L}{\theta_R - \theta_L} = \frac{\exp\left(\dfrac{\mathrm{Pe}}{L}x\right) - 1}{\exp(\mathrm{Pe}) - 1} \tag{7.96}$$

Hence, as Pe increases, the exact solution curve shows a strong boundary layer at $x = L$.

To demonstrate the inherent difficulty in the finite element solution, let us use two-node elements each of length h corresponding to a linearly varying temperature over each element. If we use the principle of virtual temperatures corresponding to (7.73) (that is, we use the [standard] Galerkin method), we obtain for the finite element node i the governing equation

$$\left(-1 - \frac{\mathrm{Pe}^e}{2}\right)\theta_{i-1} + 2\theta_i + \left(\frac{\mathrm{Pe}^e}{2} - 1\right)\theta_{i+1} = 0 \tag{7.97}$$

where the element Peclet number is $\mathrm{Pe}^e = vh/\alpha$.

Hence
$$\theta_i = \frac{1 - \mathrm{Pe}^e/2}{2}\theta_{i+1} + \frac{1 + \mathrm{Pe}^e/2}{2}\theta_{i-1} \tag{7.98}$$

However, this equation already shows that for high values of Pe^e, physically unrealistic results are obtained. For example, if $\theta_{i-1} = 0$ and $\theta_{i+1} = 100$, we have $\theta_i = 50(1 - \mathrm{Pe}^e/2)$, which gives a negative value if $\mathrm{Pe}^e > 2$!

Figure 7.5 shows results obtained in the solution of the model problem in Fig. 7.4 with the two-node element discretization for the case $\mathrm{Pe} = 20$ when using increasingly finer meshes. Actually, the analytical solution of (7.97) shows that for a reasonably accurate response prediction we need Pe^e smaller than 2. This result is also reflected in Fig. 7.5 and means that a very fine mesh is required when Pe is large. In practical analyses, flows of very high Peclet and Reynolds numbers ($\mathrm{Re} \sim 10^6$) need be solved, and the finite element discretization scheme discussed in the previous section must be amended to be applicable to such problems.

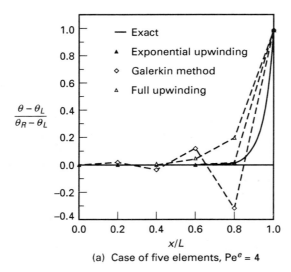

(a) Case of five elements, $\mathrm{Pe}^e = 4$

Figure 7.5 Solution of problem in Fig. 7.4 using two-node elements. $\mathrm{Pe} = 20$. The exponential upwinding, Petrov-Galerkin, and Galerkin least squares methods give the exact values at the nodes.

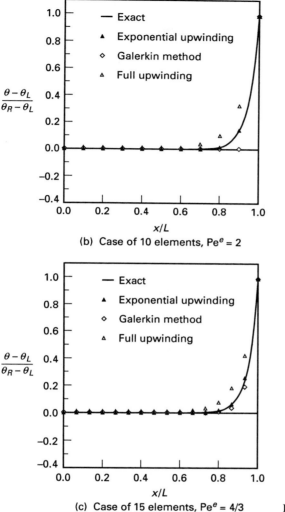

(b) Case of 10 elements, $Pe^e = 2$

(c) Case of 15 elements, $Pe^e = 4/3$ **Figure 7.5** (*continued*)

The shortcoming exposed above was recognized and overcome early by researchers using finite difference methods (see R. Courant, E. Isaacson, and M. Rees [A]). Namely, considering (7.97), we realize that this equation is also obtained when central differencing is used to solve (7.94) (see Section 3.3.5). Hence, the same solution inaccuracies are seen when the commonly employed central difference method is used to solve (7.94).

The remedy designed to overcome the above difficulties is to use upwinding. In the finite difference upwind scheme, we use

$$\frac{d\theta}{dx}\Big|_i \doteq \frac{\theta_i - \theta_{i-1}}{h} \qquad \text{if } v > 0$$

$$\frac{d\theta}{dx}\Big|_i \doteq \frac{\theta_{i+1} - \theta_i}{h} \qquad \text{if } v < 0$$

(7.99)

In the following discussion we first assume $v > 0$ and then we generalize the results to consider any value of v [see (7.115)].

If $v > 0$, the finite difference approximation of (7.94) is

$$(-1 - \text{Pe}^e)\theta_{i-1} + (2 + \text{Pe}^e)\theta_i - \theta_{i+1} = 0 \tag{7.100}$$

Figure 7.5 shows the results obtained with this upwinding (denoted as "full upwinding") for the problem being considered and shows that the oscillating solution behavior is no longer present.

This solution improvement is explained by the nature of the (exact) analytical solution: if the flow is in the positive x-direction, the values of θ are influenced more by the upstream value θ_L than by the downstream value θ_R. Indeed, when Pe is large, the value of θ is close to the upstream value θ_L over much of the solution domain. The same observation holds when the flow is in the negative x-direction, but then θ_R is of course the upstream value.

The intuitive implication of this observation is that in the finite difference discretization of (7.94), it should be appropriate to give more weight to the upstream value, and this is in essence accomplished in (7.100). Of course, it is desirable to further improve on the solution accuracy, and for the relatively simple (one-dimensional) equation (7.94), such improvement is obtained using different approaches. We briefly present below three such techniques that are actually closely related and result in excellent accuracy in one-dimensional analysis cases. However, the generalization of these methods to obtain small solution errors using relatively coarse discretizations in general two- and three-dimensional flow conditions is a difficult matter (see the end of this section).

Exponential Scheme

The basic idea of the exponential scheme is to match the numerical solution to the analytical (exact) solution, which is known in the case considered here (see D. B. Spalding [A] and S. V. Patankar [A] for the development in control volume finite difference procedures).

To introduce the scheme, let us rewrite (7.94) in the form

$$\frac{df}{dx} = 0 \tag{7.101}$$

where the flux f is given by the convective minus diffusive parts,

$$f = v\theta - \alpha\frac{d\theta}{dx} \tag{7.102}$$

The finite difference approximation of the relation in (7.101) for station i gives

$$f|_{i+1/2} - f|_{i-1/2} = 0 \tag{7.103}$$

This equation of course also corresponds to satisfying flux equilibrium for the control volume between the stations $i + \frac{1}{2}$ and $i - \frac{1}{2}$.

We now use the exact solution in (7.96) to express $f_{i+1/2}$ and $f_{i-1/2}$ in terms of the temperature values at the stations $i - 1, i, i + 1$. Hence, using (7.96) for the interval i to

$i + 1$, we obtain

$$f_{i+1/2} = v\left[\theta_i + \frac{\theta_i - \theta_{i+1}}{\exp{(\mathrm{Pe}^e)} - 1}\right] \qquad (7.104)$$

Similarly, we obtain an expression for $f_{i-1/2}$, and the relation (7.103) gives

$$(-1 - c)\theta_{i-1} + (2 + c)\theta_i - \theta_{i+1} = 0 \qquad (7.105)$$

where $$c = \exp{(\mathrm{Pe}^e)} - 1 \qquad (7.106)$$

We notice that for $\mathrm{Pe}^e = 0$ the relation in (7.105) reduces to the use of the central difference method (and the Galerkin method) corresponding to the diffusive term only (because the convective term is zero) and that (7.105) has the form of (7.100) with c replacing Pe^e. This scheme based on the analytical solution of the problem in Fig. 7.4 of course gives the exact solution even when only very few elements are used in the discretization (see Fig. 7.5). The scheme also yields very accurate solutions when the velocity v varies along the length of the domain considered and when source terms are included. A computational disadvantage is that the exponential functions need to be evaluated, and in practice it is sufficiently accurate and somewhat more effective to use a polynomial approximation instead of the (exact) analytical solution, which is referred to as the power law method (see S. V. Patankar [A] and Exercise 7.23).

Petrov-Galerkin Method

The principle of virtual temperatures, as presented and used in Section 7.2, represents an application of the classical Galerkin method in which the same trial functions are used to express the weighting and the solution (see Section 3.3.3). However, in principle, different functions may be employed, and for certain types of problems such an approach can lead to increased solution accuracy.

In the Petrov-Galerkin method, different functions are employed for the weighting than for the solution quantities. Let us assume that we are still using two-node elements to discretize the domain of the problem in Fig. 7.4. Then the ith equation is

$$\int_{-h}^{+h} \tilde{h}_i v \frac{dh_j}{dx}\theta_j\, dx + \int_{-h}^{+h} \frac{d\tilde{h}_i}{dx}\alpha \frac{dh_j}{dx}\theta_j\, dx = 0 \qquad j = i - 1, i, i + 1 \qquad (7.107)$$

where $\tilde{h}_i$ denotes the weighting function and the h_j are the usual functions of linear temperature distributions between nodes $i - 1$, i, and $i + 1$ (see Fig. 7.6).

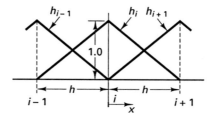

Figure 7.6 Finite element functions used in (7.107)

The basic idea is now to choose $\tilde{h}_i$ such as to obtain optimal accuracy. An efficient scheme is to use

$$\tilde{h}_i = h_i + \gamma \frac{h}{2} \frac{dh_i}{dx} \qquad \text{for } v > 0$$

$$\tilde{h}_i = h_i - \gamma \frac{h}{2} \frac{dh_i}{dx} \qquad \text{for } v < 0 \qquad (7.108)$$

Using this weighting function in (7.107), we obtain for the case $v > 0$,

$$\left[-1 - \frac{\text{Pe}^e}{2}(\gamma + 1) \right] \theta_{i-1} + (2 + \gamma \, \text{Pe}^e)\theta_i + \left[-\frac{\text{Pe}^e}{2}(\gamma - 1) - 1 \right] \theta_{i+1} = 0 \qquad (7.109)$$

We note that with $\gamma = 0$ the standard Galerkin finite element equation in (7.97) is recovered, and when $\gamma = 1$, the full upwind finite difference scheme in (7.100) is obtained.

The variable γ can be evaluated such that nodal exact values are obtained for all values of Pe^e (see I. Christie, D. F. Griffiths, A. R. Mitchell, and O. C. Zienkiewicz [A] and Exercise 7.19)

$$\gamma = \coth\left(\frac{\text{Pe}^e}{2}\right) - \frac{2}{\text{Pe}^e} \qquad (7.110)$$

The case $v < 0$ is solved similarly. Of course, the results of our test problem in Fig. 7.5 using the Petrov-Galerkin method with the γ value given above are the same as those using the exponential upwinding.

Galerkin Least Squares Method

In the Galerkin least squares method, the basic Galerkin equation is supplemented with a least squares expression so as to obtain good solution accuracy (see T. J. R. Hughes, L. P. Franca, and G. M. Hulbert [A]).

We introduced the least squares method in Section 3.3.3. For the problem in (7.94), we have, corresponding to (3.13),

$$L_{2m}[h_i] = v \frac{dh_i}{dx} - \alpha \frac{d^2 h_i}{dx^2} \qquad (7.111)$$

and

$$R_h = v \frac{d\theta_h}{dx} - \alpha \frac{d^2 \theta_h}{dx^2} \qquad (7.112)$$

where the subscript h denotes the finite element solution corresponding to the mesh with elements of size h.

In the Galerkin least squares method the equation for the nodal variable θ_i is generated by using the classical Galerkin expression and adding a factor τ times the least squares expression in (3.16). The factor τ is determined to obtain good solution accuracy.

Using for our problem the two-node finite element discretization and evaluating the residual element by element [hence, the second derivative terms in (7.111) and (7.112) are zero], the ith equation is

$$\int_{-h}^{+h} h_i v \frac{dh_j}{dx} \theta_j \, dx + \int_{-h}^{+h} \frac{dh_i}{dx} \alpha \frac{dh_j}{dx} \theta_j \, dx + \int_{-h}^{+h} \left(v \frac{dh_i}{dx} \right) \tau \left(v \frac{dh_j}{dx} \theta_j \right) dx = 0 \qquad j = i - 1, i, i + 1$$

$$(7.113)$$

where the last integral on the left-hand side corresponds to (3.16) and τ is an as-yet-undetermined parameter. To evaluate τ we can match the relation in (7.113) with the exact analytical solution (as we have done for the exponential scheme and the Petrov-Galerkin method), and thus we obtain

$$\tau = \frac{h}{2v} \coth \frac{Pe^e}{2} - \frac{\alpha}{v^2} \tag{7.114}$$

Of course, the results of the test problem in Fig. 7.5 are by construction the same (nodal exact) results as those obtained using the exponential scheme and the Petrov-Galerkin method.

Comparison of Methods

It is interesting at this point to compare the exponential method, the Petrov-Galerkin method, and the Galerkin least squares procedure. Such a comparison shows that the equations (7.105), (7.109), and (7.113) with the optimal values of c, γ, and τ, respectively, are identical within a factor [which has no effect because the right-hand side of the equations is zero (see Exercise 7.21)]. Of course, for this reason, the solutions are identical. (However, we should note that different solutions from the exponential scheme and the Petrov-Galerkin method must in general be expected if a general source term is included in (7.94) and treated differently, whereas for the linear interpolations used here, the Galerkin least squares method always gives the same solution as the Petrov-Galerkin scheme).

A second interesting observation and valuable interpretation is that all these methods are in essence equivalent to the Galerkin approximation with an additional diffusion term. Namely, if we write the Galerkin solution of (7.94) with an additional diffusion term $\alpha\beta$, we obtain

$$\int_{-h}^{+h} \left[h_i v \frac{dh_j}{dx} \theta_j + \frac{dh_i}{dx} (1 + \beta)\alpha \frac{dh_j}{dx} \theta_j \right] dx = 0 \qquad j = i - 1, i, i + 1 \tag{7.115}$$

where β is a nondimensional constant, and we now consider v to be positive or negative. The solution of (7.115) is

$$-(1 + q)\theta_{i-1} + 2\theta_i - (1 - q)\theta_{i+1} = 0 \tag{7.116}$$

where

$$q = \frac{Pe^e}{2} \frac{1}{1 + \beta} \tag{7.117}$$

The value of β depends on which method is used. Of course, $\beta = 0$ is the standard Galerkin technique, and comparing, for example, (7.115) with (7.113), we find for the Galerkin least squares method

$$\beta = \frac{v\tau}{h} Pe^e \tag{7.118}$$

Table 7.5 summarizes the value of β for the various upwinding procedures considered above. The table also includes the power law, which closely approximates the exponential scheme and is computationally less expensive (see Fig. 7.7). *Note that Table 7.5 does not suggest that we solve (7.94) with the diffusivity $(1 + \beta)\alpha$. Instead, the discretized equations obtained with the Galerkin method are constructed for the diffusivity $(1 + \beta)\alpha$ in order to obtain an accurate solution of (7.94).*

TABLE 7.5 *Additional diffusion term $\beta\alpha$ used in the Galerkin method corresponding to various upwinding procedures*

Procedure	Factor β
Standard Galerkin	0.0
Full upwinding	$\dfrac{\lvert Pe^e \rvert}{2}$
Exponential scheme, Petrov-Galerkin, and Galerkin least squares	$\dfrac{Pe^e}{2}\coth\dfrac{Pe^e}{2} - 1$
Power law	$\dfrac{\lvert Pe^e \rvert}{2} - 1 + \max\{1 - 0.1\lvert Pe^e \rvert, 0.0\}^5$

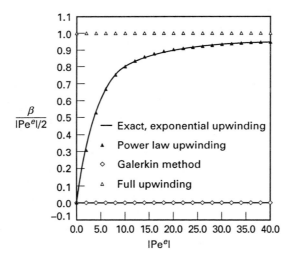

$\dfrac{\beta}{\lvert Pe^e\rvert/2}$

— Exact, exponential upwinding

▲ Power law upwinding

◇ Galerkin method

△ Full upwinding

$\lvert Pe^e \rvert$

Figure 7.7   Value of β in (7.115) for different methods

The formulas given in Table 7.5 are quite general and are applicable to varying element size and velocity v but of course assume one-dimensional flow and no source term.

Of course, Table 7.5 only lists some techniques, and additional schemes have been proposed; see, for example, N. Kondo, N. Tosaka, and T. Nishimura [A].

Finally we should also mention that the use of element internal bubble functions is equivalent to introducing upwinding. These functions couple only to the degrees of freedom of the specific element considered. The approach used is to compute the response including the bubble functions and to then, in essence, ignore the response in the bubbles. As an example, in one-dimensional response analysis, parabolic instead of linear elements may be used. Then the parabolic variation (beyond the linear variation) corresponds to the bubble response (see F. Brezzi and A. Russo [A] and Exercise 7.25).

Generalization of Techniques

As we pointed out earlier, although we considered the heat transfer problem, the same numerical procedures are also employed in the solution of the Navier-Stokes equations. Here the Reynolds number is of course used instead of the Peclet number to determine the parameters for upwinding.

The three schemes—the exponential scheme, the Petrov-Galerkin technique, and Galerkin least squares method—are closely related (because they all are based on matching the analytical solution of our simple model problem) and give accurate solutions of quite general one-dimensional flow problems. With such excellent experiences in the analysis of one-dimensional problems, these approaches appear attractive for the development of solution schemes for general two- and three-dimensional flow conditions. However, effective and accurate solution schemes for two- and three-dimensional complex flows have been difficult to reach.

In finite difference control volume methods, the exponential and power law schemes (see Exercise 7.18) have been quite simply applied to the different coordinate directions using the respective flow velocities, and generalizations have also been achieved; see, for example, W. J. Minkowycz, E. M. Sparrow, G. E. Schneider, and R. H. Pletcher [A].

For finite element analysis, the Petrov-Galerkin and Galerkin least squares techniques have been developed for general two- and three-dimensional solutions by applying, in essence, the one-dimensional schemes along the streamlines within each element. In the Petrov-Galerkin method the velocity resultant along the streamlines is used to establish the element Peclet number and hence the function $\tilde{h}_i$, resulting in the streamline upwind Petrov-Galerkin (SuPG) method (see A. N. Brooks and T. J. R. Hughes [A] and C. Johnson, U. Nävert, and J. Pitkäranta [A]). In the Galerkin least squares method, a tensor τ is used, the elements of which are a function of the Peclet number (see L. P. Franca, S. L. Frey, and T. J. R. Hughes [A]). Of course, the two techniques can also be combined.

Another, related approach is to use the techniques of the control volume finite difference method (notably the exponential or power law method) and embed these techniques in low-order finite elements. The diffusion part of the governing equations can then be discretized using the standard Galerkin method, whereas the convection part can be treated with the power law upwinding as given in Table 7.5. Of course, the finite elements used should also satisfy the inf-sup condition, so that a stable and convergent solution scheme is employed for low and high Reynolds and Peclet number flows. Experiences with such a scheme using the 4/3-c triangular and 5/4-c tetrahedral elements for two- and three-dimensional flows (see Table 4.7) in which the upwinding is applied measured on the flow through the element faces are presented by K. J. Bathe, H. Zhang and M. H. Wang [A].

7.4.4 Exercises

7.15. Starting with the basic equations (7.57) to (7.60), derive (7.65) and then also derive (7.67) and (7.68).

7.16. Show in detail that the matrix expressions for the two-dimensional planar flow conditions given in (7.77) to (7.89) are correct.

7.17. Consider that the matrix equations in (7.77) are to be solved for the steady-state case using a full Newton-Raphson iteration. Develop the coefficient matrix and give all details of the evaluations to be performed (but do not perform any integrations). Assume constant material properties and proceed as indicated in Sections 6.3.1 and 8.4.1.

7.18. Derive the expressions for upwinding given in (7.105) and (7.106).

7.19. Derive the expressions for upwinding given in (7.109) and (7.110).

7.20. Derive the expressions for upwinding given in (7.113) and (7.114).

7.21. Show analytically that the equations (7.105), (7.109), and (7.113) give identical solutions.

7.22. Show that the solution of (7.115) is given by (7.116) and (7.117).

7.23. Prove that the values of β in Table 7.5 are correct and show that the value of β given for the power law is close to the value of the exponential scheme.

7.24. Derive the governing finite element equation for the solution of (7.94) for node 20 of the assemblage of the two-node elements shown.
  (a) Use the Petrov-Galerkin method.
  (b) Use full upwinding.

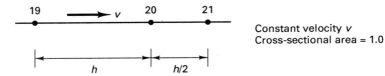

Constant velocity v
Cross-sectional area = 1.0

7.25. Consider the three-node one-dimensional element shown for the solution of (7.94). Show that the bubble function $\tilde{h}_3$ introduces, in essence, upwinding in the element. [*Hint:* Apply the Galerkin procedure to the element and evaluate the value of β when comparing the equations you have established with (7.115).]

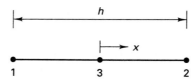

$$h_1 = \frac{1}{2}\left(1 - \frac{2x}{h}\right); \quad h_2 = \frac{1}{2}\left(1 + \frac{2x}{h}\right)$$
$$\tilde{h}_3 = 1 - \left(\frac{2x}{h}\right)^2$$

7.26. Consider the three-node element with the "hat function" instead of a parabola corresponding to the middle node for the solution of (7.94). Show that this hat function $\hat{h}_3$ introduces, in essence, upwinding in the element (see Exercise 7.25).

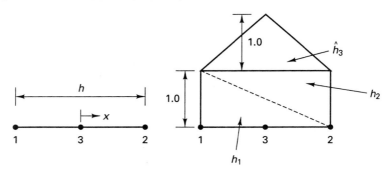

7.27. Consider the water-filled cavity acted upon by gravity as shown. Use a computer program to calculate (with a very coarse mesh) the velocities (to be calculated as zero, of course) and the pressure distribution in the water. Prescribe that the velocities are zero on the boundary (but calculate "unknown" velocities in the domain).

$$g = 10$$
$$\rho = 1.0$$
$$p = 0 \text{ at } z = 0$$

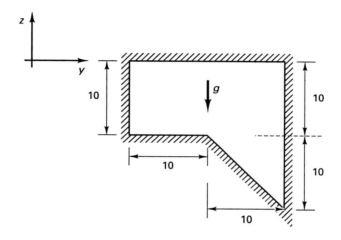

7.28. Use a computer program to analyze the fully developed flow between two concentric cylinders rotating at speeds ω_1 and ω_2 as shown. Verify that an accurate solution has been obtained.

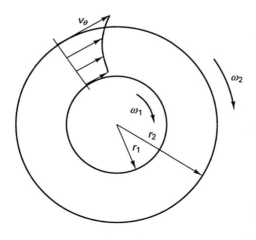

$$r_1 = 1;\ r_2 = 2;$$
$$\omega_1 = 1;\ \omega_2 = 2;$$
$$\rho = 1;\ \mu = 1;$$

7.29. Use a computer program to analyze the forced convection steady-state flow between two parallel plates as shown. Verify that an accurate solution has been obtained.

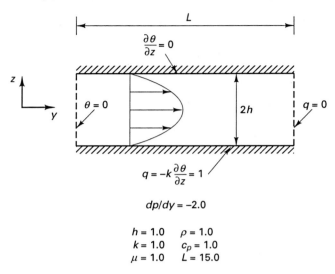

$$\frac{\partial \theta}{\partial z} = 0$$

$\theta = 0$ $2h$ $q = 0$

$$q = -k\frac{\partial \theta}{\partial z} = 1$$

$$dp/dy = -2.0$$

$h = 1.0$	$\rho = 1.0$
$k = 1.0$	$c_p = 1.0$
$\mu = 1.0$	$L = 15.0$

7.30. Use a computer program to analyze the steady-state conjugate heat transfer in a pipe. The analysis problem is described in the figure. Verify that accurate results have been obtained (see J. H. Lienhard [A]).

q_w = heat flow input on external surface of pipe

$$\frac{dp}{dz} = -4$$

$L = 10.0$	For solid:	For fluid:
$t = 0.1$	$k_s = 1.0$	$k_f = 1.0$
$R = 1.0$		$\rho = 1.0$
		$c_p = 5.0$

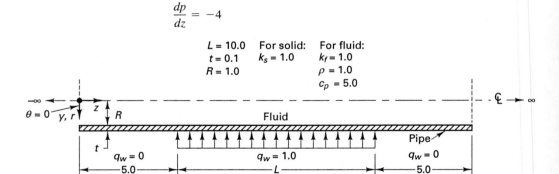

$\theta = 0$ y, r z R Fluid   Pipe

$q_w = 0$ $q_w = 1.0$ $q_w = 0$

$\longleftarrow$ 5.0 $\longrightarrow$ | $\longleftarrow$ L $\longrightarrow$ | $\longleftarrow$ 5.0 $\longrightarrow$

CHAPTER EIGHT

Solution of Equilibrium Equations in Static Analysis

8.1 INTRODUCTION

So far we have considered the derivation and calculation of the equilibrium equations of a finite element system. This included the selection and calculation of efficient elements and the efficient assemblage of the element matrices into the global finite element system matrices. However, the overall effectiveness of an analysis depends to a large degree on the numerical procedures used for the solution of the system equilibrium equations. As discussed earlier, the accuracy of the analysis can, in general, be improved if a more refined finite element mesh is used. Therefore, in practice, an analyst tends to employ larger and larger finite element systems to approximate the actual structure. However, this means that the cost of an analysis and, in fact, its practical feasibility depend to a considerable degree on the algorithms available for the solution of the resulting systems of equations. Because of the requirement that large systems be solved, much research effort has gone into optimizing the equation solution algorithms. During the early use of the finite element method, equations of the order 10,000 were in many cases consider   ently equations of the order 100,000 are solved without much dif

Depending on the kind and number of elements used   topology of the finite element mesh, in a linear static analysi   of the equilibrium equations can be a considerable percen   whereas in dynamic analysis or in nonlinear analysis, this   Therefore, if inappropriate techniques for the solution of the   the total cost of analysis is affected a great deal, and inde   say 100 times, larger than is necessary.

In addition to considering the actual computer effor   the equilibrium equations, it is important to realize that   possible if inappropriate numerical procedures are used.   analysis is simply too costly using the slow solution n

The
Gauss e
However,
simultaneous
S. Martin, G. Pet

analysis may not be possible because the solution procedures are unstable. We will observe that the stability of the solution procedures is particularly important in dynamic analysis.

In this chapter we are concerned with the solution of the simultaneous equations that arise in the static analysis of structures and solids, and we discuss first at length (see Sections 8.2 to 8.3) the solution of the equations that arise in linear analysis,

$$\mathbf{KU} = \mathbf{R} \tag{8.1}$$

where $\mathbf{K}$ is the stiffness matrix, $\mathbf{U}$ is the displacement vector, and $\mathbf{R}$ is the load vector of the finite element system. Since $\mathbf{R}$ and $\mathbf{U}$ may be functions of time t, we may also consider (8.1) as the dynamic equilibrium equations of a finite element system in which inertia and velocity-dependent damping forces have been neglected. It should be realized that since velocities and accelerations do not enter (8.1), we can evaluate the displacements at any time t independent of the displacement history, which is not the case in dynamic analysis (see Chapter 9). However, these thoughts suggest that the algorithms used for the evaluation of $\mathbf{U}$ in (8.1) may also be employed as part of the solution algorithms used in dynamic analysis. This is indeed the case; we will see in the following chapters that the procedures discussed here will be the basis of the algorithms employed for eigensolutions and direct step-by-step integrations. Furthermore, as noted already in Chapter 6 and further discussed in Section 8.4, the solution of (8.1) also represents a very important basic step of solution in a nonlinear analysis. Therefore, a detailed study of the procedures used to solve (8.1) is very important.

Although we consider explicitly in this chapter the solution of the equilibrium equations that arise in the analysis of solids and structures, the techniques are quite general and are entirely and directly applicable to all those analyses that lead to symmetric (positive definite) coefficient matrices (see Chapters 3 and 7). The only sets of equations presented earlier whose solution we do not consider in detail are those arising in the analysis of incompressible viscous fluid flow (see Section 7.4)—because in such analysis a nonsymmetric coefficient matrix is obtained—but for that case most basic concepts and procedures given below are still applicable and can be directly extended (see Exercise 8.11).

Essentially, there are two different classes of methods for the solution of the equations in (8.1): direct solution techniques and iterative solution methods. In a direct solution the equations in (8.1) are solved using a number of steps and operations that are predetermined in an exact manner, whereas iteration is used when an iterative solution method is employed. Either solution scheme will be seen to have certain advantages, and we discuss both approaches in this chapter. At present, direct techniques are employed in most cases, but for large systems iterative methods can be much more effective.

8.2 DIRECT SOLUTIONS USING ALGORITHMS BASED ON GAUSS ELIMINATION

most effective direct solution techniques currently used are basically applications of limination, which C. F. Gauss proposed over a century ago (see C. F. Gauss [A]). although the basic Gauss solution scheme can be applied to almost any set of linear equations (see, for example, J. H. Wilkinson [A], B. Noble [A], and R. rs, and J. H. Wilkinson [A]), the effectiveness in finite element analysis depends on the specific properties of the finite element stiffness matrix: symmetry, positive definiteness, and bandedness.

In the following we consider first the Gauss elimination procedure as it is used in the solution of positive definite, symmetric, and banded systems. We briefly consider the solution of symmetric indefinite systems in Section 8.2.5.

8.2.1 Introduction to Gauss Elimination

We propose to introduce the Gauss solution procedure by studying the solution of the equations $\mathbf{KU} = \mathbf{R}$ derived in Example 3.27 with the parameters $L = 5$, $EI = 1$; i.e.,

$$
\begin{bmatrix}
5 & -4 & 1 & 0 \\
-4 & 6 & -4 & 1 \\
1 & -4 & 6 & -4 \\
0 & 1 & -4 & 5
\end{bmatrix}
\begin{bmatrix}
U_1 \\ U_2 \\ U_3 \\ U_4
\end{bmatrix}
=
\begin{bmatrix}
0 \\ 1 \\ 0 \\ 0
\end{bmatrix}
\tag{8.2}
$$

In this case the stiffness matrix $\mathbf{K}$ corresponds to a simply supported beam with four translational degrees of freedom, as shown in Fig. 8.1. (We should recall that the equilibrium equations have been derived by finite differences; but, in this case, they have the same properties as in finite element analysis.)

The Mathematical Operations

Let us first consider the basic mathematical operations of Gauss elimination. We proceed in the following systematic steps:

Step 1: Subtract a multiple of the first equation in (8.2) from the second and third equations to obtain zero elements in the first column of $\mathbf{K}$. This means that $-\frac{4}{5}$ times the first row is subtracted from the second row, and $\frac{1}{5}$ times the first row is subtracted from the third row. The resulting equations are

$$
\begin{bmatrix}
5 & -4 & 1 & 0 \\
0 & \frac{14}{5} & -\frac{16}{5} & 1 \\
0 & -\frac{16}{5} & \frac{29}{5} & -4 \\
0 & 1 & -4 & 5
\end{bmatrix}
\begin{bmatrix}
U_1 \\ U_2 \\ U_3 \\ U_4
\end{bmatrix}
=
\begin{bmatrix}
0 \\ 1 \\ 0 \\ 0
\end{bmatrix}
\tag{8.3}
$$

Step 2: Considering next the equations in (8.3), subtract $-\frac{16}{14}$ times the second equation from the third equation and $\frac{5}{14}$ times the second equation from the fourth equation. The resulting equations are

$$
\begin{bmatrix}
5 & -4 & 1 & 0 \\
0 & \frac{14}{5} & -\frac{16}{5} & 1 \\
0 & 0 & \frac{15}{7} & -\frac{20}{7} \\
0 & 0 & -\frac{20}{7} & \frac{65}{14}
\end{bmatrix}
\begin{bmatrix}
U_1 \\ U_2 \\ U_3 \\ U_4
\end{bmatrix}
=
\begin{bmatrix}
0 \\ 1 \\ \frac{8}{7} \\ -\frac{5}{14}
\end{bmatrix}
\tag{8.4}
$$

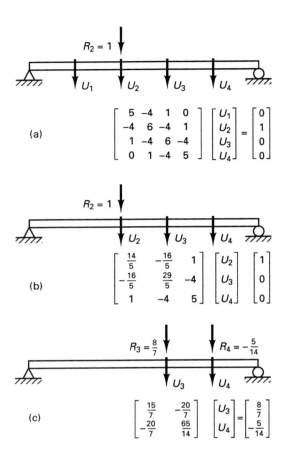

(a)

(b)

(c)

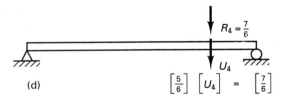

(d)

Figure 8.1   Stiffness matrices and load vectors considered in the Gauss elimination solution of the simply supported beam. The stiffness matrices in (b), (c), and (d) are the entries below the dashed lines in (8.3), (8.4), and (8.5).

Step 3: Subtract $-\frac{20}{15}$ times the third equation from the fourth equation in (8.4). This gives

$$
\begin{bmatrix}
5 & -4 & 1 & 0 \\
0 & \frac{14}{5} & -\frac{16}{5} & 1 \\
0 & 0 & \frac{15}{7} & -\frac{20}{7} \\
0 & 0 & 0 & \frac{5}{6}
\end{bmatrix}
\begin{bmatrix}
U_1 \\ U_2 \\ U_3 \\ U_4
\end{bmatrix}
=
\begin{bmatrix}
0 \\ 1 \\ \frac{8}{7} \\ \frac{7}{6}
\end{bmatrix}
\tag{8.5}
$$

Using (8.5), we can now simply solve for the unknowns U_4, U_3, U_2, and U_1:

$$U_4 = \frac{\frac{7}{6}}{\frac{5}{6}} = \frac{7}{5}; \qquad U_3 = \frac{\frac{8}{7} - (-\frac{20}{7})U_4}{\frac{15}{7}} = \frac{12}{5}$$

$$U_2 = \frac{1 - (-\frac{16}{5})U_3 - (1)U_4}{\frac{14}{5}} = \frac{13}{5}$$

$$U_1 = \frac{0 - (-4)\frac{13}{5} - (1)\frac{12}{5} - (0)\frac{7}{5}}{5} = \frac{8}{5}$$

(8.6)

The procedure in the solution is therefore to subtract in step number i in succession multiples of equation i from equations $i + 1$, $i + 2$, . . . , n, where $i = 1, 2, . . . , n - 1$. In this way the coefficient matrix $\mathbf{K}$ of the equations is reduced to upper triangular form, i.e., a form in which all elements below the diagonal elements are zero. Starting with the last equation, it is then possible to solve for all unknowns in the order U_n, U_{n-1}, . . . , U_1.

It is important to note that at the end of step i the lower right submatrix of order $n - i$ [indicated by dashed lines in (8.3) to (8.5)] is symmetric. Therefore, the elements above and including the diagonal can give all elements of the coefficient matrix at all times of the solution. We will see in Section (8.2.3) that in the computer implementation we work with only the upper triangular part of the matrix.

Another important observation is that this solution assumes in step i a nonzero ith diagonal element in the current coefficient matrix. It is the nonzero value of the ith diagonal element in the coefficient matrix that makes it possible to reduce the elements below it to zero. Also, in the back-substitution for the solution of the displacements, we again divide by the diagonal elements of the coefficient matrix. Fortunately, in the analysis of displacement-based finite element systems, all diagonal elements of the coefficient matrix are positive at all times of the solution, which is another property that makes the application of the Gauss elimination procedure very effective. (This property is not necessarily preserved when the stiffness matrices are derived using a mixed formulation or by finite differences; see Sections 3.3.4 and 4.4.2). We will prove in Section 8.2.5 that the diagonal elements must remain larger than zero, but this property is also observed by considering the physical process of Gauss elimination.

The Physical Process

In order to identify the physical process corresponding to the mathematical operations in Gauss elimination, we note first that the operations on the coefficient matrix $\mathbf{K}$ are independent of the elements in the load vector $\mathbf{R}$. Therefore, let us consider now only the operations on the coefficient matrix $\mathbf{K}$ and for ease of explanation again use the above example and Fig. 8.1. We consider that no loads are applied and hence have

$$\begin{bmatrix} 5 & -4 & 1 & 0 \\ -4 & 6 & -4 & 1 \\ 1 & -4 & 6 & -4 \\ 0 & 1 & -4 & 5 \end{bmatrix} \begin{bmatrix} U_1 \\ U_2 \\ U_3 \\ U_4 \end{bmatrix} = \begin{bmatrix} 0 \\ 0 \\ 0 \\ 0 \end{bmatrix}$$

(8.7)

Using the condition given by the first equation, i.e.,

$$5U_1 - 4U_2 + U_3 = 0$$

we can write

$$U_1 = \tfrac{4}{5}U_2 - \tfrac{1}{5}U_3 \tag{8.8}$$

and eliminate U_1 from the three equations remaining in (8.7). We thus obtain

$$-4(\tfrac{4}{5}U_2 - \tfrac{1}{5}U_3) + 6U_2 - 4U_3 + U_4 = 0$$

$$(\tfrac{4}{5}U_2 - \tfrac{1}{5}U_3) - 4U_2 + 6U_3 - 4U_4 = 0$$

$$U_2 - 4U_3 + 5U_4 = 0$$

or, in matrix form,

$$\begin{bmatrix} \tfrac{14}{5} & -\tfrac{16}{5} & 1 \\ -\tfrac{16}{5} & \tfrac{29}{5} & -4 \\ 1 & -4 & 5 \end{bmatrix} \begin{bmatrix} U_2 \\ U_3 \\ U_4 \end{bmatrix} = \begin{bmatrix} 0 \\ 0 \\ 0 \end{bmatrix} \tag{8.9}$$

Comparing (8.9) with (8.3), we observe that the coefficient matrix in (8.9) is actually the lower right 3×3 submatrix of the coefficient matrix in (8.3). However, we obtained the coefficient matrix of (8.9) by using (8.7) and the condition in (8.8), which expresses that no force is applied at the degree of freedom 1 of the beam. It follows that the coefficient matrix in (8.9) is, in fact, the stiffness matrix of the beam that corresponds to the degrees of freedom 2, 3, and 4 when no force is applied at the degree of freedom 1, i.e., when the degree of freedom 1 has been "released" (which we shall also refer to as "statically condensed out"). By the same reasoning, we have obtained in (8.4) the stiffness matrix of the beam when the first two degrees of freedom have been released; and in (8.5), the element (4, 4) of the coefficient matrix represents the stiffness matrix of the beam corresponding to degree of freedom 4 when the degrees of freedom 1, 2, and 3 have all been released. These stiffness matrices are given in Figs. 8.1(b) to (d).

Let us gain further insight into the Gauss elimination process by considering a (hypothetical) laboratory experiment—that is, a Gedankenexperiment. Suppose that in the laboratory we construct a physical beam corresponding to the model shown in Fig. 8.1. At the locations where the degrees of freedom are measured in Fig. 8.1(a), we fasten clamps to the beam with a force-measuring device, as shown in Fig. 8.2. We now impose the displacements shown in Figs. 8.3(a) to (d) to the beam and measure the required forces. These forces correspond to the columns of the stiffness matrix in (8.2). (Of course, depending on the appropriateness of our mathematical model, the accuracy of our numerical representation,

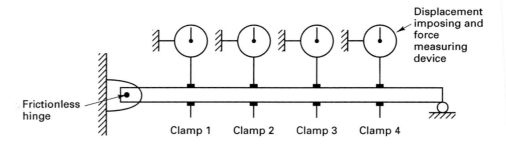

Figure 8.2 Experimental set-up for measurements on beam

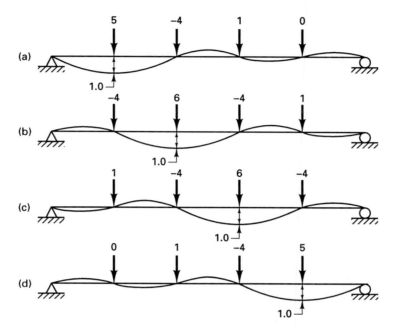

Figure 8.3   Experimental results of forces (given to one digit) in clamps due to unit displacements. (Note that the zero force in the top and bottom results is unrealistic with the given beam curvature but the value of the force is so small that we neglect it.)

and the accuracy of the laboratory measurements, the measured forces will be slightly different, but in our Gedankenexperiment we neglect that difference.)

We now remove clamp 1 and repeat the experiment in the laboratory on the *same* physical beam. The results are shown in Fig. 8.4. The measured forces now correspond to the columns in the stiffness matrix (8.9) [shown also in Fig. 8.1(b)]. Next, we also remove clamp 2 and continue the experiment to obtain the force measurements shown in Fig. 8.5. These results correspond to the stiffness matrix in Fig. 8.1(c). Finally, we also remove clamp 3, and the force measurement gives the result shown in Fig. 8.6, which corresponds to the stiffness given in Fig. 8.1(d).

The important point of our Gedankenexperiment is that the mathematical operations of Gauss elimination correspond to releasing degrees of freedom, one degree of freedom at a time, until only one degree of freedom is left (in our example U_4). The process of releasing a degree of freedom corresponds physically to removing the corresponding clamp. Hence, at every stage of the Gauss elimination a new stiffness matrix of the same physical structure is established, but this matrix corresponds to fewer degrees of freedom than were previously used.

Of course, in a laboratory experiment we are free to establish stiffness matrices of the structure considered corresponding to any arbitrary set of selected degrees of freedom. Indeed, considering the beam in Fig. 8.2, we could by measurements establish first the stiffness in Fig. 8.1(d), then the stiffness matrix in Fig. 8.1(c), then the stiffness matrix in Fig. 8.1(b), and finally the stiffness matrix in Fig. 8.1(a), or use any other order of measurements. Also, we could move the clamps to any other locations and introduce more clamps,

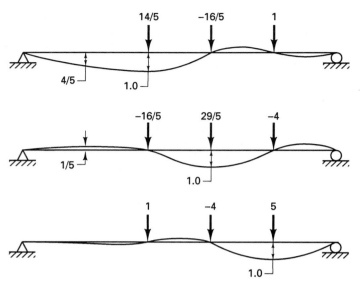

Figure 8.4   Experimental results of forces in clamps due to unit displacements with clamp 1 not present.

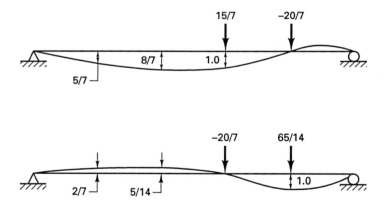

Figure 8.5   Experimental results of forces in clamps due to unit displacements with clamps 1 and 2 not present.

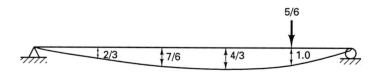

Figure 8.6   Experimental results of forces in clamps due to unit displacement with clamps 1, 2, and 3 not present.

and then establish stiffness matrices for the corresponding displacement degrees of freedom. However, in the finite element analysis we need a certain number of degrees of freedom to accurately describe the behavior of the structure (see Section 4.3), which results in a specific finite element model, and then we are able to establish the stiffness matrices of only this finite element model with certain degrees of freedom released. Gauss elimination is the process of releasing degrees of freedom.

EXAMPLE 8.1:   Assume that you know a laboratory technician who knows nothing about finite elements and equation solutions. She/he has performed an experiment using clamps that measure forces on a beam structure in the laboratory; see Fig. E8.1. By moving the clamps to "unit" and "zero" positions, the following forces have been measured.

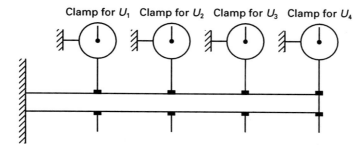

Figure E8.1   Beam with clamps

The result of the first experiment is

$$\begin{array}{c} \\ \text{Forces in clamps} \\ \text{due to } U_1 = 1 \text{ and} \\ U_2 = U_3 = U_4 = 0 \end{array} \begin{array}{c} \\ F_1 \\ F_2 \\ F_3 \\ F_4 \end{array} \begin{array}{cccc} U_1 & U_2 & U_3 & U_4 \\ \begin{bmatrix} 7 & -4 & 1 & 0 \\ -4 & 6 & -4 & 1 \\ 1 & -4 & 5 & -2 \\ 0 & 1 & -2 & 1 \end{bmatrix} \end{array} \qquad (a)$$

The technician has in a second experiment removed the clamp for U_2 and repeated the measurement to obtain the following forces.

The result of the second experiment is

$$\begin{array}{c} \\ \text{Forces in clamps} \\ \text{due to } U_1 = 1 \\ \text{and } U_3 = U_4 = 0 \end{array} \begin{array}{c} \\ F_1 \\ F_3 \\ F_4 \end{array} \begin{array}{ccc} U_1 & U_3 & U_4 \\ \begin{bmatrix} \frac{13}{3} & \frac{-5}{3} & \frac{2}{3} \\ \frac{-5}{3} & \frac{10}{3} & \frac{-4}{3} \\ \frac{2}{3} & \frac{-4}{3} & \frac{5}{6} \end{bmatrix} \end{array} \qquad (b)$$

You are suspicious of whether she/he measured the forces correctly in this second experiment. Assume that the first experiment was correctly performed. Check whether the second experiment was also correctly performed.

The stiffness matrix (b) is correct if it is obtained from (a) after releasing the degree of freedom U_2. Performing Gauss elimination on U_2, we obtain from the matrix in (a),

$$\mathbf{K} = \begin{bmatrix} \frac{13}{3} & -\frac{5}{3} & \frac{2}{3} \\ -\frac{5}{3} & \frac{7}{3} & -\frac{4}{3} \\ \frac{2}{3} & -\frac{4}{3} & \frac{5}{6} \end{bmatrix}$$

Hence, we see that the measurement was not correctly performed for the force in clamp 3 when $U_3 = 1$ and $U_1 = U_4 = 0$.

So far we have assumed that no loads are applied to the structure since the operations on the stiffness matrix are independent of the operations on the load vector. When the load vector is not a null vector, the elimination of degrees of freedom proceeds as described above, but in this case the equation used to eliminate a displacement variable from the remaining equations involves a load term. In the elimination the effect of this load is carried over to the remaining degrees of freedom. Therefore, in summary, the physical process of the Gauss elimination procedure is that n stiffness matrices of order $n, n - 1, \ldots, 1$, corresponding to the $n - i$ last degrees of freedom, $i = 0, 1, 2, \ldots, n - 1$, respectively, of the *same* physical system are established. In addition, the appropriate load vectors corresponding to the n stiffness matrices are calculated. These load vectors are such that the corresponding displacements at the unreleased degrees of freedom are the displacements calculated for the system when described by all n degrees of freedom. The unknown displacements are then obtained by considering in succession the systems with only one, two, . . . , degrees of freedom (these correspond to the last, two last, . . . , of the original number of degrees of freedom).

We can now explain why, because of physical reasons, all diagonal elements in the Gauss elimination procedure must remain positive. This follows because the final ith diagonal element is the stiffness at degree of freedom i when the first $i - 1$ degrees of freedom of the system have been released, and this stiffness should be positive. If a zero (or negative) diagonal element occurs in the Gauss elimination, *the structure is not stable.* An example of such a case is shown in Fig. 8.7, where after the release of degrees of freedom U_1, U_2, and U_3, the last diagonal element is zero.

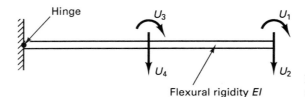

Figure 8.7   Example of an unstable structure

So far we have considered that the Gauss elimination proceeds in succession from the first to the $(n - 1)$st degree of freedom. However, we may in the same way perform the elimination backward (i.e., from the last to the second degree of freedom), or we may choose any desirable order, as we already indicated in the discussion of the physical laboratory experiment shown in Fig. 8.2.

EXAMPLE 8.2:   Obtain the solution to the equilibrium equations of the beam in Fig. 8.1 by eliminating the displacement variables in the order U_3, U_2, U_4.

We may either write down the individual equations during the elimination process or directly perform Gauss elimination in the prescribed order. In the latter case we obtain, eliminating U_3,

$$\begin{bmatrix} \frac{29}{6} & -\frac{10}{3} & 0 & \frac{2}{3} \\ -\frac{10}{3} & \frac{10}{3} & 0 & -\frac{5}{3} \\ 1 & -4 & 6 & -4 \\ \frac{2}{3} & -\frac{5}{3} & 0 & \frac{7}{3} \end{bmatrix} \begin{bmatrix} U_1 \\ U_2 \\ U_3 \\ U_4 \end{bmatrix} = \begin{bmatrix} 0 \\ 1 \\ 0 \\ 0 \end{bmatrix}$$

Next, we eliminate U_2 and obtain

$$\begin{bmatrix} \frac{3}{2} & 0 & 0 & -1 \\ -\frac{10}{3} & \frac{10}{3} & 0 & -\frac{5}{3} \\ 1 & -4 & 6 & -4 \\ -1 & 0 & 0 & \frac{3}{2} \end{bmatrix} \begin{bmatrix} U_1 \\ U_2 \\ U_3 \\ U_4 \end{bmatrix} = \begin{bmatrix} 1 \\ 1 \\ 0 \\ \frac{1}{2} \end{bmatrix}$$

and finally we eliminate U_4,

$$\begin{bmatrix} \frac{5}{6} & 0 & 0 & 0 \\ -\frac{10}{3} & \frac{10}{3} & 0 & -\frac{5}{3} \\ 1 & -4 & 6 & -4 \\ -1 & 0 & 0 & \frac{3}{2} \end{bmatrix} \begin{bmatrix} U_1 \\ U_2 \\ U_3 \\ U_4 \end{bmatrix} = \begin{bmatrix} \frac{4}{3} \\ 1 \\ 0 \\ \frac{1}{2} \end{bmatrix}$$

The solution for the displacements is now obtained as follows:

$$U_1 = \frac{8}{5}$$

$$U_4 = \frac{\frac{1}{2} - (-1)\frac{8}{5}}{\frac{3}{2}} = \frac{7}{5}$$

$$U_2 = \frac{1 - (-\frac{10}{3})\frac{8}{5} - (-\frac{5}{3})\frac{7}{5}}{\frac{10}{3}} = \frac{13}{5}$$

$$U_3 = \frac{0 - (1)\frac{8}{5} - (-4)\frac{7}{5} - (-4)\frac{13}{5}}{6} = \frac{12}{5}$$

which is the solution obtained earlier.

8.2.2 The LDL^T Solution

We have seen in the preceding section that the basic procedure of the Gauss elimination solution is to reduce the equations to correspond to an upper triangular coefficient matrix from which the unknown displacements **U** can be calculated by a back-substitution. We now want to formalize the solution procedure using appropriate matrix operations. An additional important purpose of the discussion is to introduce a notation that can be used throughout the following presentations. The actual computer implementation is given in the next section.

Considering the operations performed in the Gauss elimination solution presented in the preceding section, the reduction of the stiffness matrix **K** to upper triangular form can be written

$$\mathbf{L}_{n-1}^{-1} \ldots \mathbf{L}_2^{-1} \mathbf{L}_1^{-1} \mathbf{K} = \mathbf{S} \tag{8.10}$$

where $\mathbf{S}$ is the final upper triangular matrix and

$$
\mathbf{L}_i^{-1} = \begin{bmatrix}
1 & & & & & & \\
 & \cdot & & & \text{elements} & & \\
 & & \cdot & & \text{not shown} & & \\
 & & & \cdot & \text{are zeros}^1 & & \\
 & & & 1 & & & \cdot \\
 & & & -l_{i+1,i} & \cdot & & \\
 & & & -l_{i+2,i} & & \cdot & \\
 & & & \cdot & & & \cdot \\
 & & & \cdot & & & \\
 & & & -l_{ni} & & & 1
\end{bmatrix} \quad ; \quad l_{i+j,i} = \frac{k_{i+j,i}^{(i)}}{k_{ii}^{(i)}} \tag{8.11}
$$

The elements $l_{i+j,i}$ are the Gauss multiplying factors, and the right superscript (i) indicates that an element of the matrix $\mathbf{L}_{i-1}^{-1} \ldots \mathbf{L}_2^{-1}\mathbf{L}_1^{-1}\mathbf{K}$ is used.

We now note that $\mathbf{L}_i$ is obtained by simply reversing the signs of the off-diagonal elements in $\mathbf{L}_i^{-1}$. Therefore, we obtain

$$
\mathbf{K} = \mathbf{L}_1\mathbf{L}_2 \ldots \mathbf{L}_{n-1}\mathbf{S} \tag{8.12}
$$

where
$$
\mathbf{L}_i = \begin{bmatrix}
1 & & & & & & \\
 & \cdot & & & & & \\
 & & \cdot & & & & \\
 & & & \cdot & & & \\
 & & & 1 & & & \\
 & & & l_{i+1,i} & \cdot & & \\
 & & & l_{i+2,i} & & \cdot & \\
 & & & \cdot & & & \cdot \\
 & & & \cdot & & & \\
 & & & l_{ni} & & & 1
\end{bmatrix} \tag{8.13}
$$

Hence, we can write

$$
\mathbf{K} = \mathbf{L}\mathbf{S} \tag{8.14}
$$

where $\mathbf{L} = \mathbf{L}_1\mathbf{L}_2 \ldots \mathbf{L}_{n-1}$; i.e., $\mathbf{L}$ is a lower unit triangular matrix,

$$
\mathbf{L} = \begin{bmatrix}
1 & & & & & & \\
l_{21} & 1 & & & & & \\
l_{31} & l_{32} & 1 & & & & \\
l_{41} & l_{42} & & 1 & & & \\
\cdot & \cdot & & & \cdot & & \\
\cdot & \cdot & & & & \cdot & \\
\cdot & \cdot & & & & & \\
 & & & & & 1 & \\
l_{n1} & \cdot & & \cdot & & l_{n,n-1} & 1
\end{bmatrix} \tag{8.15}
$$

Since $\mathbf{S}$ is an upper triangular matrix and the diagonal elements are the pivots in the Gauss elimination, we can write $\mathbf{S} = \mathbf{D}\tilde{\mathbf{S}}$, where $\mathbf{D}$ is a diagonal matrix storing the diagonal

---

[1] Throughout this book, elements not shown in matrices are zero.

elements of $\mathbf{S}$; i.e., $d_{ii} = s_{ii}$. Substituting for $\mathbf{S}$ into (8.14) and noting that $\mathbf{K}$ is symmetric and the decomposition is unique, we obtain $\tilde{\mathbf{S}} = \mathbf{L}^T$, and hence,

$$\mathbf{K} = \mathbf{L}\mathbf{D}\mathbf{L}^T \tag{8.16}$$

It is this $\mathbf{L}\mathbf{D}\mathbf{L}^T$ decomposition of $\mathbf{K}$ that can be used effectively to obtain the solution of the equations in (8.1) in the following two steps:

$$\mathbf{L}\mathbf{V} = \mathbf{R} \tag{8.17}$$

$$\mathbf{D}\mathbf{L}^T\mathbf{U} = \mathbf{V} \tag{8.18}$$

where in (8.17) the load vector $\mathbf{R}$ is reduced to obtain $\mathbf{V}$,

$$\mathbf{V} = \mathbf{L}_{n-1}^{-1} \ldots \mathbf{L}_2^{-1}\mathbf{L}_1^{-1}\mathbf{R} \tag{8.19}$$

and in (8.18) the solution $\mathbf{U}$ is obtained by a back-substitution,

$$\mathbf{L}^T\mathbf{U} = \mathbf{D}^{-1}\mathbf{V} \tag{8.20}$$

In the implementation the vector $\mathbf{V}$ is frequently calculated at the same time as the matrices $\mathbf{L}_i^{-1}$ are established. This was done in the example solution of the simply supported beam in Section 8.2.1.

It should be noted that in practice the matrix multiplications to obtain $\mathbf{L}$ in (8.15) and $\mathbf{V}$ in (8.19) are not formally carried out, but that $\mathbf{L}$ and $\mathbf{V}$ are established by directly modifying $\mathbf{K}$ and $\mathbf{R}$. This is discussed further in the next section, in which the computer implementation of the solution procedure is presented. However, before proceeding, consider the example in Section 8.2.1 for the derivation of the matrices defined above.

EXAMPLE 8.3: Establish the matrices $\mathbf{L}_i^{-1}$, $i = 1, 2, 3$, $\mathbf{S}$, $\mathbf{L}$, and $\mathbf{D}$ and the vector $\mathbf{V}$ corresponding to the stiffness matrix and the load vector of the simply supported beam treated in Section 8.2.1.

Using the information given in Section 8.2.1, we can directly write down the required matrices:

$$\mathbf{L}_1^{-1} = \begin{bmatrix} 1 & & & \\ \frac{4}{5} & 1 & & \\ -\frac{1}{5} & 0 & 1 & \\ 0 & 0 & 0 & 1 \end{bmatrix}; \quad \mathbf{L}_2^{-1} = \begin{bmatrix} 1 & & & \\ 0 & 1 & & \\ 0 & \frac{8}{7} & 1 & \\ 0 & -\frac{5}{14} & 0 & 1 \end{bmatrix}$$

$$\mathbf{L}_3^{-1} = \begin{bmatrix} 1 & & & \\ 0 & 1 & & \\ 0 & 0 & 1 & \\ 0 & 0 & \frac{4}{3} & 1 \end{bmatrix}; \quad \mathbf{S} = \begin{bmatrix} 5 & -4 & 1 & 0 \\ & \frac{14}{5} & -\frac{16}{5} & 1 \\ & & \frac{15}{7} & -\frac{20}{7} \\ & & & \frac{5}{6} \end{bmatrix}$$

where the matrix $\mathbf{L}_i^{-1}$ stores in the ith column the multipliers that were used in the elimination of the ith equation and the matrix $\mathbf{S}$ is the upper triangular matrix obtained in (8.5). The matrix $\mathbf{D}$ is a diagonal matrix with the pivot elements on its diagonal. In this case,

$$\mathbf{D} = \begin{bmatrix} 5 & & & \\ & \frac{14}{5} & & \\ & & \frac{15}{7} & \\ & & & \frac{5}{6} \end{bmatrix}$$

To obtain $\mathbf{L}$ we use (8.15); hence,

$$
\mathbf{L} = \begin{bmatrix} 1 & & & \\ -\frac{4}{5} & 1 & & \\ \frac{1}{5} & -\frac{8}{7} & 1 & \\ 0 & \frac{5}{14} & -\frac{4}{3} & 1 \end{bmatrix}
$$

and we can check that $\mathbf{S} = \mathbf{DL}^T$.

The vector $\mathbf{V}$ was obtained in (8.5):

$$
\mathbf{V} = \begin{bmatrix} 0 \\ 1 \\ \frac{8}{7} \\ \frac{7}{6} \end{bmatrix}
$$

8.2.3 Computer Implementation of Gauss Elimination— The Active Column Solution

A very important aspect of the computer implementation of the Gauss solution procedure is that a minimum solution time should be used. In addition, the high-speed storage requirements should be as small as possible to avoid the use of backup storage. However, for large systems it will nevertheless be necessary to use backup storage, and for this reason it should also be possible to modify the solution algorithm for effective out-of-core solution.

An advantage of finite element analysis is that the stiffness matrix of the element assemblage is only symmetric and positive definite but also banded; i.e., $k_{ij} = 0$ for $j > i + m_K$, where m_K is the half-bandwidth of the system (see Fig. 2.1). The fact that in finite element analysis all nonzero elements are clustered around the diagonal of the system matrices greatly reduces the total number of operations and the high-speed storage required in the equation solution. However, this property depends on the nodal point numbering in the finite element mesh, and the analyst must take care to obtain an effective nodal point numbering (see Chapter 12).

Assume that for a given finite element assemblage a specific nodal point numbering has been determined and the corresponding column heights and the stiffness matrix $\mathbf{K}$ have been calculated (see Section 12.2.3 for details). The $\mathbf{LDL}^T$ decomposition of $\mathbf{K}$ can be obtained effectively by considering each column in turn; i.e., although the Gauss elimination is carried out by rows, the final elements of $\mathbf{D}$ and $\mathbf{L}$ are calculated by columns. Using $d_{11} = k_{11}$, the algorithm for the calculation of the elements l_{ij} and d_{jj} in the jth column is, for $j = 2, \ldots, n$,

$$
\left.\begin{aligned}
g_{m_j,j} &= k_{m_j,j} \\
g_{ij} &= k_{ij} - \sum_{r=m_m}^{i-1} l_{ri} g_{rj} \qquad i = m_j + 1, \ldots, j - 1
\end{aligned}\right\} \tag{8.21}
$$

where m_j is the row number of the first nonzero element in column j and $m_m = \max\{m_i, m_j\}$ (see Fig. 12.2). The variables m_i, $i = 1, \ldots, n$, define the skyline of the matrix; also, the values $i - m_i$ are the column heights and the maximum column height is the half-bandwidth m_K. The elements g_{ij} in (8.21) are defined only as intermediate quantities, and the calculation is completed using

$$l_{ij} = \frac{g_{ij}}{d_{ii}} \qquad i = m_j, \ldots, j - 1 \tag{8.22}$$

$$d_{jj} = k_{jj} - \sum_{r=m_j}^{j-1} l_{rj} g_{rj} \tag{8.23}$$

It should be noted that the summations in (8.21) and (8.23) do not involve multiplications with zero elements outside the skyline of the matrix and that the l_{ij} are elements of the matrix $\mathbf{L}^T$ rather than of $\mathbf{L}$. We refer to the solution algorithm given in (8.21) to (8.23) [actually with (8.24) and (8.25)] as the *active column solution or the skyline (or column) reduction method.*

Considering the storage arrangements in the reduction, the element l_{ij} when calculated for use in (8.23) immediately replaces g_{ij}, and d_{jj} replaces k_{jj}. Therefore, at the end of the reduction we have elements d_{jj} in the storage locations previously used by k_{jj}, and l_{rj} is stored in the locations of k_{rj}, $j > r$.

In order to get familiar with the solution algorithm, we consider the following examples.

EXAMPLE 8.4:   Use the solution algorithm given in (8.21) to (8.23) to calculate the triangular factors $\mathbf{D}$ and $\mathbf{L}^T$ of the stiffness matrix of the beam considered in Example 8.3.

The initial elements considered are, when written in their respective matrix locations,

$$\begin{bmatrix} 5 & -4 & 1 & \\ & 6 & -4 & 1 \\ & & 6 & -4 \\ & & & 5 \end{bmatrix}$$

with $m_1 = 1$, $m_2 = 1$, $m_3 = 1$, and $m_4 = 2$. Using (8.21) to (8.23), we obtain, for $j = 2$,

$$d_{11} = k_{11} = 5$$

$$g_{12} = k_{12} = -4$$

$$l_{12} = \frac{g_{12}}{d_{11}} = -\frac{4}{5}$$

$$d_{22} = k_{22} - l_{12}g_{12} = 6 - (-4)(-\tfrac{4}{5}) = \tfrac{14}{5}$$

and thus the resulting matrix elements are now, using a dotted line to separate the reduced from the unreduced columns,

$$\begin{bmatrix} 5 & -\frac{4}{5} & \vdots & 1 & \\ & \frac{14}{5} & \vdots & -4 & 1 \\ & & \vdots & 6 & -4 \\ & & \vdots & & 5 \end{bmatrix}$$

Next, we obtain, for $j = 3$,

$$g_{13} = k_{13} = 1$$

$$g_{23} = k_{23} - l_{12}g_{13} = -4 - (-\tfrac{4}{5})(1) = -\tfrac{16}{5}$$

$$l_{13} = \frac{g_{13}}{d_{11}} = \frac{1}{5}$$

$$l_{23} = \frac{g_{23}}{d_{22}} = \frac{-\frac{16}{5}}{\frac{14}{5}} = -\frac{8}{7}$$

$$d_{33} = k_{33} - l_{13}g_{13} - l_{23}g_{23} = 6 - (\tfrac{1}{5})(1) - (-\tfrac{8}{7})(-\tfrac{16}{5}) = \tfrac{15}{7}$$

and the resulting matrix elements are

$$\begin{bmatrix} 5 & -\frac{4}{5} & \frac{1}{5} & \vdots & \\ & \frac{14}{5} & -\frac{8}{7} & \vdots & 1 \\ & & \frac{15}{7} & \vdots & -4 \\ & & & \vdots & 5 \end{bmatrix}$$

Finally, we have, for $j = 4$,

$$g_{24} = k_{24} = 1$$

$$g_{34} = k_{34} - l_{23}g_{24} = -4 - (-\tfrac{8}{7})(1) = -\tfrac{20}{7}$$

$$l_{24} = \frac{g_{24}}{d_{22}} = \frac{1}{\frac{14}{5}} = \frac{5}{14}$$

$$l_{34} = \frac{g_{34}}{d_{33}} = \frac{-\frac{20}{7}}{\frac{15}{7}} = -\frac{4}{3}$$

$$d_{44} = k_{44} - l_{24}g_{24} - l_{34}g_{34} = 5 - (\tfrac{5}{14})(1) - (-\tfrac{4}{3})(-\tfrac{20}{7}) = \tfrac{5}{6}$$

and the final elements stored are

$$\begin{bmatrix} 5 & -\frac{4}{5} & \frac{1}{5} & \\ & \frac{14}{5} & -\frac{8}{7} & \frac{5}{14} \\ & & \frac{15}{7} & -\frac{4}{3} \\ & & & \frac{5}{6} \end{bmatrix}$$

We should note that the elements of $\mathbf{D}$ are stored on the diagonal and the elements l_{ij} have replaced the elements $k_{ij}, j > i$.

Although the details of the solution procedure have already been demonstrated in Example 8.4, the importance of using the column reduction method could not be shown, since the skyline coincides with the band. The effectiveness of the skyline reduction scheme is more apparent in the factorization of the following matrix.

EXAMPLE 8.5:   Use the solution algorithm given in (8.21) to (8.23) to evaluate the triangular factors $\mathbf{D}$ and $\mathbf{L}^T$ of the stiffness matrix $\mathbf{K}$, where

$$\mathbf{K} = \begin{bmatrix} 2 & -2 & & & -1 \\ & 3 & -2 & & 0 \\ & & 5 & -3 & 0 \\ & \text{Symmetric} & & 10 & 4 \\ & & & & 10 \end{bmatrix}$$

For this matrix we have $m_1 = 1$, $m_2 = 1$, $m_3 = 2$, $m_4 = 3$, and $m_5 = 1$.

The algorithm gives, in this case with $d_{11} = 2$, for $j = 2$,

$$g_{12} = k_{12} = -2$$

$$l_{12} = \frac{g_{12}}{d_{11}} = \frac{-2}{2} = -1$$

$$d_{22} = k_{22} - l_{12}g_{12} = 3 - (-1)(-2) = 1$$

and thus the resulting matrix elements are

$$\begin{bmatrix} 2 & -1 & \vdots & & & -1 \\ & 1 & \vdots & -2 & & 0 \\ & & \vdots & 5 & -3 & 0 \\ & & \vdots & & 10 & 4 \\ & & \vdots & & & 10 \end{bmatrix}$$

For $j = 3$, $\qquad\qquad g_{23} = k_{23} = -2$

$$l_{23} = \frac{g_{23}}{d_{22}} = \frac{-2}{1} = -2$$

$$d_{33} = k_{33} - l_{23}g_{23} = 5 - (-2)(-2) = 1$$

and the coefficient array is now

$$\begin{bmatrix} 2 & -1 & & \vdots & & -1 \\ & 1 & -2 & \vdots & & 0 \\ & & 1 & \vdots & -3 & 0 \\ & & & \vdots & 10 & 4 \\ & & & \vdots & & 10 \end{bmatrix}$$

For $j = 4$, $\qquad\qquad g_{34} = k_{34} = -3$

$$l_{34} = \frac{g_{34}}{d_{33}} = \frac{-3}{1} = -3$$

$$d_{44} = k_{44} - l_{34}g_{34} = 10 - (-3)(-3) = 1$$

and the resulting matrix elements are

$$\begin{bmatrix} 2 & -1 & & & \vdots & -1 \\ & 1 & -2 & & \vdots & 0 \\ & & 1 & -3 & \vdots & 0 \\ & & & 1 & \vdots & 4 \\ & & & & \vdots & 10 \end{bmatrix}$$

Finally we have, for $j = 5$,

$$g_{15} = k_{15} = -1$$

$$g_{25} = k_{25} - l_{12}g_{15} = 0 - (-1)(-1) = -1$$

$$g_{35} = k_{35} - l_{23}g_{25} = 0 - (-2)(-1) = -2$$

$$g_{45} = k_{45} - l_{34}g_{35} = +4 - (-3)(-2) = -2$$

$$l_{15} = \frac{g_{15}}{d_{11}} = \frac{-1}{2} = -\frac{1}{2}$$

$$l_{25} = \frac{g_{25}}{d_{22}} = \frac{-1}{1} = -1$$

$$l_{35} = \frac{g_{35}}{d_{33}} = \frac{-2}{1} = -2$$

$$l_{45} = \frac{g_{45}}{d_{44}} = \frac{-2}{1} = -2$$

$$d_{55} = k_{55} - l_{15}g_{15} - l_{25}g_{25} - l_{35}g_{35} - l_{45}g_{45}$$

$$= 10 - (-\tfrac{1}{2})(-1) - (-1)(-1) - (-2)(-2) - (-2)(-2) = \tfrac{1}{2}$$

and the final matrix elements are

$$\begin{bmatrix} 2 & -1 & & & -\frac{1}{2} \\ & 1 & -2 & & -1 \\ & & 1 & -3 & -2 \\ & & & 1 & -2 \\ & & & & \frac{1}{2} \end{bmatrix}$$

As in Example 8.4, we have the elements of $\mathbf{D}$ and $\mathbf{L}^T$ replacing the elements k_{ii} and $k_{ij}, j > i$ of the original matrix $\mathbf{K}$, respectively.

In the preceding discussion we considered only the decomposition of the stiffness matrix $\mathbf{K}$, which constitutes the main part of the equation solution. Once the $\mathbf{L}$, $\mathbf{D}$ factors of $\mathbf{K}$ have been obtained, the solution for $\mathbf{U}$ is calculated using (8.19) and (8.20), where it may be noted that the reduction of $\mathbf{R}$ in (8.19) can be performed at the same time as the stiffness matrix $\mathbf{K}$ is decomposed or may be carried out separately afterward. The equation to be used is similar to (8.23); i.e., we have $V_1 = R_1$ and calculate for $i = 2, \ldots, n$,

$$V_i = R_i - \sum_{r=m_i}^{i-1} l_{ri} V_r \tag{8.24}$$

where R_i and V_i are the ith elements of $\mathbf{R}$ and $\mathbf{V}$. Considering the storage arrangements, the element V_i replaces R_i.

The back-substitution in (8.20) is performed by evaluating successively U_n, $U_{n-1}, \ldots, U_1$. This is achieved by first calculating $\overline{\mathbf{V}}$, where $\overline{\mathbf{V}} = \mathbf{D}^{-1}\mathbf{V}$. Then using $\overline{\mathbf{V}}^{(n)} = \overline{\mathbf{V}}$, we have $U_n = \overline{V}_n^{(n)}$ and we calculate for $i = n, \ldots, 2$,

$$\left. \begin{aligned} \overline{V}_r^{(i-1)} &= \overline{V}_r^{(i)} - l_{ri} U_i; \qquad r = m_i, \ldots, i-1 \\ U_{i-1} &= \overline{V}_{i-1}^{(i-1)} \end{aligned} \right\} \tag{8.25}$$

where the superscript $(i-1)$ indicates that the element is calculated in the evaluation of U_{i-1}. It should be noted that $\overline{V}_k^{(j)}$ for all j is stored in the storage location of V_k, i.e., the original storage location of R_k.

EXAMPLE 8.6:   Use the algorithm given in (8.24) and (8.25) to calculate the solution to the problem $\mathbf{KU} = \mathbf{R}$, when $\mathbf{K}$ is the stiffness matrix considered in Example 8.5 and

$$\mathbf{R} = \begin{bmatrix} 0 \\ 1 \\ 0 \\ 0 \\ 0 \end{bmatrix}$$

In the solution we employ the $\mathbf{D}$, $\mathbf{L}^T$ factors of $\mathbf{K}$ calculated in Example 8.5. Using (8.24) for the forward reduction, we obtain

$$V_1 = R_1 = 0$$

$$V_2 = R_2 - l_{12} V_1 = 1 - 0 = 1$$

$$V_3 = R_3 - l_{23} V_2 = 0 - (-2)(1) = 2$$

$$V_4 = R_4 - l_{34} V_3 = 0 - (-3)(2) = 6$$

$$V_5 = R_5 - l_{15} V_1 - l_{25} V_2 - l_{35} V_3 - l_{45} V_4$$

$$= 0 - 0 - (-1)(1) - (-2)(2) - (-2)(6) = 17$$

Immediately after calculation of V_i, the element replaces R_i. Thus, we now have in the vector that initially stored the loads,

$$\mathbf{V} = \begin{bmatrix} 0 \\ 1 \\ 2 \\ 6 \\ 17 \end{bmatrix}$$

The first step in the back-substitution is to evaluate $\overline{\mathbf{V}}$, where $\overline{\mathbf{V}} = \mathbf{D}^{-1}\mathbf{V}$. Here we obtain

$$\overline{\mathbf{V}} = \begin{bmatrix} 0 \\ 1 \\ 2 \\ 6 \\ 34 \end{bmatrix} \tag{a}$$

and thus, $\qquad\qquad\qquad\qquad U_5 = \overline{V}_5 = 34$

Now we use (8.25) with $\overline{\mathbf{V}}^{(5)} = \overline{\mathbf{V}}$ of (a). Hence we obtain, for $i = 5$,

$$\overline{V}_1^{(4)} = \overline{V}_1^{(5)} - l_{15} U_5 = 0 - (-\tfrac{1}{2})(34) = 17$$

$$\overline{V}_2^{(4)} = \overline{V}_2^{(5)} - l_{25} U_5 = 1 - (-1)(34) = 35$$

$$\overline{V}_3^{(4)} = \overline{V}_3^{(5)} - l_{35} U_5 = 2 - (-2)(34) = 70$$

$$\overline{V}_4^{(4)} = \overline{V}_4^{(5)} - l_{45} U_5 = 6 - (-2)(34) = 74$$

and $\qquad\qquad\qquad\qquad U_4 = \overline{V}_4^{(4)} = 74$

For $i = 4$, $\qquad\qquad \overline{V}_3^{(3)} = \overline{V}_3^{(4)} - l_{34} U_4 = 70 - (-3)(74) = 292$

and $$U_3 = \bar{V}_3^{(3)} = 292$$

For $i = 3$, $$\bar{V}_2^{(2)} = \bar{V}_2^{(3)} - l_{23}U_3 = 35 - (-2)(292) = 619$$

and $$U_2 = \bar{V}_2^{(2)} = 619$$

For $i = 2$, $$\bar{V}_1^{(1)} = \bar{V}_1^{(2)} - l_{12}U_2 = 17 - (-1)(619) = 636$$

and $$U_1 = \bar{V}_1^{(1)} = 636$$

The elements stored in the vector that initially stored the loads are after step $i = 5, 4, 3, 2$, respectively:

$$\begin{bmatrix} 17 \\ 35 \\ 70 \\ 74 \\ 34 \end{bmatrix} ; \begin{bmatrix} 17 \\ 35 \\ 292 \\ 74 \\ 34 \end{bmatrix} ; \begin{bmatrix} 17 \\ 619 \\ 292 \\ 74 \\ 34 \end{bmatrix} ; \begin{bmatrix} 636 \\ 619 \\ 292 \\ 74 \\ 34 \end{bmatrix}$$

where the last vector gives the solution $\mathbf{U}$.

Considering the effectiveness of the active column solution algorithm, it should be noted that for a specific matrix $\mathbf{K}$ the algorithm frequently gives an efficient solution because no operations are performed on zero elements outside the skyline, which also implies that only the elements below the skyline need be stored. However, the total number of operations performed is not an absolute minimum because, in addition, all those multiplications could be skipped in (8.21) to (8.25) for which l_{ri} or g_{rj} is zero. This skipping of course requires additional logic, but is effective if there are many such cases, which is the main premise on which sparse solvers are based. These solvers, which can be very effective in large three-dimensional solutions, avoid the storage of elements that remain zero and skip the relevant operations, see, for example, A. George, J. R. Gilbert, and J. W. H. Liu (eds.) [A].

To evaluate the efficiency of the active column solution, let us consider a system with constant column heights, i.e. a half-bandwidth m_K such that $m_K = i - m_i$ for all $i, i > m_K$, and perform an operation count based on (8.16) to (8.25). We define one operation to consist of one multiplication (or division), which is nearly always followed by an addition. In this case the number of operations required for the $\mathbf{LDL}^T$ decomposition of $\mathbf{K}$ are approximately $n[m_K + (m_K - 1) + \cdots + 1] \doteq \frac{1}{2}nm_K^2$, and for the reduction and back-substitution of a load vector, an additional number of approximately $2nm_K$ operations are needed. In practice, systems with exactly constant column heights are encountered rather seldom and therefore these operation counts should be refined to $\frac{1}{2}\sum_i (i - m_i)^2$ and $2\sum_i (i - m_i)$, respectively. However, we frequently still use the constant half-bandwidth formulas with a mean or effective half-bandwidth merely to obtain an indication of the required solution effort.

Since the number of operations is governed by the pattern of the nonzero elements in the matrix, algorithms have been developed that reorder the equations so as to increase the effectiveness of the equation solution. When the active column solution scheme is used, the reordering is to reduce the column heights for an effective solution (see E. Cuthill and J. McKee [A] and N. E. Gibbs, W. G. Poole, Jr., and P. K. Stockmeyer [A]), while when a sparse solver is used the reordering is to reduce the total number of operations taking due account of not operating on elements that remain zero throughout the solution. This requirement for a sparse solver means that the number of fill-in elements (elements that originally are zero but become nonzero) should be small (see A. George, J. R. Gilbert, and J. W. H. Liu (eds.) [A]). The use of such reordering procedures, while generally not giving the actual optimal ordering of the equations, is very important because in practice the initial ordering of the equations is usually generated without regard to the efficiency of the equation solution but merely with regard to the effectiveness of the definition of the model.

The solution algorithm in (8.21) to (8.25) has been presented in two-dimensional matrix notation; e.g., element (r, j) of $\mathbf{K}$ has been denoted by k_{rj}. Also, to demonstrate the working of the algorithm, in Examples 8.4 and 8.5 the elements considered in the reduction have been displayed in their corresponding matrix locations. However, in actual computer solution, the active columns of the matrix $\mathbf{K}$ are stored effectively in a one-dimensional array. Assume that the storage scheme discussed in Chapter 12 is used; i.e., the pertinent elements of $\mathbf{K}$ are stored in the one-dimensional array A of length NWK and the addresses of the diagonal elements of $\mathbf{K}$ are stored in MAXA. An effective subroutine that uses the algorithm presented above [i.e., the relations in (8.21) to (8.25)] but operates on the stiffness matrix using this storage scheme is given next.

Subroutine COLSOL.   Program COLSOL is an active column solver to obtain the $\mathbf{LDL}^T$ factorization of a stiffness matrix or reduce and back-substitute the load vector. The complete process gives the solution of the finite element equilibrium equations. The argument variables and use of the subroutine are defined by means of comments in the program.

```
      SUBROUTINE COLSOL (A,V,MAXA,NN,NWK,NNM,KKK,IOUT)            COL00001
C . . . . . . . . . . . . . . . . . . . . . . . . . . . . . .   COL00002
C .                                                          .   COL00003
C .    P R O G R A M                                         .   COL00004
C .       TO SOLVE FINITE ELEMENT STATIC EQUILIBRIUM EQUATIONS IN .  COL00005
C .       CORE, USING COMPACTED STORAGE AND COLUMN REDUCTION SCHEME . COL00006
C .                                                          .   COL00007
C .    - - INPUT VARIABLES - -                               .   COL00008
C .       A(NWK)    = STIFFNESS MATRIX STORED IN COMPACTED FORM .  COL00009
C .       V(NN)     = RIGHT-HAND-SIDE LOAD VECTOR            .   COL00010
C .       MAXA(NNM) = VECTOR CONTAINING ADDRESSES OF DIAGONAL .   COL00011
C .                   ELEMENTS OF STIFFNESS MATRIX IN A      .   COL00012
C .       NN        = NUMBER OF EQUATIONS                    .   COL00013
C .       NWK       = NUMBER OF ELEMENTS BELOW SKYLINE OF MATRIX . COL00014
C .       NNM       = NN + 1                                 .   COL00015
C .       KKK       = INPUT FLAG                             .   COL00016
C .           EQ. 1   TRIANGULARIZATION OF STIFFNESS MATRIX  .   COL00017
C .           EQ. 2   REDUCTION AND BACK-SUBSTITUTION OF LOAD VECTOR . COL00018
C .       IOUT      = UNIT NUMBER USED FOR OUTPUT            .   COL00019
C .                                                          .   COL00020
C .    - - OUTPUT - -                                        .   COL00021
C .       A(NWK)    = D AND L - FACTORS OF STIFFNESS MATRIX  .   COL00022
C .       V(NN)     = DISPLACEMENT VECTOR                    .   COL00023
C .                                                          .   COL00024
C . . . . . . . . . . . . . . . . . . . . . . . . . . . . . .   COL00025
      IMPLICIT DOUBLE PRECISION (A-H,O-Z)                        COL00026
C . . . . . . . . . . . . . . . . . . . . . . . . . . . . . .   COL00027
C .    THIS PROGRAM IS USED IN SINGLE PRECISION ARITHMETIC ON CRAY . COL00028
C .    EQUIPMENT AND DOUBLE PRECISION ARITHMETIC ON IBM MACHINES, . COL00029
C .    ENGINEERING WORKSTATIONS AND PCS. DEACTIVATE ABOVE LINE FOR . COL00030
C .    SINGLE PRECISION ARITHMETIC.                          .   COL00031
C . . . . . . . . . . . . . . . . . . . . . . . . . . . . . .   COL00032
      DIMENSION A(NWK),V(NN),MAXA(NNM)                           COL00033
C                                                                COL00034
C     PERFORM L*D*L(T) FACTORIZATION OF STIFFNESS MATRIX         COL00035
C                                                                COL00036
      IF (KKK-2) 40,150,150                                      COL00037
   40 DO 140 N=1,NN                                              COL00038
      KN=MAXA(N)                                                 COL00039
      KL=KN + 1                                                  COL00040
```

```
         KU=MAXA(N+1) - 1                                    COL00041
         KH=KU - KL                                          COL00042
         IF (KH) 110,90,50                                   COL00043
   50    K=N - KH                                            COL00044
         IC=0                                                COL00045
         KLT=KU                                              COL00046
         DO 80 J=1,KH                                        COL00047
         IC=IC + 1                                           COL00048
         KLT=KLT - 1                                         COL00049
         KI=MAXA(K)                                          COL00050
         ND=MAXA(K+1) - KI - 1                               COL00051
         IF (ND) 80,80,60                                    COL00052
   60    KK=MIN0(IC,ND)                                      COL00053
         C=0.                                                COL00054
         DO 70 L=1,KK                                        COL00055
   70    C=C + A(KI+L)*A(KLT+L)                              COL00056
         A(KLT)=A(KLT) - C                                   COL00057
   80    K=K + 1                                             COL00058
   90    K=N                                                 COL00059
         B=0.                                                COL00060
         DO 100 KK=KL,KU                                     COL00061
         K=K - 1                                             COL00062
         KI=MAXA(K)                                          COL00063
         C=A(KK)/A(KI)                                       COL00064
         B=B + C*A(KK)                                       COL00065
  100    A(KK)=C                                             COL00066
         A(KN)=A(KN) - B                                     COL00067
  110    IF (A(KN)) 120,120,140                              COL00068
  120    WRITE (IOUT,2000) N,A(KN)                           COL00069
         GO TO 800                                           COL00070
  140    CONTINUE                                            COL00071
         GO TO 900                                           COL00072
C                                                            COL00073
C        REDUCE RIGHT-HAND-SIDE LOAD VECTOR                  COL00074
C                                                            COL00075
  150    DO 180 N=1,NN                                       COL00076
         KL=MAXA(N) + 1                                      COL00077
         KU=MAXA(N+1) - 1                                    COL00078
         IF (KU-KL) 180,160,160                              COL00079
  160    K=N                                                 COL00080
         C=0.                                                COL00081
         DO 170 KK=KL,KU                                     COL00082
         K=K - 1                                             COL00083
  170    C=C + A(KK)*V(K)                                    COL00084
         V(N)=V(N) - C                                       COL00085
  180    CONTINUE                                            COL00086
C                                                            COL00087
C        BACK-SUBSTITUTE                                     COL00088
C                                                            COL00089
         DO 200 N=1,NN                                       COL00090
         K=MAXA(N)                                           COL00091
  200    V(N)=V(N)/A(K)                                      COL00092
         IF (NN.EQ.1) GO TO 900                              COL00093
         N=NN                                                COL00094
         DO 230 L=2,NN                                       COL00095
         KL=MAXA(N) + 1                                      COL00096
         KU=MAXA(N+1) - 1                                    COL00097
         IF (KU-KL) 230,210,210                              COL00098
  210    K=N                                                 COL00099
         DO 220 KK=KL,KU                                     COL00100
         K=K - 1                                             COL00101
  220    V(K)=V(K) - A(KK)*V(N)                              COL00102
  230    N=N - 1                                             COL00103
         GO TO 900                                           COL00104
C                                                            COL00105
  800    STOP                                                COL00106
  900    RETURN                                              COL00107
C                                                            COL00108
 2000    FORMAT (//' STOP - STIFFNESS MATRIX NOT POSITIVE DEFINITE',//,  COL00109
        1           ' NONPOSITIVE PIVOT FOR EQUATION ',I8,//,            COL00110
        2           ' PIVOT = ',E20.12 )                    COL00111
         END                                                COL00112
```

8.2.4 Cholesky Factorization, Static Condensation, Substructures, and Frontal Solution

In addition to the $\mathbf{LDL}^T$ decomposition described in the preceding sections, various other schemes are used that are closely related. All methods are applications of the basic Gauss elimination procedure.

In the *Cholesky factorization* the stiffness matrix is decomposed as follows:

$$\mathbf{K} = \tilde{\mathbf{L}}\tilde{\mathbf{L}}^T \tag{8.26}$$

where

$$\tilde{\mathbf{L}} = \mathbf{LD}^{1/2} \tag{8.27}$$

Therefore, the Cholesky factors could be calculated from the $\mathbf{D}$ and $\mathbf{L}$ factors, but, more generally, the elements of $\tilde{\mathbf{L}}$ are calculated directly. An operation count shows that slightly more operations are required in the equation solution if the Cholesky factorization is used rather than the $\mathbf{LDL}^T$ decomposition. In addition, the Cholesky factorization is suitable only for the solution of positive definite systems, for which all diagonal elements d_{ii} are positive, because otherwise complex arithmetic would be required. On the other hand, the $\mathbf{LDL}^T$ decomposition can also be used effectively on indefinite systems (see Section 8.2.5).

Considering a main use of the Cholesky factorization, the decomposition is employed effectively in the transformation of a generalized eigenproblem to the standard form (see Section 10.2.5).

EXAMPLE 8.7: Calculate the Cholesky factor $\tilde{\mathbf{L}}$ of the stiffness matrix $\mathbf{K}$ of the simply supported beam treated in Section 8.2.1 and in Examples 8.2 to 8.4.

The $\mathbf{L}$ and $\mathbf{D}$ factors of the beam stiffness matrix have been given in Example 8.3. Rounding to three significant decimals, we have

$$\mathbf{L} = \begin{bmatrix} 1.000 & & & \\ -0.800 & 1.000 & & 0 \\ 0.200 & -1.143 & 1.000 & \\ 0.000 & 0.357 & -1.333 & 1.000 \end{bmatrix}; \quad \mathbf{D} = \begin{bmatrix} 5.000 & & & \\ & 2.800 & & \\ & & 2.143 & \\ & & & 0.833 \end{bmatrix}$$

Hence,

$$\tilde{\mathbf{L}} = \begin{bmatrix} 1.000 & & & \\ -0.800 & 1.000 & & \\ 0.200 & -1.143 & 1.000 & \\ 0.000 & 0.357 & -1.333 & 1.000 \end{bmatrix} \begin{bmatrix} 2.236 & & & \\ & 1.673 & & \\ & & 1.464 & \\ & & & 0.913 \end{bmatrix}$$

or

$$\tilde{\mathbf{L}} = \begin{bmatrix} 2.236 & & & \\ -1.789 & 1.673 & & \\ 0.447 & -1.912 & 1.464 & \\ 0 & 0.597 & -1.952 & 0.913 \end{bmatrix}$$

An algorithm that in some cases can effectively be used in the solution of the equilibrium equations is *static condensation* (see E. L. Wilson [B]). The name "static condensation" refers to dynamic analysis, for which the solution technique is demonstrated in Section 10.3.1. *Static condensation is employed to reduce the number of element degrees of freedom and thus, in effect, to perform part of the solution of the total finite element system equilibrium equations prior to assembling the structure matrices* **K** *and* **R**. Consider the three-node truss element in Example 8.8. Since the degree of freedom at the midnode does not correspond to a degree of freedom of any other element, we can eliminate it to obtain the element stiffness matrix that corresponds to the degrees of freedom 1 and 3 only. The elimination of the degree of freedom 2 is carried out using, in essence, Gauss elimination, as presented in Section 8.2.1 (see Example 8.1).

In order to establish the equations used in static condensation, we assume that the stiffness matrix and corresponding displacement and force vectors of the element under consideration are partitioned into the form

$$\begin{bmatrix} \mathbf{K}_{aa} & \mathbf{K}_{ac} \\ \mathbf{K}_{ca} & \mathbf{K}_{cc} \end{bmatrix} \begin{bmatrix} \mathbf{U}_a \\ \mathbf{U}_c \end{bmatrix} = \begin{bmatrix} \mathbf{R}_a \\ \mathbf{R}_c \end{bmatrix} \tag{8.28}$$

where $\mathbf{U}_a$ and $\mathbf{U}_c$ are the vectors of displacements to be retained and condensed out, respectively. The matrices $\mathbf{K}_{aa}$, $\mathbf{K}_{ac}$, and $\mathbf{K}_{cc}$ and vectors $\mathbf{R}_a$ and $\mathbf{R}_c$ correspond to the displacement vectors $\mathbf{U}_a$ and $\mathbf{U}_c$.

Using the second matrix equation in (8.28), we obtain

$$\mathbf{U}_c = \mathbf{K}_{cc}^{-1}(\mathbf{R}_c - \mathbf{K}_{ca}\mathbf{U}_a) \tag{8.29}$$

The relation in (8.29) is used to substitute for $\mathbf{U}_c$ into the first matrix equation in (8.28) to obtain the condensed equations

$$(\mathbf{K}_{aa} - \mathbf{K}_{ac}\mathbf{K}_{cc}^{-1}\mathbf{K}_{ca})\mathbf{U}_a = \mathbf{R}_a - \mathbf{K}_{ac}\mathbf{K}_{cc}^{-1}\mathbf{R}_c \tag{8.30}$$

Comparing (8.30) with the Gauss solution scheme introduced in Section 8.2.1, it is seen that static condensation is, in fact, Gauss elimination on the degrees of freedom $\mathbf{U}_c$ (see Example 8.8). In practice, therefore, static condensation is carried out effectively by using Gauss elimination sequentially on each degree of freedom to be condensed out, instead of following through the formal matrix procedure given in (8.28) to (8.30), where it is valuable to keep the physical meaning of Gauss elimination in mind (see Section 8.2.1). Since the system stiffness matrix is obtained by direct addition of the element stiffness matrices, we realize that when condensing out internal element degrees of freedom, in fact, part of the total Gauss solution is already carried out on the element level.

The advantage of using static condensation on the element level is that the order of the system matrices is reduced, which may mean that use of backup storage is prevented. In addition, if subsequent elements are identical, the stiffness matrix of only the first element needs to be derived, and performing static condensation on the element internal degrees of freedom also reduces the computer effort required. It should be noted, though, that if static condensation is actually carried out for each element (and no advantage is taken of possible identical finite elements), the total effort involved in the static condensation on all element stiffness matrices and in the Gauss elimination solution of the resulting assembled equilibrium equations is, in fact, the same as using Gauss elimination on the system equations established from the uncondensed element stiffness matrices.

EXAMPLE 8.8: The stiffness matrix of the truss element in Fig. E8.8 is given on the next page. Use static condensation as given in (8.28) to (8.30) to condense out the internal element degree of freedom. Then use Gauss elimination directly on the internal degree of freedom.

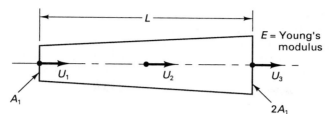

Figure E8.8   Truss element with linearly varying area

We have for the element,

$$\frac{EA_1}{6L}\begin{bmatrix} 17 & -20 & 3 \\ -20 & 48 & -28 \\ 3 & -28 & 25 \end{bmatrix}\begin{bmatrix} U_1 \\ U_2 \\ U_3 \end{bmatrix} = \begin{bmatrix} R_1 \\ R_2 \\ R_3 \end{bmatrix} \qquad (a)$$

In order to apply the equations in (8.28) to (8.30), we rearrange the equations in (a) to obtain

$$\frac{EA_1}{6L}\begin{bmatrix} 17 & 3 & -20 \\ 3 & 25 & -28 \\ -20 & -28 & 48 \end{bmatrix}\begin{bmatrix} U_1 \\ U_3 \\ U_2 \end{bmatrix} = \begin{bmatrix} R_1 \\ R_3 \\ R_2 \end{bmatrix}$$

The relation in (8.30) now gives

$$\frac{EA_1}{6L}\left\{\begin{bmatrix} 17 & 3 \\ 3 & 25 \end{bmatrix} - \begin{bmatrix} -20 \\ -28 \end{bmatrix}\begin{bmatrix} \frac{1}{48} \end{bmatrix}\begin{bmatrix} -20 & -28 \end{bmatrix}\right\}\begin{bmatrix} U_1 \\ U_3 \end{bmatrix} = \begin{bmatrix} R_1 + \frac{20}{48}R_2 \\ R_3 + \frac{28}{48}R_2 \end{bmatrix}$$

or

$$\frac{13}{9}\frac{EA_1}{L}\begin{bmatrix} 1 & -1 \\ -1 & 1 \end{bmatrix}\begin{bmatrix} U_1 \\ U_3 \end{bmatrix} = \begin{bmatrix} R_1 + \frac{5}{12}R_2 \\ R_3 + \frac{7}{12}R_2 \end{bmatrix}$$

Also, (8.29) yields $$U_2 = \frac{1}{24}\left(\frac{3L}{EA_1}R_2 + 10U_1 + 14U_3\right) \qquad (b)$$

Using Gauss elimination directly on (a) for U_2, we obtain

$$\frac{EA_1}{6L}\begin{bmatrix} 17 - \dfrac{(20)(20)}{48} & 0 & 3 - \dfrac{(20)(28)}{48} \\ -20 & 48 & -28 \\ 3 - \dfrac{(20)(28)}{48} & 0 & 25 - \dfrac{(28)(28)}{48} \end{bmatrix}\begin{bmatrix} U_1 \\ U_2 \\ U_3 \end{bmatrix} = \begin{bmatrix} R_1 + \frac{20}{48}R_2 \\ R_2 \\ R_3 + \frac{28}{48}R_2 \end{bmatrix} \qquad (c)$$

But separating the equations for U_1 and U_3 from the equation for U_2, we can rewrite the relation in (c) as

$$\frac{13}{9}\frac{EA_1}{L}\begin{bmatrix} 1 & -1 \\ -1 & 1 \end{bmatrix}\begin{bmatrix} U_1 \\ U_3 \end{bmatrix} = \begin{bmatrix} R_1 + \frac{5}{12}R_2 \\ R_3 + \frac{7}{12}R_2 \end{bmatrix}$$

and

$$U_2 = \frac{1}{24}\left[\frac{3L}{EA_1}R_2 + 10U_1 + 14U_3\right]$$

which are the relations obtained using the formal static condensation procedure.

EXAMPLE 8.9: Use the stiffness matrix of the three degree of freedom truss element in Example 8.8 to establish the equilibrium equations of the structure shown in Fig. E8.9. Use Gauss elimination directly on degrees of freedom U_2 and U_4. Show that the resulting equilibrium equations are identical to those obtained when the two degree of freedom truss element stiffness matrix derived in Example 8.8 (the internal degree of freedom has been condensed out) is used to assemble the stiffness matrix corresponding to U_1, U_3, and U_5.

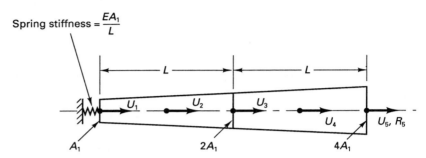

Figure E8.9 Structure composed of two truss elements of Fig. E8.8 and a spring support

The stiffness matrix of the three-element assemblage in Fig. E8.9 is obtained using the direct stiffness method; i.e., we calculate

$$\mathbf{K} = \sum_{m=1}^{3} \mathbf{K}^{(m)} \tag{a}$$

where

$$\mathbf{K}^{(1)} = \frac{EA_1}{6L} \begin{bmatrix} 6 & 0 & 0 & 0 & 0 \\ 0 & 0 & 0 & 0 & 0 \\ 0 & 0 & 0 & 0 & 0 \\ 0 & 0 & 0 & 0 & 0 \\ 0 & 0 & 0 & 0 & 0 \end{bmatrix}$$

$$\mathbf{K}^{(2)} = \frac{EA_1}{6L} \begin{bmatrix} 17 & -20 & 3 & 0 & 0 \\ -20 & 48 & -28 & 0 & 0 \\ 3 & -28 & 25 & 0 & 0 \\ 0 & 0 & 0 & 0 & 0 \\ 0 & 0 & 0 & 0 & 0 \end{bmatrix}$$

$$\mathbf{K}^{(3)} = \frac{EA_1}{6L} \begin{bmatrix} 0 & 0 & 0 & 0 & 0 \\ 0 & 0 & 0 & 0 & 0 \\ 0 & 0 & 34 & -40 & 6 \\ 0 & 0 & -40 & 96 & -56 \\ 0 & 0 & 6 & -56 & 50 \end{bmatrix}$$

Hence the equilibrium equations of the structure are

$$\frac{EA_1}{6L} \begin{bmatrix} 23 & -20 & 3 & 0 & 0 \\ -20 & 48 & -28 & 0 & 0 \\ 3 & -28 & 59 & -40 & 6 \\ 0 & 0 & -40 & 96 & -56 \\ 0 & 0 & 6 & -56 & 50 \end{bmatrix} \begin{bmatrix} U_1 \\ U_2 \\ U_3 \\ U_4 \\ U_5 \end{bmatrix} = \begin{bmatrix} 0 \\ 0 \\ 0 \\ 0 \\ R_5 \end{bmatrix}$$

Using Gauss elimination on degrees of freedom U_2 and U_4, we obtain

$$\frac{EA_1}{6L}\begin{bmatrix} 23 - \dfrac{(20)(20)}{48} & 0 & 3 - \dfrac{(20)(28)}{48} & 0 & 0 \\ -20 & 48 & -28 & 0 & 0 \\ 3 - \dfrac{(20)(28)}{48} & 0 & 59 - \dfrac{(28)(28)}{48} - \dfrac{(40)(40)}{96} & 0 & 6 - \dfrac{(40)(56)}{96} \\ 0 & 0 & -40 & 96 & -56 \\ 0 & 0 & 6 - \dfrac{(40)(56)}{96} & 0 & 50 - \dfrac{(56)(56)}{96} \end{bmatrix}\begin{bmatrix} U_1 \\ U_2 \\ U_3 \\ U_4 \\ U_5 \end{bmatrix} = \begin{bmatrix} 0 \\ 0 \\ 0 \\ 0 \\ R_5 \end{bmatrix} \quad \text{(b)}$$

Now, extracting the equilibrium equations corresponding to degrees of freedom 1, 3, and 5 and degrees of freedom 2 and 4 separately, we have

$$\frac{13}{9}\frac{EA_1}{L}\begin{bmatrix} \frac{22}{13} & -1 & 0 \\ -1 & 3 & -2 \\ 0 & -2 & 2 \end{bmatrix}\begin{bmatrix} U_1 \\ U_3 \\ U_5 \end{bmatrix} = \begin{bmatrix} 0 \\ 0 \\ R_5 \end{bmatrix} \quad \text{(c)}$$

and

$$U_2 = \tfrac{1}{12}[5U_1 + 7U_3]$$
$$U_4 = \tfrac{1}{12}[5U_3 + 7U_5] \quad \text{(d)}$$

However, using the two degree of freedom truss element stiffness matrix derived in Example 8.8 to directly assemble the structure stiffness matrix corresponding to degrees of freedom 1, 3, and 5, we use as element stiffness matrices in (a),

$$\mathbf{K}^{(1)} = \frac{13}{9}\frac{EA_1}{L}\begin{bmatrix} \frac{9}{13} & 0 & 0 \\ 0 & 0 & 0 \\ 0 & 0 & 0 \end{bmatrix}$$

$$\mathbf{K}^{(2)} = \frac{13}{9}\frac{EA_1}{L}\begin{bmatrix} 1 & -1 & 0 \\ -1 & 1 & 0 \\ 0 & 0 & 0 \end{bmatrix} \quad \text{(e)}$$

$$\mathbf{K}^{(3)} = \frac{13}{9}\frac{EA_1}{L}\begin{bmatrix} 0 & 0 & 0 \\ 0 & 2 & -2 \\ 0 & -2 & 2 \end{bmatrix} \quad \text{(f)}$$

and obtain the stiffness matrix in (c). Also, the relation (b) in Example 8.8 corresponds to relations (d) in this example. It should be noted that the total effort to solve the equilibrium equations using the condensed truss element stiffness matrix is less than when the original three degree of freedom element stiffness matrix is used because in the first case the internal degree of freedom was statically condensed out only once, whereas in (b) the element internal degree of freedom is, in fact, statically condensed out twice. The direct solution using the condensed element stiffness matrices in (e) and (f) is, however, possible only because these stiffness matrices are multiples of each other.

As indicated in Example 8.9, it can be particularly effective to employ static condensation when the same element is used many times. An application of this concept is employed in *substructure analysis,* in which the total structure is considered to be an assemblage of substructures (see, for example, J. S. Przemieniecki [A] and M. F. Rubinstein [A]). Each substructure, in turn, is idealized as an assemblage of finite elements, and all internal degrees of freedom are statically condensed out. The total structure stiffness is formed by assembling the condensed substructure stiffness matrices. Therefore, *in effect, a substructure is used in the same way as an individual finite element with internal degrees of freedom that are statically condensed out prior to the element assemblage process.* If many substructures are identical, it is effective to establish a library of substructures from which a condensed total structure stiffness matrix is formed.

It should be noted that the unreduced complete structure stiffness matrix is never calculated in substructure analysis, and *input data are required only for each substructure in the library plus information on the assemblage of the substructures* to make up the complete structure. Typical applications of finite element analysis using substructuring are found in the analysis of buildings and ship hulls, where the substructure technique has allowed economical analysis of very large finite element systems. The use of substructuring can also be effective in the analysis of structures with local nonlinearities in static and dynamic response calculations (see K. J. Bathe and S. Gracewski [A]).

As a simple example of substructuring, we refer to Example 8.9, in which each substructure is composed simply of one element, and the uncondensed and condensed stiffness matrix of a typical substructure was given in Example 8.8.

The effectiveness of analysis using the basic substructure concept described above can in many cases still be improved on by defining different levels of substructures; i.e., since each substructure can be looked on as a "super-finite element," it is possible to define second, third, etc., levels of substructuring. In a similar procedure, two substructures are always combined to define the next-higher-level substructure until the final substructure is, in fact, the actual structure under consideration. The procedure may be employed in one-, two-, or three-dimensional analysis and, as pointed out earlier, is indeed only an effective application of Gauss elimination, in which advantage is taken of the repetition of submatrices, which are the stiffness matrices that correspond to the identical substructures. The possibility of using the solution procedure effectively therefore depends on whether the structure is made up of repetitive substructures, and this is the reason the procedure can be very effective in special-purpose programs.

EXAMPLE 8.10:   Use substructuring to evaluate the stiffness matrix and the load vector corresponding to the end nodal point degrees of freedom U_1 and U_9 of the bar in Fig. E8.10.

The basic element of which the bar is composed is the three degree of freedom truss element considered in Example 8.8. The equilibrium equations of the element corresponding to the two degrees of freedom U_1 and U_3 as shown in Fig. E8.10 are

$$\frac{13}{9} \frac{A_1 E}{L} \begin{bmatrix} 1 & -1 \\ -1 & 1 \end{bmatrix} \begin{bmatrix} U_1 \\ U_3 \end{bmatrix} = \begin{bmatrix} R_1 + \frac{5}{12} R_2 \\ R_3 + \frac{7}{12} R_2 \end{bmatrix} \tag{a}$$

Since the internal degree of freedom U_2 has been statically condensed out to obtain the equilibrium relations in (a), we may regard the two degree of freedom element as a first-level substructure. We should recall that once U_1 and U_3 have been calculated, we can evaluate U_2 using the relation (b) in Example 8.8:

$$U_2 = \frac{1}{24} \left(\frac{3L}{EA_1} R_2 + 10U_1 + 14U_3 \right) \tag{b}$$

It is now effective to evaluate a second-level substructure corresponding to degrees of freedom U_1 and U_5 of the bar. For this purpose we use the stiffness matrix and load vector in (a)

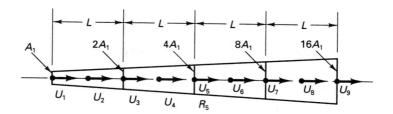

Bar with linearly varying area

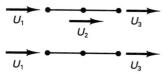

(a) First-level substructure

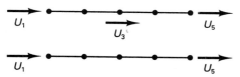

(b) Second-level substructure

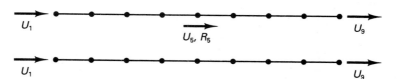

(c) Third-level substructure and actual structure

Figure E8.10   Analysis of bar using substructuring

to evaluate the equilibrium relations corresponding to U_1, U_3, and U_5:

$$\frac{13}{9}\frac{A_1E}{L}\begin{bmatrix} 1 & -1 & 0 \\ -1 & 3 & -2 \\ 0 & -2 & 2 \end{bmatrix}\begin{bmatrix} U_1 \\ U_3 \\ U_5 \end{bmatrix} = \begin{bmatrix} R_1 + \frac{5}{12}R_2 \\ R_3 + \frac{7}{12}R_2 + \frac{5}{12}R_4 \\ R_5 + \frac{7}{12}R_4 \end{bmatrix} \qquad \text{(c)}$$

The relation for calculating U_4 is similar to the one in (b):

$$U_4 = \frac{1}{24}\left(\frac{3L}{2EA_1}R_4 + 10U_3 + 14U_5\right)$$

Using Gauss elimination on the equations in (c) to condense out U_3, we obtain

$$\frac{13}{9}\frac{A_1E}{L}\begin{bmatrix} \frac{2}{3} & 0 & -\frac{2}{3} \\ -1 & 3 & -2 \\ -\frac{2}{3} & 0 & \frac{2}{3} \end{bmatrix}\begin{bmatrix} U_1 \\ U_3 \\ U_5 \end{bmatrix} = \begin{bmatrix} R_1 + \frac{22}{36}R_2 + \frac{1}{3}R_3 + \frac{5}{36}R_4 \\ R_3 + \frac{7}{12}R_2 + \frac{5}{12}R_4 \\ \frac{14}{36}R_2 + \frac{2}{3}R_3 + \frac{31}{36}R_4 + R_5 \end{bmatrix}$$

or $\quad \left(\dfrac{2}{3}\right)\left(\dfrac{13}{9}\right)\dfrac{A_1 E}{L}\begin{bmatrix} 1 & -1 \\ -1 & 1 \end{bmatrix}\begin{bmatrix} U_1 \\ U_5 \end{bmatrix} = \begin{bmatrix} R_1 + \frac{22}{36} R_2 + \frac{1}{3} R_3 + \frac{5}{36} R_4 \\ \frac{14}{36} R_2 + \frac{2}{3} R_3 + \frac{31}{36} R_4 + R_5 \end{bmatrix}$ (d)

and $\quad U_3 = \dfrac{1}{3}\left[\dfrac{9}{13}\dfrac{L}{A_1 E}\left(R_3 + \dfrac{7}{12} R_2 + \dfrac{5}{12} R_4\right) + U_1 + 2U_5\right]$

We should note that the stiffness matrix of the second-level substructure in (d) is simply $\frac{2}{3}$ times the stiffness matrix of the first-level substructure in (a). Therefore, we could continue to build up even higher-level substructures in an analogous manner; i.e., the stiffness matrix of the nth-level substructure would simply be a factor times the stiffness matrix given in (a).

In most cases loads are applied only at the boundary degrees of freedom between substructures, such as in this example. Using the stiffness matrix of the second-level substructure to assemble the stiffness matrix of the complete bar and assembling the actual load vector for this example, we obtain

$$\dfrac{2}{3}\left(\dfrac{13}{9}\right)\dfrac{A_1 E}{L}\begin{bmatrix} 1 & -1 & 0 \\ -1 & 5 & -4 \\ 0 & -4 & 4 \end{bmatrix}\begin{bmatrix} U_1 \\ U_5 \\ U_9 \end{bmatrix} = \begin{bmatrix} 0 \\ R_5 \\ 0 \end{bmatrix}$$

Eliminating U_5, we have

$$\left(\dfrac{4}{5}\right)\left(\dfrac{2}{3}\right)\left(\dfrac{13}{9}\right)\dfrac{A_1 E}{L}\begin{bmatrix} 1 & -1 \\ -1 & 1 \end{bmatrix}\begin{bmatrix} U_1 \\ U_9 \end{bmatrix} = \begin{bmatrix} \frac{1}{5} R_5 \\ \frac{4}{5} R_5 \end{bmatrix}$$

where the stiffness matrix is simply the third-level substructure stiffness matrix corresponding to the algorithm given above. We also have

$$U_5 = \dfrac{1}{5}\left(\dfrac{27}{36}\dfrac{L}{A_1 E} R_5 + U_1 + 4U_9\right)$$

To solve for specific displacements, it is necessary to impose boundary conditions on the bar, hence obtain U_1 and U_9, and then obtain the internal bar displacements using previously derived relations. It should be noted that corresponding relations must also be employed to evaluate U_6 to U_8.

So far, we have not mentioned how to proceed in the solution if the total system matrix cannot be contained in high-speed storage. If substructuring is used, it is effective to keep the size of each uncondensed substructure stiffness matrix small enough so that the static condensation of the internal degrees of freedom can be carried out in high-speed core. Therefore, disk storage would mainly be required to store the required information for the calculation of the displacements of the substructure internal nodes as expressed in (8.29).

However, it may be necessary to use multilevel substructuring (i.e., to define substructures of substructures) in order that the final equations to be solved can be taken into high-speed storage.

In general, it is important to use disk storage effectively since a great deal of reading and writing can be very expensive and indeed may limit the system size that can be solved, because not enough backup storage may be available. In out-of-core solutions the particular scheme used for solving the system equilibrium equations is largely coupled with the specific procedure employed to assemble the element stiffness matrices to the global structure stiffness matrix. In many programs the structure stiffness matrix is assembled prior to performing the Gauss solution. In the program ADINA the equations are assembled in blocks that can be taken into high-speed core. The block sizes (number of columns per block) are automatically established in the program and depend on the high-speed storage available. The solution of the system equations is then obtained in an effective manner by first reducing the blocks of the stiffness matrix and load vectors consecutively and then performing the back-substitution. Similar procedures are presently used in many analysis programs.

Instead of first assembling the complete structure stiffness matrix, we may assemble and reduce the equations at the same time. A specific solution scheme proposed by B. M. Irons [D] called the *frontal solution method* has been used effectively. In the solution procedure only those equations that are actually required for the elimination of a specific degree of freedom are assembled, the degree of freedom considered is statically condensed out, and so on.

As an example, consider the analysis of the plane stress finite element idealization of the sheet in Fig. 8.8. There are two equations associated with each node of the finite element mesh, namely, the equations corresponding to the U and V displacements, respectively. In the frontal solution scheme the equations are statically condensed out in the order of the elements; i.e., the first equations considered would be those corresponding to nodes 1, 2, ... To be able to eliminate the degrees of freedom of node 1 it is only necessary to assemble the final equations that correspond to that node. This means that only the stiffness matrix of element 1 needs to be calculated, after which the degrees of freedom corresponding to node 1 are statically condensed out. Next (for the elimination of the equations corresponding to node 2), the final equations corresponding to the degrees of freedom at node 2 are required, meaning that the stiffness matrix of element 2 must be calculated and added to the previously reduced matrix. Now the degrees of freedom corresponding to node 2 are statically condensed out; and so on.

It may now be realized that *the complete procedure, in effect, consists of statically condensing out one degree of freedom after the other and always assembling only those equations (or rather element stiffness matrices) that are actually required during the specific condensation to be performed.* The finite elements that must be considered for the

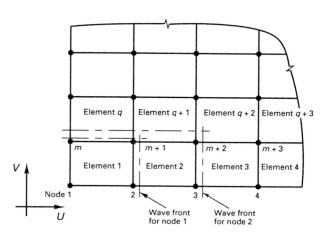

Figure 8.8 Frontal solution of plane stress finite element idealization

static condensation of the equations corresponding to one specific node define the wave front at that time, as shown in Fig. 8.8.

In principle, the frontal solution is Gauss elimination and the important aspect is the specific computer implementation. Since the equations are assembled in the order of the elements, the length of the wave front and therefore the half-bandwidth dealt with are determined by the element numbering. Therefore, an effective ordering of the elements is necessary, and we note that *if the element numbering in the frontal solution corresponds to the nodal point numbering in the active column solution (see Section 8.2.3), the same number of basic (i.e., excluding indexing) numerical operations is performed in both solutions.* An advantage of the wave front solution is that elements can be added with relative ease because no nodal point renumbering is necessary to preserve a small bandwidth. But a disadvantage is that if the wave front is large, the total high-speed storage required may well exceed the storage that is available, in which case additional out-of-core operations are required that suddenly decrease the effectiveness of the method by a great amount. Also, the active column solution is implemented in a compact stand-alone solver that is independent of the finite elements processed, whereas a frontal solver is intimately coupled to the finite elements and may require more indexing in the solution.

8.2.5 Positive Definiteness, Positive Semidefiniteness, and the Sturm Sequence Property

In the Gauss elimination discussed so far, we implicitly assumed that the stiffness matrix **K** is positive definite, that is, that the structure considered is properly restrained and stable. As discussed in Sections 2.5 and 2.6, positive definiteness of the stiffness matrix means that for any displacement vector **U**, we have

$$\mathbf{U}^T \mathbf{K} \mathbf{U} > 0 \tag{8.31}$$

Since $\frac{1}{2} \mathbf{U}^T \mathbf{K} \mathbf{U}$ is the strain energy stored in the system for the displacement vector **U**, (8.31) expresses that for any displacement vector **U** the strain energy of a system with a positive definite stiffness matrix is positive.

Note that the stiffness matrix of a finite element is not positive definite unless the element has been properly restrained, i.e., the rigid body motions have been suppressed. Instead, the stiffness matrix of an unrestrained finite element is positive semidefinite,

$$\mathbf{U}^T \mathbf{K} \mathbf{U} \geq 0 \tag{8.32}$$

where $\mathbf{U}^T \mathbf{K} \mathbf{U} = 0$ when **U** corresponds to a rigid body mode. Considering the finite element assemblage process, it should be realized that positive semidefinite element matrices are added to obtain the positive semidefinite stiffness matrix corresponding to the complete structure. The stiffness matrix of the structure is then rendered positive definite by eliminating the rows and columns that correspond to the restrained degrees of freedom, i.e., by eliminating the possibility for the structure to undergo rigid body motions.

It is instructive to consider in more detail the meaning of positive definiteness of the structure stiffness matrix. In Section 2.5, we discussed the representation of a matrix by its eigenvalues and eigenvectors. Following the development given in Section 2.5, the eigenproblem for the stiffness matrix **K** can be written

$$\mathbf{K} \boldsymbol{\phi} = \lambda \boldsymbol{\phi} \tag{8.33}$$

The solutions to (8.33) are the eigenpairs $(\lambda_i, \boldsymbol{\phi}_i)$, $i = 1, \ldots, n$, and the complete solution can be written

$$\mathbf{K}\boldsymbol{\Phi} = \boldsymbol{\Phi}\boldsymbol{\Lambda}$$

where $\boldsymbol{\Phi}$ is a matrix of the orthonormalized eigenvectors, $\boldsymbol{\Phi} = [\boldsymbol{\phi}_1, \ldots, \boldsymbol{\phi}_n]$, and $\boldsymbol{\Lambda}$ is a diagonal matrix of the corresponding eigenvalues, $\boldsymbol{\Lambda} = \text{diag}(\lambda_i)$. Since $\boldsymbol{\Phi}^T\boldsymbol{\Phi} = \boldsymbol{\Phi}\boldsymbol{\Phi}^T = \mathbf{I}$, we also have

$$\boldsymbol{\Phi}^T\mathbf{K}\boldsymbol{\Phi} = \boldsymbol{\Lambda} \tag{8.34}$$

and

$$\mathbf{K} = \boldsymbol{\Phi}\boldsymbol{\Lambda}\boldsymbol{\Phi}^T \tag{8.35}$$

Referring to Section 2.6, we recall that λ_i of $\mathbf{K}$ represents the minimum that can be reached by the Rayleigh quotient when an orthonormality constraint is satisfied on the eigenvectors $\boldsymbol{\phi}_1, \ldots, \boldsymbol{\phi}_{i-1}$:

with

$$\left.\begin{aligned} \lambda_i &= \min\left\{\frac{\boldsymbol{\phi}^T\mathbf{K}\boldsymbol{\phi}}{\boldsymbol{\phi}^T\boldsymbol{\phi}}\right\} \\ \boldsymbol{\phi}^T\boldsymbol{\phi}_r &= 0; \quad \text{for } r = 1, 2, \ldots, i - 1 \end{aligned}\right\} \tag{8.36}$$

Therefore, $\frac{1}{2}\lambda_1$ is the minimum strain energy that can be stored in the element assemblage, and the corresponding displacement vector is $\boldsymbol{\phi}_1$. For a positive definite system stiffness matrix, we therefore have $\lambda_1 > 0$. On the other hand, for the stiffness matrix of an unrestrained system, we have $\lambda_1 = \lambda_2 = \cdots = \lambda_m = 0$, where m is the number of rigid body modes present, $m < n$. As the system is restrained, the number of eigenvalues of $\mathbf{K}$ is decreased by 1 for each degree of freedom that is eliminated, and a zero eigenvalue is lost if the restraint results in the elimination of a rigid body mode.

EXAMPLE 8.11:   Determine whether the deletion of the four degrees of freedom of the plane stress element in Fig. E8.11 results in the elimination of the rigid body modes.

The plane stress element has three rigid body modes: (1) uniform horizontal translation, (2) uniform vertical translation, and (3) in-plane rotation. Consider the sequential deletion of the degrees of freedom, as shown in Fig. E8.11. The deletion of U_4 results in eliminating the horizontal translation rigid body mode. Similarly the deletion of V_4 results in the deletion of

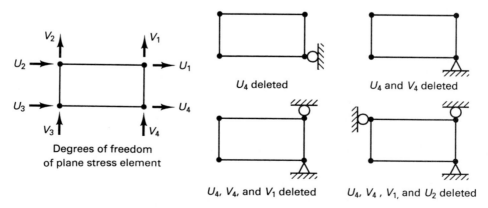

Figure E8.11   Deletion of degrees of freedom of plane stress element

the vertical translation rigid body mode. However, deleting V_1 in addition does not result in the elimination of the last rigid body mode; i.e., the in-plane rotation rigid body mode is eliminated only with the additional deletion of U_2. Therefore, the deletion of U_4 and V_4 and V_1 and U_2 eliminates all rigid body modes of the element, although we should note that, in fact, by the deletion of U_4, V_4, and U_2 alone we would achieve the same result.

The transformation performed in (8.34) has important meaning. Considering the relation and referring to Section 2.5, we realize that in (8.34) a change of basis is performed. The new basis vectors are the finite element interpolations corresponding to the eigenvectors of $\mathbf{K}$, and in this basis the operator is represented by a diagonal matrix with the eigenvalues of $\mathbf{K}$ on its diagonal. We may therefore look at $\mathbf{\Lambda}$ as being the stiffness matrix of the system when the finite element displacement functions used in the principle of virtual work in (4.7) are those corresponding to nodal point displacements ϕ_i, $i = 1, \ldots, n$, instead of unit nodal point displacements U_i, $i = 1, \ldots, n$ (see Section 4.2.1). The relation in (8.34) is therefore a statement of virtual work resulting in a diagonal stiffness matrix. If the system considered is properly restrained, all stiffness coefficients in $\mathbf{\Lambda}$ are positive; i.e., the stiffness matrix $\mathbf{\Lambda}$ (and hence $\mathbf{K}$) is positive definite, whereas for an unrestrained system some diagonal elements in $\mathbf{\Lambda}$ are zero.

Before studying the solution of nonpositive definite systems of equations, another most important observation should be discussed. In Section 2.6 we introduced the Sturm sequence property of the leading principal minors of a matrix. We should note here the physical meaning of the Sturm sequence. *Let $\mathbf{K}^{(r)}$ be the matrix of order $n - r$ obtained by deleting from $\mathbf{K}$ the last r rows and columns and consider the eigenproblem*

$$\mathbf{K}^{(r)}\mathbf{\phi}^{(r)} = \lambda^{(r)}\mathbf{\phi}^{(r)} \tag{8.37}$$

where $\mathbf{\phi}^{(r)}$ is a vector of order $n - r$. We say that (8.37) is the eigenproblem of the rth associated constraint problem of the problem $\mathbf{K}\mathbf{\phi} = \lambda\mathbf{\phi}$. Then we have shown in Section 2.6 that the eigenvalues of the $(r + 1)$st constraint problem separate those of the rth constraint problem,

$$\lambda_1^{(r)} \leq \lambda_1^{(r+1)} \leq \lambda_2^{(r)} \leq \lambda_2^{(r+1)} \leq \cdots \leq \lambda_{n-r-1}^{(r)} \leq \lambda_{n-r-1}^{(r+1)} \leq \lambda_{n-r}^{(r)} \tag{8.38}$$

As an example, the eigenproblems of the simply supported beam discussed in Section 8.2.1 and of its associated constraint problems can be considered. Figure 8.9 shows the eigenvalues calculated and, in particular, displays their separation property. We should note that as we proceed from the $(r + 1)$st constraint problem to the rth constraint problem by including the $(n - r)$th degree of freedom, the new system has an eigenvalue smaller than (or equal to) the smallest eigenvalue of the $(r + 1)$st constraint problem, and also an eigenvalue larger than (or equal to) the largest eigenvalue of the $(r + 1)$st constraint problem.

Using the separation property of the eigenvalues and realizing that any rows and columns may be interchanged at convenience to become the last rows and columns in the matrix $\mathbf{K}$, it follows that if the stiffness matrix corresponding to the n degrees of freedom is positive definite (i.e., $\lambda_1 > 0$), then any stiffness matrix obtained by deleting any rows and corresponding columns is also positive definite. Furthermore, the smallest eigenvalue of the new matrix can only have increased, and the largest eigenvalue can only have decreased. This conclusion applies also if the matrix $\mathbf{K}$ is positive semidefinite and would apply if it were indefinite since we showed the eigenvalue separation theorem to be applicable to all symmetric matrices.

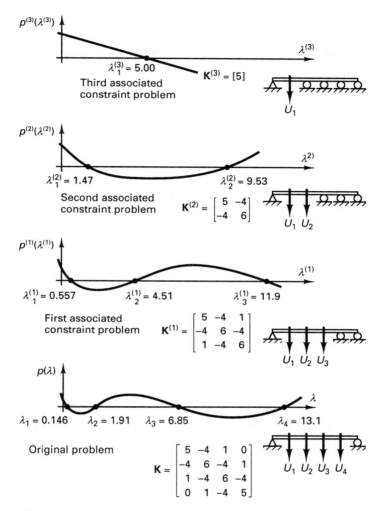

Figure 8.9 Eigenvalue solutions of simply supported beam and of associated constraint problems

We shall encounter the use of the Sturm sequence property of the leading principal minors more extensively in the design of eigenvalue solution algorithms (see Chapter 11). However, in the following we use the property to yield more insight into the solution of a set of simultaneous equations with a symmetric positive definite, positive semidefinite, or indefinite coefficient matrix. A symmetric indefinite coefficient matrix will be encountered in the solution of eigenproblems.

We showed in Sections 8.2.1 and 8.2.2 that if $\mathbf{K}$ is the stiffness matrix of a properly restrained structure, we can factorize $\mathbf{K}$ into the form

$$\mathbf{K} = \mathbf{L}\mathbf{D}\mathbf{L}^T \tag{8.39}$$

where $\mathbf{L}$ is a lower unit triangular matrix and $\mathbf{D}$ is a diagonal matrix, with $d_{ii} > 0$. It follows that

$$\det \mathbf{K} = \det \mathbf{L} \det \mathbf{D} \det \mathbf{L}^T$$

$$= \prod_{i=1}^{n} d_{ii} > 0 \qquad (8.40)$$

This result can also be obtained by considering the characteristic polynomial of $\mathbf{K}$, defined as

$$p(\lambda) = \det(\mathbf{K} - \lambda \mathbf{I}) \qquad (8.41)$$

Since λ_1 is the smallest root of $p(\lambda)$ and $\lambda_1 > 0$ for $\mathbf{K}$ being positive definite, it follows that $\det \mathbf{K} > 0$. However, it does not yet follow that $d_{ii} > 0$ for all i.

In order to formally prove that $d_{ii} > 0$, $i = 1, \ldots , n$, when $\mathbf{K}$ is positive definite, and to identify what happens during the factorization of $\mathbf{K}$, it is expedient to compare the triangular factors of $\mathbf{K}$ with those of $\mathbf{K}^{(i)}$, where $\mathbf{K}^{(i)}$ is the stiffness matrix of the ith associated constraint problem. Assuming that the factors $\mathbf{L}$ and $\mathbf{D}$ of $\mathbf{K}$ have been calculated, we have, for the associated constraint problems,

$$\mathbf{K}^{(i)} = \mathbf{L}^{(i)} \mathbf{D}^{(i)} \mathbf{L}^{(i)T} \qquad i = 1, \ldots , n - 1 \qquad (8.42)$$

where $\mathbf{L}^{(i)}$ and $\mathbf{D}^{(i)}$ are analogously the factors of $\mathbf{K}^{(i)}$. Since $\mathbf{L}$ is a lower-unit triangular matrix and $\mathbf{D}$ is a diagonal matrix, the factors $\mathbf{L}^{(i)}$ and $\mathbf{D}^{(i)}$ are obtained from $\mathbf{L}$ and $\mathbf{D}$, respectively, by striking out the last i rows and columns. Therefore, $\mathbf{L}^{(i)}$ and $\mathbf{D}^{(i)}$ are the leading principal submatrices of $\mathbf{L}$ and $\mathbf{D}$, respectively, and they are actually evaluated in the factorization of $\mathbf{K}$. However, because $\lambda_1^{(i)} > 0$, it now follows that we can use the argument in (8.39) and (8.40) starting with $i = n - 1$ to show that $d_{ii} > 0$ for all i. Therefore, the factorization of $\mathbf{K}$ into $\mathbf{LDL}^T$ is indeed possible if $\mathbf{K}$ is positive definite. We demonstrate the result in the following example.

EXAMPLE 8.12:   Consider the simply supported beam in Fig. 8.9 and the associated constraint problems. The same beam was used in Section 8.2.1. Establish the $\mathbf{L}^{(i)}$ and $\mathbf{D}^{(i)}$ factors of the matrices $\mathbf{K}^{(i)}$, $i = 1, 2, 3$, and show that d_{ii} must be greater than zero because $\lambda_1 > 0$. The required triangular factorizations are

$$[5] = [1][5][1] \qquad (a)$$

$$\begin{bmatrix} 5 & -4 \\ -4 & 6 \end{bmatrix} = \begin{bmatrix} 1 & 0 \\ -\frac{4}{5} & 1 \end{bmatrix} \begin{bmatrix} 5 & 0 \\ 0 & \frac{14}{5} \end{bmatrix} \begin{bmatrix} 1 & -\frac{4}{5} \\ 0 & 1 \end{bmatrix} \qquad (b)$$

$$\begin{bmatrix} 5 & -4 & 1 \\ -4 & 6 & -4 \\ 1 & -4 & 6 \end{bmatrix} = \begin{bmatrix} 1 & 0 & 0 \\ -\frac{4}{5} & 1 & 0 \\ \frac{1}{5} & -\frac{8}{7} & 1 \end{bmatrix} \begin{bmatrix} 5 & 0 & 0 \\ 0 & \frac{14}{5} & 0 \\ 0 & 0 & \frac{15}{7} \end{bmatrix} \begin{bmatrix} 1 & -\frac{4}{5} & \frac{1}{5} \\ 0 & 1 & -\frac{8}{7} \\ 0 & 0 & 1 \end{bmatrix} \qquad (c)$$

where the matrices $\mathbf{L}^{(i)}$ and $\mathbf{D}^{(i)}$ are obtained from the $\mathbf{L}$ and $\mathbf{D}$ factors given in Example 8.3 by striking out the last i rows and columns. [As a check, we may want to calculate the product of the matrices on the right sides of the relations in (a) to (c) to obtain the matrices on the left sides.]

Considering the elements d_{ii}, we have $\lambda_1^{(3)} \geq \lambda_1^{(2)} \geq \lambda_1^{(1)} \geq \lambda_1 > 0$. But using the relation (a), we have $\lambda_1^{(3)} = d_{11}$; hence $d_{11} > 0$. Next we consider $\mathbf{K}^{(2)}$. Since $\lambda_1^{(2)} > 0$, we have, using (8.39) and (8.40), $d_{11}d_{22} > 0$, which means that $d_{22} > 0$. Similarly, considering $\mathbf{K}^{(1)}$, we have $\lambda_1^{(1)} > 0$, and hence $d_{11}d_{22}d_{33} > 0$, from which it follows that $d_{33} > 0$. Finally, considering $\mathbf{K}$, we have $\lambda_1 > 0$, and hence $d_{11}d_{22}d_{33}d_{44} > 0$. Therefore, $d_{44} > 0$ also.

Assume next that the matrix $\mathbf{K}$ is the stiffness matrix of a finite element assemblage that is unrestrained. In this case, $\mathbf{K}$ is positive semidefinite, $\lambda = 0.0$ is a root, and det $\mathbf{K}$ is zero, which, using (8.40), means that d_{ii} for some i must be zero. Therefore, the factorization of $\mathbf{K}$ as shown in the preceding sections is, in general, not possible because a pivot element will be zero. It is again instructive to consider the associated constraint problems. When $\mathbf{K}$ is positive semidefinite, we note that the characteristic polynomial corresponding to $\mathbf{K}^{(i)}$ will have a zero eigenvalue, and this zero eigenvalue will be retained in all matrices $\mathbf{K}^{(i-1)}, \ldots, \mathbf{K}$. This follows because, first, the Sturm sequence property ensures that the smallest eigenvalue of $\mathbf{K}^{(i-1)}$ is smaller or equal to the smallest eigenvalue of $\mathbf{K}^{(i)}$, and second, $\mathbf{K}$ has no negative eigenvalues. For the ith associated constraint problem, we will therefore have

$$\det (\mathbf{L}^{(i)}\mathbf{D}^{(i)}\mathbf{L}^{(i)T}) = 0 \tag{8.43}$$

from which it follows that an element of $\mathbf{D}^{(i)}$ is zero. However, assuming that the zero root occurs only in the ith associated constraint problem [i.e., det $(\mathbf{L}^{(r)}\mathbf{D}^{(r)}\mathbf{L}^{(r)T}) > 0$ for $r > i$], it follows that $d_{n-i,n-i}$ is zero. In summary therefore, if $\mathbf{K}$ is positive semidefinite, the factorization of $\mathbf{K}$ into $\mathbf{LDL}^T$ (i.e., the Gauss elimination process) will break down at the time a zero diagonal element d_{kk} is encountered, which means that the $(n - k)$th associated constraint problem with a zero eigenvalue prevents the continuation of the factorization process.

In the case of a positive semidefinite matrix, a zero diagonal element must be encountered at some stage of the factorization. However, considering the decomposition of an indefinite matrix (i.e., some of the eigenvalues of the matrix are negative and some are positive), a zero diagonal element is encountered only if one of the associated constraint problems has a zero eigenvalue. Namely, as in the case of a positive semidefinite matrix, d_{kk} is zero if the $(n - k)$th associated constraint problem has a zero eigenvalue. However, if none of the associated constraint problems has a zero eigenvalue, all elements d_{ii} are nonzero and, in exact arithmetic, no difficulties are encountered in the factorization. We shall discuss the decomposition of indefinite coefficient matrices further in the solution of eigenproblems (see Section 11.4.2). Figure 8.10 shows typical cases that use the simply supported beam in Fig. 8.9 on spring supports for which, in the decompositions, we would and would not encounter a zero diagonal element.

Assume that a zero diagonal element d_{ii} is encountered in the Gauss elimination. To be able to proceed with the solution, it is necessary to interchange the ith row with another row, say the jth row, where $j > i$. The new diagonal element should not be zero, and to increase solution accuracy, it should be large (see Section 8.2.6). This row interchange corresponds to a rearranging of the equations, where it should be noted that the row interchange results in the coefficient matrix no longer being symmetric. On the other hand, symmetry would be preserved if we were to interchange not only the ith and jth rows but also the corresponding columns to obtain a nonzero diagonal element in row i, which is not always possible (see Example 10.4). In effect, the interchange of columns and rows corresponds to a rearranging of the associated constraint problems in such a way that these have nonzero eigenvalues.

The remedy of row interchanges assumes that it can be arranged for the new diagonal element to be nonzero. In fact, this will always be the case unless the matrix has a zero eigenvalue of multiplicity m and $i = n - m + 1$. In this case the matrix is singular and d_{ii}

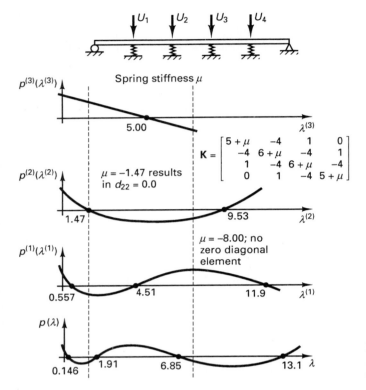

Figure 8.10 Simply supported beam on spring supports; negative spring stiffness can result in solution difficulties.

is zero, but all other elements of the last m rows of the upper triangular factor of the coefficient matrix are also zero, and the factorization of the matrix has already been completed. In other words, since the number of rows that are made up of only zero elements is equal to the multiplicity m of the zero eigenvalue, the last $m - 1$ matrices $\mathbf{L}_{n-1}^{-1}$, $\mathbf{L}_{n-2}^{-1}, \ldots, \mathbf{L}_{n-m+1}^{-1}$ in (8.10) cannot and need not be calculated. We shall therefore be able to solve for m linearly independent solutions by assuming appropriate values for the m last entries of the solution vector.

Consider the following example.

EXAMPLE 8.13: Consider the beam element in Fig. E8.13(a). The stiffness matrix of the element is

$$\mathbf{K} = \begin{bmatrix} 12 & -6 & -12 & -6 \\ -6 & 4 & 6 & 2 \\ -12 & 6 & 12 & 6 \\ -6 & 2 & 6 & 4 \end{bmatrix}$$

Show that Gauss elimination results in the third and fourth row consisting of only zero elements and evaluate formally the rigid body mode displacements.

Using the procedure in (8.10), we expect to arrive at a matrix $\mathbf{S}$ with its last two rows consisting of only zero elements because the beam element has two rigid body modes corre-

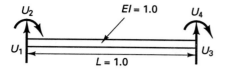

(a) Initial degree of freedom numbering

(b) Degree of freedom numbering
that requires column and row interchange

Figure E8.13   Beam element with two rigid body modes

sponding to vertical translation and rotation. We have

$$\mathbf{L}_1^{-1} = \begin{bmatrix} 1 & & & \\ \frac{1}{2} & 1 & & \\ 1 & 0 & 1 & \\ \frac{1}{2} & 0 & 0 & 1 \end{bmatrix}$$

Hence,

$$\mathbf{L}_1^{-1}\mathbf{K} = \begin{bmatrix} 12 & -6 & -12 & -6 \\ 0 & 1 & 0 & -1 \\ 0 & 0 & 0 & 0 \\ 0 & -1 & 0 & 1 \end{bmatrix}$$

Then

$$\mathbf{L}_2^{-1} = \begin{bmatrix} 1 & & & \\ 0 & 1 & & \\ 0 & 0 & 1 & \\ 0 & 1 & 0 & 1 \end{bmatrix}$$

and

$$\mathbf{S} = \mathbf{L}_2^{-1}\mathbf{L}_1^{-1}\mathbf{K} = \begin{bmatrix} 12 & -6 & -12 & -6 \\ 0 & 1 & 0 & -1 \\ 0 & 0 & 0 & 0 \\ 0 & 0 & 0 & 0 \end{bmatrix} \qquad (a)$$

Therefore, as expected, the last two rows in $\mathbf{S}$ consist of zero elements, and $\mathbf{L}_3^{-1}$ cannot and need not be calculated. We should also note that if the numbering of the degrees of freedom of the beam element were initially as in Fig. E8.13(b), we would need to interchange rows and columns 2 with rows and columns 3 in order to be able to continue with the triangularization. This, however, is equivalent to using the degree of freedom numbering that we were concerned with in the first place, i.e., the numbering in Fig. E8.13(a).

Using the matrix $\mathbf{S}$ in (a), we can now formally evaluate the rigid body mode displacements of the beam, i.e., solve the equations $\mathbf{KU} = \mathbf{0}$ to obtain two linearly independent solutions for $\mathbf{U}$.

First, assume that $U_4 = 1$ and $U_3 = 0$; then using $\mathbf{S}$, we obtain

$$12U_1 - 6U_2 = 6$$

$$U_2 = 1$$

Hence, $U_1 = 1$, $U_2 = 1$, $U_3 = 0$, $U_4 = 1$

Then assume that $U_4 = 0$, $U_3 = 1$, to obtain

$$12U_1 - 6U_2 = 12$$

$$U_2 = 0$$

Hence, $U_1 = 1,$ $U_2 = 0,$ $U_3 = 1,$ $U_4 = 0$

It should be noted that the rigid body displacement vectors are not unique, but instead the two-dimensional subspace spanned by any two linearly independent rigid body mode vectors is unique. Therefore, any rigid body displacement vector can be written as

$$\begin{bmatrix} U_1 \\ U_2 \\ U_3 \\ U_4 \end{bmatrix} = \gamma_1 \begin{bmatrix} 1 \\ 1 \\ 0 \\ 1 \end{bmatrix} + \gamma_2 \begin{bmatrix} 1 \\ 0 \\ 1 \\ 0 \end{bmatrix} \tag{b}$$

where γ_1 and γ_2 are constants. Note that the rank of $\mathbf{K}$ is 2 and the kernel of $\mathbf{K}$ is given by the two basis vectors in (b) (see Section 2.3).

8.2.6 Solution Errors

In the preceding sections we presented various algorithms for the solution of $\mathbf{KU} = \mathbf{R}$. We applied the solution procedures to some small problems for instructive purposes, but in practical analysis the methods are employed on large systems of equations using a digital computer. It is important to note that the elements of the matrices and the computational results can then be represented to only a fixed number of digits, which introduces errors in the solution. The aim in this section is to discuss the solution errors that can occur in Gauss elimination and to give guidelines for avoiding the introduction of large errors.

In order to identify the source of the errors, let us assume that we use a computer in which a number is represented using t digits in single precision. Then, to increase accuracy, double-precision arithmetic may be specified, in which case each number is approximately represented using $2t$ (or more) digits. As an example, on IBM computers single-precision numbers are represented with 6 digits, whereas double-precision numbers are represented with 16 digits.

Considering the finite digit arithmetical operations, the t digits may be used quite differently in different machines. However, most computers, in effect, perform the arithmetic operations and afterward "chop off" all digits beyond the number of digits carried. Therefore, for demonstration purposes we assume in this section that the computer at hand first adds, subtracts, multiplies, and divides two numbers exactly, and then to obtain the finite precision results, chops off all digits beyond the t digits used.

In order to demonstrate the finite precision arithmetic, assume that we want to solve the system of equations

$$\begin{bmatrix} 3.42521 & -3.42521 \\ -3.42521 & 101.2431 \end{bmatrix} \begin{bmatrix} U_1 \\ U_2 \end{bmatrix} = \begin{bmatrix} 1.3021 \\ 0.0 \end{bmatrix} \tag{8.44}$$

where $\mathbf{K}$ and $\mathbf{R}$ are given "exactly." The exact solution is (to 10 digits)

$$U_1 = 0.3934633449; \qquad U_2 = 0.0133114709 \tag{8.45}$$

Assume now that for a (hypothetical) computer at hand, $t = 3$; i.e., each number is represented to only three digits. In this case the solution to the equations in (8.44) would be obtained by first representing $\mathbf{K}$ and $\mathbf{R}$ using only the first three digits in each number and then calculating the solution by always using only three-digit representations with chopping off of the additional digits. Employing the basic Gauss elimination algorithm (see Section 8.2.1), the solution would be as follows:

$$\begin{bmatrix} 3.42 & -3.42 \\ -3.42 & 101 \end{bmatrix} \begin{bmatrix} \hat{U}_1 \\ \hat{U}_2 \end{bmatrix} = \begin{bmatrix} 1.30 \\ 0 \end{bmatrix} \tag{8.46}$$

where the hats over U_1 and U_2 indicate that the solution of (8.46) is different from the solution of (8.44). Using that with chopping to three digits,

$$101 - \left(\frac{-3.42}{3.42}\right)(-3.42) = 101 - (-1)(-3.42) = 97.5$$

we obtain

$$\begin{bmatrix} 3.42 & -3.42 \\ 0.0 & 97.5 \end{bmatrix} \begin{bmatrix} \overline{U}_1 \\ \overline{U}_2 \end{bmatrix} = \begin{bmatrix} 1.30 \\ 1.30 \end{bmatrix} \tag{8.47}$$

where the bars over U_1 and U_2 indicate that we solve (8.46) approximately. Continuing to use three-digit chopping arithmetic, we have

$$\left.\begin{aligned} \overline{U}_2 &= \frac{1.30}{97.5} = 0.0133 \\ \overline{U}_1 &= \frac{1}{3.42}[1.30 - (-3.42)(0.0133)] = \frac{1}{3.42}(1.34) \\ &= 0.391 \end{aligned}\right\} \tag{8.48}$$

and

Referring to the above example, we can identify two kinds of errors: a *truncation error* and *a round-off error*. The truncation error is the error arising because the exact matrix **K** and load vector **R** in (8.44) are represented to only three-digit precision, as given in (8.46). The round-off error is the error that arises in the solution of (8.46) because only three-digit arithmetic is used. Considering the situations in which each type of error would be large, we note that the truncation error can be large if the absolute magnitude of the elements in the matrix **K** including the diagonal elements varies by a large amount. The round-off error can be large if a small diagonal element d_{ii} is used that creates a large multiplier l_{ij}. The reason that the truncation and round-off errors are large under the above conditions is that the basic operation in the factorization is a subtraction of a multiple of the pivot row from the rows below it. If in this operation numbers of widely different magnitudes are subtracted—that have, however, been represented to only a fixed number of digits—the errors in this basic operation can be relatively large.

To identify the round-off errors and the truncation errors individually in the example, we need to solve (8.46) exactly, in which case we obtain

$$\begin{bmatrix} 3.42 & -3.42 \\ 0 & 97.58 \end{bmatrix} \begin{bmatrix} \hat{U}_1 \\ \hat{U}_2 \end{bmatrix} = \begin{bmatrix} 1.30 \\ 1.30 \end{bmatrix} \tag{8.49}$$

and

$$\hat{U}_1 = 0.3934393613$$
$$\hat{U}_2 = 0.0133224020 \tag{8.50}$$

The error in the solution arising from initial truncation is therefore

$$\hat{\mathbf{r}} = \begin{bmatrix} U_1 \\ U_2 \end{bmatrix} - \begin{bmatrix} \hat{U}_1 \\ \hat{U}_2 \end{bmatrix} = \begin{bmatrix} 0.0000239836 \\ -0.0000109311 \end{bmatrix} \tag{8.51}$$

and the round-off error is

$$\bar{\mathbf{r}} = \begin{bmatrix} \hat{U}_1 \\ \hat{U}_2 \end{bmatrix} - \begin{bmatrix} \overline{U}_1 \\ \overline{U}_2 \end{bmatrix} = \begin{bmatrix} 0.0024393613 \\ 0.0000224020 \end{bmatrix} \tag{8.52}$$

The total error $\mathbf{r}$ is the sum of $\bar{\mathbf{r}}$ and $\hat{\mathbf{r}}$, or

$$\mathbf{r} = \begin{bmatrix} U_1 \\ U_2 \end{bmatrix} - \begin{bmatrix} \overline{U}_1 \\ \overline{U}_2 \end{bmatrix} = \begin{bmatrix} 0.0024633449 \\ 0.0000114709 \end{bmatrix} \tag{8.53}$$

In this evaluation of the solution errors, we used the exact solutions to (8.44) and (8.49). In practical analyses, these exact solutions cannot be obtained; instead, double-precision arithmetic could be employed to calculate close approximations to them.

Consider now that in a specific analysis the solution obtained to the equations $\mathbf{KU} = \mathbf{R}$ is $\overline{\mathbf{U}}$; i.e., because of truncation and round-off errors, $\overline{\mathbf{U}}$ is calculated instead of $\mathbf{U}$. It appears that the error in the solution can be obtained by evaluating a residual $\Delta\mathbf{R}$, where

$$\Delta\mathbf{R} = \mathbf{R} - \mathbf{K}\overline{\mathbf{U}} \tag{8.54}$$

In practice, $\Delta\mathbf{R}$ would be calculated using double-precision arithmetic. Substituting $\mathbf{KU}$ for $\mathbf{R}$ into (8.54), we have for the solution error $\mathbf{r} = \mathbf{U} - \overline{\mathbf{U}}$,

$$\mathbf{r} = \mathbf{K}^{-1}\,\Delta\mathbf{R} \tag{8.55}$$

meaning that *although $\Delta\mathbf{R}$ may be small, the error in the solution may still be large.* On the other hand, for an accurate solution $\Delta\mathbf{R}$ must be small. Therefore, a small residual $\Delta\mathbf{R}$ is a necessary but not a sufficient condition for an accurate solution.

> **EXAMPLE 8.14:**   Calculate $\Delta\mathbf{R}$ and $\mathbf{r}$ for the introductory example considered above.
>
> Using the values for $\mathbf{R}$, $\mathbf{K}$, and $\overline{\mathbf{U}}$ given in (8.44) and (8.48), respectively, we obtain, using (8.54),
>
> $$\Delta\mathbf{R} = \begin{bmatrix} 1.3021 \\ 0 \end{bmatrix} - \begin{bmatrix} 3.42521 & -3.42521 \\ -3.42521 & 101.2431 \end{bmatrix} \begin{bmatrix} 0.391 \\ 0.0133 \end{bmatrix}$$
>
> or
> $$\Delta\mathbf{R} = \begin{bmatrix} 0.00839818 \\ -0.00042520 \end{bmatrix}$$
>
> Hence, using (8.55), we have
>
> $$\mathbf{r} = \begin{bmatrix} 0.00253338 \\ 0.00008151 \end{bmatrix}$$
>
> In this case, $\Delta\mathbf{R}$ and $\mathbf{r}$ are both relatively small because $\mathbf{K}$ is well-conditioned.

> **EXAMPLE 8.15:**   Consider the system of equations
>
> $$\begin{bmatrix} 4.855 & -4 & 1 & 0 \\ -4 & 5.855 & -4 & 1 \\ 1 & -4 & 5.855 & -4 \\ 0 & 1 & -4 & 4.855 \end{bmatrix} \begin{bmatrix} U_1 \\ U_2 \\ U_3 \\ U_4 \end{bmatrix} = \begin{bmatrix} -1.59 \\ 1 \\ 1 \\ -1.64 \end{bmatrix}$$
>
> Use six-digit arithmetic with chopping to calculate the solution.

Following the basic Gauss elimination process, we have

$$
\begin{bmatrix}
4.85500 & -4 & 1 & 0 \\
0 & 2.55944 & -3.17610 & 1 \\
0 & -3.17610 & 5.64902 & -4 \\
0 & 1 & -4 & 4.85500
\end{bmatrix}
\begin{bmatrix}
\bar{U}_1 \\ \bar{U}_2 \\ \bar{U}_3 \\ \bar{U}_4
\end{bmatrix}
=
\begin{bmatrix}
-1.59000 \\ -0.309980 \\ 1.32719 \\ -1.64000
\end{bmatrix}
$$

$$
\begin{bmatrix}
4.85500 & -4 & 1 & 0 \\
0 & 2.55944 & -3.17610 & 1 \\
0 & 0 & 1.70771 & -2.75907 \\
0 & 0 & -2.75907 & 4.46429
\end{bmatrix}
\begin{bmatrix}
\bar{U}_1 \\ \bar{U}_2 \\ \bar{U}_3 \\ \bar{U}_4
\end{bmatrix}
=
\begin{bmatrix}
-1.59000 \\ -0.309980 \\ 0.942827 \\ -1.51888
\end{bmatrix}
$$

$$
\begin{bmatrix}
4.85500 & -4 & 1 & 0 \\
 & 2.55944 & -3.17610 & 1 \\
 & & 1.70771 & -2.75907 \\
 & & & 0.006600
\end{bmatrix}
\begin{bmatrix}
\bar{U}_1 \\ \bar{U}_2 \\ \bar{U}_3 \\ \bar{U}_4
\end{bmatrix}
=
\begin{bmatrix}
-1.59000 \\ -0.309980 \\ 0.942827 \\ 0.004390
\end{bmatrix}
$$

The back-substitution yields
$$
\bar{\mathbf{U}} =
\begin{bmatrix}
0.686706 \\ 1.63768 \\ 1.62674 \\ 0.665151
\end{bmatrix}
$$

The exact answer (to seven digits) is

$$
\mathbf{U} =
\begin{bmatrix}
0.7037247 \\ 1.6652256 \\ 1.6542831 \\ 0.6821567
\end{bmatrix}
$$

Evaluating $\mathbf{\Delta R}$ as given in (8.54), we obtain

$$
\mathbf{\Delta R} =
\begin{bmatrix}
-1.59 \\ 1 \\ 1 \\ -1.64
\end{bmatrix}
-
\begin{bmatrix}
-1.59002237 \\ 0.99998340 \\ 0.99994470 \\ -1.639971895
\end{bmatrix}
=
\begin{bmatrix}
0.00002237 \\ 0.00001660 \\ 0.00005530 \\ -0.000028105
\end{bmatrix}
$$

Also evaluating $\mathbf{r}$, we have
$$
\mathbf{r} =
\begin{bmatrix}
0.01702 \\ 0.02756 \\ 0.02754 \\ 0.01701
\end{bmatrix}
$$

We therefore see that $\mathbf{\Delta R}$ is relatively much smaller than $\mathbf{r}$. Indeed, the displacement errors are of the order 1 to 2 percent, although the load errors seem to indicate an accurate solution of the equations.

Considering (8.55), we must expect that solution accuracy is difficult to obtain when the smallest eigenvalue of $\mathbf{K}$ is very small or nearly zero; i.e., the system can almost undergo rigid body motion. Namely, in that case the elements in $\mathbf{K}^{-1}$ are large and the solution errors may be large although $\mathbf{\Delta R}$ is small. Also, to substantiate this conclusion, we may realize that if λ_1 of $\mathbf{K}$ is small, the solution $\mathbf{KU} = \mathbf{R}$ may be thought of as one step of inverse iteration with a shift close to λ_1. But the analysis in Section 11.2.1 shows that in such a case the solution tends to have components of the corresponding eigenvector. These components now appear as solution errors.

To obtain more information on the solution errors, an analysis can be performed that shows that it is not only a small (near zero) eigenvalue λ_1 but a large ratio of the largest to the smallest eigenvalues of $\mathbf{K}$ that determines the solution errors. Namely, in the solution of $\mathbf{KU} = \mathbf{R}$, owing to truncation and round-off errors, we may assume that we in fact solve

$$(\mathbf{K} + \delta\mathbf{K})(\mathbf{U} + \delta\mathbf{U}) = \mathbf{R} \tag{8.56}$$

Assuming that $\delta\mathbf{K}\,\delta\mathbf{U}$ is small in relation to the other terms, we have approximately

$$\delta\mathbf{U} = -\mathbf{K}^{-1}\,\delta\mathbf{K}\,\mathbf{U} \tag{8.57}$$

or, taking norms,
$$\frac{\|\delta\mathbf{U}\|}{\|\mathbf{U}\|} \leq \text{cond}\,(\mathbf{K})\frac{\|\delta\mathbf{K}\|}{\|\mathbf{K}\|} \tag{8.58}$$

where $\text{cond}(\mathbf{K})$ is the *condition number* of $\mathbf{K}$,

$$\text{cond}(\mathbf{K}) = \frac{\lambda_n}{\lambda_1} \tag{8.59}$$

Therefore, *a large condition number means that solution errors are more likely.* To evaluate an estimate of the solution errors, assume that for a t-digit precision computer,

$$\frac{\|\delta\mathbf{K}\|}{\|\mathbf{K}\|} = 10^{-t} \tag{8.60}$$

Also, assuming s-digit precision in the solution, we have

$$\frac{\|\delta\mathbf{U}\|}{\|\mathbf{U}\|} = 10^{-s} \tag{8.61}$$

Substituting (8.60) and (8.61) into (8.58), we obtain as an estimate of the number of accurate digits obtained in the solution,

$$s \geq t - \log_{10}\left[\text{cond}(\mathbf{K})\right] \tag{8.62}$$

EXAMPLE 8.16:   Calculate the condition number of the matrix $\mathbf{K}$ used in Example 8.15. Then estimate the accuracy that can be expected in the equation solution.

In this case we have

$$\lambda_1 = 0.000898$$

$$\lambda_4 = 12.9452$$

Hence,
$$\text{cond}(\mathbf{K}) = 14415.6$$

and
$$\log_{10}\left[\text{cond}(\mathbf{K})\right] = 4.15883$$

Thus the number of accurate digits using six-digit arithmetic predicted using (8.62) is

$$s \geq 6 - 4.16$$

or one- to two-digit accuracy can be expected. Comparing this result with the results obtained in Example 8.15, we observe that, indeed, only one- to two-digit accuracy was obtained.

The condition number of $\mathbf{K}$ can in practice be evaluated approximately by calculating an upper bound for λ_n, say λ_n^u,

$$\lambda_n^u = \|\mathbf{K}\| \tag{8.63}$$

where any matrix norm may be used (see Example 8.17), and evaluating a lower bound for λ_1, say λ_1^l, using inverse iteration (see Section 11.2.1). We thus have

$$\mathrm{cond}(\mathbf{K}) \doteq \frac{\lambda_n^u}{\lambda_1^l} \tag{8.64}$$

EXAMPLE 8.17: Calculate an estimate of the condition number of the matrix $\mathbf{K}$ used in Example 8.15.

Here we have, using the ∞ norm (see Section 2.7),

$$\|\mathbf{K}\|_\infty = 14.855$$

and by inverse iteration we obtain $\lambda_1 = 0.0009$. Hence,

$$\log_{10}(\mathrm{cond}\ (\mathbf{K})) = 4.2176$$

and the conclusions reached in Example 8.16 are still valid.

The preceding considerations on round-off and truncation errors yield the following two important results:

1. Both types of errors can be expected to be large if structures with widely varying stiffness are analyzed. Large stiffness differences may be due to different material moduli, or they may be the result of the finite element modeling used, in which case a more effective model can frequently be chosen. This may be achieved by the use of finite elements that are nearly equal in size and have almost the same lengths in each dimension, the use of master-slave degrees of freedom, i.e., constraint equations (see Section 4.2.2 and Example 8.19), and relative degrees of freedom (see Example 8.20).

2. Since truncation errors are most significant, to improve the solution accuracy it is necessary to evaluate both the stiffness matrix $\mathbf{K}$ and the solution of $\mathbf{KU} = \mathbf{R}$ in double precision. It is not sufficient (a) to evaluate $\mathbf{K}$ in single precision and then solve the equations in double precision (see Example 8.18), or (b) to evaluate $\mathbf{K}$ in single precision, solve the equations in single precision using a Gauss elimination procedure, and then iterate for an improvement in the solution employing, for example, the Gauss-Seidel method.

We demonstrate these two conclusions by means of some simple examples.

EXAMPLE 8.18: Consider the simple spring system in Fig. E8.18. Calculate the displacements when $k = 1$, $K = 10,000$ using four-digit arithmetic. The equilibrium equations of the system are

$$\begin{bmatrix} K & -K & 0 \\ -K & 2K & -K \\ 0 & -K & K+k \end{bmatrix} \begin{bmatrix} U_1 \\ U_2 \\ U_3 \end{bmatrix} = \begin{bmatrix} 1 \\ 0 \\ 1 \end{bmatrix}$$

Stiffness k Stiffness K Stiffness K

U_3 U_2 U_1

$R_3 = 1$ $R_2 = 0$ $R_1 = 1$ **Figure E8.18** Simple spring system

Substituting $K = 10,000$, $k = 1$ and using four-digit arithmetic, we have

$$\begin{bmatrix} 10,000 & -10,000 & 0 \\ -10,000 & 20,000 & -10,000 \\ 0 & -10,000 & 10,000 \end{bmatrix} \begin{bmatrix} U_1 \\ U_2 \\ U_3 \end{bmatrix} = \begin{bmatrix} 1 \\ 0 \\ 1 \end{bmatrix}$$

The triangularization of the coefficient matrix gives

$$\begin{bmatrix} 10,000 & -10,000 & 0 \\ 0 & 10,000 & -10,000 \\ 0 & 0 & 0 \end{bmatrix} \begin{bmatrix} U_1 \\ U_2 \\ U_3 \end{bmatrix} = \begin{bmatrix} 1.0 \\ 1.0 \\ 2.0 \end{bmatrix}$$

Hence, a solution is not possible, because $d_{nn} = 0.0$.

To obtain a solution we may employ higher-digit arithmetic. In practice, this would mean that double-precision arithmetic would be used, i.e., in this case, eight- instead of four-digit arithmetic.

Using eight-digit arithmetic (indeed five digits would be sufficient), we obtain the exact solution as follows:

$$\begin{bmatrix} 10,000 & -10,000 & 0 \\ -10,000 & 20,000 & -10,000 \\ 0 & -10,000 & 10,001 \end{bmatrix} \begin{bmatrix} U_1 \\ U_2 \\ U_3 \end{bmatrix} = \begin{bmatrix} 1 \\ 0 \\ 1 \end{bmatrix}$$

$$\begin{bmatrix} 10,000 & -10,000 & 0 \\ 0 & 10,000 & -10,000 \\ 0 & 0 & 1 \end{bmatrix} \begin{bmatrix} U_1 \\ U_2 \\ U_3 \end{bmatrix} = \begin{bmatrix} 1.0 \\ 1.0 \\ 2.0 \end{bmatrix}$$

Hence,
$$\mathbf{U} = \begin{bmatrix} 2.0002 \\ 2.0001 \\ 2.0 \end{bmatrix}$$

This example shows that a sufficient number of digits carried in the arithmetic may be vital for the solution not to break down.

EXAMPLE 8.19: Use the master-slave solution procedure to analyze the system considered in Fig. E8.18.

The basic assumption in the master-slave analysis is the use of the constraint equations

$$U_1 = U_2 = U_3$$

The equilibrium equation governing the system is thus

$$kU_1 = 2$$

Substituting for k, we obtain $U_1 = 2$

and the complete solution is

$$\mathbf{U} = \begin{bmatrix} 2.0 \\ 2.0 \\ 2.0 \end{bmatrix}$$

This solution is approximate. However, comparing the solution with the exact result (see Example 8.18), we find that the main response is properly predicted.

EXAMPLE 8.20:   Use relative degrees of freedom to analyze the system in Fig. E8.18.

Using relative degrees of freedom, the displacement degrees of freedom defined are U_3, Δ_1, and Δ_2, where

$$U_2 = U_3 + \Delta_2$$

$$U_1 = U_2 + \Delta_1$$

or we have

$$\begin{bmatrix} U_1 \\ U_2 \\ U_3 \end{bmatrix} = \begin{bmatrix} 1 & 1 & 1 \\ 0 & 1 & 1 \\ 0 & 0 & 1 \end{bmatrix} \begin{bmatrix} \Delta_1 \\ \Delta_2 \\ U_3 \end{bmatrix} \qquad (a)$$

The matrix relating the degrees of freedom Δ_1, Δ_2, and U_3 to the degrees of freedom U_1, U_2, and U_3 is the matrix $\mathbf{T}$. The equilibrium equations for the system using relative degrees of freedom are $(\mathbf{T}^T \mathbf{K} \mathbf{T}) \mathbf{U}_{\text{rel}} = \mathbf{T}^T \mathbf{R}$; i.e., the equilibrium equations are now

$$\begin{bmatrix} 10,000 & 0 & 0 \\ 0 & 10,000 & 0 \\ 0 & 0 & 1.0 \end{bmatrix} \begin{bmatrix} \Delta_1 \\ \Delta_2 \\ U_3 \end{bmatrix} = \begin{bmatrix} 1.0 \\ 1.0 \\ 2.0 \end{bmatrix} \qquad (b)$$

with the solution

$$\Delta_1 = 0.0001$$

$$\Delta_2 = 0.0001$$

$$U_3 = 2.0$$

Hence, we obtain

$$U_1 = 2.0002$$

$$U_2 = 2.0001$$

$$U_3 = 2.0000$$

Therefore, using four-digit arithmetic, we obtain the exact solution of the system if relative degrees of freedom are used (see Example 8.18). However, it should be noted that the equilibrium equations corresponding to the relative degrees of freedom would have to be formed directly, i.e., without the transformation used in this example.

8.2.7 Exercises

8.1. Consider the cantilever beam in Example 8.1 with the given stiffness matrix. Calculate the experimental results that you expect to obtain in a laboratory experiment for the stiffnesses of the beam, as described in Figs. 8.3 to 8.6 for the simply supported beam discussed in the text. That is, give the forces in the clamps and the deflected shapes of the cantilever beam corresponding to the stiffness measurements of the four cases: all four clamps present, clamp 1 removed, clamps 1 and 2 removed, and clamps 1, 2, and 3 removed.

8.2. Given the stiffness matrix of the cantilever beam in Example 8.1, calculate the stiffness matrix corresponding to U_2 and U_4 only, that is, with the degrees of freedom U_1 and U_3 released. Then calculate and plot the deflected shapes of the beam described by U_2 and U_4 only when $U_2 = 1$, $U_4 = 0$ and when $U_2 = 0$, $U_4 = 1$.

8.3. A laboratory experiment is performed to obtain the stiffness matrix of a structure. The clamps shown are used, and the following 4×4 stiffness matrix is measured:

$$\mathbf{K} = \begin{bmatrix} 14 & -6 & 1 & 0 \\ -6 & 14 & -7 & 1 \\ 1 & -7 & 16 & -8 \\ 0 & 1 & -8 & 18 \end{bmatrix}$$

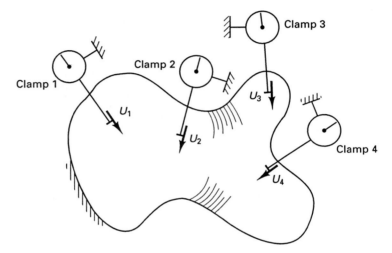

All clamps are firmly attached to structure

Clamp 2 is then removed, and the following 3×3 stiffness matrix is measured:

$$\tilde{\mathbf{K}} = \begin{bmatrix} \frac{80}{7} & -2 & \frac{3}{7} \\ -2 & \frac{25}{2} & -\frac{15}{2} \\ \frac{3}{7} & -\frac{15}{2} & 17 \end{bmatrix}$$

While you are sure that the matrix $\mathbf{K}$ has been correctly established, there is some doubt as to whether the matrix $\tilde{\mathbf{K}}$ has been measured correctly because clamp 3 might not have worked properly. Check whether the stiffness elements in $\tilde{\mathbf{K}}$ are correct, and if there is an error, give the details of the error.

8.4. The stiffness matrix of the beam element shown in (a) is given as

$$\mathbf{K} = EI \begin{array}{c} \begin{array}{cccc} U_1 & U_2 & U_3 & U_4 \end{array} \\ \begin{bmatrix} 12 & -6 & -12 & -6 \\ -6 & 4 & 6 & 2 \\ -12 & 6 & 12 & 6 \\ -6 & 2 & 6 & 4 \end{bmatrix} \end{array}$$

Calculate the stiffness of the element assemblage in (b) corresponding to the degree of freedom θ only.

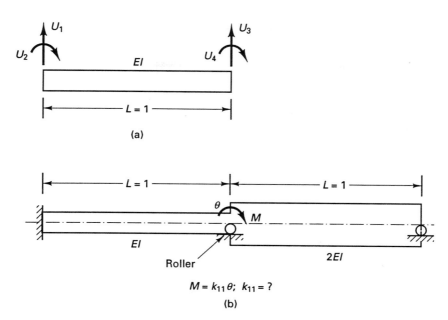

(a)

$$M = k_{11}\theta; \quad k_{11} = ?$$

(b)

8.5. The cantilever beam in Example 8.1 is loaded with a concentrated force corresponding to U_2; hence, the governing equations are

$$\begin{bmatrix} 7 & -4 & 1 & 0 \\ -4 & 6 & -4 & 1 \\ 1 & -4 & 5 & -2 \\ 0 & 1 & -2 & 1 \end{bmatrix} \begin{bmatrix} U_1 \\ U_2 \\ U_3 \\ U_4 \end{bmatrix} = \begin{bmatrix} 0 \\ 1 \\ 0 \\ 0 \end{bmatrix}$$

Calculate the displacement solution by performing Gauss elimination on the displacement variables in the order U_4, U_3, and U_1.

8.6. Consider the four-node finite element shown with its boundary conditions. Assume that Gauss elimination is performed in the usual order for U_1, U_2, . . . , and so on, i.e., from the lowest to the highest degree of freedom number. Determine for cases 1 to 3 whether any zero diagonal element will be encountered in the elimination process, and if so, at what stage of the solution this will be the case.

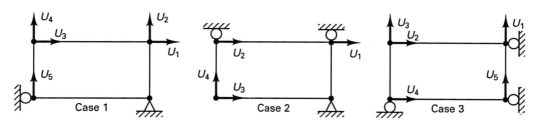

8.7. Establish the $\mathbf{LDL}^T$ factorization of the cantilever beam stiffness matrix $\mathbf{K}$ in Example 8.1 ($\mathbf{K}$ is the result of the first experiment; see Exercise 8.5). Use this factorization to calculate det $\mathbf{K}$ and to calculate the Cholesky factor $\tilde{\mathbf{L}}$ of $\mathbf{K}$.

8.8. Prove that corresponding to (8.10) and (8.14) we indeed have $\mathbf{S} = \mathbf{D}\tilde{\mathbf{S}}$ and $\tilde{\mathbf{S}} = \mathbf{L}^T$.

8.9. Consider the equations

$$
\begin{bmatrix} 2 & -1 & 0 \\ -1 & 2 & -1 \\ 0 & -1 & 2 \end{bmatrix} \begin{bmatrix} U_1 \\ U_2 \\ U_2 \end{bmatrix} = \begin{bmatrix} 1 \\ 0 \\ 0 \end{bmatrix}
$$

Establish the $\mathbf{LDL}^T$ factorization of the coefficient matrix and then solve the equations as given in (8.19) and (8.20). Finally, also calculate the Cholesky factor $\tilde{\mathbf{L}}$ of the coefficient matrix.

8.10. Consider the equations

$$
\begin{bmatrix} 2 & -1 & 0 \\ -1 & 2 & -1 \\ 0 & -1 & 2+k \end{bmatrix} \begin{bmatrix} U_1 \\ U_2 \\ U_2 \end{bmatrix} = \begin{bmatrix} 1 \\ 0 \\ 0 \end{bmatrix}
$$

Establish for which value(s) of k **(a)** the coefficient matrix is indefinite and **(b)** the equations cannot be solved.

8.11. Use the basic steps of Gauss elimination given in Section 8.2.1 to solve the following nonsymmetric set of equations. Then show that these solution steps can be written in the form (8.10) to (8.20), except that we need to replace $\mathbf{L}^T$ in these equations by an upper unit triangular matrix $\mathbf{L}_u$. Establish $\mathbf{L}_u$.

$$
\begin{bmatrix} 3 & -1 & 0 \\ -2 & 4 & -1 \\ 0 & -2 & 3 \end{bmatrix} \begin{bmatrix} U_1 \\ U_2 \\ U_3 \end{bmatrix} = \begin{bmatrix} 0 \\ 1 \\ 0 \end{bmatrix}
$$

8.12. Carry out Exercise 8.11 but use the following set of equations:

$$
\begin{bmatrix} 4 & -1 & 0 \\ 2 & 6 & -2 \\ 0 & -1 & 4 \end{bmatrix} \begin{bmatrix} U_1 \\ U_2 \\ U_3 \end{bmatrix} = \begin{bmatrix} 1 \\ 0 \\ 0 \end{bmatrix}
$$

8.13. Establish the $\mathbf{LDL}^T$ factorization of the following set of equations:

$$
\begin{bmatrix} 2 & -1 & 0 & \vdots & -1 \\ -1 & 2 & -1 & \vdots & 0 \\ 0 & -1 & 2 & \vdots & 1 \\ \cdots & \cdots & \cdots & & \cdots \\ -1 & 0 & 1 & \vdots & 0 \end{bmatrix} \begin{bmatrix} U_1 \\ U_2 \\ U_3 \\ \\ \lambda \end{bmatrix} = \begin{bmatrix} 0 \\ 1 \\ 0 \\ \cdots \\ 0 \end{bmatrix}
$$

Here U_1, U_2, and U_3 are displacements and λ is a Lagrange multiplier (force) (see Section 3.4.1).

Also establish a simple finite element model whose response is governed by these equations.

8.14. Consider the following set of equations

$$
\begin{bmatrix} \mathbf{K} & \mathbf{K}_\lambda^T \\ \mathbf{K}_\lambda & 0 \end{bmatrix} \begin{bmatrix} \mathbf{U} \\ \lambda \end{bmatrix} = \begin{bmatrix} \mathbf{R} \\ \mathbf{R}_\lambda \end{bmatrix}
$$

where $\mathbf{K}$ is a symmetric positive definite matrix of order n ($\mathbf{K}$ corresponds to a finite element model properly supported to not contain rigid body modes), and the $\mathbf{K}_\lambda$ matrix and $\mathbf{R}_\lambda$ vector correspond to p constraint equations (as, for example, are encountered in contact analysis; see Section 6.7). The vector λ contains the Lagrange multipliers.

Show that as long as the constraint equations are linearly independent and $p < n$, we can use the solution procedure in (8.10) to (8.20) to solve for the unknown displacements and Lagrange multipliers.

8.15. Consider the structural model in Example 8.9 and assume that a stiffness of $k_i = (EA_1/L) \times i$ is added to the degree of freedom u_i, $i = 1, 2, \ldots, 5$. Hence, these stiffness values are only an addition to the diagonal elements of the original stiffness matrix given in Example 8.9. Use substructuring to solve for the stiffness matrix of the resulting structure defined by the degrees of freedom U_1, U_3, and U_5 only.

8.16. Use substructuring to solve for the 3×3 stiffness matrix and corresponding force vector of the bar structure in Fig. E8.10 corresponding to the degrees of freedom U_1, U_7, and U_9.

8.17. Consider the cantilever beam in Example 8.1 and its stiffness matrix (which is given in the result of the first experiment; see Exercise 8.5). Calculate the eigenvalues of the original problem and of the associated constraint problems and thus show that the Sturm sequence property holds in this case. (*Hint:* See Fig. 8.9.)

8.18. Consider the stiffness matrix in Exercise 8.4. Calculate the eigenvalues of the original problem and of the associated constraint problems and thus show that the Sturm sequence property holds in this case. (*Hint:* See Figure 8.9.)

8.19. Consider the following matrix:

$$\begin{bmatrix} 10 & -10 & 0 \\ -10 & 10 + k & -k \\ 0 & -k & 10 + k \end{bmatrix}$$

Evaluate the value of k such that the condition number of the matrix is about 10^8.

8.20. Calculate the exact condition number of the simply supported beam stiffness matrix in Fig. 8.1(a) and an approximation thereof using a norm. [*Hint:* See Fig. 8.9 and (8.63).]

8.3 ITERATIVE SOLUTION METHODS

In many analyses some form of direct solution based on Gauss elimination to solve the equilibrium equations $\mathbf{KU} = \mathbf{R}$ is very efficient (see Section 8.2). It is interesting to note, however, that during the initial developments of the finite element method, iterative solution algorithms have been employed (see R. W. Clough and E. L. Wilson [A]).

A basic disadvantage of an iterative solution is that the time of solution can be estimated only very approximately because the number of iterations required for convergence depends on the condition number of the matrix $\mathbf{K}$ and whether the acceleration schemes used are effective for the particular case considered. It is primarily for this reason that the use of iterative methods in finite element analysis was largely abandoned during the 1960s and 1970s, while the direct methods of solution have been refined and rendered extremely effective (see Section 8.2).

However, when considering very large finite element systems, a direct method of solution can require a large amount of storage and computer time. The basic reason is that the required storage is proportional to nm_K, where n = number of equations, m_K = half-bandwidth, and a measure of the number of operations is $\frac{1}{2}nm_K^2$. Since the half-bandwidth is (roughly) proportional to $\sqrt{n}$, we recognize that as n increases, the demands on storage and computation time can become very large. In practice, the available storage on a computer frequently limits the size of finite element system that can be solved.

On the other hand, in an iterative solution the required storage is much less because we need to store only the actually nonzero matrix elements under the skyline of the matrix, a pointer array that indicates the location of each nonzero element, and some arrays, also of small size measured on the value of nm_K, for example, for the preconditioner and iteration vectors. The nonzero matrix elements under the skyline are only a small fraction of all the elements under the skyline, as we demonstrate in the following example.

EXAMPLE 8.21: Consider the finite element model of three-dimensional elements shown in Fig. E8.21. Estimate the number of matrix elements under the skyline (to be stored in a direct solution) and the number of actually nonzero matrix elements (to be stored in an iterative solution).

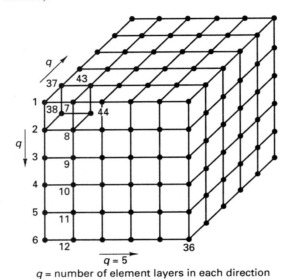

Figure E8.21   Assemblage of eight-node three-dimensional elements, 3 degrees of freedom per node

q = number of element layers in each direction

The half-bandwidth is given by the maximum difference in nodal point numbers in an element. Here we have for q element layers in each direction,

$$m_K = [(q + 1)^2 + q + 3] \times 3 - 1$$

or when q is large

$$m_K \doteq 3q^2 \qquad (a)$$

For the problem considered, the column heights are practically constant, and hence the number of elements under the skyline is about

$$nm_K \doteq (3q^3)(3q^2) = 9q^5$$

On the other hand, the number of actually nonzero elements in the skyline is determined by the fact that each nodal point i actually couples to only the directly surrounding nodal points. For an interior nodal point and eight-node elements the coupling pertains to 27 nodal points, hence the "compressed" half-bandwidth is

$$m_K|_{\text{compressed}} = \tfrac{27}{2} \times 3 \sim 40 \qquad (b)$$

and we note that this result is independent of the number of elements and the number of nodal points used in the model. Namely, the result in (b) depends only on how many elements couple into a typical nodal point. Comparing (a) and (b) we observe that the number of nonzero elements under the skyline increases only *linearly* with n, and the percentage measured on all elements under the skyline is very small when q is large.

The fact that considerable storage can be saved in an iterative solution has prompted a large amount of research effort to develop increasingly effective iterative schemes. The key to effectiveness is of course to reach convergence within a reasonable number of iterations.

As we shall see, of major importance in an iterative scheme is therefore a procedure to accelerate convergence when slow convergence is observed. The fact that effective acceleration procedures have become available for many applications has rendered iterative methods very attractive.

In the next sections we first consider the classical Gauss-Seidel iterative procedure and then the conjugate gradient method. The Gauss-Seidel method was used in the early applications of the finite element method (see R. W. Clough and E. L. Wilson [A]) and continues to find use. However, the conjugate gradient method presented here is particularly attractive.

8.3.1 The Gauss-Seidel Method

Our objective is to calculate iteratively the solution to the equations $\mathbf{KU} = \mathbf{R}$. Let $\mathbf{U}^{(1)}$ be an initial estimate for the displacements $\mathbf{U}$. If no better value is known, $\mathbf{U}^{(1)}$ may be the null vector.

In the Gauss-Seidel iteration (see L. Seidel [A] and R. S. Varga [A]), we then evaluate for $s = 1, 2, \ldots$:

$$U_i^{(s+1)} = k_{ii}^{-1}\left(R_i - \sum_{j=1}^{i-1} k_{ij} U_j^{(s+1)} - \sum_{j=i+1}^{n} k_{ij} U_j^{(s)} \right) \tag{8.65}$$

where $U_i^{(s)}$ and R_i are the ith component of $\mathbf{U}$ and $\mathbf{R}$ and s indicates the cycle of iteration. Alternatively, we may write in matrix form,

$$\mathbf{U}^{(s+1)} = \mathbf{K}_D^{-1}(\mathbf{R} - \mathbf{K}_L \mathbf{U}^{(s+1)} - \mathbf{K}_L^T \mathbf{U}^{(s)}) \tag{8.66}$$

where $\mathbf{K}_D$ is a diagonal matrix, $\mathbf{K}_D = \mathrm{diag}(k_{ii})$, and $\mathbf{K}_L$ is a lower triangular matrix with the elements k_{ij} such that

$$\mathbf{K} = \mathbf{K}_L + \mathbf{K}_D + \mathbf{K}_L^T \tag{8.67}$$

The iteration is continued until the change in the current estimate of the displacement vector is small enough, i.e., until

$$\frac{\| \mathbf{U}^{(s+1)} - \mathbf{U}^{(s)} \|_2}{\| \mathbf{U}^{(s+1)} \|_2} < \epsilon \tag{8.68}$$

where ϵ is the convergence tolerance. The number of iterations depends on the "quality" of the starting vector $\mathbf{U}^{(1)}$ and on the conditioning of the matrix $\mathbf{K}$. But it is important to note that the iteration will always converge, provided that $\mathbf{K}$ is positive definite. Furthermore, the rate of convergence can be increased using overrelaxation, in which case the iteration is as follows:

$$\mathbf{U}^{(s+1)} = \mathbf{U}^{(s)} + \beta \mathbf{K}_D^{-1}(\mathbf{R} - \mathbf{K}_L \mathbf{U}^{(s+1)} - \mathbf{K}_D \mathbf{U}^{(s)} - \mathbf{K}_L^T \mathbf{U}^{(s)}) \tag{8.69}$$

where β is the overrelaxation factor. The optimum value of β depends on the matrix **K** but is usually between 1.3 and 1.9.

EXAMPLE 8.22:   Use the Gauss-Seidel iteration to solve the system of equations considered in Section 8.2.1.

The equations to be solved are

$$
\begin{bmatrix}
5 & -4 & 1 & 0 \\
-4 & 6 & -4 & 1 \\
1 & -4 & 6 & -4 \\
0 & 1 & -4 & 5
\end{bmatrix}
\begin{bmatrix} U_1 \\ U_2 \\ U_3 \\ U_4 \end{bmatrix}
=
\begin{bmatrix} 0 \\ 1 \\ 0 \\ 0 \end{bmatrix}
$$

In the solution we use (8.69), which in this case becomes

$$
\begin{bmatrix} U_1 \\ U_2 \\ U_3 \\ U_4 \end{bmatrix}^{(s+1)}
=
\begin{bmatrix} U_1 \\ U_2 \\ U_3 \\ U_4 \end{bmatrix}^{(s)}
+ \beta
\begin{bmatrix} \frac{1}{5} & & & \\ & \frac{1}{6} & & \\ & & \frac{1}{6} & \\ & & & \frac{1}{5} \end{bmatrix}
$$

$$
\times \left\{
\begin{bmatrix} 0 \\ 1 \\ 0 \\ 0 \end{bmatrix}
-
\begin{bmatrix}
0 & & & \\
-4 & 0 & & \\
1 & -4 & 0 & \\
0 & 1 & -4 & 0
\end{bmatrix}
\begin{bmatrix} U_1 \\ U_2 \\ U_3 \\ U_4 \end{bmatrix}^{(s+1)}
-
\begin{bmatrix}
5 & -4 & 1 & 0 \\
& 6 & -4 & 1 \\
& & 6 & -4 \\
& & & 5
\end{bmatrix}
\begin{bmatrix} U_1 \\ U_2 \\ U_3 \\ U_4 \end{bmatrix}^{(s)}
\right\}
$$

We use as an initial guess

$$
\mathbf{U}^{(1)} = \begin{bmatrix} 0 \\ 0 \\ 0 \\ 0 \end{bmatrix}
$$

Consider first the solution without overrelaxation, i.e., $\beta = 1$. We obtain

$$
\begin{bmatrix} U_1 \\ U_2 \\ U_3 \\ U_4 \end{bmatrix}^{(2)}
=
\begin{bmatrix} 0 \\ 0.167 \\ 0.111 \\ 0.0556 \end{bmatrix};
\qquad
\begin{bmatrix} U_1 \\ U_2 \\ U_3 \\ U_4 \end{bmatrix}^{(3)}
=
\begin{bmatrix} 0.111 \\ 0.305 \\ 0.222 \\ 0.116 \end{bmatrix}
$$

Using the convergence limit in (8.68) with $\epsilon = 0.001$, we have convergence after 104 iterations and

$$
\begin{bmatrix} U_1 \\ U_2 \\ U_3 \\ U_4 \end{bmatrix}^{(104)}
=
\begin{bmatrix} 1.59 \\ 2.59 \\ 2.39 \\ 1.39 \end{bmatrix}
$$

with the exact solution being

$$
\begin{bmatrix} U_1 \\ U_2 \\ U_3 \\ U_4 \end{bmatrix}
=
\begin{bmatrix} 1.60 \\ 2.60 \\ 2.40 \\ 1.40 \end{bmatrix}
$$

We now vary β and recalculate the solution. The following table gives the number of iterations required for convergence with $\epsilon = 0.001$ as a function of β:

β	1.0	1.1	1.2	1.3	1.4	1.5	1.6	1.7	1.8	1.9
Number of iterations	104	88	74	61	49	37	23	30	43	82

Hence, for this example, we find that the minimum number of iterations is required at $\beta = 1.6$.

It is instructive to identify the physical process that is followed in the solution procedure. For this purpose we note that on the right-hand side of (8.69) we evaluate an out-of-balance force corresponding to degree of freedom i,

$$Q_i^{(s)} = R_i - \sum_{j=1}^{i-1} k_{ij} U_j^{(s+1)} - \sum_{j=i}^{n} k_{ij} U_j^{(s)} \tag{8.70}$$

and then calculate an improved value for the corresponding displacement component $U_i^{(s+1)}$ using

$$U_i^{(s+1)} = U_i^{(s)} + \beta k_{ii}^{-1} Q_i^{(s)} \tag{8.71}$$

where $i = 1, \ldots, n$. Assuming that $\beta = 1$, the correction to $U_i^{(s)}$ in (8.71) is calculated by applying the out-of-balance force $Q_i^{(s)}$ to the ith nodal degree of freedom, with all other nodal displacements kept fixed. The process is therefore identical to the moment-distribution procedure, which has been used extensively in hand calculation analysis of frames (see E. Lightfoot [A]). However, faster convergence is achieved if the acceleration factor β is used.

In the above equations, we summed over all off-diagonal elements [see (8.65) and (8.70)]. However, in practice we would of course include in the summation only those degrees of freedom that correspond to nonzero entries in the stiffness matrix. As we pointed out earlier, only the nonzero matrix elements would be stored and be operated on.

8.3.2 Conjugate Gradient Method with Preconditioning

One of the most effective and simple iterative methods (when used with preconditioning) for solving $\mathbf{KU} = \mathbf{R}$ is the conjugate gradient algorithm of M. R. Hestenes and E. Stiefel [A] (see also J. K. Reid [A] and G. H. Golub and C. F. van Loan [A]).

The algorithm is based on the idea that the solution of $\mathbf{KU} = \mathbf{R}$ minimizes the total potential $\Pi = \frac{1}{2}\mathbf{U}^T\mathbf{KU} - \mathbf{U}^T\mathbf{R}$ [see (4.96) to (4.98)]. Hence, the task in the iteration is, given an approximation $\mathbf{U}^{(s)}$ to $\mathbf{U}$ for which the total potential is $\Pi^{(s)}$, to find an improved approximation $\mathbf{U}^{(s+1)}$ for which $\Pi^{(s+1)} < \Pi^{(s)}$. However, not only do we want the total potential to decrease in each iteration but we also want $\mathbf{U}^{(s+1)}$ to be calculated efficiently and the decrease in the total potential to occur rapidly. Then the iteration will converge fast.

In the conjugate gradient method, we use in the sth iteration the linearly independent vectors $\mathbf{p}^{(1)}, \mathbf{p}^{(2)}, \mathbf{p}^{(3)}, \ldots, \mathbf{p}^{(s)}$ and calculate the minimum of the total potential in the space spanned by these vectors. This gives $\mathbf{U}^{(s+1)}$ (see Exercise 8.23). Also, we establish the additional basis vector $\mathbf{p}^{(s+1)}$ used in the subsequent iteration.

The algorithm can be summarized as follows.

Choose the starting iteration vector $\mathbf{U}^{(1)}$ (frequently $\mathbf{U}^{(1)}$ is the null vector).
Calculate the residual $\mathbf{r}^{(1)} = \mathbf{R} - \mathbf{K}\mathbf{U}^{(1)}$. If $\mathbf{r}^{(1)} = \mathbf{0}$, quit.
Else:

    Set $\mathbf{p}^{(1)} = \mathbf{r}^{(1)}$.
    Calculate for $s = 1, 2, \ldots,$

$$\alpha_s = \frac{\mathbf{r}^{(s)T}\mathbf{r}^{(s)}}{\mathbf{p}^{(s)T}\mathbf{K}\mathbf{p}^{(s)}}$$

$$\mathbf{U}^{(s+1)} = \mathbf{U}^{(s)} + \alpha_s\mathbf{p}^{(s)}$$

$$\mathbf{r}^{(s+1)} = \mathbf{r}^{(s)} - \alpha_s\mathbf{K}\mathbf{p}^{(s)} \tag{8.72}$$

$$\beta_s = \frac{\mathbf{r}^{(s+1)T}\mathbf{r}^{(s+1)}}{\mathbf{r}^{(s)T}\mathbf{r}^{(s)}}$$

$$\mathbf{p}^{(s+1)} = \mathbf{r}^{(s+1)} + \beta_s\mathbf{p}^{(s)}$$

We continue iterating until $\|\mathbf{r}^{(s)}\| \leq \epsilon$, where ϵ is the convergence tolerance. A convergence criterion on $\|\mathbf{U}^{(s)}\|$ could also be used.

The conjugate gradient algorithm satisfies two important orthogonality properties regarding the direction vectors $\mathbf{p}^{(i)}$ and the residuals $\mathbf{r}^{(i)}$, namely, we have (see Exercise 8.22)

$$\mathbf{p}^{(i)T}\mathbf{K}\mathbf{p}^{(j)} = 0 \qquad \text{all } i, j \text{ but } i \neq j \tag{8.73}$$

and
$$\mathbf{P}^{(j)T}\mathbf{r}^{(j+1)} = \mathbf{0} \tag{8.74}$$

where
$$\mathbf{P}^{(j)} = [\mathbf{p}^{(1)}, \ldots, \mathbf{p}^{(j)}] \tag{8.75}$$

The orthogonality property in (8.73) means that the minimum of the total potential over the space spanned by $\mathbf{p}^{(1)}, \ldots, \mathbf{p}^{(s)}$ is obtained by using the minimum over the space spanned by $\mathbf{p}^{(1)}, \ldots, \mathbf{p}^{(s-1)}$ (i.e., the solution of the previous iteration) and minimizing the total potential with respect to only a multiplier of $\mathbf{p}^{(s)}$. This process gives α_s and the improved iterative solution $\mathbf{U}^{(s+1)}$.

The orthogonality in (8.74) means that the $(j + 1)$st residual is orthogonal to all direction vectors used. This equation shows that convergence to the solution $\mathbf{U}$ will be reached and, in exact arithmetic, convergence is achieved in at most n iterations. Of course, in practice, we want convergence to be reached (to a reasonable convergence tolerance) in much fewer than n iterations.

The rate of convergence of the conjugate gradient algorithm depends on the condition number of the matrix $\mathbf{K}$, defined as $\text{cond}(\mathbf{K}) = \lambda_n/\lambda_1$, where λ_1 is the smallest eigenvalue and λ_n is the largest eigenvalue of $\mathbf{K}$ (see Section 8.2.6). The larger the condition number, the slower the convergence, and in practice, when the matrix is ill-conditioned, convergence can be very slow. For this reason, the conjugate gradient algorithm as given in (8.72) is hardly effective.

At this point, we should also note that the properties above enumerated are valid only in exact arithmetic. In practice, because of the finite precision arithmetic, the orthogonality properties in (8.73) and (8.74) are not exactly satisfied, but this loss of orthogonality is not detrimental.

To increase the rate of convergence of the solution algorithm, preconditioning is used. The basic idea is that instead of solving $\mathbf{KU} = \mathbf{R}$, we solve

$$\tilde{\mathbf{K}}\tilde{\mathbf{U}} = \tilde{\mathbf{R}} \tag{8.76}$$

where

$$\tilde{\mathbf{K}} = \mathbf{C}_L^{-1}\mathbf{K}\mathbf{C}_R^{-1}$$
$$\tilde{\mathbf{U}} = \mathbf{C}_R\mathbf{U} \tag{8.77}$$
$$\tilde{\mathbf{R}} = \mathbf{C}_L^{-1}\mathbf{R}$$

The nonsingular matrix $\mathbf{K}_p = \mathbf{C}_L\mathbf{C}_R$ is called the preconditioner. The objective with this transformation is to obtain a matrix $\tilde{\mathbf{K}}$ with a much improved condition number. Various preconditioners have been proposed (see G. H. Golub and C. F. van Loan [A], T. A. Manteuffel [A], and J. A. Meijerink and H. A. van der Vorst [A]), but one approach is particularly valuable, namely, using some incomplete Cholesky factors of $\mathbf{K}$.

In this approach a reasonable matrix $\mathbf{K}_p$ is obtained from inexact factors of $\mathbf{K}$ such that any equation solution with $\mathbf{K}_p$ as coefficient matrix can be calculated very efficiently. In principle, many different incomplete Cholesky factors of $\mathbf{K}$ could be calculated. In one scheme, incomplete Cholesky factors of $\mathbf{K}$ are obtained by performing the usual factorization, as described in Section 8.2, but considering only and operating only on those locations where $\mathbf{K}$ has nonzero entries. Hence, all matrix elements below the skyline that originally are zero remain zero during the factorization and therefore need not be stored.

Instead of considering all initially nonzero elements in $\mathbf{K}$, we may also decide to include in the factorization only those elements that are larger in magnitude than a certain threshold and set all other elements to zero. This approach leads to additional storage savings. Also, it can be effective to scale all diagonal elements in relation to the off-diagonal elements prior to performing the incomplete factorization, and of course we may use an exact factorization of certain submatrices in $\mathbf{K}$ to establish the incomplete factors (see Exercises 8.27 and 8.28). Clearly, there are many different possibilities, and various interesting relations between different approaches can be derived (see, for example, G. H. Golub and C. F. van Loan [A]).

Let $\bar{\mathbf{L}}$ and $\bar{\mathbf{L}}^T$ be the chosen incomplete Cholesky factors of $\mathbf{K}$; then in the preconditioning with these factors we use the matrix $\mathbf{K}_p = \bar{\mathbf{L}}\bar{\mathbf{L}}^T$ with $\mathbf{C}_L = \bar{\mathbf{L}}$ and $\mathbf{C}_R = \bar{\mathbf{L}}^T$.

Whichever preconditioner $\mathbf{K}_p$ is employed, using the conjugate gradient algorithm of (8.72) for the problem in (8.76), we thus arrive at the following algorithm.

Choose the starting iteration vector $\mathbf{U}^{(1)}$.
Calculate the residual $\mathbf{r}^{(1)} = \mathbf{R} - \mathbf{K}\mathbf{U}^{(1)}$. If $\mathbf{r}^{(1)} = \mathbf{0}$, quit.
Else:

    Calculate $\mathbf{z}^{(1)} = \mathbf{K}_p^{-1}\mathbf{r}^{(1)}$.
    Set $\mathbf{p}^{(1)} = \mathbf{z}^{(1)}$.

Calculate for $s = 1, 2, \ldots$, until a convergence tolerance is reached,

$$\alpha_s = \frac{\mathbf{z}^{(s)T}\mathbf{r}^{(s)}}{\mathbf{p}^{(s)T}\mathbf{K}\mathbf{p}^{(s)}}$$

$$\mathbf{U}^{(s+1)} = \mathbf{U}^{(s)} + \alpha_s\mathbf{p}^{(s)}$$

$$\mathbf{r}^{(s+1)} = \mathbf{r}^{(s)} - \alpha_s\mathbf{K}\mathbf{p}^{(s)}$$

$$\mathbf{z}^{(s+1)} = \mathbf{K}_p^{-1}\mathbf{r}^{(s+1)} \tag{8.78}$$

$$\beta_s = \frac{\mathbf{z}^{(s+1)T}\mathbf{r}^{(s+1)}}{\mathbf{z}^{(s)T}\mathbf{r}^{(s)}}$$

$$\mathbf{p}^{(s+1)} = \mathbf{z}^{(s+1)} + \beta_s\mathbf{p}^{(s)}$$

In this iteration we define an intermediate vector $\mathbf{z}^{(s)}$, which is equal to $\mathbf{r}^{(s)}$ if no preconditioning is used (i.e., when $\mathbf{K}_p = \mathbf{I}$). Of course, the matrix $\mathbf{K}_p$ need not be calculated, but rather $\mathbf{z}^{(s+1)}$ is directly computed using $\mathbf{r}^{(s+1)}$. Also, all multiplications with $\mathbf{K}$ are performed by operating on only the nonzero elements in the matrix. Note that the iteration in (8.78) reduces to the iteration in (8.72) when no preconditioning is employed and that convergence would be immediate if $\mathbf{K}_p$ were equal to $\mathbf{K}$.

We assume in this iteration that $\mathbf{K}_p$ is nonsingular. In practice, this condition is usually met, and if not, we may slightly perturb the coefficient matrix (or rather its factors) so as to be able to solve for $\mathbf{z}^{(s)}$.

While we still cannot predict how fast convergence will be achieved in the iteration, practical experience with the iterative scheme in (8.78) has shown that very significant savings in required storage and computer time are frequently realized (see K. J. Bathe, J. Walczak, and H. Zhang [A]). Of course, the required number of iterations depends on the structure of the matrix $\mathbf{K}$, its condition number, the details of the preconditioning used, and the accuracy to be achieved.

We considered in this section only the case of a symmetric coefficient matrix, and should note that also of much interest is the iterative solution of equations with nonsymmetric coefficient matrices (as we encounter in the analysis of fluid flows). Here the benefits of savings in storage and computing time can be even more significant. For nonsymmetric coefficient matrices, the conjugate gradient method has been generalized and other iterative schemes, notably, the generalized minimal residual (GMRes) method, have been developed and researched (see, for example, R. Fletcher [A], Y. Saad and M. H. Schultz [A], and L. H. Tan and K. J. Bathe [A]).

Finally, we should also recognize that there is the possibility of combining the direct and iterative solution schemes discussed above. As an example, the substructuring procedures described in Section 8.2.4 might be used to assemble governing equations (after static condensation of the internal degrees of freedom of the substructures) that are solved using conjugate gradient iteration. Such combinations can lead to a variety of procedures that may display considerable advantage in specific applications.

8.3.3 Exercises

8.21. Solve the system of equations given using the Gauss-Seidel iterative method. Use the overrelaxation factor β, and study the convergence properties as β is varied from 1.0 to 2.0.

$$\begin{bmatrix} 3 & -1 & 0 \\ -1 & 2 & -1 \\ 0 & -1 & 1 \end{bmatrix}\begin{bmatrix} U_1 \\ U_2 \\ U_3 \end{bmatrix} = \begin{bmatrix} 0 \\ 1 \\ 0 \end{bmatrix}$$

8.22. Show that the orthogonality properties (8.73) and (8.74) hold in the conjugate gradient iteration technique (using exact arithmetic).

8.23. Show that with the conjugate gradient algorithm in (8.72), the minimum of Π in the space spanned by the vectors $\mathbf{p}^{(1)}, \ldots, \mathbf{p}^{(s)}$ is obtained by using the minimum of Π in the space spanned by $\mathbf{p}^{(1)}, \ldots, \mathbf{p}^{(s-1)}$ and the solution for α_s given by the algorithm.

8.24. Derive the preconditioned incomplete Cholesky conjugate gradient algorithm in (8.78) from the standard algorithm in (8.72).

8.25. Solve the system of equations in Exercise 8.21 using the conjugate gradient algorithm (without preconditioning).

8.26. Solve the system of equations in Exercise 8.21 using the conjugate gradient method with preconditioning. Use the following preconditioner:

$$\mathbf{K}_p = \begin{bmatrix} 3 & & \\ & 2 & \\ & & 1 \end{bmatrix}$$

8.27. Consider the following system of equations:

$$\begin{bmatrix} 5 & -1 & -1 & -1 \\ -1 & 2 & 0 & 0 \\ -1 & 0 & 2 & 0 \\ -1 & 0 & 0 & 2 \end{bmatrix}\begin{bmatrix} U_1 \\ U_2 \\ U_3 \\ U_4 \end{bmatrix} = \begin{bmatrix} 0 \\ 0 \\ 0 \\ 1 \end{bmatrix}$$

(a) Solve the equations using the preconditioned conjugate gradient algorithm with $\mathbf{K}_p$ corresponding to the incomplete Cholesky factors that are obtained by performing the factorization on $\mathbf{K}$ as usual but ignoring all zero elements.

(b) Solve the equations using the preconditioned conjugate gradient algorithm with the preconditioner

$$\mathbf{K}_p = \begin{bmatrix} 5 & -1 & & \\ -1 & 2 & & \\ & & 2 & \\ & & & 2 \end{bmatrix}$$

8.28. Consider the simply supported beam problem in Fig. 8.1, governed by the equations,

$$\begin{bmatrix} 5 & -4 & 1 & 0 \\ -4 & 6 & -4 & 1 \\ 1 & -4 & 6 & -4 \\ 0 & 1 & -4 & 5 \end{bmatrix}\begin{bmatrix} U_1 \\ U_2 \\ U_3 \\ U_4 \end{bmatrix} = \begin{bmatrix} 0 \\ 1 \\ 0 \\ 0 \end{bmatrix}$$

Solve this set of equations by the conjugate gradient method using two different preconditioners that you shall propose.

8.29. Consider the cantilever beam in Example 8.1 with a concentrated load corresponding to degree of freedom U_4. The governing equations are

$$
\begin{bmatrix}
7 & -4 & 1 & 0 \\
-4 & 6 & -4 & 1 \\
1 & -4 & 5 & -2 \\
0 & 1 & -2 & 1
\end{bmatrix}
\begin{bmatrix}
U_1 \\
U_2 \\
U_3 \\
U_4
\end{bmatrix}
=
\begin{bmatrix}
0 \\
0 \\
0 \\
1
\end{bmatrix}
$$

Solve this set of equations by the conjugate gradient method using two different preconditioners that you shall propose.

8.30. Assume that each eight-node element in Fig. E8.21 is replaced by a 20-node three-dimensional element. Estimate the number of matrix elements under the skyline (to be stored in a direct solution) and the number of actually nonzero matrix elements (to be stored in an iterative solution.)

8.4 SOLUTION OF NONLINEAR EQUATIONS

We discussed in Sections 6.1 and 6.2 that the basic equations to be solved in nonlinear analysis are, at time $t + \Delta t$,

$$
{}^{t+\Delta t}\mathbf{R} - {}^{t+\Delta t}\mathbf{F} = \mathbf{0} \tag{8.79}
$$

where the vector ${}^{t+\Delta t}\mathbf{R}$ stores the externally applied nodal loads and ${}^{t+\Delta t}\mathbf{F}$ is the vector of nodal point forces that are equivalent to the element stresses. Both vectors in (8.79) are evaluated using the principle of virtual displacements. Since the nodal point forces ${}^{t+\Delta t}\mathbf{F}$ depend nonlinearly on the nodal point displacements, it is necessary to iterate in the solution of (8.79). We introduced in Section 6.1 the Newton–Raphson iteration, in which, assuming that the loads are independent of the deformations, we solve for $i = 1, 2, 3, \ldots$

$$
\Delta \mathbf{R}^{(i-1)} = {}^{t+\Delta t}\mathbf{R} - {}^{t+\Delta t}\mathbf{F}^{(i-1)} \tag{8.80}
$$

$$
{}^{t+\Delta t}\mathbf{K}^{(i-1)} \Delta \mathbf{U}^{(i)} = \Delta \mathbf{R}^{(i-1)} \tag{8.81}
$$

$$
{}^{t+\Delta t}\mathbf{U}^{(i)} = {}^{t+\Delta t}\mathbf{U}^{(i-1)} + \Delta \mathbf{U}^{(i)} \tag{8.82}
$$

with

$$
{}^{t+\Delta t}\mathbf{U}^{(0)} = {}^{t}\mathbf{U}; \qquad {}^{t+\Delta t}\mathbf{F}^{(0)} = {}^{t}\mathbf{F} \tag{8.83}
$$

These equations were obtained by linearizing the response of the finite element system about the conditions at time $t + \Delta t$, iteration $(i - 1)$. In each iteration we calculate in (8.80) an out-of-balance load vector that yields an increment in displacements obtained in (8.81), and we continue the iteration until the out-of-balance load vector $\Delta \mathbf{R}^{(i-1)}$ or the displacement increments $\Delta \mathbf{U}^{(i)}$ are sufficiently small.

The objective in this section is to discuss the above iterative scheme and others for the solution of (8.81) in more detail. Important ingredients of all solution schemes to be presented are the calculation of the vector ${}^{t+\Delta t}\mathbf{F}^{(i)}$ and the tangent stiffness matrix ${}^{t+\Delta t}\mathbf{K}^{(i-1)}$, and the solution of equations of the form (8.81). The appropriate evaluation of nodal point force vectors and tangent stiffness matrices was discussed in Chapter 6, and the solution of the linearized equations in (8.81) was presented in Sections 8.2 and 8.3; hence, the only, but very important, aspect of concern now is the construction of iterative schemes of the form (8.80) to (8.82) that display good convergence characteristics and can be employed effectively.

The methods we now present are basic techniques that in practice would be combined in a self-adaptive procedure that chooses load steps, iterative method, and convergence criteria automatically depending on the problem considered and solution accuracy sought.

8.4.1 Newton-Raphson Schemes

The most frequently used iteration schemes for the solution of nonlinear finite element equations are the Newton-Raphson iteration given in (8.80) to (8.83) and closely related techniques. Because of the importance of the Newton-Raphson method, let us derive the procedure in a more formal manner.

The finite element equilibrium requirements amount to finding the solution of the equations

$$\mathbf{f}(\mathbf{U}^*) = \mathbf{0} \tag{8.84}$$

where

$$\mathbf{f}(\mathbf{U}^*) = {}^{t+\Delta t}\mathbf{R}(\mathbf{U}^*) - {}^{t+\Delta t}\mathbf{F}(\mathbf{U}^*) \tag{8.85}$$

We denote here and in the following the complete array of the solution as $\mathbf{U}^*$ but realize that this vector may also contain variables other than displacements, for example, pressure variables and rotations (see Sections 6.4 and 6.5).

Assume that in the iterative solution we have evaluated ${}^{t+\Delta t}\mathbf{U}^{(i-1)}$; then a Taylor series expansion gives

$$\mathbf{f}(\mathbf{U}^*) = \mathbf{f}({}^{t+\Delta t}\mathbf{U}^{(i-1)}) + \left[\frac{\partial \mathbf{f}}{\partial \mathbf{U}}\right]\bigg|_{{}^{t+\Delta t}\mathbf{U}^{(i-1)}} (\mathbf{U}^* - {}^{t+\Delta t}\mathbf{U}^{(i-1)}) + \text{higher-order terms} \tag{8.86}$$

Substituting from (8.85) into (8.86) and using (8.84), we obtain

$$\left[\frac{\partial \mathbf{F}}{\partial \mathbf{U}}\right]\bigg|_{{}^{t+\Delta t}\mathbf{U}^{(i-1)}} (\mathbf{U}^* - {}^{t+\Delta t}\mathbf{U}^{(i-1)}) + \text{higher-order terms} = {}^{t+\Delta t}\mathbf{R} - {}^{t+\Delta t}\mathbf{F}^{(i-1)} \tag{8.87}$$

where we assumed that the externally applied loads are deformation-independent [see (6.83) and (6.84) regarding deformation-dependent loading].

Neglecting the higher-order terms in (8.87), we can calculate an increment in the displacements,

$$ {}^{t+\Delta t}\mathbf{K}^{(i-1)} \Delta \mathbf{U}^{(i)} = {}^{t+\Delta t}\mathbf{R} - {}^{t+\Delta t}\mathbf{F}^{(i-1)} \tag{8.88}$$

where ${}^{t+\Delta t}\mathbf{K}^{(i-1)}$ is the current tangent stiffness matrix

$$ {}^{t+\Delta t}\mathbf{K}^{(i-1)} = \left[\frac{\partial \mathbf{F}}{\partial \mathbf{U}}\right]\bigg|_{{}^{t+\Delta t}\mathbf{U}^{(i-1)}} \tag{8.89}$$

and the improved displacement solution is

$$ {}^{t+\Delta t}\mathbf{U}^{(i)} = {}^{t+\Delta t}\mathbf{U}^{(i-1)} + \Delta \mathbf{U}^{(i)} \tag{8.90}$$

The relations in (8.88) and (8.90) constitute the Newton-Raphson solution of (8.79). Since an incremental analysis is performed with time (or load) steps of size Δt (see Chapter 6), the initial conditions in this iteration are ${}^{t+\Delta t}\mathbf{K}^{(0)} = {}^{t}\mathbf{K}$, ${}^{t+\Delta t}\mathbf{F}^{(0)} = {}^{t}\mathbf{F}$ and ${}^{t+\Delta t}\mathbf{U}^{(0)} = {}^{t}\mathbf{U}$. The iteration is continued until appropriate convergence criteria are satisfied as discussed in Section 8.4.4.

A characteristic of this iteration is that a new tangent stiffness matrix is calculated in *each* iteration, which is why this method is also referred to as the *full* Newton-Raphson method. We shall mention below methods in which a current tangent stiffness matrix is not used, and these techniques are therefore not full Newton-Raphson methods (but related techniques).

Figure 8.11 illustrates the process of solution when used for a single degree of freedom system. The nonlinear response characteristics are such that convergence is rapidly obtained. However, we can imagine a more complex response characteristic with a starting

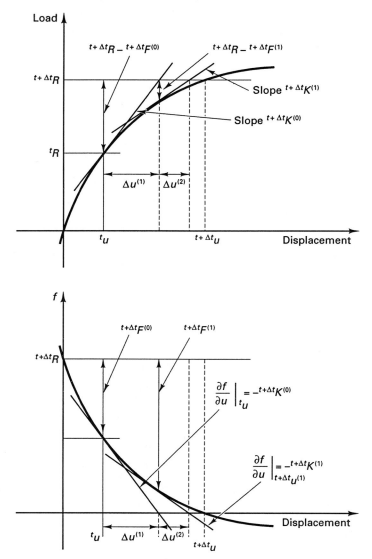

Figure 8.11 Illustration of Newton-Raphson iteration in solution of a (generic) single degree of freedom system. Top shows load-displacement relation, bottom shows iteration for zero of function **f** used in (8.84). Here $f = {}^{t+\Delta t}R - {}^{t+\Delta t}F(u)$.

point of iteration for which the procedure does not converge (see Exercise 8.31). Hence, the representation in Fig. 8.11 is rather simplistic because a very special case is considered—that of a well-behaved *single* degree of freedom system. In the solution of systems with many degrees of freedom, the response curves will in general be rather nonsmooth and complicated.

The Newton-Raphson iteration is demonstrated in the solution of a simple problem as follows.

EXAMPLE 8.23:   For a single degree of freedom system we have

$$^{t+\Delta t}R = 10; \qquad ^{t+\Delta t}F = 4 + 2\left|\left(^{t+\Delta t}U\right)^{1/2}\right|$$

and $^{t}U = 1$. Use the Newton-Raphson iteration to calculate $^{t+\Delta t}U$.

In this case we have, corresponding to (8.88) as the governing equation,

$$\left(\frac{1}{\left|\left(^{t+\Delta t}U^{(i-1)}\right)^{1/2}\right|}\right)\Delta U^{(i)} = 6 - 2\left|\sqrt{^{t+\Delta t}U^{(i-1)}}\right| \tag{a}$$

Using (a) with $^{t+\Delta t}U^{(0)} = 1$, we obtain

$$^{t+\Delta t}U^{(1)} = 5.0000; \qquad ^{t+\Delta t}U^{(2)} = 8.4164$$

$$^{t+\Delta t}U^{(3)} = 8.9902; \qquad ^{t+\Delta t}U^{(4)} = 9.0000$$

and convergence is achieved in four iterations.

Since the Newton-Raphson iteration is so widely used in finite element analysis and indeed represents the primary solution scheme for nonlinear finite element equations, it is appropriate that we summarize some major properties of the method (see, for example, D. P. Bertsekas [A]).

The first property is
If the tangent stiffness matrix $^{t+\Delta t}\mathbf{K}^{(i-1)}$ is nonsingular, if $\mathbf{f}$ and its first derivatives with respect to the solution variables (i.e. the elements of the tangent stiffness matrix) are continuous in a neighborhood of $\mathbf{U}^*$, and if $^{t+\Delta t}\mathbf{U}^{(i-1)}$ lies in that neighborhood, then $^{t+\Delta t}\mathbf{U}^{(i)}$ will be closer to $\mathbf{U}^*$ than $^{t+\Delta t}\mathbf{U}^{(i-1)}$ and the sequence of iterative solutions generated by the algorithm (8.88) to (8.90) converges to $\mathbf{U}^*$.

The second property is
If the tangent stiffness matrix also satisfies

$$\left\|^{t+\Delta t}\mathbf{K}\big|_{\mathbf{U}_1} - {}^{t+\Delta t}\mathbf{K}\big|_{\mathbf{U}_2}\right\| \le L\|\mathbf{U}_1 - \mathbf{U}_2\| \tag{8.91}$$

for all $\mathbf{U}_1$ and $\mathbf{U}_2$ in the neighborhood of $\mathbf{U}^*$ and $L > 0$, then convergence is quadratic. This means that if the error after iteration i is of order ϵ, then the error after iteration $i + 1$ will be of the order ϵ^2. The condition in (8.91) is referred to as *Lipschitz continuity;* it is stronger than mere continuity in the stiffness matrix but weaker than differentiability of the matrix.

The practical consequence of these properties is that if the current solution iterate is sufficiently close to the solution $\mathbf{U}^*$ and if the tangent stiffness matrix does not change abruptly, we can expect rapid (i.e., quadratic) convergence. The assumption is of course that the exact tangent stiffness matrix is used in the iteration; that is, (8.89) must be satisfied, meaning that $^{t+\Delta t}\mathbf{K}^{(i-1)}$ must be evaluated *consistent* with the evaluation of $^{t+\Delta t}\mathbf{F}^{(i-1)}$ (see Chapter 6 and in particular Sections 6.3.1 and 6.6.3). On the other hand, if the current solution iterate is not sufficiently close to $\mathbf{U}^*$ and/or the stiffness matrix used is not the exact tangent matrix and/or changes abruptly, then the iteration may diverge.

In an effective finite element program, the exact tangent stiffness matrix will be used, if possible, and hence the primary procedure for reaching convergence (if convergence difficulties are encountered) is to decrease the magnitude of the load step.

Considering the Newton-Raphson iteration it is recognized that in general the major computational cost per iteration lies in the calculation and factorization of the tangent stiffness matrix. Since these calculations can be quite expensive when large-order systems are considered, the use of a modification of the full Newton-Raphson algorithm can be effective.

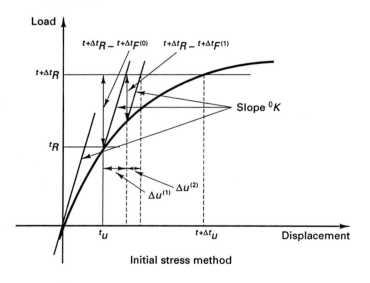

Initial stress method

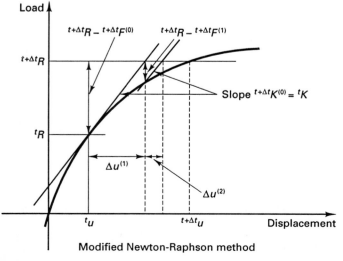

Modified Newton-Raphson method

Figure 8.12   Illustration of initial stress and modified Newton-Raphson methods. The problem in Fig. 8.11 is considered.

One such modification is to use the initial stiffness matrix $^0\mathbf{K}$ in (8.88) and thus operate on the equations:

$$^0\mathbf{K} \, \Delta\mathbf{U}^{(i)} = {}^{t+\Delta t}\mathbf{R} - {}^{t+\Delta t}\mathbf{F}^{(i-1)} \tag{8.92}$$

with the initial conditions $^{t+\Delta t}\mathbf{F}^{(0)} = {}^t\mathbf{F}$, $^{t+\Delta t}\mathbf{U}^{(0)} = {}^t\mathbf{U}$. In this case only the matrix $^0\mathbf{K}$ needs to be factorized, thus avoiding the expense of recalculating and factorizing many times the coefficient matrix in (8.88). This *"initial stress" method* corresponds to a linearization of the response about the initial configuration of the finite element system and may converge very slowly or even diverge.

In the *modified Newton-Raphson iteration* an approach somewhat in between the full Newton-Raphson iteration and the initial stress method is employed. In this method we use

$$^{\tau}\mathbf{K} \, \Delta\mathbf{U}^{(i)} = {}^{t+\Delta t}\mathbf{R} - {}^{t+\Delta t}\mathbf{F}^{(i-1)} \tag{8.93}$$

with the initial conditions $^{t+\Delta t}\mathbf{F}^{(0)} = {}^t\mathbf{F}$, $^{t+\Delta t}\mathbf{U}^{(0)} = {}^t\mathbf{U}$, and τ corresponds to one of the accepted equilibrium configurations at times $0, \Delta t, 2\,\Delta t, \ldots,$ or t (see Example 6.4). The modified Newton-Raphson iteration involves fewer stiffness reformations than the full Newton-Raphson iteration and bases the stiffness matrix update on an accepted equilibrium configuration. The choice of time steps when the stiffness matrix should be updated depends on the degree of nonlinearity in the system response; i.e. the more nonlinear the response, the more often the updating should be performed.

Figure 8.12 illustrates the performance of the initial stress and the modified Newton-Raphson methods for the single degree of freedom system already considered in Fig. 8.11.

With the very large range of system properties and nonlinearities that may be encountered in engineering analysis, we find that the effectiveness of the above solution approaches depends on the specific problem considered. The most powerful procedure for reaching convergence is the full Newton-Raphson iteration in (8.88) to (8.90), but if the initial stress or modified Newton-Raphson method can be employed, the solution cost may be reduced significantly. Hence, in practice, these solution options can also be very valuable, and an automatic procedure that self-adaptively chooses an effective technique is most attractive.

8.4.2 The BFGS Method

As an alternative to forms of Newton-Raphson iteration, a class of methods known as matrix update methods or quasi-Newton methods has been developed for iteration on nonlinear systems of equations (see J. E. Dennis, Jr. [A]). These methods involve updating the coefficient matrix (or rather its inverse) to provide a secant approximation to the matrix from iteration $(i-1)$ to (i). That is, defining a displacement increment

$$\boldsymbol{\delta}^{(i)} = {}^{t+\Delta t}\mathbf{U}^{(i)} - {}^{t+\Delta t}\mathbf{U}^{(i-1)} \tag{8.94}$$

and an increment in the out-of-balance loads, using (8.80),

$$\boldsymbol{\gamma}^{(i)} = \Delta\mathbf{R}^{(i-1)} - \Delta\mathbf{R}^{(i)} \tag{8.95}$$

the updated matrix $^{t+\Delta t}\mathbf{K}^{(i)}$ should satisfy the quasi-Newton equation

$$^{t+\Delta t}\mathbf{K}^{(i)} \, \boldsymbol{\delta}^{(i)} = \boldsymbol{\gamma}^{(i)} \tag{8.96}$$

These quasi-Newton methods provide a compromise between the full re-formation of the stiffness matrix performed in the full Newton-Raphson method and the use of a stiffness matrix from a previous configuration as is done in the modified Newton-Raphson method. Among the quasi-Newton methods available, the BFGS (*B*royden-*F*letcher-*G*oldfarb-*S*hanno) method appears to be most effective.

In the BFGS method, the following procedure is employed in iteration (i) to evaluate $^{t+\Delta t}\mathbf{U}^{(i)}$ and $^{t+\Delta t}\mathbf{K}^{(i)}$, where $^{t+\Delta t}\mathbf{K}^{(0)} = {}^{t}\mathbf{K}$ (see H. Matthies and G. Strang [A] and K. J. Bathe and A. P. Cimento [A]).

Step 1: Evaluate a displacement vector increment:

$$\Delta\overline{\mathbf{U}} = ({}^{t+\Delta t}\mathbf{K}^{-1})^{(i-1)}({}^{t+\Delta t}\mathbf{R} - {}^{t+\Delta t}\mathbf{F}^{(i-1)}) \tag{8.97}$$

This displacement vector defines a "direction" for the actual displacement increment.

Step 2: Perform a line search in the direction $\Delta\overline{\mathbf{U}}$ to satisfy "equilibrium" in this direction. In this line search we evaluate the displacement vector

$$^{t+\Delta t}\mathbf{U}^{(i)} = {}^{t+\Delta t}\mathbf{U}^{(i-1)} + \beta\,\Delta\overline{\mathbf{U}} \tag{8.98}$$

where β is a scalar multiplier, and we calculate the out-of-balance loads corresponding to these displacements $({}^{t+\Delta t}\mathbf{R} - {}^{t+\Delta t}\mathbf{F}^{(i)})$. The parameter β is varied until the component of the out-of-balance loads in the direction $\Delta\overline{\mathbf{U}}$, as defined by the inner product $\Delta\overline{\mathbf{U}}^T({}^{t+\Delta t}\mathbf{R} - {}^{t+\Delta t}\mathbf{F}^{(i)})$, is small. This condition is satisfied when, for a convergence tolerance STOL, the following equation is satisfied:

$$\Delta\overline{\mathbf{U}}^T({}^{t+\Delta t}\mathbf{R} - {}^{t+\Delta t}\mathbf{F}^{(i)}) \leq \text{STOL } \Delta\overline{\mathbf{U}}^T({}^{t+\Delta t}\mathbf{R} - {}^{t+\Delta t}\mathbf{F}^{(i-1)}) \tag{8.99}$$

The final value of β for which (8.99) is satisfied determines $^{t+\Delta t}\mathbf{U}^{(i)}$ in (8.98). We can now calculate $\boldsymbol{\delta}^{(i)}$ and $\boldsymbol{\gamma}^{(i)}$ using (8.94) and (8.95) and proceed with the evaluation of the matrix update that satisfies (8.96).

Step 3: Evaluate the correction to the coefficient matrix. In the BFGS method the updated matrix can be expressed in product form:

$$({}^{t+\Delta t}\mathbf{K}^{-1})^{(i)} = \mathbf{A}^{(i)^T}({}^{t+\Delta t}\mathbf{K}^{-1})^{(i-1)}\mathbf{A}^{(i)} \tag{8.100}$$

where the matrix $\mathbf{A}^{(i)}$ is an $n \times n$ matrix of the simple form

$$\mathbf{A}^{(i)} = \mathbf{I} + \mathbf{v}^{(i)}\,\mathbf{w}^{(i)^T} \tag{8.101}$$

The vectors $\mathbf{v}^{(i)}$ and $\mathbf{w}^{(i)}$ are calculated from the known nodal point forces and displacements using

$$\mathbf{v}^{(i)} = -\left(\frac{\boldsymbol{\delta}^{(i)^T}\boldsymbol{\gamma}^{(i)}}{\boldsymbol{\delta}^{(i)^T}\,{}^{t+\Delta t}\mathbf{K}^{(i-1)}\boldsymbol{\delta}^{(i)}}\right)^{1/2}{}^{t+\Delta t}\mathbf{K}^{(i-1)}\,\boldsymbol{\delta}^{(i)} - \boldsymbol{\gamma}^{(i)} \tag{8.102}$$

and

$$\mathbf{w}^{(i)} = \frac{\boldsymbol{\delta}^{(i)}}{\boldsymbol{\delta}^{(i)^T}\,\boldsymbol{\gamma}^{(i)}} \tag{8.103}$$

The vector $^{t+\Delta t}\mathbf{K}^{(i-1)}\,\boldsymbol{\delta}^{(i)}$ in (8.102) is equal to $\beta({}^{t+\Delta t}\mathbf{R} - {}^{t+\Delta t}\mathbf{F}^{(i-1)})$ and has already been computed.

Since the product defined in (8.100) is positive definite and symmetric, to avoid numerically dangerous updates, the condition number $c^{(i)}$ of the updating matrix $\mathbf{A}^{(i)}$ is calculated:

$$c^{(i)} = \left(\frac{\boldsymbol{\delta}^{(i)^T}\,\boldsymbol{\gamma}^{(i)}}{\boldsymbol{\delta}^{(i)^T}\,{}^{t+\Delta t}\mathbf{K}^{(i-1)}\,\boldsymbol{\delta}^{(i)}}\right)^{1/2} \tag{8.104}$$

This condition number is then compared with some preset tolerance, a large number, and the updating is not performed if the condition number exceeds this tolerance.

Considering the actual computations involved, it should be recognized that using the matrix updates defined above, the calculation of the search direction in (8.97) can be rewritten as

$$\Delta\overline{\mathbf{U}} = (\mathbf{I} + \mathbf{w}^{(i-1)}\,\mathbf{v}^{(i-1)^T}) \cdots (\mathbf{I} + \mathbf{w}^{(1)}\,\mathbf{v}^{(1)^T})^T\mathbf{K}^{-1}(\mathbf{I} + \mathbf{v}^{(1)}\,\mathbf{w}^{(1)^T}) \cdots$$
$$(\mathbf{I} + \mathbf{v}^{(i-1)}\,\mathbf{w}^{(i-1)^T})(^{t+\Delta t}\mathbf{R} - {}^{t+\Delta t}\mathbf{F}^{(i-1)}) \tag{8.105}$$

Hence, the search direction can be computed without explicitly calculating the updated matrices or performing any additional costly matrix factorizations as required in the full Newton-Raphson method.

As pointed out above, the line search is an integral part of the solution method. Of course, such line searches as performed in (8.98) and (8.99) can also be used in the Newton-Raphson methods presented in Section 8.4.1. With the line search performed within an iteration (*i*), the expense of the iteration increases, but fewer iterations may be needed for convergence. Also, the line search may prevent divergence of the iterations, and in practice, this increased robustness is the major reason why a line search can in general be effective.

We demonstrate the BFGS iteration in the following simple example.

EXAMPLE 8.24: Use the BFGS iteration method to solve for $^{t+\Delta t}U$ of the system considered in Example 8.23. Omit the line searches in the solution.

Since this is a single degree of freedom system, the solution for $^{t+\Delta t}U$ could be evaluated using only line searches, i.e., by applying (8.99), provided STOL is a tight enough convergence tolerance. However, to demonstrate in this example the basic steps of the BFGS method more clearly [the use of relations (8.94) to (8.96)], we do not include line searches in the iterative solution.

In this analysis (8.97) reduces to

$$\Delta\overline{U} = (^{t+\Delta t}K^{-1})^{(i-1)}(6 - 2|\sqrt{^{t+\Delta t}U^{(i-1)}}|)$$

with $(^{t+\Delta t}K^{-1})^{(0)} = 1$, $^{t+\Delta t}U^{(0)} = 1$ and using $\beta = 1.0$, we obtain the following values:

i	$^{t+\Delta t}U^{(i-1)}$	$\Delta\overline{U} = \delta^{(i)}$	$^{t+\Delta t}U^{(i)}$	$\gamma^{(i)}$	$(^{t+\Delta t}K^{-1})^{(i)}$
1	1.000	4.000	5.000	2.472	1.618
2	5.000	2.472	7.472	0.995	2.485
3	7.472	1.324	8.796	0.465	2.850
4	8.796	0.194	8.991	0.065	2.982
5	8.991	0.009	9.000	0.003	2.999

and convergence is achieved after five iterations.

8.4.3 Load-Displacement-Constraint Methods

An important requirement of a nonlinear analysis is frequently the calculation of the collapse load of a structure. Figure 8.13 illustrates schematically the response of a structural model that we might seek. For very small loads the load-displacement response is linear.

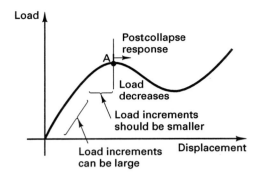

Figure 8.13 Collapse response of a structural model (the graph depicts schematically the load that is carried by a structure)

Then, as the load increases, the structural response becomes increasingly nonlinear and at point A the collapse load is reached. The response beyond point A is referred to as postcollapse or postbuckling response. We note that in Fig. 8.13 the load first decreases in this regime and then increases again as the displacement increases. Of course, the response depicted in Fig. 8.13 is a simplistic and generic representation because in the analysis of a multiple degree of freedom system a multidimensional "response surface" must be imagined, but Fig. 8.13 shows the essence of our requirements.

In order to calculate the response in Fig. 8.13 initially relatively large load increments can be employed, but as the collapse of the structural model is approached, the load increments must become smaller and there is also the difficulty of traversing the collapse point. At that point, the stiffness matrix is singular (the slope of the load-displacement response curve is zero), and beyond that point a special solution procedure that allows for a decrease in load and an increase in displacement must be used to calculate the ensuing response.

To solve for the response shown schematically in Fig. 8.13, a load-displacement-constraint method can be used, as in essence proposed by E. Riks [A]. The basic idea of such methods is to introduce a load multiplier that increases or decreases the intensity of the applied loads, so as to obtain fast convergence in each load step, to be able to traverse the collapse point and evaluate the postcollapse response.

Various efficient schemes have been proposed in which some numerical details can be important (see M. A. Crisfield [A], E. Ramm [A], and K. J. Bathe and E. N. Dvorkin [C]). However, we shall present in the following only the general approach of these methods and will omit some details that can be found in the references.

A basic assumption in the analysis is that the load vector varies proportionally during the response calculation. The governing finite element equations at time $t + \Delta t$ are

$$^{t+\Delta t}\lambda \mathbf{R} - {}^{t+\Delta t}\mathbf{F} = \mathbf{0} \tag{8.106}$$

where $^{t+\Delta t}\lambda$ is a (scalar) load multiplier, unknown and to be determined, and $\mathbf{R}$ is the reference load vector for the n degrees of freedom of the finite element model. This vector can contain any loading on the structure but is constant throughout the response calculation. The vector $^{t+\Delta t}\mathbf{F}$ is our usual vector of n nodal point forces corresponding to the element stresses at time $t+\Delta t$ [see (8.79)]. The value of the load multiplier can increase or decrease, and the increment per step should in general also change, depending on the structural response characteristics.

Since (8.106) represents n equations in $n + 1$ unknowns, we need an additional equation that is used to determine the load multiplier. If we apply one of the previously presented methods to solve (8.106), we obtain

$$^{\tau}\mathbf{K}\,\Delta\mathbf{U}^{(i)} = (^{t+\Delta t}\lambda^{(i-1)} + \Delta\lambda^{(i)})\mathbf{R} - {}^{t+\Delta t}\mathbf{F}^{(i-1)} \tag{8.107}$$

where the coefficient matrix $^{\tau}\mathbf{K}$ corresponds to the solution schemes discussed in the previous sections.

The unknowns in the n equations (8.107) are the vector of displacement increments[2] $\Delta\mathbf{U}^{(i)}$ and the load multiplier increment $\Delta\lambda^{(i)}$. The additional equation required for solution is a constraint equation between $\Delta\lambda^{(i)}$ and $\Delta\mathbf{U}^{(i)}$, of the form,

$$f(\Delta\lambda^{(i)}, \Delta\mathbf{U}^{(i)}) = 0 \tag{8.108}$$

Let us define within a load step

$$\mathbf{U}^{(i)} = {}^{t+\Delta t}\mathbf{U}^{(i)} - {}^{t}\mathbf{U} \tag{8.109}$$

and

$$\lambda^{(i)} = {}^{t+\Delta t}\lambda^{(i)} - {}^{t}\lambda \tag{8.110}$$

Hence, $\mathbf{U}^{(i)}$ represents the *total* increment in displacements within the load step [up to iteration (i)] and $\lambda^{(i)}$ represents the corresponding total increment in load multiplier. An effective constraint equation is given by the spherical constant arc length criterion (see M. A. Crisfield [A] and E. Ramm [A]),

$$(\lambda^{(i)})^2 + \frac{\mathbf{U}^{(i)^T}\mathbf{U}^{(i)}}{\beta} = (\Delta l)^2 \tag{8.111}$$

where Δl is the arc length for the step and β is a normalizing factor (to render the terms dimensionless). Figure 8.14(a) illustrates this criterion. In practice, the magnitude of Δl is selected based on the history of iterations in the previous steps and is reduced in the current step if convergence difficulties are encountered. Typically, Δl should be large when the response is almost linear and should be small when the response is highly nonlinear.

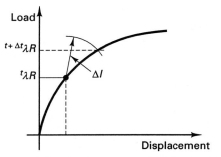

(a) Spherical constant arc length criterion

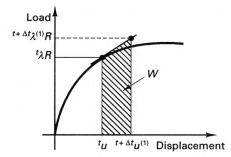

(b) Constant increment of external work criterion

Figure 8.14   Load-displacement-constraint criteria (single degree of freedom simplification)

Another effective constraint equation (see K. J. Bathe and E. N. Dvorkin [C]), is the scheme of constant increment of external work given by

---

[2] This vector also contains in general, of course, other variables such as rotations and pressures, and $\mathbf{R}$ and $^{t+\Delta t}\mathbf{F}^{(i-1)}$ contain the corresponding entries.

$$({}^{t}\lambda + \tfrac{1}{2}\,\Delta\lambda^{(1)})\mathbf{R}^{T}\,\Delta\mathbf{U}^{(1)} = W$$

(8.112)

and $$({}^{t+\Delta t}\lambda^{(i-1)} + \tfrac{1}{2}\,\Delta\lambda^{(i)})\mathbf{R}^{T}\,\Delta\mathbf{U}^{(i)} = 0 \qquad i = 2, 3, \ldots$$

where W is selected based on the history of iterations in the previous incremental steps. Figure 8.14(b) illustrates this constraint equation. The use of this scheme can be particularly effective near collapse points.

To solve the governing equations we may rewrite (8.107) to obtain

$$^{\tau}\mathbf{K}\,\Delta\overline{\mathbf{U}}^{(i)} = {}^{t+\Delta t}\lambda^{(i-1)}\mathbf{R} - {}^{t+\Delta t}\mathbf{F}^{(i-1)}$$

(8.113)

$$^{\tau}\mathbf{K}\,\Delta\overline{\overline{\mathbf{U}}} = \mathbf{R}$$

(8.114)

and hence, $$\Delta\mathbf{U}^{(i)} = \Delta\overline{\mathbf{U}}^{(i)} + \Delta\lambda^{(i)}\,\Delta\overline{\overline{\mathbf{U}}}$$

(8.115)

Employing the spherical constant arc length criterion (8.111), we then use

$$\lambda^{(i)} = \lambda^{(i-1)} + \Delta\lambda^{(i)}$$

(8.116)

and $$\mathbf{U}^{(i)} = \mathbf{U}^{(i-1)} + \Delta\overline{\mathbf{U}}^{(i)} + \Delta\lambda^{(i)}\,\Delta\overline{\overline{\mathbf{U}}}$$

(8.117)

Substituting from (8.116) and (8.117) into (8.111) gives a quadratic equation in $\Delta\lambda^{(i)}$. We select the appropriate value to proceed with the solution (see Exercise 8.35).

Using the constant increment in external work criterion, $\Delta\lambda^{(1)}$ is directly calculated from (8.112) and then the $\Delta\lambda^{(i)}$ values for $i = 2, 3, \ldots$, are obtained from (8.112) as

$$\Delta\lambda^{(i)} = -\,\frac{\mathbf{R}^{T}\,\Delta\overline{\mathbf{U}}^{(i)}}{\mathbf{R}^{T}\,\Delta\overline{\overline{\mathbf{U}}}}$$

(8.118)

The relation (8.112) also admits the solution ${}^{t+\Delta t}\lambda^{(i)} = -{}^{t+\Delta t}\lambda^{(i-1)}$, but this solution corresponds to a load reversal, which we disregard.

A complete solution algorithm based on the above load-displacement-constraint procedures must of course also contain a special scheme to start the incremental solution and must have procedures to self-adaptively select Δl and/or W. Also, the algorithm should stop iterating when divergence is imminent and then restart itself with new iterative parameters. Complete solution methods with these ingredients are very valuable and are in common use for the analysis of the collapse response of structures.

8.4.4 Convergence Criteria

If an incremental solution strategy based on iterative methods is to be effective, realistic criteria should be used for the termination of the iteration. At the end of each iteration, the solution obtained should be checked to see whether it has converged within preset tolerances or whether the iteration is diverging. If the convergence tolerances are too loose, inaccurate results are obtained, and if the tolerances are too tight, much computational effort is spent to obtain needless accuracy. Similarly, an ineffective divergence check can terminate the iteration when the solution is not actually diverging or force the iteration to search for an unattainable solution. The objective in this section is to discuss briefly some convergence criteria.

Since we are seeking the displacement configuration corresponding to time $t + \Delta t$, it is natural to require that the displacements at the end of each iteration be within a certain tolerance of the true displacement solution. Hence, a realistic convergence criterion is

$$\frac{\|\Delta\mathbf{U}^{(i)}\|_{2}}{\|{}^{t+\Delta t}\mathbf{U}\|_{2}} \leq \epsilon_{D}$$

(8.119)

where ϵ_D is a displacement convergence tolerance. The vector $^{t+\Delta t}\mathbf{U}$ is not known and must be approximated. Frequently, it is appropriate to use in (8.119) the last calculated value $^{t+\Delta t}\mathbf{U}^{(i)}$ as an approximation to $^{t+\Delta t}\mathbf{U}$ and a sufficiently small value ϵ_D. However, in some analyses the actual solution may still be far from the value obtained when convergence is measured using (8.119) with $^{t+\Delta t}\mathbf{U}^{(i)}$. This is the case when the calculated displacements change only little in each iteration but continue to change for many iterations, as may occur, for example, in elastoplastic analysis under loading conditions when the modified Newton-Raphson iteration is used.

A second convergence criterion is obtained by measuring the out-of-balance load vector. For example, we may require that the norm of the out-of-balance load vector be within a preset tolerance ϵ_F of the original load increment

$$\left\| {}^{t+\Delta t}\mathbf{R} - {}^{t+\Delta t}\mathbf{F}^{(i)} \right\|_2 \le \epsilon_F \left\| {}^{t+\Delta t}\mathbf{R} - {}^{t}\mathbf{F} \right\|_2 \tag{8.120}$$

A difficulty with this criterion is that the displacement solution does not enter the termination criterion. As an illustration of this difficulty, consider an elastoplastic truss with a very small strain-hardening modulus entering the plastic region. In this case, the out-of-balance loads may be very small while the displacements may still be much in error. Hence, the convergence criteria in (8.119) and (8.120) may have to be used with very small values of ϵ_D and ϵ_F. Also, the expressions must be modified appropriately when quantities of different units are measured (such as displacements, rotations, pressures, and so on).

In order to provide some indication of when both the displacements and the forces are near their equilibrium values, a third convergence criterion may be useful in which the increment in internal energy during each iteration (i.e., the amount of work done by the out-of-balance loads on the displacement increments) is compared to the initial internal energy increment. Convergence is assumed to be reached when, with ϵ_E a preset energy tolerance,

$$\Delta\mathbf{U}^{(i)T}({}^{t+\Delta t}\mathbf{R} - {}^{t+\Delta t}\mathbf{F}^{(i-1)}) \le \epsilon_E(\Delta\mathbf{U}^{(1)T}({}^{t+\Delta t}\mathbf{R} - {}^{t}\mathbf{F})) \tag{8.121}$$

Since this convergence criterion contains both the displacements and the forces, it is in practice an attractive measure. Some experiences with these convergence measures are given by K. J. Bathe and A. P. Cimento [A]. An important point is that the convergence tolerances ϵ_D, ϵ_F, and ϵ_E may need to be quite small in some solutions in order to reach a good solution accuracy. In general, use of the full Newton-Raphson method in the incremental solution leads to a higher accuracy in the solution than use of the modified Newton-Raphson method since, if convergence occurs, the solution error diminishes quite rapidly in the last iterations of the full Newton-Raphson method (consider, for example, Exercises 8.40 and 9.31).

8.4.5 Exercises

8.31. Consider the single degree of freedom system shown.
   (a) Use the full Newton-Raphson iteration method, the initial stress method, and the BFGS method to calculate the response of the system.
   (b) Establish a value of the constant c for which the full Newton-Raphson method will not converge.

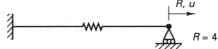

F = force in the spring = $u + cu^3$; $c = 0.1$

8.32. Consider the single degree of freedom system in Exercise 8.31 but with $F = \sin(u/L)$, $L = 1.0$, and $R = 0.5$. Perform the solution as in Exercise 8.31(a).

8.33. Consider the system in Exercise 8.31 and solve for the response by line searching *only*. (Hence do not perform any Newton-type iteration.)

8.34. Consider the four-node plane stress element shown.
  (a) Use a computer program to calculate the stiffness coefficient corresponding to the displacement u_1^1. [*Hint:* Use (8.89) in finite difference form.]
  (b) Also calculate this stiffness coefficient using the formulation given in Chapter 6.

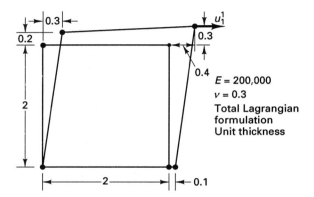

8.35. Derive the quadratic equation for $\Delta\lambda^{(i)}$ used in the spherical constant arc length criterion and calculate the roots of this equation. Discuss the solutions and identify which solution you would use in the practical implementation.

8.36. Use a computer program to solve for the collapse and postbuckling response of the simple arch structure considered in Example 6.3.

8.37. Use a computer program to solve for the collapse response of the three element truss shown. Compare your results with an analytical solution. (*Hint:* Use a large displacement formulation and a load-displacement-constraint solution method. You may also refer to the paper by P. G. Hodge, K. J. Bathe, and E. N. Dvorkin [A].)

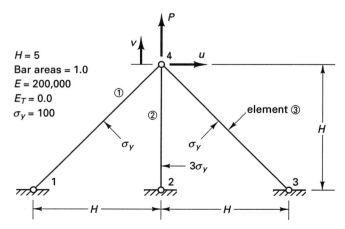

8.38. Use a computer program to calculate the collapse and postcollapse response of the structure shown. Consider various areas A_1 that you choose.

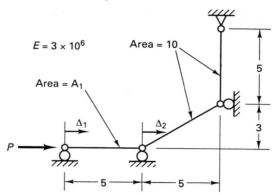

8.39. Use a computer progam to calculate the response of the plane stress cantilever shown. Use the von Mises yield condition with isotropic hardening and increase the load P until full collapse of the structure.

   Compare the solution efficiencies when using the full Newton-Raphson, modified Newton-Raphson, and the BFGS methods and also use a load-displacement-constraint procedure.

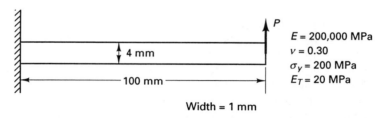

Width = 1 mm

8.40. Use a computer program to solve for the large displacement response of the cantilever beam shown below. Increase P to reach a tip deflection of $\Delta \doteq 10$ in. Compare the solution efficiencies when using the full Newton-Raphson and modified Newton-Raphson methods, with or without line searches, and the BFGS method.

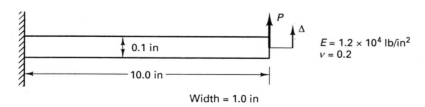

Width = 1.0 in

CHAPTER NINE

Solution of Equilibrium Equations in Dynamic Analysis

9.1 INTRODUCTION

In Section 4.2.1 we derived the equations of equilibrium governing the linear dynamic response of a system of finite elements

$$\mathbf{M\ddot{U}} + \mathbf{C\dot{U}} + \mathbf{KU} = \mathbf{R} \tag{9.1}$$

where $\mathbf{M}$, $\mathbf{C}$, and $\mathbf{K}$ are the mass, damping, and stiffness matrices; $\mathbf{R}$ is the vector of externally applied loads; and $\mathbf{U}$, $\mathbf{\dot{U}}$, and $\mathbf{\ddot{U}}$ are the displacement, velocity, and acceleration vectors of the finite element assemblage. It should be recalled that (9.1) was derived from considerations of statics at time t; i.e., (9.1) may be written

$$\mathbf{F}_I(t) + \mathbf{F}_D(t) + \mathbf{F}_E(t) = \mathbf{R}(t) \tag{9.2}$$

where $\mathbf{F}_I(t)$ are the inertia forces, $\mathbf{F}_I(t) = \mathbf{M\ddot{U}}$, $\mathbf{F}_D(t)$ are the damping forces, $\mathbf{F}_D(t) = \mathbf{C\dot{U}}$, and $\mathbf{F}_E(t)$ are the elastic forces, $\mathbf{F}_E(t) = \mathbf{KU}$, all of them being time-dependent. Therefore, in dynamic analysis, in principle, static equilibrium at time t, which includes the effect of acceleration-dependent inertia forces and velocity-dependent damping forces, is considered. Vice versa, in static analysis the equations of motion in (9.1) are considered, with inertia and damping effects neglected.

The choice for a static or dynamic analysis (i.e., for including or neglecting velocity- and acceleration-dependent forces in the analysis) is usually decided by engineering judgment, the objective thereby being to reduce the analysis effort required. However, it should be realized that the assumptions of a static analysis should be justified since otherwise the analysis results are meaningless. Indeed, in nonlinear analysis the assumption of neglecting inertia and damping forces may be so severe that a solution may be difficult or impossible to obtain.

Mathematically, (9.1) represents a system of linear differential equations of second order and, in principle, the solution to the equations can be obtained by standard procedures for the solution of differential equations with constant coefficients (see, for example,

L. Collatz [A]). However, the procedures proposed for the solution of general systems of differential equations can become very expensive if the order of the matrices is large—unless specific advantage is taken of the special characteristics of the coefficient matrices **K**, **C**, and **M**. In practical finite element analysis, we are therefore mainly interested in a few effective methods and we will concentrate in the next sections on the presentation of those techniques. The procedures that we will consider are divided into two methods of solution: direct integration and mode superposition. Although the two techniques may at first sight appear to be quite different, in fact, they are closely related, and the choice for one method or the other is determined only by their numerical effectiveness.

In the following we consider first (see Sections 9.2 to 9.4) the solution of the linear equilibrium equations (9.1), and then we discuss the solution of the nonlinear equations of finite element systems idealizing structures and solids (see Section 9.5). Finally, we show in Section 9.6 how the basic concepts discussed are also directly applicable to the analysis of heat transfer and fluid flow.

9.2 DIRECT INTEGRATION METHODS

In direct integration the equations in (9.1) are integrated using a numerical step-by-step procedure, the term "direct" meaning that prior to the numerical integration, no transformation of the equations into a different form is carried out. In essence, direct numerical integration is based on two ideas. First, instead of trying to satisfy (9.1) at any time t, it is aimed to satisfy (9.1) only at discrete time intervals Δt apart. This means that, basically, (static) equilibrium, which includes the effect of inertia and damping forces, is sought at discrete time points within the interval of solution. Therefore, it appears that all solution techniques employed in static analysis can probably also be used effectively in direct integration. The second idea on which a direct integration method is based is that a variation of displacements, velocities, and accelerations within each time interval Δt is assumed. As will be discussed in detail, it is the form of the assumption on the variation of displacements, velocities, and accelerations within each time interval that determines the accuracy, stability, and cost of the solution procedure.

In the following, assume that the displacement, velocity, and acceleration vectors at time 0, denoted by $^0\mathbf{U}, ^0\dot{\mathbf{U}}$, and $^0\ddot{\mathbf{U}}$, respectively, are known and let the solution to (9.1) be required from time 0 to time T. In the solution the time span under consideration, T, is subdivided into n equal time intervals Δt (i.e., $\Delta t = T/n$), and the integration scheme employed establishes an approximate solution at times $\Delta t, 2\Delta t, 3\Delta t, \ldots, t, t + \Delta t, \ldots, T$. Since an algorithm calculates the solution at the next required time from the solutions at the previous times considered, we derive the algorithms by assuming that the solutions at times $0, \Delta t, 2\Delta t, \ldots, t$ are known and that the solution at time $t + \Delta t$ is required next. The calculations performed to obtain the solution at time $t + \Delta t$ are typical for calculating the solution at time Δt later than considered so far and thus establish the general algorithm which can be used to calculate the solutions at all discrete time points.

In the following sections a few commonly used effective direct integration methods are presented. The derivations are given for a constant time step Δt (as commonly used in linear analysis), but are easily extended to varying time step sizes (as employed in nonlinear analysis [see Section 9.5]). Considerations of accuracy, selection of time step size, and a discussion of the advantages of one method over the other are postponed until Section 9.4. Many additional results are presented in T. Belytschko and T. J. R. Hughes (eds.) [A].

9.2.1 The Central Difference Method

If the equilibrium relation in (9.1) is regarded as a system of ordinary differential equations with constant coefficients, it follows that any convenient finite difference expressions to approximate the accelerations and velocities in terms of displacements can be used. Therefore, a large number of different finite difference expressions could theoretically be employed. However, the solution scheme should be effective, and it follows that only a few methods need to be considered. One procedure that can be very effective in the solution of certain problems is the central difference method, in which it is assumed that

$$\ddot{u}_o = \frac{\left(\frac{u_1 - u_0}{t}\right) - \left(\frac{u_0 - u_{-1}}{t}\right)}{t}$$

$$^t\ddot{\mathbf{U}} = \frac{1}{\Delta t^2}(^{t-\Delta t}\mathbf{U} - 2\,^t\mathbf{U} + ^{t+\Delta t}\mathbf{U}) \tag{9.3}$$

The error in the expansion (9.3) is of order $(\Delta t)^2$, and to have the same order of error in the velocity expansion, we can use

$$\dot{u}_o = \frac{u_1 - u_{-1}}{2t}$$

$$^t\dot{\mathbf{U}} = \frac{1}{2\Delta t}(\overset{\text{negative}}{-}\,^{t-\Delta t}\mathbf{U} + ^{t+\Delta t}\mathbf{U}) \tag{9.4}$$

The displacement solution for time $t + \Delta t$ is obtained by considering (9.1) at time t, i.e.,

$$\mathbf{M}\,^t\ddot{\mathbf{U}} + \mathbf{C}\,^t\dot{\mathbf{U}} + \mathbf{K}\,^t\mathbf{U} = {}^t\mathbf{R} \tag{9.5}$$

Substituting the relations for $^t\ddot{\mathbf{U}}$ and $^t\dot{\mathbf{U}}$ in (9.3) and (9.4), respectively, into (9.5), we obtain

$$\left(\frac{1}{\Delta t^2}\mathbf{M} + \frac{1}{2\Delta t}\mathbf{C}\right)^{t+\Delta t}\mathbf{U} = {}^t\mathbf{R} - \left(\mathbf{K} - \frac{2}{\Delta t^2}\mathbf{M}\right)^t\mathbf{U} - \left(\frac{1}{\Delta t^2}\mathbf{M} - \frac{1}{2\Delta t}\mathbf{C}\right)^{t-\Delta t}\mathbf{U} \tag{9.6}$$

from which we can solve for $^{t+\Delta t}\mathbf{U}$. It should be noted that the solution of $^{t+\Delta t}\mathbf{U}$ is thus based on using the equilibrium conditions at time t; i.e., $^{t+\Delta t}\mathbf{U}$ is calculated by using (9.5). For this reason the integration procedure is called an *explicit integration method*, and it is noted that such integration schemes do not require a factorization of the (effective) stiffness matrix in the step-by-step solution. On the other hand, the Houbolt, Wilson, and Newmark methods, considered in the next sections, use the equilibrium conditions at time $t + \Delta t$ and are called *implicit integration methods*.

A second observation is that using the central difference method, the calculation of $^{t+\Delta t}\mathbf{U}$ involves $^t\mathbf{U}$ and $^{t-\Delta t}\mathbf{U}$. Therefore, to calculate the solution at time Δt, a special starting procedure must be used. Since $^0\mathbf{U}$, $^0\dot{\mathbf{U}}$, and $^0\ddot{\mathbf{U}}$ are known [note that with $^0\mathbf{U}$ and $^0\dot{\mathbf{U}}$ known, $^0\ddot{\mathbf{U}}$ can be calculated using (9.1) at time 0; see Example 9.1], the relations in (9.3) and (9.4) can be used to obtain $^{-\Delta t}\mathbf{U}$; i.e., we have

$$^{-\Delta t}U_i = {}^0U_i - \Delta t\,^0\dot{U}_i + \frac{\Delta t^2}{2}\,^0\ddot{U}_i \tag{9.7}$$

where the subscript i indicates the ith element of the vector considered. Table 9.1 summarizes the time integration scheme as it might be implemented in the computer.

We discuss below the fact that the method is only effective when each time step solution can be performed very efficiently (because a small time step size and therefore a large number of time steps generally need to be used). For this reason, the method is largely

TABLE 9.1   *Step-by-step solution using central difference method (general mass and damping matrices)*

A. *Initial calculations:*

   1. Form stiffness matrix $\mathbf{K}$, mass matrix $\mathbf{M}$, and damping matrix $\mathbf{C}$.

   2. Initialize $^0\mathbf{U}$, $^0\dot{\mathbf{U}}$, and $^0\ddot{\mathbf{U}}$.

   3. Select time step Δt, $\Delta t \le \Delta t_{cr}$, and calculate integration constants:

$$a_0 = \frac{1}{\Delta t^2}; \qquad a_1 = \frac{1}{2\,\Delta t}; \qquad a_2 = 2a_0; \qquad a_3 = \frac{1}{a_2}$$

   4. Calculate $^{-\Delta t}\mathbf{U} = {}^0\mathbf{U} - \Delta t\,{}^0\dot{\mathbf{U}} + a_3\,{}^0\ddot{\mathbf{U}}$.

   5. Form effective mass matrix $\hat{\mathbf{M}} = a_0\mathbf{M} + a_1\mathbf{C}$.

   6. Triangularize $\hat{\mathbf{M}}$: $\hat{\mathbf{M}} = \mathbf{LDL}^T$.

B. *For each time step:*

   1. Calculate effective loads at time t:

$$^t\hat{\mathbf{R}} = {}^t\mathbf{R} - (\mathbf{K} - a_2\mathbf{M})\,{}^t\mathbf{U} - (a_0\mathbf{M} - a_1\mathbf{C})\,{}^{t-\Delta t}\mathbf{U}$$

   2. Solve for displacements at time $t + \Delta t$:

$$\mathbf{LDL}^T\,{}^{t+\Delta t}\mathbf{U} = {}^t\hat{\mathbf{R}}$$

   3. If required, evaluate accelerations and velocities at time t:

$$^t\ddot{\mathbf{U}} = a_0({}^{t-\Delta t}\mathbf{U} - 2\,{}^t\mathbf{U} + {}^{t+\Delta t}\mathbf{U})$$

$$^t\dot{\mathbf{U}} = a_1(-{}^{t-\Delta t}\mathbf{U} + {}^{t+\Delta t}\mathbf{U})$$

---

applied only when a lumped mass matrix can be assumed and velocity-dependent damping can be neglected. Then (9.6) reduces to

$$\left(\frac{1}{\Delta t^2}\mathbf{M}\right){}^{t+\Delta t}\mathbf{U} = {}^t\hat{\mathbf{R}} \tag{9.8}$$

where

$$^t\hat{\mathbf{R}} = {}^t\mathbf{R} - \left(\mathbf{K} - \frac{2}{\Delta t^2}\mathbf{M}\right){}^t\mathbf{U} - \left(\frac{1}{\Delta t^2}\mathbf{M}\right){}^{t-\Delta t}\mathbf{U} \tag{9.9}$$

Therefore, if the mass matrix is diagonal, the system of equations in (9.1) can be solved without factorizing a matrix; i.e., only matrix multiplications are required to obtain the right-hand-side effective load vector $^t\hat{\mathbf{R}}$ after which the displacement components are obtained using

$$^{t+\Delta t}U_i = {}^t\hat{R}_i\left(\frac{\Delta t^2}{m_{ii}}\right) \tag{9.10}$$

where $^{t+\Delta t}U_i$ and $^t\hat{R}_i$ denote the ith components of the vectors $^{t+\Delta t}\mathbf{U}$ and $^t\hat{\mathbf{R}}$, respectively, m_{ii} is the ith diagonal element of the mass matrix, and it is assumed that $m_{ii} > 0$.

    If the stiffness matrix of the element assemblage is not to be triangularized, it is also not necessary to assemble the matrix. We have shown in Section 4.2.1 [see (4.30)] that

$$\mathbf{K}\,{}^t\mathbf{U} = \sum_i \mathbf{K}^{(i)}\,{}^t\mathbf{U} = \sum_i {}^t\mathbf{F}^{(i)} \tag{9.11}$$

which means that $\mathbf{K}\,{}^t\mathbf{U}$ as required in (9.9) can be evaluated on the element level by summing the contributions from each element to the effective load vector. Hence, $^t\hat{\mathbf{R}}$ can be evaluated efficiently using

$$
{}^t\hat{\mathbf{R}} = {}^t\mathbf{R} - \sum_i {}^t\mathbf{F}^{(i)} - \frac{1}{\Delta t^2}\mathbf{M}({}^{t - \Delta t}\mathbf{U} - 2\,{}^t\mathbf{U}) \tag{9.12}
$$

where ${}^t\mathbf{F}^{(i)}$ is evaluated and added in compacted form (see Section 12.2.3).

Another advantage of using the central difference method in the form given in (9.10) now becomes apparent. Since no stiffness matrix of the complete element assemblage needs to be calculated, the solution can essentially be carried out on the element level and relatively little high speed storage is required. Using this approach, systems of very large order have been solved effectively.

However, we have already mentioned that for solution a relatively small time step size must generally be used. Actually, an important consideration in the use of the central difference scheme is that the integration method requires that the time step Δt be smaller than a critical value, Δt_{cr}, which can be calculated from the mass and stiffness properties of the complete element assemblage. More specifically, we will show in Section 9.4.2 that to obtain a valid solution,

$$
\Delta t \le \Delta t_{cr} = \frac{T_n}{\pi} \tag{9.13}
$$

where T_n is the smallest period of the finite element assemblage with n degrees of freedom. The period T_n could be calculated using one of the techniques discussed in Chapter 11, or a lower bound on T_n may be evaluated using norms (see Section 2.7). In practice we frequently estimate an appropriate time step Δt using the considerations given in Section 9.4.4.

In the solution using (9.10), it was assumed that $m_{ii} > 0$ for all i. The relation in (9.13) states this requirement once more because a zero diagonal element in a diagonal mass matrix means that the element assemblage has a zero period (see Section 10.2.4). In general, all diagonal elements of the mass matrix can be assumed to be larger than zero, in which case (9.13) gives a limit on the magnitude of the time step Δt that can be used in the integration. In the analysis of some problems (namely, for wave propagation problems) (9.13) does not require an unduly small time step; but, in other cases (namely, for structural dynamics problems) the time step small enough for accuracy of integration can be many times larger than Δt_{cr} obtained from (9.13).

These thoughts point toward the importance of establishing an effective finite element discretization and time step for a dynamic solution. We discuss these issues in Section 9.4, but already mention the following considerations now.

Assume that we solve using the central difference method a large system of equilibrium equations. The time step for the integration would be selected using (9.13). Assume that we now change the smallest diagonal element of the mass matrix to become very small and, in fact, nearly zero. As enumerated above, a diagonal element in the mass matrix cannot be exactly zero because T_n would then be zero and the integration would not be possible. However, as the diagonal element in the mass matrix approaches zero, the smallest period of the system, and hence Δt_{cr}, approaches zero. Therefore, the reduction of one element m_{ii} necessitates a severe reduction in the time step size that can be used in the integration. On the other hand, since the order of the system is large, we can envisage a certain dynamic loading for which we would hardly expect that the response of the element assemblage changes very much when the smallest element m_{ii} is reduced, even to become zero. Hence, the cost of analysis would in that case be unduly large only because of one very small diagonal element in the mass matrix. The same condition is also reached when an element in the stiffness matrix is changed to become large.

Integration schemes that require the use of a time step Δt smaller than a critical time step Δt_{cr}, such as the central difference method, are said to be conditionally stable. If a time step larger than Δt_{cr} is used, the integration is unstable, meaning that, for example, any errors resulting from round-off in the computer grow and make the response calculations worthless in most cases. The concept of stability of integration is very important, and we will discuss it further in Section 9.4. However, at this stage it is useful to consider the following example.

EXAMPLE 9.1:   Consider a simple system for which the governing equilibrium equations are

$$\begin{bmatrix} 2 & 0 \\ 0 & 1 \end{bmatrix} \begin{bmatrix} \ddot{U}_1 \\ \ddot{U}_2 \end{bmatrix} + \begin{bmatrix} 6 & -2 \\ -2 & 4 \end{bmatrix} \begin{bmatrix} U_1 \\ U_2 \end{bmatrix} = \begin{bmatrix} 0 \\ 10 \end{bmatrix} \tag{a}$$

The free-vibration periods of the system are given in Example 9.6, where we find that $T_1 = 4.45$, $T_2 = 2.8$. Use the central difference method in direct integration with time steps (1) $\Delta t = T_2/10$ and (2) $\Delta t = 10T_2$ to calculate the response of the system for 12 steps. Assume that $^0\mathbf{U} = \mathbf{0}$ and $^0\dot{\mathbf{U}} = \mathbf{0}$.

The first step is to calculate $^0\ddot{\mathbf{U}}$ using the equations in (a) at time 0; i.e., we use

$$\begin{bmatrix} 2 & 0 \\ 0 & 1 \end{bmatrix} {}^0\ddot{\mathbf{U}} + \begin{bmatrix} 6 & -2 \\ -2 & 4 \end{bmatrix} \begin{bmatrix} 0 \\ 0 \end{bmatrix} = \begin{bmatrix} 0 \\ 10 \end{bmatrix}$$

Hence, $^0\ddot{\mathbf{U}} = \begin{bmatrix} 0 \\ 10 \end{bmatrix}$

Now we follow the calculations in Table 9.1.

Consider case (1), in which $\Delta t = 0.28$. We then have (listed to three digits)

$$a_0 = \frac{1}{(0.28)^2} = 12.8; \qquad a_1 = \frac{1}{(2)(0.28)} = 1.79$$

$$a_2 = 2a_0 = 25.5; \qquad a_3 = \frac{1}{a_2} = 0.0392$$

Hence, $^{-\Delta t}\mathbf{U} = \begin{bmatrix} 0 \\ 0 \end{bmatrix} - 0.28 \begin{bmatrix} 0 \\ 0 \end{bmatrix} + 0.0392 \begin{bmatrix} 0 \\ 10 \end{bmatrix} = \begin{bmatrix} 0 \\ 0.392 \end{bmatrix}$

$$\hat{\mathbf{M}} = 12.8 \begin{bmatrix} 2 & 0 \\ 0 & 1 \end{bmatrix} + 1.79 \begin{bmatrix} 0 & 0 \\ 0 & 0 \end{bmatrix}$$

$$= \begin{bmatrix} 25.5 & 0 \\ 0 & 12.8 \end{bmatrix}$$

The effective loads at time t are

$$^t\hat{\mathbf{R}} = \begin{bmatrix} 0 \\ 10 \end{bmatrix} + \begin{bmatrix} 45.0 & 2 \\ 2 & 21.5 \end{bmatrix} {}^t\mathbf{U} - \begin{bmatrix} 25.5 & 0 \\ 0 & 12.8 \end{bmatrix} {}^{t-\Delta t}\mathbf{U}$$

Hence, we need to solve the following equations for each time step,

$$\begin{bmatrix} 25.5 & 0 \\ 0 & 12.8 \end{bmatrix} {}^{t+\Delta t}\mathbf{U} = {}^t\hat{\mathbf{R}} \tag{b}$$

The solution of the equations in (b) is trivial because the coefficient matrix is diagonal. Calculating the solution to (b) for each time step, we obtain

Time	Δt	$2\Delta t$	$3\Delta t$	$4\Delta t$	$5\Delta t$	$6\Delta t$	$7\Delta t$	$8\Delta t$	$9\Delta t$	$10\Delta t$	$11\Delta t$	$12\Delta t$
^tU	0	0.0307	0.168	0.487	1.02	1.70	2.40	2.91	3.07	2.77	2.04	1.02
	0.392	1.45	2.83	4.14	5.02	5.26	4.90	4.17	3.37	2.78	2.54	2.60

The solution obtained is compared with the exact results in Example 9.7.

Consider now case (2), in which $\Delta t = 28$. Following through the same calculations, we find that

$$^{\Delta t}\mathbf{U} = \begin{bmatrix} 0 \\ 3.83 \times 10^3 \end{bmatrix}; \qquad {}^{2\Delta t}\mathbf{U} = \begin{bmatrix} 3.03 \times 10^6 \\ -1.21 \times 10^7 \end{bmatrix}$$

and the calculated displacements continue to increase. Since the time step Δt is about 6 times larger than T_1 and 10 times larger than T_2, we can certainly not expect accuracy in the numerical integration. But of particular interest is whether the calculated values decrease or increase. The increase in the values as observed in this example is a consequence of the time integration scheme not being stable. As pointed out above, the time step Δt must not be larger than Δt_{cr} for stability in the integration using the central difference method, where $\Delta t_{cr} = (1/\pi)T_2$. In this case the time step Δt is much larger, and the calculated response increases without bound. This is the typical phenomenon of instability. We shall see in Examples 9.2 to 9.4 that the response predicted using $\Delta t = 28$ with the unconditionally stable Houbolt, Wilson θ, and Newmark methods is also very inaccurate but does not increase.

We discussed above the main disadvantage of the central difference method: the scheme is only conditionally stable. Various other integration methods are also conditionally stable (see, for example, L. Collatz [A]). Since the effective use of conditionally stable methods is limited to certain problems, we consider in the following sections commonly employed integration schemes which are unconditionally stable. The effectiveness of unconditionally stable integration schemes derives from the fact that to obtain accuracy in the integration, the time step Δt can be selected without a requirement such as (9.13), and in many cases Δt can be orders of magnitude larger than (9.13) would allow. However, the integration methods discussed in the following are implicit; i.e., a triangularization of the stiffness matrix $\mathbf{K}$, or rather of an effective stiffness matrix, is required for solution.

9.2.2 The Houbolt Method

The Houbolt integration scheme is somewhat related to the previously discussed central difference method in that standard finite difference expressions are used to approximate the acceleration and velocity components in terms of the displacement components. The following finite difference expansions are employed in the Houbolt integration method (see J. C. Houbolt [A]):   *using $-2\Delta t$ interval*

$$^{t+\Delta t}\ddot{\mathbf{U}} = \frac{1}{\Delta t^2}(2\ ^{t+\Delta t}\mathbf{U} - 5\ ^t\mathbf{U} + 4\ ^{t-\Delta t}\mathbf{U} - {}^{t-2\Delta t}\mathbf{U}) \tag{9.14}$$

and
$$^{t+\Delta t}\dot{\mathbf{U}} = \frac{1}{6\Delta t}(11\ ^{t+\Delta t}\mathbf{U} - 18\ ^{t}\mathbf{U} + 9\ ^{t-\Delta t}\mathbf{U} - 2\ ^{t-2\Delta t}\mathbf{U}) \tag{9.15}$$

which are two backward-difference formulas with errors of order $(\Delta t)^2$.

In order to obtain the solution at time $t + \Delta t$, we now consider (9.1) at time $t + \Delta t$ (and not at time t as for the central difference method), which gives

$$\mathbf{M}\ ^{t+\Delta t}\ddot{\mathbf{U}} + \mathbf{C}\ ^{t+\Delta t}\dot{\mathbf{U}} + \mathbf{K}\ ^{t+\Delta t}\mathbf{U} = {}^{t+\Delta t}\mathbf{R} \tag{9.16}$$

Substituting (9.14) and (9.15) into (9.16) and arranging all known vectors on the right-hand side, we obtain for the solution of $^{t+\Delta t}\mathbf{U}$,

$$\left(\frac{2}{\Delta t^2}\mathbf{M} + \frac{11}{6\Delta t}\mathbf{C} + \mathbf{K}\right)\ ^{t+\Delta t}\mathbf{U} = {}^{t+\Delta t}\mathbf{R} + \left(\frac{5}{\Delta t^2}\mathbf{M} + \frac{3}{\Delta t}\mathbf{C}\right)\ ^{t}\mathbf{U}$$

$$- \left(\frac{4}{\Delta t^2}\mathbf{M} + \frac{3}{2\Delta t}\mathbf{C}\right)\ ^{t-\Delta t}\mathbf{U} + \left(\frac{1}{\Delta t^2}\mathbf{M} + \frac{1}{3\Delta t}\mathbf{C}\right)\ ^{t-2\Delta t}\mathbf{U} \tag{9.17}$$

As shown in (9.17), the solution of $^{t+\Delta t}\mathbf{U}$ requires knowledge of $^{t}\mathbf{U}$, $^{t-\Delta t}\mathbf{U}$, and $^{t-2\Delta t}\mathbf{U}$. Although the knowledge of $^{0}\mathbf{U}$, $^{0}\dot{\mathbf{U}}$, and $^{0}\ddot{\mathbf{U}}$ is useful to start the Houbolt integration scheme, it is more accurate to calculate $^{\Delta t}\mathbf{U}$ and $^{2\Delta t}\mathbf{U}$ by some other means; i.e., we employ special starting procedures. One way of proceeding is to integrate (9.1) for the solution of $^{\Delta t}\mathbf{U}$ and $^{2\Delta t}\mathbf{U}$ using a different integration scheme, possibly a conditionally stable method such as the central difference scheme with a fraction of Δt as the time step (see Example 9.2). Table 9.2 summarizes the Houbolt integration procedure for use in a computer program.

TABLE 9.2   *Step-by-step solution using Houbolt integration method*

A. *Initial calculations:*

1. Form stiffness matrix $\mathbf{K}$, mass matrix $\mathbf{M}$, and damping matrix $\mathbf{C}$.
2. Initialize $^{0}\mathbf{U}$, $^{0}\dot{\mathbf{U}}$, and $^{0}\ddot{\mathbf{U}}$.
3. Select time step Δt and calculate integration constants:

$$a_0 = \frac{2}{\Delta t^2}; \qquad a_1 = \frac{11}{6\Delta t}; \qquad a_2 = \frac{5}{\Delta t^2}; \qquad a_3 = \frac{3}{\Delta t}; \qquad a_4 = -2a_0;$$

$$a_5 = \frac{-a_3}{2}; \qquad a_6 = \frac{a_0}{2}; \qquad a_7 = \frac{a_3}{9}$$

4. Use special starting procedure to calculate $^{\Delta t}\mathbf{U}$ and $^{2\Delta t}\mathbf{U}$.
5. Calculate effective stiffness matrix $\hat{\mathbf{K}}$: $\hat{\mathbf{K}} = \mathbf{K} + a_0\mathbf{M} + a_1\mathbf{C}$.
6. Triangularize $\hat{\mathbf{K}}$: $\hat{\mathbf{K}} = \mathbf{L}\mathbf{D}\mathbf{L}^T$.

B. *For each time step:*

1. Calculate effective load at time $t + \Delta t$:

$$^{t+\Delta t}\hat{\mathbf{R}} = {}^{t+\Delta t}\mathbf{R} + \mathbf{M}(a_2\ ^{t}\mathbf{U} + a_4\ ^{t-\Delta t}\mathbf{U} + a_6\ ^{t-2\Delta t}\mathbf{U}) + \mathbf{C}(a_3\ ^{t}\mathbf{U} + a_5\ ^{t-\Delta t}\mathbf{U} + a_7\ ^{t-2\Delta t}\mathbf{U})$$

2. Solve for displacements at time $t + \Delta t$:

$$\mathbf{L}\mathbf{D}\mathbf{L}^T\ ^{t+\Delta t}\mathbf{U} = {}^{t+\Delta t}\hat{\mathbf{R}}$$

3. If required, evaluate accelerations and velocities at time $t + \Delta t$:

$$^{t+\Delta t}\ddot{\mathbf{U}} = a_0\ ^{t+\Delta t}\mathbf{U} - a_2\ ^{t}\mathbf{U} - a_4\ ^{t-\Delta t}\mathbf{U} - a_6\ ^{t-2\Delta t}\mathbf{U}$$

$$^{t+\Delta t}\dot{\mathbf{U}} = a_1\ ^{t+\Delta t}\mathbf{U} - a_3\ ^{t}\mathbf{U} - a_5\ ^{t-\Delta t}\mathbf{U} - a_7\ ^{t-2\Delta t}\mathbf{U}$$

A basic difference between the Houbolt method in Table 9.2 and the central difference scheme in Table 9.1 is the appearance of the stiffness matrix $\mathbf{K}$ as a factor to the required displacements $^{t+\Delta t}\mathbf{U}$. The term $\mathbf{K}\,^{t+\Delta t}\mathbf{U}$ appears because in (9.16) equilibrium is considered at time $t + \Delta t$ and not at time t as in the central difference method. The Houbolt method is, for this reason, an implicit integration scheme, whereas the central difference method was an explicit procedure. With regard to the time step Δt that can be used in the integration, there is no critical time step limit and Δt can in general be selected much larger than given in (9.13) for the central difference method.

A noteworthy point is that the step-by-step solution scheme based on the Houbolt method reduces directly to a static analysis if mass and damping effects are neglected, whereas the central difference method solution in Table 9.1 could not be used. In other words, if $\mathbf{C} = \mathbf{0}$ and $\mathbf{M} = \mathbf{0}$, the solution method in Table 9.2 yields the static solution for time-dependent loads.

EXAMPLE 9.2: Use the Houbolt direct integration scheme to calculate the response of the system considered in Example 9.1.

First, we consider the case $\Delta t = 0.28$. We then have, following Table 9.2, and showing three digits,

$$a_0 = 25.5; \qquad a_1 = 6.55; \qquad a_2 = 63.8; \qquad a_3 = 10.7;$$

$$a_4 = -51.0; \qquad a_5 = -5.36; \qquad a_6 = 12.8; \qquad a_7 = 1.19$$

To start the integration we need $^{\Delta t}\mathbf{U}$ and $^{2\Delta t}\mathbf{U}$. Let us here use simply the values calculated with the central difference method in Example 9.1, i.e.,

$$^{\Delta t}\mathbf{U} = \begin{bmatrix} 0.0 \\ 0.392 \end{bmatrix}; \qquad ^{2\Delta t}\mathbf{U} = \begin{bmatrix} 0.0307 \\ 1.45 \end{bmatrix}$$

Next we calculate $\hat{\mathbf{K}}$ and obtain

$$\hat{\mathbf{K}} = \begin{bmatrix} 6 & -2 \\ -2 & 4 \end{bmatrix} + 25.5 \begin{bmatrix} 2 & 0 \\ 0 & 1 \end{bmatrix} = \begin{bmatrix} 57 & -2 \\ -2 & 29.5 \end{bmatrix}$$

For each time step we need $^{t+\Delta t}\hat{\mathbf{R}}$, which is in this case

$$^{t+\Delta t}\hat{\mathbf{R}} = \begin{bmatrix} 0 \\ 10 \end{bmatrix} + \begin{bmatrix} 2 & 0 \\ 0 & 1 \end{bmatrix}(63.8\ ^{t}\mathbf{U} - 51.0\ ^{t-\Delta t}\mathbf{U} + 12.8\ ^{t-2\Delta t}\mathbf{U})$$

Solving $\hat{\mathbf{K}}\,^{t+\Delta t}\mathbf{U} = {}^{t+\Delta t}\hat{\mathbf{R}}$ for 12 time steps, we obtain

Time	Δt	$2\Delta t$	$3\Delta t$	$4\Delta t$	$5\Delta t$	$6\Delta t$	$7\Delta t$	$8\Delta t$	$9\Delta t$	$10\Delta t$	$11\Delta t$	$12\Delta t$
$^{t}\mathbf{U}$	0	0.0307	0.167	0.461	0.923	1.50	2.11	2.60	2.86	2.80	2.40	1.72
	0.392	1.45	2.80	4.08	5.02	5.43	5.31	4.77	4.01	3.24	2.63	2.28

The solution obtained is compared with the exact results in Example 9.7.

Next we consider the case $\Delta t = 28$ in order to observe the unconditional stability of the Houbolt operator. To start the integration we use the exact response at times Δt and $2\Delta t$ (see Example 9.7),

$$^{\Delta t}\mathbf{U} = \begin{bmatrix} 2.19 \\ 2.24 \end{bmatrix}; \qquad ^{2\Delta t}\mathbf{U} = \begin{bmatrix} 2.92 \\ 3.12 \end{bmatrix}$$

It is interesting to compare $\hat{\mathbf{K}}$ with $\mathbf{K}$,

$$\hat{\mathbf{K}} = \begin{bmatrix} 6 & -2 \\ -2 & 4 \end{bmatrix} + 0.00255 \begin{bmatrix} 2 & 0 \\ 0 & 1 \end{bmatrix} = \begin{bmatrix} 6.0051 & -2.0000 \\ -2.0000 & 4.00255 \end{bmatrix}$$

where it is noted that $\hat{\mathbf{K}}$ is almost equal to $\mathbf{K}$. The displacement response over 12 time steps is given in the following table:

Time	Δt	$2\Delta t$	$3\Delta t$	$4\Delta t$	$5\Delta t$	$6\Delta t$	$7\Delta t$	$8\Delta t$	$9\Delta t$	$10\Delta t$	$11\Delta t$	$12\Delta t$
${}^t\mathbf{U}$	2.19	2.92	1.00	1.00	1.00	1.00	1.00	1.00	1.00	1.00	1.00	1.00
	2.24	3.12	3.00	3.00	3.00	3.00	3.00	3.00	3.00	3.00	3.00	3.00

The static solution is

$$ {}^t\mathbf{U} = \begin{bmatrix} 1.0 \\ 3.0 \end{bmatrix} $$

Therefore, the displacement response very rapidly approaches the static solution.

9.2.3 The Wilson θ Method

The Wilson θ method is essentially an extension of the linear acceleration method, in which a linear variation of acceleration from time t to time $t + \Delta t$ is assumed. Referring to Fig. 9.1, in the Wilson θ method the acceleration is assumed to be linear from time t to time $t + \theta \Delta t$, where $\theta \geq 1.0$ (see E. L. Wilson, I. Farhoomand, and K. J. Bathe [A]). When $\theta = 1.0$, the method reduces to the linear acceleration scheme, but we will show in Section 9.4 that for unconditional stability we need to use $\theta \geq 1.37$, and usually we employ $\theta = 1.40$.

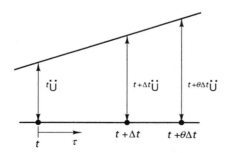

Figure 9.1   Linear acceleration assumption of Wilson θ method

Let τ denote the increase in time, where $0 \leq \tau \leq \theta \Delta t$; then for the time interval t to $t + \theta \Delta t$, it is assumed that

$$ {}^{t+\tau}\ddot{\mathbf{U}} = {}^t\ddot{\mathbf{U}} + \frac{\tau}{\theta \Delta t}({}^{t+\theta\Delta t}\ddot{\mathbf{U}} - {}^t\ddot{\mathbf{U}}) \tag{9.18} $$

Integrating (9.18), we obtain

$$ {}^{t+\tau}\dot{\mathbf{U}} = {}^t\dot{\mathbf{U}} + {}^t\ddot{\mathbf{U}}\tau + \frac{\tau^2}{2\theta \Delta t}({}^{t+\theta\Delta t}\ddot{\mathbf{U}} - {}^t\ddot{\mathbf{U}}) \tag{9.19} $$

and
$$^{t+\tau}\mathbf{U} = {}^t\mathbf{U} + {}^t\dot{\mathbf{U}}\tau + \frac{1}{2}{}^t\ddot{\mathbf{U}}\tau^2 + \frac{1}{6\theta\,\Delta t}\tau^3({}^{t+\theta\Delta t}\ddot{\mathbf{U}} - {}^t\ddot{\mathbf{U}})$$
(9.20)

Using (9.19) and (9.20), we have at time $t + \theta\,\Delta t$,

$$^{t+\theta\Delta t}\dot{\mathbf{U}} = {}^t\dot{\mathbf{U}} + \frac{\theta\,\Delta t}{2}({}^{t+\theta\Delta t}\ddot{\mathbf{U}} + {}^t\ddot{\mathbf{U}})$$
(9.21)

$$^{t+\theta\Delta t}\mathbf{U} = {}^t\mathbf{U} + \theta\,\Delta t\,{}^t\dot{\mathbf{U}} + \frac{\theta^2\,\Delta t^2}{6}({}^{t+\theta\Delta t}\ddot{\mathbf{U}} + 2\,{}^t\ddot{\mathbf{U}})$$
(9.22)

from which we can solve for $^{t+\theta\Delta t}\ddot{\mathbf{U}}$ and $^{t+\theta\Delta t}\dot{\mathbf{U}}$ in terms of $^{t+\theta\Delta t}\mathbf{U}$:

$$^{t+\theta\Delta t}\ddot{\mathbf{U}} = \frac{6}{\theta^2\,\Delta t^2}({}^{t+\theta\Delta t}\mathbf{U} - {}^t\mathbf{U}) - \frac{6}{\theta\,\Delta t}{}^t\dot{\mathbf{U}} - 2\,{}^t\ddot{\mathbf{U}}$$
(9.23)

and
$$^{t+\theta\Delta t}\dot{\mathbf{U}} = \frac{3}{\theta\,\Delta t}({}^{t+\theta\Delta t}\mathbf{U} - {}^t\mathbf{U}) - 2\,{}^t\dot{\mathbf{U}} - \frac{\theta\,\Delta t}{2}{}^t\ddot{\mathbf{U}}$$
(9.24)

To obtain the solution for the displacements, velocities, and accelerations at time $t + \Delta t$, the equilibrium equations (9.1) are considered at time $t + \theta\,\Delta t$. However, because the accelerations are assumed to vary linearly, a linearly extrapolated load vector is used; i.e., the equation employed is

$$\mathbf{M}\,^{t+\theta\Delta t}\ddot{\mathbf{U}} + \mathbf{C}\,^{t+\theta\Delta t}\dot{\mathbf{U}} + \mathbf{K}\,^{t+\theta\Delta t}\mathbf{U} = {}^{t+\theta\Delta t}\overline{\mathbf{R}}$$
(9.25)

where
$$^{t+\theta\Delta t}\overline{\mathbf{R}} = {}^t\mathbf{R} + \theta({}^{t+\Delta t}\mathbf{R} - {}^t\mathbf{R})$$
(9.26)

TABLE 9.3 *Step-by-step solution using Wilson θ integration method*

A. *Initial calculations:*
1. Form stiffness matrix $\mathbf{K}$, mass matrix $\mathbf{M}$, and damping matrix $\mathbf{C}$.
2. Initialize $^0\mathbf{U}$, $^0\dot{\mathbf{U}}$, and $^0\ddot{\mathbf{U}}$.
3. Select time step Δt and calculate integration constants, $\theta = 1.4$ (usually):

$$a_0 = \frac{6}{(\theta\,\Delta t)^2}; \qquad a_1 = \frac{3}{\theta\,\Delta t}; \qquad a_2 = 2a_1; \qquad a_3 = \frac{\theta\,\Delta t}{2}; \qquad a_4 = \frac{a_0}{\theta};$$

$$a_5 = \frac{-a_2}{\theta}; \qquad a_6 = 1 - \frac{3}{\theta}; \qquad a_7 = \frac{\Delta t}{2}; \qquad a_8 = \frac{\Delta t^2}{6}$$

4. Form effective stiffness matrix $\hat{\mathbf{K}}$: $\hat{\mathbf{K}} = \mathbf{K} + a_0\mathbf{M} + a_1\mathbf{C}$.
5. Triangularize $\hat{\mathbf{K}}$: $\hat{\mathbf{K}} = \mathbf{LDL}^T$.

B. *For each time step:*
1. Calculate effective loads at time $t + \theta\,\Delta t$:
$$^{t+\theta\Delta t}\hat{\mathbf{R}} = {}^t\mathbf{R} + \theta({}^{t+\Delta t}\mathbf{R} - {}^t\mathbf{R}) + \mathbf{M}(a_0\,{}^t\mathbf{U} + a_2\,{}^t\dot{\mathbf{U}} + 2\,{}^t\ddot{\mathbf{U}}) + \mathbf{C}(a_1\,{}^t\mathbf{U} + 2\,{}^t\dot{\mathbf{U}} + a_3\,{}^t\ddot{\mathbf{U}})$$
2. Solve for displacements at time $t + \theta\,\Delta t$:
$$\mathbf{LDL}^T\,{}^{t+\theta\Delta t}\mathbf{U} = {}^{t+\theta\Delta t}\hat{\mathbf{R}}$$
3. Calculate displacements, velocities, and accelerations at time $t + \Delta t$:
$$^{t+\Delta t}\ddot{\mathbf{U}} = a_4({}^{t+\theta\Delta t}\mathbf{U} - {}^t\mathbf{U}) + a_5\,{}^t\dot{\mathbf{U}} + a_6\,{}^t\ddot{\mathbf{U}}$$
$$^{t+\Delta t}\dot{\mathbf{U}} = {}^t\dot{\mathbf{U}} + a_7({}^{t+\Delta t}\ddot{\mathbf{U}} + {}^t\ddot{\mathbf{U}})$$
$$^{t+\Delta t}\mathbf{U} = {}^t\mathbf{U} + \Delta t\,{}^t\dot{\mathbf{U}} + a_8({}^{t+\Delta t}\ddot{\mathbf{U}} + 2\,{}^t\ddot{\mathbf{U}})$$

Substituting (9.23) and (9.24) into (9.25), an equation is obtained from which $^{t+\theta\Delta t}\mathbf{U}$ can be solved. Then substituting $^{t+\theta\Delta t}\mathbf{U}$ into (9.23), we obtain $^{t+\theta\Delta t}\ddot{\mathbf{U}}$, which is used in (9.18) to (9.20), all evaluated at $\tau = \Delta t$ to calculate $^{t+\Delta t}\ddot{\mathbf{U}}$, $^{t+\Delta t}\dot{\mathbf{U}}$ and $^{t+\Delta t}\mathbf{U}$. The complete algorithm used in the integration is given in Table 9.3.

As pointed out earlier, the Wilson θ method is also an implicit integration method because the stiffness matrix $\mathbf{K}$ is a coefficient matrix to the unknown displacement vector. It may also be noted that no special starting procedures are needed since the displacements, velocities, and accelerations at time $t + \Delta t$ are expressed in terms of the same quantities at time t only.

EXAMPLE 9.3: Calculate the displacement response of the system considered in Examples 9.1 and 9.2 using the Wilson θ method. Use $\theta = 1.4$.

First we consider the case $\Delta t = 0.28$. Following the steps of calculations in Table 9.3, we have

$$^{0}\mathbf{U} = \begin{bmatrix} 0 \\ 0 \end{bmatrix}; \qquad ^{0}\dot{\mathbf{U}} = \begin{bmatrix} 0 \\ 0 \end{bmatrix}; \qquad ^{0}\ddot{\mathbf{U}} = \begin{bmatrix} 0 \\ 10 \end{bmatrix}$$

where $^{0}\ddot{\mathbf{U}}$ was evaluated in Example 9.1. Then (listed to three digits)

$a_0 = 39.0; \qquad a_1 = 7.65; \qquad a_2 = 15.3; \qquad a_3 = 0.196; \qquad a_4 = 27.9;$

$a_5 = -10.9; \qquad a_6 = -1.14; \qquad a_7 = 0.14; \qquad a_8 = 0.0131$

and

$$\hat{\mathbf{K}} = \begin{bmatrix} 6 & -2 \\ -2 & 4 \end{bmatrix} + 39.0 \begin{bmatrix} 2 & 0 \\ 0 & 1 \end{bmatrix} = \begin{bmatrix} 84.1 & -2 \\ -2 & 43.0 \end{bmatrix}$$

For each time step we need to evaluate

$$^{t+\theta\Delta t}\hat{\mathbf{R}} = \begin{bmatrix} 0 \\ 10 \end{bmatrix} + \begin{bmatrix} 0 \\ 0 \end{bmatrix} + \begin{bmatrix} 2 & 0 \\ 0 & 1 \end{bmatrix}(39.0\,{}^{t}\mathbf{U} + 15.3\,{}^{t}\dot{\mathbf{U}} + 2\,{}^{t}\ddot{\mathbf{U}})$$

$$\hat{\mathbf{K}}\,{}^{t+\theta\Delta t}\mathbf{U} = {}^{t+\theta\Delta t}\hat{\mathbf{R}}$$

and then calculate

$$^{t+\Delta t}\ddot{\mathbf{U}} = 27.9({}^{t+\theta\Delta t}\mathbf{U} - {}^{t}\mathbf{U}) - 10.9\,{}^{t}\dot{\mathbf{U}} - 1.14\,{}^{t}\ddot{\mathbf{U}}$$

$$^{t+\Delta t}\dot{\mathbf{U}} = {}^{t}\dot{\mathbf{U}} + 0.14({}^{t+\Delta t}\ddot{\mathbf{U}} + {}^{t}\ddot{\mathbf{U}})$$

$$^{t+\Delta t}\mathbf{U} = {}^{t}\mathbf{U} + 0.28\,{}^{t}\dot{\mathbf{U}} + 0.0131({}^{t+\Delta t}\ddot{\mathbf{U}} + 2\,{}^{t}\ddot{\mathbf{U}})$$

Time	Δt	$2\Delta t$	$3\Delta t$	$4\Delta t$	$5\Delta t$	$6\Delta t$	$7\Delta t$	$8\Delta t$	$9\Delta t$	$10\Delta t$	$11\Delta t$	$12\Delta t$
$^{t}\mathbf{U}$	0.00605	0.0525	0.196	0.490	0.952	1.54	2.16	2.67	2.92	2.82	2.33	1.54
	0.366	1.34	2.64	3.92	4.88	5.31	5.18	4.61	3.82	3.06	2.52	2.29

The solution obtained is compared with the exact results in Example 9.7.

Consider now the direct integration with a time step $\Delta t = 28$. In this case we have

$$\hat{\mathbf{K}} = \begin{bmatrix} 6 & -2 \\ -2 & 4 \end{bmatrix} + 0.0039 \begin{bmatrix} 2 & 0 \\ 0 & 1 \end{bmatrix} = \begin{bmatrix} 6.0078 & -2 \\ -2 & 4.0039 \end{bmatrix}$$

where we note that $\hat{\mathbf{K}}$ is nearly equal to $\mathbf{K}$, as in the integration using the Houbolt method.

This displacement response obtained over 12 time steps is

Time	Δt	$2\Delta t$	$3\Delta t$	$4\Delta t$	$5\Delta t$	$6\Delta t$	$7\Delta t$	$8\Delta t$	$9\Delta t$	$10\Delta t$	$11\Delta t$	$12\Delta t$
${}^t\mathbf{U}$	1.09	2.82	−2.61	5.86	−4.47	6.59	−4.38	5.97	−3.46	4.92	−2.39	3.89
	1123.	−834.	674.	−519.	406.	−308.	242.	−181.	144.	−105.	86.1	−60.9

Here it should be noted that the initial conditions on the accelerations, i.e., ${}^0\ddot{\mathbf{U}} = \begin{bmatrix} 0 \\ 10 \end{bmatrix}$, cause the large initial displacement response. This response is damped out with increasing time. If we use ${}^0\ddot{\mathbf{U}} = \begin{bmatrix} 0 \\ 0 \end{bmatrix}$, the calculated displacement response is

Time	Δt	$2\Delta t$	$3\Delta t$	$4\Delta t$	$5\Delta t$	$6\Delta t$	$7\Delta t$	$8\Delta t$	$9\Delta t$	$10\Delta t$	$11\Delta t$	$12\Delta t$
${}^t\mathbf{U}$	0.363	1.44	0.632	1.29	0.782	1.17	0.875	1.09	0.929	1.05	0.960	1.03
	1.09	4.33	1.89	3.87	2.32	3.52	2.60	3.31	2.77	3.18	2.86	3.11

where it is observed that the static solution is approached (see Example 9.2).

9.2.4 The Newmark Method

The Newmark integration scheme can also be understood to be an extension of the linear acceleration method. The following assumptions are used (see N. M. Newmark [A]):

$$ {}^{t+\Delta t}\dot{\mathbf{U}} = {}^t\dot{\mathbf{U}} + [(1 - \delta)\,{}^t\ddot{\mathbf{U}} + \delta\,{}^{t+\Delta t}\ddot{\mathbf{U}}]\,\Delta t \tag{9.27} $$

$$ {}^{t+\Delta t}\mathbf{U} = {}^t\mathbf{U} + {}^t\dot{\mathbf{U}}\,\Delta t + [(\tfrac{1}{2} - \alpha)\,{}^t\ddot{\mathbf{U}} + \alpha\,{}^{t+\Delta t}\ddot{\mathbf{U}}]\,\Delta t^2 \tag{9.28} $$

where α and δ are parameters that can be determined to obtain integration accuracy and stability. When $\delta = \tfrac{1}{2}$ and $\alpha = \tfrac{1}{6}$, relations (9.27) and (9.28) correspond to the linear acceleration method (which is also obtained using $\theta = 1$ in the Wilson θ method). Newmark originally proposed as an unconditionally stable scheme the constant-average-acceleration method (also called trapezoidal rule), in which case $\delta = \tfrac{1}{2}$ and $\alpha = \tfrac{1}{4}$ (see Fig. 9.2).

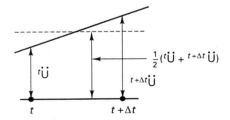

$\frac{1}{2}({}^t\ddot{\mathbf{U}} + {}^{t+\Delta t}\ddot{\mathbf{U}})$

Figure 9.2 Newmark's constant-average-acceleration scheme

In addition to (9.27) and (9.28), for solution of the displacements, velocities, and accelerations at time $t + \Delta t$, the equilibrium equations (9.1) at time $t + \Delta t$ are also considered:

$$ \mathbf{M}\,{}^{t+\Delta t}\ddot{\mathbf{U}} + \mathbf{C}\,{}^{t+\Delta t}\dot{\mathbf{U}} + \mathbf{K}\,{}^{t+\Delta t}\mathbf{U} = {}^{t+\Delta t}\mathbf{R} \tag{9.29} $$

Solving from (9.28) for $^{t+\Delta t}\ddot{\mathbf{U}}$ in terms of $^{t+\Delta t}\mathbf{U}$ and then substituting for $^{t+\Delta t}\ddot{\mathbf{U}}$ into (9.27), we obtain equations for $^{t+\Delta t}\ddot{\mathbf{U}}$ and $^{t+\Delta t}\dot{\mathbf{U}}$, each in terms of the unknown displacements $^{t+\Delta t}\mathbf{U}$ only. These two relations for $^{t+\Delta t}\dot{\mathbf{U}}$ and $^{t+\Delta t}\ddot{\mathbf{U}}$ are substituted into (9.29) to solve for $^{t+\Delta t}\mathbf{U}$, after which, using (9.27) and (9.28), $^{t+\Delta t}\ddot{\mathbf{U}}$ and $^{t+\Delta t}\dot{\mathbf{U}}$ can also be calculated.

The complete algorithm using the Newmark integration scheme is given in Table 9.4. The close relationship between the computer implementations of the Newmark method and the Wilson θ method should be noted (see also Exercise 9.3.)

TABLE 9.4 *Step-by-step solution using Newmark integration method*

A. *Initial calculations:*
1. Form stiffness matrix $\mathbf{K}$, mass matrix $\mathbf{M}$, and damping matrix $\mathbf{C}$.
2. Initialize $^0\mathbf{U}$, $^0\dot{\mathbf{U}}$, and $^0\ddot{\mathbf{U}}$.
3. Select time step Δt and parameters α and δ and calculate integration constants:
$$\delta \geq 0.50; \qquad \alpha \geq 0.25(0.5 + \delta)^2$$
$$a_0 = \frac{1}{\alpha\,\Delta t^2}; \qquad a_1 = \frac{\delta}{\alpha\,\Delta t}; \qquad a_2 = \frac{1}{\alpha\,\Delta t}; \qquad a_3 = \frac{1}{2\alpha} - 1;$$
$$a_4 = \frac{\delta}{\alpha} - 1; \qquad a_5 = \frac{\Delta t}{2}\left(\frac{\delta}{\alpha} - 2\right); \qquad a_6 = \Delta t(1 - \delta); \qquad a_7 = \delta\,\Delta t$$

4. Form effective stiffness matrix $\hat{\mathbf{K}}$: $\hat{\mathbf{K}} = \mathbf{K} + a_0\mathbf{M} + a_1\mathbf{C}$.
5. Triangularize $\hat{\mathbf{K}}$: $\hat{\mathbf{K}} = \mathbf{LDL}^T$.

B. *For each time step:*
1. Calculate effective loads at time $t + \Delta t$:
$$^{t+\Delta t}\hat{\mathbf{R}} = {}^{t+\Delta t}\mathbf{R} + \mathbf{M}(a_0\,{}^t\mathbf{U} + a_2\,{}^t\dot{\mathbf{U}} + a_3\,{}^t\ddot{\mathbf{U}}) + \mathbf{C}(a_1\,{}^t\mathbf{U} + a_4\,{}^t\dot{\mathbf{U}} + a_5\,{}^t\ddot{\mathbf{U}})$$
2. Solve for displacements at time $t + \Delta t$:
$$\mathbf{LDL}^T\,{}^{t+\Delta t}\mathbf{U} = {}^{t+\Delta t}\hat{\mathbf{R}}$$
3. Calculate accelerations and velocities at time $t + \Delta t$:
$$^{t+\Delta t}\ddot{\mathbf{U}} = a_0({}^{t+\Delta t}\mathbf{U} - {}^t\mathbf{U}) - a_2\,{}^t\dot{\mathbf{U}} - a_3\,{}^t\ddot{\mathbf{U}}$$
$$^{t+\Delta t}\dot{\mathbf{U}} = {}^t\dot{\mathbf{U}} + a_6\,{}^t\ddot{\mathbf{U}} + a_7\,{}^{t+\Delta t}\ddot{\mathbf{U}}$$

EXAMPLE 9.4: Calculate the displacement response of the system considered in Examples 9.1 to 9.3 using the Newmark method. Use $\alpha = 0.25$, $\delta = 0.5$.

Consider first the case $\Delta t = 0.28$. Following the steps of calculations given in Table 9.4, we have
$$^0\mathbf{U} = \begin{bmatrix} 0 \\ 0 \end{bmatrix}; \qquad ^0\dot{\mathbf{U}} = \begin{bmatrix} 0 \\ 0 \end{bmatrix}; \qquad ^0\ddot{\mathbf{U}} = \begin{bmatrix} 0 \\ 10 \end{bmatrix}$$

The integration constants are (showing three digits)
$$a_0 = 51.0; \qquad a_1 = 7.14; \qquad a_2 = 14.3; \qquad a_3 = 1.00;$$
$$a_4 = 1.00; \qquad a_5 = 0.00; \qquad a_6 = 0.14; \qquad a_7 = 0.14$$

Thus the effective stiffness matrix is
$$\hat{\mathbf{K}} = \begin{bmatrix} 6 & -2 \\ -2 & 4 \end{bmatrix} + 51.0\begin{bmatrix} 2 & 0 \\ 0 & 1 \end{bmatrix} = \begin{bmatrix} 108 & -2 \\ -2 & 55 \end{bmatrix}$$

For each time step we need to evaluate

$$^{t+\Delta t}\hat{\mathbf{R}} = \begin{bmatrix} 0 \\ 10 \end{bmatrix} + \begin{bmatrix} 2 & 0 \\ 0 & 1 \end{bmatrix}(51\ ^{t}\mathbf{U} + 14.3\ ^{t}\dot{\mathbf{U}} + 1.0\ ^{t}\ddot{\mathbf{U}})$$

Then

$$\hat{\mathbf{K}}\ ^{t+\Delta t}\mathbf{U} = {}^{t+\Delta t}\hat{\mathbf{R}}$$

and

$$^{t+\Delta t}\ddot{\mathbf{U}} = 51.0(^{t+\Delta t}\mathbf{U} - {}^{t}\mathbf{U}) - 14.3\ ^{t}\dot{\mathbf{U}} - 1.0\ ^{t}\ddot{\mathbf{U}}$$

$$^{t+\Delta t}\dot{\mathbf{U}} = {}^{t}\dot{\mathbf{U}} + 0.14\ ^{t}\ddot{\mathbf{U}} + 0.14\ ^{t+\Delta t}\ddot{\mathbf{U}}$$

Performing these calculations, we obtain

Time	Δt	$2\Delta t$	$3\Delta t$	$4\Delta t$	$5\Delta t$	$6\Delta t$	$7\Delta t$	$8\Delta t$	$9\Delta t$	$10\Delta t$	$11\Delta t$	$12\Delta t$
$^{t}\mathbf{U}$	0.00673	0.0505	0.189	0.485	0.961	1.58	2.23	2.76	3.00	2.85	2.28	1.40
	0.364	1.35	2.68	4.00	4.95	5.34	5.13	4.48	3.64	2.90	2.44	2.31

The solution obtained is compared with the exact results in Example 9.7.

Next we employ the time step $\Delta t = 28.0$. In this case we have

$$\hat{\mathbf{K}} = \begin{bmatrix} 6 & -2 \\ -2 & 4 \end{bmatrix} + 0.0051 \begin{bmatrix} 2 & 0 \\ 0 & 1 \end{bmatrix} = \begin{bmatrix} 6.0102 & -2.0000 \\ -2.0000 & 4.0051 \end{bmatrix}$$

Therefore, $\hat{\mathbf{K}}$ is, as in the integrations using the Houbolt and Wilson θ methods, nearly equal to $\mathbf{K}$.

Using the initial conditions $^{0}\ddot{\mathbf{U}} = \begin{bmatrix} 0 \\ 10 \end{bmatrix}$, we obtain as the displacement response,

Time	Δt	$2\Delta t$	$3\Delta t$	$4\Delta t$	$5\Delta t$	$6\Delta t$	$7\Delta t$	$8\Delta t$	$9\Delta t$	$10\Delta t$	$11\Delta t$	$12\Delta t$
$^{t}\mathbf{U}$	1.99	0.028	1.94	0.112	1.83	0.248	1.67	0.429	1.47	0.648	1.23	0.894
	5.99	0.045	5.90	0.177	5.72	0.393	5.47	0.685	5.14	1.04	4.76	1.45

However, using as initial conditions $^{0}\ddot{\mathbf{U}} = \begin{bmatrix} 0 \\ 0 \end{bmatrix}$, we obtain

Time	Δt	$2\Delta t$	$3\Delta t$	$4\Delta t$	$5\Delta t$	$6\Delta t$	$7\Delta t$	$8\Delta t$	$9\Delta t$	$10\Delta t$	$11\Delta t$	$12\Delta t$
$^{t}\mathbf{U}$	0.996	1.01	0.982	1.02	0.969	1.04	0.957	1.05	0.947	1.06	0.940	1.06
	2.99	3.02	2.97	3.04	2.95	3.06	2.93	3.08	2.91	3.09	2.90	3.11

and the solution slightly oscillates about the static response.

9.2.5 The Coupling of Different Integration Operators

So far we have assumed that all dynamic equilibrium equations are solved using the same time integration scheme. As discussed in Section 9.4, the choice of which method to use for an effective solution depends on the problem to be analyzed. However, for certain kinds of problems it may be advantageous to use different operators to integrate the response in different regions of the total element assemblage (see, for example, T. Belytschko, H. J. Yen, and R. Mullen [A] and T. Belytschko and T. J. R. Hughes (eds.) [A]). This is particularly the case when the stiffness and mass characteristics (i.e., the characteristic time constants) of the total element assemblage are quite different in different parts of the element assemblage. An example is the analysis of fluid-structure systems, in which the fluid is very flexible when measured on the stiffness of the structure. Here the explicit time integration of the fluid response using the conditionally stable central difference method and an implicit unconditionally stable time integration of the structural response (using, for example, the Newmark method) may be a natural choice (see Section 9.4). The reasons are that, first, the physical phenomenon to be analyzed may be a wave propagation in the fluid and a structural vibration of the structure, and second, the critical time step size for an explicit time integration of the fluid response is usually much larger than the time step required for explicit time integration of the structural response. The result may be that by proper choice of the finite element idealizations of the fluid and the structure, the explicit time integration of the fluid response and implicit time integration of the structural response can be performed with a time step that is relatively large but small enough to yield a stable and accurate solution. Of course, it may also be efficient to use different time step sizes for the explicit and implicit integrations, with one time step size being a multiple of the other.

The use of a combination of operators for the integration of dynamic response raises the questions of which methods to choose and how to couple them. There are a large number of possibilities, but in general the selection of the schemes depends on their stability and accuracy characteristics, including the effects due to the operator coupling, and the overall effectiveness of the resulting time integration. We demonstrate the use of explicit-implicit time integration in the analysis of the simple problem considered in Examples 9.1 to 9.4.

EXAMPLE 9.5:   Solve for U_1 and U_2 of the simple system considered in Example 9.1 using the explicit central difference method for U_1 and the implicit trapezoidal rule (Newmark's method with $\alpha = \frac{1}{4}$, $\delta = \frac{1}{2}$) for U_2.

In the explicit integration we consider the equilibrium at time t to calculate the displacement for time $t + \Delta t$. For degree of freedom 1, we have

$$2\,{}^{t}\ddot{U}_1 + 6\,{}^{t}U_1 - 2\,{}^{t}U_2 = 0 \tag{a}$$

In the implicit integration we consider the equilibrium at time $t + \Delta t$ to calculate the displacement for time $t + \Delta t$. Thus, we have for degree of freedom 2,

$$ {}^{t+\Delta t}\ddot{U}_2 - 2\,{}^{t+\Delta t}U_1 + 4\,{}^{t+\Delta t}U_2 = 10 \tag{b}$$

For (a) we now use the central difference method,

$$ {}^{t}\ddot{U}_1 = \frac{{}^{t+\Delta t}U_1 - 2\,{}^{t}U_1 + {}^{t-\Delta t}U_1}{(\Delta t)^2} \tag{c}$$

and for (b) we use the trapezoidal rule,

$$ {}^{t+\Delta t}\dot{U}_2 = {}^{t}\dot{U}_2 + \frac{\Delta t}{2}({}^{t}\ddot{U}_2 + {}^{t+\Delta t}\ddot{U}_2) $$

$$ {}^{t+\Delta t}U_2 = {}^{t}U_2 + {}^{t}\dot{U}_2\,\Delta t + \frac{(\Delta t)^2}{4}({}^{t}\ddot{U}_2 + {}^{t+\Delta t}\ddot{U}_2) \tag{d}$$

The initial conditions are

$$^0U_1 = {}^0\dot{U}_1 = {}^0\ddot{U}_1 = {}^0U_2 = {}^0\dot{U}_2 = 0; \qquad {}^0\ddot{U}_2 = 10$$

Hence, using (9.7) to obtain the starting value $^{-\Delta t}U_1$, we obtain $^{-\Delta t}U_1 = 0$.

We can now use, for each time step, (a) and (c) to solve for $^{t+\Delta t}U_1$ and then (b) and (d) to solve for $^{t+\Delta t}U_2$. We should note that in this solution we evaluate $^{t+\Delta t}U_1$ by projecting ahead from the equilibrium configuration at time t of the degree of freedom 1, and we then accept this value of $^{t+\Delta t}U_1$ to evaluate $^{t+\Delta t}U_2$ implicitly. Using this procedure we obtain with $\Delta t = 0.28$ the following data:

Time	Δt	$2\Delta t$	$3\Delta t$	$4\Delta t$	$5\Delta t$	$6\Delta t$	$7\Delta t$	$8\Delta t$	$9\Delta t$	$10\Delta t$	$11\Delta t$	$12\Delta t$
^tU	0.	.0285	.156	.457	.962	1.63	2.33	2.88	3.11	2.90	2.24	1.25
	.364	1.35	2.68	3.98	4.93	5.32	5.12	4.50	3.70	2.99	2.54	2.39

This solution compares with the response calculated in Example 9.1. If, however, we now try to obtain a solution with $\Delta t = 28$, we find that the solution is unstable; i.e., the predicted displacements very rapidly grow out of bound.

As demonstrated in the preceding example, the use of explicit-implicit time integration requires that the time step be small enough for stability in the explicitly integrated domain, while special considerations need to be given to the interface conditions. In an alternative solution approach, a single implicit time integration scheme is used for the complete domain, but the stiffness of the very flexible part is not added to the coefficient matrix, and dynamic equilibrium is satisfied by iteration (see, for example, K. J. Bathe and V. Sonnad [A] and Section 8.3.2).

9.2.6 Exercises

9.1. Consider the two degree of freedom system

$$\begin{bmatrix} 1 & 0 \\ 0 & 2 \end{bmatrix}\begin{bmatrix} \ddot{U}_1 \\ \ddot{U}_2 \end{bmatrix} + \begin{bmatrix} 8 & -3 \\ -3 & 4 \end{bmatrix}\begin{bmatrix} U_1 \\ U_2 \end{bmatrix} = \begin{bmatrix} 10 \\ 0 \end{bmatrix}$$

with the initial conditions $^0\mathbf{U} = {}^0\dot{\mathbf{U}} = \mathbf{0}$. Use the central difference method to calculate the response of the system to a reasonable accuracy for time 0 to time 4.

9.2. Consider the same system equations as in Exercise 9.1 but use the trapezoidal rule to calculate the system response.

9.3. Develop a computational scheme for which the Wilson θ method and the trapezoidal rule are special cases. Give the computational scheme in tabular form (as Table 9.3 for the Wilson θ method).

9.4. Consider a single degree of freedom system. Show that by selecting in the Newmark method the specific values $\alpha = 0$, $\delta = \frac{1}{2}$, the equations of the central difference method are obtained.

9.5. Consider the single degree of freedom equation

$$2\ddot{U} + 4U = 0; \qquad {}^0U = 10^{-12}; \qquad {}^0\dot{U} = 0$$

(which is obtained by setting $U_1 = 0$ in the system in Exercise 9.1).

Assume that the time step used in the time integration is $1.01 \times \Delta t_{cr}$. Estimate after how many time steps the solution will reach overflow (which is, for the computer used, given by 10^{30}).

9.6. Solve the equations given in Exercise 9.1 by using the central difference method for the time integration of U_1 and the trapezoidal rule for the time integration of U_2.

9.3 MODE SUPERPOSITION

Tables 9.2 to 9.4, summarizing the implicit direct integration schemes, show that if a diagonal mass matrix and no damping are assumed, the number of operations for one time step are—as a rough estimate—somewhat larger than $2nm_K$, where n and m_K are the order and half-bandwidth of the stiffness matrix considered, respectively (assuming constant column heights or a mean half-bandwidth, see Section 8.2.3). The $2nm_K$ operations are required for the solution of the system equations in each time step. The initial triangular factorization of the effective stiffness matrix requires additional operations. Furthermore, if a consistent mass matrix is used or a damping matrix is included in the analysis, an additional number of operations proportional to nm_K is required per time step. Therefore, neglecting the operations for the initial calculations, a total number of about $\alpha nm_K s$ operations is required in the complete integration, where α depends on the characteristics of the matrices used and s is the number of time steps.

Using the central difference method, the number of operations per step is usually much less (for the reasons given in Section 9.2.1).

These considerations show that the number of operations required in a direct integration solution are directly proportional to the number of time steps and that the use of implicit direct integration can be expected to be effective only when the response for a relatively short duration (i.e., for not too many time steps) is required. If the integration must be carried out for many time steps, it may be more effective to first transform the equilibrium equations (9.1) into a form in which the step-by-step solution is less costly. In particular, since the number of operations required is directly proportional to the half-bandwidth m_K of the stiffness matrix, a reduction in m_K would decrease proportionally the cost of the step-by-step solution.

It is important at this stage to fully recognize what we have proposed to pursue. We recall that (9.1) are the equilibrium equations obtained when the finite element interpolation functions are used in the evaluation of the virtual work equation (4.7) (see Section 4.2.1). The resulting matrices $\mathbf{K}$, $\mathbf{M}$, and $\mathbf{C}$ have a bandwidth that is determined by the numbering of the finite element nodal points. Therefore, the topology of the finite element mesh determines the order and bandwidth of the system matrices. In order to reduce the bandwidth of the system matrices, we may rearrange the nodal point numbering; however, there is a limit on the minimum bandwidth that can be obtained in this way, and we therefore set out to follow a different procedure.

9.3.1 Change of Basis to Modal Generalized Displacements

We propose to transform the equilibrium equations into a more effective form for direct integration by using the following transformation on the n finite element nodal point displacements in $\mathbf{U}$,

$$\mathbf{U}(t) = \mathbf{PX}(t) \tag{9.30}$$

where $\mathbf{P}$ is an $n \times n$ square matrix and $\mathbf{X}(t)$ is a time-dependent vector of order n. The transformation matrix $\mathbf{P}$ is still unknown and will have to be determined. The components of $\mathbf{X}$ are referred to as *generalized displacements*. Substituting (9.30) into (9.1) and premultiplying by $\mathbf{P}^T$, we obtain

$$\tilde{\mathbf{M}}\ddot{\mathbf{X}}(t) + \tilde{\mathbf{C}}\dot{\mathbf{X}}(t) + \tilde{\mathbf{K}}\mathbf{X}(t) = \tilde{\mathbf{R}}(t) \tag{9.31}$$

where $\tilde{\mathbf{M}} = \mathbf{P}^T\mathbf{M}\mathbf{P};$ $\tilde{\mathbf{C}} = \mathbf{P}^T\mathbf{C}\mathbf{P};$ $\tilde{\mathbf{K}} = \mathbf{P}^T\mathbf{K}\mathbf{P};$ $\tilde{\mathbf{R}} = \mathbf{P}^T\mathbf{R}$ (9.32)

It should be noted that this transformation is obtained by substituting (9.30) into (4.8) to express the element displacements in terms of the generalized displacements,

$$\mathbf{u}^{(m)}(x, y, z, t) = \mathbf{H}^{(m)}\mathbf{P}\mathbf{X}(t) \tag{9.33}$$

and then using (9.33) in the virtual work equation (4.7). Therefore, in essence, to obtain (9.31) from (9.1), a change of basis from the finite element displacement basis to a generalized displacement basis has been performed (see Section 2.5).

The objective of the transformation is to obtain new system stiffness, mass, and damping matrices $\tilde{\mathbf{K}}$, $\tilde{\mathbf{M}}$, and $\tilde{\mathbf{C}}$, which have a smaller bandwidth than the original system matrices, and the transformation matrix $\mathbf{P}$ should be selected accordingly. In addition, it should be noted that $\mathbf{P}$ must be nonsingular (i.e., the rank of $\mathbf{P}$ must be n) in order to have a unique relation between any vectors $\mathbf{U}$ and $\mathbf{X}$ as expressed in (9.30).

In theory, there can be many different transformation matrices $\mathbf{P}$, which would reduce the bandwidth of the system matrices. However, in practice, an effective transformation matrix is established using the displacement solutions of the free-vibration equilibrium equations with damping neglected,

$$\mathbf{M}\ddot{\mathbf{U}} + \mathbf{K}\mathbf{U} = \mathbf{0} \tag{9.34}$$

The solution to (9.34) can be postulated to be of the form

$$\mathbf{U} = \boldsymbol{\phi} \sin \omega(t - t_0) \tag{9.35}$$

where $\boldsymbol{\phi}$ is a vector of order n, t is the time variable, t_0 is a time constant, and ω is a constant identified to represent the frequency of vibration (radians/second) of the vector $\boldsymbol{\phi}$.

Substituting (9.35) into (9.34), we obtain the generalized eigenproblem, from which $\boldsymbol{\phi}$ and ω must be determined,

$$\mathbf{K}\boldsymbol{\phi} = \omega^2\mathbf{M}\boldsymbol{\phi} \tag{9.36}$$

The eigenproblem in (9.36) yields the n eigensolutions $(\omega_1^2, \boldsymbol{\phi}_1), (\omega_2^2, \boldsymbol{\phi}_2), \ldots, (\omega_n^2, \boldsymbol{\phi}_n)$, where the eigenvectors are $\mathbf{M}$-orthonormalized (see Section 10.2.1); i.e.,

$$\boldsymbol{\phi}_i^T\mathbf{M}\boldsymbol{\phi}_j \begin{cases} = 1; & i = j \\ = 0; & i \neq j \end{cases} \tag{9.37}$$

and $$0 \leq \omega_1^2 \leq \omega_2^2 \leq \omega_3^2 \leq \cdots \leq \omega_n^2 \tag{9.38}$$

The vector $\boldsymbol{\phi}_i$ is called the ith-mode shape vector, and ω_i is the corresponding frequency of vibration (radians/second). It should be emphasized that (9.34) is satisfied using any of the n displacement solutions $\boldsymbol{\phi}_i \sin \omega_i(t - t_0)$, $i = 1, 2, \ldots, n$. For a physical interpretation of ω_i and $\boldsymbol{\phi}_i$, see Example 9.6 and Exercise 9.8.

Defining a matrix $\mathbf{\Phi}$ whose columns are the eigenvectors $\mathbf{\phi}_i$ and a diagonal matrix $\mathbf{\Omega}^2$, which stores the eigenvalues ω_i^2 on its diagonal; i.e.,

$$\mathbf{\Phi} = [\mathbf{\phi}_1, \mathbf{\phi}_2, \ldots, \mathbf{\phi}_n]; \qquad \mathbf{\Omega}^2 = \begin{bmatrix} \omega_1^2 & & & \\ & \omega_2^2 & & \\ & & \cdot & \\ & & & \cdot \\ & & & & \omega_n^2 \end{bmatrix} \tag{9.39}$$

we can write the n solutions to (9.36) as

$$\mathbf{K}\mathbf{\Phi} = \mathbf{M}\mathbf{\Phi}\mathbf{\Omega}^2 \tag{9.40}$$

Since the eigenvectors are $\mathbf{M}$-orthonormal, we have

$$\mathbf{\Phi}^T\mathbf{K}\mathbf{\Phi} = \mathbf{\Omega}^2; \qquad \mathbf{\Phi}^T\mathbf{M}\mathbf{\Phi} = \mathbf{I} \tag{9.41}$$

It is now apparent that the matrix $\mathbf{\Phi}$ would be a suitable transformation matrix $\mathbf{P}$ in (9.30). Using

$$\mathbf{U}(t) = \mathbf{\Phi}\mathbf{X}(t) \tag{9.42}$$

we obtain equilibrium equations that correspond to the modal generalized displacements

$$\ddot{\mathbf{X}}(t) + \mathbf{\Phi}^T\mathbf{C}\mathbf{\Phi}\dot{\mathbf{X}}(t) + \mathbf{\Omega}^2\mathbf{X}(t) = \mathbf{\Phi}^T\mathbf{R}(t) \tag{9.43}$$

The initial conditions on $\mathbf{X}(t)$ are obtained using (9.42) and the $\mathbf{M}$-orthonormality of $\mathbf{\Phi}$; i.e., at time 0 we have

$$^0\mathbf{X} = \mathbf{\Phi}^T\mathbf{M}\,{}^0\mathbf{U}; \qquad ^0\dot{\mathbf{X}} = \mathbf{\Phi}^T\mathbf{M}\,{}^0\dot{\mathbf{U}} \tag{9.44}$$

The equations in (9.43) show that if a damping matrix is not included in the analysis, the finite element equilibrium equations are decoupled when using in the transformation matrix $\mathbf{P}$ the free-vibration mode shapes of the finite element system. Since the derivation of the damping matrix can in many cases not be carried out explicitly and the damping effects can be included only approximately, it is reasonable to use a damping matrix that includes all required effects but at the same time allows an effective solution of the equilibrium equations. In many analyses damping effects are neglected altogether, and it is this case that we shall discuss first.

EXAMPLE 9.6:   Calculate the transformation matrix $\mathbf{\Phi}$ for the problem considered in Examples 9.1 to 9.4 and thus establish the decoupled equations of equilibrium in the basis of mode shape vectors.

For the system under consideration we have

$$\mathbf{K} = \begin{bmatrix} 6 & -2 \\ -2 & 4 \end{bmatrix}; \qquad \mathbf{M} = \begin{bmatrix} 2 & 0 \\ 0 & 1 \end{bmatrix}; \qquad \mathbf{R} = \begin{bmatrix} 0 \\ 10 \end{bmatrix}$$

The generalized eigenproblem to be solved is therefore

$$\begin{bmatrix} 6 & -2 \\ -2 & 4 \end{bmatrix}\mathbf{\phi} = \omega^2 \begin{bmatrix} 2 & 0 \\ 0 & 1 \end{bmatrix}\mathbf{\phi}$$

The solution is obtained by one of the methods given in Chapters 10 and 11. Here we simply give the two solutions without derivations:

$$\omega_1^2 = 2; \qquad \boldsymbol{\Phi}_1 = \begin{bmatrix} \dfrac{1}{\sqrt{3}} \\[2mm] \dfrac{1}{\sqrt{3}} \end{bmatrix}$$

$$\omega_2^2 = 5; \qquad \boldsymbol{\Phi}_2 = \begin{bmatrix} \dfrac{1}{2}\sqrt{\dfrac{2}{3}} \\[4mm] -\sqrt{\dfrac{2}{3}} \end{bmatrix}$$

Therefore, considering the free-vibration equilibrium equations of the system

$$\begin{bmatrix} 2 & 0 \\ 0 & 1 \end{bmatrix} \ddot{\mathbf{U}}(t) + \begin{bmatrix} 6 & -2 \\ -2 & 4 \end{bmatrix} \mathbf{U}(t) = \mathbf{0} \tag{a}$$

the following two solutions are possible:

$$\mathbf{U}_1(t) = \begin{bmatrix} \dfrac{1}{\sqrt{3}} \\[2mm] \dfrac{1}{\sqrt{3}} \end{bmatrix} \sin \sqrt{2}\,(t - t_0^1) \quad \text{and} \quad \mathbf{U}_2(t) = \begin{bmatrix} \dfrac{1}{2}\sqrt{\dfrac{2}{3}} \\[4mm] -\sqrt{\dfrac{2}{3}} \end{bmatrix} \sin \sqrt{5}\,(t - t_0^2)$$

That the vectors $\mathbf{U}_1(t)$ and $\mathbf{U}_2(t)$ indeed satisfy the relation in (a) can be verified simply by substituting $\mathbf{U}_1$ and $\mathbf{U}_2$ into the equilibrium equations. The actual solution to the equations in (a) is of the form

$$\mathbf{U}(t) = \alpha \begin{bmatrix} \dfrac{1}{\sqrt{3}} \\[2mm] \dfrac{1}{\sqrt{3}} \end{bmatrix} \sin \sqrt{2}\,(t - t_0^1) + \beta \begin{bmatrix} \dfrac{1}{2}\sqrt{\dfrac{2}{3}} \\[4mm] -\sqrt{\dfrac{2}{3}} \end{bmatrix} \sin \sqrt{5}\,(t - t_0^2)$$

where α, β, t_0^1, and t_0^2 are determined by the initial conditions on $\mathbf{U}$ and $\dot{\mathbf{U}}$. In particular, if we impose initial conditions corresponding to α (or β) only, we find that the system vibrates in the corresponding eigenvector with frequency $\sqrt{2}$ rad/sec (or $\sqrt{5}$ rad/sec). The general procedure of solution for α, β, t_1^0, and t_2^0 is discussed in Section 9.3.2.

Having evaluated $(\omega_1^2, \boldsymbol{\Phi}_1)$ and $(\omega_2^2, \boldsymbol{\Phi}_2)$ for the problem in Examples 9.1 to 9.4, we arrive at the following equilibrium equations in the basis of eigenvectors:

$$\ddot{\mathbf{X}}(t) + \begin{bmatrix} 2 & 0 \\ 0 & 5 \end{bmatrix} \mathbf{X}(t) = \begin{bmatrix} \dfrac{1}{\sqrt{3}} & \dfrac{1}{\sqrt{3}} \\[4mm] \dfrac{1}{2}\sqrt{\dfrac{2}{3}} & -\sqrt{\dfrac{2}{3}} \end{bmatrix} \begin{bmatrix} 0 \\ 10 \end{bmatrix}$$

or

$$\ddot{\mathbf{X}}(t) + \begin{bmatrix} 2 & 0 \\ 0 & 5 \end{bmatrix} \mathbf{X}(t) = \begin{bmatrix} \dfrac{10}{\sqrt{3}} \\[4mm] -10\sqrt{\dfrac{2}{3}} \end{bmatrix}$$

9.3.2 Analysis with Damping Neglected

If velocity-dependent damping effects are not included in the analysis, (9.43) reduces to

$$\ddot{\mathbf{X}}(t) + \mathbf{\Omega}^2 \mathbf{X}(t) = \mathbf{\Phi}^T \mathbf{R}(t) \tag{9.45}$$

i.e., n individual equations of the form

$$\left.\begin{array}{l} \ddot{x}_i(t) + \omega_i^2 x_i(t) = r_i(t) \\ r_i(t) = \mathbf{\phi}_i^T \mathbf{R}(t) \end{array}\right\} \quad i = 1, 2, \ldots, n \tag{9.46}$$

with
$$x_i|_{t=0} = \mathbf{\phi}_i^T \mathbf{M}\,^0\mathbf{U}$$
$$\dot{x}_i|_{t=0} = \mathbf{\phi}_i^T \mathbf{M}\,^0\dot{\mathbf{U}}$$

We note that the ith typical equation in (9.46) is the equilibrium equation of a single degree of freedom system with unit mass and stiffness ω_i^2 and initial conditions established from (9.44). The solution to each equation in (9.46) can be obtained using the integration algorithms in Tables 9.1 to 9.4 or can be calculated using the Duhamel integral:

$$x_i(t) = \frac{1}{\omega_i} \int_0^t r_i(\tau) \sin \omega_i(t - \tau)\, d\tau + \alpha_i \sin \omega_i t + \beta_i \cos \omega_i t \tag{9.47}$$

where α_i and β_i are determined from the initial conditions in (9.46). The Duhamel integral in (9.47) may have to be evaluated numerically. In addition, it should be noted that various other integration methods could also be used in the solution of (9.46).

For the complete response, the solution to all n equations in (9.46), $i = 1, 2, \ldots, n$, must be calculated and then the finite element nodal point displacements are obtained by superposition of the response in each mode; i.e., using (9.42), we obtain

$$\mathbf{U}(t) = \sum_{i=1}^{n} \mathbf{\phi}_i x_i(t) \tag{9.48}$$

Therefore, in summary, the response analysis by mode superposition requires, first, the solution of the eigenvalues and eigenvectors of the problem in (9.36), then the solution of the decoupled equilibrium equations in (9.46), and finally, the superposition of the response in each eigenvector as expressed in (9.48). In the analysis, the eigenvectors are the free-vibration mode shapes of the finite element assemblage. As mentioned earlier, the choice between mode superposition analysis and direct integration described in Section 9.2 is merely one of numerical effectiveness. The solutions obtained using either procedure are identical within the numerical errors of the time integration schemes used [if the same time integration methods are used in direct integration and the solution of (9.46), the same numerical errors are present] and the round-off errors in the computer.

EXAMPLE 9.7: Use mode superposition to calculate the displacement response of the system considered in Examples 9.1 to 9.4 and 9.6.

(1) Calculate the exact response by integrating each of the two decoupled equilibrium equations exactly.

(2) Use the Newmark method with time step $\Delta t = 0.28$ for the time integration.

We established the decoupled equilibrium equations of the system under consideration in Example 9.6; i.e., the two equilibrium equations to be solved are

$$\ddot{x}_1 + 2x_1 = \frac{10}{\sqrt{3}}; \ \ddot{x}_2 + 5x_2 = -10\sqrt{\frac{2}{3}} \tag{a}$$

The initial conditions on the system are $\mathbf{U}\,|_{t=0} = \mathbf{0}$, $\dot{\mathbf{U}}\,|_{t=0} = \mathbf{0}$, and hence, using (9.46), we have

$$x_1\,|_{t=0} = 0 \qquad \dot{x}_1\,|_{t=0} = 0 \tag{b}$$
$$x_2\,|_{t=0} = 0 \qquad \dot{x}_2\,|_{t=0} = 0$$

Also, to obtain $\mathbf{U}$ we need to use the relation in (9.42), which, using the eigenvectors calculated in Example 9.6, gives

$$\mathbf{U}(t) = \begin{bmatrix} \dfrac{1}{\sqrt{3}} & \dfrac{1}{2}\sqrt{\dfrac{2}{3}} \\[3mm] \dfrac{1}{\sqrt{3}} & -\sqrt{\dfrac{2}{3}} \end{bmatrix} \mathbf{X}(t) \tag{c}$$

The exact solutions to the equations in (a) and (b) are

$$x_1 = \frac{5}{\sqrt{3}}(1 - \cos\sqrt{2}\,t); \ x_2 = 2\sqrt{\frac{2}{3}}(-1 + \cos\sqrt{5}\,t) \tag{d}$$

Hence, using (c), we have

$$\mathbf{U}(t) = \begin{bmatrix} \dfrac{1}{\sqrt{3}} & \dfrac{1}{2}\sqrt{\dfrac{2}{3}} \\[3mm] \dfrac{1}{\sqrt{3}} & -\sqrt{\dfrac{2}{3}} \end{bmatrix} \begin{bmatrix} \dfrac{5}{\sqrt{3}}(1 - \cos\sqrt{2}t) \\[3mm] 2\sqrt{\dfrac{2}{3}}(-1 + \cos\sqrt{5}t) \end{bmatrix} \tag{e}$$

Evaluating the displacements from (e) for times $\Delta t, 2\Delta t, \ldots, 12\Delta t$, where $\Delta t = 0.28$, we obtain

Time	Δt	$2\Delta t$	$3\Delta t$	$4\Delta t$	$5\Delta t$	$6\Delta t$	$7\Delta t$	$8\Delta t$	$9\Delta t$	$10\Delta t$	$11\Delta t$	$12\Delta t$
${}^t\mathbf{U}$	0.003	0.038	0.176	0.486	0.996	1.66	2.338	2.861	3.052	2.806	2.131	1.157
	0.382	1.41	2.78	4.09	5.00	5.29	4.986	4.277	3.457	2.806	2.484	2.489

The results obtained are compared in Fig. E9.7 with the response predicted using the central difference, Houbolt, Wilson θ, and Newmark methods in Examples 9.1 to 9.4, respectively. The discussion in Section 9.4 will show that the time step Δt selected for the direct integrations is relatively large, and with this in mind it may be noted that the direct integration schemes predict a fair approximation to the exact response of the system.

Instead of evaluating the exact response as given in (d) we could use a numerical integration scheme to solve the equations in (a). Here we employ the Newmark method and obtain

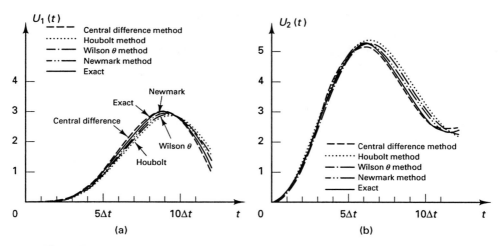

Figure E9.7   Displacement response of system considered in Examples 9.1, 9.2, 9.3, 9.4, and 9.7

Time	Δt	$2\Delta t$	$3\Delta t$	$4\Delta t$	$5\Delta t$	$6\Delta t$
$x_1(t)$	0.2258	0.8199	1.807	2.379	4.123	5.064
$x_2(t)$	−0.3046	−0.7920	−2.1239	−2.939	−3.258	−2.632

	$7\Delta t$	$8\Delta t$	$9\Delta t$	$10\Delta t$	$11\Delta t$	$12\Delta t$
	5.579	5.774	5.521	4.855	3.866	2.773
	−2.161	−1.156	−0.3307	−0.004083	−0.2482	−1.088

The solution for $U_1(t)$ and $U_2(t)$ is now evaluated by substituting for $\mathbf{X}(t)$ in the relation given in (c). As expected, it is found that the displacement response thus predicted is the same as the response obtained when using the Newmark method in direct integration.

As discussed so far, the only difference between a mode superposition and a direct integration analysis is that prior to the time integration, a change of basis is carried out, namely, from the finite element coordinate basis to the basis of eigenvectors of the generalized eigenproblem $\mathbf{K}\boldsymbol{\phi} = \omega^2 \mathbf{M}\boldsymbol{\phi}$. Since mathematically the same space is spanned by the n eigenvectors as by the n nodal point finite element displacements, the same solution must be obtained in both analyses. The choice of whether to use direct integration or mode superposition will therefore be decided by considerations of effectiveness only. However, this choice can only be made once an important additional aspect of mode superposition has been presented. This aspect relates to the distribution and frequency content of the loading and renders the mode superposition solution of some structures much more effective than use of direct integration.

Consider the decoupled equilibrium equations in (9.46). We note that if $r_i(t) = 0$, $i = 1, \ldots, n$, and either the initial displacements $^0\mathbf{U}$ or the initial velocities $^0\dot{\mathbf{U}}$ are a multiple of $\boldsymbol{\phi}_j$, and only of $\boldsymbol{\phi}_j$, then only $x_j(t)$ is nonzero and the structure will vibrate only in this mode shape. In practice, such transient response will decrease in magnitude due to damping (see Section 9.3.3) and frequently the effect of the external loading is more important.

Therefore, consider next that $^0\mathbf{U} = {}^0\dot{\mathbf{U}} = \mathbf{0}$, and that the loading is of the form $\mathbf{R}(t) = \mathbf{M}\boldsymbol{\phi}_j f(t)$, where $f(t)$ is an arbitrary function of t. In such a case, since $\boldsymbol{\phi}_i^T\mathbf{M}\boldsymbol{\phi}_j = \delta_{ij}$ (δ_{ij} = Kronecker delta), we would have that only $x_j(t)$ is nonzero. These are rather stringent conditions, and in general analysis can hardly be expected to apply exactly to many of the n equations in (9.46) because the loading is in general arbitrary. However, in addition to the fact that the loading may be nearly orthogonal to $\boldsymbol{\phi}_i$, it is also the frequency content of the loading that determines whether the ith equation in (9.46) will contribute significantly to the response. Namely, the response $x_i(t)$ is relatively large if the excitation frequency contained in r_i lies near ω_i.

To demonstrate these basic considerations we introduce the following example.

EXAMPLE 9.8: Consider a one degree of freedom system with the equilibrium equation

$$\ddot{x}(t) + \omega^2 x(t) = R \sin \hat{\omega}t$$

and initial conditions

$$x\big|_{t=0} = 0, \qquad \dot{x}\big|_{t=0} = 1 \tag{a}$$

Use the Duhamel integral to calculate the displacement response.

We note that the system is subjected to a periodic force input and a nonzero initial velocity. Using the relation in (9.47), we obtain

$$x(t) = \frac{R}{\omega} \int_0^t \sin \hat{\omega}\tau \sin \omega(t - \tau)\, d\tau + \alpha \sin \omega t + \beta \cos \omega t$$

Evaluating the integral, we obtain

$$x(t) = \frac{R/\omega^2}{1 - \hat{\omega}^2/\omega^2} \sin \hat{\omega}t + \alpha \sin \omega t + \beta \cos \omega t \tag{b}$$

We now need to use the initial conditions to evaluate α and β. The solution at time $t = 0$ is

$$x\big|_{t=0} = \beta$$

$$\dot{x}\big|_{t=0} = \frac{R\hat{\omega}/\omega^2}{1 - \hat{\omega}^2/\omega^2} + \alpha\omega$$

Using the conditions in (a), we obtain

$$\beta = 0; \qquad \alpha = \frac{1}{\omega} - \frac{R\hat{\omega}/\omega^3}{1 - \hat{\omega}^2/\omega^2}$$

Substituting for α and β into (b), we thus have

$$x(t) = \frac{R/\omega^2}{1 - \hat{\omega}^2/\omega^2} \sin \hat{\omega}t + \left(\frac{1}{\omega} - \frac{R\hat{\omega}/\omega^3}{1 - \hat{\omega}^2/\omega^2}\right) \sin \omega t$$

which may also be written as

$$x(t) = Dx_{\text{stat}} + x_{\text{trans}} \tag{d}$$

where x_{stat} is the static response of the system,

$$x_{\text{stat}} = \frac{R}{\omega^2} \sin \hat{\omega}t$$

x_{trans} is the transient response,

$$x_{\text{trans}} = \left(\frac{1}{\omega} - \frac{R\hat{\omega}/\omega^3}{1 - \hat{\omega}^2/\omega^2} \right) \sin \omega t$$

and *D is the dynamic load factor,* indicating resonance when $\hat{\omega} = \omega$,

$$D = \frac{1}{1 - \hat{\omega}^2/\omega^2}$$

The analysis of the response of the single degree of freedom system considered in this example showed that the complete response is the sum of two contributions:

1. A dynamic response obtained by multiplying the static response by a dynamic load factor (this is the particular solution of the governing differential equation), and
2. An additional dynamic response which we called the transient response.

These observations pertain also to an actual practical analysis of a multiple degree of freedom system because, first, the complete response is obtained as a superposition of the response measured in each modal degree of freedom, and second, the actual loading can be represented in a Fourier decomposition as a superposition of harmonic sine and cosine contributions. Therefore, the above two observations apply to each modal response corresponding to each Fourier component of the loading.

An important difference between an actual practical response analysis and the solution in Example 9.8 is, however, that in practice the effect of damping must be included as discussed in Section 9.3.3. The presence of damping reduces the dynamic load factor (which then cannot be infinite) and damps out the transient response.

Figure 9.3 shows the dynamic load factor as a function of $\hat{\omega}/\omega$ (and the damping ratio ξ discussed in Section 9.3.3). The information in Fig. 9.3 is obtained by solving (9.54) as in Example 9.8. If we apply the information given in this figure to the analysis of an actual practical system, we recognize that the response in the modes with $\hat{\omega}/\omega$ large is negligible (the loads vary so rapidly that the system does not move), and that the static response is measured when $\hat{\omega}/\omega$ is close to zero (the loads vary so slowly that the system simply follows the loads statically). Therefore, in the analysis of a multiple degree of freedom system, the response in the high frequencies of the system (that are much larger than the highest frequencies contained in the loads) is simply a static response.

The essence of a mode superposition solution of a dynamic response is that frequently only a small fraction of the total number of decoupled equations needs to be considered in order to obtain a good approximate solution to the exact solution of (9.1). Most frequently, only the first p equilibrium equations in (9.46) need to be used; i.e., we need to include in the analysis the equations (9.46) only for $i = 1, 2, \ldots, p$, where $p \ll n$, in order to obtain a good approximate solution. This means that we need to solve only for the lowest p eigenvalues and corresponding eigenvectors of the problem in (9.36) and we only sum in

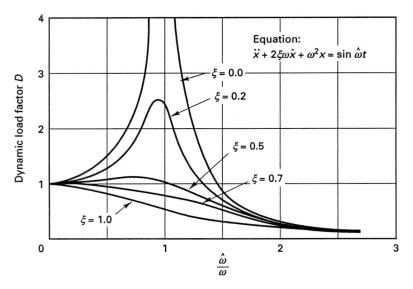

Figure 9.3   The dynamic load factor

(9.48) the response in the first p modes; i.e., we use

$$\mathbf{U}^p(t) = \sum_{i=1}^{p} \boldsymbol{\phi}_i x_i(t) \qquad (9.49)$$

where $\mathbf{U}^p$ approximates the exact solution $\mathbf{U}$ of (9.1).

The reason that only the lowest modes are considered in a practical finite element analysis lies in the complete modeling process for dynamic analysis. Namely, so far, we have been concerned only with the exact solution of the finite element system equilibrium equations in (9.1). However, what we really want to obtain is a good approximation to the actual exact response of the mathematical model under consideration. We showed in Section 4.3.3 that under certain conditions the finite element analysis can be understood to be a Ritz analysis. In such case, upper bounds to the exact frequencies of the mathematical model are obtained. Moreover, in general, even when the monotonic convergence conditions are not satisfied, the finite element analysis approximates the lowest exact frequencies best, and little or no accuracy can be expected in approximating the higher frequencies and mode shapes. Therefore, there is usually little justification for including the dynamic response in the mode shapes with the high frequencies in the analysis. In fact, the finite element mesh should be chosen such that all important exact frequencies and vibration mode shapes of the mathematical model are well approximated, and then the solution needs to be calculated including only the response in these modes. However, this can be achieved precisely using mode superposition analysis by considering only the important modes of the finite element system.

It is primarily because of the fact that in a mode superposition analysis only a few modes may need to be considered that the mode superposition procedure can be much more effective than direct integration. However, it also follows that the effectiveness of mode superposition depends on the number of modes that must be included in the analysis. *In general, the structure considered and the spatial distribution and frequency content of the loading determine the number of modes to be used.* For earthquake loading, in some cases only the 10 lowest modes need to be considered, although the order of the system n may be quite large. On the other hand, for blast or shock loading, many more modes generally need to be included, and p may be as large as $2n/3$. Finally, in vibration excitation analysis, only a few intermediate frequencies may be excited, such as all frequencies between the lower and upper frequency limits ω_l and ω_u, respectively.

Considering the problem of selecting the number of modes to be included in the mode superposition analysis, it should always be kept in mind that an approximate solution to the dynamic equilibrium equations in (9.1) is sought. Therefore, if not enough modes are considered, the equations in (9.1) are not solved accurately enough. But this means, in effect, that equilibrium, including the inertia forces, is not satisfied for the approximate response calculated. Denoting by $\mathbf{U}^p$ the response predicted by mode superposition when p modes are considered, an indication of the accuracy of analysis at any time t is obtained by calculating an error measure ϵ^p, such as

$$\epsilon^p(t) = \frac{\| \mathbf{R}(t) - [\mathbf{M}\ddot{\mathbf{U}}^p(t) + \mathbf{K}\mathbf{U}^p(t)] \|_2}{\| \mathbf{R}(t) \|_2} \tag{9.50}$$

where we assume that $\| \mathbf{R}(t) \|_2 \neq 0$. If a good approximate solution of the system equilibrium equations in (9.1) has been obtained, $\epsilon^p(t)$ will be small at any time t. But $\mathbf{U}^p(t)$ must have been obtained by an accurate calculation of the response in each of the p modes considered because in this way the only error is due to not including enough modes in the analysis.

The error measure ϵ^p calculated in (9.50) determines how well equilibrium including inertia forces is satisfied and is a measure of the nodal point loads not balanced by inertia and elastic nodal point forces [see (9.2)]. Alternatively, we may say that ϵ^p is a measure of that part of the external load vector that has not been included in the mode superposition analysis. Since we have $\mathbf{R} = \Sigma_{i=1}^n r_i \mathbf{M} \boldsymbol{\phi}_i$, we can evaluate

$$\Delta \mathbf{R} = \mathbf{R} - \sum_{i=1}^{p} r_i (\mathbf{M} \boldsymbol{\phi}_i) \tag{9.51}$$

For a properly modeled problem the response to $\Delta \mathbf{R}$ should be at most a static response. Therefore, a good correction $\Delta \mathbf{U}$ to the mode superposition solution $\mathbf{U}^p$ can be obtained from

$$\mathbf{K} \, \Delta \mathbf{U}(t) = \Delta \mathbf{R}(t) \tag{9.52}$$

where the solution of (9.52) may be required only for certain times at which the maximum response is measured. We call $\Delta \mathbf{U}$ calculated from (9.52) the *static correction.*

In summary, therefore, assuming that the decoupled equations in (9.46) have been solved accurately, the errors in a mode superposition analysis using $p < n$ are due to the fact that not enough modes have been used, whereas the errors in a direct integration analysis arise because too large a time step is employed.

From the preceding discussion it may appear that the mode superposition procedure has an inherent advantage over direct integration in that the response corresponding to the higher, probably inaccurate frequencies of the finite element system is not included in the analysis. However, assuming that in the finite element analysis all important frequencies are represented accurately, meaning that negligible dynamic response is calculated in the modes that are not represented accurately, the inclusion of the finite element system dynamic response in these latter modes will not seriously affect the accuracy of the solution. In addition, we will discuss in Section 9.4 that in implicit direct integration, advantage can be taken also of integrating accurately only the first p equations in (9.46). This is achieved by using an unconditionally stable direct integration method and selecting an appropriate integration time step Δt, which, in general, is much larger than the integration step used with a conditionally stable integration scheme.

9.3.3 Analysis with Damping Included

The general form of the equilibrium equations of the finite element system in the basis of the eigenvectors $\boldsymbol{\phi}_i$, $i = 1, \ldots, n$ was given in (9.43), which shows that provided damping effects are neglected, the equilibrium equations decouple and the time integration can be carried out individually for each equation. Considering the analysis of systems in which damping effects cannot be neglected, we still would like to deal with decoupled equilibrium equations in (9.43), and use essentially the same computational procedure whether damping effects are included or neglected. In general, the damping matrix $\mathbf{C}$ cannot be constructed from element damping matrices, such as the mass and stiffness matrices of the element assemblage, and it is introduced to approximate the overall energy dissipation during the system response (see, for example, R. W. Clough and J. Penzien [A]). The mode superposition analysis is particularly effective if it can be assumed that damping is proportional, in which case

$$\boldsymbol{\phi}_i^T \mathbf{C} \boldsymbol{\phi}_j = 2\omega_i \xi_i \delta_{ij} \tag{9.53}$$

where ξ_i is a modal damping parameter and δ_{ij} is the Kronecker delta ($\delta_{ij} = 1$ for $i = j$, $\delta_{ij} = 0$ for $i \neq j$). Therefore, using (9.53), it is assumed that the eigenvectors $\boldsymbol{\phi}_i$, $i = 1$, $2, \ldots, n$, are also $\mathbf{C}$-orthogonal and the equations in (9.43) reduce to n equations of the form

$$\ddot{x}_i(t) + 2\omega_i \xi_i \dot{x}_i(t) + \omega_i^2 x_i(t) = r_i(t) \tag{9.54}$$

where $r_i(t)$ and the initial conditions on $x_i(t)$ have already been defined in (9.46). We note that (9.54) is the equilibrium equation governing motion of the single degree of freedom system considered in (9.46) when ξ_i is the damping ratio.

If the relation in (9.53) is used to account for damping effects, the procedure of solution of the finite element equilibrium equations in (9.43) is the same as in the case when damping is neglected (see Section 9.3.2), except that the response in each mode is obtained by solving (9.54). This response can be calculated using an integration scheme such as those given in Tables 9.1 to 9.4 or by evaluating the Duhamel integral to obtain

$$x_i(t) = \frac{1}{\bar{\omega}_i} \int_0^t r_i(\tau) e^{-\xi_i \omega_i(t-\tau)} \sin \bar{\omega}_i(t - \tau) \, d\tau + e^{-\xi_i \omega_i t}(\alpha_i \sin \bar{\omega}_i t + \beta_i \cos \bar{\omega}_i t) \tag{9.55}$$

where
$$\bar{\omega}_i = \omega_i \sqrt{1 - \xi_i^2}$$

and α_i and β_i are calculated using the initial conditions in (9.46).

In considering the implications of using (9.53) to take account of damping effects, the following observations are made. First, the assumption in (9.53) means that the total damping in the structure is the sum of individual damping in each mode. The damping in one mode could be observed, for example, by imposing initial conditions corresponding to that mode only (say $^0\mathbf{U} = \boldsymbol{\phi}_i$ for mode i) and measuring the amplitude decay during the free damped vibration. In fact, the ability to measure values for the damping ratios ξ_i, and thus approximate in many cases in a realistic manner the damping behavior of the complete structural system, is an important consideration. A second observation relating to the mode superposition analysis is that for the numerical solution of the finite element equilibrium equations in (9.1) using the decoupled equations in (9.54), we do not calculate the damping matrix $\mathbf{C}$ but only the stiffness and mass matrices $\mathbf{K}$ and $\mathbf{M}$.

Damping effects can therefore readily be taken into account in mode superposition analysis provided that (9.53) is satisfied. However, assume that it would be numerically more effective to use direct step-by-step integration when realistic damping ratios ξ_i, $i = 1, \ldots, r$ are known. In that case, it is necessary to evaluate the matrix $\mathbf{C}$ explicitly, which when substituted into (9.53) yields the established damping ratios ξ_i. If $r = 2$, Rayleigh damping can be assumed, which is of the form

$$\mathbf{C} = \alpha \mathbf{M} + \beta \mathbf{K} \tag{9.56}$$

where α and β are constants to be determined from two given damping ratios that correspond to two unequal frequencies of vibration.

EXAMPLE 9.9:   Assume that for a multiple degree of freedom system $\omega_1 = 2$ and $\omega_2 = 3$, and that in those two modes we require 2 percent and 10 percent critical damping, respectively; i.e., we require $\xi_1 = 0.02$ and $\xi_2 = 0.10$. Establish the constants α and β for Rayleigh damping in order that a direct step-by-step integration can be carried out.

In Rayleigh damping we have

$$\mathbf{C} = \alpha \mathbf{M} + \beta \mathbf{K} \tag{a}$$

But using the relation in (9.53) we obtain, using (a),

$$\boldsymbol{\phi}_i^T(\alpha \mathbf{M} + \beta \mathbf{K})\boldsymbol{\phi}_i = 2\omega_i \xi_i$$

or

$$\alpha + \beta \omega_i^2 = 2\omega_i \xi_i \tag{b}$$

Using this relation for ω_1, ξ_1 and ω_2, ξ_2, we obtain two equations for α and β,

$$\alpha + 4\beta = 0.08$$
$$\alpha + 9\beta = 0.60 \tag{c}$$

The solution of (c) is $\alpha = -0.336$ and $\beta = 0.104$. Thus, the damping matrix to be used is

$$\mathbf{C} = -0.336\mathbf{M} + 0.104\mathbf{K} \tag{d}$$

With the damping matrix given, we can now establish the damping ratio that is specified at any value of ω_i, when the Rayleigh damping matrix in (d) is used. Namely, the relation in (b) gives

$$\xi_i = \frac{-0.336 + 0.104\omega_i^2}{2\omega_i}$$

for all values of ω_i.

In actual analysis it may well be that the damping ratios are known for many more than two frequencies. In that case two average values, say $\bar{\xi}_1$ and $\bar{\xi}_2$, are used to evaluate α and β. Consider the following example.

EXAMPLE 9.10: Assume that the approximate damping to be specified for a multiple degree of freedom system is as follows:

$$\xi_1 = 0.002; \qquad \omega_1 = 2; \qquad \xi_2 = 0.03; \qquad \omega_2 = 3$$

$$\xi_3 = 0.04; \qquad \omega_3 = 7; \qquad \xi_4 = 0.10; \qquad \omega_4 = 15$$

$$\xi_5 = 0.14; \qquad \omega_5 = 19$$

Choose appropriate Rayleigh damping parameters α and β.

As in Example 9.9, we determine α and β from the relation

$$\alpha + \beta\omega_i^2 = 2\omega_i\xi_i \qquad (a)$$

However, only two pairs of values, $\bar{\xi}_1$, $\bar{\omega}_1$ and $\bar{\xi}_2$, $\bar{\omega}_2$, determine α and β. Considering the spacing of the frequencies, we use

$$\bar{\xi}_1 = 0.03; \qquad \bar{\omega}_1 = 4$$
$$\bar{\xi}_2 = 0.12; \qquad \bar{\omega}_2 = 17 \qquad (b)$$

For the values in (b) we obtain, using (a),

$$\alpha + 16\beta = 0.24$$

$$\alpha + 289\beta = 4.08$$

Hence $\alpha = 0.01498$, $\beta = 0.01405$, and we obtain

$$\mathbf{C} = 0.01498\mathbf{M} + 0.01405\mathbf{K} \qquad (c)$$

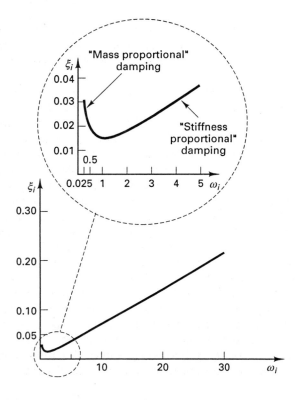

Figure E9.10 Damping as a function of frequency

We can now calculate which actual damping ratios are employed when the damping matrix **C** in (c) is used. From (a) we obtain

$$\xi_i = \frac{0.01498 + 0.01405\omega_i^2}{2\omega_i}$$

Figure E9.10 shows the relation of ξ_i as a function of ω_i, where, based on the use of ξ_i in (9.54), we also indicate the "mass proportional" and "stiffness proportional" damping regions.

The procedure of calculating α and β in Examples 9.9 and 9.10 may suggest the use of a more general damping matrix if more than only two damping ratios are used to establish **C**. Assume that the r damping ratios ξ_i, $i = 1, 2, \ldots, r$ are given to define **C**. Then a damping matrix that satisfies the relation in (9.53) is obtained using the Caughey series,

$$\mathbf{C} = \mathbf{M} \sum_{k=0}^{r-1} a_k [\mathbf{M}^{-1} \mathbf{K}]^k \tag{9.57}$$

where the coefficients a_k, $k = 0, \ldots, r - 1$, are calculated from the r simultaneous equations

$$\xi_i = \tfrac{1}{2}\left(\frac{a_0}{\omega_i} + a_1 \omega_i + a_2 \omega_i^3 + \cdots + a_{r-1} \omega_i^{2r-3}\right)$$

We should note that with $r = 2$, (9.57) reduces to Rayleigh damping, as presented in (9.56). An important observation is that if $r > 2$, the damping matrix **C** in (9.57) is, in general, a full matrix. Since the cost of analysis is increased by a very significant amount if the damping matrix is not banded, in most practical analyses using direct integration, Rayleigh damping is assumed. A disadvantage of Rayleigh damping is that the higher modes are considerably more damped than the lower modes, for which the Rayleigh constants have been selected (see Example 9.10).

In practice, reasonable Rayleigh coefficients in the analysis of a specific structure may often be selected using available information on the damping characteristics of a typical similar structure; i.e., approximately the same α and β values are used in the analysis of similar structures. The magnitude of the Rayleigh coefficients is to a large extent determined by the energy dissipation characteristics of the construction, including the materials.

In the above discussion we assumed that the damping characteristics of the structure can be represented appropriately using proportional damping, either in a mode superposition analysis or in a direct integration procedure. In many analyses, the assumption of proportional damping [i.e., that (9.53) is satisfied] is adequate. However, in the analysis of structures with widely varying material properties, nonproportional damping may need to be used. For example, in the analysis of foundation-structure interaction problems, significantly more damping may be observed in the foundation than in the surface structure. In this case it may be reasonable to assign in the construction of the damping matrix different Rayleigh coefficients α and β to different parts of the structure, which results in a damping matrix that does not satisfy the relation in (9.53). Another case of nonproportional damping is encountered when concentrated dampers corresponding to specific degrees of freedom (e.g., at the support points of a structure) are specified.

The solution of the finite element system equilibrium equations with nonproportional damping can be obtained using the direct integration algorithms in Tables 9.1 to 9.4 without modifications because the property of the damping matrix did not enter into the derivation of the solution procedures. On the other hand, considering mode superposition analysis using the free-vibration mode shapes with damping neglected as base vectors, we find that $\mathbf{\Phi}^T\mathbf{C}\mathbf{\Phi}$ in (9.43) is in the case of nonproportional damping a full matrix. In other words, the equilibrium equations in the basis of mode shape vectors are no longer decoupled. But, if it can be assumed that the primary response of the system is still contained in the subspace spanned by $\mathbf{\phi}_1, \ldots, \mathbf{\phi}_p$, it is necessary to consider only the first p equations in (9.43). Assuming that the coupling in the damping matrix $\mathbf{\Phi}^T\mathbf{C}\mathbf{\Phi}$ between $x_i, i = 1, \ldots, p$, and $x_i, i = p + 1, \ldots, n$, can be neglected, the first p equations in (9.43) decouple from the equations $p + 1$ to n and can be solved by direct integration using the algorithms in Tables 9.1 to 9.4 (see Example 9.11). In an alternative analysis procedure, the decoupling of the finite element equilibrium equations is achieved by solving a quadratic eigenproblem, in which case complex frequencies and vibration mode shapes are calculated (see J. H. Wilkinson [A]).

EXAMPLE 9.11:   Consider the solution of the equilibrium equations

$$\begin{bmatrix} \tfrac{1}{2} & & \\ & 1 & \\ & & \tfrac{1}{2} \end{bmatrix} \ddot{\mathbf{U}} + \begin{bmatrix} 0.1 & & \\ & 0 & \\ & & 0.5 \end{bmatrix} \dot{\mathbf{U}} + \begin{bmatrix} 2 & -1 & 0 \\ -1 & 4 & -1 \\ 0 & -1 & 2 \end{bmatrix} \mathbf{U} = \mathbf{R}(t) \qquad (a)$$

The free-vibration mode shapes with damping neglected and corresponding frequencies of vibration are calculated in Example 10.4 and are

$$\mathbf{\Phi} = \begin{bmatrix} \dfrac{1}{\sqrt{2}} & 1 & -\dfrac{1}{\sqrt{2}} \\ \dfrac{1}{\sqrt{2}} & 0 & \dfrac{1}{\sqrt{2}} \\ \dfrac{1}{\sqrt{2}} & -1 & -\dfrac{1}{\sqrt{2}} \end{bmatrix} ; \qquad \mathbf{\Omega}^2 = \begin{bmatrix} 2 & & \\ & 4 & \\ & & 6 \end{bmatrix}$$

Transform the equilibrium equations in (a) to equilibrium relations in the mode shape basis. Using $\mathbf{U} = \mathbf{\Phi}\mathbf{X}$, we obtain corresponding to (9.43) the equilibrium relations

$$\ddot{\mathbf{X}}(t) + \begin{bmatrix} 0.3 & -0.2\sqrt{2} & -0.3 \\ -0.2\sqrt{2} & 0.6 & 0.2\sqrt{2} \\ -0.3 & 0.2\sqrt{2} & 0.3 \end{bmatrix} \dot{\mathbf{X}}(t) + \begin{bmatrix} 2 & & \\ & 4 & \\ & & 6 \end{bmatrix} \mathbf{X}(t)$$

$$= \begin{bmatrix} \dfrac{1}{\sqrt{2}} & \dfrac{1}{\sqrt{2}} & \dfrac{1}{\sqrt{2}} \\ 1 & 0 & -1 \\ -\dfrac{1}{\sqrt{2}} & \dfrac{1}{\sqrt{2}} & -\dfrac{1}{\sqrt{2}} \end{bmatrix} \mathbf{R}(t) \qquad (b)$$

If it were now known that because of the specific loading applied, the primary response lies only in the first mode, we could obtain an approximate response by solving only

$$\ddot{x}_1(t) + 0.3\dot{x}_1(t) + 2x_1(t) = \begin{bmatrix} \dfrac{1}{\sqrt{2}} & \dfrac{1}{\sqrt{2}} & \dfrac{1}{\sqrt{2}} \end{bmatrix} \mathbf{R}(t) \qquad (c)$$

and then calculating

$$\mathbf{U}(t) = \begin{bmatrix} \dfrac{1}{\sqrt{2}} \\[2ex] \dfrac{1}{\sqrt{2}} \\[2ex] \dfrac{1}{\sqrt{2}} \end{bmatrix} x_1(t)$$

However, it should be noted that because $\mathbf{\Phi}^T \mathbf{C} \mathbf{\Phi}$ in (b) is full, the solution of $x_1(t)$ from (c) does not give the actual response in the first mode because the damping coupling has been neglected.

9.3.4 Exercises

9.7. Obtain the solution of the finite element equations in Exercise 9.1 by mode superposition using all modes of the system (see Example 9.6).

9.8. Consider the finite element system in Exercise 9.1.
   (a) Establish a load vector which will excite only the second mode of the system.
   (b) Assume that $\mathbf{R} = \mathbf{0}$ and $^0\mathbf{U} = \mathbf{0}$ but $^0\dot{\mathbf{U}} \neq \mathbf{0}$. Establish a value of $^0\dot{\mathbf{U}}$ which will make the system vibrate only in its first mode.

9.9. Calculate the curve corresponding to $\xi = 0.2$ given in Fig. 9.3.

9.10. Perform a mode superposition solution of the equations given in Exercise 9.1 but using only the lowest mode. Also, evaluate the static correction [i.e., in (9.51) we have $p = 1$].

9.11. Establish a damping matrix $\mathbf{C}$ for the system considered in Exercise 9.1, which gives the modal damping parameters $\xi_1 = 0.02$, $\xi_2 = 0.08$.

9.12. A finite element system has the following frequencies: $\omega_1 = 1.2$, $\omega_2 = 2.3$, $\omega_3 = 2.9$, $\omega_4 = 3.1$, $\omega_5 = 4.9$, $\omega_6 = 10.1$. The modal damping parameters at ω_1 and ω_4 shall be $\xi_1 = 0.04$, $\xi_4 = 0.10$, respectively. Calculate a Rayleigh damping matrix and evaluate the damping ratios used at the other frequencies.

9.4 ANALYSIS OF DIRECT INTEGRATION METHODS

In the preceding sections we presented the two principal procedures used for the solution of the dynamic equilibrium equations

$$\mathbf{M}\ddot{\mathbf{U}}(t) + \mathbf{C}\dot{\mathbf{U}}(t) + \mathbf{K}\mathbf{U}(t) = \mathbf{R}(t) \tag{9.58}$$

where the matrices and vectors have been defined in Section 9.1. The two procedures were mode superposition and direct integration. The integration schemes considered were the central difference method, the Houbolt method, the Wilson θ method, and the Newmark integration procedure (see Tables 9.1 to 9.4). We stated that using the central difference scheme, a time step Δt smaller than a critical time step Δt_{cr} has to be used; but when employing the other three integration schemes, a similar time step limitation is not applicable.

An important observation was that the cost of a direct integration analysis (i.e., the number of operations required) is directly proportional to the number of time steps required for solution. It follows that the selection of an appropriate time step in direct integration is of much importance. On one hand, the time step must be small enough to obtain accuracy in the solution; but, on the other hand, the time step must not be smaller than necessary because with such time step the solution is more costly than actually required. The aim in this section is to discuss in detail the problem of selecting an appropriate time step Δt for direct integration. The two fundamental concepts to be considered are those of stability and accuracy of the integration schemes. The analysis of the stability and accuracy characteristics of the integration methods results in guidelines for the selection of an appropriate time step.

A first fundamental observation for the analysis of a direct integration method is the relation between mode superposition and direct integration. We pointed out in Section 9.3 that, in essence, using either procedure the solution is obtained by numerical integration. However, in the mode superposition analysis, a change of basis from the finite element nodal displacements to the basis of eigenvectors of the generalized eigenproblem,

$$\mathbf{K}\boldsymbol{\phi} = \omega^2 \mathbf{M}\boldsymbol{\phi} \tag{9.59}$$

is performed prior to the time integration. Writing

$$\mathbf{U}(t) = \boldsymbol{\Phi}\mathbf{X}(t) \tag{9.60}$$

where the columns in $\boldsymbol{\Phi}$ are the $\mathbf{M}$-orthonormalized eigenvectors (free-vibration modes) $\boldsymbol{\phi}_1, \ldots, \boldsymbol{\phi}_n$, and substituting for $\mathbf{U}(t)$ into (9.58) we obtain

$$\ddot{\mathbf{X}}(t) + \boldsymbol{\Delta}\dot{\mathbf{X}}(t) + \boldsymbol{\Omega}^2\mathbf{X}(t) = \boldsymbol{\Phi}^T\mathbf{R}(t) \tag{9.61}$$

where $\boldsymbol{\Omega}^2$ is a diagonal matrix listing the eigenvalues of (9.59) (free-vibration frequencies squared) $\omega_1^2, \ldots, \omega_n^2$. Assuming that the damping is proportional, $\boldsymbol{\Delta}$ is a diagonal matrix, $\boldsymbol{\Delta} = \text{diag}(2\omega_i\xi_i)$, where ξ_i is the damping ratio in the ith mode.

The equation in (9.61) consists of n uncoupled equations, which can be solved, for example, using the Duhamel integral. Alternatively, one of the numerical integration schemes discussed as direct integration procedures may be used. Because the periods of vibration T_i, $i = 1, \ldots, n$, are known, where $T_i = 2\pi/\omega_i$, we can choose in the numerical integration of each equation in (9.61) an appropriate time step that ensures a required level of accuracy. On the other hand, if all n equations in (9.61) are integrated using the same time step Δt, then the mode superposition analysis is completely equivalent to a direct integration analysis in which the same integration scheme and the same time step Δt are used. In other words, the solution of the finite element system equilibrium equations would be identical using either procedure. Therefore, *to study the accuracy of direct integration, we may focus attention on the integration of the equations in (9.61) with a common time step Δt instead of considering (9.58). In this way, the variables to be considered in the stability and accuracy analysis of the direct integration method are only Δt, ω_i, and ξ_i, $i = 1, \ldots, n$, and not all elements of the stiffness, mass, and damping matrices. Furthermore, because all n equations in (9.61) are similar, we only need to study the integration of one typical row in (9.61), which may be written*

$$\ddot{x} + 2\xi\omega\dot{x} + \omega^2 x = r \tag{9.62}$$

and is the equilibrium equation governing motion of a single degree of freedom system with free-vibration period T, damping ratio ξ, and applied load r.

It may be mentioned here that this procedure of changing basis, i.e., using the transformation in (9.60), is also used in the convergence analysis of eigenvalue and eigenvector solution methods (see Section 11.2). The reason for carrying out the transformation in Section 11.2 is the same, namely, many fewer variables need to be considered in the analysis.

Considering the solution characteristics of a direct integration method, the problem is, therefore, to estimate the integration errors in the solution of (9.62) as a function of $\Delta t / T$, ξ, and r. For such investigations, see, for example, L. Collatz [A] and R. D. Richtmyer and K. W. Morton [A]. In the following discussion we employ a relatively simple procedure in which the first step is to evaluate an approximation and load operator that relates explicitly the unknown required variables at time $t + \Delta t$ to previously calculated quantities (see K. J. Bathe and E. L. Wilson [A]).

9.4.1 Direct Integration Approximation and Load Operators

As discussed in the derivation of the direct integration methods (see Section 9.2), assume that we have obtained the required solution for the discrete times $0, \Delta t, 2\Delta t, 3\Delta t, \ldots,$ $t - \Delta t, t$ and that the solution for time $t + \Delta t$ is required next. Then for the specific integration method considered, we aim to establish the following recursive relationship:

$$^{t+\Delta t}\hat{\mathbf{X}} = \mathbf{A} \, ^{t}\hat{\mathbf{X}} + \mathbf{L}(^{t+\nu}r) \tag{9.63}$$

where $^{t+\Delta t}\hat{\mathbf{X}}$ and $^{t}\hat{\mathbf{X}}$ are vectors storing the solution quantities (e.g., displacements, velocities) and $^{t+\nu}r$ is the load at time $t + \nu$. We will see that ν may be 0, Δt, or $\theta \, \Delta t$ for the integration methods considered. The matrix $\mathbf{A}$ and vector $\mathbf{L}$ are the *integration approximation and load operators,* respectively. Each quantity in (9.63) depends on the specific integration scheme employed. However, before deriving the matrices and vectors corresponding to the different integration procedures, we note that (9.63) can be used to calculate the solution at any time $t + n\Delta t$, namely, applying (9.63) recursively, we obtain

$$^{t+n\Delta t}\hat{\mathbf{X}} = \mathbf{A}^{n} \, ^{t}\hat{\mathbf{X}} + \mathbf{A}^{n-1}\mathbf{L}(^{t+\nu}r) + \mathbf{A}^{n-2}\mathbf{L}(^{t+\Delta t+\nu}r) + \cdots$$
$$+ \mathbf{A}\,\mathbf{L}(^{t+(n-2)\Delta t+\nu}r) + \mathbf{L}(^{t+(n-1)\Delta t+\nu}r) \tag{9.64}$$

It is this relation that we will use for the study of the stability and accuracy of the integration methods. In the following sections we derive the operators $\mathbf{A}$ and $\mathbf{L}$ for the different integration methods considered, where we refer to the presentations in Sections 9.2.1 to 9.2.4.

The central difference method. In the central difference integration scheme we use (9.3) and (9.4) to approximate the acceleration and velocity at time t, respectively. The equilibrium equation (9.62) is considered at time t; i.e., we use

$$^{t}\ddot{x} + 2\xi\omega \, ^{t}\dot{x} + \omega^{2} \, ^{t}x = \, ^{t}r \tag{9.65}$$

$$^{t}\ddot{x} = \frac{1}{\Delta t^{2}}(^{t-\Delta t}x - 2 \, ^{t}x + \, ^{t+\Delta t}x) \tag{9.66}$$

$$^{t}\dot{x} = \frac{1}{2\Delta t}(-^{t-\Delta t}x + \, ^{t+\Delta t}x) \tag{9.67}$$

Substituting (9.66) and (9.67) into (9.65) and solving for $^{t+\Delta t}x$, we obtain

$$^{t+\Delta t}x = \frac{2 - \omega^{2} \, \Delta t^{2}}{1 + \xi\omega \, \Delta t} \, ^{t}x - \frac{1 - \xi\omega \, \Delta t}{1 + \xi\omega \, \Delta t} \, ^{t-\Delta t}x + \frac{\Delta t^{2}}{1 + \xi\omega \, \Delta t} \, ^{t}r \tag{9.68}$$

The solution (9.68) can now be written in the form (9.63); i.e., we have

$$\begin{bmatrix} {}^{t+\Delta t}x \\ {}^{t}x \end{bmatrix} = \mathbf{A} \begin{bmatrix} {}^{t}x \\ {}^{t-\Delta t}x \end{bmatrix} + \mathbf{L}\,{}^{t}r \tag{9.69}$$

where

$$\mathbf{A} = \begin{bmatrix} \dfrac{2 - \omega^2\,\Delta t^2}{1 + \xi\omega\,\Delta t} & -\dfrac{1 - \xi\omega\,\Delta t}{1 + \xi\omega\,\Delta t} \\ 1 & 0 \end{bmatrix} \tag{9.70}$$

and

$$\mathbf{L} = \begin{bmatrix} \dfrac{\Delta t^2}{1 + \xi\omega\,\Delta t} \\ 0 \end{bmatrix} \tag{9.71}$$

As we pointed out in Section 9.2.1, the method is usually employed with $\xi = 0$.

The Houbolt method.   In the Houbolt integration scheme the equilibrium equation (9.62) is considered at time $t + \Delta t$ and two backward difference formulas are used for the acceleration and velocity at time $t + \Delta t$; i.e., we use

$$^{t+\Delta t}\ddot{x} + 2\xi\omega\,{}^{t+\Delta t}\dot{x} + \omega^2\,{}^{t+\Delta t}x = {}^{t+\Delta t}r \tag{9.72}$$

$$^{t+\Delta t}\ddot{x} = \frac{1}{\Delta t^2}(2\,{}^{t+\Delta t}x - 5\,{}^{t}x + 4\,{}^{t-\Delta t}x - {}^{t-2\Delta t}x) \tag{9.73}$$

$$^{t+\Delta t}\dot{x} = \frac{1}{6\Delta t}(11\,{}^{t+\Delta t}x - 18\,{}^{t}x + 9\,{}^{t-\Delta t}x - 2\,{}^{t-2\Delta t}x) \tag{9.74}$$

Substituting (9.73) and (9.74) into (9.72), we can establish the relation

$$\begin{bmatrix} {}^{t+\Delta t}x \\ {}^{t}x \\ {}^{t-\Delta t}x \end{bmatrix} = \mathbf{A} \begin{bmatrix} {}^{t}x \\ {}^{t-\Delta t}x \\ {}^{t-2\Delta t}x \end{bmatrix} + \mathbf{L}\,{}^{t+\Delta t}r \tag{9.75}$$

where

$$\mathbf{A} = \begin{bmatrix} \dfrac{5\beta}{\omega^2\,\Delta t^2} + 6\kappa & -\left(\dfrac{4\beta}{\omega^2\,\Delta t^2} + 3\kappa\right) & \dfrac{\beta}{\omega^2\,\Delta t^2} + \dfrac{2\kappa}{3} \\ 1 & 0 & 0 \\ 0 & 1 & 0 \end{bmatrix} \tag{9.76}$$

$$\beta = \left(\frac{2}{\omega^2\,\Delta t^2} + \frac{11\xi}{3\omega\,\Delta t} + 1\right)^{-1}; \qquad \kappa = \frac{\xi\beta}{\omega\,\Delta t} \tag{9.77}$$

and

$$\mathbf{L} = \begin{bmatrix} \dfrac{\beta}{\omega^2} \\ 0 \\ 0 \end{bmatrix} \tag{9.78}$$

The Wilson θ method.   The basic assumption in the Wilson θ method is that the acceleration varies linearly over the time interval from t to $t + \theta\,\Delta t$, where $\theta \geq 1$ and is determined to obtain optimum stability and accuracy characteristics. Let τ denote the increase in time from time t, where $0 \leq \tau \leq \theta\,\Delta t$; then for the time interval t to $t + \theta\,\Delta t$, we have

$$^{t+\tau}\ddot{x} = {}^{t}\ddot{x} + ({}^{t+\Delta t}\ddot{x} - {}^{t}\ddot{x})\frac{\tau}{\Delta t} \tag{9.79}$$

$$^{t+\tau}\dot{x} = {}^{t}\dot{x} + {}^{t}\ddot{x}\,\tau + ({}^{t+\Delta t}\ddot{x} - {}^{t}\ddot{x})\frac{\tau^2}{2\Delta t} \tag{9.80}$$

$$^{t+\tau}x = {}^{t}x + {}^{t}\dot{x}\,\tau + \tfrac{1}{2}{}^{t}\ddot{x}\,\tau^2 + ({}^{t+\Delta t}\ddot{x} - {}^{t}\ddot{x})\frac{\tau^3}{6\Delta t} \tag{9.81}$$

At time $t + \Delta t$ we have

$$^{t+\Delta t}\dot{x} = {}^{t}\dot{x} + ({}^{t+\Delta t}\ddot{x} + {}^{t}\ddot{x})\frac{\Delta t}{2} \tag{9.82}$$

$$^{t+\Delta t}x = {}^{t}x + {}^{t}\dot{x}\,\Delta t + (2\,{}^{t}\ddot{x} + {}^{t+\Delta t}\ddot{x})\frac{\Delta t^2}{6} \tag{9.83}$$

Furthermore, in the Wilson θ method the equilibrium equation (9.62) is considered at time $t + \theta\,\Delta t$ [with an extrapolated load; see (9.25)], which gives

$$^{t+\theta\Delta t}\ddot{x} + 2\xi\omega\,{}^{t+\theta\Delta t}\dot{x} + \omega^2\,{}^{t+\theta\Delta t}x = {}^{t+\theta\Delta t}r \tag{9.84}$$

Using (9.79) to (9.81) at time $\tau = \theta\,\Delta t$ to substitute into (9.84), an equation is obtained with $^{t+\Delta t}\ddot{x}$ as the only unknown. Solving for $^{t+\Delta t}\ddot{x}$ and substituting into (9.82) and (9.83), the following relationship of the form (9.63) is established:

$$\begin{bmatrix} {}^{t+\Delta t}\ddot{x} \\ {}^{t+\Delta t}\dot{x} \\ {}^{t+\Delta t}x \end{bmatrix} = \mathbf{A}\begin{bmatrix} {}^{t}\ddot{x} \\ {}^{t}\dot{x} \\ {}^{t}x \end{bmatrix} + \mathbf{L}\,{}^{t+\theta\Delta t}r \tag{9.85}$$

where

$$\mathbf{A} = \begin{bmatrix} 1 - \dfrac{\beta\theta^2}{3} - \dfrac{1}{\theta} - \kappa\theta & \dfrac{1}{\Delta t}(-\beta\theta - 2\kappa) & \dfrac{1}{\Delta t^2}(-\beta) \\[2ex] \Delta t\left(1 - \dfrac{1}{2\theta} - \dfrac{\beta\theta^2}{6} - \dfrac{\kappa\theta}{2}\right) & 1 - \dfrac{\beta\theta}{2} - \kappa & \dfrac{1}{\Delta t}\left(-\dfrac{\beta}{2}\right) \\[2ex] \Delta t^2\left(\dfrac{1}{2} - \dfrac{1}{6\theta} - \dfrac{\beta\theta^2}{18} - \dfrac{\kappa\theta}{6}\right) & \Delta t\left(1 - \dfrac{\beta\theta}{6} - \dfrac{\kappa}{3}\right) & 1 - \dfrac{\beta}{6} \end{bmatrix} \tag{9.86}$$

$$\beta = \left(\frac{\theta}{\omega^2\,\Delta t^2} + \frac{\xi\theta^2}{\omega\,\Delta t} + \frac{\theta^3}{6}\right)^{-1}; \qquad \kappa = \frac{\xi\beta}{\omega\,\Delta t} \tag{9.87}$$

and

$$\mathbf{L} = \begin{bmatrix} \dfrac{\beta}{\omega^2\,\Delta t^2} \\[2ex] \dfrac{\beta}{2\omega^2\,\Delta t} \\[2ex] \dfrac{\beta}{6\omega^2} \end{bmatrix} \tag{9.88}$$

The Newmark method. In the Newmark integration scheme the equilibrium equation (9.62) is considered at time $t + \Delta t$; i.e., we use

$$^{t+\Delta t}\ddot{x} + 2\xi\omega\,^{t+\Delta t}\dot{x} + \omega^2\,^{t+\Delta t}x = \,^{t+\Delta t}r \tag{9.89}$$

and the following expansions are employed for the velocity and displacement at time $t + \Delta t$:

$$^{t+\Delta t}\dot{x} = \,^{t}\dot{x} + [(1 - \delta)\,^{t}\ddot{x} + \delta\,^{t+\Delta t}\ddot{x}]\,\Delta t \tag{9.90}$$

$$^{t+\Delta t}x = \,^{t}x + \,^{t}\dot{x}\,\Delta t + [(\tfrac{1}{2} - \alpha)\,^{t}\ddot{x} + \alpha\,^{t+\Delta t}\ddot{x}]\,\Delta t^2 \tag{9.91}$$

where δ and α are parameters to be chosen to obtain optimum stability and accuracy. Newmark proposed as an unconditionally stable scheme the constant-average-acceleration method, in which case $\delta = \tfrac{1}{2}$ and $\alpha = \tfrac{1}{4}$.

Substituting for $^{t+\Delta t}\dot{x}$ and $^{t+\Delta t}x$ into (9.89), we can solve for $^{t+\Delta t}\ddot{x}$ and then use (9.90) and (9.91) to calculate $^{t+\Delta t}\dot{x}$ and $^{t+\Delta t}x$. We thus can establish the relation

$$\begin{bmatrix} ^{t+\Delta t}\ddot{x} \\ ^{t+\Delta t}\dot{x} \\ ^{t+\Delta t}x \end{bmatrix} = \mathbf{A} \begin{bmatrix} ^{t}\ddot{x} \\ ^{t}\dot{x} \\ ^{t}x \end{bmatrix} + \mathbf{L}\,^{t+\Delta t}r \tag{9.92}$$

where

$$\mathbf{A} = \begin{bmatrix} -(\tfrac{1}{2} - \alpha)\beta - 2(1 - \delta)\kappa & \dfrac{1}{\Delta t}(-\beta - 2\kappa) & \dfrac{1}{\Delta t^2}(-\beta) \\[2mm] \Delta t[1 - \delta - (\tfrac{1}{2} - \alpha)\delta\beta - 2(1 - \delta)\delta\kappa] & 1 - \beta\delta - 2\delta\kappa & \dfrac{1}{\Delta t}(-\beta\delta) \\[2mm] \Delta t^2[\tfrac{1}{2} - \alpha - (\tfrac{1}{2} - \alpha)\alpha\beta - 2(1 - \delta)\alpha\kappa] & \Delta t(1 - \alpha\beta - 2\alpha\kappa) & (1 - \alpha\beta) \end{bmatrix} \tag{9.93}$$

$$\beta = \left(\frac{1}{\omega^2\,\Delta t^2} + \frac{2\xi\delta}{\omega\,\Delta t} + \alpha\right)^{-1}; \qquad \kappa = \frac{\xi\beta}{\omega\,\Delta t} \tag{9.94}$$

and

$$\mathbf{L} = \begin{bmatrix} \dfrac{\beta}{\omega^2\,\Delta t^2} \\[2mm] \dfrac{\beta\delta}{\omega^2\,\Delta t} \\[2mm] \dfrac{\alpha\beta}{\omega^2} \end{bmatrix} \tag{9.95}$$

We should note the close relationship between the Newmark operators in (9.93) and (9.95) and the Wilson θ method operators in (9.86) and (9.88). That is, using $\delta = \tfrac{1}{2}$, $\alpha = \tfrac{1}{6}$, and $\theta = 1.0$, the same approximation and load operators are obtained in both methods. This should be expected because for these parameters both methods assume a linear variation of acceleration over the time interval t to $t + \Delta t$.

9.4.2 Stability Analysis

The aim in the numerical integration of the finite element system equilibrium equations is to evaluate a good approximation to the actual dynamic response of the structure under consideration. In order to predict the dynamic response of the structure accurately, it would seem that all system equilibrium equations in (9.58) must be integrated to high precision, and this means that all n equations of the form (9.62) need to be integrated accurately. Since in direct integration the same time step is used for each equation of the form (9.62), Δt would have to be selected corresponding to the smallest period in the system, which may mean that the time step is very small indeed. As an estimate of Δt thus required, it appears that if the smallest period is T_n, Δt would have to be about $T_n/10$ (or smaller; see Section 9.4.3). However, we discussed in Section 9.3.2 that in many analyses practically all dynamic response lies in only some modes of vibration and that for this reason only some mode shapes are considered in mode superposition analysis. In addition, it was pointed out that in many analyses there is little justification to include the response predicted in the higher modes because the frequencies and mode shapes of the finite element mesh can be only crude approximations to the "exact" quantities. Therefore, the finite element idealization has to be chosen in such a way that the lowest p frequencies and mode shapes of the structure are predicted accurately, where p is determined by the distribution and frequency content of the loading.

It can therefore be concluded that in many analyses we are interested in integrating only the first p equations of the n equations in (9.61) accurately. This means that we would be able to revise Δt to be about $T_p/10$, i.e., T_p/T_n times larger than our first estimate. In practical analysis the ratio T_p/T_n can be very large, say of the order 1000, meaning that the analysis would be much more effective using $\Delta t = T_p/10$. However, assuming that we select a time step Δt of magnitude $T_p/10$, we realize that in the direct integration also the response in the higher modes is automatically integrated with the same time step. Since we cannot possibly integrate accurately the response in those modes for which Δt is larger than half the natural period T, an important question is: What "response" is predicted in the numerical integration of (9.62) when $\Delta t/T$ is large? This is, in essence, the question of stability of an integration scheme. Stability of an integration method means that the physical initial conditions for the equations with a large value $\Delta t/T$ must not be amplified artificially and thus render worthless any accuracy in the integration of the lower mode response. Stability also means that any "initial" conditions at time t given by errors in the displacements, velocities, and accelerations, which may be due to round-off in the computer, do not grow in the integration. Stability is ensured if the time step is small enough to integrate accurately the response in the highest-frequency component. But this may require a very small step, and, as was pointed out earlier, the accurate integration of the high-frequency response predicted by the finite element assemblage is in many cases not justified and therefore not necessary.

The stability of an integration method is therefore determined by examining the behavior of the numerical solution for arbitrary initial conditions. Therefore, we consider the integration of (9.62) when no load is satisfied; i.e., $r = 0$. The solution for prescribed initial conditions only as obtained from (9.64) is, hence,

$$^{t+n\Delta t}\hat{\mathbf{X}} = \mathbf{A}^n \, ^t\hat{\mathbf{X}} \tag{9.96}$$

Considering the stability of integration methods, we have procedures that are unconditionally stable and that are only conditionally stable. *An integration method is unconditionally stable if the solution for any initial conditions does not grow without bound for any time step Δt, in particular when $\Delta t/T$ is large. The method is only conditionally stable if the above only holds provided that $\Delta t/T$ is smaller than or equal to a certain value, usually called the stability limit.*

For the stability analysis we use the spectral decomposition of $\mathbf{A}$ given by $\mathbf{A} = \mathbf{PJP}^{-1}$, where $\mathbf{P}$ is the matrix of eigenvectors of $\mathbf{A}$, and $\mathbf{J}$ is the Jordan canonical form of $\mathbf{A}$ with eigenvalues λ_i of $\mathbf{A}$ on its diagonal. We considered in Section 2.5 the case of $\mathbf{A}$ being symmetric, in which case $\mathbf{J} = \mathbf{\Lambda}$ [see (2.108)], $\mathbf{P} = \mathbf{V}$, and $\mathbf{P}^{-1} = \mathbf{V}^T$. However, the approximation operator $\mathbf{A}$ is in general a nonsymmetric matrix, and we therefore must use the more general decomposition $\mathbf{A} = \mathbf{PJP}^{-1}$, in which $\mathbf{J}$ is not necessarily a diagonal matrix but may exhibit unit elements on the superdiagonal line (corresponding to multiple eigenvalues), (see, for example, J. H. Wilkinson [A]).

Of course, using the above spectral decomposition, we have

$$\mathbf{A}^n = \mathbf{PJ}^n\mathbf{P}^{-1} \tag{9.97}$$

and with this expression we can determine the stability of the time integration scheme.

Let $\rho(\mathbf{A})$ be the spectral radius $\mathbf{A}$ defined as

$$\rho(\mathbf{A}) = \max_{i=1,2,\ldots} |\lambda_i| \tag{9.98}$$

where the absolute value sign requires the evaluation of the absolute magnitude of λ_i in the complex plane. Then our stability criterion is that

1. If all eigenvalues are distinct, we must have $\rho(\mathbf{A}) \leq 1$, whereas
2. If $\mathbf{A}$ contains multiple eigenvalues, we require that all such eigenvalues be (in modulus) smaller than 1.[1]

If this stability criterion is fulfilled, we have $\mathbf{J}^n$ and hence $\mathbf{A}^n$ bounded for $n \to \infty$. Furthermore, if $\rho(\mathbf{A}) < 1$, we have $\mathbf{J}^n \to \mathbf{0}$ and hence $\mathbf{A}^n \to \mathbf{0}$, and the decrease in $\mathbf{A}^n$ is more rapid when $\rho(\mathbf{A})$ is small.

Since the stability of an integration method depends only on the eigenvalues of the approximation operator, it may be convenient to apply a similarity transformation on $\mathbf{A}$ before evaluating the eigenvalues. In the case of the Newmark method and the Wilson θ method we apply the similarity transformation $\mathbf{D}^{-1}\mathbf{AD}$, where $\mathbf{D}$ is a diagonal matrix with $d_{ii} = (\Delta t)^i$. As might be expected, we then find that the spectral radii and therefore the stability of the integration methods depend only on the time ratio $\Delta t/T$, the damping ratio ξ, and the integration parameters used. Therefore, for given $\Delta t/T$ and ξ, it is possible in the Wilson θ method and in the Newmark method to vary the parameters θ and α, δ, repectively, to obtain optimum stability and accuracy characteristics.

Consider as a simple example the stability analysis of the central difference method.

EXAMPLE 9.12:   Analyze the central difference method for its integration stability. Consider the case $\xi = 0.0$ used in (9.8) to (9.12).

We need to calculate the spectral radius of the approximation operator given in (9.70) when $\xi = 0$. The eigenvalue problem $\mathbf{Au} = \lambda\mathbf{u}$ to be solved is

$$\begin{bmatrix} 2 - \omega^2 \, \Delta t^2 & -1 \\ 1 & 0 \end{bmatrix} \mathbf{u} = \lambda\mathbf{u} \tag{a}$$

---

[1] The Jordan form of a 2×2 nonsymmetric matrix with λ an eigenvalue of multiplicity 2 would be $\mathbf{J} = \begin{bmatrix} \lambda & \alpha \\ 0 & \lambda \end{bmatrix}$, with $\alpha = 0$ or $\alpha = 1$. Hence, $\mathbf{J}^n = \begin{bmatrix} \lambda^n & \alpha n\lambda^{n-1} \\ 0 & \lambda^n \end{bmatrix}$ and $\mathbf{J}^n$ is not bounded when $\alpha = 1$ and $|\lambda| = 1$. In the case $\alpha = 0$ we could actually allow $|\lambda| = 1$.

The eigenvalues are the roots of the characteristic polynomial $p(\lambda)$ (see Section 2.5) defined as

$$p(\lambda) = (2 - \omega^2 \, \Delta t^2 - \lambda)(-\lambda) + 1$$

Hence,

$$\lambda_1 = \frac{2 - \omega^2 \, \Delta t^2}{2} + \sqrt{\frac{(2 - \omega^2 \, \Delta t^2)^2}{4} - 1}$$

$$\lambda_2 = \frac{2 - \omega^2 \, \Delta t^2}{2} - \sqrt{\frac{(2 - \omega^2 \, \Delta t^2)^2}{4} - 1}$$

For stability we need that the absolute values of λ_1 and λ_2 be smaller than or equal to 1; i.e., the spectral radius $\rho(\mathbf{A})$ of the matrix $\mathbf{A}$ in (a) must satisfy the condition $\rho(\mathbf{A}) \le 1$, and this gives the condition $\Delta t / T \le 1/\pi$. Hence, the central difference method is stable provided that $\Delta t \le \Delta t_{cr}$, where $\Delta t_{cr} = T_n/\pi$. It is interesting to note that this same time step stability limit is also applicable when $\xi > 0$ (see Exercise 9.14).

By the same procedure as employed in Example 9.12, the Wilson θ, Newmark, and Houbolt methods can be analyzed for stability using the corresponding approximation operators; Fig. 9.4 shows the stability characteristics. It is noted that the central difference method is only conditionally stable as evaluated in Example 9.12 and that the Newmark, Wilson θ, and Houbolt methods are unconditionally stable.

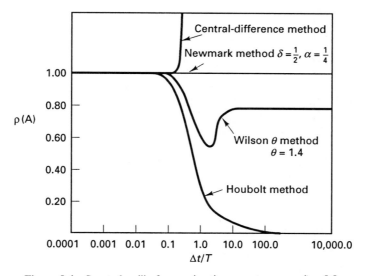

Figure 9.4   Spectral radii of approximation operators, case $\xi = 0.0$

In order to evaluate an optimum value of θ for the Wilson θ method, the variation of the spectral radius of the approximation operator as a function of θ must be calculated as shown in Fig. 9.5. It is seen that unconditional stability is obtained when $\theta \ge 1.37$ (see K. J. Bathe and E. L. Wilson [A]). This information must be supplemented by the accuracy of the method in order to arrive at the optimum value of θ (see Section 9.4.3).

Considering the Newmark method, the two parameters α and δ can be varied to obtain optimum stability and accuracy. The integration scheme is unconditionally stable provided

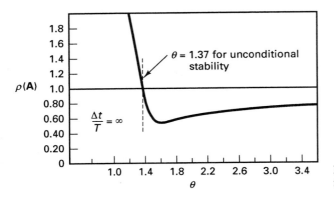

Figure 9.5   Spectral radius $\rho(A)$ as a function of θ in the Wilson θ method

that $\delta \geq 0.5$ and $\alpha \geq 0.25(\delta + 0.5)^2$. We will see in the next section that the method corresponding to $\delta = 0.5$ and $\alpha = 0.25$ has the most desirable accuracy characteristics.

Although only the most widely used integration schemes have been discussed, the above considerations already show that the analyst has to make a choice as to which method to use. This choice is influenced by the accuracy characteristics of the method, i.e., the accuracy that can be obtained in the integration for a given time step Δt.

9.4.3 Accuracy Analysis

The decision as to which integration operator to use in a practical analysis is governed by the cost of solution, which in turn is determined by the number of time steps required in the integration. If a conditionally stable algorithm such as the central difference method is employed, the time step size, and hence the number of time steps for a given time range considered, is determined by the critical time step Δt_{cr}, and not much choice is available. However, using an unconditionally stable operator, the time step has to be chosen to yield an accurate and effective solution. Because the direct integration of the equilibrium equations in (9.58) is equivalent to integrating simultaneously all n decoupled equations of the form (9.62), we can study the integration accuracy obtained in the solution of (9.58) by assessing the accuracy obtained in the integration of (9.62) as a function of $\Delta t/T$, ξ, and r. The solution to (9.62) was given in (9.64), and it is this equation that we use to assess the integration errors.

Let us consider for a simple accuracy analysis the solution of the initial value problem defined by

$$\ddot{x} + \omega^2 x = 0$$

and

$$\left. {}^0x = 1.0; \qquad {}^0\dot{x} = 0.0; \qquad {}^0\ddot{x} = -\omega^2} \right\} \qquad (9.99)$$

for which the exact solution is $x = \cos \omega t$. For a complete analysis we would have to consider also the initial value problem corresponding to ${}^0x = 0.0$, ${}^0\dot{x} = \omega$, ${}^0\ddot{x} = 0$ with the exact solution $x = \sin \omega t$, and the solution for a general loading condition. In addition, the influence of the damping parameter ξ would need to be investigated. However, the significant solution characteristics can be demonstrated by considering only the numerical solution of the problem in (9.99).

The Newmark and Wilson θ methods can be used directly with the initial conditions given in (9.99). However, in the Houbolt method, the initial conditions are defined only by initial displacements, and in the following study the exact displacement values for $^{\Delta t}x$ and $^{2\Delta t}x$ obtained using the solution $x = \cos \omega t$ have been employed.

The numerical solution of (9.99) using the different integration methods shows that the errors in the integrations can be measured in terms of period elongation and amplitude decay. Figure 9.6 shows the percentage period elongations and amplitude decays in the implicit integration schemes discussed as a function of $\Delta t / T$. These relationships have been obtained by evaluating (9.64) and comparing the exact solution $x = \cos \omega t$ with the numerical solutions. It should be noted that (9.64) yields the solution only at the discrete time points Δt apart. To obtain maximum displacements, as required in Fig. 9.6, the relations in (9.80), (9.81) and (9.90), (9.91), respectively, have been employed in the Wilson θ and Newmark methods, and an interpolating polynomial of order 3, which fits the displacements at the discrete time points Δt apart, has been used in the Houbolt method (see K. J. Bathe and E. L. Wilson [A]).

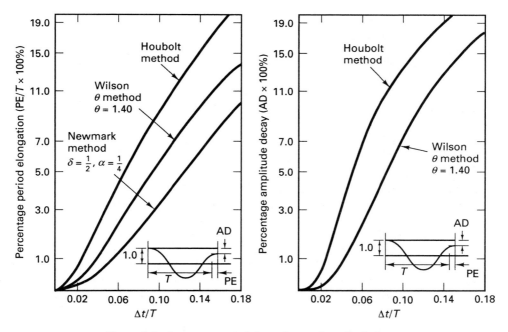

Figure 9.6   Percentage period elongations and amplitude decays

The curves in Fig. 9.6 show that, in general, the numerical integrations using any of the methods are accurate when $\Delta t / T$ is smaller than about 0.01. However, when the time step/period ratio is larger, the varous integration methods exhibit quite different characteristics. Notably, for a given ratio $\Delta t / T$, the Wilson θ method with $\theta = 1.4$ introduces less amplitude decay and period elongation than the Houbolt method, and the Newmark constant-average-acceleration method introduces only period elongation and no amplitude decay.

The characteristics of the integration errors exhibited in Fig. 9.6 are used in the discussion of the simultaneous integration of all n equations of form (9.62) as required in the solution of (9.61) and thus in the solution of (9.58). We observe that the equations for which the time step/period ratio is small are integrated accurately, but that the response in the equations for which $\Delta t/T$ is large is not obtained with any precision.

These considerations lead to the choice of an appropriate time step Δt. Using the central difference method, the time step has to be chosen such that Δt is smaller than or equal to Δt_{cr} evaluated in Example 9.12. Only in the exceptional case in which the loading or initial conditions significantly excite the highest frequencies do we need to use a much smaller time step than Δt_{cr}. However, using one of the unconditionally stable schemes, we realize that the time step Δt can be much larger and should be only small enough that the response in all modes that significantly contribute to the total structural response is calculated accurately. The other modal response components are not evaluated accurately, but the errors are unimportant because the response measured in those components is negligible, and does not grow artificially.

Using one of the unconditionally stable algorithms, the time Δt can be chosen by referring to the integration errors displayed in Fig. 9.6. Since an important phenomenon is the amplitude decay observed in the numerical integration of the modes for which $\Delta t/T$ is large, consider the following demonstrative case. Assume that using the Wilson θ method with $\theta = 1.4$, a time step is selected that gives $\Delta t/T_1 = 0.01$, where T_1 is the fundamental period of a six degree of freedom system and $T_{i+1} = T_i/10$, $i = 1, \ldots, 5$. Let the initial conditions in each mode be those given in (9.99) and let the integration be performed for 100 time steps. Figure 9.7 shows the response calculated in the fundamental and higher modes. It is observed that the amplitude decay caused by the numerical integration errors effectively "filters" the high mode response out of the solution. The same effect is obtained using the Houbolt method, whereas when the Newmark constant-average-acceleration scheme is employed, which does not introduce amplitude decay, the high-frequency response is retained in the solution. In order to obtain amplitude decay using the Newmark method, it is necessary to employ $\delta > 0.5$ and correspondingly $\alpha = \frac{1}{4}(\delta + 0.5)^2$.

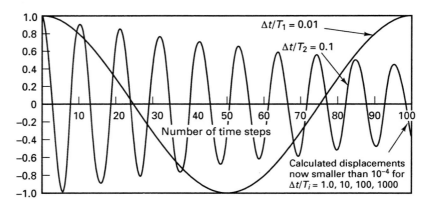

Figure 9.7   Displacement response predicted with increasing $\Delta t/T$ ratio; Wilson θ method, $\theta = 1.4$

Of course, these considerations may be regarded as rather theoretical because in a practical analysis the initial conditions on the second to sixth modes should be negligible for the above integration time step to be realistic. Therefore, the filtering should not actually be required, and because of the smallest numerical errors, the Newmark method appears to be most effective.

In most practical analyses, little difference in the computational effort using either the Newmark or Wilson θ method is observed because the errors resulting in the period elongations require about the same time step using either procedure. On the other hand, the Houbolt method has the disadvantage that special starting procedures must be used.

It should be realized that the stability and accuracy analyses given in this section assume that a linear finite element analysis is carried out. Some important additional considerations are required in the analysis of nonlinear response (see Section 9.5).

9.4.4 Some Practical Considerations

In order to obtain an effective solution of a dynamic response, it is important to choose an appropriate time integration scheme. This choice depends on the finite element idealization, which in turn depends on the actual physical problem to be analyzed. It follows therefore that the selection of an appropriate finite element idealization of a problem and the choice of an effective integration scheme for the response solution are closely related and must be considered together. The finite element model and time integration scheme are chosen differently depending on whether a structural dynamics or a wave propagation problem is solved.

Structural Dynamics

The basic consideration in the selection of an appropriate finite element model of a structural dynamics problem is that only the lowest modes (or only a few intermediate modes) of a physical system are being excited by the load vector. We discussed this consideration already in Section 9.3.2, where we addressed the problem of how many modes need to be included in a mode superposition analysis. Referring to Section 9.3.2, we can conclude that if a Fourier analysis of the dynamic load input shows that only frequencies below ω_u are contained in the loading, then the finite element mesh should at most represent accurately the frequencies to about $\omega_{co} = 4\omega_u$ of the actual system. There is no need to represent the higher frequencies of the actual physical system accurately in the finite element system because the dynamic response contribution in these frequencies is negligible; i.e., for values of $\hat{\omega}/\omega$ in Fig. 9.3 smaller than 0.25, an almost static response is measured and this response is directly included in the direct integration step-by-step dynamic response calculations. We should also note that the static displacement response in the higher modes is small if the mode shapes are almost orthogonal to the load vector and/or the frequencies are high, see (9.46) (i.e., when the structure is very stiff in these mode shapes). When the static response is small it may well be expedient to use ω_{co} closer to ω_u than given by the factor 4 used above. This reduction of ω_{co} may be considerable, for example, in earthquake response analysis of certain structures.

The complete procedure for the modeling of a structural vibration problem is therefore:

1. Identify the frequencies significantly contained in the loading, using a Fourier analysis if necessary. These frequencies may change as a function of time. Let the highest frequency significantly contained in the loading be ω_u.
2. Choose a finite element mesh that can accurately represent the static response and accurately represents all frequencies up to about $\omega_{co} = 4\omega_u$.

3. Perform the direct integration analysis. The time step Δt for this solution should equal about $\frac{1}{20} T_{co}$, where $T_{co} = 2\pi/\omega_{co}$ (or be smaller for stability reasons when the central difference method is used).

Note that if a mode superposition solution were used for this step (as described in Section 9.3), then ω_{co} would be the highest frequency to be included in the solution. Hence p in (9.49) is equal to the number of modes with frequencies smaller than or equal to ω_{co}.

When analyzing a structural dynamics problem, in most cases, an implicit unconditionally stable time integration is most effective. Then the time step Δt need generally be only $\frac{1}{20} T_{co}$ (and not smaller, unless convergence difficulties are encountered in the iteration in a nonlinear response calculation; see Section 9.5.2). If an implicit time integration is employed, it is frequently effective to use higher-order finite elements, for example, the 9- and 27-node elements (see Section 5.3) in two- and three-dimensional analysis, respectively, and a consistent mass idealization. The higher-order elements are effective in the representation of bending behavior, but generally need to be employed with a consistent load vector so that the midside and the corner nodes are subjected to their appropriate load contributions in the analysis.

The observation that the use of higher-order elements can be effective with implicit time integration in the analysis of structural dynamics problems is consistent with the fact that higher-order elements have generally been found to be efficient in static analysis, and structural dynamics problems can be thought of as "static problems including inertia effects." If, on the other hand, the finite element idealization consists of many elements, it can be more efficient to use explicit time integration with a lumped mass matrix, in which case no effective stiffness matrix is assembled and triangularized but a much smaller time step Δt must generally be employed in the solution.

Wave Propagation

The major difference between a structural dynamics problem and a wave propagation problem can be understood to be that in a wave propagation problem a large number of frequencies are excited in the system. It follows that one way to analyze a wave propagation problem is to use a sufficiently high cutoff frequency ω_{co} to obtain enough solution accuracy. The difficulties are in identifying the cutoff frequency to be used and in establishing a corresponding finite element model.

Instead of using these considerations to obtain an appropriate finite element mesh for the analysis of a wave propagation problem, it is generally more effective to employ the concepts used in finite difference solutions.

If we assume that the critical wavelength to be represented is L_w, the total time for this wave to travel past a point is

$$t_w = \frac{L_w}{c} \tag{9.100}$$

where c is the wave speed. Assuming that n time steps are necessary to represent the travel of the wave,

$$\Delta t = \frac{t_w}{n} \tag{9.101}$$

and the "effective length" of a finite element should be

$$L_e = c \, \Delta t \tag{9.102}$$

This effective length and corresponding time step must be able to represent the complete wave travel accurately and are chosen differently depending on the kind of element idealization and time integration scheme used.

Although a special case, the effectiveness of using (9.102) becomes apparent when a one-dimensional analysis of a bar is performed with a lumped mass idealization and the central difference method. If a uniform bar free at both ends and subjected to a sudden constant step load is idealized as an assemblage of two-node truss elements each of length $c \, \Delta t$, the exact wave propagation response is obtained in the solution of the model. It is also interesting to note that the time step Δt given in (9.102) then corresponds to the stability limit T_n/π derived in Example 9.12, i.e., $\omega_n = 2c/L_e$, and the nonzero (highest) frequency of a single unconstrained element is ω_n. Hence, *the most accurate solution is obtained by integrating with a time step equal to the stability limit and the solution is less accurate when a smaller time step is employed!* This deterioration in the accuracy of the predicted solution when Δt is smaller than Δt_{cr} is most pronounced when a relatively coarse spatial discretization is used.

In more complex two- and three-dimensional analyses, the exact solution is generally not obtained, and L_e is chosen depending on whether the central difference method or an implicit method is employed for solution.

If the explicit central difference method is used, a lumped mass matrix should be employed, and in this case low-order finite elements in uniform meshes are probably most effective; i.e. the four- and eight-node elements in Figs. 5.4 and 5.5 are frequently employed in two- and three-dimensional analyses, respectively. Using these elements, we construct a mesh as uniform as possible and L_e is equal to the *smallest distance between any two of the nodes of the mesh employed.* This length determines Δt as given by (9.102). If higher-order (parabolic or cubic) continuum elements are used, again a mesh as uniform as possible should be constructed with the same measure L_e, but the time step has to be further reduced because the interior nodes are "stiffer" than the corner nodes. Also, if structural (beam, plate, or shell) elements are included in the mesh, the time step size Δt may be governed by the flexural modes in these elements so that the distances between nodes do not alone determine Δt (see Table 9.5). Since the condition is always that $\Delta t \leq T_n/\pi$, where T_n is the smallest period of the mesh, we aim to use, for an effective solution, an inexpensively calculated lower bound on T_n. This bound is given by the smallest period $T_n^{(m)}$ of any element, considered individually, measured over all elements in the mesh, as we show in the following example.

EXAMPLE 9.13:   Let ω_n be the largest frequency of an assembled finite element mesh and let $\omega_n^{(m)}$ be the largest frequency of element m. Show that

$$\omega_n \leq \max_{(m)} \omega_n^{(m)} \tag{a}$$

where $\max_{(m)} \omega_n^{(m)}$ is the largest element frequency of all elements in the mesh.

Hence, for the central difference method we can then use the time step

$$\Delta t = \frac{2}{\max\limits_{(m)} \omega_n^{(m)}} \leq \Delta t_{cr}$$

Using the Rayleigh quotient (see Section 2.6), we have with $\mathbf{K}^{(m)}$ and $\mathbf{M}^{(m)}$ defined in (4.19) and (4.25),

$$(\omega_n)^2 = \frac{\boldsymbol{\phi}_n^T \left(\sum_m \mathbf{K}^{(m)} \right) \boldsymbol{\phi}_n}{\boldsymbol{\phi}_n^T \left(\sum_m \mathbf{M}^{(m)} \right) \boldsymbol{\phi}_n} \tag{b}$$

Let

$$\mathcal{U}^{(m)} = \boldsymbol{\phi}_n^T \mathbf{K}^{(m)} \boldsymbol{\phi}_n \qquad \text{and} \qquad \mathcal{I}^{(m)} = \boldsymbol{\phi}_n^T \mathbf{M}^{(m)} \boldsymbol{\phi}_n$$

then

$$(\omega_n)^2 = \frac{\sum_m \mathcal{U}^{(m)}}{\sum_m \mathcal{I}^{(m)}} \tag{c}$$

Now consider the Rayleigh quotient for a single element,

$$\rho^{(m)} = \frac{\boldsymbol{\phi}_n^T \mathbf{K}^{(m)} \boldsymbol{\phi}_n}{\boldsymbol{\phi}_n^T \mathbf{M}^{(m)} \boldsymbol{\phi}_n} = \frac{\mathcal{U}^{(m)}}{\mathcal{I}^{(m)}} \tag{d}$$

Since $\mathbf{M}^{(m)}$ and $\mathbf{K}^{(m)}$ are of the same size as $\mathbf{K}$, we could theoretically imagine $\mathcal{U}^{(m)}$ and $\mathcal{I}^{(m)}$ to be zero (but not for all m). However, in any case we have for each element (see Section 2.6)

$$\mathcal{U}^{(m)} \leq (\omega_n^{(m)})^2 \mathcal{I}^{(m)}$$

and therefore from (c),

$$(\omega_n)^2 \leq \frac{\sum_m (\omega_n^{(m)})^2 \mathcal{I}^{(m)}}{\sum_m \mathcal{I}^{(m)}}$$

$$\leq \left[\max_m \left(\omega_n^{(m)} \right)^2 \right] \frac{\sum_m \mathcal{I}^{(m)}}{\sum_m \mathcal{I}^{(m)}}$$

which proves (a). Note that in (b) we used the $\mathbf{K}^{(m)}$ and $\mathbf{M}^{(m)}$ matrices of element m defined in (4.19) and (4.25), that is with all boundary conditions (and the actions of the other elements) removed. Of course, the same proof is applicable if some elements are constrained at certain degrees of freedom (applied to the assemblage of elements).

For some elements the smallest period can be established exactly in closed form, whereas for more complex (distorted and curved) elements, a lower bound on $T_n^{(m)}$ may have to be employed. Table 9.5 summarizes some results.

The condition that $\Delta t \leq$ ("element length"/wave speed) is referred to as the CFL condition after R. Courant, K. Friedrichs, and H. Lewy [A]. We also use the Courant (or CFL) number $\Delta t / \Delta t_{cr}$ to indicate the size of time step actually used in a dynamic solution.

The choice of the effective length L_e, and hence time step Δt, is considerably simpler if an implicit unconditionally stable time integration method is used. In this case, L_e can be chosen according to (9.100) to (9.102) as $L_e = L_w/n$ in *the direction of the wave travel,* and then Δt follows from (9.102). Nonuniform meshes and low- or high-order elements can be used, and when high-order elements are employed, a consistent mass matrix is usually appropriate.

These considerations have been put forward for linear dynamic analysis but are largely also applicable in nonlinear analysis. An important point in nonlinear analysis is that the periods and wave velocities represented in the finite element system change during its

TABLE 9.5 *Central difference method critical time steps for some elements:*
$\Delta t_{cr}^{(m)} = T_n^{(m)}/\pi = 2/\omega_n^{(m)}$

Two-node truss element:

$$\mathbf{K}^{(m)} = \frac{AE}{L}\begin{bmatrix} 1 & -1 \\ -1 & 1 \end{bmatrix}; \qquad \mathbf{M}^{(m)} = \frac{\rho L}{2}\begin{bmatrix} 1 & 0 \\ 0 & 1 \end{bmatrix}$$

$$\Delta t_{cr}^{(m)} = \frac{L}{c};$$

Two-node beam element (see Example 4.1):

$$\mathbf{K}^{(m)} = \frac{EI}{L}\begin{bmatrix} \dfrac{12}{L^2} & -\dfrac{6}{L} & -\dfrac{12}{L^2} & -\dfrac{6}{L} \\ & 4 & \dfrac{6}{L} & 2 \\ & & \dfrac{12}{L^2} & \dfrac{6}{L} \\ \text{Sym.} & & & 4 \end{bmatrix}$$

$$\mathbf{M}^{(m)} = \frac{\rho AL}{24}\begin{bmatrix} 12 & 0 & 0 & 0 \\ & L^2 & 0 & 0 \\ \text{Sym.} & & 12 & 0 \\ & & & L^2 \end{bmatrix}$$

$$\Delta t_{cr}^{(m)} = \sqrt{\frac{A}{48I}\frac{L^2}{c}}$$

Four-node square plane stress element (see Example 4.6):

$$\mathbf{K}^{(m)} = \frac{Et}{1-\nu^2}\begin{bmatrix} \dfrac{3-\nu}{6} & & \begin{array}{l}\text{Elements are} \\ \text{function of } \nu\end{array} \\ & \ddots & \\ \text{Sym.} & & \\ & & \dfrac{3-\nu}{6} \end{bmatrix}$$

$$\mathbf{M}^{(m)} = \frac{\rho L^2 t}{4}\begin{bmatrix} 1 & & & \\ & 1 & \text{Zeros} & \\ & & \ddots & \\ & & 1 & \\ & & & 1 \end{bmatrix}$$

$$\Delta t_{cr}^{(m)} = \frac{L}{c}\sqrt{1-\nu}$$

where E = Young's modulus, ν = Poisson's ratio, L = length (side length) of element, A = cross-sectional area of element, ρ = mass density, I = flexural moment of inertia, t = thickness of plane stress element, c = one-dimensional wave speed = $\sqrt{E/\rho}$

response. Therefore, the selection of the time step size must take into account that in structural dynamics problems the significantly excited frequencies change magnitudes and that in a wave propagation problem the value of c in (9.102) is not constant.

We discuss additional considerations pertaining to nonlinear analysis in Section 9.5. Let us now present an example demonstrating the above modeling features.

EXAMPLE 9.14:   Consider the bar shown in Fig. E9.14(a) initially at rest and subjected to a concentrated end load. The response of the bar at time 0.01 sec is sought.

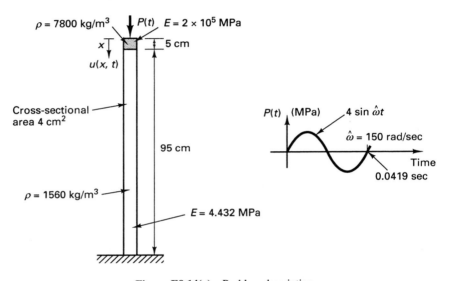

Figure E9.14(a)   Problem description

Solve this problem using two-node truss elements
(i) With the mode superposition method and
(ii) By direct integration with the trapezoidal rule and the central difference method.

We note that the bar is made of two materials (giving a stiff and a flexible section), and that the choice of truss elements to model the bar implies the use of a one-dimensional mathematical model (see Example 3.17). Of course, in practice, the actual problem and solution may be of much more complex nature, and we use this simplified problem statement and mathematical model merely to demonstrate the modeling and solution procedures discussed above.

To solve this problem we need to first select a discretization that accurately represents a sufficient number of the exact frequencies and corresponding mode shapes. Using lumped and consistent mass representations, the frequencies listed in Table E9.14 are calculated with discretizations using 20 and 40 equal-length elements. In this analysis we note that the frequencies of the lumped mass models are always below the frequencies of the consistent mass models. Because of the relatively stiff short section of the bar at its top, the twentieth frequency in the 20-element models is considerably higher than the nineteenth frequency (and the thirty-ninth and fortieth frequencies of the 40-element models are much higher than the thirty-eighth frequency).

TABLE E9.14   *Predicted frequencies (radians/second)*

Frequency number	Lumped mass matrix assumption		Consistent mass matrix assumption	
	20-element model	40-element model	20-element model	40-element model
1	7.02516E + 01	7.02648E + 01	7.02770E + 01	7.02712E + 01
2	2.19037E + 02	2.19393E + 02	2.19812E + 02	2.19587E + 02
3	3.78880E + 02	3.80576E + 02	3.82932E + 02	3.81591E + 02
4	5.43097E + 02	5.47936E + 02	5.55239E + 02	5.50977E + 02
5	7.06967E + 02	7.17610E + 02	7.34395E + 02	7.24482E + 02
6	8.67764E + 02	8.87724E + 02	9.20054E + 02	9.00834E + 02
⋮	⋮	⋮	⋮	⋮
19	2.12481E + 03	2.89023E + 03	3.65556E + 03	3.47009E + 03
20	1.93925E + 05	3.01715E + 03	3.25207E + 05	3.69646E + 03
⋮		⋮		⋮
38		4.26046E + 03		7.36679E + 03
39		2.73219E + 05		3.36596E + 05
40		3.97280E + 05		6.76577E + 05

The frequency of the load application lies between the first and second frequencies of the model. Using $4 \times \hat{\omega}$ as the cutoff frequency, we note that it should be sufficient to include the response of four modes in the mode superposition solution, i.e., to use $p = 4$ in (9.49). However, for instructive purposes we consider the response corresponding to $p = 1, 2, \ldots, 5$. We also note that the 20-element models are predicting the significantly excited frequencies to sufficient accuracy (we compare the frequencies of the 20-element models with those of the 40-element models), and we use these models for the response solution.

For the mode superposition solution we use the consistent mass model and obtain at time 0.01 sec the results shown in Figs. E9.14(b) and (c).

Figures E9.14(b) and (c) illustrate how, as we increase the number of modes included in the response prediction, the predicted response converges. The predicted response using four modes is almost the same as using five modes. However, we also note that the static correction [i.e., use of (9.52)] improves the response prediction very significantly when only one, two, or three modes are used in the superposition solution. The modal solutions have been obtained by numerical integration of the decoupled equation (9.46) with a time step $\Delta t = 0.0004$ (which is about $T_5/20$).

For the direct integration with the trapezoidal rule we also use the consistent mass 20-element model and the same time step as in the mode superposition solution. This time step ensures that the response in the modes $\boldsymbol{\phi}_1$ to $\boldsymbol{\phi}_5$ is accurately integrated. Figure E9.14(d) shows the calculated response and the excellent comparison with the mode superposition solution.

For the central difference method solution we use the 20-element lumped mass model. The time step needs to be sufficiently small for stability. If we use the highest frequency in the model, we obtain $\Delta t_{cr} = 2/\omega_{20} = 1.03 \times 10^{-5}$ sec, and if we use the formula given in Table 9.5, we obtain $\Delta t_{cr} \geq \min_{m=1,\ldots,20} \Delta t_{cr}^{(m)} = 0.98 \times 10^{-5}$ sec. Therefore, in practice, we would use $\Delta t = 0.98 \times 10^{-5}$ sec, but here we can use $\Delta t = 1.0 \times 10^{-5}$ sec. Note that whereas we need

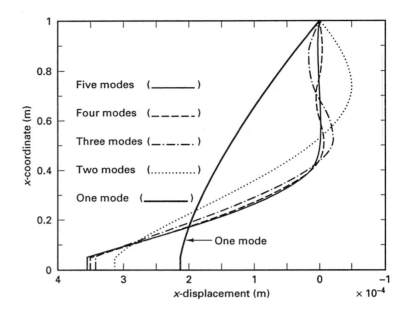

Figure E9.14(b)   Solution using mode superposition without static correction

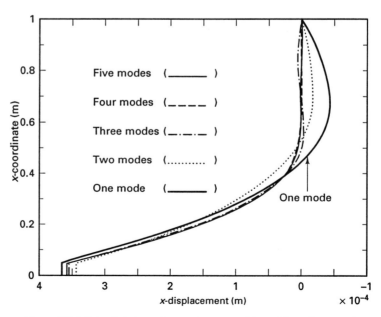

Figure E9.14(c)   Solution using mode superposition with static correction

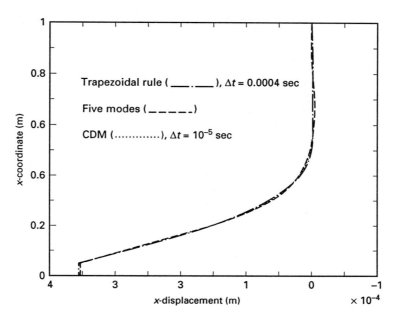

Figure E9.14(d)   Comparison of solutions obtained by mode superposition and direct integration

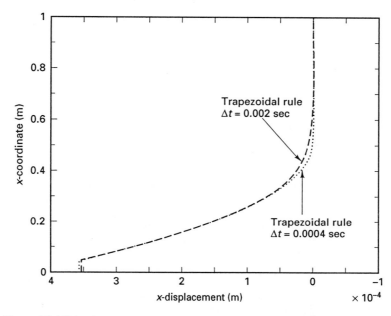

Figure E9.14(e)   Comparison of direct integration solutions using the trapezoidal rule

only 25 time steps with the trapezoidal rule (hence the CFL number $\doteq$ 40), we require 1000 time steps with the central difference method. Of course, this is due to the relatively stiff top part of the bar. The solution using the central difference method compares very well with the mode superposition and implicit direct integration (by the trapezoidal rule) solutions [see Fig. E9.14(d)].

Finally, let us investigate the solution accuracy if we were to increase the time step size using the trapezoidal rule of time integration. If we consider the third frequency $\omega_3 = 382.93$ rad/sec, we have $\hat{\omega}/\omega_3 \doteq 0.39$. Figure 9.3 shows that for this frequency and the larger frequencies the increase in response above the static response is less than 50 percent. However, the static response in a mode ϕ_i decreases proportionally with the factor $1/\omega_i^2$ and is in any case included in the direct time integration. If we use $\Delta t = 0.002$ sec, we still integrate the third mode dynamic response with about 5 percent accuracy (see Fig. 9.6) (and of course the first and second mode responses more accurately). Hence, the choice of the time step $\Delta t = 0.002$ sec appears reasonable (the CFL number is then approximately 200).

Figure E9.14(e) indeed shows that the solution with the time step $\Delta t = 0.002$ sec is not far from the solution with the smaller time step. This result corresponds also to the results given in Fig. E9.14(c), where it is seen that the mode superposition solution using three modes is already quite accurate, provided the static correction is included. Hence, the selection and use of the finer time step $\Delta t = 0.0004$ sec for the trapezoidal rule integration was conservative.

9.4.5 Exercises

9.13. Evaluate the direct integration approximation and load operators for the integration method proposed by H. M. Hilber, T. J. R. Hughes, and R. L. Taylor [A], in which the assumptions of the Newmark method [see (9.27) and (9.28)] and the following equation are employed

$$\mathbf{M}^{t+\Delta t}\ddot{\mathbf{U}} + (1+\gamma)\,\mathbf{C}^{t+\Delta t}\dot{\mathbf{U}} - \gamma\mathbf{C}^{t}\dot{\mathbf{U}} + (1+\gamma)\,\mathbf{K}^{t+\Delta t}\mathbf{U}$$
$$- \gamma\mathbf{K}^{t}\mathbf{U} = (1+\gamma)^{t+\Delta t}\mathbf{R} - \gamma^{t}\mathbf{R}$$

with γ a parameter to be selected. Consider the case $\delta = \frac{1}{2}$, $\alpha = \frac{1}{4}$ in the Newmark assumption.

9.14. Assume that the central difference method is used to solve the dynamic equilibrium equations including proportional damping [that is, we have $\xi > 0$ in (9.62)]. Show that the critical time step is still given by $2/\omega_n$.

9.15 Consider the spectral radii corresponding to the Houbolt, Wilson θ ($\theta = 1.4$), and Newmark ($\delta = \frac{1}{2}$, $\alpha = \frac{1}{4}$) methods. Show that the values given in Fig. 9.4 for $\Delta t/T = 10,000$ are correct.

9.16. Calculate the percentage period elongations and amplitude decays of the Houbolt, Wilson θ ($\theta = 1.4$), and Newmark ($\delta = \frac{1}{2}$, $\alpha = \frac{1}{4}$) methods corresponding to the initial value problem in (9.99) for the case $\Delta t/T = 0.10$. Thus, show that the values given in Fig. 9.6 are correct.

9.17. Use a computer program to solve for the lowest six frequencies of the cantilever shown. Consider three different mathematical models: a Hermitian beam model, a plane stress model, and a fully three-dimensional model. In each case, choose appropriate finite element discretizations and consider the lumped and consistent mass matrix assumptions. Verify that accurate results have been obtained.

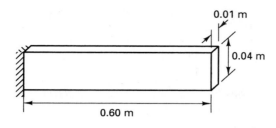

Young's modulus E = 200,000 MPa
Poisson's ratio v = 0.3
Mass density ρ = 7800 kg/m³

9.18. Use a computer program to solve for the lowest six frequencies of the curved cantilever shown. Use the isoparametric mixed interpolated beam element with two, three, or four nodes and use the lumped or consistent mass matrix. Verify that you have obtained accurate results.

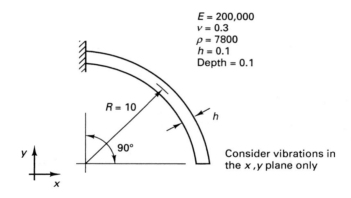

E = 200,000
v = 0.3
ρ = 7800
h = 0.1
Depth = 0.1

R = 10

h

90°

Consider vibrations in the x, y plane only

9.19. Consider the problem of a concentrated load P traveling over a simply supported beam. Use a computer program to solve this problem for various values of velocity v.

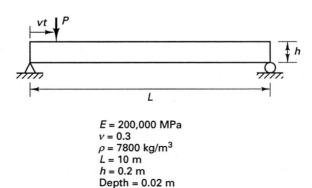

E = 200,000 MPa
v = 0.3
ρ = 7800 kg/m³
L = 10 m
h = 0.2 m
Depth = 0.02 m

9.20. An 11-story tapered tower is subjected to an air blast as shown. Use a computer program to solve for the response of the tower.

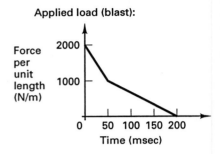

11 story tapered tower

3.2 m

Girder properties:
$E = 2.07 \times 10^{11}$ Pa
$v = 0.3$
$A = 0.01$ m^2
$A_s = 0.009$ m^2
$I = 8.33 \times 10^{-5}$ m^4
$\rho = 7800$ kg/m^3

32 m

Pressure induced by blast

6.4 m

Applied load (blast):

Force per unit length (N/m)

2000

1000

0   50 100 150 200

Time (msec)

9.5 SOLUTION OF NONLINEAR EQUATIONS IN DYNAMIC ANALYSIS

The solution of the nonlinear dynamic response of a finite element system is, in essence, obtained using the procedures already discussed: the incremental formulations presented in Chapter 6, the iterative solution procedures discussed in Section 8.4, and the time integration algorithms presented in this chapter. Hence, the major basic procedures used in a nonlinear dynamic response solution have already been presented, and we only need to briefly summarize in the following how these procedures are employed together in a nonlinear dynamic analysis.

9.5.1 Explicit Integration

The most common explicit time integration operator used in nonlinear dynamic analysis is probably the central difference operator. As in linear analysis (see Section 9.2), the equilibrium of the finite element system is considered at time t in order to calculate the displacements at time $t + \Delta t$. Neglecting the effect of a damping matrix, we operate for each discrete time step solution on the equations,

$$\mathbf{M}\,{}^{t}\ddot{\mathbf{U}} = {}^{t}\mathbf{R} - {}^{t}\mathbf{F} \tag{9.103}$$

where the nodal point force vector ${}^{t}\mathbf{F}$ is evaluated as discussed in Section 6.3. The solution for the nodal point displacements at time $t + \Delta t$ is obtained using the central difference approximation for the accelerations [given in (9.3)] to substitute for ${}^{t}\ddot{\mathbf{U}}$ in (9.103). Thus, as in linear analysis, if we know ${}^{t-\Delta t}\mathbf{U}$ and ${}^{t}\mathbf{U}$, the relations in (9.3) and (9.103) are employed to calculate ${}^{t+\Delta t}\mathbf{U}$. The solution therefore simply corresponds to a forward marching in time; the main advantage of the method is that with $\mathbf{M}$ a diagonal matrix the solution of ${}^{t+\Delta t}\mathbf{U}$ does not involve a triangular factorization of a coefficient matrix.

The shortcoming in the use of the central difference method lies in the severe time step restriction: for stability, the time step size Δt must be smaller than a critical time step Δt_{cr}, which is equal to T_n/π, where T_n is the smallest period in the finite element system. This time step restriction was derived considering a linear system (see Example 9.12), but the result is also applicable to nonlinear analysis, since for each time step the nonlinear response calculation may be thought of—in an approximate way—as a linear analysis. However, whereas in a linear analysis the stiffness properties remain constant, in a nonlinear analysis these properties change during the response calculations. These changes in the material and/or geometric conditions enter into the evaluation of the force vector ${}^t\mathbf{F}$ as discussed in Chapter 6. Since therefore the value of T_n is not constant during the response calculation, the time step Δt needs to be decreased if the system stiffens, and this time step adjustment must be performed in a conservative manner so that the condition $\Delta t \leq T_n/\pi$ is satisfied with certainty at all times.

To emphasize this point, consider an analysis in which the time step is always smaller than the critical time step except for a few successive solution steps, and for these solution steps the time step Δt is just slightly larger than the critical time step. In such a case, the analysis results may not show an "obvious" solution instability but instead a significant solution error is accumulated over the solution steps for which the time step size was larger than the critical value for stability. The situation is quite different from what is observed in linear analysis, where the solution quickly "blows up" if the time step is larger than the critical time step size for stability. This phenomenon is demonstrated somewhat in the response predicted for the simple one degree of freedom spring-mass system shown in Fig. 9.8. In the solution the time step Δt is slightly larger than the critical time step for stability in the stiff region of the spring. Since the time step corresponds to a stable time step for small spring displacements, the response calculations are partly stable and partly unstable. The calculated response is shown in Fig 9.8, and it is observed that although the predicted displacements are grossly in error, the solution does not blow up. Hence, if this single degree of freedom system corresponded to a higher frequency in a large finite element model, a significant error accumulation could take place without an obvious blow-up of the solution.

The proper choice of the time step Δt is therefore a most important factor. Guidelines for the choice of Δt have been given in Section 9.4.4.

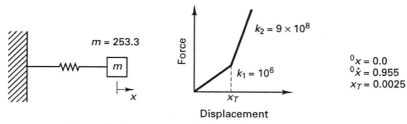

Force-displacement relation in tension and compression

Figure 9.8 Response of bilinear elastic system as predicted using the central difference method; $\Delta t_{cr} = 0.001061027$; the accurate response with displacement $\ll 0.1$ was calculated with $\Delta t = 0.000106103$; the "unstable" response was calculated with $\Delta t = 0.00106103$.

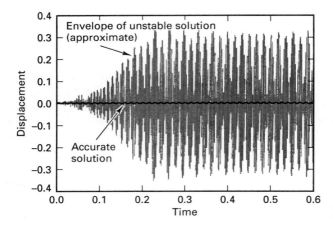

Figure 9.8   *(continued)*

9.5.2 Implicit Integration

All the implicit time integration schemes discussed previously for linear dynamic analysis can also be employed in nonlinear dynamic response calculations. A very common technique used is the trapezoidal rule, which is Newmark's method with $\delta = \frac{1}{2}$ and $\alpha = \frac{1}{4}$, and we use this method to demonstrate the basic additional considerations involved in a nonlinear analysis.

As in linear analysis, using implicit time integration, we consider the equilibrium of the system at time $t + \Delta t$. This requires in nonlinear analysis that an iteration be performed. Using, for instance, the modified Newton-Raphson iteration, the governing equilibrium equations are (see Section 6.3.2, neglecting the effects of a damping matrix):

$$\mathbf{M}\,^{t+\Delta t}\ddot{\mathbf{U}}^{(k)} + {}^{t}\mathbf{K}\,\Delta\mathbf{U}^{(k)} = {}^{t+\Delta t}\mathbf{R} - {}^{t+\Delta t}\mathbf{F}^{(k-1)} \tag{9.104}$$

$$^{t+\Delta t}\mathbf{U}^{(k)} = {}^{t+\Delta t}\mathbf{U}^{(k-1)} + \Delta\mathbf{U}^{(k)} \tag{9.105}$$

Using the trapezoidal rule of time integration, the following assumptions are employed:

$$^{t+\Delta t}\mathbf{U} = {}^{t}\mathbf{U} + \frac{\Delta t}{2}({}^{t}\dot{\mathbf{U}} + {}^{t+\Delta t}\dot{\mathbf{U}}) \tag{9.106}$$

$$^{t+\Delta t}\dot{\mathbf{U}} = {}^{t}\dot{\mathbf{U}} + \frac{\Delta t}{2}({}^{t}\ddot{\mathbf{U}} + {}^{t+\Delta t}\ddot{\mathbf{U}}) \tag{9.107}$$

Using the relations in (9.105) to (9.107), we thus obtain

$$^{t+\Delta t}\ddot{\mathbf{U}}^{(k)} = \frac{4}{\Delta t^2}({}^{t+\Delta t}\mathbf{U}^{(k-1)} - {}^{t}\mathbf{U} + \Delta\mathbf{U}^{(k)}) - \frac{4}{\Delta t}\,{}^{t}\dot{\mathbf{U}} - {}^{t}\ddot{\mathbf{U}} \tag{9.108}$$

and substituting into (9.104), we have

$$^{t}\hat{\mathbf{K}}\,\Delta\mathbf{U}^{(k)} = {}^{t+\Delta t}\mathbf{R} - {}^{t+\Delta t}\mathbf{F}^{(k-1)} - \mathbf{M}\left(\frac{4}{\Delta t^2}({}^{t+\Delta t}\mathbf{U}^{(k-1)} - {}^{t}\mathbf{U}) - \frac{4}{\Delta t}\,{}^{t}\dot{\mathbf{U}} - {}^{t}\ddot{\mathbf{U}}\right) \tag{9.109}$$

where
$$'\hat{\mathbf{K}} = {}'\mathbf{K} + \frac{4}{\Delta t^2}\mathbf{M} \tag{9.110}$$

We now notice that the iterative equations in dynamic nonlinear analysis using implicit time integration are of the same form as the equations that we considered in static nonlinear analysis, except that both the coefficient matrix and the nodal point force vector contain contributions from the inertia of the system. We can therefore directly conclude that all iterative solution strategies discussed in Section 8.4 for static analysis are also directly applicable to the solution of (9.109). However, since the inertia of the system renders its dynamic response, in general, "more smooth" than its static response, convergence of the iteration can, in general, be expected to be more rapid than in static analysis, and the convergence behavior can be improved by decreasing Δt. The numerical reason for the better convergence characteristics in a dynamic analysis as Δt decreases lies in the contribution of the mass matrix to the coefficient matrix. This contribution increases and ultimately becomes dominant as the time step decreases (see Section 8.4.1).

It is interesting to note that in the first solutions of nonlinear dynamic finite element response, equilibrium iterations were not performed in the step-by-step incremental analysis; i.e., the relation in (9.109) was simply solved for $k = 1$ and the incremental displacement $\Delta \mathbf{U}^{(1)}$ was accepted as an accurate approximation to the actual displacement increment from time t to time $t + \Delta t$. However, it was then recognized that the iteration can actually be of utmost importance (see K. J. Bathe and E. L. Wilson [B]) since any error admitted in the incremental solution at a particular time directly affects in a path-dependent manner the solution at any subsequent time. Indeed, because any nonlinear dynamic response is highly path-dependent, the analysis of a nonlinear dynamic problem requires iteration at each time step more stringently than does a static analysis.

A simple demonstration of this observation is given in Fig. 9.9. This figure shows the results obtained in the analysis of a simple pendulum that was idealized as a truss element with a concentrated mass at its free end. The pendulum was released from a horizontal position, and the response was calculated for about one period of oscillation. In the analysis the convergence tolerances already discussed in Section 8.4.4 were used, but including the

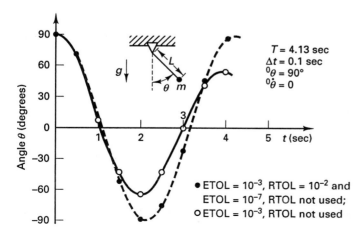

Figure 9.9 Analysis of simple pendulum using trapezoidal rule, RNORM = mg

effect of inertia, i.e., convergence is reached when the following conditions are satisfied:

$$\frac{\left\| {}^{t+\Delta t}\mathbf{R} - {}^{t+\Delta t}\mathbf{F}^{(i-1)} - \mathbf{M} {}^{t+\Delta t}\ddot{\mathbf{U}}^{(i-1)} \right\|_2}{\text{RNORM}} \leq \text{RTOL} \tag{9.111}$$

and

$$\frac{\Delta \mathbf{U}^{(i)T}({}^{t+\Delta t}\mathbf{R} - {}^{t+\Delta t}\mathbf{F}^{(i-1)} - \mathbf{M} {}^{t+\Delta t}\ddot{\mathbf{U}}^{(i-1)})}{\Delta \mathbf{U}^{(1)T}({}^{t+\Delta t}\mathbf{R} - {}^{t}\mathbf{F} - \mathbf{M} {}^{t}\ddot{\mathbf{U}})} \leq \text{ETOL} \tag{9.112}$$

in which RTOL is a force tolerance and ETOL is an energy tolerance. Figure 9.9 demonstrates the importance of iterating and doing so with a sufficiently tight convergence tolerance. In this analysis energy is lost if the convergence tolerance is not tight enough, but depending on the problem being considered, the predicted response may also blow up if iteration is not used. In practice, it is frequently the case that only a few iterations per time step are required to obtain a stable solution.

Therefore, in summary, for a nonlinear dynamic analysis using implicit time integration, the analyst should employ an operator that is unconditionally stable in linear analysis (a good choice is the trapezoidal rule), use equilibrium iterations with tight enough convergence tolerances, and select the time step size based on the guidelines given in Section 9.4.4 and on the fact that convergence in the equilibrium iterations must be achieved.

9.5.3 Solution Using Mode Superposition

In considering linear analysis, we discussed in Section 9.3 that the essence of mode superposition is a transformation from the element nodal point degrees of freedom to the generalized degrees of freedom of the vibration mode shapes. Since the dynamic equilibrium equations in the basis of the mode shape vectors decouple (assuming proportional damping), mode superposition analysis can be very effective in linear analysis if only some vibration modes are excited by the loading. The same basic principles are also applicable in nonlinear analysis; however, in this case the vibration mode shapes and frequencies change, and to transform the coefficient matrix in (9.109) into diagonal form the free-vibration mode shapes of the system at time t need to be used in the transformation. The calculation of the vibration mode shapes and frequencies at time t, when these quantities have been calculated at a previous time, could be achieved economically using the subspace iteration method (see Section 11.6). However, the complete mode superposition analysis of nonlinear dynamic response is generally effective only when the solution can be obtained without updating the stiffness matrix too frequently. In this case, the governing finite element equilibrium equations for the solution of the response at time $t + \Delta t$ are

$$\mathbf{M} {}^{t+\Delta t}\ddot{\mathbf{U}}^{(k)} + {}^{\tau}\mathbf{K} \, \Delta\mathbf{U}^{(k)} = {}^{t+\Delta t}\mathbf{R} - {}^{t+\Delta t}\mathbf{F}^{(k-1)} \qquad k = 1, 2, \ldots \tag{9.113}$$

where ${}^{\tau}\mathbf{K}$ is the stiffness matrix corresponding to the configuration at some previous time τ. In the mode superposition analysis we now use

$$ {}^{t+\Delta t}\mathbf{U} = \sum_{i=r}^{s} \boldsymbol{\phi}_i \, {}^{t+\Delta t}x_i \tag{9.114}$$

where ${}^{t+\Delta t}x_i$ is the ith generalized modal displacement at time $t + \Delta t$ and

$$ {}^{\tau}\mathbf{K}\boldsymbol{\phi}_i = \omega_i^2 \mathbf{M}\boldsymbol{\phi}_i; \qquad i = r, \ldots, s \tag{9.115}$$

that is, ω_i, $\boldsymbol{\phi}_i$ are free-vibration frequencies (radians/second) and mode shape vectors of the system at time τ. Using (9.114) in the usual way, the equations in (9.113) are transformed to

$$^{t+\Delta t}\ddot{\mathbf{X}}^{(k)} + \mathbf{\Omega}^2\,\Delta\mathbf{X}^{(k)} = \mathbf{\Phi}^T(^{t+\Delta t}\mathbf{R} - {}^{t+\Delta t}\mathbf{F}^{(k-1)}) \qquad k = 1, 2, \ldots \qquad (9.116)$$

where

$$\mathbf{\Omega}^2 = \begin{bmatrix} \omega_r^2 & & \\ & \ddots & \\ & & \omega_s^2 \end{bmatrix}; \qquad \mathbf{\Phi} = [\boldsymbol{\phi}_r, \ldots, \boldsymbol{\phi}_s]; \qquad {}^{t+\Delta t}\mathbf{X} = \begin{bmatrix} {}^{t+\Delta t}x_r \\ \vdots \\ \vdots \\ {}^{t+\Delta t}x_s \end{bmatrix} \qquad (9.117)$$

The relations in (9.116) are the equilibrium equations at time $t + \Delta t$ in the generalized modal displacements of time τ; the corresponding mass matrix is an identity matrix, the stiffness matrix is $\mathbf{\Omega}^2$, the external load vector is $\mathbf{\Phi}^T {}^{t+\Delta t}\mathbf{R}$, and the force vector corresponding to the element stresses at the end of iteration $(k - 1)$ is $\mathbf{\Phi}^T {}^{t+\Delta t}\mathbf{F}^{(k-1)}$. The solution of (9.116) can be obtained using, for example, the trapezoidal rule of time integration (see Section 9.5.2).

In general, the use of mode superposition in nonlinear dynamic analysis can be effective if only a relatively few mode shapes need to be considered in the analysis. Such conditions may be encountered, for example, in the analysis of earthquake response and vibration excitation, and it is in these areas that the technique has been employed.

9.5.4 Exercises

9.21. Consider the simple pendulum idealization shown. Use a finite element program to solve for the response of the system (see Fig. 9.9).

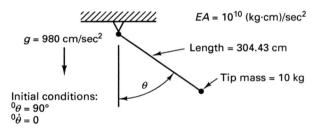

$EA = 10^{10}$ (kg·cm)/sec²

$g = 980$ cm/sec²

Length = 304.43 cm

Tip mass = 10 kg

θ

Initial conditions:
$^0\theta = 90°$
$^0\dot{\theta} = 0$

One truss element with tip concentrated mass is employed

9.22. Consider the cantilever beam shown. The beam is initially at rest when the tip load P is suddenly applied. Use a finite element program to solve for the dynamic response of the beam, allowing for the large displacement effects. Use the trapezoidal rule, the central difference method and, if available, also mode superposition to solve for the response.

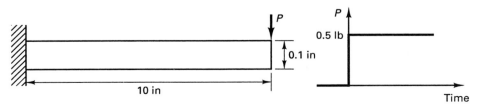

P

P

0.5 lb

0.1 in

10 in

Time

Young's modulus $E = 1.2 \times 10^6$ lb/in²
Poisson's ratio $\nu = 0.2$
Mass density $\rho = 1.0 \times 10^{-4}$ (lb·sec²)/in⁴
Width = 1 in

9.23. Use a computer program to solve for the dynamic buckling load of the arch considered in Fig. 6.23.

9.24. Use a computer program to analyze the pipe whip problem described in the figure. You can perform a direct integration solution or a mode superposition solution. (These types of problems are of importance in the analysis of postulated accident conditions; see, for example, S. N. Ma and K. J. Bathe [A].)

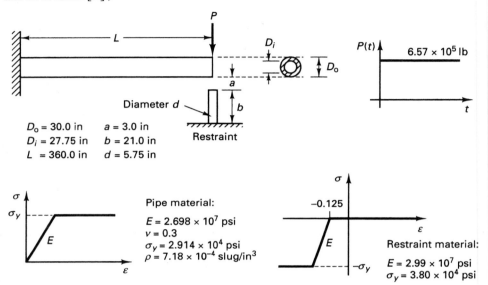

$D_o = 30.0$ in $a = 3.0$ in
$D_i = 27.75$ in $b = 21.0$ in
$L = 360.0$ in $d = 5.75$ in

Pipe material:
$E = 2.698 \times 10^7$ psi
$\nu = 0.3$
$\sigma_y = 2.914 \times 10^4$ psi
$\rho = 7.18 \times 10^{-4}$ slug/in^3

Restraint material:
$E = 2.99 \times 10^7$ psi
$\sigma_y = 3.80 \times 10^4$ psi

9.6 SOLUTION OF NONSTRUCTURAL PROBLEMS; HEAT TRANSFER AND FLUID FLOWS

Although we considered in the previous sections the solution of the dynamic response of structures and solids, it should be recognized that many of the basic concepts discussed are also directly applicable to the analysis of other types of problems. Namely, in the solution of a nonstructural problem, the choice lies again between the use of explicit or implicit time integration, mode superposition analysis needs to be considered, and it may also be advantageous to use different time integration schemes for different domains of the complete element assemblage (see Section 9.2.5). The stability and accuracy properties of the time integration schemes used are analyzed in basically the same way as in structural analysis, and the important basic observations made concerning nonlinear structural analysis are also applicable to the analysis of nonlinear nonstructural problems.

9.6.1 The α-Method of Time Integration

The nonstructural problems that we have in mind are heat transfer, field problems, and fluid flow (see Chapter 7). The major difference in the time integration of the governing equations of these problems, when compared to structural analysis, is that we now deal only with first derivatives in time. Therefore, time integration operators different from those discussed in the previous sections are employed.

Based on the discussion in Section 9.4 we can present a time integration scheme used in the analysis of heat transfer and fluid flows by considering a typical one degree of freedom equilibrium equation,

$$\dot{\eta} + \lambda\eta = r; \qquad \eta|_{t=0} = {}^{0}\eta \tag{9.118}$$

where, for example, considering a heat transfer problem, η is the unknown temperature, λ is the diffusivity, and r is the heat input to the system. The α-method of time integration can be employed effectively for the solution of (9.118) and is given by the following assumptions:

$$
\begin{aligned}
{}^{t+\alpha\Delta t}\dot{\eta} &= ({}^{t+\Delta t}\eta - {}^{t}\eta)/\Delta t \\
{}^{t+\alpha\Delta t}\eta &= (1 - \alpha)\,{}^{t}\eta + \alpha\,{}^{t+\Delta t}\eta
\end{aligned}
\tag{9.119}
$$

where α is a constant that is chosen to yield optimum stability and accuracy properties. To solve for ${}^{t+\Delta t}\eta$ we proceed as described in Section 9.2. Namely, if ${}^{t}\eta$ is known, we can use (9.118) at time $t + \alpha\,\Delta t$ and (9.119) to solve for ${}^{t+\Delta t}\eta$, and so on. This α-method was already used in Section 6.6.3 in the solution of the inelastic response of finite element systems.

The properties of the integration procedure depend on the value of α that is employed. The following procedures are in frequent use (see, for example, L. Collatz [A]).

$\alpha = 0$,   explicit Euler forward method, stable provided $\Delta t \leq 2/\lambda$, first-order accurate in Δt

$\alpha = \frac{1}{2}$,   implicit trapezoidal rule, unconditionally stable, second-order accurate in Δt

$\alpha = 1$,   implicit Euler backward method, unconditionally stable, first-order accurate in Δt.

To evaluate these stability properties we proceed as in Section 9.4.2. Now we use (9.118), with $r = 0$ and λ constant, at time $t + \alpha\,\Delta t$, substitute from (9.119), and solve for the variable η at time $t + \Delta t$ in terms of all known quantities.

$$
{}^{t+\Delta t}\eta = \frac{1 - (1 - \alpha)\lambda\,\Delta t}{1 + \alpha\lambda\,\Delta t}\,{}^{t}\eta \tag{9.120}
$$

Therefore, for stability we need

$$
\left| \frac{1 - (1 - \alpha)\lambda\,\Delta t}{1 + \alpha\lambda\,\Delta t} \right| \leq 1 \tag{9.121}
$$

which shows that the α-method is unconditionally stable if $\alpha \geq \frac{1}{2}$. In the case $\alpha < \frac{1}{2}$, the method is only stable provided

$$
\Delta t \leq \frac{2}{(1 - 2\alpha)\lambda} \tag{9.122}
$$

These results have been used in the summary given above for the cases $\alpha = 0, \frac{1}{2}$, and 1.

To evaluate the accuracy properties we proceed in a similar manner as in Section 9.4.3 but now consider the initial value problem

$$
\dot{\eta} + \lambda\eta = 0; \qquad {}^{0}\eta = 1 \tag{9.123}
$$

Assume that we perform the numerical solution of (9.123) for a time period $1/\lambda$, with time step magnitude $1/n\lambda$, where n is the number of time steps used for the time period $1/\lambda$. Then we can define as our error measure the percentage in absolute difference between the numerical and exact solutions at time $1/\lambda$. Figure 9.10 shows this error measure for the Euler forward and backward methods and the trapezoidal rule.

The information in Fig. 9.10 is useful for a direct integration solution if the largest value of λ in the finite element mesh, for which the response is to be accurately integrated, is known. Namely, the relation in (9.118) can be considered as the governing differential equation in time for the mode shape corresponding to the value λ (see the discussion in Sections 9.3.2 and 9.4.4).

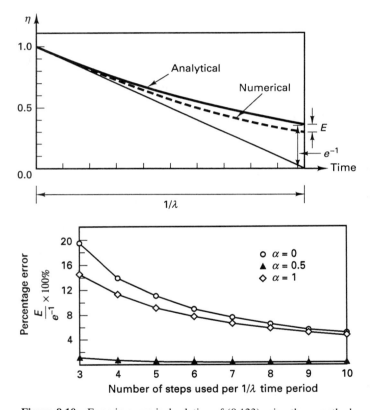

Figure 9.10   Error in numerical solution of (9.123) using the α method

However, in actual analysis, we need to select the finite element discretization, the time integration scheme, and the time step Δt. The following considerations are then useful.

Consider a one-dimensional heat transfer condition in a continuous medium, as shown in Fig. 9.11. The uniform initial temperature is θ_i, when suddenly the free surface at $x = 0$ is subjected to a temperature θ_0. The governing differential equation of equilibrium of this problem was derived in Example 3.16.

The exact solution of the mathematical model gives the temperature distributions shown schematically in Fig. 9.11(b). This figure also shows the penetration depth γ

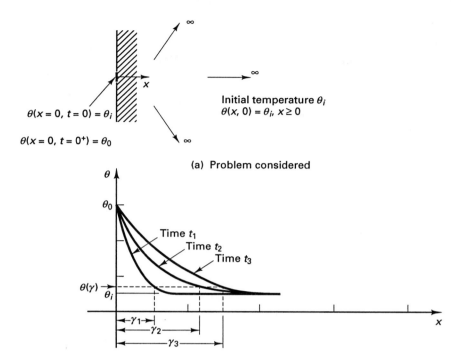

(a) Problem considered

$\theta(x = 0, t = 0) = \theta_i$

$\theta(x = 0, t = 0^+) = \theta_0$

Initial temperature θ_i
$\theta(x, 0) = \theta_i,\ x \geq 0$

(b) Penetration depths at three different times (schematic presentation)

Figure 9.11   Analysis of continuous medium

defined as

$$\gamma = 4\sqrt{at} \tag{9.124}$$

where a is the thermal diffusity,[2] $a = k/\rho c$. At this distance,

$$\frac{\theta(\gamma) - \theta_i}{\theta_0 - \theta_i} < 0.01 \tag{9.125}$$

(see Fig.9.11).

This penetration depth is also used for the problem when instead of an imposed temperature, suddenly a heat flux is imposed. In this case we have

$$\frac{\theta(\gamma) - \theta_i}{\theta^S - \theta_i} < 0.01 \tag{9.126}$$

where θ^S is the surface temperature at time t.

The finite element discretization is chosen by use of γ. Assume that t_{min} is the minimum time at which temperature results are desired. Then, if N is the number of

---

[2] We use here the symbol a to denote the diffusivity (instead of α in Section 7.4), because the symbol α is here used to denote the time integration parameter.

elements needed to discretize the penetration depth, we use

$$\Delta x = \frac{4}{N} \sqrt{a t_{\min}} \tag{9.127}$$

Typically, for two-node elements, we use $N = 6$ to 10, and this element size would be used throughout the mesh.

Next, the time step Δt for the integration scheme must be chosen. Assume that we use two-node elements and a lumped heat capacity matrix. If the Euler forward method is employed, the stability limit dictates the time step to be (see Exercise 9.27),

$$\Delta t \leq \frac{(\Delta x)^2}{2a} \tag{9.128}$$

Whereas using the trapezoidal rule or Euler backward method we can employ

$$\Delta t = \frac{(\Delta x)^2}{a} \tag{9.129}$$

or an even larger time step.

When using the implicit methods, $\alpha = 1$ or $\frac{1}{2}$, it is, however, frequently effective to use higher-order (parabolic) elements and the consistent heat capacity matrix because significantly better accuracy might be achieved. In this case Δx is the distance between adjacent nodes.

These considerations are also directly useful in two- and three-dimensional analysis. In these cases we use the Euler forward method with the low-order elements (four-node quadrilateral elements in two-dimensional analysis and eight-node brick elements in three-dimensional analysis) and a lumped heat capacity matrix, and a mesh as close as possible to a uniform mesh. The time step is given by (9.128), where Δx is now the smallest distance between any nodes. On the other hand, with the trapezoidal rule or Euler backward method, we usually use the parabolic elements (nine-node elements in two-dimensional analysis and 27-node elements in three-dimensional analysis), the consistent heat capacity matrix, and a time step of magnitude (9.129), where Δx is again the smallest distance between any nodes.

Finally, let us demonstrate the application of the α-method of time integration in two examples.

EXAMPLE 9.15: Develop the equations to be solved in a nonlinear transient heat transfer analysis using the Euler backward method and the full Newton-Raphson method.

The governing equations in a nonlinear heat transfer analysis using an implicit time integration procedure are (see Section 7.2.3)

$$^{t+\Delta t}\mathbf{C}^{(i)}\,^{t+\Delta t}\dot{\boldsymbol{\theta}}^{(i)} + {}^{t+\Delta t}\mathbf{K}^{(i-1)}\,\Delta\boldsymbol{\theta}^{(i)} = {}^{t+\Delta t}\tilde{\mathbf{Q}}^{(i-1)} \tag{a}$$

where $^{t+\Delta t}\tilde{\mathbf{Q}}^{(i-1)}$ is a vector of nodal point heat flows corresponding to time $t + \Delta t$ and iteration $(i - 1)$. Using the Euler backward method, we have

$$^{t+\Delta t}\dot{\boldsymbol{\theta}}^{(i)} = \frac{{}^{t+\Delta t}\boldsymbol{\theta}^{(i-1)} + \Delta\boldsymbol{\theta}^{(i)} - {}^{t}\boldsymbol{\theta}}{\Delta t}$$

and hence (a) reduces to

$$\left({}^{t+\Delta t}\mathbf{K}^{(i-1)} + \frac{1}{\Delta t}\,{}^{t+\Delta t}\mathbf{C}^{(i)}\right)\Delta\boldsymbol{\theta}^{(i)} = {}^{t+\Delta t}\tilde{\mathbf{Q}}^{(i-1)} - {}^{t+\Delta t}\mathbf{C}^{(i)}\,{}^{t+\Delta t}\dot{\boldsymbol{\theta}}^{(i-1)} \tag{b}$$

where

$$t+\Delta t\dot{\boldsymbol{\theta}}^{(i-1)} = \frac{t+\Delta t\boldsymbol{\theta}^{(i-1)} - t\boldsymbol{\theta}}{\Delta t}$$

For solution the relation (b) is further linearized (corresponding to a full Newton-Raphson iteration) using

$$\left(t+\Delta t\mathbf{K}^{(i-1)} + \frac{1}{\Delta t}\, t+\Delta t\mathbf{C}^{(i-1)} \right) \Delta\boldsymbol{\theta}^{(i)} = t+\Delta t\tilde{\mathbf{Q}}^{(i-1)} - t+\Delta t\mathbf{C}^{(i-1)}\, t+\Delta t\dot{\boldsymbol{\theta}}^{(i-1)}$$

EXAMPLE 9.16:   Referring to Example 9.15, develop the equations to be solved in incompressible fluid flow without heat transfer using the Euler backward method.

The governing finite element equations in fluid flow are given in (7.74) and (7.75), which we can restate as

$$\begin{bmatrix} \mathbf{M} & 0 \\ 0 & 0 \end{bmatrix} \begin{bmatrix} \dot{\mathbf{V}} \\ \dot{\mathbf{P}} \end{bmatrix} + \begin{bmatrix} \mathbf{K} & \mathbf{K}_p \\ \mathbf{K}_p^T & 0 \end{bmatrix} \begin{bmatrix} \mathbf{V} \\ \mathbf{P} \end{bmatrix} = \begin{bmatrix} \mathbf{R} \\ 0 \end{bmatrix} \tag{a}$$

where the vector $\mathbf{V}$ denotes all velocity degrees of freedom and $\mathbf{P}$ lists all pressure degrees of freedom.

We note that the fully incompressible flow condition results in the zero diagonal elements corresponding to the pressure degrees of freedom. Hence, an implicit time integration is necessary. In the Euler backward integration we use (now showing the superscripts denoting time and iteration number),

$$\left(\begin{bmatrix} \mathbf{K} & \mathbf{K}_p \\ \mathbf{K}_p^T & 0 \end{bmatrix} \bigg|_{\substack{\text{evaluated at} \\ t+\Delta t\mathbf{V}^{(i-1)},\ t+\Delta t\mathbf{P}^{(i-1)}}} + \frac{1}{\Delta t}\begin{bmatrix} \mathbf{M} & 0 \\ 0 & 0 \end{bmatrix} \right) \begin{bmatrix} \Delta\mathbf{V}^{(i)} \\ \Delta\mathbf{P}^{(i)} \end{bmatrix}$$

$$= \begin{bmatrix} t+\Delta t\mathbf{R} \\ 0 \end{bmatrix} - \left(\begin{bmatrix} \mathbf{M} & 0 \\ 0 & 0 \end{bmatrix} \begin{bmatrix} t+\Delta t\dot{\mathbf{V}}^{(i-1)} \\ t+\Delta t\dot{\mathbf{P}}^{(i-1)} \end{bmatrix} + \begin{bmatrix} \mathbf{K} & \mathbf{K}_p \\ \mathbf{K}_p^T & 0 \end{bmatrix} \bigg|_{\substack{\text{evaluated at} \\ t+\Delta t\mathbf{V}^{(i-1)},\ t+\Delta t\mathbf{P}^{(i-1)}}} \begin{bmatrix} t+\Delta t\mathbf{V}^{(i-1)} \\ t+\Delta t\mathbf{P}^{(i-1)} \end{bmatrix} \right) \tag{b}$$

The equations in (b) correspond simply to a solution by successive substitution because the coefficient matrices are not tangent matrices. A Newton-Raphson type of iteration would have to be developed as described in Sections 6.3.1 and 8.4.1.

In practice, the simple iteration in (b) frequently works quite well, particularly if the time step Δt is sufficiently small. However, the right-hand-side vector must then be very efficiently calculated by minimizing the multiplications actually required.

In the preceding example solutions, we considered nonlinear systems with an implicit time integration scheme. Hence, as pointed out in Section 9.5.2, it is important to iterate for the solution. In heat transfer analysis we can also employ the explicit Euler forward method, in which case no iteration is performed, but the time step Δt must be smaller than $2/\lambda_n$, where λ_n is the largest eigenvalue of the problem $\mathbf{K}\boldsymbol{\phi} = \lambda\mathbf{C}\boldsymbol{\phi}$, with $\mathbf{K}$ and $\mathbf{C}$ changing in nonlinear analysis (see Exercise 9.25). This time step can be estimated from (9.128) or the matrices of the individual finite elements (see Example 9.13 and Exercise 9.27). On the other hand, in incompressible fluid flow solutions, an unconditionally stable implicit time integration method must be used for the pressure equations, whereas implicit or explicit integration can be performed for the velocity and temperature equations (see Section 9.2.5 for an example of coupling integration schemes, and Exercise 9.28).

9.6.2 Exercises

9.25. The governing heat transfer equations of a general linear finite element system are

$$C\dot{\theta} + K\theta = Q$$

$$\theta|_{\text{time }0} = {}^0\theta \qquad\qquad\qquad\text{(a)}$$

(i) Consider the unforced system with $Q = 0$, assume $\theta = \phi e^{-\lambda t}$, and develop the eigenproblem

$$K\phi = \lambda C\phi \qquad\qquad\qquad\text{(b)}$$

(ii) Use the eigensolutions of (b) and show how to solve the equations in (a) by mode superposition.

(iii) Assume now the specific case

$$C = \begin{bmatrix} \frac{1}{2} & 0 \\ 0 & 1 \end{bmatrix}; \qquad K = \begin{bmatrix} 2 & -1 \\ -1 & 1 \end{bmatrix}$$

$$Q = \begin{bmatrix} 1 \\ 0 \end{bmatrix}$$

and obtain the solution using the mode superposition proposed in part (ii).

9.26. Assume that for the general system in Exercise 9.25 a mode superposition solution is performed using only the modes corresponding to the smallest p eigenvalues (i.e., using only the equations corresponding to $\lambda_1, \ldots, \lambda_p$). Show how the error in the solution of the governing finite element equations could be evaluated and also develop a correction scheme similar to the static correction used in the dynamic analysis of structural systems [see (9.52)].

9.27. Assume that the Euler forward method is used in the solution of the governing heat transfer equation $C\dot{\theta} + K\theta = Q$. Show how the critical time step can be evaluated from the individual element matrices. (*Hint*: See Example 9.13.) Apply your result to evaluate the critical time step for the finite element model of the one-dimensional heat transfer problem shown and compare your result with the value given in (9.128).

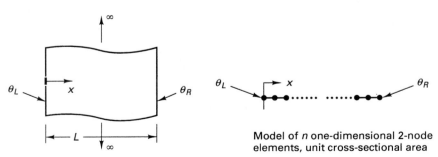

Uniform slab of material constants
k, ρc; initial temperature θ_i;
suddenly θ_L and θ_R are applied

Model of n one-dimensional 2-node
elements, unit cross-sectional area

9.28. Consider the governing finite element equations of incompressible transient fluid flow (7.74) to (7.76). Propose a time integration scheme in which the pressure equations are integrated implicitly and the velocity and temperature equations are integrated explicitly (see Section 9.2.5).

9.29. Use a finite element program to solve for the transient response of the mathematical model shown in the figure in Exercise 9.27. Choose a reasonable finite element discretization and select a time integration scheme and an appropriate time step Δt. Show that your results are reasonably accurate. In this analysis, $k = 0.10$, $pc = 0.01$, $\theta_i = 70$, $\theta_R = 70$, $\theta_L = 400$, $L = 10$.

9.30. Proceed as in Exercise 9.29 but for the two-dimensional mathematical model of a corner where the surface temperature θ^S is suddenly applied at time 0^+.

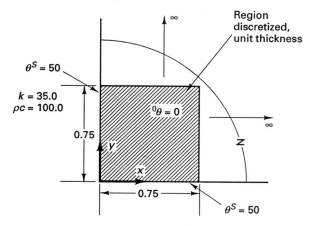

9.31. Use a computer program to solve for the transient response of a fluid between two rotating cylinders. Use the same geometries and material properties as in Exercise 7.28. Assume that the cylinders are initially at rest and that the full rotational velocities are developed in the time interval 0 to 1.

    Compare your results with the analytically calculated steady-state solution (see, for example, F. M. White [A]).

9.32. Use a computer program to solve for the transient response of a fluid between two plates; see the figure for the data to be used. The bottom plate is at rest, and the top plate starts from rest and with a linear increase reaches a steady-state velocity V. The fluid is subjected to a pressure gradient.

    Compare your results with the analytically calculated steady-state solution (see, for example, H. Schlichting [A]).

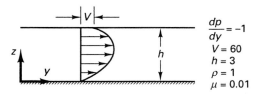

CHAPTER TEN

Preliminaries to the Solution of Eigenproblems

10.1 INTRODUCTION

In various sections of the preceding chapters we encountered eigenproblems and the statement of their solutions. We did not at that time discuss how to obtain the required eigenvalues and eigenvectors. It is the purpose of this and the next chapter to describe the actual solution procedures used to solve the eigenproblems of interest. Before presenting the algorithms, we discuss in this chapter some important basic considerations for the solution of eigenproblems.

First, let us briefly summarize the eigenproblems that we want to solve. The simplest problem encountered is the standard eigenproblem,

$$\mathbf{K}\boldsymbol{\phi} = \lambda\boldsymbol{\phi} \tag{10.1}$$

where $\mathbf{K}$ is the stiffness matrix of a single finite element or of an element assemblage. We recall that $\mathbf{K}$ has order n, and for an element assemblage the half-bandwidth m_K (i.e., the total bandwidth is $2m_K + 1$), and that $\mathbf{K}$ is positive semidefinite or positive definite. There are n eigenvalues and corresponding eigenvectors satisfying (10.1). The ith eigenpair is denoted as $(\lambda, \boldsymbol{\phi}_i)$, where the eigenvalues are ordered according to their magnitudes:

$$0 \leq \lambda_1 \leq \lambda_2 \cdots \leq \lambda_{n-1} \leq \lambda_n \tag{10.2}$$

The solution for p eigenpairs can be written

$$\mathbf{K}\boldsymbol{\Phi} = \boldsymbol{\Phi}\boldsymbol{\Lambda} \tag{10.3}$$

where $\boldsymbol{\Phi}$ is an $n \times p$ matrix with its columns equal to the p eigenvectors and $\boldsymbol{\Lambda}$ is a $p \times p$ diagonal matrix listing the corresponding eigenvalues. As an example, (10.3) may represent the solution to the lowest p eigenvalues and corresponding eigenvectors of $\mathbf{K}$, in which case $\boldsymbol{\Phi} = [\boldsymbol{\phi}_1, \ldots, \boldsymbol{\phi}_p]$ and $\boldsymbol{\Lambda} = \text{diag}(\lambda_i), i = 1, \ldots, p$. We recall that if $\mathbf{K}$ is positive definite,

$\lambda_i > 0$, $i = 1, \ldots, n$, and if $\mathbf{K}$ is positive semidefinite, $\lambda_i \geq 0$, $i = 1, \ldots, n$, where the number of zero eigenvalues is equal to the number of rigid body modes in the system.

The solution of the eigenvalue problem in (10.1) is, for example, sought in the evaluation of an element stiffness matrix or in the calculation of the condition number of a structure stiffness matrix. We discussed in Section 4.3.2 that the representation of the element stiffness matrix in its canonical form (i.e., in the eigenvector basis) is used to evaluate the effectiveness of the element. In this case all eigenvalues and vectors of $\mathbf{K}$ must be calculated. On the other hand, to evaluate the condition number of a stiffness matrix, only the smallest and largest eigenvalues are required (see Section 8.2.6).

Before proceeding to the generalized eigenproblems, we should mention that other standard eigenproblems may also need to be solved. For example, we may require the eigenvalues of the mass matrix $\mathbf{M}$, in which case $\mathbf{M}$ replaces $\mathbf{K}$ in (10.1). Similarly, we may want to solve for the eigenvalues of a conductivity or heat capacity matrix in heat flow analysis (see Section 7.2).

A very frequently considered eigenproblem is the one to be solved in vibration mode superposition analysis (see Section 9.3). In this case we consider the generalized eigenproblem,

$$\mathbf{K}\boldsymbol{\phi} = \lambda \mathbf{M}\boldsymbol{\phi} \tag{10.4}$$

where $\mathbf{K}$ and $\mathbf{M}$ are, respectively, the stiffness matrix and mass matrix of the finite element assemblage. The eigenvalues λ_i and eigenvectors $\boldsymbol{\phi}_i$ are the free vibration frequencies (radians/second) squared, ω_i^2, and corresponding mode shape vectors, respectively. The properties of $\mathbf{K}$ are as discussed above. The mass matrix may be banded, in which case its half-bandwidth m_M is equal to m_K, or $\mathbf{M}$ may be diagonal with $m_{ii} \geq 0$; i.e., some diagonal elements may possibly be zero. A banded mass matrix, obtained in a consistent mass analysis, is always positive definite, whereas a lumped mass matrix is positive definite only if all diagonal elements are larger than zero. In general, a diagonal mass matrix is positive semidefinite.

In analogy to (10.3), the solution for p eigenvalues and corresponding eigenvectors of (10.4) can be written

$$\mathbf{K}\boldsymbol{\Phi} = \mathbf{M}\boldsymbol{\Phi}\boldsymbol{\Lambda} \tag{10.5}$$

where the columns in $\boldsymbol{\Phi}$ are the eigenvectors and $\boldsymbol{\Lambda}$ is a diagonal matrix listing the corresponding eigenvalues.

Of course, the generalized eigenproblem in (10.4) reduces to the standard eigenproblem in (10.1) if $\mathbf{M}$ is an identity matrix. In other words, the eigenvalues and eigenvectors in (10.3) can also be thought of as frequencies squared and vibration mode shapes of the system when unit mass is specified at each degree of freedom. Corresponding to the possible eigenvalues in the solution of (10.1), the generalized eigenproblem in (10.4) has eigenvalues $\lambda_i \geq 0$, $i = 1, \ldots, n$, where the number of zero eigenvalues is again equal to the number of rigid body modes in the system.

Two additional generalized eigenproblems should be mentioned briefly. A second problem is solved in linearized buckling analysis, in which case we consider (see Section 6.8.2)

$${}^{t}\mathbf{K}\boldsymbol{\phi} = \lambda\, {}^{t-\Delta t}\mathbf{K}\boldsymbol{\phi} \tag{10.6}$$

where $^{t-\Delta t}\mathbf{K}$ and $^{t}\mathbf{K}$ are the stiffness matrices corresponding to times (i.e., load levels) $t - \Delta t$ and t, respectively.

A third generalized eigenproblem is encountered in heat transfer analysis, where we consider the equation

$$\mathbf{K}\boldsymbol{\phi} = \lambda \mathbf{C}\boldsymbol{\phi} \tag{10.7}$$

where $\mathbf{K}$ is the heat conductivity matrix and $\mathbf{C}$ is the heat capacity matrix. The eigenvalues and eigenvectors are the thermal eigenvalues and mode shapes, respectively. The solution of (10.7) is required in heat transfer analysis using mode superposition (see Exercise 9.25). The matrices $\mathbf{K}$ and $\mathbf{C}$ in (10.7) are positive definite or positive semidefinite, so that the eigenvalues of (10.7) are $\lambda_i \geq 0$, $i = 1, \ldots, n$.

In this and the next chapter we discuss the solution of the eigenproblems $\mathbf{K}\boldsymbol{\phi} = \lambda\boldsymbol{\phi}$ and $\mathbf{K}\boldsymbol{\phi} = \lambda\mathbf{M}\boldsymbol{\phi}$ in (10.1) and (10.4). These eigenproblems are encountered frequently in practice. However, it should be realized that all algorithms to be presented are also applicable to the solution of other eigenproblems, provided they are of the same form and the matrices satisfy the appropriate conditions of positive definiteness, semidefiniteness, and so on. For example, to solve the problem in (10.7), the mass matrix $\mathbf{M}$ simply needs to be replaced by the heat capacity matrix $\mathbf{C}$, and the matrix $\mathbf{K}$ is the heat conductivity matrix.

Considering the actual computer solution of the required eigenproblems, we recall that in the introduction to equation solution procedures in static analysis (see Section 8.1), we observed the importance of using effective calculation procedures. This is even more so in eigensystem calculations because the solution of eigenvalues and corresponding eigenvectors requires, in general, much more computer effort than the solution of static equilibrium equations. A particularly important consideration is that the solution algorithms must be stable, which is more difficult to achieve in eigensolutions.

A variety of eigensystem solution methods have been developed and are reported in the literature (see, for example, J. H. Wilkinson [A]). Most of the techniques have been devised for rather general matrices. However, in finite element analysis we are concerned with the solution of the specific eigenproblems summarized above, in which each of the matrices has specific properties such as being banded, positive definite, and so on. The eigensystem solution algorithms should take advantage of these properties in order to make a more economical solution possible.

The objective in this chapter is to lay the foundation for a thorough understanding of effective eigensolution methods. This is accomplished by first discussing the properties of the matrices, eigenvalues, and eigenvectors of the problems of interest and then presenting some approximate solution techniques. The actual solution methods recommended for use are presented in Chapter 11.

10.2 FUNDAMENTAL FACTS USED IN THE SOLUTION OF EIGENSYSTEMS

Before the working of any eigensystem solution procedure can be properly studied, it is necessary first to thoroughly understand the different properties of the matrices and eigenvalues and eigenvectors considered. In particular, we will find that all solution methods are, in essence, based on these fundamental properties. We therefore want to summarize in this section the important properties of the matrices and their eigensystems, although some of the material has already been presented in other sections of the book. As pointed out in Section 10.1, we consider the eigenproblem $\mathbf{K}\boldsymbol{\phi} = \lambda \mathbf{M}\boldsymbol{\phi}$, which reduces to $\mathbf{K}\boldsymbol{\phi} = \lambda \boldsymbol{\phi}$ when $\mathbf{M} = \mathbf{I}$, but the observations made are equally applicable to other eigenproblems of interest.

10.2.1 Properties of the Eigenvectors

It was stated that the solution of the generalized eigenproblem $\mathbf{K}\boldsymbol{\phi} = \lambda \mathbf{M}\boldsymbol{\phi}$ yields n eigenvalues $\lambda_1, \ldots, \lambda_n$, ordered as shown in (10.2), and corresponding eigenvectors $\boldsymbol{\phi}_1, \ldots, \boldsymbol{\phi}_n$. Each eigenpair $(\lambda_i, \boldsymbol{\phi}_i)$ satisfies (10.4); i.e.; we have

$$\mathbf{K}\boldsymbol{\phi}_i = \lambda_i \mathbf{M}\boldsymbol{\phi}_i; \qquad i = 1, \ldots, n \tag{10.8}$$

The significance of (10.8) should be well understood. The equation says that if we establish a vector $\lambda_i \mathbf{M}\boldsymbol{\phi}_i$ and use it as a load vector $\mathbf{R}$ in the equation $\mathbf{KU} = \mathbf{R}$, then $\mathbf{U} = \boldsymbol{\phi}_i$. This thought may immediately suggest the use of static solution algorithms for the calculation of an eigenvector. We will see later that the $\mathbf{LDL}^T$ decomposition algorithm is indeed an important part of eigensolution procedures.

The equation in (10.8) also shows that an eigenvector is defined only within a multiple of itself; i.e., we also have

$$\mathbf{K}(\alpha\,\boldsymbol{\phi}_i) = \lambda_i \mathbf{M}(\alpha\,\boldsymbol{\phi}_i) \tag{10.9}$$

where α is a nonzero constant. Therefore, with $\boldsymbol{\phi}_i$ being an eigenvector, $\alpha\,\boldsymbol{\phi}_i$ is also an eigenvector, and we say that an eigenvector is defined only by its direction in the n-dimensional space considered. However, in our discussion we refer to *the* eigenvectors $\boldsymbol{\phi}_i$ as satisfying (10.8) and also the relation $\boldsymbol{\phi}_i^T \mathbf{M}\boldsymbol{\phi}_i = 1$, which fixes the lengths of the eigenvectors, i.e., the absolute magnitude of the elements in each eigenvector. However, we may note that the eigenvectors are still defined only within a multiplier of -1.

An important relation which the eigenvectors satisfy is that of $\mathbf{M}$-orthonormality; i.e., we have

$$\boldsymbol{\phi}_i^T \mathbf{M}\boldsymbol{\phi}_j = \delta_{ij} \tag{10.10}$$

where δ_{ij} is the Kronecker delta. This relation follows from the orthonormality of the eigenvectors of standard eigenproblems (see Section 2.5) and is discussed further in Section 10.2.5. Premultiplying (10.8) by $\boldsymbol{\phi}_j$ transposed and using the condition in (10.10), we obtain

$$\boldsymbol{\phi}_i^T \mathbf{K}\boldsymbol{\phi}_j = \lambda_i \delta_{ij} \tag{10.11}$$

meaning that the eigenvectors are also $\mathbf{K}$-orthogonal. When using the relations in (10.10) and (10.11) it should be kept in mind that the $\mathbf{M}$- and $\mathbf{K}$-orthogonality follow from (10.8) and that (10.8) is the basic equation to be satisfied. In other words, if we believe that we have an eigenvector and eigenvalue, then as a check we should substitute them into (10.8) (see Example 10.3).

So far we have made no mention of multiple eigenvalues and corresponding eigenvectors. It is important to realize that in this case the eigenvectors are not unique but that we can always choose a set of $\mathbf{M}$-orthonormal eigenvectors which span the subspace that corresponds to a multiple eigenvalue (see Section 2.5). In other words, assume that λ_i has multiplicity m (i.e., $\lambda_i = \lambda_{i+1} = \cdots = \lambda_{i+m-1}$); then we can choose m eigenvectors

$\boldsymbol{\phi}_i, \ldots, \boldsymbol{\phi}_{i+m-1}$ that span the m-dimensional subspace corresponding to the eigenvalues of magnitude λ_i and which satisfy the orthogonality relation in (10.10) and (10.11). However, the eigenvectors are not unique; instead, the eigenspace corresponding to λ_i is unique. We demonstrate the results by means of some examples.

EXAMPLE 10.1: The stiffness matrix and mass matrix of a two degree of freedom system are

$$\mathbf{K} = \begin{bmatrix} 5 & -2 \\ -2 & 2 \end{bmatrix}; \qquad \mathbf{M} = \begin{bmatrix} \frac{5}{4} & 0 \\ 0 & \frac{1}{5} \end{bmatrix}$$

It is believed that the two eigenpairs of the problem $\mathbf{K}\boldsymbol{\phi} = \lambda\boldsymbol{\phi}$ are

$$(d_1, \mathbf{v}_1) = \left(1, \begin{bmatrix} \frac{1}{\sqrt{5}} \\ \frac{2}{\sqrt{5}} \end{bmatrix}\right); \qquad (d_2, \mathbf{v}_2) = \left(6, \begin{bmatrix} \frac{2}{\sqrt{5}} \\ -\frac{1}{\sqrt{5}} \end{bmatrix}\right) \tag{a}$$

and the two eigenpairs of the problem $\mathbf{K}\boldsymbol{\phi} = \lambda\mathbf{M}\boldsymbol{\phi}$ are

$$(g_1, \mathbf{w}_1) = \left(2, \begin{bmatrix} \frac{4}{5} \\ 1 \end{bmatrix}\right); \qquad (g_2, \mathbf{w}_2) = \left(12, \begin{bmatrix} \frac{2}{5} \\ -2 \end{bmatrix}\right) \tag{b}$$

Verify that we indeed have in (a) and (b) the eigensolutions of the problems $\mathbf{K}\boldsymbol{\phi} = \lambda\boldsymbol{\phi}$ and $\mathbf{K}\boldsymbol{\phi} = \lambda\mathbf{M}\boldsymbol{\phi}$, respectively.

Consider first the problem $\mathbf{K}\boldsymbol{\phi} = \lambda\boldsymbol{\phi}$. The values given in (a) are indeed the eigensolution if they satisfy the relation in (10.8) with $\mathbf{M} = \mathbf{I}$ and, to fix the lengths of the vectors, the orthonormality relations in (10.10) with $\mathbf{M} = \mathbf{I}$. Substituting into (10.3), which expresses the relation in (10.8) for all eigenpairs, we have

$$\begin{bmatrix} 5 & -2 \\ -2 & 2 \end{bmatrix} \begin{bmatrix} \frac{1}{\sqrt{5}} & \frac{2}{\sqrt{5}} \\ \frac{2}{\sqrt{5}} & -\frac{1}{\sqrt{5}} \end{bmatrix} = \begin{bmatrix} \frac{1}{\sqrt{5}} & \frac{2}{\sqrt{5}} \\ \frac{2}{\sqrt{5}} & -\frac{1}{\sqrt{5}} \end{bmatrix} \begin{bmatrix} 1 & 0 \\ 0 & 6 \end{bmatrix}$$

or

$$\begin{bmatrix} \frac{1}{\sqrt{5}} & \frac{12}{\sqrt{5}} \\ \frac{2}{\sqrt{5}} & -\frac{6}{\sqrt{5}} \end{bmatrix} = \begin{bmatrix} \frac{1}{\sqrt{5}} & \frac{12}{\sqrt{5}} \\ \frac{2}{\sqrt{5}} & -\frac{6}{\sqrt{5}} \end{bmatrix}$$

Evaluating (10.10), we obtain

$$\mathbf{v}_1^T\mathbf{v}_1 = \begin{bmatrix} \frac{1}{\sqrt{5}} & \frac{2}{\sqrt{5}} \end{bmatrix} \begin{bmatrix} \frac{1}{\sqrt{5}} \\ \frac{2}{\sqrt{5}} \end{bmatrix} = 1$$

$$\mathbf{v}_2^T\mathbf{v}_1 = \begin{bmatrix} \frac{2}{\sqrt{5}} & -\frac{1}{\sqrt{5}} \end{bmatrix} \begin{bmatrix} \frac{1}{\sqrt{5}} \\ \frac{2}{\sqrt{5}} \end{bmatrix} = 0$$

$$\mathbf{v}_2^T\mathbf{v}_2 = \begin{bmatrix} \dfrac{2}{\sqrt{5}} & -\dfrac{1}{\sqrt{5}} \end{bmatrix} \begin{bmatrix} \dfrac{2}{\sqrt{5}} \\ -\dfrac{1}{\sqrt{5}} \end{bmatrix} = 1$$

$$\mathbf{v}_1^T\mathbf{v}_2 = \mathbf{v}_2^T\mathbf{v}_1 = 0$$

Therefore, the relations in (10.3) and (10.10) are satisfied, and we have $\lambda_1 = d_1$, $\lambda_2 = d_2$, $\boldsymbol{\phi}_1 = \mathbf{v}_1$, and $\boldsymbol{\phi}_2 = \mathbf{v}_2$.

To check whether we have in (b) the eigensolution to $\mathbf{K}\boldsymbol{\phi} = \lambda\mathbf{M}\boldsymbol{\phi}$, we proceed in an analogous way. Substituting into (10.5), we have

$$\begin{bmatrix} 5 & -2 \\ -2 & 2 \end{bmatrix} \begin{bmatrix} \frac{4}{5} & \frac{2}{5} \\ 1 & -2 \end{bmatrix} = \begin{bmatrix} \frac{5}{4} & 0 \\ 0 & \frac{1}{5} \end{bmatrix} \begin{bmatrix} \frac{4}{5} & \frac{2}{5} \\ 1 & -2 \end{bmatrix} \begin{bmatrix} 2 & 0 \\ 0 & 12 \end{bmatrix}$$

or

$$\begin{bmatrix} 2 & 6 \\ \frac{2}{5} & -\frac{24}{5} \end{bmatrix} = \begin{bmatrix} 2 & 6 \\ \frac{2}{5} & -\frac{24}{5} \end{bmatrix}$$

and evaluating (10.10), we obtain

$$\mathbf{w}_1^T\mathbf{M}\mathbf{w}_1 = \begin{bmatrix} \frac{4}{5} & 1 \end{bmatrix} \begin{bmatrix} \frac{5}{4} & 0 \\ 0 & \frac{1}{5} \end{bmatrix} \begin{bmatrix} \frac{4}{5} \\ 1 \end{bmatrix} = 1$$

$$\mathbf{w}_2^T\mathbf{M}\mathbf{w}_1 = \begin{bmatrix} \frac{2}{5} & -2 \end{bmatrix} \begin{bmatrix} \frac{5}{4} & 0 \\ 0 & \frac{1}{5} \end{bmatrix} \begin{bmatrix} \frac{4}{5} \\ 1 \end{bmatrix} = 0$$

$$\mathbf{w}_2^T\mathbf{M}\mathbf{w}_2 = \begin{bmatrix} \frac{2}{5} & -2 \end{bmatrix} \begin{bmatrix} \frac{5}{4} & 0 \\ 0 & \frac{1}{5} \end{bmatrix} \begin{bmatrix} \frac{2}{5} \\ -2 \end{bmatrix} = 1$$

$$\mathbf{w}_1^T\mathbf{M}\mathbf{w}_2 = \mathbf{w}_2^T\mathbf{M}\mathbf{w}_1 = 0$$

Hence, the relations in (10.5) and (10.10) are satisfied and we have

$$\lambda_1 = g_1; \qquad \lambda_2 = g_2; \qquad \boldsymbol{\phi}_1 = \mathbf{w}_1; \qquad \boldsymbol{\phi}_2 = \mathbf{w}_2$$

EXAMPLE 10.2:   Consider the eigenproblem

$$\mathbf{K}\boldsymbol{\phi} = \lambda\boldsymbol{\phi} \qquad \text{with } \mathbf{K} = \begin{bmatrix} 2 & & \\ & 2 & \\ & & 3 \end{bmatrix}$$

and show that the eigenvectors corresponding to the multiple eigenvalue are not unique.

The eigenvalues of $\mathbf{K}$ are $\lambda_1 = 2$, $\lambda_2 = 2$, and $\lambda_3 = 3$, and a set of eigenvectors is

$$\boldsymbol{\phi}_1 = \begin{bmatrix} 1 \\ 0 \\ 0 \end{bmatrix}; \qquad \boldsymbol{\phi}_2 = \begin{bmatrix} 0 \\ 1 \\ 0 \end{bmatrix}; \qquad \boldsymbol{\phi}_3 = \begin{bmatrix} 0 \\ 0 \\ 1 \end{bmatrix} \qquad \text{(a)}$$

where $\boldsymbol{\phi}_3$ is unique. These values could be checked as in Example 10.1. However, any linear combinations of $\boldsymbol{\phi}_1$ and $\boldsymbol{\phi}_2$ given in (a) that satisfy the orthonormality conditions in (10.10) with

$\mathbf{M} = \mathbf{I}$ would also be eigenvectors. For example, we could use

$$\boldsymbol{\phi}_1 = \begin{bmatrix} \dfrac{1}{\sqrt{2}} \\ \dfrac{1}{\sqrt{2}} \\ 0 \end{bmatrix} \quad \text{and} \quad \boldsymbol{\phi}_2 = \begin{bmatrix} \dfrac{1}{\sqrt{2}} \\ -\dfrac{1}{\sqrt{2}} \\ 0 \end{bmatrix}$$

That these are indeed eigenvectors corresponding to $\lambda_1 = \lambda_2 = 2$ can again be checked as in Example 10.1. It should be noted that any eigenvectors $\boldsymbol{\phi}_1$ and $\boldsymbol{\phi}_2$ provide a basis for the unique two-dimensional eigenspace that corresponds to λ_1 and λ_2.

The solution to (10.4) for all p required eigenvalues and corresponding eigenvectors was established in (10.5). Using the relations in (10.10) and (10.11), we may now write

$$\boldsymbol{\Phi}^T \mathbf{K} \boldsymbol{\Phi} = \boldsymbol{\Lambda} \tag{10.12}$$

and

$$\boldsymbol{\Phi}^T \mathbf{M} \boldsymbol{\Phi} = \mathbf{I} \tag{10.13}$$

where the p columns of $\boldsymbol{\Phi}$ are the eigenvectors. *It is very important to note that (10.12) and (10.13) are conditions that the eigenvectors must satisfy, but that if the $\mathbf{M}$-orthonormality and $\mathbf{K}$-orthogonality are satisfied, the p vectors need not necessarily be eigenvectors unless $p = n$.* In other words, assume that $\mathbf{X}$ stores p vectors, $p < n$, and that $\mathbf{X}^T \mathbf{K} \mathbf{X} = \mathbf{D}$ and $\mathbf{X}^T \mathbf{M} \mathbf{X} = \mathbf{I}$; then the vectors in $\mathbf{X}$ and the diagonal elements in $\mathbf{D}$ may or may not be eigenvectors and eigenvalues of (10.4). However, if $p = n$, then $\mathbf{X} = \boldsymbol{\Phi}$ and $\mathbf{D} = \boldsymbol{\Lambda}$ because only the eigenvectors span the complete n-dimensional space and diagonalize the matrices $\mathbf{K}$ and $\mathbf{M}$. To underline this observation we present the following example.

EXAMPLE 10.3:   Consider the eigenproblem $\mathbf{K}\boldsymbol{\phi} = \lambda \mathbf{M}\boldsymbol{\phi}$, where

$$\mathbf{K} = \begin{bmatrix} 2 & -1 & 0 \\ -1 & 4 & -1 \\ 0 & -1 & 2 \end{bmatrix}; \quad \mathbf{M} = \begin{bmatrix} \frac{1}{2} & 0 & 0 \\ 0 & 1 & 0 \\ 0 & 0 & \frac{1}{2} \end{bmatrix}$$

and the two vectors

$$\mathbf{v}_1 = \begin{bmatrix} 1 \\ \dfrac{1}{\sqrt{2}} \\ 0 \end{bmatrix}; \quad \mathbf{v}_2 = \begin{bmatrix} 1 \\ -\dfrac{1}{\sqrt{2}} \\ 0 \end{bmatrix}$$

Show that the vectors $\mathbf{v}_1$ and $\mathbf{v}_2$ satisfy the orthogonality relations in (10.12) and (10.13) [i.e., the relations in (10.11) and (10.10)] but that they are not eigenvectors.

For the check we let $\mathbf{v}_1$ and $\mathbf{v}_2$ be the columns in $\boldsymbol{\Phi}$, and we evaluate (10.12) and (10.13). Thus, we obtain

$$\begin{bmatrix} 1 & \dfrac{1}{\sqrt{2}} & 0 \\ 1 & -\dfrac{1}{\sqrt{2}} & 0 \end{bmatrix} \begin{bmatrix} 2 & -1 & 0 \\ -1 & 4 & -1 \\ 0 & -1 & 2 \end{bmatrix} \begin{bmatrix} 1 & 1 \\ \dfrac{1}{\sqrt{2}} & -\dfrac{1}{\sqrt{2}} \\ 0 & 0 \end{bmatrix} = \begin{bmatrix} (4 - \sqrt{2}) & 0 \\ 0 & (4 + \sqrt{2}) \end{bmatrix} \tag{a}$$

and

$$\begin{bmatrix} 1 & \dfrac{1}{\sqrt{2}} & 0 \\[2ex] 1 & -\dfrac{1}{\sqrt{2}} & 0 \end{bmatrix} \begin{bmatrix} \dfrac{1}{2} & & \\[1ex] & 1 & \\[1ex] & & \dfrac{1}{2} \end{bmatrix} \begin{bmatrix} 1 & 1 \\[1ex] \dfrac{1}{\sqrt{2}} & -\dfrac{1}{\sqrt{2}} \\[1ex] 0 & 0 \end{bmatrix} = \begin{bmatrix} 1 & 0 \\ 0 & 1 \end{bmatrix}$$

Hence, the orthogonality relations are satisfied. To show that $\mathbf{v}_1$ and $\mathbf{v}_2$ are not eigenvectors, we employ (10.8). For example,

$$\mathbf{K}\mathbf{v}_1 = \begin{bmatrix} 2 - \dfrac{1}{\sqrt{2}} \\[2ex] -1 + \dfrac{4}{\sqrt{2}} \\[2ex] -\dfrac{1}{\sqrt{2}} \end{bmatrix}; \qquad \mathbf{M}\mathbf{v}_1 = \begin{bmatrix} \dfrac{1}{2} \\[2ex] \dfrac{1}{\sqrt{2}} \\[2ex] 0 \end{bmatrix}$$

However, the vector $\mathbf{K}\mathbf{v}_1$ cannot be equal to the vector $\alpha \mathbf{M}\mathbf{v}_1$, where α is a scalar; i.e., $\mathbf{K}\mathbf{v}_1$ is not parallel to $\mathbf{M}\mathbf{v}_1$, and therefore $\mathbf{v}_1$ is not an eigenvector. Similarly, $\mathbf{v}_2$ is not an eigenvector and the values $(4 - \sqrt{2})$ and $(4 + \sqrt{2})$ calculated in (a) are not eigenvalues. The actual eigenvalues and corresponding eigenvectors are given in Example 10.4.

In the preceding presentation we considered the properties of the eigenvectors of the problem $\mathbf{K}\boldsymbol{\phi} = \lambda \mathbf{M}\boldsymbol{\phi}$, and we should now briefly comment on the properties of the eigenvectors calculated in the solution of the other eigenvalue problems of interest. The comment is simple: the orthogonality relations discussed here hold equally for the eigenvectors of the problems encountered in buckling analysis and heat transfer analysis. That is, we also have in buckling analysis, using the notation in (10.6),

$$\left. \begin{array}{ll} \boldsymbol{\phi}_i^{T\ t-\Delta t}\mathbf{K}\boldsymbol{\phi}_j = \delta_{ij}; & \boldsymbol{\phi}_i^{T\ t}\mathbf{K}\boldsymbol{\phi}_j = \lambda_i \delta_{ij} \\[1ex] \boldsymbol{\Phi}^{T\ t-\Delta t}\mathbf{K}\boldsymbol{\Phi} = \mathbf{I}; & \boldsymbol{\Phi}^{T\ t}\mathbf{K}\boldsymbol{\Phi} = \boldsymbol{\Lambda} \end{array} \right\} \tag{10.14}$$

and in heat transfer analysis, using the notation in (10.7), we have

$$\left. \begin{array}{ll} \boldsymbol{\phi}_i^T \mathbf{C}\boldsymbol{\phi}_j = \delta_{ij}; & \boldsymbol{\phi}_i^T \mathbf{K}\boldsymbol{\phi}_j = \lambda_i \delta_{ij} \\[1ex] \boldsymbol{\Phi}^T \mathbf{C}\boldsymbol{\Phi} = \mathbf{I}; & \boldsymbol{\Phi}^T \mathbf{K}\boldsymbol{\Phi} = \boldsymbol{\Lambda} \end{array} \right\} \tag{10.15}$$

As for the eigenproblem $\mathbf{K}\boldsymbol{\phi} = \lambda \mathbf{M}\boldsymbol{\phi}$, the proof of the relations in (10.14) and (10.15) depends on the fact that the generalized eigenproblems can be transformed to a standard form. We discuss this matter further in Section 10.2.5.

10.2.2 The Characteristic Polynomials of the Eigenproblem $\mathbf{K}\boldsymbol{\phi} = \lambda \mathbf{M}\boldsymbol{\phi}$ and of Its Associated Constraint Problems

An important property of the eigenvalues of the problem $\mathbf{K}\boldsymbol{\phi} = \lambda \mathbf{M}\boldsymbol{\phi}$ is that they are the roots of the characteristic polynomial,

$$p(\lambda) = \det(\mathbf{K} - \lambda \mathbf{M}) \tag{10.16}$$

We can show that this property derives from the basic relation in (10.8). Rewriting (10.8) in the form

$$(\mathbf{K} - \lambda_i \mathbf{M})\boldsymbol{\phi}_i = \mathbf{0} \tag{10.17}$$

we observe that (10.8) can be satisfied only for nontrivial $\boldsymbol{\phi}_i$ (i.e., $\boldsymbol{\phi}_i$ not being equal to a null vector) provided that the matrix $\mathbf{K} - \lambda_i \mathbf{M}$ is singular. This means that if we factorize $\mathbf{K} - \lambda_i \mathbf{M}$ into a unit lower triangular matrix $\mathbf{L}$ and an upper triangular matrix $\mathbf{S}$ using Gauss elimination, we have $s_{nn} = 0$. However, since

$$p(\lambda_i) = \det \mathbf{LS} = \prod_{i=1}^{n} s_{ii} \tag{10.18}$$

it follows that $p(\lambda_i) = 0$. Furthermore, if λ_i has multiplicity m, we also have $s_{n-1,n-1} = \cdots = s_{n-m+1,n-m+1} = 0$. We should note that in the factorization of $\mathbf{K} - \lambda_i \mathbf{M}$, interchanges may be needed, in which case the factorization of $\mathbf{K} - \lambda_i \mathbf{M}$ with its rows and possibly its columns interchanged is obtained (each row and each column interchange then introduces a sign change in the determinant which must be taken into account; see Section 2.2). If no interchanges are carried out, or row and corresponding column interchanges are performed, which in practice is nearly always possible (but see Example 10.4 for a case where it is not possible), the coefficient matrix remains symmetric. In this case we can write for (10.18)

$$p(\lambda_i) = \det \mathbf{LDL}^T = \prod_{i=1}^{n} d_{ii} \tag{10.19}$$

where $\mathbf{LDL}^T$ is the factorization of $\mathbf{K} - \lambda_i \mathbf{M}$ or of the matrix derived from it by interchanging rows and corresponding columns, i.e., using a different ordering for the system degrees of freedom (see Section 8.2.5). The condition $s_{nn} = 0$ is now $d_{nn} = 0$, and when λ_i has multiplicity m, the last m elements in $\mathbf{D}$ are zero.

In Section 8.2.5 we discussed the Sturm sequence property of the characteristic polynomials of the constraint problems associated with the problem $\mathbf{K}\boldsymbol{\phi} = \lambda\boldsymbol{\phi}$. The same properties that we observed in that discussion are applicable also to the characteristic polynomials of the constraint problems associated with the problem $\mathbf{K}\boldsymbol{\phi} = \lambda\mathbf{M}\boldsymbol{\phi}$. The proof follows from the fact that the generalized eigenproblem $\mathbf{K}\boldsymbol{\phi} = \lambda\mathbf{M}\boldsymbol{\phi}$ can be transformed to a standard eigenproblem for which the Sturm sequence property of the characteristic polynomials holds. Referring the proof to Section 10.2.5, Example 10.11, let us summarize the important result.

The eigenproblem of the rth associated constraint problem corresponding to $\mathbf{K}\boldsymbol{\phi} = \lambda\mathbf{M}\boldsymbol{\phi}$ is given by

$$\mathbf{K}^{(r)}\boldsymbol{\phi}^{(r)} = \lambda^{(r)}\mathbf{M}^{(r)}\boldsymbol{\phi}^{(r)} \tag{10.20}$$

where all matrices are of order $n - r$ and $\mathbf{K}^{(r)}$ and $\mathbf{M}^{(r)}$ are obtained by deleting from $\mathbf{K}$ and $\mathbf{M}$ the last r rows and columns. The characteristic polynomial of the rth associated constraint problem is

$$p^{(r)}(\lambda^{(r)}) = \det(\mathbf{K}^{(r)} - \lambda^{(r)}\mathbf{M}^{(r)}) \tag{10.21}$$

and as for the special case $\mathbf{M} = \mathbf{I}$, the eigenvalues of the $(r + 1)$st constraint problem separate those of the rth constraint problem; i.e., as stated in (8.38), we again have

$$\lambda_1^{(r)} \leq \lambda_1^{(r+1)} \leq \lambda_2^{(r)} \leq \lambda_2^{(r+1)} \leq \cdots \leq \lambda_{n-r-1}^{(r)} \leq \lambda_{n-r-1}^{(r+1)} \leq \lambda_{n-r}^{(r)} \tag{10.22}$$

Consider the following example.

EXAMPLE 10.4: Consider the eigenproblem $\mathbf{K}\boldsymbol{\phi} = \lambda\mathbf{M}\boldsymbol{\phi}$, where

$$\mathbf{K} = \begin{bmatrix} 2 & -1 & 0 \\ -1 & 4 & -1 \\ 0 & -1 & 2 \end{bmatrix}; \qquad \mathbf{M} = \begin{bmatrix} \frac{1}{2} & & \\ & 1 & \\ & & \frac{1}{2} \end{bmatrix}$$

(a) Calculate the eigenvalues using the characteristic polynomial as defined in (10.16).

(b) Solve for the eigenvectors $\boldsymbol{\phi}_i$, $i = 1, 2, 3$, by using the relation in (10.17) and the $\mathbf{M}$-orthonormality condition of the eigenvectors.

(c) Calculate the eigenvalues of the associated constraint problems and show that the eigenvalue separation property given in (10.22) holds.

Using (10.16), we obtain the characteristic polynomial

$$p(\lambda) = (2 - \tfrac{1}{2}\lambda)(4 - \lambda)(2 - \tfrac{1}{2}\lambda) - (-1)(-1)(2 - \tfrac{1}{2}\lambda) - (-1)(-1)(2 - \tfrac{1}{2}\lambda)$$

Hence, $\qquad\qquad\qquad p(\lambda) = -\tfrac{1}{4}\lambda^3 + 3\lambda^2 - 11\lambda + 12$

and we have $\qquad\qquad \lambda_1 = 2; \qquad \lambda_2 = 4; \qquad \lambda_3 = 6$

To obtain the corresponding eigenvectors, we use the relation in (10.17). For λ_1 we have

$$\begin{bmatrix} 1 & -1 & 0 \\ -1 & 2 & -1 \\ 0 & -1 & 1 \end{bmatrix}\boldsymbol{\phi}_1 = \mathbf{0} \tag{a}$$

The coefficient matrix $\mathbf{K} - \lambda_1\mathbf{M}$ in (a) can be factorized into $\mathbf{LDL}^T$ without interchanges. Using the procedure described in Section 8.2.2, we obtain

$$\begin{bmatrix} 1 & & \\ -1 & 1 & \\ 0 & -1 & 1 \end{bmatrix}\begin{bmatrix} 1 & & \\ & 1 & \\ & & 0 \end{bmatrix}\begin{bmatrix} 1 & -1 & 0 \\ & 1 & -1 \\ & & 1 \end{bmatrix}\boldsymbol{\phi}_1 = \mathbf{0} \tag{b}$$

We note that $d_{33} = 0.0$. To evaluate $\boldsymbol{\phi}_1$, we obtain from (b),

$$\begin{bmatrix} 1 & -1 & 0 \\ & 1 & -1 \\ & & 0 \end{bmatrix}\boldsymbol{\phi}_1 = \mathbf{0}$$

Using also $\boldsymbol{\phi}_1^T\mathbf{M}\boldsymbol{\phi}_1 = 1$, we have

$$\boldsymbol{\phi}_1^T = \begin{bmatrix} \dfrac{1}{\sqrt{2}} & \dfrac{1}{\sqrt{2}} & \dfrac{1}{\sqrt{2}} \end{bmatrix}$$

To obtain $\boldsymbol{\phi}_2$ and $\boldsymbol{\phi}_3$, we proceed in an analogous way. Evaluating $\mathbf{K} - \lambda_2\mathbf{M}$, we obtain from (10.17),

$$\begin{bmatrix} 0 & -1 & 0 \\ -1 & 0 & -1 \\ 0 & -1 & 0 \end{bmatrix}\boldsymbol{\phi}_2 = \mathbf{0}$$

In this case we cannot factorize the coefficient matrix preserving symmetry; i.e., we need to interchange only the first and second rows (and not the corresponding columns). This row interchange results into the relation

$$
\begin{bmatrix}
-1 & 0 & -1 \\
0 & -1 & 0 \\
0 & -1 & 0
\end{bmatrix} \boldsymbol{\phi}_2 = \mathbf{0}
$$

Factorizing the coefficient matrix into a unit lower triangular matrix $\mathbf{L}$ and an upper triangular matrix $\mathbf{S}$, we obtain

$$
\begin{bmatrix}
1 & & \\
0 & 1 & \\
0 & 1 & 1
\end{bmatrix}
\begin{bmatrix}
-1 & 0 & -1 \\
& -1 & 0 \\
& & 0
\end{bmatrix} \boldsymbol{\phi}_2 = \mathbf{0}
$$

and hence, $s_{33} = 0$. To solve for $\boldsymbol{\phi}_2$, we use

$$
\begin{bmatrix}
-1 & 0 & -1 \\
& -1 & 0 \\
& & 0
\end{bmatrix} \boldsymbol{\phi}_2 = \mathbf{0}
$$

and $\boldsymbol{\phi}_2^T \mathbf{M} \boldsymbol{\phi}_2 = 1$. Thus, we obtain

$$
\boldsymbol{\phi}_2^T = [-1 \quad 0 \quad 1]
$$

To calculate $\boldsymbol{\phi}_3$, we evaluate $\mathbf{K} - \lambda_3 \mathbf{M}$ and have

$$
\begin{bmatrix}
-1 & -1 & 0 \\
-1 & -2 & -1 \\
0 & -1 & -1
\end{bmatrix} \boldsymbol{\phi}_3 = \mathbf{0}
$$

The coefficient matrix can be factorized into $\mathbf{LDL}^T$ without interchanges; i.e., we have

$$
\begin{bmatrix}
1 & & \\
1 & 1 & \\
0 & 1 & 1
\end{bmatrix}
\begin{bmatrix}
-1 & & \\
& -1 & \\
& & 0
\end{bmatrix}
\begin{bmatrix}
1 & 1 & 0 \\
& 1 & 1 \\
& & 1
\end{bmatrix} \boldsymbol{\phi}_3 = \mathbf{0}
$$

We note that $d_{33} = 0$. To calculate $\boldsymbol{\phi}_3$ we use

$$
\begin{bmatrix}
-1 & -1 & 0 \\
& -1 & -1 \\
& & 0
\end{bmatrix} \boldsymbol{\phi}_3 = \mathbf{0}
$$

and $\boldsymbol{\phi}_3^T \mathbf{M} \boldsymbol{\phi}_3 = 1$. Hence,

$$
\boldsymbol{\phi}_3^T = \left[\frac{1}{\sqrt{2}} \quad -\frac{1}{\sqrt{2}} \quad \frac{1}{\sqrt{2}} \right]
$$

The eigenvalues of the first associated constraint problem are obtained from the solution of

$$
\begin{bmatrix}
2 & -1 \\
-1 & 4
\end{bmatrix} \boldsymbol{\phi}^{(1)} = \lambda^{(1)}
\begin{bmatrix}
\frac{1}{2} & 0 \\
0 & 1
\end{bmatrix} \boldsymbol{\phi}^{(1)}
$$

Hence,

$$
p^{(1)}(\lambda^{(1)}) = \tfrac{1}{2}\lambda^{(1)2} - 4\lambda^{(1)} + 7
$$

and

$$
\lambda_1^{(1)} = 4 - \sqrt{2}; \qquad \lambda_2^{(1)} = 4 + \sqrt{2}
$$

Also $\lambda_1^{(2)} = 4$, and hence the eigenvalue separation property given in (10.22) is in this case:

1. For the eigenvalues of the first and second associated constraint problems,

$$4 - \sqrt{2} < 4 < 4 + \sqrt{2}$$

2. For the eigenvalues of $\mathbf{K}\boldsymbol{\phi} = \lambda\mathbf{M}\boldsymbol{\phi}$ and the first associated constraint problem,

$$2 < (4 - \sqrt{2}) < 4 < (4 + \sqrt{2}) < 6$$

An important fact that follows from the property of the separation of eigenvalues as expressed in (10.22) is the following. Assume that we can factorize the matrix $\mathbf{K} - \mu\mathbf{M}$ into $\mathbf{L}\mathbf{D}\mathbf{L}^T$; i.e., none of the associated constraint problems has a zero eigenvalue. For simplicity of discussion let us first assume that all eigenvalues are distinct; i.e., there are no multiple eigenvalues. *The important fact is that in the decomposition of* $\mathbf{K} - \mu\mathbf{M}$, *the number of negative elements in* $\mathbf{D}$ *is equal to the number of eigenvalues smaller than* μ. Conversely, if $\lambda_i < \mu < \lambda_{i+1}$, there are exactly i negative diagonal elements in $\mathbf{D}$. The proof is obtained using the separation property in (10.22) and is relatively easily outlined by the following considerations. Referring to Fig. 10.1, assume that in the sketch of the characteristic polynomials we connect by straight lines all eigenvalues $\lambda_1^{(r)}$, $r = 0, 1, \ldots$, with $\lambda_1^{(0)} = \lambda_1$, and call the resulting curve C_1. Similarly, we establish curves $C_2, C_3, \ldots$, as indicated in Fig. 10.1. Consider now that $\lambda_i < \mu < \lambda_{i+1}$ and draw a vertical line corresponding to μ in the figure of the characteristic polynomials; i.e., this line establishes where μ lies in relation to the eigenvalues of the associated constraint problems. We note that the line corresponding to μ must cross the curves $C_1, \ldots, C_i$ and because of the eigenvalue

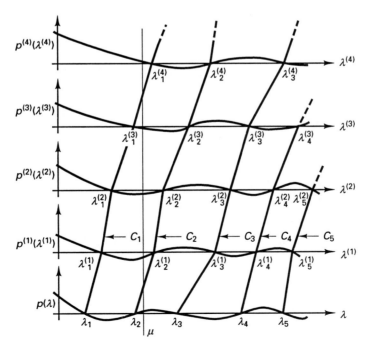

Figure 10.1 Construction of curves C_i for the characteristic polynomials of the problem $\mathbf{K}\boldsymbol{\phi} = \lambda\mathbf{M}\boldsymbol{\phi}$ and of the associated constraint problems

separation property cannot cross the curves $C_{i+1}, \ldots, C_n$. However, since

$$p^{(r)}(\mu) = \prod_{i=1}^{n-r} d_{ii} \tag{10.23}$$

and since each crossing of μ with an envelope C_k corresponds to a negative element appearing in **D**, we have exactly i negative elements in **D**.

These considerations also hold in the case of multiple eigenvalues; i.e., in Fig. 10.1 we would merely find that some eigenvalues are equal, but the argument given above would not change.

The property that the number of negative elements in **D** is equal to the number of eigenvalues smaller than μ can be used directly in the solution of eigenvalues (see Section 11.4.3). Namely, by assuming a shift μ and checking whether μ is smaller or larger than the required eigenvalue, we can successively reduce the interval in which the eigenvalue must lie. We demonstrate the solution procedure in the following example.

EXAMPLE 10.5: Use the fact that the number of negative elements in **D**, where $\mathbf{LDL}^T = \mathbf{K} - \mu\mathbf{M}$, is equal to the number of eigenvalues smaller than μ in order to calculate λ_2 of $\mathbf{K}\boldsymbol{\phi} = \lambda\mathbf{M}\boldsymbol{\phi}$, where

$$\mathbf{K} = \begin{bmatrix} 2 & -1 & 0 \\ -1 & 4 & -1 \\ 0 & -1 & 2 \end{bmatrix}; \qquad \mathbf{M} = \begin{bmatrix} \frac{1}{2} & & \\ & 1 & \\ & & \frac{1}{2} \end{bmatrix}$$

The three eigenvalues of the problem have already been calculated in Example 10.4. We now proceed in the following systematic steps.

1. Let us assume $\mu = 1$ and evaluate $\mathbf{LDL}^T$ of $\mathbf{K} - \mu\mathbf{M}$,

$$\mathbf{K} - \mu\mathbf{M} = \begin{bmatrix} \frac{3}{2} & -1 & 0 \\ -1 & 3 & -1 \\ 0 & -1 & \frac{3}{2} \end{bmatrix}$$

Hence, $\qquad \mathbf{LDL}^T = \begin{bmatrix} 1 & & \\ -\frac{2}{3} & 1 & \\ 0 & -\frac{3}{7} & 1 \end{bmatrix} \begin{bmatrix} \frac{3}{2} & & \\ & \frac{7}{3} & \\ & & \frac{15}{14} \end{bmatrix} \begin{bmatrix} 1 & -\frac{2}{3} & 0 \\ & 1 & -\frac{3}{7} \\ & & 1 \end{bmatrix}$

Since all elements in **D** are larger than zero, we have $\lambda_1 > 1$.

2. We now try $\mu = 8$, where

$$\mathbf{K} - \mu\mathbf{M} = \begin{bmatrix} -2 & -1 & 0 \\ -1 & -4 & -1 \\ 0 & -1 & -2 \end{bmatrix}$$

and $\qquad \mathbf{LDL}^T = \begin{bmatrix} 1 & & \\ \frac{1}{2} & 1 & \\ 0 & \frac{2}{7} & 1 \end{bmatrix} \begin{bmatrix} -2 & & \\ & -\frac{7}{2} & \\ & & -\frac{12}{7} \end{bmatrix} \begin{bmatrix} 1 & \frac{1}{2} & 0 \\ & 1 & \frac{2}{7} \\ & & 1 \end{bmatrix}$

Since all three diagonal elements are smaller than zero, it follows that $\lambda_3 < 8$.

3. The next estimate μ should logically lie between 1 and 8; we choose $\mu = 5$, for which

$$\mathbf{K} - \mu\mathbf{M} = \begin{bmatrix} -\frac{1}{2} & -1 & 0 \\ -1 & -1 & -1 \\ 0 & -1 & -\frac{1}{2} \end{bmatrix}$$

and
$$\mathbf{LDL}^T = \begin{bmatrix} 1 & & \\ 2 & 1 & \\ 0 & -1 & 1 \end{bmatrix} \begin{bmatrix} -\frac{1}{2} & & \\ & 1 & \\ & & -\frac{3}{2} \end{bmatrix} \begin{bmatrix} 1 & 2 & 0 \\ & 1 & -1 \\ & & 1 \end{bmatrix}$$

Since two negative elements are in $\mathbf{D}$, we have $\lambda_2 < 5$.

4. The next estimate must lie between 1 and 5. Let us use $\mu = 3$, in which case

$$\mathbf{K} - \mu\mathbf{M} = \begin{bmatrix} \frac{1}{2} & -1 & 0 \\ -1 & 1 & -1 \\ 0 & -1 & \frac{1}{2} \end{bmatrix}$$

and
$$\mathbf{LDL}^T = \begin{bmatrix} 1 & & \\ -2 & 1 & \\ 0 & 1 & 1 \end{bmatrix} \begin{bmatrix} \frac{1}{2} & & \\ & -1 & \\ & & \frac{3}{2} \end{bmatrix} \begin{bmatrix} 1 & -2 & 0 \\ & 1 & 1 \\ & & 1 \end{bmatrix}$$

Hence $\lambda_2 > 3$, because there is only one negative element in $\mathbf{D}$.

The pattern of the solution procedure has now been established. So far we know that $3 < \lambda_2 < 5$. In order to obtain a closer estimate on λ_2 we would continue choosing a shift μ in the interval 3 to 5 and investigate whether the new shift is smaller or larger than λ_2. By always choosing an appropriate new shift, the required eigenvalue can be determined very accurately (see Section 11.4.3). It should be noted that we did not need to use interchanges in the factorizations of $\mathbf{K} - \mu\mathbf{M}$ carried out above.

10.2.3 Shifting

An important procedure that is used extensively in the solution of eigenvalues and eigenvectors is shifting. The purpose of shifting is to accelerate the calculations of the required eigensystem. In the solution $\mathbf{K}\boldsymbol{\phi} = \lambda\mathbf{M}\boldsymbol{\phi}$, we perform a shift ρ on $\mathbf{K}$ by calculating

$$\hat{\mathbf{K}} = \mathbf{K} - \rho\mathbf{M} \tag{10.24}$$

and we then consider the eigenproblem

$$\hat{\mathbf{K}}\boldsymbol{\psi} = \mu\mathbf{M}\boldsymbol{\psi} \tag{10.25}$$

To identify how the eigenvalues and eigenvectors of $\mathbf{K}\boldsymbol{\phi} = \lambda\mathbf{M}\boldsymbol{\phi}$ are related to those of the problem $\hat{\mathbf{K}}\boldsymbol{\psi} = \mu\mathbf{M}\boldsymbol{\psi}$ we rewrite (10.25) in the form

$$\mathbf{K}\boldsymbol{\psi} = \gamma\mathbf{M}\boldsymbol{\psi} \tag{10.26}$$

where $\gamma = \rho + \mu$. However, (10.26) is, in fact, the eigenproblem $\mathbf{K}\boldsymbol{\phi} = \lambda\mathbf{M}\boldsymbol{\phi}$, and since the solution of this problem is unique, we have

$$\lambda_i = \rho + \mu_i; \qquad \boldsymbol{\phi}_i = \boldsymbol{\psi}_i \tag{10.27}$$

In other words, the eigenvectors of $\hat{\mathbf{K}}\boldsymbol{\psi} = \mu\mathbf{M}\boldsymbol{\psi}$ are the same as the eigenvectors of $\mathbf{K}\boldsymbol{\phi} = \lambda\mathbf{M}\boldsymbol{\phi}$, but the eigenvalues have been decreased by ρ. A frequent application of shifting occurs in the calculation of rigid body modes when an algorithm is to be used that is not designed explicitly to calculate zero eigenvalues. We illustrate such an application in the following example.

EXAMPLE 10.6: Consider the eigenproblem

$$\begin{bmatrix} 3 & -3 \\ -3 & 3 \end{bmatrix} \boldsymbol{\phi} = \lambda \begin{bmatrix} 2 & 1 \\ 1 & 2 \end{bmatrix} \boldsymbol{\phi} \tag{a}$$

Calculate the eigenvalues and eigenvectors. Then impose a shift $\rho = -2$ and solve again for the eigenvalues and corresponding eigenvectors.

To calculate the eigenvalues we use the characteristic polynomial

$$p(\lambda) = \det(\mathbf{K} - \lambda\mathbf{M}) = 3\lambda^2 - 18\lambda$$

and thus obtain $\lambda_1 = 0$, $\lambda_2 = 6$. To calculate $\boldsymbol{\phi}_1$ and $\boldsymbol{\phi}_2$ we use the relation in (10.17) and the mass orthonormality condition $\boldsymbol{\phi}_i^T\mathbf{M}\boldsymbol{\phi}_i = 1$. We have

$$\begin{bmatrix} 3 & -3 \\ -3 & 3 \end{bmatrix} \boldsymbol{\phi}_1 = \mathbf{0}; \qquad \text{hence,} \quad \boldsymbol{\phi}_1 = \begin{bmatrix} \dfrac{1}{\sqrt{6}} \\ \dfrac{1}{\sqrt{6}} \end{bmatrix} \tag{b}$$

and

$$\begin{bmatrix} -9 & -9 \\ -9 & -9 \end{bmatrix} \boldsymbol{\phi}_2 = \mathbf{0}; \qquad \text{hence,} \quad \boldsymbol{\phi}_2 = \begin{bmatrix} \dfrac{1}{\sqrt{2}} \\ -\dfrac{1}{\sqrt{2}} \end{bmatrix} \tag{c}$$

Imposing a shift of $\rho = -2$, we obtain the problem

$$\begin{bmatrix} 7 & -1 \\ -1 & 7 \end{bmatrix} \boldsymbol{\phi} = \lambda \begin{bmatrix} 2 & 1 \\ 1 & 2 \end{bmatrix} \boldsymbol{\phi} \tag{d}$$

Proceeding as before, we have

$$p(\lambda) = \lambda^2 - 10\lambda + 16$$

and obtain as the roots $\lambda_1 = 2$, $\lambda_2 = 8$. Hence the eigenvalues have increased by 2; i.e., they have decreased by ρ.

The eigenvectors would be calculated using (10.17). However, we note that this relation again yields the equations in (b) and (c), and therefore the eigenvectors of the problem in (d) are those of the problem in (a).

An important observation resulting from the above discussion is that, in principle, we need only solution algorithms to calculate the eigenvalues and corresponding eigenvectors of the problem $\mathbf{K}\boldsymbol{\phi} = \lambda\mathbf{M}\boldsymbol{\phi}$ when all eigenvalues are larger than zero. This follows, because if rigid body modes are present, we may always operate on a shifted stiffness matrix that renders all eigenvalues positive.

Extensive applications of shifting are given in Chapter 11, where the various eigensystem solution algorithms are discussed.

10.2.4 Effect of Zero Mass

When using a lumped mass matrix, $\mathbf{M}$ is diagonal with positive and possibly some zero diagonal elements. If all elements m_{ii} are larger than zero, the eigenvalues λ_i can usually not be obtained without the use of an eigenvalue solution algorithm as described in Chapter 11.

However, if $\mathbf{M}$ has some zero diagonal elements, say r diagonal elements in $\mathbf{M}$ are zero, we can immediately say that the problem $\mathbf{K}\boldsymbol{\phi} = \lambda\mathbf{M}\boldsymbol{\phi}$ has the eigenvalues $\lambda_n = \lambda_{n-1} = \cdots = \lambda_{n-r+1} = \infty$ and can also construct the corresponding eigenvectors by inspection.

To obtain the above result, let us recall the fundamental objective in an eigensolution. It is important to remember that all we require is a vector $\boldsymbol{\phi}$ and scalar λ that satisfy the equation

$$\mathbf{K}\boldsymbol{\phi} = \lambda\mathbf{M}\boldsymbol{\phi} \tag{10.4}$$

where $\boldsymbol{\phi}$ is nontrivial; i.e., $\boldsymbol{\phi}$ is a vector with at least one element in it nonzero. In other words, if we have a vector $\boldsymbol{\phi}$ and scalar λ that satisfy (10.4), then λ and $\boldsymbol{\phi}$ are an eigenvalue λ_i and eigenvector $\boldsymbol{\phi}_i$, respectively, where it should be noted that it does not matter how $\boldsymbol{\phi}$ and λ have been obtained. If, for example, we can guess $\boldsymbol{\phi}$ and λ, we should certainly take advantage of it. This may be the case when rigid body modes are present in the structural element assemblage. Thus, if we know that the element assemblage can undergo a rigid body mode, we have $\lambda_1 = 0$ and need to seek $\boldsymbol{\phi}_1$ to satisfy the equation $\mathbf{K}\boldsymbol{\phi}_1 = \mathbf{0}$. In general, the solution of $\boldsymbol{\phi}_1$ must be obtained using an equation solver, but in a simple finite element assemblage we may be able to identify $\boldsymbol{\phi}_1$ by inspection.

In the case of r zero diagonal elements in a diagonal mass matrix $\mathbf{M}$, we can always immediately establish r eigenvalues and corresponding eigenvectors. Rewriting the eigenproblem in (10.4) in the form

$$\mathbf{M}\boldsymbol{\phi} = \mu\mathbf{K}\boldsymbol{\phi} \tag{10.28}$$

where $\mu = \lambda^{-1}$, we find that if $m_{kk} = 0$, we have an eigenpair $(\mu_i, \boldsymbol{\phi}_i) = (0, \mathbf{e}_k)$; i.e.,

$$\boldsymbol{\phi}_i^T = [0 \quad 0 \quad \ldots \quad 0 \quad \underset{\underset{k\text{th element}}{\uparrow}}{1} \quad 0 \quad \ldots \quad 0]; \qquad \mu_i = 0 \tag{10.29}$$

That $\boldsymbol{\phi}_i$ and μ_i in (10.29) are indeed an eigenvector and eigenvalue of (10.28) is verified by simply substituting into (10.28) and noting that $(\mu_i, \boldsymbol{\phi}_i)$ is a nontrivial solution. Since $\mu = \lambda^{-1}$, we therefore found that an eigenpair of $\mathbf{K}\boldsymbol{\phi} = \lambda\mathbf{M}\boldsymbol{\phi}$ is given by $(\lambda_i, \boldsymbol{\phi}_i) = (\infty, \mathbf{e}_k)$. Considering the case of r zero diagonal elements in $\mathbf{M}$, it follows that there are r infinite eigenvalues, and the corresponding eigenvectors can be taken to be unit vectors with each unit vector having the 1 in a location corresponding to a zero mass element in $\mathbf{M}$. Since λ_n is then an eigenvalue of multiplicity r, the corresponding eigenvectors are not unique (see Section 10.2.1). In addition, we note that the length of an eigenvector cannot be fixed using the condition of $\mathbf{M}$-orthonormality. We demonstrate how we establish the eigenvalues and eigenvectors by means of a brief example.

EXAMPLE 10.7:   Consider the eigenproblem

$$\begin{bmatrix} 2 & -1 & & \\ -1 & 2 & -1 & \\ & -1 & 2 & -1 \\ & & -1 & 1 \end{bmatrix} \boldsymbol{\phi} = \lambda \begin{bmatrix} 0 & & & \\ & 2 & & \\ & & 0 & \\ & & & 1 \end{bmatrix} \boldsymbol{\phi}$$

Establish λ_3, λ_4 and $\boldsymbol{\phi}_3$, $\boldsymbol{\phi}_4$.

There are two zero diagonal elements in $\mathbf{M}$; hence, $\lambda_3 = \infty$, $\lambda_4 = \infty$. As corresponding eigenvectors we can use

$$\boldsymbol{\phi}_3 = \begin{bmatrix} 1 \\ 0 \\ 0 \\ 0 \end{bmatrix} \qquad \boldsymbol{\phi}_4 = \begin{bmatrix} 0 \\ 0 \\ 1 \\ 0 \end{bmatrix} \tag{a}$$

Alternatively, any linear combination of $\boldsymbol{\phi}_3$ and $\boldsymbol{\phi}_4$ given in (a) would represent an eigenvector. We should note that $\boldsymbol{\phi}_i^T \mathbf{M} \boldsymbol{\phi}_i = 0$ for $i = 3, 4$, and therefore the magnitude of the elements in $\boldsymbol{\phi}_i$ cannot be fixed using the $\mathbf{M}$-orthonormality condition.

10.2.5 Transformation of the Generalized Eigenproblem $\mathbf{K}\boldsymbol{\phi} = \lambda\mathbf{M}\boldsymbol{\phi}$ to a Standard Form

The most common eigenproblems that are encountered in general scientific analysis are standard eigenproblems, and most other eigenproblems can be reduced to a standard form. For this reason, the solution of standard eigenproblems has attracted much attention in numerical analysis, and many solution algorithms are available. The purpose of this section is to show how the eigenproblem $\mathbf{K}\boldsymbol{\phi} = \lambda\mathbf{M}\boldsymbol{\phi}$ can be reduced to a standard form. The implications of the transformation are twofold. First, because the transformation is possible, use can be made of the various solution algorithms available for standard eigenproblems. We will see that the effectiveness of the eigensolution procedure employed depends to a large degree on the decision whether or not to carry out a transformation to a standard form. Second, *if a generalized eigenproblem can be written in standard form, the properties of the eigenvalues, eigenvectors, and characteristic polynomials of the generalized eigenproblem can be deduced from the properties of the corresponding quantities of the standard eigenproblem.* Realizing that the properties of standard eigenproblems are more easily assessed, it is to a large extent for the second reason that the transformation to a standard eigenproblem is important to be studied. Indeed, after presenting the transformation procedures, we will show how the properties of the eigenvectors (see Section 10.2.1) and the properties of the characteristic polynomials (see Section 10.2.2) of the problem $\mathbf{K}\boldsymbol{\phi} = \lambda\mathbf{M}\boldsymbol{\phi}$ are derived from the corresponding properties of the standard eigenproblem.

In the following we assume that $\mathbf{M}$ is positive definite. This is the case when $\mathbf{M}$ is diagonal with $m_{ii} > 0$, $i = 1, \ldots, n$, or $\mathbf{M}$ is banded, as in a consistent mass analysis. If $\mathbf{M}$ is diagonal with some zero diagonal elements, we first need to perform static condensation on the massless degrees of freedom as described in Section 10.3.1. Assuming that $\mathbf{M}$ is positive definite, we can transform the generalized eigenproblem $\mathbf{K}\boldsymbol{\phi} = \lambda\mathbf{M}\boldsymbol{\phi}$ given in (10.4) by using a decomposition of $\mathbf{M}$ of the form

$$\mathbf{M} = \mathbf{S}\mathbf{S}^T \tag{10.30}$$

where $\mathbf{S}$ is any nonsingular matrix. Substituting for $\mathbf{M}$ into (10.4), we have

$$\mathbf{K}\boldsymbol{\phi} = \lambda\mathbf{S}\mathbf{S}^T\boldsymbol{\phi} \tag{10.31}$$

Premultiplying both sides of (10.31) by $\mathbf{S}^{-1}$ and defining a vector,

$$\tilde{\boldsymbol{\phi}} = \mathbf{S}^T\boldsymbol{\phi} \tag{10.32}$$

we obtain the standard eigenproblem,

$$\tilde{\mathbf{K}}\tilde{\boldsymbol{\phi}} = \lambda\tilde{\boldsymbol{\phi}} \tag{10.33}$$

where

$$\tilde{\mathbf{K}} = \mathbf{S}^{-1}\mathbf{K}\mathbf{S}^{-T} \tag{10.34}$$

One of two decompositions of $\mathbf{M}$ is used in general: the Cholesky factorization or the spectral decomposition of $\mathbf{M}$. The Cholesky factorization of $\mathbf{M}$ is obtained as described in Section 8.2.4 and yields $\mathbf{M} = \tilde{\mathbf{L}}_{\mathrm{M}}\tilde{\mathbf{L}}_{\mathrm{M}}^{T}$. In (10.30) to (10.34) we therefore have

$$\mathbf{S} = \tilde{\mathbf{L}}_{\mathrm{M}} \tag{10.35}$$

The spectral decomposition of $\mathbf{M}$ requires solution of the complete eigensystem of $\mathbf{M}$. Denoting the matrix of orthonormal eigenvectors by $\mathbf{R}$ and the diagonal matrix of eigenvalues by $\mathbf{D}^2$, we have

$$\mathbf{M} = \mathbf{R}\mathbf{D}^2\mathbf{R}^T \tag{10.36}$$

and we use in (10.30) to (10.34),

$$\mathbf{S} = \mathbf{R}\mathbf{D} \tag{10.37}$$

It should be noted that when $\mathbf{M}$ is diagonal, the matrices $\mathbf{S}$ in (10.35) and (10.37) are the same, but when $\mathbf{M}$ is banded, they are different.

Considering the effectiveness of the solution of the required eigenvalues and eigenvectors of (10.33), it is most important that $\tilde{\mathbf{K}}$ has the same bandwidth as $\mathbf{K}$ when $\mathbf{M}$ is diagonal. However, when $\mathbf{M}$ is banded, $\tilde{\mathbf{K}}$ in (10.33) is in general a full matrix, which makes the transformation ineffective in almost all large-order finite element analyses. This will become more apparent in Chapter 11 when various eigensystem solution algorithms are discussed.

Comparing the Cholesky factorization and the spectral decomposition of $\mathbf{M}$, it may be noted that the use of the Cholesky factors is in general computationally more efficient than the use of the spectral decomposition because fewer operations are involved in calculating $\tilde{\mathbf{L}}_{\mathrm{M}}$ than $\mathbf{R}$ and $\mathbf{D}$. However, the spectral decomposition of $\mathbf{M}$ may yield a more accurate solution of $\mathbf{K}\boldsymbol{\phi} = \lambda\mathbf{M}\boldsymbol{\phi}$. Assume that $\mathbf{M}$ is ill-conditioned with respect to inversion; then the transformation process to the standard eigenproblem is also ill-conditioned. In that case it is important to employ the more stable transformation procedure. Using the Cholesky factorization of $\mathbf{M}$ without pivoting, we find that $\tilde{\mathbf{L}}_{\mathrm{M}}^{-1}$ has large elements in many locations because of the coupling in $\mathbf{M}$ and $\tilde{\mathbf{L}}_{\mathrm{M}}^{-1}$. Consequently, $\tilde{\mathbf{K}}$ is calculated with little precision, and the lowest eigenvalues and corresponding eigenvectors are determined inaccurately.

On the other hand, using the spectral decomposition of $\mathbf{M}$, good accuracy may be obtained in the elements of $\mathbf{R}$ and $\mathbf{D}^2$, although some elements in $\mathbf{D}^2$ are small in relation to the other elements. The ill-conditioning of $\mathbf{M}$ is now concentrated in only the small elements of $\mathbf{D}^2$, and considering $\tilde{\mathbf{K}}$, only those rows and columns that correspond to the small elements in $\mathbf{D}$ have large elements, and the eigenvalues of normal size are more likely to be preserved accurately.

Consider the following examples of transforming the generalized eigenvalue problem $\mathbf{K}\boldsymbol{\phi} = \lambda\mathbf{M}\boldsymbol{\phi}$ to a standard form.

EXAMPLE 10.8: Consider the problem $\mathbf{K}\boldsymbol{\phi} = \lambda\mathbf{M}\boldsymbol{\phi}$, where

$$\mathbf{K} = \begin{bmatrix} 3 & -1 & 0 \\ -1 & 2 & -1 \\ 0 & -1 & 1 \end{bmatrix}; \qquad \mathbf{M} = \begin{bmatrix} 2 & 1 & 0 \\ 1 & 3 & 1 \\ 0 & 1 & 2 \end{bmatrix}$$

Use the Cholesky factorization of $\mathbf{M}$ to calculate the matrix $\tilde{\mathbf{K}}$ of a corresponding standard eigenproblem.

We first calculate the $\mathbf{LDL}^T$ decomposition of $\mathbf{M}$,

$$\mathbf{M} = \begin{bmatrix} 1 & & \\ \frac{1}{2} & 1 & \\ 0 & \frac{2}{5} & 1 \end{bmatrix} \begin{bmatrix} 2 & & \\ & \frac{5}{2} & \\ & & \frac{8}{5} \end{bmatrix} \begin{bmatrix} 1 & \frac{1}{2} & 0 \\ & 1 & \frac{2}{5} \\ & & 1 \end{bmatrix}$$

Hence, the Cholesky factor of $\mathbf{M}$ is (see Section 8.2.4)

$$\tilde{\mathbf{L}}_M = \begin{bmatrix} \sqrt{2} & & \\ \dfrac{1}{\sqrt{2}} & \sqrt{\dfrac{5}{2}} & \\ 0 & \sqrt{\dfrac{2}{5}} & \sqrt{\dfrac{8}{5}} \end{bmatrix}$$

and

$$\tilde{\mathbf{L}}_M^{-1} = \begin{bmatrix} \dfrac{1}{\sqrt{2}} & & \\ -\dfrac{1}{\sqrt{10}} & \sqrt{\dfrac{2}{5}} & \\ \dfrac{1}{\sqrt{40}} & -\dfrac{1}{\sqrt{10}} & \sqrt{\dfrac{5}{8}} \end{bmatrix}$$

The matrix of the standard eigenproblem $\tilde{\mathbf{K}} = \tilde{\mathbf{L}}_M^{-1}\mathbf{K}\tilde{\mathbf{L}}_M^{-T}$ is in this case,

$$\tilde{\mathbf{K}} = \begin{bmatrix} \dfrac{3}{2} & -\dfrac{\sqrt{5}}{2} & \dfrac{\sqrt{5}}{4} \\ -\dfrac{\sqrt{5}}{2} & \dfrac{3}{2} & -\dfrac{5}{4} \\ \dfrac{\sqrt{5}}{4} & -\dfrac{5}{4} & \dfrac{3}{2} \end{bmatrix}$$

EXAMPLE 10.9: Consider the generalized eigenproblem in Example 10.8. Use the spectral decomposition of $\mathbf{M}$ to calculate the matrix $\tilde{\mathbf{K}}$ of a corresponding standard eigenproblem.

The eigenvalues and corresponding eigenvectors of the problem $\mathbf{M}\boldsymbol{\phi} = \lambda\boldsymbol{\phi}$ can be calculated as shown in Example 10.4. We obtain $\lambda_1 = 1$, $\lambda_2 = 2$, $\lambda_3 = 4$, and

$$\boldsymbol{\phi}_1 = \begin{bmatrix} \dfrac{1}{\sqrt{3}} \\ -\dfrac{1}{\sqrt{3}} \\ \dfrac{1}{\sqrt{3}} \end{bmatrix}; \qquad \boldsymbol{\phi}_2 = \begin{bmatrix} \dfrac{1}{\sqrt{2}} \\ 0 \\ -\dfrac{1}{\sqrt{2}} \end{bmatrix}; \qquad \boldsymbol{\phi}_3 = \begin{bmatrix} \dfrac{1}{\sqrt{6}} \\ \dfrac{2}{\sqrt{6}} \\ \dfrac{1}{\sqrt{6}} \end{bmatrix}$$

Hence, the decomposition $\mathbf{M} = \mathbf{R}\mathbf{D}^2\mathbf{R}^T$ is

$$\mathbf{M} = \begin{bmatrix} \dfrac{1}{\sqrt{3}} & \dfrac{1}{\sqrt{2}} & \dfrac{1}{\sqrt{6}} \\[8pt] -\dfrac{1}{\sqrt{3}} & 0 & \dfrac{2}{\sqrt{6}} \\[8pt] \dfrac{1}{\sqrt{3}} & -\dfrac{1}{\sqrt{2}} & \dfrac{1}{\sqrt{6}} \end{bmatrix} \begin{bmatrix} 1 & & \\ & 2 & \\ & & 4 \end{bmatrix} \begin{bmatrix} \dfrac{1}{\sqrt{3}} & -\dfrac{1}{\sqrt{3}} & \dfrac{1}{\sqrt{3}} \\[8pt] \dfrac{1}{\sqrt{2}} & 0 & -\dfrac{1}{\sqrt{2}} \\[8pt] \dfrac{1}{\sqrt{6}} & \dfrac{2}{\sqrt{6}} & \dfrac{1}{\sqrt{6}} \end{bmatrix}$$

Noting that $\mathbf{S} = \mathbf{R}\mathbf{D}$ and $\mathbf{S}^{-1} = \mathbf{D}^{-1}\mathbf{R}^T$ because $\mathbf{R}\mathbf{R}^T = \mathbf{I}$, we obtain

$$\mathbf{S}^{-1} = \begin{bmatrix} \dfrac{1}{\sqrt{3}} & -\dfrac{1}{\sqrt{3}} & \dfrac{1}{\sqrt{3}} \\[8pt] \dfrac{1}{2} & 0 & -\dfrac{1}{2} \\[8pt] \dfrac{1}{2\sqrt{6}} & \dfrac{1}{\sqrt{6}} & \dfrac{1}{2\sqrt{6}} \end{bmatrix}$$

The matrix of the standard eigenproblem is $\tilde{\mathbf{K}} = \mathbf{S}^{-1}\mathbf{K}\mathbf{S}^{-T}$; i.e.,

$$\tilde{\mathbf{K}} = \begin{bmatrix} \dfrac{10}{3} & \dfrac{1}{\sqrt{3}} & -\dfrac{1}{3\sqrt{2}} \\[8pt] \dfrac{1}{\sqrt{3}} & 1 & \dfrac{1}{2\sqrt{6}} \\[8pt] -\dfrac{1}{3\sqrt{2}} & \dfrac{1}{2\sqrt{6}} & \dfrac{1}{6} \end{bmatrix}$$

We should note that the matrix $\tilde{\mathbf{K}}$ obtained here is different from the matrix $\tilde{\mathbf{K}}$ derived in Example 10.8.

In the above discussion we considered only the factorization of $\mathbf{M}$ into $\mathbf{M} = \mathbf{S}\mathbf{S}^T$ and then the transformation of $\mathbf{K}\boldsymbol{\phi} = \lambda\mathbf{M}\boldsymbol{\phi}$ into the form given in (10.33). We pointed out that this transformation can yield inaccurate results if $\mathbf{M}$ is ill-conditioned. In such a case it seems natural to avoid the decomposition of $\mathbf{M}$ and instead use a factorization of $\mathbf{K}$. Rewriting $\mathbf{K}\boldsymbol{\phi} = \lambda\mathbf{M}\boldsymbol{\phi}$ in the form $\mathbf{M}\boldsymbol{\phi} = (1/\lambda)\mathbf{K}\boldsymbol{\phi}$, we can use an analogous procedure to obtain the eigenproblem

$$\tilde{\mathbf{M}}\tilde{\boldsymbol{\phi}} = \frac{1}{\lambda}\tilde{\boldsymbol{\phi}} \tag{10.38}$$

where

$$\tilde{\mathbf{M}} = \mathbf{S}^{-1}\mathbf{M}\mathbf{S}^{-T} \tag{10.39}$$

$$\mathbf{K} = \mathbf{S}\mathbf{S}^T \tag{10.40}$$

$$\tilde{\boldsymbol{\phi}} = \mathbf{S}^T\boldsymbol{\phi} \tag{10.41}$$

and $\mathbf{S}$ is obtained using the Cholesky factor or spectral decomposition of $\mathbf{K}$. If $\mathbf{K}$ is well-conditioned, the transformation is also well-conditioned. However, since $\mathbf{K}$ is always banded, $\tilde{\mathbf{M}}$ is always a full matrix, and the transformation is usually inefficient for the solution of $\mathbf{K}\boldsymbol{\phi} = \lambda\mathbf{M}\boldsymbol{\phi}$.

As we pointed out earlier, the possibility of actually solving a generalized eigenproblem by first transforming it into a standard form is only one reason why we considered the above transformations. The second reason is that the properties of the eigensolution of the generalized eigenproblem can be deduced from the properties of the solution of the corresponding standard eigenproblem. Specifically, we can derive the orthogonality properties of the eigenvectors as given in (10.10) and (10.11), and the Sturm sequence property of the characteristic polynomials of the eigenproblem $\mathbf{K}\boldsymbol{\phi} = \lambda \mathbf{M}\boldsymbol{\phi}$ and of its associated constraint problems as given in (10.22). In both cases no fundamentally new concepts need be proved; instead, the corresponding properties of the standard eigenproblem, which is obtained from the generalized eigenproblem, are used. We give the proofs in the following examples as an application of the transformation of a generalized eigenproblem to a standard form.

EXAMPLE 10.10: Show that the eigenvectors of the problem $\mathbf{K}\boldsymbol{\phi} = \lambda \mathbf{M}\boldsymbol{\phi}$ are $\mathbf{M}$- and $\mathbf{K}$-orthogonal and discuss the orthogonality of the eigenvectors of the problems ${}^t\mathbf{K}\boldsymbol{\phi} = \lambda^{t-\Delta t}\mathbf{K}\boldsymbol{\phi}$ given in (10.6) and $\mathbf{K}\boldsymbol{\phi} = \lambda \mathbf{C}\boldsymbol{\phi}$ given in (10.7).

The eigenvector orthogonality is proved by transforming the generalized eigenproblem to a standard form and using the fact that the eigenvectors of a standard eigenproblem with a symmetric matrix are orthogonal. Consider first the problem $\mathbf{K}\boldsymbol{\phi} = \lambda \mathbf{M}\boldsymbol{\phi}$ and assume that $\mathbf{M}$ is positive definite. Then we can use the transformation in (10.30) to (10.34) to obtain, as an equivalent eigenproblem,

$$\tilde{\mathbf{K}}\tilde{\boldsymbol{\phi}} = \lambda \tilde{\boldsymbol{\phi}}$$

where
$$\mathbf{M} = \mathbf{S}\mathbf{S}^T; \qquad \tilde{\mathbf{K}} = \mathbf{S}^{-1}\mathbf{K}\mathbf{S}^{-T}; \qquad \tilde{\boldsymbol{\phi}} = \mathbf{S}^T\boldsymbol{\phi}$$

But since the eigenvectors $\tilde{\boldsymbol{\phi}}_i$ of the problem $\tilde{\mathbf{K}}\tilde{\boldsymbol{\phi}} = \lambda \tilde{\boldsymbol{\phi}}$ have the properties (see Section 2.7)

$$\tilde{\boldsymbol{\phi}}_i^T \tilde{\boldsymbol{\phi}}_j = \delta_{ij}; \qquad \tilde{\boldsymbol{\phi}}_i^T \tilde{\mathbf{K}}\tilde{\boldsymbol{\phi}}_j = \lambda_i \delta_{ij}$$

we have, substituting $\tilde{\boldsymbol{\phi}}_i = \mathbf{S}^T\boldsymbol{\phi}_i$, $\tilde{\boldsymbol{\phi}}_j = \mathbf{S}^T\boldsymbol{\phi}_j$,

$$\boldsymbol{\phi}_i^T \mathbf{M}\boldsymbol{\phi}_j = \delta_{ij}; \qquad \boldsymbol{\phi}_i^T \mathbf{K}\boldsymbol{\phi}_j = \lambda_i \delta_{ij} \qquad \text{(a)}$$

If $\mathbf{M}$ is not positive definite, we consider the eigenproblem $\mathbf{M}\boldsymbol{\phi} = (1/\lambda)\mathbf{K}\boldsymbol{\phi}$ (with $\mathbf{K}$ positive definite or a shift must be imposed; see Section 10.2.3). We now use the transformation

$$\tilde{\mathbf{M}}\tilde{\boldsymbol{\phi}} = \left(\frac{1}{\lambda}\right)\tilde{\boldsymbol{\phi}}$$

where
$$\mathbf{K} = \mathbf{S}\mathbf{S}^T; \qquad \tilde{\mathbf{M}} = \mathbf{S}^{-1}\mathbf{M}\mathbf{S}^{-T}; \qquad \tilde{\boldsymbol{\phi}} = \mathbf{S}^T\boldsymbol{\phi}$$

and the properties
$$\tilde{\boldsymbol{\phi}}_i^T \tilde{\boldsymbol{\phi}}_j = \delta_{ij}; \qquad \tilde{\boldsymbol{\phi}}_i^T \tilde{\mathbf{M}}\tilde{\boldsymbol{\phi}}_j = \left(\frac{1}{\lambda_i}\right)\delta_{ij}$$

Substituting for $\tilde{\boldsymbol{\phi}}_i$ and $\tilde{\boldsymbol{\phi}}_j$, we obtain

$$\boldsymbol{\phi}_i^T \mathbf{K}\boldsymbol{\phi}_j = \delta_{ij}; \qquad \boldsymbol{\phi}_i^T \mathbf{M}\boldsymbol{\phi}_j = \left(\frac{1}{\lambda_i}\right)\delta_{ij} \qquad \text{(b)}$$

with the eigenvectors now being $\mathbf{K}$-orthonormalized, because the problem $\mathbf{M}\boldsymbol{\phi} = (1/\lambda)\mathbf{K}\boldsymbol{\phi}$ was considered. To obtain the same vectors as in the problem $\mathbf{K}\boldsymbol{\phi} = \lambda \mathbf{M}\boldsymbol{\phi}$, we need to multiply the eigenvectors $\boldsymbol{\phi}_i$ of the problem $\mathbf{M}\boldsymbol{\phi} = (1/\lambda)\mathbf{K}\boldsymbol{\phi}$ by the factors $\sqrt{\lambda_i}$, $i = 1, \ldots, n$.

Considering these proofs, we note that we arranged the eigenproblems in such a way that the matrix associated with the eigenvalue, i.e., the matrix on the right-hand side of the eigenvalue problem, is positive definite. This is necessary to be able to carry out the transformation of the generalized eigenproblem to a standard form and thus derive the eigenvector orthogonality properties in (a) and (b). However, considering the problems ${}^{t}\mathbf{K}\boldsymbol{\phi} = \lambda^{t-\Delta t}\mathbf{K}\boldsymbol{\phi}$ and $\mathbf{K}\boldsymbol{\phi} = \lambda\mathbf{C}\boldsymbol{\phi}$ given in (10.6) and (10.7), we can proceed in a similar manner. The results would be the eigenvector orthogonality properties given in (10.14) and (10.15).

EXAMPLE 10.11:   Prove the Sturm sequence property of the characteristic polynomials of the problem $\mathbf{K}\boldsymbol{\phi} = \lambda\mathbf{M}\boldsymbol{\phi}$ and the associated constraint problems. Demonstrate the proof for the following matrices:

$$\mathbf{K} = \begin{bmatrix} 3 & -1 & \\ -1 & 2 & -1 \\ & -1 & 1 \end{bmatrix}; \qquad \mathbf{M} = \begin{bmatrix} 4 & 4 & \\ 4 & 8 & 4 \\ & 4 & 8 \end{bmatrix} \qquad \text{(a)}$$

The proof that we consider here is based on the transformation of the eigenproblems $\mathbf{K}\boldsymbol{\phi} = \lambda\mathbf{M}\boldsymbol{\phi}$ and $\mathbf{K}^{(r)}\boldsymbol{\phi}^{(r)} = \lambda^{(r)}\mathbf{M}^{(r)}\boldsymbol{\phi}^{(r)}$ to standard eigenproblems, for which the characteristic polynomials are known to form a Sturm sequence (see Sections 2.6 and 8.2.5).

As in Example 10.10, we assume first that $\mathbf{M}$ is positive definite. In this case we can transform the problem $\mathbf{K}\boldsymbol{\phi} = \lambda\mathbf{M}\boldsymbol{\phi}$ into the form

$$\tilde{\mathbf{K}}\tilde{\boldsymbol{\phi}} = \lambda\tilde{\boldsymbol{\phi}}$$

where $\qquad \tilde{\mathbf{K}} = \tilde{\mathbf{L}}_\mathbf{M}^{-1}\mathbf{K}\tilde{\mathbf{L}}_\mathbf{M}^{-T}; \qquad \mathbf{M} = \tilde{\mathbf{L}}_\mathbf{M}\tilde{\mathbf{L}}_\mathbf{M}^{T}; \qquad \tilde{\boldsymbol{\phi}} = \tilde{\mathbf{L}}_\mathbf{M}^{T}\boldsymbol{\phi}$

and $\tilde{\mathbf{L}}_\mathbf{M}$ is the Cholesky factor of $\mathbf{M}$.

Considering the eigenproblems $\tilde{\mathbf{K}}\tilde{\boldsymbol{\phi}} = \lambda\tilde{\boldsymbol{\phi}}$ and $\tilde{\mathbf{K}}^{(r)}\tilde{\boldsymbol{\phi}}^{(r)} = \lambda^{(r)}\tilde{\boldsymbol{\phi}}^{(r)}$, $r = 1, \ldots, n-1$ [see (8.37)], we know that the characteristic polynomials form a Sturm sequence. On the other hand, if we consider the eigenproblem $\mathbf{K}\boldsymbol{\phi} = \lambda\mathbf{M}\boldsymbol{\phi}$ and the eigenproblems of its associated constraint problems, i.e., $\mathbf{K}^{(r)}\boldsymbol{\phi}^{(r)} = \lambda^{(r)}\mathbf{M}^{(r)}\boldsymbol{\phi}^{(r)}$ [see (10.20)], we note that *the problems* $\tilde{\mathbf{K}}^{(r)}\tilde{\boldsymbol{\phi}}^{(r)} = \lambda^{(r)}\tilde{\boldsymbol{\phi}}^{(r)}$ *and* $\mathbf{K}^{(r)}\boldsymbol{\phi}^{(r)} = \lambda^{(r)}\mathbf{M}^{(r)}\boldsymbol{\phi}^{(r)}$ *have the same eigenvalues.* Namely, $\tilde{\mathbf{K}}^{(r)}\boldsymbol{\phi}^{(r)} = \lambda^{(r)}\tilde{\boldsymbol{\phi}}^{(r)}$ is a standard eigenproblem corresponding to $\mathbf{K}^{(r)}\boldsymbol{\phi}^{(r)} = \lambda^{(r)}\mathbf{M}^{(r)}\boldsymbol{\phi}^{(r)}$; i.e., instead of eliminating the r rows and columns from $\tilde{\mathbf{K}}$ (to obtain $\tilde{\mathbf{K}}^{(r)}$), we can also calculate $\tilde{\mathbf{K}}^{(r)}$ as follows:

$$\tilde{\mathbf{K}}^{(r)} = \tilde{\mathbf{L}}_\mathbf{M}^{(r)-1}\mathbf{K}^{(r)}\tilde{\mathbf{L}}_\mathbf{M}^{(r)-T}; \qquad \mathbf{M}^{(r)} = \tilde{\mathbf{L}}_\mathbf{M}^{(r)}\tilde{\mathbf{L}}_\mathbf{M}^{(r)T}; \qquad \tilde{\boldsymbol{\phi}}^{(r)} = \tilde{\mathbf{L}}_\mathbf{M}^{(r)T}\boldsymbol{\phi}^{(r)} \qquad \text{(b)}$$

Note that $\tilde{\mathbf{L}}_\mathbf{M}^{(r)}$ and $\tilde{\mathbf{L}}_\mathbf{M}^{(r)-1}$ can be obtained simply by deleting the last r rows and columns of $\tilde{\mathbf{L}}_\mathbf{M}$ and $\tilde{\mathbf{L}}_\mathbf{M}^{-1}$, respectively.

Hence, the Sturm sequence property also holds for the characteristic polynomials of $\mathbf{K}\boldsymbol{\phi} = \lambda\mathbf{M}\boldsymbol{\phi}$ and the associated constraint problems.

For the example to be considered, we have

$$\tilde{\mathbf{L}}_\mathbf{M} = \begin{bmatrix} 2 & 0 & 0 \\ 2 & 2 & 0 \\ 0 & 2 & 2 \end{bmatrix} \qquad \text{(c)}$$

Hence,

$$\tilde{\mathbf{K}} = \begin{bmatrix} \frac{1}{2} & 0 & 0 \\ -\frac{1}{2} & \frac{1}{2} & 0 \\ \frac{1}{2} & -\frac{1}{2} & \frac{1}{2} \end{bmatrix}\begin{bmatrix} 3 & -1 & 0 \\ -1 & 2 & -1 \\ 0 & -1 & 1 \end{bmatrix}\begin{bmatrix} \frac{1}{2} & -\frac{1}{2} & \frac{1}{2} \\ 0 & \frac{1}{2} & -\frac{1}{2} \\ 0 & 0 & \frac{1}{2} \end{bmatrix} = \begin{bmatrix} \frac{3}{4} & -1 & 1 \\ -1 & \frac{7}{4} & -2 \\ 1 & -2 & \frac{5}{2} \end{bmatrix} \qquad \text{(d)}$$

Using $\tilde{\mathbf{K}}$ in (d) to obtain $\tilde{\mathbf{K}}^{(1)}$ and $\tilde{\mathbf{K}}^{(2)}$, we have

$$\tilde{\mathbf{K}}^{(1)} = \begin{bmatrix} \frac{3}{4} & -1 \\ -1 & \frac{7}{4} \end{bmatrix}; \qquad \tilde{\mathbf{K}}^{(2)} = \begin{bmatrix} \frac{3}{4} \end{bmatrix}$$

On the other hand, we can obtain the same matrices $\tilde{\mathbf{K}}^{(1)}$ and $\tilde{\mathbf{K}}^{(2)}$ using the relations in (b),

$$\tilde{\mathbf{K}}^{(1)} = \tilde{\mathbf{L}}_M^{(1)-1} \mathbf{K}^{(1)} \tilde{\mathbf{L}}_M^{(1)-T}; \qquad \tilde{\mathbf{K}}^{(2)} = \tilde{\mathbf{L}}_M^{(2)-1} \mathbf{K}^{(2)} \tilde{\mathbf{L}}_M^{(2)-T}$$

where $\mathbf{K}^{(r)}$ and $\mathbf{M}^{(r)}$ (to calculate $\tilde{\mathbf{L}}_M^{(r)}$) are obtained from $\mathbf{K}$ and $\mathbf{M}$ in (a).

In the preceding discussion we assumed that $\mathbf{M}$ is positive definite. If $\mathbf{M}$ is positive semidefinite, we can consider the problem $\mathbf{M}\boldsymbol{\phi} = (1/\lambda)\mathbf{K}\boldsymbol{\phi}$ instead, in which $\mathbf{K}$ is positive definite (this may mean that a shift has to be imposed; see Section 10.2.3) and thus show that the Sturm sequence property still holds.

It may be noted that it follows from this discussion that the characteristic polynomials of the eigenproblems ${}^t\mathbf{K}\boldsymbol{\phi} = \lambda^{t-\Delta t}\mathbf{K}\boldsymbol{\phi}$ and $\mathbf{K}\boldsymbol{\phi} = \lambda\mathbf{C}\boldsymbol{\phi}$ given in (10.6) and (10.7) and of their associated constraint problems also form a Sturm sequence.

10.2.6 Exercises

10.1. Consider the generalized eigenproblem

$$\begin{bmatrix} 6 & -1 & 0 \\ -1 & 4 & -1 \\ 0 & -1 & 2 \end{bmatrix} \boldsymbol{\phi} = \lambda \begin{bmatrix} 2 & 0 & 0 \\ 0 & 2 & 1 \\ 0 & 1 & 1 \end{bmatrix} \boldsymbol{\phi}$$

(a) Calculate the eigenvalues and eigenvectors and show explicitly that the eigenvectors are $\mathbf{M}$-orthogonal.

(b) Find two vectors that are $\mathbf{M}$-orthogonal but are not eigenvectors.

10.2. Calculate the eigenvalues of the eigenproblem in Exercise 10.1 and of its associated constraint problems. Show that the eigenvalues satisfy the separation property (10.22).

10.3. Consider the eigenproblem

$$\begin{bmatrix} 2 & -1 & 0 \\ -1 & 2 & 0 \\ 0 & 0 & 3 \end{bmatrix} \boldsymbol{\phi} = \lambda \begin{bmatrix} 1 & & \\ & 2 & \\ & & \frac{3}{2} \end{bmatrix} \boldsymbol{\phi}$$

(a) Calculate the eigenvalues and eigenvectors of the problem. Also, calculate the eigenvalues of the associated constraint problems [see (10.20)].

(b) Establish two vectors that are $\mathbf{M}$-orthogonal but are not eigenvectors.

10.4. Calculate the eigenvalues and eigenvectors of the problem

$$\begin{bmatrix} 6 & -1 \\ -1 & 4 \end{bmatrix} \boldsymbol{\phi} = \lambda \begin{bmatrix} 2 & 0 \\ 0 & 0 \end{bmatrix} \boldsymbol{\phi}$$

Then apply a shift $\rho = 3$ on $\mathbf{K}$ and calculate the eigenvalues and eigenvectors of the new problem [see (10.25)].

10.5. Transform the generalized eigenproblem in Exercise 10.1 into a standard form.

10.6. (a) The eigenvalues and eigenvectors of the problem

$$\mathbf{K}\boldsymbol{\phi} = \lambda\boldsymbol{\phi}$$

are

$$\lambda_1 = 1; \qquad \boldsymbol{\phi}_1 = \frac{1}{\sqrt{2}}\begin{bmatrix} 1 \\ 1 \end{bmatrix}$$

$$\lambda_2 = 4; \qquad \boldsymbol{\phi}_2 = \frac{1}{\sqrt{2}}\begin{bmatrix} 1 \\ -1 \end{bmatrix}$$

Calculate $\mathbf{K}$.

(b) The eigenvalues and eigenvectors of the problem

$$\mathbf{K}\boldsymbol{\phi} = \lambda \mathbf{M}\boldsymbol{\phi}$$

are
$$\lambda_1 = 1; \qquad \boldsymbol{\phi}_1 = \frac{1}{\sqrt{3}}\begin{bmatrix} 1 \\ 1 \end{bmatrix}$$

$$\lambda_2 = 4; \qquad \boldsymbol{\phi}_2 = \sqrt{\frac{2}{3}}\begin{bmatrix} -\frac{1}{2} \\ 1 \end{bmatrix}$$

Calculate $\mathbf{K}$ and $\mathbf{M}$. Are the $\mathbf{K}$ and $\mathbf{M}$ matrices in **(a)** and **(b)** unique?

10.3 APPROXIMATE SOLUTION TECHNIQUES

It is apparent from the nature of a dynamic problem that a dynamic response calculation must be substantially more costly than a static analysis. Whereas in a static analysis the solution is obtained in one step, in dynamics the solution is required at a number of discrete time points over the time interval considered. Indeed, we found that in a direct step-by-step integration solution, an equation of statics, which includes the effects of inertia and damping forces, is considered at the end of each discrete time step (see Section 9.2). Considering a mode superposition analysis, the main computational effort is spent in the calculation of the required frequencies and mode shapes, which also requires considerably more effort than a static analysis. It is therefore natural that much attention has been directed toward effective algorithms for the calculation of the required eigensystem in the problem $\mathbf{K}\boldsymbol{\phi} = \lambda \mathbf{M}\boldsymbol{\phi}$. In fact, because the "exact" solution of the required eigenvalues and corresponding eigenvectors can be prohibitively expensive when the order of the system is large and a "conventional" technique is used, approximate techniques of solution have been developed. The purpose of this section is to present the major approximate methods that have been designed and are currently still in use.

The approximate solution techniques have primarily been developed to calculate the lowest eigenvalues and corresponding eigenvectors in the problem $\mathbf{K}\boldsymbol{\phi} = \lambda \mathbf{M}\boldsymbol{\phi}$ when the order of the system is large. Most programs use exact solution techniques in the analysis of small-order systems. However, the problem of calculating the few lowest eigenpairs of relatively large-order systems is very important and is encountered in all branches of structural engineering and in particular in earthquake response analysis. In the following sections we present three major techniques. *The aim in the presentation is not to advocate the implementation of any one of these methods but rather to describe their practical use, their limitations, and the assumptions employed. Moreover, the relationships between the approximate techniques are described, and in Section 11.6 we will, in fact, find that the approximate techniques considered here can be understood to be a first iteration (and may be used as such) in the subspace iteration algorithm.*

10.3.1 Static Condensation

We have already encountered the procedure of static condensation in the solution of static equilibrium equations, where we showed that static condensation is, in fact, an application of Gauss elimination (see Section 8.2.4). In static condensation we eliminated those degrees of freedom that are not required to appear in the global finite element assemblage. For example, the displacement degrees of freedom at the internal nodes of a finite element can be condensed out because they do not take part in imposing interelement continuity. We mentioned in Section 8.2.4 that the term "static condensation" was actually coined in dynamic analysis.

The basic assumption of static condensation in the calculation of frequencies and mode shapes is that the mass of the structure can be lumped at only some specific degrees of freedom without much effect on the accuracy of the frequencies and mode shapes of interest. In the case of a lumped mass matrix with some zero diagonal elements, some of the mass lumping has already been carried out. However, additional mass lumping is in general required. Typically, the ratio of mass degrees of freedom to the total number of degrees of freedom may be somewhere between $\frac{1}{2}$ and $\frac{1}{10}$. The more mass lumping is performed, the less computer effort is required in the solution; however, the more probable it is also that the required frequencies and mode shapes are not predicted accurately. We shall have more to say about this later.

Assume that the mass lumping has been carried out. By partitioning the matrices, we can then write the eigenproblem in the form

$$\begin{bmatrix} \mathbf{K}_{aa} & \mathbf{K}_{ac} \\ \mathbf{K}_{ca} & \mathbf{K}_{cc} \end{bmatrix} \begin{bmatrix} \boldsymbol{\phi}_a \\ \boldsymbol{\phi}_c \end{bmatrix} = \lambda \begin{bmatrix} \mathbf{M}_a & \mathbf{0} \\ \mathbf{0} & \mathbf{0} \end{bmatrix} \begin{bmatrix} \boldsymbol{\phi}_a \\ \boldsymbol{\phi}_c \end{bmatrix} \tag{10.42}$$

where $\boldsymbol{\phi}_a$ and $\boldsymbol{\phi}_c$ are the displacements at the mass and the massless degrees of freedom, respectively, and $\mathbf{M}_a$ is a diagonal mass matrix. The relation in (10.42) gives the condition

$$\mathbf{K}_{ca}\boldsymbol{\phi}_a + \mathbf{K}_{cc}\boldsymbol{\phi}_c = \mathbf{0} \tag{10.43}$$

which can be used to eliminate $\boldsymbol{\phi}_c$. From (10.43) we obtain

$$\boldsymbol{\phi}_c = -\mathbf{K}_{cc}^{-1}\mathbf{K}_{ca}\boldsymbol{\phi}_a \tag{10.44}$$

and substituting into (10.42), we obtain the reduced eigenproblem

$$\mathbf{K}_a\boldsymbol{\phi}_a = \lambda\mathbf{M}_a\boldsymbol{\phi}_a \tag{10.45}$$

where $\qquad\qquad \mathbf{K}_a = \mathbf{K}_{aa} - \mathbf{K}_{ac}\mathbf{K}_{cc}^{-1}\mathbf{K}_{ca} \tag{10.46}$

The solution of the generalized eigenproblem in (10.45) is in most cases obtained by transforming the problem first into a standard form as described in Section 10.2.5. Since $\mathbf{M}_a$ is a diagonal mass matrix with all its diagonal elements positive and probably not small, the transformation is in general well-conditioned.

The analogy to the use of static condensation in static analysis should be noted. Realizing that the right-hand side of (10.42) may be understood to be a load vector $\mathbf{R}$, where

$$\mathbf{R} = \begin{bmatrix} \lambda\mathbf{M}_a\boldsymbol{\phi}_a \\ \mathbf{0} \end{bmatrix} \tag{10.47}$$

we can use Gauss elimination on the massless degrees of freedom in the same way as we do on the degrees of freedom associated with the interior nodes of an element or a substructure (see Section 8.2.4).

One important aspect should be observed when comparing the static condensation procedure on the massless degrees of freedom in (10.42) to (10.46) on the one side, with Gauss elimination or static condensation in static analysis on the other side. Considering (10.47), we find that the loads at the $\boldsymbol{\phi}_a$ degrees of freedom depend on the eigenvalue (free-vibration frequency squared) and eigenvector (mode shape displacements). This means that in (10.45) a further reduction of the number of degrees of freedom to be considered is not possible. This is a basic difference to static condensation as applied in static analysis, where the loads are given explicitly and their effect can be carried over to the remaining degrees of freedom.

EXAMPLE 10.12:   Use static condensation to calculate the eigenvalues and eigenvectors of the problem $\mathbf{K}\boldsymbol{\phi} = \lambda\mathbf{M}\boldsymbol{\phi}$, where

$$\mathbf{K} = \begin{bmatrix} 2 & -1 & 0 & 0 \\ -1 & 2 & -1 & 0 \\ 0 & -1 & 2 & -1 \\ 0 & 0 & -1 & 1 \end{bmatrix}; \qquad \mathbf{M} = \begin{bmatrix} 0 & & & \\ & 2 & & \\ & & 0 & \\ & & & 1 \end{bmatrix}$$

First we rearrange columns and rows to obtain the form given in (10.42), which is

$$\begin{bmatrix} 2 & 0 & -1 & -1 \\ 0 & 1 & 0 & -1 \\ -1 & 0 & 2 & 0 \\ -1 & -1 & 0 & 2 \end{bmatrix}\begin{bmatrix} \boldsymbol{\phi}_a \\ \boldsymbol{\phi}_c \end{bmatrix} = \lambda \begin{bmatrix} 2 & & & \\ & 1 & & \\ & & 0 & \\ & & & 0 \end{bmatrix}\begin{bmatrix} \boldsymbol{\phi}_a \\ \boldsymbol{\phi}_c \end{bmatrix}$$

Hence, $\mathbf{K}_a$ given in (10.46) is in this case,

$$\mathbf{K}_a = \begin{bmatrix} 2 & 0 \\ 0 & 1 \end{bmatrix} - \begin{bmatrix} -1 & -1 \\ 0 & -1 \end{bmatrix}\begin{bmatrix} \frac{1}{2} & 0 \\ 0 & \frac{1}{2} \end{bmatrix}\begin{bmatrix} -1 & 0 \\ -1 & -1 \end{bmatrix} = \begin{bmatrix} 1 & -\frac{1}{2} \\ -\frac{1}{2} & \frac{1}{2} \end{bmatrix}$$

The eigenproblem $\mathbf{K}_a\boldsymbol{\phi}_a = \lambda\mathbf{M}_a\boldsymbol{\phi}_a$ is, therefore,

$$\begin{bmatrix} 1 & -\frac{1}{2} \\ -\frac{1}{2} & \frac{1}{2} \end{bmatrix}\boldsymbol{\phi}_a = \lambda \begin{bmatrix} 2 & \\ & 1 \end{bmatrix}\boldsymbol{\phi}_a$$

and we have

$$\det(\mathbf{K}_a - \lambda\mathbf{M}_a) = 2\lambda^2 - 2\lambda + \tfrac{1}{4}$$

Hence,

$$\lambda_1 = \frac{1}{2} - \frac{\sqrt{2}}{4}; \qquad \lambda_2 = \frac{1}{2} + \frac{\sqrt{2}}{4}$$

The corresponding eigenvectors are calculated using

$$(\mathbf{K}_a - \lambda_i\mathbf{M}_a)\boldsymbol{\phi}_{a_i} = \mathbf{0}; \qquad \boldsymbol{\phi}_{a_i}^T\mathbf{M}_a\boldsymbol{\phi}_{a_i} = 1$$

Hence

$$\boldsymbol{\phi}_{a_1} = \begin{bmatrix} \frac{1}{2} \\ \frac{\sqrt{2}}{2} \end{bmatrix}; \qquad \boldsymbol{\phi}_{a_2} = \begin{bmatrix} -\frac{1}{2} \\ \frac{\sqrt{2}}{2} \end{bmatrix}$$

Using (10.44), we obtain

$$\boldsymbol{\phi}_{c_1} = -\begin{bmatrix} \frac{1}{2} & 0 \\ 0 & \frac{1}{2} \end{bmatrix}\begin{bmatrix} -1 & 0 \\ -1 & -1 \end{bmatrix}\begin{bmatrix} \frac{1}{2} \\ \frac{\sqrt{2}}{2} \end{bmatrix} = \begin{bmatrix} \frac{1}{4} \\ \frac{1+\sqrt{2}}{4} \end{bmatrix}$$

$$\boldsymbol{\phi}_{c_2} = -\begin{bmatrix} \frac{1}{2} & 0 \\ 0 & \frac{1}{2} \end{bmatrix}\begin{bmatrix} -1 & 0 \\ -1 & -1 \end{bmatrix}\begin{bmatrix} -\frac{1}{2} \\ \frac{\sqrt{2}}{2} \end{bmatrix} = \begin{bmatrix} -\frac{1}{4} \\ \frac{-1+\sqrt{2}}{4} \end{bmatrix}$$

Therefore, the solution to the eigenproblem $\mathbf{K}\boldsymbol{\phi} = \lambda\mathbf{M}\boldsymbol{\phi}$ is

$$\lambda_1 = \frac{1}{2} - \frac{\sqrt{2}}{4}; \qquad \boldsymbol{\phi}_1 = \begin{bmatrix} \dfrac{1}{4} \\[2mm] \dfrac{1}{2} \\[2mm] \dfrac{1 + \sqrt{2}}{4} \\[2mm] \dfrac{\sqrt{2}}{2} \end{bmatrix}$$

$$\lambda_2 = \frac{1}{2} + \frac{\sqrt{2}}{4}; \qquad \boldsymbol{\phi}_2 = \begin{bmatrix} -\dfrac{1}{4} \\[2mm] -\dfrac{1}{2} \\[2mm] \dfrac{-1 + \sqrt{2}}{4} \\[2mm] \dfrac{\sqrt{2}}{2} \end{bmatrix}$$

$$\lambda_3 = \infty; \qquad \boldsymbol{\phi}_3 = \begin{bmatrix} 1 \\ 0 \\ 0 \\ 0 \end{bmatrix}$$

$$\lambda_4 = \infty; \qquad \boldsymbol{\phi}_4 = \begin{bmatrix} 0 \\ 0 \\ 1 \\ 0 \end{bmatrix}$$

In the above discusssion we gave the formal matrix equations for carrying out static condensation. The main computational effort is in calculating $\mathbf{K}_a$ given in (10.46), where it should be noted that in practice a formal inversion of $\mathbf{K}_{cc}$ is not performed. Instead, $\mathbf{K}_a$ can be obtained conveniently using the Cholesky factor $\tilde{\mathbf{L}}_{cc}$ of $\mathbf{K}_{cc}$. If we factorize $\mathbf{K}_{cc}$,

$$\mathbf{K}_{cc} = \tilde{\mathbf{L}}_c \tilde{\mathbf{L}}_c^T \tag{10.48}$$

we can calculate $\mathbf{K}_a$ in the following way:

$$\mathbf{K}_a = \mathbf{K}_{aa} - \mathbf{Y}^T\mathbf{Y} \tag{10.49}$$

where $\mathbf{Y}$ is solved from $\qquad\qquad \tilde{\mathbf{L}}_c\mathbf{Y} = \mathbf{K}_{ca} \tag{10.50}$

As pointed out earlier, this procedure is, in fact, Gauss elimination of the massless degrees of freedom, i.e., elimination of those degrees of freedom at which no external forces (mass effects) are acting. Therefore, an alternative procedure to the one given in (10.42) to (10.50) is to directly use Gauss elimination on the $\boldsymbol{\phi}_c$ degrees of freedom without partitioning $\mathbf{K}$ into the submatrices $\mathbf{K}_{aa}$, $\mathbf{K}_{cc}$, $\mathbf{K}_{ac}$, and $\mathbf{K}_{ca}$ because Gauss elimination can be performed in any order (see Example 8.1, Section 8.2.1). However, the bandwidth of the stiffness matrix will then, in general, increase during the reduction process, and problems of storage must be considered.

For the solution of the eigenproblem $\mathbf{K}_a \boldsymbol{\phi}_a = \lambda \mathbf{M}_a \boldsymbol{\phi}_a$, it is important to note that $\mathbf{K}_a$ is, in general, a full matrix, and the solution is relatively expensive unless the order of the matrices is small.

Instead of calculating the matrix $\mathbf{K}_a$, it may be preferable to evaluate the flexibility matrix $\mathbf{F}_a = \mathbf{K}_a^{-1}$, which is obtained using

$$\begin{bmatrix} \mathbf{K}_{aa} & \mathbf{K}_{ac} \\ \mathbf{K}_{ca} & \mathbf{K}_{cc} \end{bmatrix} \begin{bmatrix} \mathbf{F}_a \\ \mathbf{F}_c \end{bmatrix} = \begin{bmatrix} \mathbf{I} \\ \mathbf{0} \end{bmatrix} \tag{10.51}$$

where $\mathbf{I}$ is a unit matrix of the same order as $\mathbf{K}_{aa}$. Therefore, in (10.51), we solve for the displacements of the structure when unit loads are applied in turn at the mass degrees of freedom. Although the degrees of freedom have been partitioned in (10.51), there is no need for it in this analysis (see Example 10.13). Having solved for $\mathbf{F}_a$, we now consider instead of (10.45) the eigenproblem

$$\left(\frac{1}{\lambda}\right) \boldsymbol{\phi}_a = \mathbf{F}_a \mathbf{M}_a \boldsymbol{\phi}_a \tag{10.52}$$

Although this eigenproblem is of a slightly different form than the generalized problem $\mathbf{K}\boldsymbol{\phi} = \lambda \mathbf{M}\boldsymbol{\phi}$, the transformation to a standard problem proceeds in much the same way (see Section 10.2.5). For the transformation we define

$$\tilde{\boldsymbol{\phi}}_a = \mathbf{M}_a^{1/2} \boldsymbol{\phi}_a \tag{10.53}$$

where $\mathbf{M}_a^{1/2}$ is a diagonal matrix with its ith diagonal element equal to the root of the ith diagonal element of $\mathbf{M}_a$. Premultiplying both sides of (10.52) by $\mathbf{M}_a^{1/2}$ and substituting the relation in (10.53), we obtain

$$\tilde{\mathbf{F}}_a \tilde{\boldsymbol{\phi}}_a = \left(\frac{1}{\lambda}\right) \tilde{\boldsymbol{\phi}}_a \tag{10.54}$$

$$\tilde{\mathbf{F}}_a = \mathbf{M}_a^{1/2} \mathbf{F}_a \mathbf{M}_a^{1/2} \tag{10.55}$$

Once the displacements $\boldsymbol{\phi}_a$ have been calculated, we obtain the complete displacement vector using

$$\begin{bmatrix} \boldsymbol{\phi}_a \\ \boldsymbol{\phi}_c \end{bmatrix} = \begin{bmatrix} \mathbf{I} \\ \mathbf{F}_c \mathbf{K}_a \end{bmatrix} \boldsymbol{\phi}_a \tag{10.56}$$

where $\mathbf{F}_c$ was calculated in (10.51). The relation in (10.56) is arrived at by realizing that the forces applied at the mass degrees of freedom to impose $\boldsymbol{\phi}_a$ are $\mathbf{K}_a \boldsymbol{\phi}_a$. Using (10.51), the corresponding displacements at all degrees of freedom are given in (10.56).

EXAMPLE 10.13:   Use the procedure given in (10.51) to (10.56) to calculate the eigenvalues and eigenvectors of the problem $\mathbf{K}\boldsymbol{\phi} = \lambda \mathbf{M}\boldsymbol{\phi}$ considered in Example 10.12.

The first step is to solve the equations

$$\begin{bmatrix} 2 & -1 & 0 & 0 \\ -1 & 2 & -1 & 0 \\ 0 & -1 & 2 & -1 \\ 0 & 0 & -1 & 1 \end{bmatrix} [\mathbf{v}_1 \quad \mathbf{v}_2] = \begin{bmatrix} 0 & 0 \\ 1 & 0 \\ 0 & 0 \\ 0 & 1 \end{bmatrix} \tag{a}$$

where we did not interchange rows and columns in $\mathbf{K}$ in order to obtain the form in (10.51).

For the solution of the equations in (a), we use the $\mathbf{LDL}^T$ decomposition of $\mathbf{K}$, where

$$\mathbf{L} = \begin{bmatrix} 1 & & & \\ -\frac{1}{2} & 1 & & \\ 0 & -\frac{2}{3} & 1 & \\ 0 & 0 & -\frac{3}{4} & 1 \end{bmatrix}; \qquad \mathbf{D} = \begin{bmatrix} 2 & & & \\ & \frac{3}{2} & & \\ & & \frac{4}{3} & \\ & & & \frac{1}{4} \end{bmatrix}$$

Hence, we obtain

$$\mathbf{v}_1^T = [1 \quad 2 \quad 2 \quad 2]; \qquad \mathbf{v}_2^T = [1 \quad 2 \quad 3 \quad 4]$$

and hence, $\qquad \mathbf{F}_a = \begin{bmatrix} 2 & 2 \\ 2 & 4 \end{bmatrix}; \qquad \mathbf{F}_c = \begin{bmatrix} 1 & 1 \\ 2 & 3 \end{bmatrix}$

$$\tilde{\mathbf{F}}_a = \begin{bmatrix} \sqrt{2} & 0 \\ 0 & 1 \end{bmatrix}\begin{bmatrix} 2 & 2 \\ 2 & 4 \end{bmatrix}\begin{bmatrix} \sqrt{2} & 0 \\ 0 & 1 \end{bmatrix} = \begin{bmatrix} 4 & 2\sqrt{2} \\ 2\sqrt{2} & 4 \end{bmatrix}$$

The solution of the eigenproblem

$$\tilde{\mathbf{F}}_a \tilde{\boldsymbol{\phi}}_a = \mu \tilde{\boldsymbol{\phi}}_a$$

gives $\qquad\qquad \mu_1 = 4 - 2\sqrt{2}; \qquad \tilde{\boldsymbol{\phi}}_{a_1} = \begin{bmatrix} -\dfrac{1}{\sqrt{2}} \\ \dfrac{1}{\sqrt{2}} \end{bmatrix}$

$$\text{(b)}$$

$$\mu_2 = 4 + 2\sqrt{2}; \qquad \tilde{\boldsymbol{\phi}}_{a_2} = \begin{bmatrix} \dfrac{1}{\sqrt{2}} \\ \dfrac{1}{\sqrt{2}} \end{bmatrix}$$

Since $\boldsymbol{\phi}_a = \mathbf{M}_a^{-1/2}\tilde{\boldsymbol{\phi}}_a$, we have

$$\boldsymbol{\phi}_{a_1} = \begin{bmatrix} \dfrac{1}{\sqrt{2}} & 0 \\ 0 & 1 \end{bmatrix}\begin{bmatrix} -\dfrac{1}{\sqrt{2}} \\ \dfrac{1}{\sqrt{2}} \end{bmatrix} = \begin{bmatrix} -\dfrac{1}{2} \\ \dfrac{1}{\sqrt{2}} \end{bmatrix}; \qquad \boldsymbol{\phi}_{a_2} = \begin{bmatrix} \dfrac{1}{2} \\ \dfrac{1}{\sqrt{2}} \end{bmatrix} \qquad \text{(c)}$$

The vectors $\boldsymbol{\phi}_{c_1}$, and $\boldsymbol{\phi}_{c_2}$ are calculated using (10.56); hence,

$$\boldsymbol{\phi}_{c_1} = \begin{bmatrix} -\dfrac{1}{4} \\ \dfrac{-1 + \sqrt{2}}{4} \end{bmatrix}; \qquad \boldsymbol{\phi}_{c_2} = \begin{bmatrix} \dfrac{1}{4} \\ \dfrac{1 + \sqrt{2}}{4} \end{bmatrix} \qquad \text{(d)}$$

Since $\mu = 1/\lambda$ we realize that in (b) to (d) we have the same solution as obtained in Example 10.12.

Considering the different procedures of eliminating the massless degrees of freedom, the results of the eigensystem analysis are the same irrespective of the procedure followed, i.e., whether $\mathbf{K}_a$ or $\mathbf{F}_a$ is established and whether the eigenproblem in (10.45) or in (10.52) is solved. The basic assumption in the analysis is that resulting from mass lumping. As we discussed in Section 10.2.4, each zero mass corresponds to an infinite frequency in the system. Therefore, in approximating the original system equation $\mathbf{K}\boldsymbol{\phi} = \lambda\mathbf{M}\boldsymbol{\phi}$ by the equation in (10.42), we replace, in fact, some of the frequencies of $\mathbf{K}\boldsymbol{\phi} = \lambda\mathbf{M}\boldsymbol{\phi}$ by infinite frequencies and assume that the lowest frequencies solved from either equation are not much different. The accuracy with which the lowest frequencies of $\mathbf{K}\boldsymbol{\phi} = \lambda\mathbf{M}\boldsymbol{\phi}$ are approximated by solving $\mathbf{K}_a\boldsymbol{\phi}_a = \lambda\mathbf{M}_a\boldsymbol{\phi}_a$ depends on the specific mass lumping chosen and may be adequate or crude indeed. In general, more accuracy can be expected if more mass degrees of freedom are included. However, realizing that the static condensation results in $\mathbf{K}_a$ having a larger bandwidth than $\mathbf{K}$ (and $\mathbf{F}_a$ is certainly full), the computational effort required in the solution of the reduced eigenproblem increases rapidly as the order of $\mathbf{K}_a$ becomes large (see Section 11.3). On the other hand, if sufficient mass degrees of freedom for accuracy of solution are selected, we may no longer want to calculate the complete eigensystem of $\mathbf{K}_a\boldsymbol{\phi}_a = \lambda\mathbf{M}_a\boldsymbol{\phi}_a$ but only the smallest eigenvalues and corresponding vectors. However, in this case we may just as well consider the problem $\mathbf{K}\boldsymbol{\phi} = \lambda\mathbf{M}\boldsymbol{\phi}$ without mass lumping and solve directly only for the eigenvalues and vectors of interest using one of the algorithms described in Chapter 11.

In summary, the main shortcoming of the mass lumping procedure followed by static condensation is that the accuracy of solution depends to a large degree on the experience of the analyst in distributing the mass appropriately and that the solution accuracy is actually not assessed. We consider the following example to show the approximation that can typically result.

EXAMPLE 10.14: In Example 10.4 we calculated the eigensystem of the problem $\mathbf{K}\boldsymbol{\phi} = \lambda\mathbf{M}\boldsymbol{\phi}$, where $\mathbf{K}$ and $\mathbf{M}$ are given in the example. To evaluate an approximation to the smallest eigenvalue and corresponding eigenvector, consider instead the following eigenproblem, in which the mass is lumped

$$\begin{bmatrix} 2 & -1 & 0 \\ -1 & 4 & -1 \\ 0 & -1 & 2 \end{bmatrix}\boldsymbol{\phi} = \lambda\begin{bmatrix} 0 & & \\ & 2 & \\ & & 0 \end{bmatrix}\boldsymbol{\phi} \tag{a}$$

Using the procedure given in (10.51) to (10.56), we obtain

$$\mathbf{F}_a = [\tfrac{1}{3}]; \qquad \mathbf{F}_c = \begin{bmatrix} \tfrac{1}{6} \\ \tfrac{1}{6} \end{bmatrix}$$

Hence, $\lambda_1 = \tfrac{3}{2}$, $\boldsymbol{\phi}_{a_1} = [1/\sqrt{2}]$, and

$$\boldsymbol{\phi}_{c_1} = \begin{bmatrix} \dfrac{1}{2\sqrt{2}} \\ \dfrac{1}{2\sqrt{2}} \end{bmatrix}$$

The solution of the eigenproblem in (a) for the smallest eigenvalue and corresponding eigenvector is hence

$$\lambda_1 = \tfrac{3}{2}; \qquad \boldsymbol{\phi}_1 = \begin{bmatrix} \dfrac{1}{2\sqrt{2}} \\ \dfrac{1}{\sqrt{2}} \\ \dfrac{1}{2\sqrt{2}} \end{bmatrix}$$

whereas the solution of the original problem (see Example 10.4) is

$$\lambda_1 = 2; \qquad \boldsymbol{\phi}_1 = \begin{bmatrix} \dfrac{1}{\sqrt{2}} \\[2mm] \dfrac{1}{\sqrt{2}} \\[2mm] \dfrac{1}{\sqrt{2}} \end{bmatrix}$$

It should be noted that using the mass lumping procedure, the eigenvalues can be smaller—as in this example—or larger than the eigenvalues of the original system.

10.3.2 Rayleigh-Ritz Analysis

A most general technique for finding approximations to the lowest eigenvalues and corresponding eigenvectors of the problem $\mathbf{K}\boldsymbol{\phi} = \lambda\mathbf{M}\boldsymbol{\phi}$ is the Rayleigh-Ritz analysis. *The static condensation procedure in Section 10.3.1, the component mode synthesis described in the next section, and various other methods can be understood to be Ritz analyses.* As we will see, the techniques differ only in the choice of the Ritz basis vectors assumed in the analysis. In the following we first present the Rayleigh-Ritz analysis procedure in general and then show how other techniques relate to it.

The eigenproblem that we consider is

$$\mathbf{K}\boldsymbol{\phi} = \lambda\mathbf{M}\boldsymbol{\phi} \tag{10.4}$$

where we now first assume for clarity of presentation that $\mathbf{K}$ and $\mathbf{M}$ are both positive definite, which ensures that the eigenvalues are all positive; i.e., $\lambda_1 > 0$. As we pointed out in Section 10.2.3, $\mathbf{K}$ can be assumed positive definite because a shift can always be introduced to obtain a shifted stiffness matrix that satisfies this condition. As for the mass matrix, we now assume that $\mathbf{M}$ is a consistent mass matrix or a lumped mass matrix with no zero diagonal elements, which is a condition that we shall later relax.

Consider first the Rayleigh minimum principle, which states that

$$\lambda_1 = \min \rho(\boldsymbol{\phi}) \tag{10.57}$$

where the minimum is taken over all possible vectors $\boldsymbol{\phi}$, and $\rho(\boldsymbol{\phi})$ is the Rayleigh quotient

$$\rho(\boldsymbol{\phi}) = \frac{\boldsymbol{\phi}^T\mathbf{K}\boldsymbol{\phi}}{\boldsymbol{\phi}^T\mathbf{M}\boldsymbol{\phi}} \tag{10.58}$$

This Rayleigh quotient is obtained from the Rayleigh quotient of the standard eigenvalue problem $\tilde{\mathbf{K}}\tilde{\boldsymbol{\phi}} = \lambda\tilde{\boldsymbol{\phi}}$ (see Sections 2.6 and 10.2.5). Since both $\mathbf{K}$ and $\mathbf{M}$ are positive definite, $\rho(\boldsymbol{\phi})$ has finite values for all $\boldsymbol{\phi}$. Referring to Section 2.6, the bounds on the Rayleigh quotient are

$$0 < \lambda_1 \le \rho(\boldsymbol{\phi}) \le \lambda_n < \infty \tag{10.59}$$

In the Ritz analysis we consider a set of vectors $\overline{\boldsymbol{\phi}}$, which are linear combinations of the Ritz basis vectors $\boldsymbol{\psi}_i$, $i = 1, \ldots, q$; i.e., a typical vector is given by

$$\overline{\boldsymbol{\phi}} = \sum_{i=1}^{q} x_i\boldsymbol{\psi}_i \tag{10.60}$$

where the x_i are the Ritz coordinates. Since $\overline{\phi}$ is a linear combination of the Ritz basis vectors, $\overline{\phi}$ cannot be any arbitrary vector but instead lies in the subspace spanned by the Ritz basis vectors, which we call V_q (see Sections 2.3 and 11.6). It should be noted that the vectors ψ_i, $i = 1, \ldots, q$, must be linearly independent; therefore, the subspace V_q has dimension q. Also, denoting the n-dimensional space in which the matrices $\mathbf{K}$ and $\mathbf{M}$ are defined by V_n, we have that V_q is contained in V_n.

In the Rayleigh-Ritz analysis we aim to determine the specific vectors $\overline{\phi}_i$, $i = 1, \ldots, q$, which, with the constraint of lying in the subspace spanned by the Ritz basis vectors, "best" approximate the required eigenvectors. For this purpose we invoke the Rayleigh minimum principle. The use of this principle determines in what sense the solution "best" approximates the eigenvectors sought, an aspect that we shall point out during the presentation of the solution procedure.

To invoke the Rayleigh minimum principle on $\overline{\phi}$, we first evaluate the Rayleigh quotient,

$$\rho(\overline{\phi}) = \frac{\sum\limits_{j=1}^{q} \sum\limits_{i=1}^{q} x_i x_j \tilde{k}_{ij}}{\sum\limits_{j=1}^{q} \sum\limits_{i=1}^{q} x_i x_j \tilde{m}_{ij}} = \frac{\tilde{k}}{\tilde{m}} \tag{10.61}$$

where

$$\tilde{k}_{ij} = \psi_i^T \mathbf{K} \psi_j \tag{10.62}$$

$$\tilde{m}_{ij} = \psi_i^T \mathbf{M} \psi_j \tag{10.63}$$

The necessary condition for a minimum of $\rho(\overline{\phi})$ given in (10.61) is $\partial\rho(\overline{\phi})/\partial x_i = 0$, $i = 1, \ldots, q$, because the x_i are the only variables. However,

$$\frac{\partial\rho(\overline{\phi})}{\partial x_i} = \frac{2\tilde{m} \sum\limits_{j=1}^{q} x_j \tilde{k}_{ij} - 2\tilde{k} \sum\limits_{j=1}^{q} x_j \tilde{m}_{ij}}{\tilde{m}^2} \tag{10.64}$$

and using $\rho = \tilde{k}/\tilde{m}$, the condition for a minimum of $\rho(\overline{\phi})$ is

$$\sum_{j=1}^{q} (\tilde{k}_{ij} - \rho\tilde{m}_{ij})x_j = 0 \qquad \text{for } i = 1, \ldots, q \tag{10.65}$$

In actual analysis we write the q equations in (10.65) in matrix form, thus obtaining the eigenproblem

$$\tilde{\mathbf{K}}\mathbf{x} = \rho\tilde{\mathbf{M}}\mathbf{x} \tag{10.66}$$

where $\tilde{\mathbf{K}}$ and $\tilde{\mathbf{M}}$ are $q \times q$ matrices with typical elements defined in (10.62) and (10.63), respectively, and $\mathbf{x}$ is a vector of the Ritz coordinates sought:

$$\mathbf{x}^T = [x_1 \quad x_2 \quad \ldots \quad x_q] \tag{10.67}$$

The solution to (10.66) yields q eigenvalues $\rho_1, \ldots, \rho_q$, which are approximations to $\lambda_1, \ldots, \lambda_q$, and q eigenvectors,

$$\mathbf{x}_1^T = [x_1^1 \quad x_2^1 \quad \ldots \quad x_q^1]$$

$$\mathbf{x}_2^T = [x_1^2 \quad x_2^2 \quad \ldots \quad x_q^2]$$

$$\vdots \qquad \qquad \vdots$$

$$\mathbf{x}_q^T = [x_1^q \quad x_2^q \quad \ldots \quad x_q^q] \tag{10.68}$$

The eigenvectors $\mathbf{x}_i$ are used to evaluate the vectors $\overline{\boldsymbol{\phi}}_1, \ldots, \overline{\boldsymbol{\phi}}_q$, which are approximations to the eigenvectors $\boldsymbol{\phi}_1, \ldots, \boldsymbol{\phi}_q$. Using (10.68) and (10.60), we have

$$\overline{\boldsymbol{\phi}}_i = \sum_{j=1}^{q} x_j^i \, \boldsymbol{\psi}_j; \qquad i = 1, \ldots, q \tag{10.69}$$

An important feature of the eigenvalue approximations calculated in the analysis is that they are upper bound approximations to the eigenvalues of interest; i.e.,

$$\lambda_1 \leq \rho_1; \qquad \lambda_2 \leq \rho_2; \qquad \lambda_3 \leq \rho_3; \qquad \ldots; \qquad \lambda_q \leq \rho_q \leq \lambda_n \tag{10.70}$$

meaning that since $\mathbf{K}$ and $\mathbf{M}$ are assumed to be positive definite, $\tilde{\mathbf{K}}$ and $\tilde{\mathbf{M}}$ are also positive definite matrices.

The proof of the inequality in (10.70) shows the actual mechanism that is used to obtain the eigenvalue approximations ρ_i. To calculate ρ_1 we search for the minimum of $\rho(\boldsymbol{\phi})$ that can be reached by linearly combining all available Ritz basis vectors. The inequality $\lambda_1 \leq \rho_1$ follows from the Rayleigh minimum principle in (10.57) and because V_q is contained in the n-dimensional space V_n, in which $\mathbf{K}$ and $\mathbf{M}$ are defined.

The condition that is employed to obtain ρ_2 is typical of the mechanism used to calculate the approximations to the higher eigenvalues. First, we observe that for the eigenvalue problem $\mathbf{K}\boldsymbol{\phi} = \lambda \mathbf{M}\boldsymbol{\phi}$, we have

$$\lambda_2 = \min \rho(\boldsymbol{\phi}) \tag{10.71}$$

where the minimum is now taken over all possible vectors $\boldsymbol{\phi}$ in V_n that satisfy the orthogonality condition (see Section 2.6)

$$\boldsymbol{\phi}^T \mathbf{M} \boldsymbol{\phi}_1 = 0 \tag{10.72}$$

Considering the approximate eigenvectors $\overline{\boldsymbol{\phi}}_i$ obtained in the Rayleigh-Ritz analysis, we observe that

$$\overline{\boldsymbol{\phi}}_i^T \mathbf{M} \overline{\boldsymbol{\phi}}_j = \delta_{ij} \tag{10.73}$$

where δ_{ij} is the Kronecker delta, and that, therefore, in the above Rayleigh-Ritz analysis we obtained ρ_2 by evaluating

$$\rho_2 = \min \rho(\overline{\boldsymbol{\phi}}) \tag{10.74}$$

where the minimum was taken over all possible vectors $\overline{\boldsymbol{\phi}}$ in V_q that satisfy the orthogonality condition

$$\overline{\boldsymbol{\phi}}^T \mathbf{M} \overline{\boldsymbol{\phi}}_1 = 0 \tag{10.75}$$

To show that $\lambda_2 \leq \rho_2$, we consider an auxiliary problem; i.e., assume that we evaluate

$$\tilde{\rho}_2 = \min \rho(\overline{\boldsymbol{\phi}}) \tag{10.76}$$

where the minimum is taken over all vectors $\overline{\boldsymbol{\phi}}$ that satisfy the condition

$$\overline{\boldsymbol{\phi}}^T \mathbf{M} \boldsymbol{\phi}_1 = 0 \tag{10.77}$$

The problem defined in (10.76) and (10.77) is the same as the problem in (10.71) and (10.72), except that in the latter case the minimum is taken over all $\boldsymbol{\phi}$, whereas in the problem in (10.76) and (10.77) we consider all vectors $\overline{\boldsymbol{\phi}}$ in V_q. Then since V_q is contained in V_n, we have $\lambda_2 \leq \tilde{\rho}_2$. On the other hand, $\tilde{\rho}_2 \leq \rho_2$ because the most severe constraint on

$\overline{\phi}$ in (10.77) is $\overline{\phi}_1$. Therefore, we have

$$\lambda_2 \leq \tilde{\rho}_2 \leq \rho_2 \tag{10.78}$$

The basis for the calculation of $\overline{\phi}_2$, and hence ρ_2, is that the minimum of $\rho(\overline{\phi})$ is sought with the orthogonality condition in (10.75) on $\overline{\phi}_1$. Similarly, to obtain ρ_i and $\overline{\phi}_i$, we in fact minimize $\rho(\overline{\phi})$ with the orthogonality conditions $\overline{\phi}^T M \overline{\phi}_j = 0$ for $j = 1, \ldots,$ $i - 1$. Accordingly, the inequality on ρ_i in (10.70) can be proved in an analogous manner to the procedure used above for ρ_2, but all $i - 1$ constraint equations need to be satisfied.

The observation that $i - 1$ constraint equations need to be fulfilled in the evaluation of ρ_i also indicates that we can expect less accuracy in the approximation of the higher eigenvalues than in the approximation of the lower eigenvalues, for which fewer constraints are imposed. This is generally also observed in actual analysis.

Considering the procedure in practical dynamic analysis, the Ritz basis functions may be calculated from a static solution in which q load patterns are specified in $\mathbf{R}$; i.e., we consider

$$\mathbf{K\Psi} = \mathbf{R} \tag{10.79}$$

where $\mathbf{\Psi}$ is an $n \times q$ matrix storing the Ritz basis vectors; i.e., $\mathbf{\Psi} = [\boldsymbol{\psi}_1, \ldots, \boldsymbol{\psi}_q]$. The analysis is continued by evaluating the projections of $\mathbf{K}$ and $\mathbf{M}$ onto the subspace V_q spanned by the vectors $\boldsymbol{\psi}_i$, $i = 1, \ldots, q$; i.e., we calculate

$$\tilde{\mathbf{K}} = \mathbf{\Psi}^T \mathbf{K} \mathbf{\Psi} \tag{10.80}$$

and

$$\tilde{\mathbf{M}} = \mathbf{\Psi}^T \mathbf{M} \mathbf{\Psi} \tag{10.81}$$

where because of (10.79) we have

$$\tilde{\mathbf{K}} = \mathbf{\Psi}^T \mathbf{R} \tag{10.82}$$

Next we solve the eigenproblem $\tilde{\mathbf{K}} \mathbf{x} = \rho \tilde{\mathbf{M}} \mathbf{x}$, the solution of which can be written

$$\tilde{\mathbf{K}} \mathbf{X} = \tilde{\mathbf{M}} \mathbf{X} \boldsymbol{\rho} \tag{10.83}$$

where $\boldsymbol{\rho}$ is a diagonal matrix listing the eigenvalue approximations ρ_i, $\boldsymbol{\rho} = \text{diag}(\rho_i)$, and $\mathbf{X}$ is a matrix storing the $\tilde{\mathbf{M}}$- orthonormal eigenvectors $\mathbf{x}_1, \ldots, \mathbf{x}_q$. The approximations to the eigenvectors of the problem $\mathbf{K}\boldsymbol{\phi} = \lambda \mathbf{M}\boldsymbol{\phi}$ are then

$$\overline{\mathbf{\Phi}} = \mathbf{\Psi} \mathbf{X} \tag{10.84}$$

So far we have assumed that the mass matrix of the finite element system is positive definite; i.e., $\mathbf{M}$ is not a diagonal mass matrix with some zero diagonal elements. The reason for this assumption was to avoid the case $\overline{\phi}^T \mathbf{M} \overline{\phi}$ equal to zero in the calculation of the Rayleigh quotient, in which case $\rho(\overline{\phi})$ gives an infinite eigenvalue. However, the Rayleigh-Ritz analysis can be carried out as described above when $\mathbf{M}$ is a diagonal matrix with some zero diagonal elements, provided the Ritz basis vectors are selected to lie in the subspace that corresponds to the finite eigenvalues. In addition, the Ritz basis vectors must be linearly independent when considering only the mass degrees of freedom in order to obtain a positive definite matrix $\tilde{\mathbf{M}}$. One way of achieving this in practice is to excite different mass degrees of freedom in each of the load vectors in $\mathbf{R}$ in (10.79) (see Section 11.6.3 and Example 10.16).

Of particular interest are the errors that we may expect in the solution. *Although we have shown that an eigenvalue calculated from the Ritz analysis is an upper bound on the corresponding exact eigenvalue of the system, we did not establish anything about the actual error in the eigenvalue.* This error depends on the Ritz basis vectors used because the vectors $\overline{\boldsymbol{\phi}}$ are linear combinations of the Ritz basis vectors $\boldsymbol{\psi}_i$, $i = 1, \ldots, q$. We can obtain good results only if the vectors $\boldsymbol{\psi}_i$ span a subspace V_q that is close to the least dominant subspace of $\mathbf{K}$ and $\mathbf{M}$ spanned by $\boldsymbol{\phi}_1, \ldots, \boldsymbol{\phi}_q$. It should be noted that this does not mean that the Ritz basis vectors should each be close to an eigenvector sought but rather that linear combinations of the Ritz basis vectors can establish good approximations of the required eigenvectors of $\mathbf{K}\boldsymbol{\phi} = \lambda\mathbf{M}\boldsymbol{\phi}$. We further discuss the selection of good Ritz basis vectors and the approximations involved in the analysis in Section 11.6 when we present the subspace iteration method, because this method uses the Ritz analysis technique.

To demonstrate the Rayleigh-Ritz analysis procedure, consider the following examples.

EXAMPLE 10.15: Obtain approximate solutions to the eigenproblem $\mathbf{K}\boldsymbol{\phi} = \lambda\mathbf{M}\boldsymbol{\phi}$ considered in Example 10.4, where

$$\mathbf{K} = \begin{bmatrix} 2 & -1 & 0 \\ -1 & 4 & -1 \\ 0 & -1 & 2 \end{bmatrix}; \qquad \mathbf{M} = \begin{bmatrix} \frac{1}{2} & & \\ & 1 & \\ & & \frac{1}{2} \end{bmatrix}$$

The exact eigenvalues are $\lambda_1 = 2$, $\lambda_2 = 4$, $\lambda_3 = 6$.

1. Use the following load vectors to generate the Ritz basis vectors

$$\mathbf{R} = \begin{bmatrix} 1 & 0 \\ 0 & 0 \\ 0 & 1 \end{bmatrix}$$

2. Then use a different set of load vectors to generate the Ritz basis vectors

$$\mathbf{R} = \begin{bmatrix} 1 & 0 \\ 1 & 1 \\ 1 & 0 \end{bmatrix}$$

In the Ritz analysis we employ the relations in (10.79) to (10.84) and obtain, in case 1,

$$\begin{bmatrix} 2 & -1 & 0 \\ -1 & 4 & -1 \\ 0 & -1 & 2 \end{bmatrix} \boldsymbol{\Psi} = \begin{bmatrix} 1 & 0 \\ 0 & 0 \\ 0 & 1 \end{bmatrix}$$

Hence,

$$\boldsymbol{\Psi} = \begin{bmatrix} \frac{7}{12} & \frac{1}{12} \\ \frac{1}{6} & \frac{1}{6} \\ \frac{1}{12} & \frac{7}{12} \end{bmatrix}$$

and

$$\tilde{\mathbf{K}} = \frac{1}{12}\begin{bmatrix} 7 & 1 \\ 1 & 7 \end{bmatrix}; \qquad \tilde{\mathbf{M}} = \frac{1}{144}\begin{bmatrix} 29 & 11 \\ 11 & 29 \end{bmatrix}$$

The solution of the eigenproblem $\tilde{\mathbf{K}}\mathbf{x} = \rho\tilde{\mathbf{M}}\mathbf{x}$ is

$$(\rho_1, \mathbf{x}_1) = \left(2.4004, \begin{bmatrix} 1.3418 \\ 1.3418 \end{bmatrix}\right); \qquad (\rho_2, \mathbf{x}_2) = \left(4.0032, \begin{bmatrix} 2.0008 \\ -2.0008 \end{bmatrix}\right)$$

Hence, we have as eigenvalue approximations $\rho_1 = 2.40$, $\rho_2 = 4.00$, and evaluating

$$\bar{\Phi} = \begin{bmatrix} \frac{7}{12} & \frac{1}{12} \\ \frac{1}{6} & \frac{1}{6} \\ \frac{1}{12} & \frac{7}{12} \end{bmatrix} \begin{bmatrix} 1.3418 & 2.0008 \\ 1.3418 & -2.0008 \end{bmatrix} = \begin{bmatrix} 0.895 & 1.00 \\ 0.447 & 0 \\ 0.895 & -1.00 \end{bmatrix}$$

we have

$$\bar{\phi}_1 = \begin{bmatrix} 0.895 \\ 0.447 \\ 0.895 \end{bmatrix}; \qquad \bar{\phi}_2 = \begin{bmatrix} 1.00 \\ 0.00 \\ -1.00 \end{bmatrix}$$

Next we assume the load vectors in case 2 and solve

$$\begin{bmatrix} 2 & -1 & 0 \\ -1 & 4 & -1 \\ 0 & -1 & 2 \end{bmatrix} \Psi = \begin{bmatrix} 1 & 0 \\ 1 & 1 \\ 1 & 0 \end{bmatrix}$$

Hence,

$$\Psi = \begin{bmatrix} \frac{5}{6} & \frac{1}{6} \\ \frac{2}{3} & \frac{1}{3} \\ \frac{5}{6} & \frac{1}{6} \end{bmatrix}$$

and

$$\tilde{K} = \begin{bmatrix} \frac{7}{3} & \frac{2}{3} \\ \frac{2}{3} & \frac{1}{3} \end{bmatrix}; \qquad \tilde{M} = \frac{1}{36}\begin{bmatrix} 41 & 13 \\ 13 & 5 \end{bmatrix}$$

The solution of the eigenproblem $\tilde{K}x = \rho\tilde{M}x$ gives

$$(\rho_1, x_1) = (2.000, \begin{bmatrix} 0.70711 \\ 0.70711 \end{bmatrix}); \qquad (\rho_2, x_2) = (6.0000, \begin{bmatrix} -2.1213 \\ 6.3640 \end{bmatrix})$$

Hence, we have as eigenvalue approximations $\rho_1 = 2.00$, $\rho_2 = 6.00$, and evaluating

$$\bar{\Phi} = \begin{bmatrix} \frac{5}{6} & \frac{1}{6} \\ \frac{2}{3} & \frac{1}{3} \\ \frac{5}{6} & \frac{1}{6} \end{bmatrix} \begin{bmatrix} 0.70711 & -2.1213 \\ 0.70711 & 6.3640 \end{bmatrix} = \begin{bmatrix} 0.70711 & -0.70708 \\ 0.70711 & 0.70713 \\ 0.70711 & -0.70708 \end{bmatrix}$$

we have

$$\bar{\phi}_1 = \begin{bmatrix} 0.70711 \\ 0.70711 \\ 0.70711 \end{bmatrix}; \qquad \bar{\phi}_2 = \begin{bmatrix} -0.70708 \\ 0.70713 \\ -0.70708 \end{bmatrix}$$

Comparing the results with the exact solution, it is interesting to note that in case 1, $\rho_1 > \lambda_1$ and $\rho_2 = \lambda_2$, whereas in case 2, $\rho_1 = \lambda_1$ and $\rho_2 = \lambda_3$. In both cases we did not obtain good approximations to the lowest two eigenvalues, and it is clearly demonstrated that the results depend completely on the initial Ritz basis vectors chosen.

EXAMPLE 10.16:   Use the Rayleigh-Ritz analysis to calculate an approximation to λ_1 and ϕ_1 of the eigenproblem considered in Example 10.12.

We note that in this case M is positive semidefinite. Therefore, to carry out the Ritz analysis we need to choose a load vector in R that excites at least one mass. Assume that we use

$$R^T = \begin{bmatrix} 0 & 1 & 0 & 0 \end{bmatrix}$$

Then the solution of (10.79) yields (see Example 10.13)

$$\Psi^T = \begin{bmatrix} 1 & 2 & 2 & 2 \end{bmatrix}$$

Hence,
$$\tilde{\mathbf{K}} = [2]; \qquad \tilde{\mathbf{M}} = [12]$$

$$\rho_1 = \frac{1}{6}; \qquad \mathbf{x}_1 = \begin{bmatrix} 1 \\ 2\sqrt{3} \end{bmatrix}$$

and
$$\overline{\mathbf{\phi}}_1^T = \begin{bmatrix} \dfrac{1}{2\sqrt{3}} & \dfrac{1}{\sqrt{3}} & \dfrac{1}{\sqrt{3}} & \dfrac{1}{\sqrt{3}} \end{bmatrix}$$

Hence we have, as expected, $\rho_1 > \lambda_1$.

The Ritz analysis procedure presented above is a very general tool, and, as pointed out earlier, various analysis methods known under different names can actually be shown to be Ritz analyses. In Section 10.3.3 we present the component mode synthesis as a Ritz analysis. In the following we briefly want to show that the technique of static condensation as described in Section 10.3.1 is, in fact, also a Ritz analysis.

In the static condensation analysis we assumed that all mass can be lumped at q degrees of freedom. Therefore, as an approximation to the eigenproblem $\mathbf{K}\mathbf{\phi} = \lambda\mathbf{M}\mathbf{\phi}$, we obtained the following problem:

$$\begin{bmatrix} \mathbf{K}_{aa} & \mathbf{K}_{ac} \\ \mathbf{K}_{ca} & \mathbf{K}_{cc} \end{bmatrix} \begin{bmatrix} \mathbf{\phi}_a \\ \mathbf{\phi}_c \end{bmatrix} = \lambda \begin{bmatrix} \mathbf{M}_a & \mathbf{0} \\ \mathbf{0} & \mathbf{0} \end{bmatrix} \begin{bmatrix} \mathbf{\phi}_a \\ \mathbf{\phi}_c \end{bmatrix} \tag{10.42}$$

with q finite and $n - q$ infinite eigenvalues, which correspond to the massless degrees of freedom (see Section 10.2.4). To calculate the finite eigenvalues, we used static condensation on the massless degrees of freedom and arrived at the eigenproblem

$$\mathbf{K}_a\mathbf{\phi}_a = \lambda\mathbf{M}_a\mathbf{\phi}_a \tag{10.45}$$

where $\mathbf{K}_a$ is defined in (10.46). However, this solution is actually a Ritz analysis of the lumped mass model considered in (10.42). The Ritz basis vectors are the displacement patterns associated with the $\mathbf{\phi}_a$ degrees of freedom when the $\mathbf{\phi}_c$ degrees of freedom are released. Solving the equations

$$\begin{bmatrix} \mathbf{K}_{aa} & \mathbf{K}_{ac} \\ \mathbf{K}_{ca} & \mathbf{K}_{cc} \end{bmatrix} \begin{bmatrix} \mathbf{F}_a \\ \mathbf{F}_c \end{bmatrix} = \begin{bmatrix} \mathbf{I} \\ \mathbf{0} \end{bmatrix} \tag{10.51}$$

in which $\mathbf{F}_a = \mathbf{K}_a^{-1}$, we find that the Ritz basis vectors to be used in (10.80), (10.81), and (10.84) are

$$\mathbf{\Psi} = \begin{bmatrix} \mathbf{I} \\ \mathbf{F}_c\mathbf{K}_a \end{bmatrix} \tag{10.85}$$

To verify that a Ritz analysis with the base vectors in (10.85) yields in fact (10.45), we evaluate (10.80) and (10.81). Substituting for $\mathbf{\Psi}$ and $\mathbf{K}$ in (10.80), we obtain

$$\tilde{\mathbf{K}} = [\mathbf{I} \quad (\mathbf{F}_c\mathbf{K}_a)^T] \begin{bmatrix} \mathbf{K}_{aa} & \mathbf{K}_{ac} \\ \mathbf{K}_{ca} & \mathbf{K}_{cc} \end{bmatrix} \begin{bmatrix} \mathbf{I} \\ \mathbf{F}_c\mathbf{K}_a \end{bmatrix} \tag{10.86}$$

which, using (10.51), reduces to

$$\tilde{\mathbf{K}} = \mathbf{K}_a \tag{10.87}$$

Similarly, substituting for $\mathbf{\Psi}$ and $\mathbf{M}$ in (10.81), we have

$$\tilde{\mathbf{M}} = [\mathbf{I} \quad (\mathbf{F}_c\mathbf{K}_a)^T] \begin{bmatrix} \mathbf{M}_a & \mathbf{0} \\ \mathbf{0} & \mathbf{0} \end{bmatrix} \begin{bmatrix} \mathbf{I} \\ \mathbf{F}_c\mathbf{K}_a \end{bmatrix} \tag{10.88}$$

or
$$\tilde{\mathbf{M}} = \mathbf{M}_a \qquad (10.89)$$

Hence, in the static condensation we actually perform a Ritz analysis of the lumped mass model. It should be noted that in the analysis we calculate the q finite eigenvalues exactly (i.e., $\rho_i = \lambda_i$ for $i = 1, \ldots, q$) because the Ritz basis vectors span the q-dimensional subspace corresponding to the finite eigenvalues. In practice, the evaluation of the vectors $\mathbf{\Psi}$ in (10.85) is not necessary (and would be costly), and instead the Ritz analysis is better carried out using

$$\mathbf{\Psi} = \begin{bmatrix} \mathbf{F}_a \\ \mathbf{F}_c \end{bmatrix} \qquad (10.90)$$

Since the vectors in (10.90) span the same subspace as the vectors in (10.85), the same eigenvalues and eigenvectors are calculated employing either set of base vectors. Specifically, using (10.90), we obtain in the Ritz analysis the reduced eigenproblem

$$\mathbf{F}_a \mathbf{x} = \lambda \mathbf{F}_a \mathbf{M}_a \mathbf{F}_a \mathbf{x} \qquad (10.91)$$

To show that this eigenproblem is indeed equivalent to the problem in (10.45), we premultiply both sides in (10.91) by $\mathbf{K}_a$ and use the transformation $\mathbf{x} = \mathbf{K}_a \tilde{\mathbf{x}}$, giving $\mathbf{K}_a \tilde{\mathbf{x}} = \lambda \mathbf{M}_a \tilde{\mathbf{x}}$, i.e., the problem in (10.45).

EXAMPLE 10.17: Use the Ritz analysis procedure to perform static condensation of the massless degrees of freedom in the problem $\mathbf{K}\boldsymbol{\phi} = \lambda \mathbf{M}\boldsymbol{\phi}$ considered in Example 10.12.

We first need to evaluate the Ritz basis vectors given in (10.90). This was done in Example 10.13, where we found that

$$\mathbf{F}_a = \begin{bmatrix} 2 & 2 \\ 2 & 4 \end{bmatrix}; \qquad \mathbf{F}_c = \begin{bmatrix} 1 & 1 \\ 2 & 3 \end{bmatrix}$$

The Ritz reduction given in (10.91) thus yields the eigenproblem

$$\begin{bmatrix} 2 & 2 \\ 2 & 4 \end{bmatrix} \mathbf{x} = \lambda \begin{bmatrix} 12 & 16 \\ 16 & 24 \end{bmatrix} \mathbf{x}$$

Finally, we should note that the use of the Ritz basis vectors in (10.85) [(or in (10.90)] is also known as the *Guyan reduction* (see R. J. Guyan [A]). In the Guyan scheme the Ritz vectors are used to operate on a lumped mass matrix with zero elements on the diagonal as in (10.88) or on general full lumped or consistent mass matrices. In this reduction the $\boldsymbol{\phi}_a$ degrees of freedom are frequently referred to as dynamic degrees of freedom.

10.3.3 Component Mode Synthesis

As for the static condensation procedure, the component mode synthesis is, in fact, a Ritz analysis, and the method might have been presented in the previous section as a specific application. However, as was repeatedly pointed out, the most important aspect in a Ritz analysis is the selection of appropriate Ritz basis vectors because the results can be only as good as the Ritz basis vectors allow them to be. The specific scheme used in the component mode synthesis is of particular interest, which is the reason we want to devote a separate section to the discussion of the method.

The component mode synthesis has been developed to a large extent as a natural consequence of the analysis procedure followed in practice when large and complex structures are analyzed. The general practical procedure is that different groups perform the analyses of different components of the structure under consideration. For example, in a plant analysis, one group may analyze a main pipe and another group a piping system attached to it. In a first preliminary analysis, both groups work separately and model the effects of the other components on the specific component that they consider in an approximate manner. For example, in the analysis of the two piping systems referred to above, the group analyzing the side branch may assume full fixity at the point of intersection with the main pipe, and the group analyzing the main pipe may introduce a concentrated spring and mass to allow for the side branch. The advantage of considering the components of the structure separately is primarily one of time scheduling; i.e., the separate groups can work on the analyses and designs of the components at the same time. It is primarily for this reason that the component mode synthesis is very appealing in the analysis and design of large structural systems.

Assume that the preliminary analyses of the components have been carried out and that the complete structure shall now be analyzed. It is at this stage that the component mode synthesis is a natural procedure to use. Namely, with the mode shape characteristics of each component known, it appears natural to use this information in estimating the frequencies and mode shapes of the complete structure. The specific procedure may vary (see R. R. Craig, Jr. [A]), but, in essence, the mode shapes of the components are used in a Rayleigh-Ritz analysis to calculate approximate mode shapes and frequencies of the complete structure.

Consider for illustration that each component structure was obtained by fixing all its boundary degrees of freedom and denote the stiffness matrices of the component structures by $\mathbf{K}_I, \mathbf{K}_{II}, \ldots, \mathbf{K}_M$ (see Example 10.18). Assume that only component structures $L - 1$ and L connect, $L = 2, \ldots, M$; then we can write for the stiffness matrix of the complete structure,

$$\mathbf{K} = \begin{bmatrix} \mathbf{K}_I & \cdot & & & & \\ & \cdot & \cdot & \cdot & & \\ & & \cdot & \mathbf{K}_{II} & \cdot & \\ & & & \cdot & \cdot & \cdot \\ & & & & \cdot & \\ & & & & & \cdot \\ & & & & & & \mathbf{K}_M \end{bmatrix} \tag{10.92}$$

Using an analogous notation for the mass matrices, we also have

$$\mathbf{M} = \begin{bmatrix} \mathbf{M}_I & \cdot & & & & \\ & \cdot & \cdot & \cdot & & \\ & & \cdot & \mathbf{M}_{II} & \cdot & \\ & & & \cdot & \cdot & \cdot \\ & & & & \cdot & \\ & & & & & \cdot \\ & & & & & & \mathbf{M}_M \end{bmatrix} \tag{10.93}$$

Assume that the lowest eigenvalues and corresponding eigenvectors of each component structure have been calculated; i.e., we have for each component structure,

$$
\left.\begin{array}{c}
\mathbf{K}_I\,\boldsymbol{\Phi}_I = \mathbf{M}_I\,\boldsymbol{\Phi}_I\,\boldsymbol{\Lambda}_I \\[4pt]
\mathbf{K}_{II}\,\boldsymbol{\Phi}_{II} = \mathbf{M}_{II}\,\boldsymbol{\Phi}_{II}\,\boldsymbol{\Lambda}_{II} \\
\vdots \qquad\qquad \vdots \\
\mathbf{K}_M\,\boldsymbol{\Phi}_M = \mathbf{M}_M\,\boldsymbol{\Phi}_M\,\boldsymbol{\Lambda}_M
\end{array}\right\}
\tag{10.94}
$$

where $\boldsymbol{\Phi}_L$ and $\boldsymbol{\Lambda}_L$ are the matrices of calculated eigenvectors and eigenvalues of the Lth component structure.

In a component mode synthesis, approximate mode shapes and frequencies can be obtained by performing a Rayleigh-Ritz analysis with the following assumed loads on the right-hand side of (10.79),

$$
\mathbf{R} =
\begin{bmatrix}
\boldsymbol{\Phi}_I & \mathbf{0} & \mathbf{0} & \cdots \\
\mathbf{0} & \mathbf{I}_{I,\,II} & \mathbf{0} & \\
\boldsymbol{\Phi}_{II} & \mathbf{0} & \mathbf{0} & \cdots \\
\mathbf{0} & \mathbf{0} & \mathbf{I}_{II,\,III} & \\
\vdots & \vdots & \vdots & \cdots \\
\boldsymbol{\Phi}_M & \mathbf{0} & &
\end{bmatrix}
\tag{10.95}
$$

where $\mathbf{I}_{L-1,\,L}$ is a unit matrix of order equal to the connection degrees of freedom between component structures $L - 1$ and L. The unit matrices correspond to loads that are applied to the connection degrees of freedom of the component structures. Since in the derivation of the mode shape matrices used in (10.95) the component structures were fixed at their boundaries, the unit loads have the effect of releasing these connection degrees of freedom. If, on the other hand, the connection degrees of freedom have been included in the analysis of the component structures, we may dispense with the unit matrices in $\mathbf{R}$.

An important consideration is the accuracy that can be expected in the above component mode synthesis. Since a Ritz analysis is performed, all accuracy considerations discussed in Section 10.3.2 are directly applicable; i.e., the analysis yields upper bounds to the exact eigenvalues of the problem $\mathbf{K}\boldsymbol{\phi} = \lambda\mathbf{M}\boldsymbol{\phi}$. However, the actual accuracy achieved in the solution is not known, although it can be evaluated, for example, as described in Section 10.4. The fact that the solution accuracy is highly dependent on the vectors used in $\mathbf{R}$ (i.e., the Ritz basis vectors) is, as in all Ritz analyses, the main defect of the method. However, in practice, reasonable accuracy can often be obtained because the eigenvectors corresponding to the smallest eigenvalues of the component structures are used in $\mathbf{R}$. We demonstrate the analysis procedure in the following example.

EXAMPLE 10.18: Consider the eigenproblem $\mathbf{K}\boldsymbol{\phi} = \lambda\mathbf{M}\boldsymbol{\phi}$, where

$$
\mathbf{K} =
\begin{bmatrix}
2 & -1 & & & \\
-1 & 2 & -1 & & \\
& -1 & 2 & -1 & \\
& & -1 & 2 & -1 \\
& & & -1 & 1
\end{bmatrix}
; \qquad
\mathbf{M} =
\begin{bmatrix}
1 & & & & \\
& 1 & & & \\
& & 1 & & \\
& & & 1 & \\
& & & & \tfrac{1}{2}
\end{bmatrix}
$$

Use the substructure eigenproblems indicated by the dashed lines in $\mathbf{K}$ and $\mathbf{M}$ to establish the load matrix given in (10.95) for a component mode synthesis analysis. Then calculate eigenvalue and eigenvector approximations.

Here we have for substructure I,

$$\mathbf{K}_I = \begin{bmatrix} 2 & -1 \\ -1 & 2 \end{bmatrix}; \qquad \mathbf{M}_I = \begin{bmatrix} 1 & 0 \\ 0 & 1 \end{bmatrix}$$

with the eigensolution

$$\lambda_1 = 1, \qquad \tilde{\lambda}_2 = 3; \qquad \boldsymbol{\phi}_1 = \begin{bmatrix} \dfrac{\sqrt{2}}{2} \\ \dfrac{\sqrt{2}}{2} \end{bmatrix}, \qquad \boldsymbol{\phi}_2 = \begin{bmatrix} -\dfrac{\sqrt{2}}{2} \\ \dfrac{\sqrt{2}}{2} \end{bmatrix}$$

and for substructure II,

$$\mathbf{K}_{II} = \begin{bmatrix} 2 & -1 \\ -1 & 1 \end{bmatrix}; \qquad \mathbf{M}_{II} = \begin{bmatrix} 1 & 0 \\ 0 & \frac{1}{2} \end{bmatrix}$$

with the eigensolution

$$\lambda_1 = 2 - \sqrt{2}, \quad \lambda_2 = 2 + \sqrt{2}; \qquad \boldsymbol{\phi}_1 = \begin{bmatrix} \dfrac{\sqrt{2}}{2} \\ 1 \end{bmatrix}, \qquad \boldsymbol{\phi}_2 = \begin{bmatrix} -\dfrac{\sqrt{2}}{2} \\ 1 \end{bmatrix}$$

Thus we have for the matrix $\mathbf{R}$ in (10.95),

$$\mathbf{R} = \begin{bmatrix} \dfrac{\sqrt{2}}{2} & -\dfrac{\sqrt{2}}{2} & 0 \\ \dfrac{\sqrt{2}}{2} & \dfrac{\sqrt{2}}{2} & 0 \\ 0 & 0 & 1 \\ \dfrac{\sqrt{2}}{2} & -\dfrac{\sqrt{2}}{2} & 0 \\ 1 & 1 & 0 \end{bmatrix}$$

Now performing the Ritz analysis as given in (10.79) to (10.84), we obtain

$$\tilde{\mathbf{K}} = \begin{bmatrix} 22.40 & 5.328 & 7.243 \\ 5.328 & 2.257 & 1.586 \\ 7.243 & 1.586 & 3 \end{bmatrix}$$

$$\tilde{\mathbf{M}} = \begin{bmatrix} 222.4 & 50.69 & 77.69 \\ 50.69 & 11.94 & 17.59 \\ 77.69 & 17.59 & 27.5 \end{bmatrix}$$

and hence,

$$\boldsymbol{\rho} = \begin{bmatrix} 0.098 & & \\ & 2.83 & \\ & & 1.82 \end{bmatrix}$$

$$\bar{\boldsymbol{\Phi}} = \begin{bmatrix} 0.207 & -0.773 & 0.00690 \\ 0.181 & 0.0984 & -0.0655 \\ 0.509 & 1.47 & 0.443 \\ 0.594 & -0.385 & -0.166 \\ 0.655 & 0.574 & -0.978 \end{bmatrix}$$

The exact eigenvalues are

$$\lambda_1 = 0.09789 \qquad \lambda_2 = 0.824; \qquad \lambda_3 = 2.00; \qquad \lambda_4 = 3.18; \qquad \lambda_5 = 3.90$$

and hence we note that we obtained in ρ_1 a good approximation to λ_1, but ρ_2 and ρ_3 do not represent approximations to eigenvalues.

10.3.4 Exercises

10.7. Consider the eigenproblem

$$\begin{bmatrix} 6 & -1 & 0 \\ -1 & 4 & -1 \\ 0 & -1 & 2 \end{bmatrix} \boldsymbol{\phi} = \lambda \begin{bmatrix} 0 & 0 & 0 \\ 0 & 2 & 1 \\ 0 & 1 & 1 \end{bmatrix} \boldsymbol{\phi}$$

Perform the static condensation as usually performed [see (10.46)] and then by the Rayleigh-Ritz analysis procedure [see (10.51)].

10.8. Consider the eigenproblem in Exercise 10.1. Perform a Rayleigh-Ritz analysis with the two vectors

$$\boldsymbol{\psi}_1 = \begin{bmatrix} 1 \\ 1 \\ 1 \end{bmatrix}; \qquad \boldsymbol{\psi}_2 = \begin{bmatrix} 1 \\ -1 \\ 1 \end{bmatrix}$$

to calculate an approximation to the smallest eigenvalue and corresponding eigenvector.

10.9. It is being claimed that if, in the solution of the generalized eigenproblem $\mathbf{K}\boldsymbol{\phi} = \lambda\mathbf{M}\boldsymbol{\phi}$, the Ritz vectors are

$$\boldsymbol{\psi}_1 = \boldsymbol{\phi}_1 + 2\boldsymbol{\phi}_2$$
$$\boldsymbol{\psi}_2 = 3\boldsymbol{\phi}_1 - \boldsymbol{\phi}_2$$

where $\boldsymbol{\phi}_1$ and $\boldsymbol{\phi}_2$ are the eigenvectors corresponding to λ_1 and λ_2, then the Rayleigh-Ritz analysis will give the exact eigenvalues λ_1 and λ_2 and the corresponding eigenvectors $\boldsymbol{\phi}_1$ and $\boldsymbol{\phi}_2$. Show explicitly that this result is indeed obtained.

10.10. Consider the following spring system.
  (a) Evaluate the exact smallest frequency of the system.
  (b) Evaluate an approximation of the smallest frequency by using the component mode synthesis technique in Section 10.3.3. Use only the eigenvector of the smallest frequency of each component in the system.

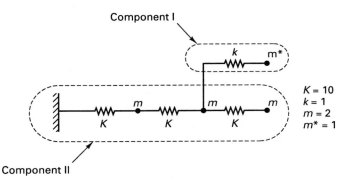

10.4 SOLUTION ERRORS

An important part of an eigenvalue and vector solution is to estimate the accuracy with which the required eigensystem has been calculated. Since an eigensystem solution is necessarily iterative, the solution should be terminated once convergence within the prescribed tolerances giving the actual accuracy has been obtained. When one of the approximate solution techniques outlined in Section 10.3 is used, an estimate of the actual solution accuracy obtained is of course also important.

10.4.1 Error Bounds

In order to identify the accuracy that has been obtained in an eigensolution, we recall that the equation to be solved is

$$\mathbf{K}\boldsymbol{\phi} = \lambda \mathbf{M}\boldsymbol{\phi} \tag{10.96}$$

Let us first assume that using any one solution procedure we obtained an approximation $\bar{\lambda}$ and $\bar{\boldsymbol{\phi}}$ to an eigenpair. Then without regard to how the values have been obtained, we can evaluate a residual vector that gives important information about the accuracy with which $\bar{\lambda}$ and $\bar{\boldsymbol{\phi}}$ approximate the eigenpair. The results are given in (10.101) to (10.104). We then present also error bound calculations useful in solutions based on inverse iterations and a simple error measure.

Standard Eigenproblem

Consider first that $\mathbf{M} = \mathbf{I}$. In that case we can write

$$\mathbf{r} = \mathbf{K}\bar{\boldsymbol{\phi}} - \bar{\lambda}\,\bar{\boldsymbol{\phi}} \tag{10.97}$$

and using the relations in (10.12) and (10.13), we have

$$\mathbf{r} = \boldsymbol{\Phi}(\boldsymbol{\Lambda} - \bar{\lambda}\mathbf{I})\boldsymbol{\Phi}^T\bar{\boldsymbol{\phi}} \tag{10.98}$$

or because $\bar{\lambda}$ is not equal but only close to an eigenvalue, we have

$$\bar{\boldsymbol{\phi}} = \boldsymbol{\Phi}(\boldsymbol{\Lambda} - \bar{\lambda}\mathbf{I})^{-1}\boldsymbol{\Phi}^T\mathbf{r} \tag{10.99}$$

Hence, because $\|\bar{\boldsymbol{\phi}}\|_2 = 1$, taking norms we obtain

$$1 \le \|(\boldsymbol{\Lambda} - \bar{\lambda}\mathbf{I})^{-1}\|_2 \, \|\mathbf{r}\|_2 \tag{10.100}$$

But since

$$\|(\boldsymbol{\Lambda} - \bar{\lambda}\mathbf{I})^{-1}\|_2 = \max_i \frac{1}{|\lambda_i - \bar{\lambda}|}$$

we have

$$\min_i |\lambda_i - \bar{\lambda}| \le \|\mathbf{r}\|_2 \tag{10.101}$$

Therefore, a conclusive statement can be made about the accuracy with which $\bar{\lambda}$ approximates an eigenvalue λ_i by evaluating $\|\mathbf{r}\|_2$ as expressed in (10.101). This is quite different from the information that could be obtained from the evaluation of the residual vector $\mathbf{r}$ in the solution of the static equilibrium equations.

Although the relation in (10.101) establishes that $\bar{\lambda}$ is close to an eigenvalue provided that $\|\mathbf{r}\|_2$ is small, it should be recognized that the relation does not tell which eigenvalue is approximated. In fact, to identify which specific eigenvalue has been approximated, it is necessary to use the Sturm sequence property (see Section 10.2.2 and the following example).

EXAMPLE 10.19:   Consider the eigenproblem $\mathbf{K}\boldsymbol{\phi} = \lambda\boldsymbol{\phi}$, where

$$\mathbf{K} = \begin{bmatrix} 3 & -1 & 0 \\ -1 & 2 & -1 \\ 0 & -1 & 3 \end{bmatrix}$$

The eigensolution is $\lambda_1 = 1$, $\lambda_2 = 3$, $\lambda_3 = 4$, and

$$\boldsymbol{\phi}_1 = \frac{1}{\sqrt{6}}\begin{bmatrix} 1 \\ 2 \\ 1 \end{bmatrix}; \qquad \boldsymbol{\phi}_2 = \frac{1}{\sqrt{2}}\begin{bmatrix} 1 \\ 0 \\ -1 \end{bmatrix}; \qquad \boldsymbol{\phi}_3 = \frac{1}{\sqrt{3}}\begin{bmatrix} 1 \\ -1 \\ 1 \end{bmatrix}$$

Assume that we calculated

$$\bar{\lambda} = 3.1 \qquad \text{and} \qquad \bar{\boldsymbol{\phi}} = \begin{bmatrix} 0.7 \\ 0.1414 \\ -0.7 \end{bmatrix}$$

as approximations to λ_2 and $\boldsymbol{\phi}_2$. Apply the error bound relation in (10.101).
    We have in this case

$$\mathbf{r} = \begin{bmatrix} 3 & -1 & 0 \\ -1 & 2 & -1 \\ 0 & -1 & 3 \end{bmatrix}\begin{bmatrix} 0.7 \\ 0.1414 \\ -0.7 \end{bmatrix} - 3.1\begin{bmatrix} 1 & & \\ & 1 & \\ & & 1 \end{bmatrix}\begin{bmatrix} 0.7 \\ 0.1414 \\ -0.7 \end{bmatrix}$$

Hence
$$\mathbf{r} = \begin{bmatrix} -0.2114 \\ -0.1555 \\ -0.2114 \end{bmatrix}; \qquad \|\mathbf{r}\|_2 = 0.3370$$

The relation in (10.101) now gives

$$|\lambda_2 - \bar{\lambda}| \le 0.3370$$

which is indeed true because $\bar{\lambda} - \lambda_2 = 0.1$.
    Assume now that we have calculated only $\bar{\lambda}$ and $\bar{\boldsymbol{\phi}}$ and do not know which eigenvalue and eigenvector they approximate. In this case we can use the relation in (10.101) to establish bounds on the unknown exact eigenvalue in order to apply Sturm sequence checks (see Section 10.2.2).
    For the example considered here we have

$$2.7630 \le \lambda_i \le 3.4370$$

Let us use as a lower bound 2.7 and as an upper bound 3.5. The $\mathbf{LDL}^T$ triangular factorization of $\mathbf{K} - \mu\mathbf{I}$ gives, at $\mu = 2.7$,

$$\begin{bmatrix} 0.3 & -1 & 0 \\ -1 & -0.7 & -1 \\ 0 & -1 & 0.3 \end{bmatrix}$$

$$= \begin{bmatrix} 1 & & \\ -3.333 & 1 & \\ 0 & 0.2479 & 1 \end{bmatrix}\begin{bmatrix} 0.3 & & \\ & -4.033 & \\ & & 0.3248 \end{bmatrix}\begin{bmatrix} 1 & -3.333 & 0 \\ & 1 & 0.2479 \\ & & 1 \end{bmatrix} \qquad (a)$$

and at $\mu = 3.5$,

$$\begin{bmatrix} -0.5 & -1 & 0 \\ -1 & -1.5 & -1 \\ 0 & -1 & -0.5 \end{bmatrix} = \begin{bmatrix} 1 & & \\ 2 & 1 & \\ 0 & -2 & 1 \end{bmatrix}\begin{bmatrix} -0.5 & & \\ & 0.5 & \\ & & -2.5 \end{bmatrix}\begin{bmatrix} 1 & 2 & 0 \\ & 1 & -2 \\ & & 1 \end{bmatrix} \qquad (b)$$

But there is one negative element in $\mathbf{D}$ in (a) and there are two negative elements in $\mathbf{D}$ in (b); hence, we can conclude that $2.7 < \lambda_2 < 3.5$. Furthermore, it follows that $\bar{\lambda}$ and $\overline{\boldsymbol{\phi}}$ are approximations to λ_2 and $\boldsymbol{\phi}_2$.

Considering now the accuracy with which $\overline{\boldsymbol{\phi}}$ approximates an eigenvector, an analysis equivalent to this one not only requires the evaluation of $\|\mathbf{r}\|_2$ but the spacing between the individual eigenvalues is also needed. In actual analysis this spacing is known only approximately because the eigenvalues have been evaluated only to a specific accuracy.

Assume that $\bar{\lambda}$ and $\overline{\boldsymbol{\phi}}$ have been calculated, where $\|\overline{\boldsymbol{\phi}}\|_2 = 1$, and that $\bar{\lambda}$ approximates the eigenvalues λ_i, $i = p, \ldots, q$. For the error analysis we also assume that the eigenvalues λ_i for all i but $i \neq p, \ldots, q$ are known (although we would need to use the calculated eigenvalues here). The final result of the accuracy analysis is that if $|\lambda_i - \bar{\lambda}| \leq \|\mathbf{r}\|_2$ for $i = p, \ldots, q$ and $|\lambda_i - \bar{\lambda}| \geq s$ for all i, $i \neq p, \ldots, q$, then there is a vector $\hat{\boldsymbol{\phi}} = \alpha_p \boldsymbol{\phi}_p + \cdots + \alpha_q \boldsymbol{\phi}_q$, for which $\|\overline{\boldsymbol{\phi}} - \hat{\boldsymbol{\phi}}\|_2 \leq \|\mathbf{r}\|_2/s$ (see Example 10.20). Therefore, if $\bar{\lambda}$ is an approximation to a single eigenvalue λ_i, the corresponding vector $\overline{\boldsymbol{\phi}}$ is an approximation to $\boldsymbol{\phi}_i$, where

$$\|\overline{\boldsymbol{\phi}} - \alpha_i \boldsymbol{\phi}_i\|_2 \leq \frac{\|\mathbf{r}\|_2}{s}; \qquad s = \min_{\substack{\text{all } j \\ j \neq i}} |\lambda_j - \bar{\lambda}| \tag{10.102}$$

However, if $\bar{\lambda}$ is close to a number of eigenvalues $\lambda_p, \ldots, \lambda_q$, then the analysis only shows that the corresponding vector $\overline{\boldsymbol{\phi}}$ is close to a vector that lies in the subspace corresponding to $\boldsymbol{\phi}_p, \ldots, \boldsymbol{\phi}_q$. In practical analysis (i.e., mode superposition in dynamic response calculations), this is most likely all that is required because the close eigenvalues may almost be dealt with as equal eigenvalues, in which case the calculated eigenvectors would also not be unique but lie in the subspace corresponding to the equal eigenvalues. In the following we first give the proof for the accuracy with which $\overline{\boldsymbol{\phi}}$ approximates an eigenvector and then demonstrate the results by means of examples.

EXAMPLE 10.20: Assume that we have calculated $\bar{\lambda}$, $\overline{\boldsymbol{\phi}}$, with $\|\overline{\boldsymbol{\phi}}\|_2 = 1$, as eigenvalue and eigenvector approximations and that $\mathbf{K}\overline{\boldsymbol{\phi}} - \bar{\lambda}\overline{\boldsymbol{\phi}} = \mathbf{r}$. Consider the case in which $|\lambda_i - \bar{\lambda}| \leq \|\mathbf{r}\|_2$ for $i = 1, \ldots, q$ and $|\lambda_i - \bar{\lambda}| \geq s$ for $i = q + 1, \ldots, n$. Show that $\|\overline{\boldsymbol{\phi}} - \hat{\boldsymbol{\phi}}\|_2 \leq \|\mathbf{r}\|_2/s$, where $\hat{\boldsymbol{\phi}}$ is a vector in the subspace that corresponds to $\boldsymbol{\phi}_1, \ldots, \boldsymbol{\phi}_q$.

The calculated eigenvector approximation $\overline{\boldsymbol{\phi}}$ can be written as

$$\overline{\boldsymbol{\phi}} = \sum_{i=1}^{n} \alpha_i \boldsymbol{\phi}_i$$

Using $\hat{\boldsymbol{\phi}} = \sum_{i=1}^{q} \alpha_i \boldsymbol{\phi}_i$, we have

$$\|\overline{\boldsymbol{\phi}} - \hat{\boldsymbol{\phi}}\|_2 = \left\| \sum_{i=q+1}^{n} \alpha_i \boldsymbol{\phi}_i \right\|_2$$

or, because $\boldsymbol{\phi}_i^T \boldsymbol{\phi}_j = \delta_{ij}$,

$$\|\overline{\boldsymbol{\phi}} - \hat{\boldsymbol{\phi}}\|_2 = \left(\sum_{i=q+1}^{n} \alpha_i^2 \right)^{1/2} \tag{a}$$

But

$$\|\mathbf{r}\|_2 = \|\mathbf{K}\overline{\boldsymbol{\phi}} - \bar{\lambda}\overline{\boldsymbol{\phi}}\|_2$$

$$= \left\| \sum_{i=1}^{n} \alpha_i (\lambda_i - \bar{\lambda}) \boldsymbol{\phi}_i \right\|_2$$

or

$$\|\mathbf{r}\|_2 = \left(\sum_{i=1}^{n} \alpha_i^2 (\lambda_i - \bar{\lambda})^2 \right)^{1/2}$$

which gives
$$\|\mathbf{r}\|_2 \geq s\left(\sum_{i=q+1}^{n} \alpha_i^2\right)^{1/2} \tag{b}$$

Hence, combining (a) and (b), we obtain

$$\|\overline{\boldsymbol{\phi}} - \tilde{\boldsymbol{\phi}}\|_2 \leq \frac{\|\mathbf{r}\|_2}{s}$$

EXAMPLE 10.21: Consider the eigenproblem in Example 10.19. Assume that λ_1 and λ_3 are known (i.e., $\lambda_1 = 1$, $\lambda_3 = 4$) and that $\overline{\lambda}$ and $\overline{\boldsymbol{\phi}}$ given in Example 10.19 have been evaluated. (In actual analysis we would have only approximations to λ_1 and λ_3, and all error bound calculations would be approximate.) Estimate the accuracy with which $\overline{\boldsymbol{\phi}}$ approximates $\boldsymbol{\phi}_2$.

For the estimate we use the relation in (10.102). In this case we have

$$\|\overline{\boldsymbol{\phi}} - \alpha_2\boldsymbol{\phi}_2\|_2 \leq \frac{0.3370}{s}$$

with
$$s = \min_{i=1,3} |\lambda_i - \overline{\lambda}|$$

Hence, since $\overline{\lambda} = 3.1$, we have $s = 0.9$ and

$$\|\overline{\boldsymbol{\phi}} - \alpha_2\boldsymbol{\phi}_2\|_2 \leq 0.3744$$

Evaluating $\|\overline{\boldsymbol{\phi}} - \boldsymbol{\phi}_2\|_2$ exactly, we have

$$\|\overline{\boldsymbol{\phi}} - \boldsymbol{\phi}_2\|_2 = \left[\left(0.7 - \frac{1}{\sqrt{2}}\right)^2 + (0.1414 - 0)^2 + \left(-0.7 + \frac{1}{\sqrt{2}}\right)^2\right]^{1/2} = 0.1418$$

EXAMPLE 10.22: Consider the eigenproblem $\mathbf{K}\boldsymbol{\phi} = \lambda\boldsymbol{\phi}$, where

$$\mathbf{K} = \begin{bmatrix} 100 & -1 \\ -1 & 100 \end{bmatrix}$$

The eigenvalues and eigenvectors of the problem are

$$\lambda_1 = 99, \ \boldsymbol{\phi}_1 = \frac{1}{\sqrt{2}}\begin{bmatrix} 1 \\ 1 \end{bmatrix}; \qquad \lambda_2 = 101, \ \boldsymbol{\phi}_2 = \frac{1}{\sqrt{2}}\begin{bmatrix} 1 \\ -1 \end{bmatrix}$$

Assume that we have calculated eigenvalue and eigenvector approximations $\overline{\lambda} = 100$, $\overline{\boldsymbol{\phi}} = \begin{bmatrix} 1 \\ 0 \end{bmatrix}$.
Evaluate $\mathbf{r}$ and thus establish the relations given in (10.101) and (10.102).

First, we calculate $\mathbf{r}$ as given in (10.97),

$$\mathbf{r} = \begin{bmatrix} 100 & -1 \\ -1 & 100 \end{bmatrix}\begin{bmatrix} 1 \\ 0 \end{bmatrix} - 100\begin{bmatrix} 1 \\ 0 \end{bmatrix} = \begin{bmatrix} 0 \\ -1 \end{bmatrix}$$

Hence, $\|\mathbf{r}\|_2 = 1$ and (10.101) yields

$$\min_{i} |\lambda_i - \overline{\lambda}| \leq 1 \tag{a}$$

Therefore, we can conclude that an eigenvalue has been approximated with about 1 percent or less error. Since we know λ_1 and λ_2, we can compare $\overline{\lambda}$ with λ_1 or λ_2 and find that (a) does indeed hold.

Considering now the eigenvector approximation $\overline{\boldsymbol{\phi}}$, we note that $\overline{\boldsymbol{\phi}}$ does not approximate either $\boldsymbol{\phi}_1$ or $\boldsymbol{\phi}_2$. This is also reflected by evaluating the relation (10.102). Assuming that $\overline{\boldsymbol{\phi}}$ is an approximation to $\boldsymbol{\phi}_1$, which gives $s = 1$, we have

$$\|\overline{\boldsymbol{\phi}} - \alpha_1\boldsymbol{\phi}_1\|_2 \leq 1$$

Similarly, assuming that $\overline{\boldsymbol{\phi}}$ is an approximation to $\boldsymbol{\phi}_2$, we obtain

$$\|\overline{\boldsymbol{\phi}} - \alpha_2\boldsymbol{\phi}_2\|_2 \leq 1$$

and in both cases the bound obtained is very large (note that $\|\boldsymbol{\phi}_1\|_2 = 1$ and $\|\boldsymbol{\phi}_2\|_2 = 1$), indicating that $\overline{\boldsymbol{\phi}}$ does not approximate an eigenvector.

Generalized Eigenproblem

Consider now that we wish to estimate the accuracy obtained in the solution of a generalized eigenproblem $\mathbf{K}\boldsymbol{\phi} = \lambda\mathbf{M}\boldsymbol{\phi}$. Assume that we have calculated as an approximation to λ_i and $\boldsymbol{\phi}_i$ the values $\overline{\lambda}$ and $\overline{\boldsymbol{\phi}}$. Then, in analogy to the calculations performed above, we can calculate an error vector $\mathbf{r}_{\mathrm{M}}$, where

$$\mathbf{r}_{\mathrm{M}} = \mathbf{K}\overline{\boldsymbol{\phi}} - \overline{\lambda}\mathbf{M}\overline{\boldsymbol{\phi}} \tag{10.103}$$

In order to relate the error vector in (10.103) to the error vector that corresponds to the standard eigenproblem, we use $\mathbf{M} = \mathbf{S}\mathbf{S}^T$, and then

$$\mathbf{r} = \tilde{\mathbf{K}}\tilde{\boldsymbol{\phi}} - \overline{\lambda}\tilde{\boldsymbol{\phi}} \tag{10.104}$$

where $\mathbf{r} = \mathbf{S}^{-1}\mathbf{r}_{\mathrm{M}}$, $\tilde{\boldsymbol{\phi}} = \mathbf{S}^T\overline{\boldsymbol{\phi}}$, and $\tilde{\mathbf{K}} = \mathbf{S}^{-1}\mathbf{K}\mathbf{S}^{-T}$ (see Section 10.2.5). It is the vector $\mathbf{S}^{-1}\mathbf{r}_{\mathrm{M}}$ that we would need to use, therefore, to calculate the error bound given in (10.101). These error bound calculations would require the factorization of $\mathbf{M}$ into $\mathbf{S}\mathbf{S}^T$, where it is assumed that $\mathbf{M}$ is positive definite.[1]

During Computations

In actual computations we frequently use the method of inverse iteration (see Sections 11.2 and 11.6), and then an error bound based on the following evaluations can be efficiently obtained (see H. Matthies [A] and also Exercise 10.11). Let

$$\mathbf{K}\overline{\boldsymbol{\phi}} = \mathbf{M}\hat{\boldsymbol{\phi}} \tag{10.105}$$

Then we have

$$\min_i |\lambda_i - \rho(\overline{\boldsymbol{\phi}})| \leq \left\{ \left(\frac{\hat{\boldsymbol{\phi}}^T\mathbf{M}\hat{\boldsymbol{\phi}}}{\overline{\boldsymbol{\phi}}^T\mathbf{M}\overline{\boldsymbol{\phi}}}\right) - [\rho(\overline{\boldsymbol{\phi}})]^2 \right\}^{1/2} \tag{10.106}$$

and

$$\min_{\substack{i \\ \lambda_i \neq 0}} \left|\frac{\lambda_i - \rho(\overline{\boldsymbol{\phi}})}{\lambda_i}\right| \leq \left\{ 1 - \frac{(\rho(\overline{\boldsymbol{\phi}}))^2}{\hat{\boldsymbol{\phi}}^T\mathbf{M}\hat{\boldsymbol{\phi}}/\overline{\boldsymbol{\phi}}^T\mathbf{M}\overline{\boldsymbol{\phi}}} \right\}^{1/2} \tag{10.107}$$

where $\rho(\overline{\boldsymbol{\phi}})$ is the Rayleigh quotient,

$$\rho(\overline{\boldsymbol{\phi}}) = \frac{\overline{\boldsymbol{\phi}}^T\mathbf{K}\overline{\boldsymbol{\phi}}}{\overline{\boldsymbol{\phi}}^T\mathbf{M}\overline{\boldsymbol{\phi}}}$$

We will see that (10.105) is the typical step in an inverse iteration, Lanczos iteration, and subspace iteration, and $\rho(\overline{\boldsymbol{\phi}})$ is in practice also almost always calculated because of the good approximation quality of the Rayleigh quotient to an eigenvalue. Notice also that the term $\hat{\boldsymbol{\phi}}^T\mathbf{M}\hat{\boldsymbol{\phi}}/\overline{\boldsymbol{\phi}}^T\mathbf{M}\overline{\boldsymbol{\phi}}$ consists of two numbers that are easily calculated in the iterations.

While the above error bounds are very effective, it is finally also of interest to consider the following simple *error measure:*

$$\epsilon = \frac{\|\mathbf{K}\overline{\boldsymbol{\phi}} - \overline{\lambda}\mathbf{M}\overline{\boldsymbol{\phi}}\|_2}{\|\mathbf{K}\overline{\boldsymbol{\phi}}\|_2} \tag{10.108}$$

---

[1] To avoid the factorization of $\mathbf{M}$ we may instead consider the problem $\mathbf{M}\boldsymbol{\phi} = \lambda^{-1}\mathbf{K}\boldsymbol{\phi}$ if the factorization of $\mathbf{K}$ is already available, and then establish bounds on λ^{-1}.

Since, physically, $\mathbf{K}\bar{\boldsymbol{\phi}}$ represents the elastic nodal point forces and $\bar{\lambda}\mathbf{M}\bar{\boldsymbol{\phi}}$ represents the inertia nodal point forces when the finite element assemblage is vibrating in the mode $\bar{\boldsymbol{\phi}}$, we evaluate in (10.108) the norm of out-of-balance nodal point forces divided by the norm of elastic nodal point forces. This quantity should be small if $\bar{\lambda}$ and $\bar{\boldsymbol{\phi}}$ are an accurate solution of an eigenpair.

If $\mathbf{M} = \mathbf{I}$, it should be noted that we can write

$$\bar{\lambda}\epsilon = \|\mathbf{r}\|_2 \tag{10.109}$$

and hence,

$$\epsilon \geq \min_i \frac{|\lambda_i - \bar{\lambda}|}{\bar{\lambda}} \tag{10.110}$$

EXAMPLE 10.23:   Consider the eigenproblem $\mathbf{K}\boldsymbol{\phi} = \lambda\mathbf{M}\boldsymbol{\phi}$, where

$$\mathbf{K} = \begin{bmatrix} 10 & -10 \\ -10 & 100 \end{bmatrix}; \qquad \mathbf{M} = \begin{bmatrix} 2 & 1 \\ 1 & 4 \end{bmatrix}$$

The exact eigenvalues and eigenvectors to 12-digit precision are

$$\lambda_1 = 3.863385512876; \qquad \boldsymbol{\phi}_1 = \begin{bmatrix} 0.640776011246 \\ 0.105070337503 \end{bmatrix}$$

$$\lambda_2 = 33.279471629982; \qquad \boldsymbol{\phi}_2 = \begin{bmatrix} -0.401041986380 \\ 0.524093989558 \end{bmatrix}$$

Assume that $\bar{\boldsymbol{\phi}} = (\boldsymbol{\phi}_1 + \delta\boldsymbol{\phi}_2)c$, where c is such that $\bar{\boldsymbol{\phi}}^T\mathbf{M}\bar{\boldsymbol{\phi}} = 1$ and $\delta = 10^{-1}, 10^{-3}$, and 10^{-6}. For each value of δ evaluate $\bar{\lambda}$ as the Rayleigh quotient of $\bar{\boldsymbol{\phi}}$ and calculate the error bounds based on (10.104), (10.106), and the error measure ϵ given in (10.108).

The following table summarizes the results obtained. The equations used to evaluate the quantities are given in (10.103) to (10.108). The results in the table show that for each value of δ the error bounds are satisfied and that ϵ is also small for an accurate solution.

δ	10^{-1}	10^{-3}	10^{-6}
$\bar{\boldsymbol{\phi}}$	0.597690792656	0.640374649073	0.640775610204
	0.156698194481	0.105594378695	0.105070861597
$\bar{\boldsymbol{\phi}}^T\mathbf{K}\bar{\boldsymbol{\phi}}$	4.154633890275	3.863414928932	3.863385512905
$\bar{\lambda}$	4.154633890275	3.863414928932	3.863385512905
$\mathbf{r}_M$	−1.207470493734	−0.008218153965	−0.000008177422
	4.605630581124	0.049838803226	0.000049870085
$\mathbf{r}$	1.634419466242	0.021106743617	0.000021152364
	1.411679295681	0.015042545327	0.000015049775
$|\lambda_1 - \bar{\lambda}|$	0.291248377399	0.000029416056	0.000000000029
Bound (10.101/10.104)	2.159667897036	0.025918580132	0.000025959936
Bound (10.106)	2.912483773983	0.029416056744	0.000029433139
Measure (10.108)	0.447113235813	0.007458208660	0.000007491764

10.4.2 Exercises

10.11. The following error bound is discussed by J. Stoer and R. Bulirsch [A]. Let $\mathbf{A}$ be a symmetric matrix and λ_i be an eigenvalue of $\mathbf{A}$; then

$$\min_i \left| \lambda_i - \frac{\mathbf{x}^T \mathbf{A} \mathbf{x}}{\mathbf{x}^T \mathbf{x}} \right| \leq \sqrt{\frac{\mathbf{x}^T \mathbf{A} \mathbf{A} \mathbf{x}}{\mathbf{x}^T \mathbf{x}} - \left(\frac{\mathbf{x}^T \mathbf{A} \mathbf{x}}{\mathbf{x}^T \mathbf{x}} \right)^2}$$

for any vector $\mathbf{x} \neq \mathbf{0}$.

Show that (10.105) to (10.107) follow from this formula.

10.12. Consider the eigenproblem in Exercise 10.1. Let

$$\hat{\boldsymbol{\phi}} = \begin{bmatrix} 1 \\ 1 \\ 1 \end{bmatrix}$$

Calculate $\overline{\boldsymbol{\phi}}$ using (10.105) and $\rho(\overline{\boldsymbol{\phi}})$. These values, $\rho(\overline{\boldsymbol{\phi}})$ and $\overline{\boldsymbol{\phi}}$, are now the best approximations to an eigenvalue and eigenvector.

Establish the error bounds (10.101) [with (10.103)] and (10.106). Also evaluate the error measure (10.108).

CHAPTER ELEVEN

Solution Methods for Eigenproblems

11.1 INTRODUCTION

In Chapter 10 we discussed the basic facts that are used in eigenvalue and vector solutions and some techniques for the calculation of approximations to the required eigensystem. The purpose of this chapter is to present effective eigensolution techniques. The methods considered here are based on the fundamental aspects discussed in Chapter 10. Therefore, for a thorough understanding of the solution techniques to be presented in this chapter, it is necessary to be very familiar with the material discussed in Chapter 10. In addition, we also employ the notation that was defined in that chapter.

As before, we concentrate on the solution of the eigenproblem

$$\mathbf{K}\boldsymbol{\phi} = \lambda\mathbf{M}\boldsymbol{\phi} \tag{11.1}$$

and, in particular, on the calculation of the smallest eigenvalues $\lambda_1, \ldots, \lambda_p$ and corresponding eigenvectors $\boldsymbol{\phi}_1, \ldots, \boldsymbol{\phi}_p$. *The solution methods that we consider here first (see Sections 11.2 to 11.4) can be subdivided into four groups, corresponding to which basic property is used as the basis of the solution algorithm (see, for example, J. H. Wilkinson [A]).*

The vector iteration methods make up the first group, in which the basic property used is that

$$\mathbf{K}\boldsymbol{\phi}_i = \lambda_i \mathbf{M}\boldsymbol{\phi}_i \tag{11.2}$$

The transformation methods constitute the second group, using

$$\boldsymbol{\Phi}^T\mathbf{K}\boldsymbol{\Phi} = \boldsymbol{\Lambda} \tag{11.3}$$

and

$$\boldsymbol{\Phi}^T\mathbf{M}\boldsymbol{\Phi} = \mathbf{I} \tag{11.4}$$

where $\boldsymbol{\Phi} = [\boldsymbol{\phi}_1, \ldots, \boldsymbol{\phi}_n]$ and $\boldsymbol{\Lambda} = \mathrm{diag}(\lambda_i)$, $i = 1, \ldots, n$. The solution methods of the third group are polynomial iteration techniques that operate on the fact that

$$p(\lambda_i) = 0 \tag{11.5}$$

where

$$p(\lambda) = \det(\mathbf{K} - \lambda\mathbf{M}) \tag{11.6}$$

The solution methods of the fourth group employ the Sturm sequence property of the characteristic polynomials

$$p(\lambda) = \det(\mathbf{K} - \lambda\mathbf{M}) \tag{11.7}$$

and

$$p^{(r)}(\lambda^{(r)}) = \det(\mathbf{K}^{(r)} - \lambda^{(r)}\mathbf{M}^{(r)}); \qquad r = 1, \ldots, n - 1 \tag{11.8}$$

where $p^{(r)}(\lambda^{(r)})$ is the characteristic polynomial of the rth associated constraint problem corresponding to $\mathbf{K}\boldsymbol{\phi} = \lambda\mathbf{M}\boldsymbol{\phi}$.

A number of solution algorithms have been developed within each of these four groups of solution methods. However, for an effective calculation of the required eigensystem of $\mathbf{K}\boldsymbol{\phi} = \lambda\mathbf{M}\boldsymbol{\phi}$, only a few techniques need to be considered, and we present important methods for finite element analysis in the following sections. Vector iteration and transformation methods are presented separately in Sections 11.2 and 11.3, respectively. However, polynomial and Sturm sequence iteration methods are presented together in one section, Section 11.4, because both of these methods use the characteristic polynomials and can be directly employed in one solution scheme. In addition to those techniques that can be classified as falling into one of the four groups, we discuss in Sections 11.5 and 11.6 the Lanczos method and the subspace iteration method, both of which use a combination of the fundamental properties given in (11.2) to (11.8).

Before presenting the solution techniques of interest, a few basic additional points should be noted. It is important to realize that *all solution methods must be iterative in nature because, basically, solving the eigenvalue problem* $\mathbf{K}\boldsymbol{\phi} = \lambda\mathbf{M}\boldsymbol{\phi}$ *is equivalent to calculating the roots of the polynomial* $p(\lambda)$, *which has order equal to the order of* $\mathbf{K}$ *and* $\mathbf{M}$. Since there are for the general case no explicit formulas available for the calculation of the roots of $p(\lambda)$ when the order of p is larger than 4, an iterative solution method has to be used. However, before iteration is started, we may choose to transform the matrices $\mathbf{K}$ and $\mathbf{M}$ into a form that allows a more economical solution of the required eigensystem (see Section 11.3.3).

Although iteration is needed in the solution of an eigenpair $(\lambda_i, \boldsymbol{\phi}_i)$, it should be noted that once one member of the eigenpair has been calculated, we can obtain the other member without further iteration. Assume that λ_i has been evaluated by iteration; then we can obtain $\boldsymbol{\phi}_i$ using (11.2); i.e., $\boldsymbol{\phi}_i$ is calculated by solving

$$(\mathbf{K} - \lambda_i\mathbf{M})\boldsymbol{\phi}_i = \mathbf{0} \tag{11.9}$$

On the other hand, if we have evaluated $\boldsymbol{\phi}_i$ by iteration, we can obtain the required eigenvalue from the Rayleigh quotient; i.e., using (11.3) and (11.4), we have

$$\lambda_i = \boldsymbol{\phi}_i^T\mathbf{K}\boldsymbol{\phi}_i; \qquad \boldsymbol{\phi}_i^T\mathbf{M}\boldsymbol{\phi}_i = 1 \tag{11.10}$$

Therefore, when considering the design of an effective solution method, a basic question is whether we should first solve for the eigenvalue λ_i and then calculate the eigenvector $\boldsymbol{\phi}_i$, or vice versa, or whether it is most economical to solve for both λ_i and $\boldsymbol{\phi}_i$ simultaneously. The answer to this question depends on the solution requirements and the properties of the matrices $\mathbf{K}$ and $\mathbf{M}$, i.e., such factors as the number of required eigenpairs, the order of $\mathbf{K}$ and $\mathbf{M}$, the bandwidth of $\mathbf{K}$, and whether $\mathbf{M}$ is banded.

The effectiveness of a solution method depends largely on two factors: first, the possibility of a reliable use of the procedure, and second, the cost of solution. The solution cost is essentially determined by the number of high-speed storage operations and an efficient use of backup storage devices. However, it is most important that a solution method can be employed in a reliable manner. This means that for well-defined stiffness and mass matrices the solution is always obtained to the required precision without solution breakdown. In practice, a solution is then interrupted only when the problem is ill-defined; for example, due to a data input error the stiffness and mass matrices are not properly defined. This solution interruption then occurs best as early as possible during the calculations, i.e., prior to any large computational expense. We should study the algorithms presented in the following with these considerations.

11.2 VECTOR ITERATION METHODS

As has been pointed out already, in the solution of an eigenvector or an eigenvalue we need to use iteration. In Section 11.1 we classified the solution methods according to the basic relation on which they operate. In the vector iteration methods the basic relation considered is

$$\mathbf{K}\boldsymbol{\phi} = \lambda \mathbf{M}\boldsymbol{\phi} \tag{11.1}$$

The aim is to satisfy the equation in (11.1) by directly operating on it. Consider that we assume a vector for $\boldsymbol{\phi}$, say $\mathbf{x}_1$, and assume a value for λ, say $\lambda = 1$. We can then evaluate the right-hand side of (11.1); i.e., we may calculate

$$\mathbf{R}_1 = (1)\mathbf{M}\mathbf{x}_1 \tag{11.11}$$

Since $\mathbf{x}_1$ is an arbitrarily assumed vector, we do not have, in general, $\mathbf{K}\mathbf{x}_1 = \mathbf{R}_1$. If $\mathbf{K}\mathbf{x}_1$ were equal to $\mathbf{R}_1$, then $\mathbf{x}_1$ would be an eigenvector and, except for trivial cases, our assumptions would have been extremely lucky. Instead, we have an equilibrium equation as encountered in static analysis (see Section 8.2), which we may write

$$\mathbf{K}\mathbf{x}_2 = \mathbf{R}_1; \qquad \mathbf{x}_2 \neq \mathbf{x}_1 \tag{11.12}$$

where $\mathbf{x}_2$ is the displacement solution corresponding to the applied forces $\mathbf{R}_1$. Since we know that we have to use iteration to solve for an eigenvector, we may now feel intuitively that $\mathbf{x}_2$ may be a better approximation to an eigenvector than $\mathbf{x}_1$ was. This is indeed the case, and by repeating the cycle we obtain an increasingly better approximation to an eigenvector.

This procedure is the basis of inverse iteration. We will see that other vector iteration techniques work in a similar way. Specifically, in forward iteration, the iterative cycle is reversed; i.e., in the first step we evaluate $\mathbf{R}_1 = \mathbf{K}\mathbf{x}_1$ and then obtain the improved approximation, $\mathbf{x}_2$, to an eigenvector by solving $\mathbf{M}\mathbf{x}_2 = \mathbf{R}_1$.

The basic steps of the vector iteration schemes and of the other solution methods that we consider later can be introduced using intuition. Namely, we need to satisfy one of the basic relations summarized in Section 11.1 and try to do so by some iterative cycle. However, the real justification for using any one of the methods derives from the fact that they do work and that they can be used economically.

11.2.1 Inverse Iteration

The technique of inverse iteration is very effectively used to calculate an eigenvector, and at the same time the corresponding eigenvalue can also be evaluated. Inverse iteration is employed in various important iteration procedures, including the subspace iteration method described in Section 11.6. It is therefore important that we discuss the method in detail.

In this section we assume that $\mathbf{K}$ is positive definite, whereas $\mathbf{M}$ may be a diagonal mass matrix with or without zero diagonal elements or may be a banded mass matrix. If $\mathbf{K}$ is only positive semidefinite, a shift should be used prior to the iteration (see Section 11.2.3).

In the following we first consider the basic equations used in inverse iteration and then present a more effective form of the technique. In the solution we assume a starting iteration vector $\mathbf{x}_1$ and then evaluate in each iteration step $k = 1, 2, \ldots$:

$$\mathbf{K}\overline{\mathbf{x}}_{k+1} = \mathbf{M}\mathbf{x}_k \tag{11.13}$$

and

$$\mathbf{x}_{k+1} = \frac{\overline{\mathbf{x}}_{k+1}}{(\overline{\mathbf{x}}_{k+1}^T \mathbf{M} \overline{\mathbf{x}}_{k+1})^{1/2}} \tag{11.14}$$

where provided that $\mathbf{x}_1$ is not $\mathbf{M}$-orthogonal to $\boldsymbol{\phi}_1$, meaning that $\mathbf{x}_1^T \mathbf{M} \boldsymbol{\phi}_1 \neq 0$, we have

$$\mathbf{x}_{k+1} \rightarrow \boldsymbol{\phi}_1 \qquad \text{as } k \rightarrow \infty$$

The basic step in the iteration is the solution of the equations in (11.13) in which we evaluate a vector $\overline{\mathbf{x}}_{k+1}$ with a direction closer to an eigenvector than had the previous iteration vector $\mathbf{x}_k$. The calculation in (11.14) merely ensures that the $\mathbf{M}$-weighted length of the new iteration vector $\mathbf{x}_{k+1}$ is unity; i.e., we want $\mathbf{x}_{k+1}$ to satisfy the mass orthonormality relation

$$\mathbf{x}_{k+1}^T \mathbf{M} \mathbf{x}_{k+1} = 1 \tag{11.15}$$

Substituting for $\mathbf{x}_{k+1}$ from (11.14) into (11.15), we find that (11.15) is indeed satisfied. If the scaling in (11.14) is not included in the iteration, the elements of the iteration vectors grow (or decrease) in each step and the iteration vectors do not converge to $\boldsymbol{\phi}_1$ but to a multiple of it. We illustrate the procedure by means of the following example.

EXAMPLE 11.1:   Consider the eigenproblem $\mathbf{K}\boldsymbol{\phi} = \lambda \mathbf{M}\boldsymbol{\phi}$, where

$$\mathbf{K} = \begin{bmatrix} 2 & -1 & 0 & 0 \\ -1 & 2 & -1 & 0 \\ 0 & -1 & 2 & -1 \\ 0 & 0 & -1 & 1 \end{bmatrix}; \qquad \mathbf{M} = \begin{bmatrix} 0 & & & \\ & 2 & & \\ & & 0 & \\ & & & 1 \end{bmatrix}$$

The eigenvalues and corresponding vectors of the problem have been evaluated in Examples 10.12 and 10.13. Use two steps of inverse iteration to evaluate an approximation to $\boldsymbol{\phi}_1$.

The first step is to decompose $\mathbf{K}$ into $\mathbf{LDL}^T$ in order to be able to solve the equations in (11.13). We obtained the triangular factors of $\mathbf{K}$ in Example 10.13.

As starting iteration vector we need a vector that is not orthogonal to $\boldsymbol{\phi}_1$. Since we do not know $\boldsymbol{\phi}_1$, we cannot make sure that $\boldsymbol{\phi}_1^T \mathbf{M} \mathbf{x}_1 \neq 0$, but we want to pick a vector that is not likely to be orthogonal to $\boldsymbol{\phi}_1$. Experience has shown that a good starting vector is in many cases a unit full vector (but see Example 11.6 for a case in which a unit full vector is a bad choice). In this example we use

$$\mathbf{x}_1^T = \begin{bmatrix} 1 & 1 & 1 & 1 \end{bmatrix}$$

and then obtain, for $k = 1$,

$$\begin{bmatrix} 2 & -1 & 0 & 0 \\ -1 & 2 & -1 & 0 \\ 0 & -1 & 2 & -1 \\ 0 & 0 & -1 & 1 \end{bmatrix} \bar{\mathbf{x}}_2 = \begin{bmatrix} 0 & & & \\ & 2 & & \\ & & 0 & \\ & & & 1 \end{bmatrix} \begin{bmatrix} 1 \\ 1 \\ 1 \\ 1 \end{bmatrix}$$

Hence,

$$\bar{\mathbf{x}}_2 = \begin{bmatrix} 3 \\ 6 \\ 7 \\ 8 \end{bmatrix}; \qquad \bar{\mathbf{x}}_2^T \mathbf{M} \bar{\mathbf{x}}_2 = 136$$

and

$$\mathbf{x}_2 = \frac{1}{\sqrt{136}} \begin{bmatrix} 3 \\ 6 \\ 7 \\ 8 \end{bmatrix}$$

Note that the zero diagonal elements in $\mathbf{M}$ do not introduce solution difficulties. Proceeding to the next iteration, $k = 2$, we use

$$\begin{bmatrix} 2 & -1 & 0 & 0 \\ -1 & 2 & -1 & 0 \\ 0 & -1 & 2 & -1 \\ 0 & 0 & -1 & 1 \end{bmatrix} \bar{\mathbf{x}}_3 = \begin{bmatrix} 0 & & & \\ & 2 & & \\ & & 0 & \\ & & & 1 \end{bmatrix} \begin{bmatrix} \dfrac{3}{\sqrt{136}} \\[2mm] \dfrac{6}{\sqrt{136}} \\[2mm] \dfrac{7}{\sqrt{136}} \\[2mm] \dfrac{8}{\sqrt{136}} \end{bmatrix}$$

Hence,

$$\bar{\mathbf{x}}_3 = \frac{1}{\sqrt{136}} \begin{bmatrix} 20 \\ 40 \\ 48 \\ 56 \end{bmatrix}; \qquad \bar{\mathbf{x}}_3^T \mathbf{M} \bar{\mathbf{x}}_3 = \frac{6336}{136}$$

and

$$\mathbf{x}_3 = \frac{1}{\sqrt{6336}} \begin{bmatrix} 20 \\ 40 \\ 48 \\ 56 \end{bmatrix}$$

Comparing $\mathbf{x}_3$ with the exact solution (see Example 10.12), we have

$$\mathbf{x}_3 = \begin{bmatrix} 0.251 \\ 0.503 \\ 0.603 \\ 0.704 \end{bmatrix} \qquad \text{and} \qquad \boldsymbol{\phi}_1 = \begin{bmatrix} 0.250 \\ 0.500 \\ 0.602 \\ 0.707 \end{bmatrix}$$

Hence, with only two iterations we have already obtained a fair approximation to $\boldsymbol{\phi}_1$.

The relations in (11.13) and (11.14) state the basic inverse iteration algorithm. However, in actual computer implementation it is more effective to iterate as follows. Assuming that $\mathbf{y}_1 = \mathbf{M}\mathbf{x}_1$, we evaluate for $k = 1, 2, \ldots,$

$$\mathbf{K}\overline{\mathbf{x}}_{k+1} = \mathbf{y}_k \tag{11.16}$$

$$\overline{\mathbf{y}}_{k+1} = \mathbf{M}\overline{\mathbf{x}}_{k+1} \tag{11.17}$$

$$\rho(\overline{\mathbf{x}}_{k+1}) = \frac{\overline{\mathbf{x}}_{k+1}^T \mathbf{y}_k}{\overline{\mathbf{x}}_{k+1}^T \overline{\mathbf{y}}_{k+1}} \tag{11.18}$$

$$\mathbf{y}_{k+1} = \frac{\overline{\mathbf{y}}_{k+1}}{(\overline{\mathbf{x}}_{k+1}^T \overline{\mathbf{y}}_{k+1})^{1/2}} \tag{11.19}$$

where, provided that $\mathbf{y}_1^T \boldsymbol{\phi}_1 \neq 0$,

$$\mathbf{y}_{k+1} \to \mathbf{M}\boldsymbol{\phi}_1 \quad \text{and} \quad \rho(\overline{\mathbf{x}}_{k+1}) \to \lambda_1 \qquad \text{as} \qquad k \to \infty$$

It should be noted that we essentially dispense in (11.16) to (11.19) with the calculation of the matrix product $\mathbf{M}\mathbf{x}_k$ in (11.13) by iterating on $\mathbf{y}_k$ rather than on $\mathbf{x}_k$. But the value of $\overline{\mathbf{y}}_{k+1}$ is evaluated in either procedure; i.e., $\overline{\mathbf{y}}_{k+1}$ must be calculated in (11.14) and is evaluated in (11.17). Using the second iteration procedure, we obtain in (11.18) an approximation to the eigenvalue λ_1 given by the Rayleigh quotient $\rho(\overline{\mathbf{x}}_{k+1})$. It is this approximation to λ_1 that is conveniently used to measure convergence in the iteration. Denoting the current approximation to λ_1 by $\lambda_1^{(k+1)}$ [i.e., $\lambda_1^{(k+1)} = \rho(\overline{\mathbf{x}}_{k+1})$], we measure convergence using

$$\frac{|\lambda_1^{(k+1)} - \lambda_1^{(k)}|}{\lambda_1^{(k+1)}} \leq tol \tag{11.20}$$

or (10.107) is used for the left-hand side in (11.20), where tol should be 10^{-2s} or smaller when the eigenvalue λ_1 is required to $2s$-digit accuracy. The use of the right-hand side of (10.107) is preferable but requires more computations, and it is in general sufficient to evaluate the error bound in (10.107) only after (11.20) has been met and to restart the iteration if the error is considered to be too large.

The eigenvector will then be accurate to about s or more digits [see text following (11.33)]. Let l be the last iteration; then we have

$$\lambda_1 \doteq \rho(\overline{\mathbf{x}}_{l+1}) \tag{11.21}$$

and

$$\boldsymbol{\phi}_1 \doteq \frac{\overline{\mathbf{x}}_{l+1}}{(\overline{\mathbf{x}}_{l+1}^T \overline{\mathbf{y}}_{l+1})^{1/2}} \tag{11.22}$$

EXAMPLE 11.2:   Use the inverse iteration procedure given in (11.16) to (11.19) to evaluate an approximation to λ_1 and $\boldsymbol{\phi}_1$ of the eigenproblem $\mathbf{K}\boldsymbol{\phi} = \lambda\mathbf{M}\boldsymbol{\phi}$ considered in Example 11.1. Use $tol = 10^{-6}$ (i.e., $s = 3$) in (11.20), in order to measure convergence.

As in Example 11.1, we start the iteration with

$$\mathbf{x}_1 = \begin{bmatrix} 1 \\ 1 \\ 1 \\ 1 \end{bmatrix}$$

Proceeding as given in (11.16) to (11.19), we obtain for $k = 1$,

$$\mathbf{y}_1 = \begin{bmatrix} 0 \\ 2 \\ 0 \\ 1 \end{bmatrix}; \quad \overline{\mathbf{x}}_2 = \begin{bmatrix} 3 \\ 6 \\ 7 \\ 8 \end{bmatrix}; \quad \overline{\mathbf{y}}_2 = \begin{bmatrix} 0 \\ 12 \\ 0 \\ 8 \end{bmatrix}; \quad \rho(\overline{\mathbf{x}}_2) = \frac{\overline{\mathbf{x}}_2^T \mathbf{y}_1}{\overline{\mathbf{x}}_2^T \overline{\mathbf{y}}_2} = 0.1470588$$

and

$$\mathbf{y}_2 = \begin{bmatrix} 0.0 \\ 1.02899 \\ 0.0 \\ 0.68599 \end{bmatrix}$$

The next iterations are carried out in the same way. The results are summarized in Table E11.2. It is seen that after five iterations, convergence has been achieved. It should be noted that the Rayleigh quotient $\rho(\overline{\mathbf{x}}_{k+1})$ converges much faster than the vector $\overline{\mathbf{x}}_{k+1}$ (see Example 11.3) and converges from above to λ_1. Using (11.21) and (11.22), we have

$$\lambda_1 \doteq 0.146447; \quad \boldsymbol{\phi}_1 \doteq \begin{bmatrix} 0.25001 \\ 0.50001 \\ 0.60355 \\ 0.70709 \end{bmatrix}$$

Also, at the end of iteration 5 we have $|\lambda_1^{\text{exact}} - \rho(\overline{\mathbf{x}}_6)|/\lambda_1^{\text{exact}} = 3.14 \times 10^{-9}$ and the right-hand side in (10.107) is 1.23×10^{-4}. Note that in this case (10.107) significantly overestimates the error.

TABLE E11.2

k	$\overline{\mathbf{x}}_{k+1}$	$\overline{\mathbf{y}}_{k+1}$	$\rho(\overline{\mathbf{x}}_{k+1})$	$\dfrac{\|\lambda_1^{(k+1)} - \lambda_1^{(k)}\|}{\lambda_1^{(k+1)}}$	$\mathbf{y}_k$
1	3	0	0.1470588	—	0
	6	12			1.02899
	7	0			0
	8	8			0.68599
2	1.71499	0	0.1464646	0.004056795132	0
	3.42997	6.85994			1.00504
	4.11597	0			0
	4.80196	4.80196			0.70353
3	1.70856	0	0.1464471	0.00011953858	0
	3.41713	6.83426			1.00087
	4.12066	0			0
	4.82418	4.82418			0.70649
4	1.70736	0	0.1464466	0.000003518989	0
	3.41472	6.82944			1.00015
	4.12121	0			0
	4.82771	4.82771			0.70700
5	1.70715	0	0.1464466	0.000000103589	0
	3.41430	6.82860			1.00003
	4.12130	0			0
	4.82830	4.82830			0.70709

In the above discussion we have merely stated the iteration scheme and its convergence. We then applied the method in two examples but did not formally prove convergence. In the following we derive the convergence properties because we believe that the proof is very instructive.

The first step in the proof of convergence and of the convergence rate given here is similar to the procedure used in the analysis of direct integration methods (see Section 9.4). The fundamental equation used in inverse iteration is the relation in (11.13). Neglecting the scaling of the elements in the iteration vector, we basically use for $k = 1, 2, \ldots,$

$$\mathbf{K}\mathbf{x}_{k+1} = \mathbf{M}\mathbf{x}_k \tag{11.23}$$

where we stated that $\mathbf{x}_{k+1}$ will now converge to a multiple of $\boldsymbol{\phi}_1$. To show convergence it is convenient (as in the analysis of direct integration procedures) to change basis from the finite element coordinate basis to the basis of eigenvectors; namely, we can write for any iteration vector $\mathbf{x}_k$,

$$\mathbf{x}_k = \boldsymbol{\Phi}\mathbf{z}_k \tag{11.24}$$

where $\boldsymbol{\Phi}$ is the matrix of eigenvectors $\boldsymbol{\Phi} = [\boldsymbol{\phi}_1, \ldots, \boldsymbol{\phi}_n]$. It should be realized that because $\boldsymbol{\Phi}$ is nonsingular, there is a unique vector $\mathbf{z}_k$ for any vector $\mathbf{x}_k$. Substituting for $\mathbf{x}_k$ and $\mathbf{x}_{k+1}$ from (11.24) into (11.23), premultiplying by $\boldsymbol{\Phi}^T$, and using the orthogonality relations $\boldsymbol{\Phi}^T\mathbf{K}\boldsymbol{\Phi} = \boldsymbol{\Lambda}$ and $\boldsymbol{\Phi}^T\mathbf{M}\boldsymbol{\Phi} = \mathbf{I}$, we obtain

$$\boldsymbol{\Lambda}\mathbf{z}_{k+1} = \mathbf{z}_k \tag{11.25}$$

where $\boldsymbol{\Lambda} = \text{diag}(\lambda_i)$. Comparing (11.25) with (11.23) we find that the iterations are of the same form with $\mathbf{K} = \boldsymbol{\Lambda}$ and $\mathbf{M} = \mathbf{I}$. We may wonder why the transformation in (11.24) is used since $\boldsymbol{\Phi}$ is unknown. However, we should realize that the transformation is employed only to investigate the convergence behavior of inverse iteration. Namely, because *in theory* (11.25) is equivalent to (11.23), the convergence properties of (11.25) are also those of (11.23). But the convergence characteristics of (11.25) are relatively easy to investigate, since the eigenvalues are the diagonal elements of $\boldsymbol{\Lambda}$ and the eigenvectors are the unit vectors $\mathbf{e}_i$, where

$$\mathbf{e}_i^T = [0 \quad \ldots \quad 0 \quad 1 \quad 0 \quad \ldots \quad 0] \tag{11.26}$$

with the 1 at the ith location.

In the presentation of the inverse iteration algorithms given in (11.13) and (11.14) and (11.16) to (11.22), we stated that the starting iteration vector $\mathbf{x}_1$ must not be $\mathbf{M}$-orthogonal to $\boldsymbol{\phi}_1$. Equivalently, in (11.25) the iteration vector $\mathbf{z}_1$ must not be orthogonal to $\mathbf{e}_1$. Assume that we use

$$\mathbf{z}_1^T = [1 \quad 1 \quad 1 \quad \ldots \quad 1] \tag{11.27}$$

We discuss the effect of this assumption in Section 11.2.6. Then using (11.25) for $k = 1, \ldots, l$, we obtain

$$\mathbf{z}_{l+1}^T = \left[\left(\frac{1}{\lambda_1}\right)^l \left(\frac{1}{\lambda_2}\right)^l \cdots \left(\frac{1}{\lambda_n}\right)^l\right] \tag{11.28}$$

Let us first assume that $\lambda_1 < \lambda_2$. To show that $\mathbf{z}_{l+1}$ converges to a multiple of $\mathbf{e}_1$ as $l \to \infty$, we multiply $\mathbf{z}_{l+1}$ in (11.28) by $(\lambda_1)^l$ to obtain

$$\overline{\mathbf{z}}_{l+1} = \begin{bmatrix} 1 \\ (\lambda_1/\lambda_2)^l \\ \cdot \\ \cdot \\ \cdot \\ (\lambda_1/\lambda_n)^l \end{bmatrix} \tag{11.29}$$

and observe that $\overline{\mathbf{z}}_{l+1}$ converges to $\mathbf{e}_1$ as $l \to \infty$. Hence, $\mathbf{z}_{l+1}$ converges to a multiple of $\mathbf{e}_1$ as $l \to \infty$.

To evaluate the order and rate of convergence, we use the convergence definition given in Section 2.7. For the iteration under consideration here we obtain

$$\lim_{l \to \infty} \frac{\| \overline{\mathbf{z}}_{l+1} - \mathbf{e}_1 \|_2}{\| \overline{\mathbf{z}}_l - \mathbf{e}_1 \|_2} = \frac{\lambda_1}{\lambda_2} \tag{11.30}$$

Hence convergence is linear, and the rate of convergence is λ_1/λ_2. This convergence rate is also shown in the iteration vector $\overline{\mathbf{z}}_{l+1}$ in (11.29); i.e., those elements in the iteration vector that should tend to zero do so with at least the ratio λ_1/λ_2 in each additional iteration. Thus, if $\lambda_2 > \lambda_1$, it is the relative magnitude of λ_1 to λ_2 that determines how fast the iteration vector converges to the eigenvector $\boldsymbol{\phi}_1$.

In this discussion we assumed that $\lambda_1 < \lambda_2$. Let us now consider the case of a multiple eigenvalue, namely, $\lambda_1 = \lambda_2 = \cdots = \lambda_m$. Then we have in (11.29),

$$\overline{\mathbf{z}}_{l+1}^T = \begin{bmatrix} 1 & 1 & \dots & 1 & \left(\dfrac{\lambda_1}{\lambda_{m+1}}\right)^l & \dots & \left(\dfrac{\lambda_1}{\lambda_n}\right)^l \end{bmatrix} \tag{11.31}$$

and the convergence rate of the iteration vector is λ_1/λ_{m+1}. Therefore, in general, the rate of convergence of the iteration vector in inverse iteration is given by the ratio of λ_1 to the next distinct eigenvalue.

In the iteration given in (11.16) to (11.22), we obtain an approximation to the eigenvalue λ_1 by evaluating the Rayleigh quotient. Corresponding to (11.18), the Rayleigh quotient calculated in the iteration of (11.25) would be

$$\rho(\mathbf{z}_{k+1}) = \frac{\mathbf{z}_{k+1}^T \mathbf{z}_k}{\mathbf{z}_{k+1}^T \mathbf{z}_{k+1}} \tag{11.32}$$

Assume that we consider the last iteration in which $k = l$. Then substituting for $\mathbf{z}_l$ and $\mathbf{z}_{l+1}$ from (11.28) into (11.32), we obtain

$$\rho(\mathbf{z}_{l+1}) = \frac{\lambda_1 \sum\limits_{i=1}^{n} (\lambda_1/\lambda_i)^{2l-1}}{\sum\limits_{i=1}^{n} (\lambda_1/\lambda_i)^{2l}} \tag{11.33}$$

Hence we have for λ_1 being a simple or multiple eigenvalue,

$$\rho(\mathbf{z}_{l+1}) \to \lambda_1 \qquad \text{as } l \to \infty$$

Also, convergence is linear with the rate equal to $(\lambda_1/\lambda_{m+1})^2$, where λ_{m+1} is defined as in (11.31). This convergence rate substantiates the observation that if an eigenvector is known with an error ϵ, then the Rayleigh quotient yields an approximation to the corresponding eigenvalue with error ϵ^2 (see Section 2.6).

Before demonstrating the results by means of a brief example, it should be recalled that we assumed in the above analysis a full unit starting iteration vector as given in (11.27). The convergence properties derived hold for any starting iteration vector that is not orthogonal to the eigenvector of interest, but the convergence rates can in many practical analyses be observed only as the number of iterations becomes large. The same observation also holds for any of the other convergence analyses that are presented in the following sections. We discuss this observation with other important practical aspects in Section 11.2.6.

EXAMPLE 11.3: For the problem considered in Example 11.2, calculate the ultimate convergence rates of the iteration vector and the Rayleigh quotient. Compare the ultimate convergence rates with those actually observed in the inverse iteration carried out in Example 11.2.

For the evaluation of the theoretical convergence rates, we need λ_1 and λ_2. We calculated the eigenvalues in Example 10.12 and found

$$\lambda_1 = \frac{1}{2} - \frac{\sqrt{2}}{4}$$

$$\lambda_2 = \frac{1}{2} + \frac{\sqrt{2}}{4}$$

Hence, the ultimate convergence rate of the iteration vector is

$$\frac{\lambda_1}{\lambda_2} = 0.17$$

and the ultimate convergence rate of the Rayleigh quotient is

$$\left(\frac{\lambda_1}{\lambda_2}\right)^2 = 0.029$$

The actual vector convergence obtained is observed by evaluating the ratio r_{k+1}, $k = 1$, $2, \ldots$, where

$$r_{k+1} = \frac{\| \mathbf{x}_{k+1} - \boldsymbol{\phi}_1 \|_2}{\| \mathbf{x}_k - \boldsymbol{\phi}_1 \|_2}$$

and we assume that $\boldsymbol{\phi}_1$ is obtained in the last iteration [see (11.22)].

For the iteration in Example 11.2, we thus obtain

$$r_2 = 0.026083; \qquad r_3 = 0.170559; \qquad r_4 = 0.167134; \qquad r_5 = 0.144251$$

Ignoring r_2 because the iteration just started, we see that the theoretical and actual convergence rates compare quite well.

Similarly, the actual convergence of the Rayleigh quotient calculated in Example 11.2 is observed by evaluating

$$\epsilon_{k+1} = \frac{| \rho(\overline{\mathbf{x}}_{k+1}) - \lambda_1 |}{| \rho(\overline{\mathbf{x}}_k) - \lambda_1 |}$$

where we use the converged value of the Rayleigh quotient for λ_1. In the iteration of Example 11.2 we have

$$\epsilon_3 = 0.028768; \qquad \epsilon_4 = 0.027778; \qquad \epsilon_5 = 0$$

Hence, we see that the theoretical and observed convergence rates again agree quite well in this solution.

11.2.2 Forward Iteration

The method of forward iteration is complementary to the inverse iteration technique in that the method yields the eigenvector corresponding to the largest eigenvalue. Whereas we assumed in inverse iteration that $\mathbf{K}$ is positive definite, we assume in this section that $\mathbf{M}$ is positive definite; otherwise, a shift must be used (see Section 11.2.3). Having chosen a starting iteration vector $\mathbf{x}_1$, in forward iteration we evaluate, for $k = 1, 2, \ldots,$

$$\mathbf{M}\overline{\mathbf{x}}_{k+1} = \mathbf{K}\mathbf{x}_k \tag{11.34}$$

and

$$\mathbf{x}_{k+1} = \frac{\overline{\mathbf{x}}_{k+1}}{(\overline{\mathbf{x}}_{k+1}^T \mathbf{M} \overline{\mathbf{x}}_{k+1})^{1/2}} \tag{11.35}$$

where provided that $\mathbf{x}_1$ is not $\mathbf{M}$-orthogonal to $\boldsymbol{\phi}_n$, we have

$$\mathbf{x}_{k+1} \to \boldsymbol{\phi}_n \qquad \text{as } k \to \infty$$

The analogy to inverse iteration should be noted; the only difference is that we solve (11.34) rather than (11.13) to obtain an improved eigenvector. This means, in practice, that in the inverse iteration we need to triangularize the matrix $\mathbf{K}$ and in the forward iteration we decompose $\mathbf{M}$.

A more effective forward iteration procedure than that in (11.34) and (11.35) would be obtained by using equations that are analogous to those in (11.16) to (11.22). Assuming that $\mathbf{y}_1 = \mathbf{K}\mathbf{x}_1$, we evaluate for $k = 1, 2, \ldots,$

$$\mathbf{M}\overline{\mathbf{x}}_{k+1} = \mathbf{y}_k \tag{11.36}$$

$$\overline{\mathbf{y}}_{k+1} = \mathbf{K}\overline{\mathbf{x}}_{k+1} \tag{11.37}$$

$$\rho(\overline{\mathbf{x}}_{k+1}) = \frac{\overline{\mathbf{x}}_{k+1}^T \overline{\mathbf{y}}_{k+1}}{\overline{\mathbf{x}}_{k+1}^T \mathbf{y}_k} \tag{11.38}$$

$$\mathbf{y}_{k+1} = \frac{\overline{\mathbf{y}}_{k+1}}{(\overline{\mathbf{x}}_{k+1}^T \mathbf{y}_k)^{1/2}} \tag{11.39}$$

where provided that $\boldsymbol{\phi}_n^T \mathbf{y}_1 \neq 0$,

$$\mathbf{y}_{k+1} \to \mathbf{K}\boldsymbol{\phi}_n \quad \text{and} \quad \rho(\overline{\mathbf{x}}_{k+1}) \to \lambda_n \qquad \text{as } k \to \infty$$

Convergence in the iteration could again be measured as given in (11.20), and denoting the last iteration by l, we have

$$\lambda_n \doteq \rho(\overline{\mathbf{x}}_{l+1}) \tag{11.40}$$

and

$$\boldsymbol{\phi}_n \doteq \frac{\overline{\mathbf{x}}_{l+1}}{(\overline{\mathbf{x}}_{l+1}^T \mathbf{y}_l)^{1/2}} \tag{11.41}$$

Considering the analysis of convergence of the iteration vector to $\boldsymbol{\phi}_n$, it can be carried out following the same procedure that was used in the evaluation of the convergence characteristics of inverse iteration. Alternatively, we may use the results that we obtained in the analysis of inverse iteration. Namely, assume that we write the eigenproblem $\mathbf{K}\boldsymbol{\phi} = \lambda \mathbf{M}\boldsymbol{\phi}$ in the form $\mathbf{M}\boldsymbol{\phi} = \lambda^{-1}\mathbf{K}\boldsymbol{\phi}$; then using inverse iteration to solve for an eigenvector and corresponding eigenvalue is equivalent to performing forward iteration on the problem

$\mathbf{K}\boldsymbol{\phi} = \lambda \mathbf{M}\boldsymbol{\phi}$. But since we converge in the inverse iteration of (11.16) to (11.22) to the smallest eigenvalue and corresponding eigenvector, and since for the problem $\mathbf{M}\boldsymbol{\phi} = \lambda^{-1}\mathbf{K}\boldsymbol{\phi}$ this eigenvalue is λ_n^{-1}, where λ_n is the largest eigenvalue of $\mathbf{K}\boldsymbol{\phi} = \lambda \mathbf{M}\boldsymbol{\phi}$, we converge in the forward iteration of (11.36) to (11.41) to λ_n and $\boldsymbol{\phi}_n$ and the convergence rate of the iteration vector is λ_{n-1}/λ_n. We should note that the Rayleigh quotient evaluated in (11.38) is $\overline{\mathbf{x}}_{k+1}^T \mathbf{K}\overline{\mathbf{x}}_{k+1}/\overline{\mathbf{x}}_{k+1}^T \mathbf{M}\overline{\mathbf{x}}_{k+1}$, i.e., just the inverse of the Rayleigh quotient for calculating an approximation to λ_n^{-1} in the problem $\mathbf{M}\boldsymbol{\phi} = \lambda^{-1}\mathbf{K}\boldsymbol{\phi}$.

We demonstrate the iteration and convergence in the following example.

EXAMPLE 11.4: Use forward iteration as given in (11.36) to (11.41) with $tol = 10^{-6}$ in (11.20) to evaluate λ_4 and $\boldsymbol{\phi}_4$ of the eigenproblem $\mathbf{K}\boldsymbol{\phi} = \lambda \mathbf{M}\boldsymbol{\phi}$, where

$$
\mathbf{K} = \begin{bmatrix} 5 & -4 & 1 & 0 \\ -4 & 6 & -4 & 1 \\ 1 & -4 & 6 & -4 \\ 0 & 1 & -4 & 5 \end{bmatrix}; \qquad \mathbf{M} = \begin{bmatrix} 2 & & & \\ & 2 & & \\ & & 1 & \\ & & & 1 \end{bmatrix}
$$

The physical problem considered in this example is the free-vibration response of the simply supported beam shown in Fig. 8.1 with the above mass matrix.

Starting the iteration with

$$
\mathbf{x}_1 = \begin{bmatrix} 1 \\ 1 \\ 1 \\ 1 \end{bmatrix}
$$

we calculate in the inverse iteration the values summarized in Table E11.4.

Hence, we need 10 iterations for a convergence tolerance of 10^{-6} in (11.20), and we then use, as given in (11.40) and (11.41),

$$
\lambda_4 \doteq 10.63845; \qquad \boldsymbol{\phi}_4 \doteq \begin{bmatrix} -0.10731 \\ 0.25539 \\ -0.72827 \\ 0.56227 \end{bmatrix}
$$

Comparing after iteration 10 the predicted value of λ_4 with the exact value, we have

$$
\frac{|\lambda_4^{\text{exact}} - \rho(\overline{\mathbf{x}}_{11})|}{\lambda_4^{\text{exact}}} = 1.92 \times 10^{-7}
$$

Also, the right-hand side in (10.107) gives 5.24×10^{-4}.

TABLE E11.4

k	$\overline{\mathbf{x}}_{k+1}$	$\overline{\mathbf{y}}_{k+1}$	$\rho(\overline{\mathbf{x}}_{k+1})$	$\mathbf{y}_{k+1}$	$\dfrac{\lvert \lambda_4^{(k+1)} - \lambda_4^{(k)} \rvert}{\lambda_4^{(k+1)}}$
1	1	6	5.93333	2.1909	—
	−0.5	−1		−0.3651	
	−1	−11		−4.0166	
	2	13.5		4.9295	
2	1.0954	2.1909	8.57887	0.3345	0.3084
	−0.1826	15.5188		2.3694	
	−4.0166	−41.9921		−6.4112	
	4.9295	40.5315		6.1882	
3	0.1672	−10.3137	10.15966	−1.1372	0.1556
	1.1847	38.2720		4.2198	
	−6.4112	−67.7914		−7.4745	
	6.1882	57.7704		6.3696	
8	−1.1285	−24.2083	10.63838	−2.2756	0.00003304
	2.7044	57.7298		5.4267	
	−7.7481	−82.4222		−7.7478	
	5.9969	63.6811		5.9861	
9	−1.1378	−24.2902	10.63844	−2.2833	0.000005584
	2.7133	57.8086		5.4340	
	−7.7478	−82.4224		−7.7476	
	5.9861	63.6351		5.9816	
10	−1.1416	−24.3237	10.63845	−2.2864	0.0000009437
	2.7170	57.8405		5.4369	
	−7.7476	−82.4219		−7.7476	
	5.9816	63.6157		5.9798	

11.2.3 Shifting in Vector Iteration

The convergence analysis of inverse iteration in Section 11.2.1 showed that assuming $\lambda_1 < \lambda_2$, the iteration vector converges with a rate λ_1/λ_2 to the eigenvector $\boldsymbol{\phi}_1$. Therefore, depending on the magnitude of λ_1 and λ_2, the convergence rate can be arbitrarily low, say $\lambda_1/\lambda_2 = 0.99999$, or can be very high, say $\lambda_1/\lambda_2 = 0.01$. Similarly, in forward iteration the convergence rate can be low or high. Therefore, a natural question must be how to improve the convergence rate in the vector iterations. We show in this section that the convergence rate can be much improved by shifting. In addition, a shift can be used to obtain convergence to an eigenpair other than $(\lambda_1, \boldsymbol{\phi}_1)$ and $(\lambda_n, \boldsymbol{\phi}_n)$ in inverse and forward iterations, respectively, and a shift is used effectively in inverse iteration when $\mathbf{K}$ is positive semidefinite and in forward iteration when $\mathbf{M}$ is diagonal with some zero diagonal elements (see Example 11.6).

Assume that a shift μ is applied as described in Section 10.2.3; then we consider the eigenproblem

$$(\mathbf{K} - \mu\mathbf{M})\boldsymbol{\phi} = \eta\mathbf{M}\boldsymbol{\phi} \qquad (11.42)$$

where the eigenvalues of the original problem $\mathbf{K}\boldsymbol{\phi} = \lambda\mathbf{M}\boldsymbol{\phi}$ and of the problem in (11.42) are related by $\eta_i = \lambda_i - \mu$, $i = 1, \ldots, n$. To analyze the convergence properties of inverse and forward iteration when applied to the problem in (11.42), we follow in all respects the procedure used in Section 11.2.1. The first step is to consider the problem in the basis of eigenvectors $\boldsymbol{\Phi}$. Using the transformation

$$\boldsymbol{\phi} = \boldsymbol{\Phi}\boldsymbol{\psi} \tag{11.43}$$

we obtain for the convergence analysis the equivalent eigenproblem

$$(\boldsymbol{\Lambda} - \mu\mathbf{I})\boldsymbol{\psi} = \eta\boldsymbol{\psi} \tag{11.44}$$

Consider first inverse iteration and assume that all eigenvalues are distinct. In that case we obtain, using the notation in Section 11.2.1,

$$\mathbf{z}_{l+1}^T = \left[\frac{1}{(\lambda_1 - \mu)^l} \quad \frac{1}{(\lambda_2 - \mu)^l} \cdots \frac{1}{(\lambda_n - \mu)^l}\right] \tag{11.45}$$

where it is assumed that all $\lambda_i - \mu$ are nonzero, but they may be positive or negative. Assume that $\lambda_i - \mu$ is smallest in absolute magnitude when $i = j$; then multiplying $\mathbf{z}_{l+1}$ by $(\lambda_j - \mu)^l$, we obtain

$$\bar{\mathbf{z}}_{l+1} = \begin{bmatrix} \left(\dfrac{\lambda_j - \mu}{\lambda_1 - \mu}\right)^l \\ \vdots \\ \left(\dfrac{\lambda_j - \mu}{\lambda_{j-1} - \mu}\right)^l \\ 1 \\ \left(\dfrac{\lambda_j - \mu}{\lambda_{j+1} - \mu}\right)^l \\ \vdots \\ \left(\dfrac{\lambda_j - \mu}{\lambda_n - \mu}\right)^l \end{bmatrix} \tag{11.46}$$

where $|(\lambda_j - \mu)/(\lambda_p - \mu)| < 1$ for all $p \neq j$. Hence, in the iteration we have $\bar{\mathbf{z}}_{l+1} \to \mathbf{e}_j$, meaning that in inverse iteration to solve (11.42), the iteration vector converges to $\boldsymbol{\phi}_j$. Furthermore, we obtain $\lambda_j = \eta_j + \mu$. The convergence rate in the iteration is determined by the element $(\lambda_j - \mu)/(\lambda_p - \mu)$ which is largest in absolute magnitude, $p \neq j$; i.e., the convergence rate r is

$$r = \max_{p \neq j} \left|\frac{\lambda_j - \mu}{\lambda_p - \mu}\right| \tag{11.47}$$

Since λ_j is nearest μ, the convergence rate of the iteration vector in (11.42) to the eigenvector $\boldsymbol{\phi}_j$ is either

$$\left|\frac{\lambda_j - \mu}{\lambda_{j-1} - \mu}\right| \quad \text{or} \quad \left|\frac{\lambda_j - \mu}{\lambda_{j+1} - \mu}\right|$$

whichever is larger. The convergence rate for a typical case is shown in Fig. 11.1.

Using the results of the above convergence analysis and of the analysis of inverse iteration without shifting (see Section 11.2.1), two additional conclusions are reached.

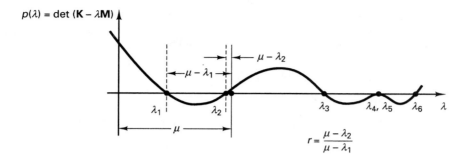

Figure 11.1 Example of vector convergence rate r in inverse iteration

First, we observe that the convergence rate of the Rayleigh quotient, which for μ nearest to λ_j converges to $\lambda_j - \mu$, is

$$\left| \frac{\lambda_j - \mu}{\lambda_{j-1} - \mu} \right|^2 \qquad \text{or} \qquad \left| \frac{\lambda_j - \mu}{\lambda_{j+1} - \mu} \right|^2$$

whichever is larger.

The second observation concerns the case of λ_j being a multiple eigenvalue. The analysis in Section 11.2.1 and the conclusions above show that if $\lambda_j = \lambda_{j+1} = \cdots = \lambda_{j+m-1}$, the rate of convergence of the iteration vector is

$$\max_{p \neq j, j+1, \ldots, j+m-1} \left| \frac{\lambda_j - \mu}{\lambda_p - \mu} \right|$$

and convergence occurs to a vector in the subspace corresponding to λ_j.

The important point in inverse iteration with shifting is that by choosing a shift near enough the specific eigenvalue of interest, we can, in theory, have a convergence rate that is as high as required; i.e., we would only need to make $|\lambda_j - \mu|$ small enough in relation to $|\lambda_p - \mu|$ defined above. However, in an actual solution scheme the difficulty is to find an appropriate μ, for which we consider various methods in the next sections.

EXAMPLE 11.5: Use inverse iteration as given in (11.16) to (11.22) in order to calculate $(\lambda_1, \boldsymbol{\phi}_1)$ of the problem $\mathbf{K}\boldsymbol{\phi} = \lambda\mathbf{M}\boldsymbol{\phi}$, where $\mathbf{K}$ and $\mathbf{M}$ are given in Example 11.4. Then impose the shift $\mu = 10$ and show that in the inverse iteration convergence occurs toward λ_4 and $\boldsymbol{\phi}_4$.

Using inverse iteration on $\mathbf{K}\boldsymbol{\phi} = \lambda\mathbf{M}\boldsymbol{\phi}$ as in Example 11.2 gives convergence after three iterations with a tolerance of 10^{-6},

$$\lambda_1 \doteq 0.09654; \qquad \boldsymbol{\phi}_1 \doteq \begin{bmatrix} 0.3126 \\ 0.4955 \\ 0.4791 \\ 0.2898 \end{bmatrix}$$

Now imposing a shift of $\mu = 10$, we obtain

$$\mathbf{K} - \mu\mathbf{M} = \begin{bmatrix} -15 & -4 & 1 & 0 \\ -4 & -14 & -4 & 1 \\ 1 & -4 & -4 & -4 \\ 0 & 1 & -4 & -5 \end{bmatrix}$$

Using inverse iteration on the problem $(\mathbf{K} - \mu\mathbf{M})\boldsymbol{\phi} = \eta\mathbf{M}\boldsymbol{\phi}$, we obtain convergence after six iterations with

$$\rho(\bar{\mathbf{x}}_7) = 0.6385; \qquad \mathbf{x}_7 = \begin{bmatrix} -0.1076 \\ 0.2556 \\ -0.7283 \\ 0.5620 \end{bmatrix}$$

Since we imposed a shift, we do know that $\mu + \rho(\bar{\mathbf{x}}_7)$ is an approximation to an eigenvalue and $\mathbf{x}_7$ is an approximation to the corresponding eigenvector. But we do not know which eigenpair has been approximated. By comparing $\mathbf{x}_7$ with the results obtained in Example 11.4 we find that

$$\lambda_4 \doteq \mu + \rho(\mathbf{x}_7) \doteq 10.6385; \qquad \boldsymbol{\phi}_4 \doteq \mathbf{x}_7$$

EXAMPLE 11.6:   Consider the unsupported beam element depicted in Fig. E8.13. Show that the usual inverse iteration algorithm of calculating λ_1 and $\boldsymbol{\phi}_1$ does not work, but that after imposing a shift the standard algorithm can again be applied.

The first step in the inverse iteration defined in (11.16) is, in this case with $\mathbf{M} = \mathbf{I}$ and $\mathbf{x}_1$ a full unit vector,

$$\begin{bmatrix} 12 & -6 & -12 & -6 \\ -6 & 4 & 6 & 2 \\ -12 & 6 & 12 & 6 \\ -6 & 2 & 6 & 4 \end{bmatrix} \bar{\mathbf{x}}_2 = \begin{bmatrix} 1 \\ 1 \\ 1 \\ 1 \end{bmatrix} \qquad \text{(a)}$$

Using Gauss elimination to solve the equations, we arrive at

$$\begin{bmatrix} 12 & -6 & -12 & -6 \\ & 1 & 0 & -1 \\ & & 0 & 0 \\ & & & 0 \end{bmatrix} \bar{\mathbf{x}}_2 = \begin{bmatrix} 1 \\ \frac{3}{2} \\ 2 \\ \frac{7}{2} \end{bmatrix}$$

and hence the equations in (a) have no solution. They have a solution only if the right-hand side [i.e., $\mathbf{x}_1$ in (11.16)] is a null vector. There would be no difficulty in modifying the solution procedure when a singular coefficient matrix is encountered, and the advantage would be that the eigenvector would be calculated in one iteration. On the other hand, if we impose a shift, we can use the standard iteration procedure, and stability problems are avoided in the calculation of other eigenvalues and eigenvectors. Assume that we use $\mu = -6$ so that all λ_i are positive. Then we have

$$\mathbf{K} - \mu\mathbf{I} = \begin{bmatrix} 18 & -6 & -12 & -6 \\ -6 & 10 & 6 & 2 \\ -12 & 6 & 18 & 6 \\ -6 & 2 & 6 & 10 \end{bmatrix}$$

The inverse iteration can now be performed in the standard manner using a full unit starting iteration vector. Convergence is achieved after five iterations to a tolerance of 10^{-6}, and we have

$$\rho(\bar{\mathbf{x}}_6) = 6.000000; \qquad \mathbf{x}_6 = \begin{bmatrix} 0.73784 \\ 0.42165 \\ 0.31625 \\ 0.42165 \end{bmatrix}$$

Hence, taking account of the shift, we have

$$\lambda_1 \doteq 0.0; \qquad \boldsymbol{\phi}_1 \doteq \mathbf{x}_6$$

We showed before that the rate of convergence in inverse iteration can be greatly increased by shifting. We may now wonder whether the convergence rate in forward iteration can be increased in a similar way. In analogy to the convergence proof of inverse iteration with a shift, we can generalize the convergence analysis of forward iteration when a shift μ is used. The final result is that the iteration vector converges to the eigenvector $\boldsymbol{\phi}_j$ that corresponds to the largest eigenvalue $|\lambda_j - \mu|$ of the problem in (11.42), where

$$|\lambda_j - \mu| = \max_{\text{all } i} |\lambda_i - \mu| \tag{11.48}$$

The convergence rate of the iteration vector is given by

$$r = \max_{p \neq j} \left| \frac{\lambda_p - \mu}{\lambda_j - \mu} \right| \tag{11.49}$$

which, in fact, is the ratio of the second largest eigenvalue to the largest eigenvalue (both measured in absolute values) of the problem $(\mathbf{K} - \mu\mathbf{M})\boldsymbol{\phi} = \eta\mathbf{M}\boldsymbol{\phi}$. In the case of λ_j being a multiple eigenvalue, say $\lambda_j = \lambda_{j+1} = \cdots = \lambda_{j+m-1}$, the iteration vector converges to a vector in the subspace corresponding to λ_j, and the rate of convergence is

$$\max_{p \neq j, j+1, \ldots, j+m-1} \left| \frac{\lambda_p - \mu}{\lambda_j - \mu} \right|$$

The main difference between the convergence rate in (11.47) and (11.49) is that in (11.47), λ_p is in the denominator, whereas in (11.49), λ_p is in the numerator. This limits the convergence rate in forward iteration and by means of shifting convergence can be obtained only to the eigenpair $(\lambda_n, \boldsymbol{\phi}_n)$ or to the eigenpair $(\lambda_1, \boldsymbol{\phi}_1)$. To achieve the highest convergence rates to $\boldsymbol{\phi}_n$ and $\boldsymbol{\phi}_1$, we need to choose $\mu = (\lambda_1 + \lambda_{n-1})/2$ and $\mu = (\lambda_2 + \lambda_n)/2$, respectively, and have the corresponding convergence rates

$$\left| \frac{\lambda_{n-1} - \dfrac{\lambda_1 + \lambda_{n-1}}{2}}{\lambda_n - \dfrac{\lambda_1 + \lambda_{n-1}}{2}} \right| \qquad \text{and} \qquad \left| \frac{\lambda_2 - \dfrac{\lambda_2 + \lambda_n}{2}}{\lambda_1 - \dfrac{\lambda_2 + \lambda_n}{2}} \right|$$

(see Fig. 11.2). Therefore, a much higher convergence rate can be obtained with shifting in

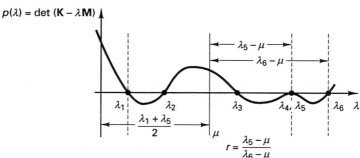

Figure 11.2 Shifting to obtain best convergence rate r in forward iteration for λ_6 (λ_6 = largest eigenvalue)

inverse iteration than using forward iteration. For this reason and because a shift can be chosen to converge to any eigenpair, inverse iteration is much more important in practical analysis, and in the algorithms presented later, we always use inverse iteration whenever vector iteration is required.

11.2.4 Rayleigh Quotient Iteration

We discussed in Section 11.2.3 that the convergence rate in inverse iteration can be much improved by shifting. In practice, the difficulty lies in choosing an appropriate shift. One possibility is to use as a shift value the Rayleigh quotient calculated in (11.18), which is an approximation to the eigenvalue sought. If a new shift using (11.18) is evaluated in each iteration, we have the Rayleigh quotient iteration (see A. M. Ostrowski [A]). In this procedure we assume a starting iteration vector $\mathbf{x}_1$, hence $\mathbf{y}_1 = \mathbf{M}\mathbf{x}_1$, a starting shift $\rho(\overline{\mathbf{x}}_1)$, which is usually zero, and then evaluate for $k = 1, 2, \ldots$:

$$[\mathbf{K} - \rho(\overline{\mathbf{x}}_k)\mathbf{M}]\overline{\mathbf{x}}_{k+1} = \mathbf{y}_k \tag{11.50}$$

$$\overline{\mathbf{y}}_{k+1} = \mathbf{M}\,\overline{\mathbf{x}}_{k+1} \tag{11.51}$$

$$\rho(\overline{\mathbf{x}}_{k+1}) = \frac{\overline{\mathbf{x}}_{k+1}^T \mathbf{y}_k}{\overline{\mathbf{x}}_{k+1}^T \overline{\mathbf{y}}_{k+1}} + \rho(\overline{\mathbf{x}}_k) \tag{11.52}$$

$$\mathbf{y}_{k+1} = \frac{\overline{\mathbf{y}}_{k+1}}{(\overline{\mathbf{x}}_{k+1}^T \overline{\mathbf{y}}_{k+1})^{1/2}} \tag{11.53}$$

where now $\mathbf{y}_{k+1} \rightarrow \mathbf{M}\boldsymbol{\phi}_i$ and $\rho(\overline{\mathbf{x}}_{k+1}) \rightarrow \lambda_i$ as $k \rightarrow \infty$

The eigenvalue λ_i and corresponding eigenvector $\boldsymbol{\phi}_i$ to which the iteration converges depend on the starting iteration vector $\mathbf{x}_1$ and the initial shift $\rho(\overline{\mathbf{x}}_1)$. If $\mathbf{x}_1$ has strong components of an eigenvector, say $\boldsymbol{\phi}_k$, and $\rho(\overline{\mathbf{x}}_2)$ provides a sufficiently close shift to the corresponding eigenvalue λ_k, then the iteration converges to the eigenpair $(\lambda_k, \boldsymbol{\phi}_k)$ and the ultimate order of convergence for both λ_k and $\boldsymbol{\phi}_k$ is cubic. Hence, in practice we need to ensure that $\mathbf{x}_1$ is reasonably close to the eigenvector of interest, and then *convergence will always be cubic*. This excellent convergence behavior is a most important observation. We may intuitively explain it by the fact that in inverse iteration the vector converges linearly, and with an error of order ϵ in the vector the Rayleigh quotient predicts the eigenvalue with an error of order ϵ^2. Since the eigenvalue approximation used as a shift has a direct effect on the approximation to be obtained for the eigenvector, and vice versa, it seems probable that in Rayleigh quotient iteration the order of convergence is cubic for both the eigenvalue and eigenvector.

To analyze the convergence characteristics of Rayleigh quotient iteration we may proceed in the same way as in the analysis of inverse iteration; i.e., we consider the iteration in the basis of the eigenvectors. In this case we use the transformation in (11.24) and write the two basic equations of Rayleigh quotient iteration [i.e., (11.50) and (11.52), respectively] in the following form:

$$[\boldsymbol{\Lambda} - \rho(\mathbf{z}_k)\mathbf{I}]\mathbf{z}_{k+1} = \mathbf{z}_k \tag{11.54}$$

$$\rho(\mathbf{z}_{k+1}) = \frac{\mathbf{z}_{k+1}^T \mathbf{z}_k}{\mathbf{z}_{k+1}^T \mathbf{z}_{k+1}} + \rho(\mathbf{z}_k) \tag{11.55}$$

where the length normalization of the iteration vector has been omitted.

To consider the convergence characteristics of the iteration vector, let us perform an approximate convergence analysis that gives insight into the working of the algorithm. Assume that the current iteration vector $\mathbf{z}_l$ is already close to the eigenvector $\mathbf{e}_1$; i.e., we have

$$\mathbf{z}_l^T = [1 \quad o(\epsilon) \quad o(\epsilon) \quad \ldots \quad o(\epsilon)] \tag{11.56}$$

where $o(\epsilon)$ denotes "of order ϵ" and $\epsilon \ll 1$. We then obtain

$$\rho(\mathbf{z}_l) = \lambda_1 + o(\epsilon^2) \tag{11.57}$$

Solving from (11.54) for $\mathbf{z}_{l+1}$, we thus have

$$\mathbf{z}_{l+1}^T = \left[\frac{1}{o(\epsilon^2)} \quad \frac{o(\epsilon)}{\lambda_2 - \lambda_1} \quad \cdots \quad \frac{o(\epsilon)}{\lambda_n - \lambda_1} \right] \tag{11.58}$$

In order to assess the convergence of the iteration vector we normalize to 1 the first component of $\mathbf{z}_{l+1}$, to obtain

$$\bar{\mathbf{z}}_{l+1}^T = [1 \quad o(\epsilon^3) \quad o(\epsilon^3) \quad \ldots \quad o(\epsilon^3)] \tag{11.59}$$

Hence, the elements that in $\bar{\mathbf{z}}_l$ have been of order ϵ are now of order ϵ^3, indicating cubic convergence.

Consider the following example to demonstrate the characteristics of Rayleigh quotient iteration.

EXAMPLE 11.7: Perform the Rayleigh quotient iteration on the problem $\mathbf{\Lambda}\boldsymbol{\phi} = \lambda\boldsymbol{\phi}$, where

$$\mathbf{\Lambda} = \begin{bmatrix} 2 & 0 \\ 0 & 6 \end{bmatrix}$$

Use as starting iteration vectors $\mathbf{x}_1$ the vectors

$$(1) \quad \mathbf{x}_1 = \begin{bmatrix} 1 \\ 1 \end{bmatrix}; \qquad (2) \quad \mathbf{x}_1 = \begin{bmatrix} 1 \\ 0.1 \end{bmatrix}$$

Using the relations given in (11.50) to (11.53) [with $\rho(\bar{\mathbf{x}}_1) = 0.0$], we obtain, in case 1,

$$\bar{\mathbf{x}}_2 = \begin{bmatrix} 0.500 \\ 0.166667 \end{bmatrix}; \qquad \rho(\bar{\mathbf{x}}_2) = 2.40$$

$$\mathbf{y}_2 = \begin{bmatrix} 0.94868 \\ 0.31623 \end{bmatrix}$$

$$\bar{\mathbf{x}}_3 = \begin{bmatrix} -2.37171 \\ 0.08784 \end{bmatrix}; \qquad \rho(\bar{\mathbf{x}}_3) = 2.00548$$

$$\mathbf{y}_3 = \begin{bmatrix} -0.99931 \\ 0.03701 \end{bmatrix}$$

$$\bar{\mathbf{x}}_4 = \begin{bmatrix} 182.37496 \\ 0.00927 \end{bmatrix}; \qquad \rho(\bar{\mathbf{x}}_4) = 2.000000$$

and

$$\mathbf{y}_4 = \begin{bmatrix} 1.0000 \\ 0.00005 \end{bmatrix}$$

Hence, we see that in three steps of iteration we have obtained a good approximation to the required eigenvalue and eigenvector.

In case 2 we have

$$\bar{\mathbf{x}}_2 = \begin{bmatrix} 0.50000 \\ 0.016667 \end{bmatrix}; \qquad \rho(\bar{\mathbf{x}}_2) = 2.00444$$

$$\mathbf{y}_2 = \begin{bmatrix} 0.99944 \\ 0.033315 \end{bmatrix}$$

and then

$$\bar{\mathbf{x}}_3 = \begin{bmatrix} -225.125 \\ 0.00834 \end{bmatrix}; \qquad \rho(\bar{\mathbf{x}}_3) = 2.000001$$

$$\mathbf{y}_3 = \begin{bmatrix} -1.00000 \\ 0.000037 \end{bmatrix}$$

We observe that in this case two iterations are sufficient to obtain a good approximation to the required eigenvalue and eigenvector because the starting iteration vector was already closer to the required eigenvector.

As was pointed out in the preceding discussion, the Rayleigh quotient iteration can, in principle, converge to any eigenpair. Therefore, if we are interested in the smallest p eigenvalues and corresponding eigenvectors, we need to supplement the Rayleigh quotient iterations by another technique to ensure convergence to one of the eigenpairs sought. For example, to calculate the smallest eigenvalue and corresponding eigenvector, we may first use the inverse iteration in (11.16) to (11.19) without shifting to obtain an iteration vector that is a good approximation of $\boldsymbol{\phi}_1$, and only then start with Rayleigh quotient iteration. However, the difficulty lies in assessing how many inverse iterations must be performed before Rayleigh quotient shifting can be started and yet convergence to $\boldsymbol{\phi}_1$ and λ_1 is achieved. Unfortunately, this question can in general not be resolved, and it is necessary to use the Sturm sequence property to make sure that the required eigenvalue and corresponding eigenvector have indeed been calculated (see Section 11.4).

11.2.5 Matrix Deflation and Gram-Schmidt Orthogonalization

In Sections 11.2.1 to 11.2.4 we discussed how an eigenvalue and corresponding eigenvector can be calculated using vector iteration. The basic inverse iteration technique converges to λ_1 and $\boldsymbol{\phi}_1$ (see Section 11.2.1), and the basic forward iteration can be used to calculate λ_n and $\boldsymbol{\phi}_n$ (see Section 11.2.2), but the methods can also be employed with shifting to calculate other eigenvalues and corresponding eigenvectors (see Section 11.2.3). Assume now that we have calculated a specific eigenpair, say $(\lambda_k, \boldsymbol{\phi}_k)$, using either method and that we require the solution of another eigenpair. To ensure that we do not converge again to λ_k and $\boldsymbol{\phi}_k$, we need to deflate either the matrices or the iteration vectors.

Matrix deflation has been applied extensively in the solution of standard eigenproblems. The problem may be $\mathbf{K}\boldsymbol{\phi} = \lambda\boldsymbol{\phi}$, i.e., when $\mathbf{M}$ is the identity matrix in $\mathbf{K}\boldsymbol{\phi} = \lambda\mathbf{M}\boldsymbol{\phi}$, or may be $\tilde{\mathbf{K}}\tilde{\boldsymbol{\phi}} = \lambda\tilde{\boldsymbol{\phi}}$, which is obtained by transforming the generalized eigenproblem into a standard form (see Section 10.2.5). We recall that this transformation is effective when $\mathbf{M}$ is diagonal and all diagonal elements are larger than zero because in such a case $\tilde{\mathbf{K}}$ has the same bandwidth as $\mathbf{K}$.

Consider the deflation of $\mathbf{K}\boldsymbol{\phi} = \lambda\boldsymbol{\phi}$ because the deflation of $\tilde{\mathbf{K}}\tilde{\boldsymbol{\phi}} = \lambda\tilde{\boldsymbol{\phi}}$ would be obtained in the same way. A stable matrix deflation can be carried out by finding an orthogonal matrix $\mathbf{P}$ whose first column is the calculated eigenvector $\boldsymbol{\phi}_k$.

Writing $\mathbf{P}$ as $$\mathbf{P} = [\boldsymbol{\phi}_k, \mathbf{p}_2, \ldots, \mathbf{p}_n] \tag{11.60}$$

we need to have $\boldsymbol{\phi}_k^T \mathbf{p}_i = 0$ for $i = 2, \ldots, n$. It then follows that

$$\mathbf{P}^T \mathbf{K} \mathbf{P} = \begin{bmatrix} \lambda_k & \mathbf{0} \\ \mathbf{0} & \mathbf{K}_1 \end{bmatrix} \tag{11.61}$$

because $\boldsymbol{\phi}_k^T \boldsymbol{\phi}_k = 1$. The important point is that $\mathbf{P}^T \mathbf{K} \mathbf{P}$ has the same eigenvalues as $\mathbf{K}$, and therefore $\mathbf{K}_1$ must have all eigenvalues of $\mathbf{K}$ except λ_k. In addition, denoting the eigenvectors of $\mathbf{P}^T \mathbf{K} \mathbf{P}$ by $\overline{\boldsymbol{\phi}}_i$, we have

$$\boldsymbol{\phi}_i = \mathbf{P} \overline{\boldsymbol{\phi}}_i \tag{11.62}$$

It is important to note that the matrix $\mathbf{P}$ is not unique and that various techniques can be used to construct an appropriate transformation matrix. Since $\mathbf{K}$ is banded, we would like to have that the transformation does not destroy the bandform (see, for example, H. Rutishauser [A]).

From this discussion it follows that once a second required eigenpair using $\mathbf{K}_1$ has been evaluated, the process of deflation can be repeated by working with $\mathbf{K}_1$ rather than with $\mathbf{K}$. Therefore, we may continue deflating until all required eigenvalues and eigenvectors have been calculated. The disadvantage of matrix deflation is that the eigenvectors have to be calculated to very high precision to avoid the accumulation of errors introduced in the deflation process.

Instead of matrix deflation, we may deflate the iteration vector in order to converge to an eigenpair other than $(\lambda_k, \boldsymbol{\phi}_k)$. The basis of vector deflation is that in order for an iteration vector to converge in forward or inverse iteration to a required eigenvector, the iteration vector must not be orthogonal to it. Hence, conversely, if the iteration vector is orthogonalized to the eigenvectors already calculated, we eliminate the possibility that the iteration converges to any one of them, and, as we will see, convergence occurs instead to another eigenvector.

A particular vector orthogonalization procedure that is employed extensively is the Gram-Schmidt method. The procedure can be used in the solution of the generalized eigenproblem $\mathbf{K}\boldsymbol{\phi} = \lambda \mathbf{M}\boldsymbol{\phi}$, where $\mathbf{M}$ can take the different forms that we encounter in finite element analysis.

In order to consider a general case, assume that we have calculated in inverse iteration the eigenvectors $\boldsymbol{\phi}_1, \boldsymbol{\phi}_2, \ldots, \boldsymbol{\phi}_m$ and that we want to $\mathbf{M}$-orthogonalize $\mathbf{x}_1$ to these eigenvectors. In Gram-Schmidt orthogonalization a vector $\tilde{\mathbf{x}}_1$, which is $\mathbf{M}$-orthogonal to the eigenvectors $\boldsymbol{\phi}_i$, $i = 1, \ldots, m$, is calculated using

$$\tilde{\mathbf{x}}_1 = \mathbf{x}_1 - \sum_{i=1}^{m} \alpha_i \boldsymbol{\phi}_i \tag{11.63}$$

where the coefficients α_i are obtained using the conditions that $\boldsymbol{\phi}_i^T \mathbf{M} \tilde{\mathbf{x}}_1 = 0$, $i = 1, \ldots, m$, and $\boldsymbol{\phi}_i^T \mathbf{M} \boldsymbol{\phi}_j = \delta_{ij}$. Premultiplying both sides of (11.63) by $\boldsymbol{\phi}_i^T \mathbf{M}$, we therefore obtain

$$\alpha_i = \boldsymbol{\phi}_i^T \mathbf{M} \mathbf{x}_1; \qquad i = 1, \ldots, m \tag{11.64}$$

In the inverse iteration we would now use $\tilde{\mathbf{x}}_1$ as the starting iteration vector instead of $\mathbf{x}_1$ and provided that $\mathbf{x}_1^T \mathbf{M} \boldsymbol{\phi}_{m+1} \neq 0$, convergence occurs (at least in theory; see Section 11.2.6) to $\boldsymbol{\phi}_{m+1}$ and λ_{m+1}.

To prove the convergence given above, we consider as before the iteration process in the basis of eigenvectors; i.e., we analyze the iteration given in (11.25) when the Gram-

Schmidt orthogonalization is included. In this case the eigenvectors corresponding to the smallest eigenvalues are $\mathbf{e}_i$, $i = 1, \ldots, m$. Carrying out the deflation of the starting iteration vector $\mathbf{z}_1$ in (11.27), we obtain

$$\tilde{\mathbf{z}}_1 = \mathbf{z}_1 - \sum_{i=1}^{m} \alpha_i \mathbf{e}_i \tag{11.65}$$

with

$$\alpha_i = \mathbf{e}_i^T \mathbf{z}_1 = 1; \qquad i = 1, \ldots, m \tag{11.66}$$

Hence,
$$\tilde{\mathbf{z}}_1^T = [0 \quad \ldots \quad 0 \quad \overset{\text{Element } m+1}{1} \quad \ldots \quad 1] \tag{11.67}$$

Using now $\tilde{\mathbf{z}}_1$ as the starting iteration vector and performing the convergence analysis as discussed in Section 11.2.1, we find that if $\lambda_{m+2} > \lambda_{m+1}$, we have $\tilde{\mathbf{z}}_{l+1} \rightarrow \mathbf{e}_{m+1}$, as was required to prove. Furthermore, we find that the rate of convergence of the eigenvector is $\lambda_{m+1}/\lambda_{m+2}$, and when λ_{m+1} is a multiple eigenvalue, the rate of convergence is given by the ratio of λ_{m+1} to the next distinct eigenvalue.

Although so far we have discussed Gram-Schmidt orthogonalization in connection with vector inverse iteration, it should be realized that the orthogonalization procedure can be used equally well in the other vector iteration methods. All convergence considerations discussed in the presentation of inverse iteration, forward iteration, and Rayleigh quotient iteration are also applicable when Gram-Schmidt orthogonalization is included if it is taken into account that convergence to the eigenvectors already calculated is not possible.

EXAMPLE 11.8: Calculate, using Gram-Schmidt orthogonalization, an appropriate starting iteration vector for the solution of the problem $\mathbf{K}\boldsymbol{\phi} = \lambda\mathbf{M}\boldsymbol{\phi}$, where $\mathbf{K}$ and $\mathbf{M}$ are given in Example 11.4. Assume that the eigenpairs $(\lambda_1, \boldsymbol{\phi}_1)$ and $(\lambda_4, \boldsymbol{\phi}_4)$ are known as obtained in Example 11.5 and that convergence to another eigenpair is sought.

To determine an appropriate starting iteration vector, we want to deflate the unit full vector of the vectors $\boldsymbol{\phi}_1$ and $\boldsymbol{\phi}_4$; i.e., (11.63) reads

$$\tilde{\mathbf{x}}_1 = \begin{bmatrix} 1 \\ 1 \\ 1 \\ 1 \end{bmatrix} - \alpha_1 \boldsymbol{\phi}_1 - \alpha_4 \boldsymbol{\phi}_4$$

where α_1 and α_4 are obtained using (11.64):

$$\alpha_1 = \boldsymbol{\phi}_1^T \mathbf{M} \mathbf{x}_1; \qquad \alpha_4 = \boldsymbol{\phi}_4^T \mathbf{M} \mathbf{x}_1$$

Substituting for $\mathbf{M}$, $\boldsymbol{\phi}_1$, and $\boldsymbol{\phi}_4$, we obtain

$$\alpha_1 = 2.385; \qquad \alpha_4 = 0.1299$$

Then, to a few-digit accuracy,

$$\tilde{\mathbf{x}}_1 = \begin{bmatrix} 0.2683 \\ -0.2149 \\ -0.04812 \\ 0.2358 \end{bmatrix}$$

11.2.6 Some Practical Considerations Concerning Vector Iterations

So far we have discussed the theory used in vector iteration techniques. However, for a proper computer implementation of the methods, it is important to interpret the theoretical results and relate them to practice. Of particular importance are practical convergence and stability considerations when any one of the techniques is used.

A first important point is that the convergence rates of the iterations may turn out to be rather theoretical when measured in practice, namely, we assumed that the starting iteration vector $\mathbf{z}_1$ in (11.27) is a unit full vector, which corresponds to a vector $\mathbf{x}_1 = \sum_{i=1}^{n} \boldsymbol{\phi}_i$. This means that the starting iteration vector is equally strong in each of the eigenvectors $\boldsymbol{\phi}_i$. We chose this starting iteration vector to identify easily the theoretical convergence rate with which the iteration vector approaches the required eigenvector. However, in practice it is hardly possible to pick $\mathbf{x}_1 = \sum_{i=1}^{n} \boldsymbol{\phi}_i$ as the starting iteration vector, and instead we have

$$\mathbf{x}_1 = \sum_{i=1}^{n} \alpha_i \boldsymbol{\phi}_i \tag{11.68}$$

where the α_i are arbitrary constants. This vector $\mathbf{x}_1$ corresponds to the following vector in the basis of eigenvectors:

$$\mathbf{z}_1 = \begin{bmatrix} \alpha_1 \\ \cdot \\ \cdot \\ \cdot \\ \alpha_n \end{bmatrix} \tag{11.69}$$

To identify the effect of the constants α_i, consider as an example the convergence analysis of inverse iteration without shifting when the starting vector in (11.68) is used and $\lambda_2 > \lambda_1$. The conclusions reached will be equally applicable to other vector iteration methods. As before, we consider the iteration in the basis of eigenvectors $\boldsymbol{\Phi}$ and require $\alpha_1 \neq 0$ in order to have $\mathbf{x}_1^T \mathbf{M} \boldsymbol{\phi}_1 \neq 0$. After l inverse iterations we now have instead of (11.29),

$$\tilde{\mathbf{z}}_{l+1} = \begin{bmatrix} 1 \\ \beta_2 \left(\dfrac{\lambda_1}{\lambda_2} \right)^l \\ \cdot \\ \cdot \\ \cdot \\ \beta_n \left(\dfrac{\lambda_1}{\lambda_n} \right)^l \end{bmatrix} \tag{11.70}$$

$$\beta_i = \frac{\alpha_i}{\alpha_1}; \qquad i = 2, \ldots, n \tag{11.71}$$

Therefore, the iteration vector obtained now has the multipliers β_i in its last $n - 1$ components. In the iteration the ith component is still decreasing with each iteration, as in (11.29) by the factor λ_1/λ_i, $i = 2, \ldots, n$, and the rate of convergence is λ_1/λ_2, as already derived in Section 11.2.1. However, in practical analysis the unknown coefficients β_i may produce the result that the theoretical convergence rate is not observed for many iterations. In practice, therefore, not only the order and rate of convergence but equally importantly the "quality" of the starting iteration vector determines the number of iterations required for convergence. Furthermore, it is important to use a high enough convergence tolerance to prevent premature acceptance of the iteration vector as an approximation to the required eigenvector.

Together with the vector iterations, we may use a matrix deflation procedure or Gram-Schmidt vector orthogonalization to obtain convergence to an eigenpair not already calculated (see Section 11.2.5). We have mentioned already that for matrix deflation, the eigenvectors have to be evaluated to relatively high precision to preserve stability. Considering the Gram-Schmidt orthogonalization, the method is sensitive to round-off errors and must also be used with care. If the technique is employed in inverse or forward iteration without shifting, it is necessary to calculate the eigenvectors to high precision in order that Gram-Schmidt orthogonalization will work. In addition, the iteration vector should be orthogonalized in each iteration to the eigenvectors already calculated.

Let us now draw an important conclusion. We pointed out earlier in the presentation of the vector iteration techniques that it is difficult (and indeed theory shows impossible) to *ensure* convergence to a specific (but arbitrarily selected) eigenvalue and corresponding eigenvector. The discussion concerning practical aspects in this section substantiates those observations, and it is concluded that the vector iteration procedures and the Gram-Schmidt orthogonalization process must be employed with care if a specific eigenvalue and corresponding eigenvector are required. We will see in Sections 11.5 and 11.6 that, in fact, both techniques are best employed and are used very effectively in conjunction with other solution strategies.

11.2.7 Exercises

11.1. Consider the generalized eigenproblem

$$\begin{bmatrix} 6 & -1 & 0 \\ -1 & 4 & -1 \\ 0 & -1 & 2 \end{bmatrix} \boldsymbol{\phi} = \lambda \begin{bmatrix} 2 & 0 & 0 \\ 0 & 2 & 1 \\ 0 & 1 & 1 \end{bmatrix} \boldsymbol{\phi}$$

with the starting vector for iteration

$$\mathbf{x}_1^T = \begin{bmatrix} 1 & 1 & 1 \end{bmatrix}$$

(a) Perform two inverse iterations and then use the Rayleigh quotient to calculate an approximation to λ_1.

(b) Perform two forward iterations and then use the Rayleigh quotient to calculate an approximation to λ_3.

11.2. Proceed as in Exercise 11.1, but for the following eigenproblem,

$$\begin{bmatrix} 2 & -1 & 0 \\ -1 & 6 & -1 \\ 0 & -1 & 8 \end{bmatrix} \boldsymbol{\phi} = \lambda \begin{bmatrix} 1 & & \\ & \frac{1}{2} & \\ & & 2 \end{bmatrix} \boldsymbol{\phi}$$

11.3. The eigenvectors corresponding to the two smallest eigenvalues $\lambda_1 = 1$, $\lambda_2 = 2$ of the problem

$$\begin{bmatrix} 2 & 1 & 0 \\ 1 & 3 & 1 \\ 0 & 1 & 2 \end{bmatrix} \boldsymbol{\phi} = \lambda \boldsymbol{\phi}$$

are

$$\boldsymbol{\phi}_1 = \frac{1}{\sqrt{3}}\begin{bmatrix} 1 \\ -1 \\ 1 \end{bmatrix}; \qquad \boldsymbol{\phi}_2 = \frac{1}{\sqrt{2}}\begin{bmatrix} 1 \\ 0 \\ -1 \end{bmatrix}$$

Let

$$\mathbf{x}_1 = \begin{bmatrix} 1 \\ 1 \\ 1 \end{bmatrix}$$

Use the Gram-Schmidt orthogonalization procedure to extract from $\mathbf{x}_1$ a vector orthogonal to $\boldsymbol{\phi}_1$ and $\boldsymbol{\phi}_2$. Show explicitly that this vector is the third eigenvector $\boldsymbol{\phi}_3$ and calculate λ_3.

11.4. Consider the eigenproblem

$$\begin{bmatrix} 2 & -1 & 0 \\ -1 & 4 & -1 \\ 0 & -1 & 2 \end{bmatrix}\boldsymbol{\phi} = \lambda \begin{bmatrix} \frac{1}{2} & & \\ & 1 & \\ & & \frac{1}{2} \end{bmatrix}\boldsymbol{\phi}$$

For this problem,

$$\boldsymbol{\phi}_1 = \frac{1}{\sqrt{2}}\begin{bmatrix} 1 \\ 1 \\ 1 \end{bmatrix}; \qquad \boldsymbol{\phi}_3 = \frac{1}{\sqrt{2}}\begin{bmatrix} 1 \\ -1 \\ 1 \end{bmatrix}$$

Use Gram-Schmidt orthogonalization to calculate $\boldsymbol{\phi}_2$ and calculate all eigenvalues.

11.3 TRANSFORMATION METHODS

We pointed out in Section 11.1 that the transformation methods comprise a group of eigensystem solution procedures that employ the basic properties of the eigenvectors in the matrix $\boldsymbol{\Phi}$,

$$\boldsymbol{\Phi}^T \mathbf{K} \boldsymbol{\Phi} = \boldsymbol{\Lambda} \tag{11.3}$$

and

$$\boldsymbol{\Phi}^T \mathbf{M} \boldsymbol{\Phi} = \mathbf{I} \tag{11.4}$$

Since the matrix $\boldsymbol{\Phi}$, of order $n \times n$, which diagonalizes $\mathbf{K}$ and $\mathbf{M}$ in the way given in (11.3) and (11.4) is unique, we can try to construct it by iteration. The basic scheme is to reduce $\mathbf{K}$ and $\mathbf{M}$ to diagonal form using successive pre- and postmultiplication by matrices $\mathbf{P}_k^T$ and $\mathbf{P}_k$, respectively, where $k = 1, 2, \ldots$. Specifically, if we define $\mathbf{K}_1 = \mathbf{K}$ and $\mathbf{M}_1 = \mathbf{M}$, we form

$$\left.\begin{aligned} \mathbf{K}_2 &= \mathbf{P}_1^T \mathbf{K}_1 \mathbf{P}_1 \\ \mathbf{K}_3 &= \mathbf{P}_2^T \mathbf{K}_2 \mathbf{P}_2 \\ &\ \ \vdots \\ \mathbf{K}_{k+1} &= \mathbf{P}_k^T \mathbf{K}_k \mathbf{P}_k \\ &\ \ \vdots \end{aligned}\right\} \tag{11.72}$$

Similarly,

$$\left.\begin{aligned} \mathbf{M}_2 &= \mathbf{P}_1^T \mathbf{M}_1 \mathbf{P}_1 \\ \mathbf{M}_3 &= \mathbf{P}_2^T \mathbf{M}_2 \mathbf{P}_2 \\ &\ \ \vdots \\ \mathbf{M}_{k+1} &= \mathbf{P}_k^T \mathbf{M}_k \mathbf{P}_k \\ &\ \ \vdots \end{aligned}\right\} \tag{11.73}$$

where the matrices $\mathbf{P}_k$ are selected to bring $\mathbf{K}_k$ and $\mathbf{M}_k$ closer to diagonal form. Then for a proper procedure we apparently need to have

$$\mathbf{K}_{k+1} \rightarrow \boldsymbol{\Lambda} \quad \text{and} \quad \mathbf{M}_{k+1} \rightarrow \mathbf{I} \qquad \text{as } k \rightarrow \infty$$

in which case, with l being the last iteration,

$$\boldsymbol{\Phi} = \mathbf{P}_1 \mathbf{P}_2 \ldots \mathbf{P}_l \tag{11.74}$$

In practice, it is not necessary that $\mathbf{M}_{k+1}$ converges to $\mathbf{I}$ and $\mathbf{K}_{k+1}$ to $\boldsymbol{\Lambda}$, but they only need to converge to diagonal form. Namely, if

$$\mathbf{K}_{k+1} \rightarrow \text{diag}(K_r) \quad \text{and} \quad \mathbf{M}_{k+1} \rightarrow \text{diag}(M_r) \qquad \text{as } k \rightarrow \infty$$

then with l indicating the last iteration and disregarding that the eigenvalues and eigenvectors may not be in the usual order,

$$\boldsymbol{\Lambda} = \text{diag}\left(\frac{K_r^{(l+1)}}{M_r^{(l+1)}}\right) \tag{11.75}$$

and

$$\boldsymbol{\Phi} = \mathbf{P}_1 \mathbf{P}_2 \ldots \mathbf{P}_l \, \text{diag}\left(\frac{1}{\sqrt{M_r^{(l+1)}}}\right) \tag{11.76}$$

Using the basic idea described above, a number of different iteration methods have been proposed. We shall discuss in the next sections only the Jacobi and the Householder-QR methods, which are believed to be most effective in finite element analysis. However, before presenting the techniques in detail we should point out one important aspect. In the above introduction it was implied that iteration is started with pre- and postmultiplication by $\mathbf{P}_1^T$ and $\mathbf{P}_1$, respectively, which is indeed the case in the Jacobi solution methods. However, alternatively, we may first aim to transform the eigenvalue problem $\mathbf{K}\boldsymbol{\phi} = \lambda \mathbf{M}\boldsymbol{\phi}$ into a form that is more economical to use in the iteration. In particular, when $\mathbf{M} = \mathbf{I}$, the first m transformations in (11.72) may be used to reduce $\mathbf{K}$ into tridiagonal form without iteration, after which the matrices $\mathbf{P}_i$, $i = m + 1, \ldots, l$, are applied in an iterative manner to bring $\mathbf{K}_{m+1}$ into diagonal form. In such a case the first matrices $\mathbf{P}_1, \ldots, \mathbf{P}_m$ may be of different form than the later applied matrices $\mathbf{P}_{m+1}, \ldots, \mathbf{P}_l$. An application of this procedure is the Householder-QR method, in which Householder matrices are used to first transform $\mathbf{K}$ into tridiagonal form and then rotation matrices are employed in the QR transformations. The same solution strategy can also be used to solve the generalized eigenproblem $\mathbf{K}\boldsymbol{\phi} = \lambda \mathbf{M}\boldsymbol{\phi}$, $\mathbf{M} \neq \mathbf{I}$, provided that the problem is first transformed into the standard form.

11.3.1 The Jacobi Method

The basic Jacobi solution method has been developed for the solution of standard eigenproblems ($\mathbf{M}$ being the identity matrix), and we consider it in this section. The method was proposed over a century ago (see C. G. J. Jacobi [A]) and has been used extensively. A major advantage of the procedure is its simplicity and stability. Since the eigenvector properties in (11.3) and (11.4) (with $\mathbf{M} = \mathbf{I}$) are applicable to all symmetric matrices $\mathbf{K}$ with no restriction on the eigenvalues, the Jacobi method can be used to calculate negative, zero, or positive eigenvalues.

Considering the standard eigenproblem $\mathbf{K}\boldsymbol{\phi} = \lambda\boldsymbol{\phi}$, the kth iteration step defined in (11.72) reduces to

$$\mathbf{K}_{k+1} = \mathbf{P}_k^T \mathbf{K}_k \mathbf{P}_k \tag{11.77}$$

where $\mathbf{P}_k$ is an orthogonal matrix; i.e., (11.73) gives

$$\mathbf{P}_k^T \mathbf{P}_k = \mathbf{I} \tag{11.78}$$

In the Jacobi solution the matrix $\mathbf{P}_k$ is a rotation matrix that is selected in such way that an off-diagonal element in $\mathbf{K}_k$ is zeroed. If element (i,j) is to be reduced to zero, the corresponding orthogonal matrix $\mathbf{P}_k$ is

$$
\mathbf{P}_k =
\begin{bmatrix}
1 & & & & & & & & & \\
 & \ddots & & & & & & & & \\
 & & 1 & & & & & & & \\
 & & & \cos\theta & & -\sin\theta & & & & \quad\text{---}\ i\text{th} \\
 & & & & 1 & & & & & \\
 & & & & & \ddots & & & & \\
 & & & & & & 1 & & & \\
 & & & \sin\theta & & \cos\theta & & & & \quad\text{---}\ j\text{th} \\
 & & & & & & & 1 & & \\
 & & & & & & & & \ddots & \\
 & & & & & & & & & 1
\end{bmatrix}
\tag{11.79}
$$

where θ is selected from the condition that element (i,j) in $\mathbf{K}_{k+1}$ be zero. Denoting element (i,j) in $\mathbf{K}_k$ by $k_{ij}^{(k)}$, we use

$$\tan 2\theta = \frac{2k_{ij}^{(k)}}{k_{ii}^{(k)} - k_{jj}^{(k)}} \qquad \text{for } k_{ii}^{(k)} \neq k_{jj}^{(k)} \tag{11.80}$$

and

$$\theta = \frac{\pi}{4} \qquad \text{for } k_{ii}^{(k)} = k_{jj}^{(k)} \tag{11.81}$$

It should be noted that the numerical evaluation of $\mathbf{K}_{k+1}$ in (11.77) requires only the linear combination of two rows and two columns. In addition, advantage should also be taken of the fact that $\mathbf{K}_k$ is symmetric for all k; i.e., we should work on only the upper (or lower) triangular part of the matrix, including its diagonal elements.

An important point to emphasize is that although the transformation in (11.77) reduces an off-diagonal element in $\mathbf{K}_k$ to zero, this element will again become nonzero during the transformations that follow. Therefore, for the design of an actual algorithm, we have to decide which element to reduce to zero. One choice is to always zero the largest off-diagonal element in $\mathbf{K}_k$. However, the search for the largest element is time-consuming, and it may be preferable to simply carry out the Jacobi transformations systematically, row by row or column by column, which is known as the *cyclic Jacobi procedure*. Running once over all off-diagonal elements is one *sweep*. The disadvantage of this procedure is that regardless of its size, an off-diagonal element is always zeroed; i.e., the element may already be nearly zero, and a rotation is still applied.

A procedure that has been used very effectively is the *threshold Jacobi method,* in which the off-diagonal elements are tested sequentially, namely, row by row (or column by column), and a rotation is applied only if the element is larger than the threshold for that sweep. To define an appropriate threshold we note that, physically, in the diagonalization of $\mathbf{K}$ we want to reduce the coupling between the degrees of freedom i and j. A measure of this coupling is given by $(k_{ij}^2/k_{ii}k_{jj})^{1/2}$, and it is this factor that can be used effectively in deciding whether to apply a rotation. In addition to having a realistic threshold tolerance, it is also necessary to measure convergence. As described above, $\mathbf{K}_{k+1} \rightarrow \mathbf{\Lambda}$ as $k \rightarrow \infty$, but in the numerical computations we seek only a close enough approximation to the eigenvalues and corresponding eigenvectors. Let l be the last iteration; i.e., we have, to the precision required,

$$\mathbf{K}_{l+1} \doteq \mathbf{\Lambda} \tag{11.82}$$

Then we say that convergence to a tolerance s has been achieved provided that

$$\frac{|k_{ii}^{(l+1)} - k_{ii}^{(l)}|}{k_{ii}^{(l+1)}} \leq 10^{-s}; \qquad i = 1, \ldots, n \tag{11.83}$$

and

$$\left[\frac{(k_{ij}^{(l+1)})^2}{k_{ii}^{(l+1)} k_{jj}^{(l+1)}} \right]^{1/2} \leq 10^{-s}; \qquad \text{all } i, j; \ i < j \tag{11.84}$$

The relation in (11.83) has to be satisfied because the element $k_{ii}^{(l+1)}$ is the current approximation to an eigenvalue, and the relation states that the current and last approximations to the eigenvalues did not change in the first s digits. This convergence measure is essentially the same as the one used in vector iteration in (11.20). The relation in (11.84) ensures that the off-diagonal elements are indeed small.

Having discussed the main aspects of the iteration, we may now summarize the actual solution procedure. The following steps have been used in a threshold Jacobi iteration.

1. Initialize the threshold for the sweep. Typically, the threshold used for sweep m may be 10^{-2m}.

2. For all i, j with $i < j$ calculate the coupling factor $[(k_{ij}^{(k)})^2/k_{ii}^{(k)} k_{jj}^{(k)}]^{1/2}$ and apply a transformation if the factor is larger than the current threshold.

3. Use (11.83) to check for convergence. If the relation in (11.83) is not satisfied, continue with the next sweep; i.e., go to step 1. If (11.83) is satisfied, check if (11.84) is also satisfied; if "yes," the iteration converged; if "no," continue with the next sweep.

So far we have stated the algorithm but we have not shown that convergence will indeed always occur. The proof of convergence has been given elsewhere (see J. H. Wilkinson [A]) and will not be repeated here because little additional insight into the working of the solution procedure would be gained. However, one important point should be noted— that convergence is quadratic once the off-diagonal elements are small. Since rapid convergence is obtained once the off-diagonal elements are small, little extra cost is involved in solving for the eigensystem to high accuracy when an approximate solution has been obtained. In practical solutions we use $m = 2$ and $s = 12$, and about six sweeps are required for solution of the eigensystem to high accuracy. A program used is given in the next section, when we discuss the solution of the generalized eigenproblem $\mathbf{K}\boldsymbol{\phi} = \lambda\mathbf{M}\boldsymbol{\phi}$.

EXAMPLE 11.9: Calculate the eigensystem of the matrix **K**, where

$$
\mathbf{K} = \begin{bmatrix} 5 & -4 & 1 & 0 \\ -4 & 6 & -4 & 1 \\ 1 & -4 & 6 & -4 \\ 0 & 1 & -4 & 5 \end{bmatrix}
$$

Use the threshold Jacobi iteration described above.

To demonstrate the solution algorithm we give one sweep in detail and then the results obtained in the next sweeps.

For sweep 1 we have as a threshold 10^{-2}. We therefore obtain the following results. For $i = 1, j = 2$:

$$\cos \theta = 0.7497; \qquad \sin \theta = 0.6618$$

and thus

$$
\mathbf{P}_1 = \begin{bmatrix} 0.7497 & -0.6618 & 0 & 0 \\ 0.6618 & 0.7497 & 0 & 0 \\ 0 & 0 & 1 & 0 \\ 0 & 0 & 0 & 1 \end{bmatrix}
$$

$$
\mathbf{P}_1^T \mathbf{K} \mathbf{P}_1 = \begin{bmatrix} 1.469 & 0 & -1.898 & 0.6618 \\ 0 & 9.531 & -3.661 & 0.7497 \\ -1.898 & -3.661 & 6 & -4 \\ 0.6618 & 0.7497 & -4 & 5 \end{bmatrix}
$$

For $i = 1, j = 3$:

$$\cos \theta = 0.9398; \qquad \sin \theta = 0.3416$$

$$
\mathbf{P}_2 = \begin{bmatrix} 0.9398 & 0 & -0.3416 & 0 \\ 0 & 1 & 0 & 0 \\ 0.3416 & 0 & 0.9398 & 0 \\ 0 & 0 & 0 & 1 \end{bmatrix}
$$

$$
\mathbf{P}_2^T \mathbf{P}_1^T \mathbf{K} \mathbf{P}_1 \mathbf{P}_2 = \begin{bmatrix} 0.7792 & -1.250 & 0 & -0.7444 \\ -1.250 & 9.531 & -3.440 & 0.7497 \\ 0 & -3.440 & 6.690 & -3.986 \\ -0.7444 & 0.7497 & -3.986 & 5 \end{bmatrix}
$$

$$
\mathbf{P}_1 \mathbf{P}_2 = \begin{bmatrix} 0.7046 & -0.6618 & -0.2561 & 0 \\ 0.6220 & 0.7497 & -0.2261 & 0 \\ 0.3416 & 0 & 0.9398 & 0 \\ 0 & 0 & 0 & 1 \end{bmatrix}
$$

For $i = 1, j = 4$:

$$\cos \theta = 0.9857; \qquad \sin \theta = 0.1687$$

$$
\mathbf{P}_3 = \begin{bmatrix} 0.9857 & 0 & 0 & -0.1687 \\ 0 & 1 & 0 & 0 \\ 0 & 0 & 1 & 0 \\ 0.1687 & 0 & 0 & 0.9857 \end{bmatrix}
$$

$$\mathbf{P}_3^T\mathbf{P}_2^T\mathbf{P}_1^T\mathbf{K}\mathbf{P}_1\mathbf{P}_2\mathbf{P}_3 = \begin{bmatrix} 0.6518 & -1.106 & -0.6725 & 0 \\ -1.106 & 9.531 & -3.440 & 0.9499 \\ -0.6725 & -3.440 & 6.690 & -3.928 \\ 0 & 0.9499 & -3.928 & 5.127 \end{bmatrix}$$

$$\mathbf{P}_1\mathbf{P}_2\mathbf{P}_3 = \begin{bmatrix} 0.6945 & -0.6618 & -0.2561 & -0.1189 \\ 0.6131 & 0.7497 & -0.2261 & -0.1050 \\ 0.3367 & 0 & 0.9398 & -0.0576 \\ 0.1687 & 0 & 0 & 0.9857 \end{bmatrix}$$

For $i = 2, j = 3$:

$$\cos\theta = 0.8312; \qquad \sin\theta = -0.5560$$

$$\mathbf{P}_4 = \begin{bmatrix} 1 & 0 & 0 & 0 \\ 0 & 0.8312 & 0.5560 & 0 \\ 0 & -0.5560 & 0.8312 & 0 \\ 0 & 0 & 0 & 1 \end{bmatrix}$$

$$\mathbf{P}_4^T\mathbf{P}_3^T\mathbf{P}_2^T\mathbf{P}_1^T\mathbf{K}\mathbf{P}_1\mathbf{P}_2\mathbf{P}_3\mathbf{P}_4 = \begin{bmatrix} 0.6518 & 0.5453 & -1.174 & 0 \\ -0.5453 & 11.83 & 0 & 2.974 \\ -1.174 & 0 & 4.388 & -2.737 \\ 0 & 2.974 & -2.737 & 5.127 \end{bmatrix}$$

$$\mathbf{P}_1\mathbf{P}_2\mathbf{P}_3\mathbf{P}_4 = \begin{bmatrix} 0.6945 & -0.4077 & -0.5808 & -0.1189 \\ 0.6131 & 0.7488 & 0.2289 & -0.1050 \\ 0.3367 & -0.5226 & 0.7812 & -0.0576 \\ 0.1682 & 0 & 0 & 0.9857 \end{bmatrix}$$

For $i = 2, j = 4$:

$$\cos\theta = 0.9349; \qquad \sin\theta = 0.3549$$

$$\mathbf{P}_5 = \begin{bmatrix} 1 & 0 & 0 & 0 \\ 0 & 0.9349 & 0 & -0.3549 \\ 0 & 0 & 1 & 0 \\ 0 & 0.3549 & 0 & 0.9349 \end{bmatrix}$$

$$\mathbf{P}_5^T\mathbf{P}_4^T\mathbf{P}_3^T\mathbf{P}_2^T\mathbf{P}_1^T\mathbf{K}\mathbf{P}_1\mathbf{P}_2\mathbf{P}_3\mathbf{P}_4\mathbf{P}_5 = \begin{bmatrix} 0.6518 & 0.5098 & -1.174 & 0.1935 \\ -0.5098 & 12.96 & 0.9713 & 0 \\ -1.174 & -0.9713 & 4.388 & -2.559 \\ 0.1935 & 0 & -2.559 & 3.999 \end{bmatrix}$$

$$\mathbf{P}_1\mathbf{P}_2\mathbf{P}_3\mathbf{P}_4\mathbf{P}_5 = \begin{bmatrix} 0.6945 & -0.4233 & -0.5808 & 0.0335 \\ 0.6131 & 0.6628 & 0.2289 & -0.3639 \\ 0.3367 & 0.5090 & 0.7812 & 0.1316 \\ 0.1687 & 0.3498 & 0 & 0.9213 \end{bmatrix}$$

To complete the sweep, we zero element (3, 4), using

$$\cos \theta = 0.7335; \qquad \sin \theta = -0.6797$$

$$\mathbf{P}_6 = \begin{bmatrix} 1 & 0 & 0 & 0 \\ 0 & 1 & 0 & 0 \\ 0 & 0 & 0.7335 & 0.6797 \\ 0 & 0 & -0.6797 & 0.7335 \end{bmatrix}$$

and hence, the approximations obtained for $\mathbf{\Lambda}$ and $\mathbf{\Phi}$ are

$$\mathbf{\Lambda} \doteq \mathbf{P}_6^T \ldots \mathbf{P}_1^T \mathbf{K} \mathbf{P}_1 \ldots \mathbf{P}_6$$

i.e.,

$$\mathbf{\Lambda} \doteq \begin{bmatrix} 0.6518 & -0.5098 & -0.9926 & -0.6560 \\ -0.5098 & 12.96 & -0.7124 & -0.6602 \\ -0.9926 & -0.7124 & 6.7596 & 0 \\ -0.6560 & -0.6602 & 0 & 1.6272 \end{bmatrix}$$

and

$$\mathbf{\Phi} \doteq \mathbf{P}_1 \ldots \mathbf{P}_6$$

i.e.,

$$\mathbf{\Phi} \doteq \begin{bmatrix} 0.6945 & -0.4233 & -0.4488 & -0.3702 \\ 0.6131 & 0.6628 & 0.4152 & -0.1113 \\ 0.3367 & -0.5090 & 0.4835 & 0.6275 \\ 0.1687 & 0.3498 & -0.6264 & 0.6759 \end{bmatrix}$$

After the second sweep we obtain

$$\mathbf{\Lambda} \doteq \begin{bmatrix} 0.1563 & -0.3635 & 0.0063 & -0.0176 \\ -0.3635 & 13.08 & -0.0020 & 0 \\ 0.0063 & -0.0020 & 6.845 & 0 \\ -0.0176 & 0 & 0 & 1.910 \end{bmatrix}$$

$$\mathbf{\Phi} \doteq \begin{bmatrix} 0.3875 & -0.3612 & -0.6017 & -0.5978 \\ 0.5884 & 0.6184 & 0.3710 & -0.3657 \\ 0.6148 & -0.5843 & 0.3714 & 0.3777 \\ 0.3546 & 0.3816 & -0.6020 & 0.6052 \end{bmatrix}$$

And after the third sweep we have

$$\mathbf{\Lambda} \doteq \begin{bmatrix} 0.1459 & & & \\ & 13.09 & & \\ & & 6.854 & \\ & & & 1.910 \end{bmatrix}$$

$$\mathbf{\Phi} \doteq \begin{bmatrix} 0.3717 & -0.3717 & -0.6015 & -0.6015 \\ 0.6015 & 0.6015 & 0.3717 & -0.3717 \\ 0.6015 & -0.6015 & 0.3717 & 0.3717 \\ 0.3717 & 0.3717 & -0.6015 & 0.6015 \end{bmatrix}$$

The approximation for $\mathbf{\Lambda}$ is diagonal to the precision given, and we can use

$$\lambda_1 \doteq 0.1459; \qquad \boldsymbol{\phi}_1 \doteq \begin{bmatrix} 0.3717 \\ 0.6015 \\ 0.6015 \\ 0.3717 \end{bmatrix}$$

$$\lambda_2 \doteq 1.910; \qquad \boldsymbol{\phi}_2 \doteq \begin{bmatrix} -0.6015 \\ -0.3717 \\ 0.3717 \\ 0.6015 \end{bmatrix}$$

$$\lambda_3 \doteq 6.854; \qquad \boldsymbol{\phi}_3 \doteq \begin{bmatrix} -0.6015 \\ 0.3717 \\ 0.3717 \\ -0.6015 \end{bmatrix}$$

$$\lambda_4 \doteq 13.09; \qquad \boldsymbol{\phi}_4 \doteq \begin{bmatrix} -0.3717 \\ 0.6015 \\ -0.6015 \\ 0.3717 \end{bmatrix}$$

It should be noted that the eigenvalues and eigenvectors did not appear in the usual order in the approximation for $\mathbf{\Lambda}$ and $\mathbf{\Phi}$.

In the following example we demonstrate the quadratic convergence when the off-diagonal elements are already small (see J. H. Wilkinson [B]).

EXAMPLE 11.10:   Consider the Jacobi solution of the eigenproblem $\mathbf{K}\boldsymbol{\phi} = \lambda\boldsymbol{\phi}$, where

$$\mathbf{K} = \begin{bmatrix} k_{11} & o(\epsilon) & o(\epsilon) \\ o(\epsilon) & k_{22} & o(\epsilon) \\ o(\epsilon) & o(\epsilon) & k_{33} \end{bmatrix}$$

The symbol $o(\epsilon)$ signifies "of order ϵ," where $\epsilon \ll k_{ii}$, $i = 1, 2, 3$. Show that after one complete sweep, all off-diagonal elements are of order ϵ^2, meaning that convergence is quadratic.

Since the rotations to be applied are small, we make the assumption that $\sin\theta = \theta$ and $\cos\theta = 1$. Hence, the relation in (11.80) gives

$$\theta = \frac{k_{ij}^{(k)}}{k_{ii}^{(k)} - k_{jj}^{(k)}}$$

In one sweep we need to set to zero, in succession, all off-diagonal elements. Using $\mathbf{K}_1 = \mathbf{K}$, we obtain $\mathbf{K}_2$ by zeroing element $(1, 2)$ in $\mathbf{K}_1$,

$$\mathbf{K}_2 = \mathbf{P}_1^T \mathbf{K}_1 \mathbf{P}_1$$

where

$$\mathbf{P}_1 = \begin{bmatrix} 1 & \dfrac{-o(\epsilon)}{k_{11} - k_{22}} & 0 \\ \dfrac{o(\epsilon)}{k_{11} - k_{22}} & 1 & 0 \\ 0 & 0 & 1 \end{bmatrix}$$

Hence,
$$\mathbf{K}_2 = \begin{bmatrix} k_{11} + o(\epsilon^2) & 0 & o(\epsilon) \\ 0 & k_{22} + o(\epsilon^2) & o(\epsilon) \\ o(\epsilon) & o(\epsilon) & k_{33} \end{bmatrix}$$

Similarly, we zero element $(1, 3)$ in $\mathbf{K}_2$ to obtain $\mathbf{K}_3$,

$$\mathbf{K}_3 = \begin{bmatrix} k_{11} + o(\epsilon^2) & o(\epsilon^2) & 0 \\ o(\epsilon^2) & k_{22} + o(\epsilon^2) & o(\epsilon) \\ 0 & o(\epsilon) & k_{33} + o(\epsilon^2) \end{bmatrix}$$

Finally, we zero element $(2, 3)$ in $\mathbf{K}_3$ and have

$$\mathbf{K}_4 = \begin{bmatrix} k_{11} + o(\epsilon^2) & o(\epsilon^2) & o(\epsilon^2) \\ o(\epsilon^2) & k_{22} + o(\epsilon^2) & 0 \\ o(\epsilon^2) & 0 & k_{33} + o(\epsilon^2) \end{bmatrix}$$

with all off-diagonal elements at least $o(\epsilon^2)$.

11.3.2 The Generalized Jacobi Method

In the previous section we discussed the solution of the standard eigenproblem $\mathbf{K}\boldsymbol{\phi} = \lambda\boldsymbol{\phi}$ using the conventional Jacobi rotation matrices in order to reduce $\mathbf{K}$ to diagonal form. To solve the generalized problem $\mathbf{K}\boldsymbol{\phi} = \lambda\mathbf{M}\boldsymbol{\phi}$, $\mathbf{M} \neq \mathbf{I}$, using the standard Jacobi method, it would be necessary to first transform the problem into a standard form. However, this transformation can be dispensed with by using a generalized Jacobi solution method that operates directly on $\mathbf{K}$ and $\mathbf{M}$ (see S. Falk and P. Langemeyer [A] and K. J. Bathe [A]). The algorithm proceeds as summarized in (11.72) to (11.76) and is a natural extension of the standard Jacobi solution scheme; i.e., the generalized method reduces to the scheme presented for the problem $\mathbf{K}\boldsymbol{\phi} = \lambda\boldsymbol{\phi}$ when $\mathbf{M}$ is an identity matrix.

Referring to the discussion in the previous section, in the generalized Jacobi iteration we use the following matrix $\mathbf{P}_k$:

$$\mathbf{P}_k = \tag{11.85}$$

where the constants α and γ are selected in such a way as to reduce to zero simultaneously elements (i, j) in $\mathbf{K}_k$ and $\mathbf{M}_k$. Therefore, the values of α and γ are a function of the elements $k_{ij}^{(k)}$, $k_{ii}^{(k)}$, $k_{jj}^{(k)}$, $m_{ij}^{(k)}$, $m_{ii}^{(k)}$, and $m_{jj}^{(k)}$, where the superscript (k) indicates that the kth iteration is considered. Performing the multiplications $\mathbf{P}_k^T\mathbf{K}_k\mathbf{P}_k$ and $\mathbf{P}_k^T\mathbf{M}_k\mathbf{P}_k$ and using the condition that $k_{ij}^{(k+1)}$ and $m_{ij}^{(k+1)}$ shall be zero, we obtain the following two equations for α and γ:

$$\alpha k_{ii}^{(k)} + (1 + \alpha\gamma)k_{ij}^{(k)} + \gamma k_{jj}^{(k)} = 0 \tag{11.86}$$

and

$$\alpha m_{ii}^{(k)} + (1 + \alpha\gamma)m_{ij}^{(k)} + \gamma m_{jj}^{(k)} = 0 \tag{11.87}$$

If

$$\frac{k_{ii}^{(k)}}{m_{ii}^{(k)}} = \frac{k_{jj}^{(k)}}{m_{jj}^{(k)}} = \frac{k_{ij}^{(k)}}{m_{ij}^{(k)}}$$

(i.e., the submatrices considered are scalar multiples, which may be regarded to be a trivial case), we use $\alpha = 0$ and $\gamma = -k_{ij}^{(k)}/k_{jj}^{(k)}$. In general, to solve for α and γ from (11.86) and (11.87), we define

$$\left.\begin{array}{l} \bar{k}_{ii}^{(k)} = k_{ii}^{(k)}m_{ij}^{(k)} - m_{ii}^{(k)}k_{ij}^{(k)} \\[4pt] \bar{k}_{jj}^{(k)} = k_{jj}^{(k)}m_{ij}^{(k)} - m_{jj}^{(k)}k_{ij}^{(k)} \\[4pt] \bar{k}^{(k)} = k_{ii}^{(k)}m_{jj}^{(k)} - k_{jj}^{(k)}m_{ii}^{(k)} \end{array}\right\} \tag{11.88}$$

and

$$\gamma = -\frac{\bar{k}_{ii}^{(k)}}{x}; \qquad \alpha = \frac{\bar{k}_{jj}^{(k)}}{x} \tag{11.89}$$

The value of x needed to obtain α and γ is then to be determined using

$$x = \frac{\bar{k}^{(k)}}{2} + \text{sign}\,(\bar{k}^{(k)})\sqrt{\left(\frac{\bar{k}^{(k)}}{2}\right)^2 + \bar{k}_{ii}^{(k)}\bar{k}_{jj}^{(k)}} \tag{11.90}$$

The relations for α and γ are used and have primarily been developed for the case of **M** being a positive definite full or banded mass matrix. In that case (and, in fact, also under less restrictive conditions), we have

$$\left(\frac{\bar{k}^{(k)}}{2}\right)^2 + \bar{k}_{ii}^{(k)}\bar{k}_{jj}^{(k)} > 0$$

and hence x is always nonzero. In addition, det $\mathbf{P}_k \neq 0$, which indeed is the necessary condition for the algorithm to work.

The generalized Jacobi solution procedure has been used a great deal in the subspace iteration method (see Section 11.6) and when a consistent mass idealization is employed. However, other situations may arise as well. Assume that **M** is a diagonal mass matrix, $\mathbf{M} \neq \mathbf{I}$ and $m_{ii} > 0$, in which case we employ in (11.88),

$$\bar{k}_{ii}^{(k)} = -m_{ii}^{(k)}k_{ij}^{(k)}; \qquad \bar{k}_{jj}^{(k)} = -m_{jj}^{(k)}k_{ij}^{(k)} \tag{11.91}$$

and otherwise (11.85) to (11.90) are used as before. However, if $\mathbf{M} = \mathbf{I}$, the relation in (11.87) yields $\alpha = -\gamma$, and we recognize that $\mathbf{P}_k$ in (11.85) is a multiple of the rotation matrix defined in (11.79) (see Example 11.11). In addition, it should be mentioned that the solution procedure can be adapted to solve the problem $\mathbf{K\phi} = \lambda\mathbf{M\phi}$ when **M** is a diagonal matrix with some zero diagonal elements.

The complete solution process is analogous to the Jacobi iteration in the solution of the problem $\mathbf{K\phi} = \lambda\mathbf{\phi}$, which was presented in the preceding section. The differences are that now a mass coupling factor $[(m_{ij}^{(k)})^2/m_{ii}^{(k)}m_{jj}^{(k)}]^{1/2}$ must also be calculated, unless **M** is diagonal, and the transformation is applied to $\mathbf{K}_k$ and $\mathbf{M}_k$. Convergence is measured by comparing successive eigenvalue approximations and by testing if all off-diagonal elements are small enough; i.e., with l being the last iteration, convergence has been achieved if

$$\frac{|\lambda_i^{(l+1)} - \lambda_i^{(l)}|}{\lambda_i^{(l+1)}} \leq 10^{-s}; \qquad i = 1, \ldots, n \tag{11.92}$$

where

$$\lambda_i^{(l)} = \frac{k_{ii}^{(l)}}{m_{ii}^{(l)}}; \qquad \lambda_i^{(l+1)} = \frac{k_{ii}^{(l+1)}}{m_{ii}^{(l+1)}} \qquad (11.93)$$

and

$$\left[\frac{(k_{ij}^{(l+1)})^2}{k_{ii}^{(l+1)}k_{jj}^{(l+1)}}\right]^{1/2} \le 10^{-s}; \qquad \left[\frac{(m_{ij}^{(l+1)})^2}{m_{ii}^{(l+1)}m_{jj}^{(l+1)}}\right]^{1/2} \le 10^{-s}; \qquad \text{all } i, j; \; i < j \qquad (11.94)$$

where 10^{-s} is the convergence tolerance.

Table 11.1 summarizes the solution procedure for the case of **M** being full (or banded) and positive definite. The relations given in Table 11.1 are employed directly in the subroutine JACOBI, which is presented at the end of this section. Table 11.1 also gives an operation count of the solution process and the storage requirements. The total number of operations in one sweep as given in the table are an upper bound because it is assumed that both matrices are full and that all off-diagonal elements are zeroed; i.e., the threshold tolerance is never passed. Considering the number of sweeps required for solution, the same experience as with the solution of standard eigenproblems holds; i.e., with $m = 2$ and $s = 12$ in the iteration (see Section 11.3.1) about six sweeps are required for solution of the eigensystem to high accuracy.

TABLE 11.1 *Summary of generalized Jacobi solution*

Operation	Calculation	Number of operations	Required storage
Calculation of coupling factors	$\dfrac{(k_{ij}^{(k)})^2}{k_{ii}^{(k)}k_{jj}^{(k)}}$; $\quad \dfrac{(m_{ij}^{(k)})^2}{m_{ii}^{(k)}m_{jj}^{(k)}}$	6	
Transformation to zero elements (i, j)	$\bar{k}_{ii}^{(k)} = k_{ii}^{(k)}m_{ij}^{(k)} - m_{ii}^{(k)}k_{ij}^{(k)}$ $\bar{k}_{jj}^{(k)} = k_{jj}^{(k)}m_{ij}^{(k)} - m_{jj}^{(k)}k_{ij}^{(k)}$ $\bar{k}^{(k)} = k_{ii}^{(k)}m_{jj}^{(k)} - k_{jj}^{(k)}m_{ii}^{(k)}$		
	$x = \dfrac{\bar{k}^{(k)}}{2} + (\text{sign } \bar{k}^{(k)})\sqrt{\left(\dfrac{\bar{k}^{(k)}}{2}\right)^2 + \bar{k}_{ii}^{(k)}\bar{k}_{jj}^{(k)}}$ $\gamma = -\dfrac{\bar{k}_{ii}^{(k)}}{x}, \; \alpha = \dfrac{\bar{k}_{jj}^{(k)}}{x}$	$4n + 12$	Using symmetry of matrices $n(n + 2)$
	$\mathbf{K}_{k+1} = \mathbf{P}_k^T\mathbf{K}_k\mathbf{P}_k, \quad \mathbf{M}_{k+1} = \mathbf{P}_k^T\mathbf{M}_k\mathbf{P}_k$		
Calculation of eigenvectors	$(\mathbf{P}_1 \ldots \mathbf{P}_{k-1})\mathbf{P}_k$	$2n$	n^2
Total for one sweep		$3n^3 + 6n^2$	$2n^2 + 2n$

The following examples demonstrate some of the characteristics of the generalized Jacobi solution algorithm.

EXAMPLE 11.11: Prove that the generalized Jacobi method reduces to the standard technique when **M** = **I**.

For the proof we need only consider the calculation of the transformation matrices that would be used to zero typical off-diagonal elements. We want to show that the transformation matrices obtained in the standard and generalized Jacobi methods are multiples of each other; namely, in that case we could, by proper scaling, obtain the standard method from the generalized scheme. Since each step of iteration consists of applying a rotation in the (i,j)th plane, we can without loss of generality consider the solution of the problem

$$\begin{bmatrix} k_{11} & k_{12} \\ k_{12} & k_{22} \end{bmatrix} \boldsymbol{\phi} = \lambda \boldsymbol{\phi}$$

Using (11.88) to (11.90), we thus obtain

$$\alpha = -\gamma; \qquad \mathbf{P}_1 = \begin{bmatrix} 1 & -\gamma \\ \gamma & 1 \end{bmatrix} \qquad\qquad \text{(a)}$$

and

$$\gamma = \frac{-k_{11} + k_{22} \pm \sqrt{(k_{11} - k_{22})^2 + 4k_{12}^2}}{2k_{12}}$$

On the other hand, in the standard Jacobi solution we use

$$\mathbf{P}_1 = \begin{bmatrix} \cos \theta & -\sin \theta \\ \sin \theta & \cos \theta \end{bmatrix}$$

which may be written as

$$\mathbf{P}_1 = \cos \theta \begin{bmatrix} 1 & -\tan \theta \\ \tan \theta & 1 \end{bmatrix} \qquad\qquad \text{(b)}$$

Thus, $\mathbf{P}_1$ in (b) would be a multiple of $\mathbf{P}_1$ in (a) if $\tan \theta = \gamma$. In the standard Jacobi method we obtain $\tan 2\theta$ using (11.80). In this case, we have

$$\tan 2\theta = \frac{2k_{12}}{k_{11} - k_{22}} \qquad\qquad \text{(c)}$$

We also have, by simple trigonometry,

$$\tan 2\theta = \frac{2 \tan \theta}{1 - \tan^2 \theta} \qquad\qquad \text{(d)}$$

Using (c) and (d), we can solve for $\tan \theta$ to be used in (b) and obtain

$$\tan \theta = \frac{-k_{11} + k_{22} \pm \sqrt{(k_{11} - k_{22})^2 + 4k_{12}^2}}{2k_{12}}$$

Hence, $\gamma = \tan \theta$ and the generalized Jacobi iteration is equivalent to the standard method when $\mathbf{M} = \mathbf{I}$.

EXAMPLE 11.12: Use the generalized Jacobi method to calculate the eigensystem of the problem $\mathbf{K}\boldsymbol{\phi} = \lambda \mathbf{M}\boldsymbol{\phi}$.

(1) In the first case let

$$\mathbf{K} = \begin{bmatrix} 1 & -1 \\ -1 & 1 \end{bmatrix}; \qquad \mathbf{M} = \begin{bmatrix} 2 & 1 \\ 1 & 2 \end{bmatrix}$$

We note that $\mathbf{K}$ is singular, and hence we expect a zero eigenvalue.

(2) Then let

$$\mathbf{K} = \begin{bmatrix} 2 & 1 \\ 1 & 2 \end{bmatrix}; \qquad \mathbf{M} = \begin{bmatrix} 2 & 0 \\ 0 & 0 \end{bmatrix}$$

in which case we have an infinite eigenvalue.

For solution, we use the relations in (11.85) to (11.90). Considering the problem in case (1), we obtain

$$\bar{k}_{11}^{(1)} = 3; \qquad \bar{k}_{22}^{(1)} = 3; \qquad \bar{k}^{(1)} = 0$$

$$x = 3; \qquad \gamma = -1; \qquad \alpha = 1$$

$$\mathbf{P}_1 = \begin{bmatrix} 1 & 1 \\ -1 & 1 \end{bmatrix}$$

Hence,
$$\mathbf{P}_1^T \mathbf{K} \mathbf{P}_1 = \begin{bmatrix} 4 & 0 \\ 0 & 0 \end{bmatrix}; \qquad \mathbf{P}_1^T \mathbf{M} \mathbf{P}_1 = \begin{bmatrix} 2 & 0 \\ 0 & 6 \end{bmatrix}$$

To obtain $\mathbf{\Lambda}$ and $\mathbf{\Phi}$ we use (11.75) and (11.76) and arrange the columns in the matrices in the appropriate order. Hence,

$$\mathbf{\Lambda} = \begin{bmatrix} 0 & \\ & 2 \end{bmatrix}; \qquad \mathbf{\Phi} = \begin{bmatrix} \dfrac{1}{\sqrt{6}} & \dfrac{1}{\sqrt{2}} \\[2ex] \dfrac{1}{\sqrt{6}} & -\dfrac{1}{\sqrt{2}} \end{bmatrix}$$

Now consider the problem in case (2). Here we have

$$\bar{k}_{11}^{(1)} = -2; \qquad \bar{k}_{22}^{(1)} = 0; \qquad \bar{k}^{(1)} = -4$$

$$x = -4; \qquad \alpha = 0; \qquad \gamma = -\tfrac{1}{2}$$

$$\mathbf{P}_1 = \begin{bmatrix} 1 & 0 \\ -\frac{1}{2} & 1 \end{bmatrix}$$

Hence,
$$\mathbf{P}_1^T \mathbf{K} \mathbf{P}_1 = \begin{bmatrix} \frac{3}{2} & 0 \\ 0 & 2 \end{bmatrix}; \qquad \mathbf{P}_1^T \mathbf{M} \mathbf{P}_1 = \begin{bmatrix} 2 & 0 \\ 0 & 0 \end{bmatrix}$$

and
$$\mathbf{\Lambda} = \begin{bmatrix} \frac{3}{4} & \\ & \infty \end{bmatrix}; \qquad \mathbf{\phi}_1 = \begin{bmatrix} \dfrac{1}{\sqrt{2}} \\[2ex] -\dfrac{1}{2\sqrt{2}} \end{bmatrix}$$

The above discussion of the generalized Jacobi solution method has already indicated in some way the advantages of the solution technique. First, the transformation of the generalized eigenproblem to the standard form is avoided. This is particularly advantageous (1) when the matrices are ill-conditioned, and (2) when the off-diagonal elements in $\mathbf{K}$ and $\mathbf{M}$ are already small or, equivalently when there are only a few nonzero off-diagonal elements. In the first case the direct solution of $\mathbf{K}\mathbf{\phi} = \lambda\mathbf{M}\mathbf{\phi}$ avoids the solution of a standard eigenproblem of a matrix with very large and very small elements (see Section 10.2.5). In the second case the eigenproblem is already nearly solved, because the zeroing of small or only a few off-diagonal elements in $\mathbf{K}$ and $\mathbf{M}$ will not result in a large change in the diagonal elements of the matrices, the ratios of which are the eigenvalues. In addition, fast convergence can be expected when the off-diagonal elements are small (see Section 11.3.1). We will see that this case arises in the subspace iteration method described in Section 11.6, which is one reason why the generalized Jacobi method is used effectively in that technique.

It should be noted that the Jacobi solution methods solve simultaneously for all eigenvalues and corresponding eigenvectors. However, in finite element analysis we require in most cases only some eigenpairs, and the use of a Jacobi solution procedure can be very inefficient, in particular when the order of **K** and **M** is large. In such cases much more effective solution methods are available, which solve only for the specific eigenvalues and eigenvectors that are actually required. However, the generalized Jacobi solution method presented in this section can be used very effectively as part of those solution strategies (see Section 11.6). When the order of the matrices **K** and **M** is relatively small, the solution of the eigenproblem is not very expensive, and the Jacobi iteration may also be attractive because of its simplicity and elegance of solution.

Subroutine JACOBI.   Program JACOBI is used to calculate all eigenvalues and corresponding eigenvectors of the generalized eigenproblem $\mathbf{K}\boldsymbol{\phi} = \lambda\mathbf{M}\boldsymbol{\phi}$. The argument variables and use of the subroutine are defined using comment lines in the program.

```
      SUBROUTINE JACOBI (A,B,X,EIGV,D,N,RTOL,NSMAX,IFPR,IOUT)         JAC00001
C ................................................................. JAC00002
C .                                                               . JAC00003
C .    P R O G R A M                                              . JAC00004
C .       TO SOLVE THE GENERALIZED EIGENPROBLEM USING THE         . JAC00005
C .       GENERALIZED JACOBI ITERATION                            . JAC00006
C .                                                               . JAC00007
C . - - INPUT VARIABLES - -                                       . JAC00008
C .       A(N,N)    = STIFFNESS MATRIX (ASSUMED POSITIVE DEFINITE) . JAC00009
C .       B(N,N)    = MASS MATRIX (ASSUMED POSITIVE DEFINITE)     . JAC00010
C .       X(N,N)    = STORAGE FOR EIGENVECTORS                    . JAC00011
C .       EIGV(N)   = STORAGE FOR EIGENVALUES                     . JAC00012
C .       D(N)      = WORKING VECTOR                              . JAC00013
C .       N         = ORDER OF MATRICES A AND B                   . JAC00014
C .       RTOL      = CONVERGENCE TOLERANCE (USUALLY SET TO 10.**-12). JAC00015
C .       NSMAX     = MAXIMUM NUMBER OF SWEEPS ALLOWED            . JAC00016
C .                   (USUALLY SET TO 15)                         . JAC00017
C .       IFPR      = FLAG FOR PRINTING DURING ITERATION          . JAC00018
C .           EQ.0    NO PRINTING                                 . JAC00019
C .           EQ.1    INTERMEDIATE RESULTS ARE PRINTED            . JAC00020
C .       IOUT      = UNIT NUMBER USED FOR OUTPUT                 . JAC00021
C .                                                               . JAC00022
C . - - OUTPUT - -                                                . JAC00023
C .       A(N,N)    = DIAGONALIZED STIFFNESS MATRIX               . JAC00024
C .       B(N,N)    = DIGONALIZED MASS MATRIX                     . JAC00025
C .       X(N,N)    = EIGENVECTORS STORED COLUMNWISE              . JAC00026
C .       EIGV(N)   = EIGENVALUES                                 . JAC00027
C .                                                               . JAC00028
C ................................................................. JAC00029
      IMPLICIT DOUBLE PRECISION (A-H,O-Z)                           JAC00030
C ................................................................. JAC00031
C .    THIS PROGRAM IS USED IN SINGLE PRECISION ARITHMETIC ON CRAY . JAC00032
C .    EQUIPMENT AND DOUBLE PRECISION ARITHMETIC ON IBM MACHINES,  . JAC00033
C .    ENGINEERING WORKSTATIONS AND PCS. DEACTIVATE ABOVE LINE FOR . JAC00034
C .    SINGLE PRECISION ARITHMETIC.                                . JAC00035
C ................................................................. JAC00036
      DIMENSION A(N,N),B(N,N),X(N,N),EIGV(N),D(N)                   JAC00037
C                                                                    JAC00038
C     INITIALIZE EIGENVALUE AND EIGENVECTOR MATRICES                 JAC00039
C                                                                    JAC00040
      DO 10 I=1,N                                                    JAC00041
      IF (A(I,I).GT.0. .AND. B(I,I).GT.0.) GO TO 4                   JAC00042
      WRITE (IOUT,2020)                                              JAC00043
      GO TO 800                                                      JAC00044
    4 D(I)=A(I,I)/B(I,I)                                             JAC00045
   10 EIGV(I)=D(I)                                                   JAC00046
      DO 30 I=1,N                                                    JAC00047
      DO 20 J=1,N                                                    JAC00048
```

```
     20 X(I,J)=0.                                                    JAC00049
     30 X(I,I)=1.                                                    JAC00050
        IF (N.EQ.1) GO TO 900                                        JAC00051
C                                                                    JAC00052
C       INITIALIZE SWEEP COUNTER AND BEGIN ITERATION                 JAC00053
C                                                                    JAC00054
        NSWEEP=0                                                     JAC00055
        NR=N - 1                                                     JAC00056
     40 NSWEEP=NSWEEP + 1                                            JAC00057
        IF (IFPR.EQ.1) WRITE (IOUT,2000) NSWEEP                      JAC00058
C                                                                    JAC00059
C       CHECK IF PRESENT OFF-DIAGONAL ELEMENT IS LARGE ENOUGH TO     JAC00060
C       REQUIRE ZEROING                                             JAC00061
C                                                                    JAC00062
        EPS=(.01)**(NSWEEP*2)                                        JAC00063
        DO 210 J=1,NR                                                JAC00064
        JJ=J + 1                                                     JAC00065
        DO 210 K=JJ,N                                                JAC00066
        EPTOLA=(A(J,K)/A(J,J))*(A(J,K)/A(K,K))                       JAC00067
        EPTOLB=(B(J,K)/B(J,J))*(B(J,K)/B(K,K))                       JAC00068
        IF (EPTOLA.LT.EPS .AND. EPTOLB.LT.EPS) GO TO 210             JAC00069
C                                                                    JAC00070
C       IF ZEROING IS REQUIRED, CALCULATE THE ROTATION MATRIX        JAC00071
C       ELEMENTS CA AND CG                                          JAC00072
C                                                                    JAC00073
        AKK=A(K,K)*B(J,K) - B(K,K)*A(J,K)                            JAC00074
        AJJ=A(J,J)*B(J,K) - B(J,J)*A(J,K)                            JAC00075
        AB=A(J,J)*B(K,K) - A(K,K)*B(J,J)                             JAC00076
        SCALE=A(K,K)*B(K,K)                                          JAC00077
        ABCH=AB/SCALE                                                JAC00078
        AKKCH=AKK/SCALE                                              JAC00079
        AJJCH=AJJ/SCALE                                              JAC00080
        CHECK=(ABCH*ABCH + 4.*AKKCH*AJJCH)/4.                        JAC00081
        IF (CHECK) 50,60,60                                          JAC00082
     50 WRITE (IOUT,2020)                                            JAC00083
        GO TO 800                                                    JAC00084
     60 SQCH=SCALE*SQRT(CHECK)                                       JAC00085
        D1=AB/2. + SQCH                                              JAC00086
        D2=AB/2. - SQCH                                              JAC00087
        DEN=D1                                                       JAC00088
        IF (ABS(D2).GT.ABS(D1)) DEN=D2                               JAC00089
        IF (DEN) 80,70,80                                            JAC00090
     70 CA=0.                                                        JAC00091
        CG=-A(J,K)/A(K,K)                                            JAC00092
        GO TO 90                                                     JAC00093
     80 CA=AKK/DEN                                                   JAC00094
        CG=-AJJ/DEN                                                  JAC00095
C                                                                    JAC00096
C       PERFORM THE GENERALIZED ROTATION TO ZERO ELEMENTS            JAC00097
C                                                                    JAC00098
     90 IF (N-2) 100,190,100                                         JAC00099
    100 JP1=J + 1                                                    JAC00100
        JM1=J - 1                                                    JAC00101
        KP1=K + 1                                                    JAC00102
        KM1=K - 1                                                    JAC00103
        IF (JM1-1) 130,110,110                                       JAC00104
    110 DO 120 I=1,JM1                                               JAC00105
        AJ=A(I,J)                                                    JAC00106
        BJ=B(I,J)                                                    JAC00107
        AK=A(I,K)                                                    JAC00108
        BK=B(I,K)                                                    JAC00109
        A(I,J)=AJ + CG*AK                                            JAC00110
        B(I,J)=BJ + CG*BK                                            JAC00111
        A(I,K)=AK + CA*AJ                                            JAC00112
    120 B(I,K)=BK + CA*BJ                                            JAC00113
    130 IF (KP1-N) 140,140,160                                       JAC00114
    140 DO 150 I=KP1,N                                               JAC00115
        AJ=A(J,I)                                                    JAC00116
        BJ=B(J,I)                                                    JAC00117
        AK=A(K,I)                                                    JAC00118
        BK=B(K,I)                                                    JAC00119
```

```
      A(J,I)=AJ + CG*AK                                        JAC00120
      B(J,I)=BJ + CG*BK                                        JAC00121
      A(K,I)=AK + CA*AJ                                        JAC00122
  150 B(K,I)=BK + CA*BJ                                        JAC00123
  160 IF (JP1-KM1) 170,170,190                                 JAC00124
  170 DO 180 I=JP1,KM1                                         JAC00125
      AJ=A(J,I)                                                JAC00126
      BJ=B(J,I)                                                JAC00127
      AK=A(I,K)                                                JAC00128
      BK=B(I,K)                                                JAC00129
      A(J,I)=AJ + CG*AK                                        JAC00130
      B(J,I)=BJ + CG*BK                                        JAC00131
      A(I,K)=AK + CA*AJ                                        JAC00132
  180 B(I,K)=BK + CA*BJ                                        JAC00133
  190 AK=A(K,K)                                                JAC00134
      BK=B(K,K)                                                JAC00135
      A(K,K)=AK + 2.*CA*A(J,K) + CA*CA*A(J,J)                  JAC00136
      B(K,K)=BK + 2.*CA*B(J,K) + CA*CA*B(J,J)                  JAC00137
      A(J,J)=A(J,J) + 2.*CG*A(J,K) + CG*CG*AK                  JAC00138
      B(J,J)=B(J,J) + 2.*CG*B(J,K) + CG*CG*BK                  JAC00139
      A(J,K)=0.                                                JAC00140
      B(J,K)=0.                                                JAC00141
C                                                              JAC00142
C     UPDATE THE EIGENVECTOR MATRIX AFTER EACH ROTATION        JAC00143
C                                                              JAC00144
      DO 200 I=1,N                                             JAC00145
      XJ=X(I,J)                                                JAC00146
      XK=X(I,K)                                                JAC00147
      X(I,J)=XJ + CG*XK                                        JAC00148
  200 X(I,K)=XK + CA*XJ                                        JAC00149
  210 CONTINUE                                                 JAC00150
C                                                              JAC00151
C     UPDATE THE EIGENVALUES AFTER EACH SWEEP                  JAC00152
C                                                              JAC00153
      DO 220 I=1,N                                             JAC00154
      IF (A(I,I).GT.0. .AND. B(I,I).GT.0.) GO TO 220           JAC00155
      WRITE (IOUT,2020)                                        JAC00156
      GO TO 800                                                JAC00157
  220 EIGV(I)=A(I,I)/B(I,I)                                    JAC00158
      IF (IFPR.EQ.0) GO TO 230                                 JAC00159
      WRITE (IOUT,2030)                                        JAC00160
      WRITE (IOUT,2010) (EIGV(I),I=1,N)                        JAC00161
C                                                              JAC00162
C     CHECK FOR CONVERGENCE                                    JAC00163
C                                                              JAC00164
  230 DO 240 I=1,N                                             JAC00165
      TOL=RTOL*D(I)                                            JAC00166
      DIF=ABS(EIGV(I)-D(I))                                    JAC00167
      IF (DIF.GT.TOL) GO TO 280                                JAC00168
  240 CONTINUE                                                 JAC00169
C                                                              JAC00170
C     CHECK OFF-DIAGONAL ELEMENTS TO SEE IF ANOTHER SWEEP IS NEEDED JAC00171
C                                                              JAC00172
      EPS=RTOL**2                                              JAC00173
      DO 250 J=1,NR                                            JAC00174
      JJ=J + 1                                                 JAC00175
      DO 250 K=JJ,N                                            JAC00176
      EPSA=(A(J,K)/A(J,J))*(A(J,K)/A(K,K))                     JAC00177
      EPSB=(B(J,K)/B(J,J))*(B(J,K)/B(K,K))                     JAC00178
      IF (EPSA.LT.EPS .AND. EPSB.LT.EPS) GO TO 250             JAC00179
      GO TO 280                                                JAC00180
  250 CONTINUE                                                 JAC00181
C                                                              JAC00182
C     FILL OUT BOTTOM TRIANGLE OF RESULTANT MATRICES, SCALE EIGENVECTORSJAC00183
C                                                              JAC00184
  255 DO 260 I=1,N                                             JAC00185
      DO 260 J=I,N                                             JAC00186
      A(J,I)=A(I,J)                                            JAC00187
  260 B(J,I)=B(I,J)                                            JAC00188
      DO 270 J=1,N                                             JAC00189
```

```
        BB=SQRT(B(J,J))                                         JAC00190
        DO 270 K=1,N                                            JAC00191
   270  X(K,J)=X(K,J)/BB                                        JAC00192
        GO TO 900                                               JAC00193
C                                                               JAC00194
C       UPDATE  D  MATRIX AND START NEW SWEEP, IF ALLOWED       JAC00195
C                                                               JAC00196
   280  DO 290 I=1,N                                            JAC00197
   290  D(I)=EIGV(I)                                            JAC00198
        IF (NSWEEP.LT.NSMAX) GO TO 40                           JAC00199
        GO TO 255                                               JAC00200
C                                                               JAC00201
   800  STOP                                                    JAC00202
   900  RETURN                                                  JAC00203
C                                                               JAC00204
  2000  FORMAT (//,' SWEEP NUMBER IN *JACOBI* = ',I8)           JAC00205
  2010  FORMAT (' ',6E20.12)                                    JAC00206
  2020  FORMAT (//,' *** ERROR *** SOLUTION STOP',/,            JAC00207
     1          ' MATRICES NOT POSITIVE DEFINITE')              JAC00208
  2030  FORMAT (//,' CURRENT EIGENVALUES IN *JACOBI* ARE',/)    JAC00209
        END                                                     JAC00210
```

11.3.3 The Householder-QR-Inverse Iteration Solution

Another most important transformation solution technique is the Householder-QR-inverse iteration (HQRI) method, although this procedure is restricted to the solution of the standard eigenproblem (see J. G. F. Francis [A], J. H. Wilkinson [B], B. N. Parlett [A, B], and R. S. Martin, C. Reinsch, and J. H. Wilkinson [A]). Therefore, if the generalized eigenproblem $\mathbf{K}\boldsymbol{\phi} = \lambda\mathbf{M}\boldsymbol{\phi}$ is considered, it must first be transformed into the standard form before the HQRI solution technique can be used. As pointed out in Section 10.2.5, this transformation is effective in only some cases.

In the following discussion, we consider the problem $\mathbf{K}\boldsymbol{\phi} = \lambda\boldsymbol{\phi}$, in which $\mathbf{K}$ may have zero (and could also have negative) eigenvalues. Therefore, it is not necessary to impose a shift prior to applying the HQRI algorithm in order to solve for only positive eigenvalues (see Section 10.2.3). The name "HQRI solution method" stands for the following three solution steps:

1. Householder transformations are employed to reduce the matrix $\mathbf{K}$ to tridiagonal form.
2. QR iteration yields all eigenvalues.
3. Using inverse iteration the required eigenvectors of the tridiagonal matrix are calculated. These vectors are transformed to obtain the eigenvectors of $\mathbf{K}$.

A basic difference from the Jacobi solution method is that the matrix is first transformed without iteration into a tridiagonal form. This matrix can then be used effectively in the QR iterative solution, in which all eigenvalues are calculated. Finally, only those eigenvectors that are actually requested are evaluated. We will note that unless many eigenvectors must be calculated, the transformation of $\mathbf{K}$ into tridiagonal form requires most of the numerical operations. In the following we consider in detail the three distinct steps carried out in the HQRI solution.

The Householder reduction.   The Householder reduction to tridiagonal form involves $n - 2$ transformations of the form (11.72); i.e., using $\mathbf{K}_1 = \mathbf{K}$, we calculate

$$\mathbf{K}_{k+1} = \mathbf{P}_k^T\mathbf{K}_k\mathbf{P}_k; \qquad k = 1, \ldots, n - 2 \qquad (11.95)$$

where the $\mathbf{P}_k$ are Householder transformation matrices (reflection matrices, see Exercise 2.6):

$$\mathbf{P}_k = \mathbf{I} - \theta\mathbf{w}_k\mathbf{w}_k^T \tag{11.96}$$

$$\theta = \frac{2}{\mathbf{w}_k^T\mathbf{w}_k} \tag{11.97}$$

To show how the vector $\mathbf{w}_k$ that defines the matrix $\mathbf{P}_k$ is calculated, we consider the case $k = 1$, which is typical. First, we partition $\mathbf{K}_1$, $\mathbf{P}_1$, and $\mathbf{w}_1$ into submatrices as follows:

$$\mathbf{P}_1 = \left[\begin{array}{c|c} 1 & \mathbf{0} \\ \hline \mathbf{0} & \overline{\mathbf{P}}_1 \end{array}\right]; \qquad \mathbf{w}_1 = \left[\begin{array}{c} 0 \\ \hline \overline{\mathbf{w}}_1 \end{array}\right]$$

$$\mathbf{K}_1 = \left[\begin{array}{c|c} k_{11} & \mathbf{k}_1^T \\ \hline \mathbf{k}_1 & \overline{\mathbf{K}}_{11} \end{array}\right] \tag{11.98}$$

where $\mathbf{K}_{11}$, $\overline{\mathbf{P}}_1$, and $\overline{\mathbf{w}}_1$ are of order $n - 1$. In the general case of step k, we have corresponding matrices of order $n - k$. Performing the multiplications in (11.95), we obtain, using the notation of (11.98),

$$\mathbf{K}_2 = \left[\begin{array}{c|c} k_{11} & \mathbf{k}_1^T\overline{\mathbf{P}}_1 \\ \hline \overline{\mathbf{P}}_1^T\mathbf{k}_1 & \overline{\mathbf{P}}_1^T\mathbf{K}_{11}\overline{\mathbf{P}}_1 \end{array}\right] \tag{11.99}$$

The condition is now that the first column and row of $\mathbf{K}_2$ should be in tridiagonal form; i.e., we want $\mathbf{K}_2$ to be in the form

$$\mathbf{K}_2 = \left[\begin{array}{c|ccccc} k_{11} & \times & 0 & \dots & 0 \\ \hline \times & & & & \\ 0 & & & & \\ \cdot & & & \overline{\mathbf{K}}_2 & \\ \cdot & & & & \\ 0 & & & & \end{array}\right] \tag{11.100}$$

where $\times$ indicates a nonzero value and

$$\overline{\mathbf{K}}_2 = \overline{\mathbf{P}}_1^T\mathbf{K}_{11}\overline{\mathbf{P}}_1 \tag{11.101}$$

The form of $\mathbf{K}_2$ in (11.100) is achieved by realizing that $\overline{\mathbf{P}}_1$ is a reflection matrix. Therefore, we can use $\overline{\mathbf{P}}_1$ to reflect the vector $\mathbf{k}_1$ of $\mathbf{K}_1$ in (11.98) into a vector that has only its first component nonzero. Since the length of the new vector must be the length of $\mathbf{k}_1$, we determine $\overline{\mathbf{w}}_1$ from the condition

$$(\mathbf{I} - \theta\overline{\mathbf{w}}_1\overline{\mathbf{w}}_1^T)\mathbf{k}_1 = \pm\|\mathbf{k}_1\|_2\mathbf{e}_1 \tag{11.102}$$

where $\mathbf{e}_1$ is a unit vector of dimension $n - 1$; i.e., $\mathbf{e}_1^T = [1 \quad 0 \quad 0 \quad \dots \quad 0]$, and the $+$ or $-$ sign can be selected to obtain the best numerical stability. Noting that we only need to solve for a multiple of $\overline{\mathbf{w}}_1$ (i.e., only the direction of the vector normal to the plane of reflection is important, see Exercise 2.6), we obtain from (11.102) as a suitable value for $\overline{\mathbf{w}}_1$,

$$\overline{\mathbf{w}}_1 = \mathbf{k}_1 + \text{sign}\,(k_{21})\|\mathbf{k}_1\|_2\mathbf{e}_1 \tag{11.103}$$

where k_{21} is element $(2, 1)$ of $\mathbf{K}_1$.

With $\overline{\mathbf{w}}_1$ defined in (11.103), the first Householder transformation, $k = 1$ in (11.95), can be carried out. In the next step, $k = 2$, we can consider the matrix $\overline{\mathbf{K}}_2$ in (11.100) in the same way as we considered $\mathbf{K}_1$ in (11.98) to (11.103) because the reduction of the first column and row of $\overline{\mathbf{K}}_2$ does not affect the first column and row in $\mathbf{K}_2$. Thus, the general algorithm for the transformation of $\mathbf{K}$ into tridiagonal form is established. We demonstrate the procedure in the following example.

EXAMPLE 11.13:   Use Householder transformation matrices to reduce $\mathbf{K}$ to tridiagonal form, where

$$\mathbf{K} = \begin{bmatrix} 5 & -4 & 1 & 0 \\ -4 & 6 & -4 & 1 \\ 1 & -4 & 6 & -4 \\ 0 & 1 & -4 & 5 \end{bmatrix}$$

Here, using (11.95) to (11.103) to reduce column 1, we have

$$\overline{\mathbf{w}}_1 = \begin{bmatrix} -4 \\ 1 \\ 0 \end{bmatrix} - 4.1231 \begin{bmatrix} 1 \\ 0 \\ 0 \end{bmatrix} = \begin{bmatrix} -8.1231 \\ 1 \\ 0 \end{bmatrix}$$

Hence,
$$\mathbf{w}_1 = \begin{bmatrix} 0 \\ -8.1231 \\ 1 \\ 0 \end{bmatrix}; \qquad \theta_1 = 0.0298575$$

$$\mathbf{P}_1 = \begin{bmatrix} 1 & 0 & 0 & 0 \\ 0 & -0.9701 & 0.2425 & 0 \\ 0 & 0.2425 & 0.9701 & 0 \\ 0 & 0 & 0 & 1 \end{bmatrix}$$

and
$$\mathbf{K}_2 = \begin{bmatrix} 5 & 4.1231 & 0 & 0 \\ 4.1231 & 7.8823 & 3.5294 & -1.9403 \\ 0 & 3.5294 & 4.1177 & -3.6380 \\ 0 & -1.9403 & -3.6380 & 5 \end{bmatrix}$$

Next we reduce column 2,

$$\overline{\mathbf{w}}_2 = \begin{bmatrix} 3.5294 \\ -1.9403 \end{bmatrix} + 4.0276 \begin{bmatrix} 1 \\ 0 \end{bmatrix} = \begin{bmatrix} 7.5570 \\ -1.9403 \end{bmatrix}$$

$$\mathbf{w}_2 = \begin{bmatrix} 0 \\ 0 \\ 7.5570 \\ -1.9403 \end{bmatrix}; \qquad \theta_2 = 0.0328553$$

$$\mathbf{P}_2 = \begin{bmatrix} 1 & 0 & 0 & 0 \\ 0 & 1 & 0 & 0 \\ 0 & 0 & -0.8763 & 0.4817 \\ 0 & 0 & 0.4817 & 0.8763 \end{bmatrix}$$

Hence,
$$\mathbf{K}_3 = \begin{bmatrix} 5 & 4.1231 & 0 & 0 \\ 4.1231 & 7.8823 & -4.0276 & 0 \\ 0 & -4.0276 & 7.3941 & 2.3219 \\ 0 & 0 & 2.3219 & 1.7236 \end{bmatrix}$$

Some important numerical aspects should be noted. First, the reduced matrices $\mathbf{K}_2$, $\mathbf{K}_3, \ldots, \mathbf{K}_{n-1}$ are symmetric. This means that in the reduction we need to store only the lower symmetric part of $\mathbf{K}$. Furthermore, to store the $\overline{\mathbf{w}}_k, k = 1, 2, \ldots, n - 2$, we can use the storage locations below the subdiagonal elements in the matrix currently being reduced.

A disadvantage of the Householder transformations is that the bandwidth is increased in the unreduced part of $\mathbf{K}_{k+1}$. Hence, in the reduction, essentially no advantage can be taken of the bandedness of $\mathbf{K}$.

An important aspect of the transformation is the evaluation of the matrix product $\overline{\mathbf{P}}_1^T \mathbf{K}_{11} \overline{\mathbf{P}}_1$ and the similar products required in the next steps. In the most general case a triple matrix product with matrices of order n requires $2n^3$ operations, and if this many operations were required, the Householder reduction would be quite uneconomical. However, by taking advantage of the special nature of the matrix $\overline{\mathbf{P}}_1$, we can evaluate the product $\overline{\mathbf{P}}_1^T \mathbf{K}_{11} \overline{\mathbf{P}}_1$ by calculating

$$\left.\begin{array}{l} \mathbf{v}_1 = \mathbf{K}_{11} \overline{\mathbf{w}}_1 \\[4pt] \mathbf{p}_1^T = \theta_1 \mathbf{v}_1^T \\[4pt] \beta_1 = \mathbf{p}_1^T \overline{\mathbf{w}}_1 \\[4pt] \mathbf{q}_1 = \mathbf{p}_1 - \theta_1 \beta_1 \overline{\mathbf{w}}_1 \end{array}\right\} \qquad (11.104)$$

and then
$$\overline{\mathbf{P}}_1^T \mathbf{K}_{11} \overline{\mathbf{P}}_1 = \mathbf{K}_{11} - \overline{\mathbf{w}}_1 \mathbf{p}_1^T - \mathbf{q}_1 \overline{\mathbf{w}}_1^T \qquad (11.105)$$

which requires only about $3m^2 + 3m$ operations, where m is the order of $\overline{\mathbf{P}}_1$ and $\mathbf{K}_{11}$ (i.e., $m = n - 1$ in this case). Hence, the multiplication $\overline{\mathbf{P}}_1^T \mathbf{K}_{11} \overline{\mathbf{P}}_1$ requires a number of operations of the order m-squared rather than m-cubed, which is a very significant reduction. We demonstrate the procedure given in (11.104) and (11.105) by reworking Example 11.13.

EXAMPLE 11.14: Use the relations given in (11.104) and (11.105) to reduce the matrix $\mathbf{K}$ in Example 11.13 to tridiagonal form.

Here we obtain for the reduction of column 1 using $\overline{\mathbf{w}}_1$ and θ_1 calculated in Example 11.13,

$$\mathbf{v}_1 = \begin{bmatrix} 6 & -4 & 1 \\ -4 & 6 & -4 \\ 1 & -4 & 5 \end{bmatrix} \overline{\mathbf{w}}_1 = \begin{bmatrix} -52.738 \\ 38.4924 \\ -12.1231 \end{bmatrix}$$

$$\mathbf{p}_1^T = [-1.5746 \quad 1.1493 \quad -0.36197]; \qquad \beta_1 = 13.9403; \qquad \mathbf{q}_1 = \begin{bmatrix} 1.8064 \\ 0.7331 \\ -0.3620 \end{bmatrix}$$

$$\overline{\mathbf{P}}_1^T \mathbf{K}_{11} \overline{\mathbf{P}}_1 = \begin{bmatrix} 6 & -4 & 1 \\ -4 & 6 & -4 \\ 1 & -4 & 5 \end{bmatrix} - \begin{bmatrix} 12.7910 & -9.335 & 2.9403 \\ -1.5746 & 1.1493 & -0.3620 \\ 0 & 0 & 0 \end{bmatrix}$$
$$- \begin{bmatrix} -14.6734 & 1.8064 & 0 \\ -5.9548 & 0.73307 & 0 \\ 2.9403 & -0.3620 & 0 \end{bmatrix}$$

or
$$\overline{\mathbf{P}}_1^T \mathbf{K}_{11} \overline{\mathbf{P}}_1 = \begin{bmatrix} 7.8823 & 3.5294 & -1.9403 \\ 3.5294 & 4.1177 & -3.6380 \\ -1.9403 & -3.6380 & 5 \end{bmatrix}$$

and hence, $\mathbf{K}_2 = \begin{bmatrix} 5 & 4.1231 & 0 & 0 \\ 4.1231 & 7.8823 & 3.5294 & -1.9403 \\ 0 & 3.5294 & 4.1177 & -3.6380 \\ 0 & -1.9403 & -3.6380 & 5 \end{bmatrix}$

Next we reduce the second column

$$\mathbf{v}_2 = \begin{bmatrix} 4.1177 & -3.6380 \\ -3.6380 & 5 \end{bmatrix} \quad \overline{\mathbf{w}}_2 = \begin{bmatrix} 38.1759 \\ -37.1941 \end{bmatrix}$$

$$\mathbf{p}_2^T = [1.2543 \quad -1.2220]; \qquad \beta_2 = 11.8497; \qquad \mathbf{q}_2 = \begin{bmatrix} -1.6878 \\ -0.4666 \end{bmatrix}$$

$$\overline{\mathbf{P}}_2^T \mathbf{K}_{22} \overline{\mathbf{P}}_2 = \begin{bmatrix} 4.1177 & -3.6380 \\ -3.6380 & 5 \end{bmatrix} - \begin{bmatrix} 9.4786 & -9.2348 \\ -2.4337 & 2.3711 \end{bmatrix} - \begin{bmatrix} -12.7550 & 3.2749 \\ -3.5263 & 0.90538 \end{bmatrix}$$

$$= \begin{bmatrix} 7.3941 & 2.3219 \\ 2.3219 & 1.7236 \end{bmatrix}$$

and hence, $\mathbf{K}_3 = \begin{bmatrix} 5 & 4.1231 & 0 & 0 \\ 4.1231 & 7.9823 & -4.0276 & 0 \\ 0 & -4.0276 & 7.3941 & 2.3219 \\ 0 & 0 & 2.3219 & 1.7236 \end{bmatrix}$

The QR iteration.   In the HQRI solution procedure, the QR iteration is applied to the tridiagonal matrix obtained by the Householder tansformation of **K**. However, it should be realized that the QR iteration could be applied to the original matrix **K** as well, and that the transformation of **K** into tridiagonal form prior to the iteration is merely carried out to improve the efficiency of solution. In the following we therefore consider first how the iteration is applied to a general symmetric matrix **K**.

The name "QR iteration" derives from the notation used in the algorithm. Namely, the basic step in the iteration is to decompose **K** into the form

$$\mathbf{K} = \mathbf{Q}\mathbf{R} \tag{11.106}$$

where **Q** is an orthogonal and **R** is an upper triangular matrix. We then form

$$\mathbf{R}\mathbf{Q} = \mathbf{Q}^T\mathbf{K}\mathbf{Q} \tag{11.107}$$

Therefore, by calculating **RQ** we in fact carry out a transformation of the form (11.72).

The factorization in (11.106) could be obtained by applying the Gram-Schmidt process to the columns of **K**. In practice, it is more effective to reduce **K** into upper triangular form using Jacobi rotation matrices; i.e., we evaluate

$$\mathbf{P}_{n,n-1}^T \ldots \mathbf{P}_{3,1}^T \mathbf{P}_{2,1}^T \mathbf{K} = \mathbf{R} \tag{11.108}$$

where the rotation matrix $\mathbf{P}_{j,i}^T$ is selected to zero element (j, i). Using (11.108), we have, corresponding to (11.106),

$$\mathbf{Q} = \mathbf{P}_{2,1}\mathbf{P}_{3,1} \ldots \mathbf{P}_{n,n-1} \tag{11.109}$$

The QR iteration algorithm is obtained by repeating the process given in (11.106) and (11.107). Using the notation $\mathbf{K}_1 = \mathbf{K}$, we form

$$\mathbf{K}_k = \mathbf{Q}_k\mathbf{R}_k \tag{11.110}$$

and then

$$\mathbf{K}_{k+1} = \mathbf{R}_k \mathbf{Q}_k \qquad (11.111)$$

where, then, disregarding that eigenvalues and eigenvectors may not be in the usual order,

$$\mathbf{K}_{k+1} \rightarrow \mathbf{\Lambda} \quad \text{and} \quad \mathbf{Q}_1 \cdots \mathbf{Q}_{k-1} \mathbf{Q}_k \rightarrow \mathbf{\Phi} \qquad \text{as } k \rightarrow \infty$$

We demonstrate the iteration process in the following example.

EXAMPLE 11.15: Use the QR iteration with $\mathbf{Q}$ obtained as a product of Jacobi rotation matrices to calculate the eigensystem of $\mathbf{K}$, where

$$\mathbf{K} = \begin{bmatrix} 5 & -4 & 1 & 0 \\ -4 & 6 & -4 & 1 \\ 1 & -4 & 6 & -4 \\ 0 & 1 & -4 & 5 \end{bmatrix}$$

The Jacobi rotation matrix $\mathbf{P}_{j,i}^T$ to zero element (j, i) in the current matrix is given by

$$\mathbf{P}_{j,i}^T = \begin{bmatrix} 1 & & & & & & & & \\ & \ddots & & & & & & & \\ & & 1 & & & & & & \\ & & & \cos\theta & & \sin\theta & & & \text{—} \ i\text{th row} \\ & & & & 1 & & & & \\ & & & & & \ddots & & & \\ & & & & & & 1 & & \\ & & & -\sin\theta & & \cos\theta & & & \text{—} \ j\text{th row} \\ & & & & & & & 1 & \\ & & & & & & & & \ddots \\ & & & & & & & & & 1 \end{bmatrix}$$

where

$$\sin\theta = \frac{\bar{k}_{ji}}{(\bar{k}_{ii}^2 + \bar{k}_{ji}^2)^{1/2}}; \qquad \cos\theta = \frac{\bar{k}_{ii}}{(\bar{k}_{ii}^2 + \bar{k}_{ji}^2)^{1/2}}$$

and the bar indicates that the elements of the current matrix are used.

Proceeding as in (11.108), we obtain for element (2, 1),

$$\sin\theta = -0.6247; \qquad \cos\theta = 0.7809$$

$$\mathbf{P}_{2,1} = \begin{bmatrix} 0.7809 & 0.6247 & 0 & 0 \\ -0.6247 & 0.7809 & 0 & 0 \\ 0 & 0 & 1 & 0 \\ 0 & 0 & 0 & 1 \end{bmatrix}$$

and

$$\mathbf{P}_{2,1}^T \mathbf{K} = \begin{bmatrix} 6.403 & -6.872 & 3.280 & -0.6247 \\ 0 & 2.186 & -2.499 & 0.7809 \\ 1 & -4 & 6 & -4 \\ 0 & 1 & -4 & 5 \end{bmatrix}$$

Next we zero element (3, 1),

$$\mathbf{P}_{3,1}^T \mathbf{P}_{2,1}^T \mathbf{K} = \begin{bmatrix} 6.481 & -7.407 & 4.166 & -1.234 \\ 0 & 2.186 & -2.499 & 0.7809 \\ 0 & -2.892 & 5.422 & -3.856 \\ 0 & 1 & -4 & 5 \end{bmatrix}$$

Noting that element (4, 1) is zero already, we continue with the factorization by zeroing element (3, 2),

$$\mathbf{P}_{3,2}^T\mathbf{P}_{3,1}^T\mathbf{P}_{2,1}^T\mathbf{K} = \begin{bmatrix} 6.481 & -7.407 & 4.166 & -1.234 \\ 0 & 3.625 & -5.832 & 3.546 \\ 0 & 0 & 1.277 & -1.703 \\ 0 & 1 & -4 & 5 \end{bmatrix}$$

Proceeding in the same manner, we obtain

$$\mathbf{P}_{4,2}^T\mathbf{P}_{3,2}^T\mathbf{P}_{3,1}^T\mathbf{P}_{2,1}^T\mathbf{K} = \begin{bmatrix} 6.481 & -7.407 & 4.166 & -1.234 \\ 0 & 3.761 & -6.686 & 4.748 \\ 0 & 0 & 1.277 & -1.703 \\ 0 & 0 & -2.305 & 3.877 \end{bmatrix}$$

and finally, $\mathbf{R}_1 = \mathbf{P}_{4,3}^T\mathbf{P}_{4,2}^T\mathbf{P}_{3,2}^T\mathbf{P}_{3,1}^T\mathbf{P}_{2,1}^T\mathbf{K}$

$$\mathbf{R}_1 = \begin{bmatrix} 6.481 & -7.407 & 4.166 & -1.234 \\ 0 & 3.761 & -6.686 & 4.748 \\ 0 & 0 & 2.635 & -4.216 \\ 0 & 0 & 0 & 0.3892 \end{bmatrix}$$

Also, we have $\mathbf{Q}_1 = \mathbf{P}_{2,1}\mathbf{P}_{3,1}\mathbf{P}_{3,2}\mathbf{P}_{4,2}\mathbf{P}_{4,3}$

$$\mathbf{Q}_1 = \begin{bmatrix} 0.7715 & 0.4558 & 0.3162 & 0.3114 \\ -0.6172 & 0.3799 & 0.4216 & 0.5449 \\ 0.1543 & -0.7597 & 0.1054 & 0.6228 \\ 0 & 0.2659 & -0.8433 & 0.4671 \end{bmatrix}$$

The first iteration step of QR is completed by calculating

$$\mathbf{K}_2 = \mathbf{R}_1\mathbf{Q}_1$$

to obtain $$\mathbf{K}_2 = \begin{bmatrix} 10.21 & -3.353 & 0.4066 & 0 \\ -3.353 & 7.771 & -3.123 & 0.1035 \\ 0.4066 & -3.123 & 3.833 & -0.3282 \\ 0 & 0.1035 & -0.3282 & 0.1818 \end{bmatrix}$$

The following results are obtained in the next steps of QR. For $k = 2$:

$$\mathbf{R}_2 = \begin{bmatrix} 10.76 & -5.723 & 1.504 & -0.0446 \\ 0 & 6.974 & -4.163 & 0.2284 \\ 0 & 0 & 2.265 & -0.2752 \\ 0 & 0 & 0 & 0.1471 \end{bmatrix}$$

$$\mathbf{Q}_1\mathbf{Q}_2 = \begin{bmatrix} 0.6024 & 0.4943 & 0.5084 & 0.3665 \\ -0.6885 & -0.0257 & 0.4099 & 0.5978 \\ 0.3873 & -0.6409 & -0.2715 & 0.6046 \\ -0.1147 & 0.5867 & 0.7070 & 0.3779 \end{bmatrix}$$

$$\mathbf{K}_3 = \mathbf{R}_2\mathbf{Q}_2 = \begin{bmatrix} 12.05 & -2.331 & 0.0856 & 0 \\ -2.331 & 7.726 & -0.9483 & 0.0022 \\ 0.0856 & -0.9483 & 2.0740 & -0.0173 \\ 0 & 0.0022 & -0.0173 & 0.1461 \end{bmatrix}$$

For $k = 3$:

$$\mathbf{R}_3 = \begin{bmatrix} 12.28 & -3.761 & 0.2785 & -0.0005 \\ 0 & 7.202 & -1.173 & 0.0044 \\ 0 & 0 & 1.938 & -0.0182 \\ 0 & 0 & 0 & 0.1459 \end{bmatrix}$$

$$\mathbf{Q}_1\mathbf{Q}_2\mathbf{Q}_3 = \begin{bmatrix} 0.5011 & 0.5302 & 0.5743 & 0.3713 \\ -0.6682 & -0.2076 & 0.3860 & 0.6012 \\ 0.5000 & -0.5157 & -0.3492 & 0.6018 \\ -0.2290 & 0.6401 & -0.6319 & 0.3722 \end{bmatrix}$$

$$\mathbf{K}_4 = \mathbf{R}_3\mathbf{Q}_3 = \begin{bmatrix} 12.77 & -1.375 & 0.0135 & 0 \\ -1.375 & 7.162 & -0.2481 & 0 \\ 0.0135 & -0.2481 & 1.922 & -0.0013 \\ 0 & 0 & -0.0013 & 0.1459 \end{bmatrix}$$

And after nine iterations, we have

$$\mathbf{R}_9 = \begin{bmatrix} 13.09 & -0.0869 & 0 & 0 \\ 0 & 6.854 & -0.0005 & 0 \\ 0 & 0 & 1.910 & 0 \\ 0 & 0 & 0 & 0.1459 \end{bmatrix}$$

$$\mathbf{Q}_1\mathbf{Q}_2\mathbf{Q}_3\mathbf{Q}_4\mathbf{Q}_5\mathbf{Q}_6\mathbf{Q}_7\mathbf{Q}_8\mathbf{Q}_9 = \begin{bmatrix} 0.3746 & 0.5997 & 0.6015 & 0.3717 \\ -0.6033 & -0.3689 & 0.3718 & 0.6015 \\ 0.5997 & -0.3746 & -0.3717 & 0.6015 \\ -0.3689 & 0.6033 & -0.6015 & 0.3718 \end{bmatrix}$$

$$\mathbf{K}_{10} = \begin{bmatrix} 13.09 & -0.0298 & 0 & 0 \\ -0.0298 & 6.8542 & -0.0001 & 0 \\ 0 & -0.0001 & 1.910 & 0 \\ 0 & 0 & 0 & 0.1459 \end{bmatrix}$$

Thus we have, after nine steps of QR iteration,

$$\lambda_1 \doteq 0.1459; \qquad \boldsymbol{\phi}_1 \doteq \begin{bmatrix} 0.3717 \\ 0.6015 \\ 0.6015 \\ 0.3718 \end{bmatrix}$$

$$\lambda_2 \doteq 1.910; \qquad \boldsymbol{\phi}_2 \doteq \begin{bmatrix} 0.6015 \\ 0.3718 \\ -0.3717 \\ -0.6015 \end{bmatrix}$$

$$\lambda_3 \doteq 6.854; \qquad \boldsymbol{\phi}_3 \doteq \begin{bmatrix} 0.5997 \\ -0.3689 \\ -0.3746 \\ 0.6033 \end{bmatrix}$$

$$\lambda_4 \doteq 13.09; \qquad \boldsymbol{\phi}_4 \doteq \begin{bmatrix} 0.3746 \\ -0.6033 \\ 0.5997 \\ -0.3689 \end{bmatrix}$$

These results can be compared with the results obtained using the Jacobi method in Example 11.9. It is interesting to note that in the above solution, λ_1 and $\boldsymbol{\phi}_1$ converged first and indeed were well predicted after only three QR iterations. This is a consequence of the fact that QR iteration is closely related to inverse iteration (see Example 11.16), in which the lowest eigenvalues and corresponding vectors converge first.

Although the QR iteration may look similar to the Jacobi solution procedure, the method is, in fact, completely different. This may be observed by studying the convergence characteristics of the QR solution procedure because it is then found that *the QR method is intimately related to inverse iteration*. In Example 11.16 we compare QR and inverse iteration, where it is assumed that the matrix $\mathbf{K}$ is nonsingular. As we may recall, this assumption is necessary for inverse iteration and can always be satisfied by using a shift (see Section 10.2.3).

EXAMPLE 11.16:   Show the theoretical relationship between QR and inverse iteration.

In the QR method, we obtain after l steps of iteration,

$$\mathbf{K}_{l+1} = \mathbf{Q}_l^T \mathbf{Q}_{l-1}^T \ldots \mathbf{Q}_1^T \mathbf{K}_1 \mathbf{Q}_1 \ldots \mathbf{Q}_{l-1} \mathbf{Q}_l$$

or

$$\mathbf{K}_{l+1} = \mathbf{P}_l^T \mathbf{K}_1 \mathbf{P}_l; \qquad \mathbf{P}_l = \mathbf{Q}_1 \ldots \mathbf{Q}_l$$

Let us define

$$\mathbf{S}_l = \mathbf{R}_l \ldots \mathbf{R}_1$$

Then we have

$$\mathbf{P}_l \mathbf{S}_l = \mathbf{P}_{l-1} \mathbf{Q}_l \mathbf{R}_l \mathbf{S}_{l-1}$$

$$= \mathbf{P}_{l-1} \mathbf{K}_l \mathbf{S}_{l-1}$$

If we note that

$$\mathbf{K}_1 \mathbf{P}_{l-1} = \mathbf{P}_{l-1} \mathbf{K}_l$$

we get

$$\mathbf{P}_l \mathbf{S}_l = \mathbf{K}_1 \mathbf{P}_{l-1} \mathbf{S}_{l-1}$$

In an analogous manner we obtain $\mathbf{P}_{l-1} \mathbf{S}_{l-1} = \mathbf{K}_1 \mathbf{P}_{l-2} \mathbf{S}_{l-2}$, and so on, and thus conclude that

$$\mathbf{P}_l \mathbf{S}_l = \mathbf{K}^l \tag{a}$$

Assuming that $\mathbf{K}$ is nonsingular, we have from (a),

$$\mathbf{P}_l = \mathbf{K}^{-l} \mathbf{S}_l^T$$

or equating columns on both sides,

$$\mathbf{P}_l \mathbf{E} = \mathbf{K}^{-l} \mathbf{S}_l^T \mathbf{E} \tag{b}$$

where $\mathbf{E}$ consists of the last p columns of $\mathbf{I}$.

Consider now inverse iteration on p vectors. This iteration process can be written

$$\mathbf{K} \mathbf{X}_k = \mathbf{X}_{k-1} \mathbf{L}_k; \qquad k = 1, 2, \ldots$$

where $\mathbf{L}_k$ is a lower triangular matrix chosen so that $\mathbf{X}_k^T \mathbf{X}_k = \mathbf{I}$. The matrix $\mathbf{L}_k$ can be determined using the Gram-Schmidt process on the iteration vectors. Hence, after l steps we have

$$\mathbf{X}_l = \mathbf{K}^{-l} \mathbf{X}_0 \overline{\mathbf{L}}_l; \qquad \overline{\mathbf{L}}_l = \mathbf{L}_1 \ldots \mathbf{L}_l \tag{c}$$

On the other hand, the relation in (b) can be written

$$\mathbf{P}_l\mathbf{E} = \mathbf{K}^{-l}\mathbf{E}\bar{\mathbf{S}}_l \qquad (d)$$

where $\bar{\mathbf{S}}_l$ consists of the last p columns and rows of $\mathbf{S}_l^T$. Using $\mathbf{X}_l^T\mathbf{X}_l = \mathbf{I}$ and $(\mathbf{P}_l\mathbf{E})^T(\mathbf{P}_l\mathbf{E}) = \mathbf{I}$, we obtain from (c) and (d), respectively,

$$\bar{\mathbf{L}}_l^{-T}\bar{\mathbf{L}}_l^{-1} = \mathbf{X}_0^T\mathbf{K}^{-2l}\mathbf{X}_0 \qquad (e)$$

and

$$\bar{\mathbf{S}}_l^{-T}\bar{\mathbf{S}}_l^{-1} = \mathbf{E}^T\mathbf{K}^{-2l}\mathbf{E} \qquad (f)$$

The equations in (e) and (f) can now be used to show the relationship between inverse iteration and the QR solution procedure. Namely, if we choose $\mathbf{X}_0 = \mathbf{E}$, we find from (e) and (f) that $\bar{\mathbf{L}}_l = \bar{\mathbf{S}}_l$ because these matrices are the Cholesky factors of the same positive definite matrix. However, referring then to (c) and (d), we can conclude that the inverse iteration yields vectors $\mathbf{X}_l$ which are the last p columns in $\mathbf{P}_l$ of the QR solution.

The relationship between the QR solution method and simple inverse iteration suggests that an acceleration of convergence in the QR iteration described in (11.110) and (11.111) should be possible. This is indeed the case and, in practice, QR iteration is used with shifting; i.e., instead of (11.110) and (11.111), the following decompositions are employed:

$$\mathbf{K}_k - \mu_k\mathbf{I} = \mathbf{Q}_k\mathbf{R}_k \qquad (11.112)$$

$$\mathbf{K}_{k+1} = \mathbf{R}_k\mathbf{Q}_k + \mu_k\mathbf{I} \qquad (11.113)$$

where then, as before,

$$\mathbf{K}_{k+1} \to \boldsymbol{\Lambda} \quad \text{and} \quad \mathbf{Q}_1 \ldots \mathbf{Q}_{k-1}\mathbf{Q}_k \to \boldsymbol{\Phi} \qquad \text{as } k \to \infty$$

However, *if μ_k is element (n, n) of $\mathbf{K}_k$, the QR iteration corresponds to Rayleigh quotient iteration, ultimately giving cubic convergence.*

As pointed out earlier, in practice the QR iteration should be applied after reduction of $\mathbf{K}$ to tridiagonal form using Householder transformation matrices; i.e., the QR solution should be applied to the matrix $\mathbf{K}_{n-1}$ in (11.95), which we now call $\mathbf{T}_1$. When the matrix is tridiagonal, the QR process is very effective; i.e., by experience about $9n^2$ operations are required for solution of all eigenvalues. It is also not necessary to formally go through the procedure discussed above and demonstrated in Example 11.15; instead, we may use explicit formulas that relate the elements in $\mathbf{T}_{k+1}$ to the elements of $\mathbf{T}_k$, $k = 1, 2, \ldots$ (see J. H. Wilkinson [A])

Calculation of eigenvectors. The eigenvalues are generally calculated to full machine precision because convergence is very rapid in the QR iteration with shifting. Once the eigenvalues have been evaluated very accurately, we calculate only the required eigenvectors of the tridiagonal matrix $\mathbf{T}_1$ by simple inverse iteration with shifts equal to the corresponding eigenvalues. Two steps of inverse iteration starting with a full unit vector are usually sufficient. The eigenvectors of $\mathbf{T}_1$ then need to be transformed with the Householder transformations used to obtain the eigenvectors of $\mathbf{K}$; i.e., denoting the ith eigenvector of $\mathbf{T}_1$ by $\boldsymbol{\psi}_i$, we have, using the transformation matrices $\mathbf{P}_k$ in (11.95),

$$\boldsymbol{\phi}_i = \mathbf{P}_1\mathbf{P}_2 \ldots \mathbf{P}_{n-2}\boldsymbol{\psi}_i \qquad (11.114)$$

With the three basic steps of the HQRI solution method described above, Table 11.2 summarizes the complete procedure and presents the high-speed storage needed and the

TABLE 11.2 *Summary of Householder-QR-inverse iteration solution*

Operation	Calculation	Number of operations	Required storage
Householder transformation	$\mathbf{K}_{k+1} = \mathbf{P}_k^T \mathbf{K}_k \mathbf{P}_k$; $k = 1, 2, \ldots, n-2$; $\mathbf{K}_1 = \mathbf{K}$	$\frac{2}{3}n^3 + \frac{3}{2}n^2$	
QR iterations	$\mathbf{T}_{k+1} = \mathbf{Q}_k^T \mathbf{T}_k \mathbf{Q}_k$; $k = 1, 2, \ldots$ $\mathbf{T}_1 = \mathbf{K}_{n-1}$	$9n^2$	Using symmetry of matrix
Calculation of p eigenvectors	$(\mathbf{K}_{n-1} - \lambda_i \mathbf{I})\mathbf{x}_i^{(k+1)} = \mathbf{x}_i^{(k)}$; $k = 1, 2$; $i = 1, 2, \ldots, p$	$10pn$	$\frac{n}{2}(n+1) + 6n$
Transformation of eigenvectors	$\boldsymbol{\phi}_i = \mathbf{P}_1 \ldots \mathbf{P}_{n-2} \mathbf{x}_i^{(3)}$; $i = 1, 2, \ldots, p$	$pn(n-1)$	
Total for all eigenvalues and p eigenvectors		$\frac{2}{3}n^3 + \frac{21}{2}n^2 + pn^2 + 9pn$	

number of operations required. It is noted that the greater part of the total number of operations is used for the Householder transformations in (11.95) and, if many eigenvectors need to be calculated, for the eigenvector transformations in (11.114). Therefore, it is seen that the calculation of the eigenvalues of $\mathbf{T}_1$ is not very expensive, but the preparation of $\mathbf{K}$ in a form that can be used effectively for the iteration process requires most of the numerical effort.

It should be noted that Table 11.2 does not include the operations required for transforming a generalized eigenproblem into a standard form. If this transformation is carried out, the eigenvectors calculated in Table 11.2 must also be transformed to the eigenvectors of the generalized eigenproblem as discussed in Section 10.2.5.

11.3.4 Exercises

11.5. Use the Jacobi method to calculate the eigenvalues and eigenvectors of the problems

$$\begin{bmatrix} 1 & -1 \\ -1 & 1 \end{bmatrix} \boldsymbol{\phi} = \lambda \begin{bmatrix} 1 & 0 \\ 0 & 1 \end{bmatrix} \boldsymbol{\phi}$$

and

$$\begin{bmatrix} 2 & -1 \\ -1 & 1 \end{bmatrix} \boldsymbol{\phi} = \lambda \begin{bmatrix} 1 & 0 \\ 0 & 2 \end{bmatrix} \boldsymbol{\phi}$$

11.6. Use the Jacobi method to calculate the eigenvalues and eigenvectors of the eigenproblem in Exercise 10.3.

11.7. Derive in detail the values for α and γ given in (11.89).

11.8. Perform the QR iteration on the eigenvalue problem

$$\begin{bmatrix} 2 & -1 \\ -1 & 1 \end{bmatrix} \boldsymbol{\phi} = \lambda \begin{bmatrix} 1 & 0 \\ 0 & 2 \end{bmatrix} \boldsymbol{\phi}$$

Note: Here you need to first transform the eigenproblem into a standard form.

11.4 POLYNOMIAL ITERATIONS AND STURM SEQUENCE TECHNIQUES

The close relationship between the calculation of the zeros of a polynomial and the evaluation of eigenvalues has been discussed in Section 10.2.2. Namely, defining the characteristic polynomial $p(\lambda)$, where

$$p(\lambda) = \det(\mathbf{K} - \lambda\mathbf{M}) \tag{11.6}$$

the zeros of $p(\lambda)$ are the eigenvalues of the eigenproblem $\mathbf{K}\boldsymbol{\phi} = \lambda\mathbf{M}\boldsymbol{\phi}$. To calculate the eigenvalues, we therefore may operate on $p(\lambda)$ to extract the zeros of the polynomial, and basically there are two strategies—explicit and implicit evaluation procedures—both of which may use the same basic iteration schemes.

In the discussion of the polynomial iteration schemes, we assume that the solution is carried out directly using $\mathbf{K}$ and $\mathbf{M}$ of the finite element assemblage, i.e., without transforming the problem into a different form. For example, if $\mathbf{M}$ is the identity matrix, we could transform $\mathbf{K}$ first into tridiagonal form as is done in the HQRI solution (see Section 11.3.3). In case $\mathbf{M} \neq \mathbf{I}$, we would need to transform the generalized eigenproblem into a standard form (see Section 10.2.5) before the Householder reduction to a tridiagonal matrix could be performed. Whichever problem we finally consider in the iterative solution of the required eigenvalues, the solution strategy would not be changed. However, if only a few eigenvalues are to be calculated, the direct solution using $\mathbf{K}$ and $\mathbf{M}$ is nearly always most effective.

In conjunction with a polynomial iteration method, it is natural and can be effective to use the Sturm sequence property discussed in Section 10.2.2. We show in this section how this property can be employed.

It should be noted that using a polynomial iteration or Sturm sequence method, only the eigenvalues are calculated. The corresponding eigenvectors can then be obtained effectively by using inverse iteration with shifting; i.e., each required eigenvector is obtained by inverse iteration at a shift equal to the corresponding eigenvalue.

These techniques—implicit polynomial iterations, Sturm sequence checks, and vector iterations—have been combined in a determinant search algorithm, efficient for small banded systems (see K. J. Bathe [A] and K. J. Bathe and E. L. Wilson [C].

11.4.1 Explicit Polynomial Iteration

In the explicit polynomial iteration methods, the first step is to write $p(\lambda)$ in the form

$$p(\lambda) = a_0 + a_1\lambda + a_2\lambda^2 + \cdots + a_n\lambda^n \tag{11.115}$$

and evaluate the polynomial coefficients $a_0, a_1, \ldots, a_n$. The second step is to calculate the roots of the polynomial. We demonstrate the procedure by means of an example.

> **EXAMPLE 11.17:** Establish the coefficients of the characteristic polynomial of the problem $\mathbf{K}\boldsymbol{\phi} = \lambda\mathbf{M}\boldsymbol{\phi}$, where $\mathbf{K}$ and $\mathbf{M}$ are the matrices used in Example 11.4.
>
> The problem is to evaluate the expression
>
> $$p(\lambda) = \det \begin{bmatrix} 5 - 2\lambda & -4 & 1 & 0 \\ -4 & 6 - 2\lambda & -4 & 1 \\ 1 & -4 & 6 - \lambda & -4 \\ 0 & 1 & -4 & 5 - \lambda \end{bmatrix}$$

Following the rules given in Section 2.2 for the evaluation of a determinant, we obtain

$$p(\lambda) = (5 - 2\lambda) \det \begin{bmatrix} 6 - 2\lambda & -4 & 1 \\ -4 & 6 - \lambda & -4 \\ 1 & -4 & 5 - \lambda \end{bmatrix}$$

$$+ (4) \det \begin{bmatrix} -4 & -4 & 1 \\ 1 & 6 - \lambda & -4 \\ 0 & -4 & 5 - \lambda \end{bmatrix} + (1) \det \begin{bmatrix} -4 & 6 - 2\lambda & 1 \\ 1 & -4 & -4 \\ 0 & 1 & 5 - \lambda \end{bmatrix}$$

Hence,
$$p(\lambda) = (5 - 2\lambda)\{(6 - 2\lambda)[(6 - \lambda)(5 - \lambda) - 16] \\ + 4[-4(5 - \lambda) + 4] + 16 - (6 - \lambda)\}$$
$$+ 4\{-4[(6 - \lambda)(5 - \lambda) - 16] + 4(5 - \lambda) - 4\}$$
$$+ \{-4[(-4)(5 - \lambda) + 4] - (6 - 2\lambda)(5 - \lambda) + 1\}$$

and the expression finally reduces to

$$p(\lambda) = 4\lambda^4 - 66\lambda^3 + 276\lambda^2 - 285\lambda + 25$$

In the general case when n is large, we cannot evaluate the polynomial coefficients as easily as in this example. The expansion of the determinant would require about n-factorial operations, which are far too many operations to make the method practical. However, other procedures have been developed; for example, the Newton identities may be used (see, for example, C. E. Fröberg [A]). Once the coefficients have been evaluated, it is necessary to employ a standard polynomial root finder, using, for example, a Newton iteration or secant iteration to evaluate the required eigenvalues.

Although the procedure seems most natural to use, one difficulty has caused the method to be almost completely abandoned for the solution of eigenvalue problems. A basic defect of the method is that small errors in the coefficients $a_0, \ldots, a_n$ cause large errors in the roots of the polynomial. But small errors are almost unavoidable, owing to round-off in the computer. Therefore, an explicit evaluation of the coefficients $a_0, \ldots, a_n$ from $\mathbf{K}$ and $\mathbf{M}$ with subsequent solution of the required eigenvalues is not effective in general analysis.

11.4.2 Implicit Polynomial Iteration

In an implicit polynomial iteration solution we evaluate the value of $p(\lambda)$ directly without calculating first the coefficients $a_0, \ldots, a_n$ in (11.115). The value of $p(\lambda)$ can be obtained effectively by decomposing $\mathbf{K} - \lambda\mathbf{M}$ into a lower-unit triangular matrix $\mathbf{L}$ and an upper triangular matrix $\mathbf{S}$; i.e., we have

$$\mathbf{K} - \lambda\mathbf{M} = \mathbf{LS} \tag{11.116}$$

where then
$$\det(\mathbf{K} - \lambda\mathbf{M}) = \prod_{i=1}^{n} s_{ii} \tag{11.117}$$

The decomposition of $\mathbf{K} - \lambda\mathbf{M}$ is obtained as discussed in Section 8.2, but, as pointed out in Section 8.2.5, may require interchanges when $\lambda > \lambda_1$. When row and corresponding column interchanges are carried out, the coefficient matrix remains symmetric and, in effect, the degree of freedom numbering has then merely been rearranged. In other words, the stiffness and mass matrices of the finite element system actually used correspond to a different degree of freedom numbering than originally specified. On the other hand, if only row interchanges are employed, a nonsymmetric coefficient matrix is obtained. However, in either case it is important to note that the required row and column interchanges could have been carried out prior to the Gauss elimination process to obtain an "effective" coefficient matrix $\mathbf{K} - \lambda\mathbf{M}$ that is considered in (11.116), and no more interchanges would then be needed. Each row or column interchange introduced merely effects a change in sign of the determinant. In practice, we do not know the actual row and column interchanges that will be required, but the realization that all interchanges could have been carried out prior to the factorization shows that we can always use the Gauss elimination procedure given in (8.10) to (8.14), provided that we admit that the "effective" initial coefficient matrix may be nonsymmetric. Consider the following example.

EXAMPLE 11.18:   Use Gauss elimination to evaluate $p(\lambda) = \det(\mathbf{K} - \lambda\mathbf{M})$, where

$$\mathbf{K} = \begin{bmatrix} 2 & -1 & 0 \\ -1 & 4 & -1 \\ 0 & -1 & 2 \end{bmatrix}; \qquad \mathbf{M} = \begin{bmatrix} 1 & & \\ & 1 & \\ & & \frac{1}{2} \end{bmatrix}; \qquad \lambda = 2$$

In this case we have
$$\mathbf{K} - \lambda\mathbf{M} = \begin{bmatrix} 0 & -1 & 0 \\ -1 & 2 & -1 \\ 0 & -1 & 1 \end{bmatrix}$$

Since the first diagonal element is zero, we need to use interchanges. Assume that we interchange the first and second rows (and not the corresponding columns); then we effectively factorize $\overline{\mathbf{K}} - \lambda\overline{\mathbf{M}}$, where

$$\overline{\mathbf{K}} = \begin{bmatrix} -1 & 4 & -1 \\ 2 & -1 & 0 \\ 0 & -1 & 2 \end{bmatrix}; \qquad \overline{\mathbf{M}} = \begin{bmatrix} 0 & 1 & 0 \\ 1 & 0 & 0 \\ 0 & 0 & \frac{1}{2} \end{bmatrix}$$

The factorization of $\overline{\mathbf{K}} - \lambda\overline{\mathbf{M}}$ is now obtained in the usual way (see Examples 10.4 and 10.5),

$$\overline{\mathbf{K}} - \lambda\overline{\mathbf{M}} = \begin{bmatrix} 1 & & \\ 0 & 1 & \\ 0 & 1 & 1 \end{bmatrix}\begin{bmatrix} -1 & 2 & -1 \\ & -1 & 0 \\ & & 1 \end{bmatrix}$$

Hence,
$$\det(\overline{\mathbf{K}} - \lambda\overline{\mathbf{M}}) = (-1)(-1)(1) = 1$$

and taking account of the fact that the row interchange has changed the sign of the determinant (see Section 2.2), we have

$$\det(\mathbf{K} - \lambda\mathbf{M}) = -1$$

As pointed out above, if in the Gauss elimination no interchanges have been carried out or each row interchange was accompanied by a corresponding column interchange, the coefficient matrix $\mathbf{K} - \lambda\mathbf{M}$ in (11.116) is symmetric. In this case we have $\mathbf{S} = \mathbf{DL}^T$, as in Section 8.2.2, and hence,

$$\det(\mathbf{K} - \lambda\mathbf{M}) = \prod_{i=1}^{n} d_{ii} \qquad (11.118)$$

In the determinant search solution method (see K. J. Bathe [A] and K. J. Bathe and E. L. Wilson [C]), we use a factorization only if it can be completed without interchanges and therefore always employ (11.118). In this case, one polynomial evaluation requires about $\frac{1}{2}nm_K^2$ operations, where n is the order of $\mathbf{K}$ and $\mathbf{M}$ and m_K is the half-bandwidth of $\mathbf{K}$.

With a method available for the evaluation of $p(\lambda)$, we can now employ a number of iteration schemes to calculate a root of the polynomial. One commonly used simple technique is the secant method, in which a linear interpolation is employed; i.e., let $\mu_{k-1} < \mu_k$, then we iterate using

$$\mu_{k+1} = \mu_k - \frac{p(\mu_k)}{p(\mu_k) - p(\mu_{k-1})}(\mu_k - \mu_{k-1}) \qquad (11.119)$$

where μ_k is the kth iterate (see Fig. 11.3). We may note that the secant method in (11.119) is an approximation to the Newton iteration,

$$\mu_{k+1} = \mu_k - \frac{p(\mu_k)}{p'(\mu_k)} \qquad (11.120)$$

where $p'(\mu_k)$ is approximated using

$$p'(\mu_k) \doteq \frac{p(\mu_k) - p(\mu_{k-1})}{\mu_k - \mu_{k-1}} \qquad (11.121)$$

An actual scheme for accurately evaluating $p'(\mu_k)$ has been tested but was not found to be effective (see K. J. Bathe [A]).

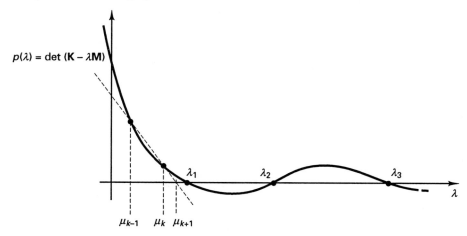

Figure 11.3   Secant iteration for calculation of λ_1

Another technique commonly used in the solution of complex eigenvalue problems is Muller's method, in which case a quadratic interpolation is employed. A disadvantage of Muller's method in the solution of $\mathbf{K\phi} = \lambda\mathbf{M\phi}$ is that although the starting values μ_k, μ_{k-1}, and μ_{k-2} are real, the calculated value μ_{k+1} may be complex.

It should be noted that so far we have not discussed to which eigenvalue any one of the iteration strategies converges. This depends on the starting iteration values. Using μ_{k-1} and μ_k both smaller than λ_1, the Newton and secant iterations converge montonically to λ_1, as shown in Fig. 11.3, and the ultimate order of convergence is quadratic and linear, respectively. In effect, convergence is achieved in the iterations because $p''(\lambda) > 0$ for

$\lambda < \lambda_1$, which is always the case for any order and bandwidth of $\mathbf{K}$ and $\mathbf{M}$. However, convergence cannot be guaranteed for arbitrary starting values μ_{k-1} and μ_k.

In an actual solution scheme, it is effective to first calculate λ_1 and then repeat the algorithm on the characteristic polynomial deflated by λ_1. This approach can be used to calculate the smallest eigenvalues in succession from λ_1 to the required value λ_p (see K. J. Bathe [A], K. J. Bathe and E. L. Wilson [C], and Exercise 11.9).

Consider the following example of a secant iteration.

EXAMPLE 11.19: Use the secant iteration to calculate λ_1 in the eigenproblem $\mathbf{K}\boldsymbol{\phi} = \lambda\mathbf{M}\boldsymbol{\phi}$, where

$$\mathbf{K} = \begin{bmatrix} 2 & -1 & 0 \\ -1 & 4 & -1 \\ 0 & -1 & 2 \end{bmatrix}; \qquad \mathbf{M} = \begin{bmatrix} \frac{1}{2} & & \\ & 1 & \\ & & \frac{1}{2} \end{bmatrix}$$

For the secant iteration we need two starting values for μ_1 and μ_2 that are lower bounds to λ_1. Let $\mu_1 = -1$ and $\mu_2 = 0$. Then we have

$$p(-1) = \det \begin{bmatrix} \frac{5}{2} & -1 & 0 \\ -1 & 5 & -1 \\ 0 & -1 & \frac{5}{2} \end{bmatrix}$$

$$= \det \begin{bmatrix} 1 & & \\ -\frac{2}{5} & 1 & \\ 0 & -\frac{5}{23} & 1 \end{bmatrix} \begin{bmatrix} \frac{5}{2} & & \\ & \frac{23}{5} & \\ & & \frac{105}{46} \end{bmatrix} \begin{bmatrix} 1 & -\frac{2}{5} & 0 \\ & 1 & -\frac{5}{23} \\ & & 1 \end{bmatrix}$$

Hence, $$p(-1) = (\tfrac{5}{2})(\tfrac{23}{5})(\tfrac{105}{46}) = 26.25$$

Similarly, $$p(0) = \det \begin{bmatrix} 2 & -1 & 0 \\ -1 & 4 & -1 \\ 0 & -1 & 2 \end{bmatrix} = 12$$

Now using (11.119), we obtain as the next shift,

$$\mu_3 = 0 - \frac{12}{12 - 26.25}[0 - (-1)]$$

Hence, $$\mu_3 = 0.8421$$

Continuing in the same way, we obtain

$$p(0.8421) = 4.7150$$
$$\mu_4 = 1.3871$$
$$p(1.3871) = 1.8467$$
$$\mu_5 = 1.7380$$
$$p(1.7380) = 0.63136$$
$$\mu_6 = 1.9203$$
$$p(1.9203) = 0.16899$$
$$\mu_7 = 1.9870$$

$$p(1.9870) = 0.026347$$

$$\mu_8 = 1.9993$$

Hence, after six iterations we have as an approximation to λ_1, $\lambda_1 \doteq 1.9993$.

11.4.3 Iteration Based on the Sturm Sequence Property

In Section 10.2.2 we discussed the Sturm sequence property of the characteristic polynomials of the problem $\mathbf{K}\boldsymbol{\phi} = \lambda \mathbf{M}\boldsymbol{\phi}$ and of its associated constraint problems. The main result was the following. Assume that for a shift μ_k, the Gauss factorization of $\mathbf{K} - \mu_k \mathbf{M}$ into $\mathbf{LDL}^T$ can be obtained. Then the number of negative elements in $\mathbf{D}$ is equal to the number of eigenvalues smaller than μ_k. This result can be used directly to construct an algorithm for the calculation of eigenvalues and corresponding eigenvectors. As in the discussion of the polynomial iteration methods, we assume in the following that the solution is performed directly using $\mathbf{K}$ and $\mathbf{M}$, although the same strategies could be used after the generalized eigenproblem has been transformed into a different form. Also, as in Section 11.4.2, the solution method to be presented solves only for the eigenvalues, and the corresponding eigenvectors would be calculated using inverse iteration with shifting (see Section 11.2.3).

Consider that we want to solve for all eigenvalues between λ_l and λ_u, where λ_l and λ_u are the lower and upper limits, respectively. For example, we may have a case such as depicted in Fig. 11.4 or λ_l may be zero, in which case we would need to solve for all eigenvalues up to the value λ_u. The basis of the solution procedure is the triangular factorization of $\mathbf{K} - \mu_k \mathbf{M}$, where μ_k is selected in such way as to obtain from the positive or negative signs of the diagonal elements in the factorization meaningful information about the unknown and required eigenvalues. The following solution procedure, known as the *bisection method,* may be used (refer to Fig. 11.4 for a typical example):

1. Factorize $\mathbf{K} - \lambda_l \mathbf{M}$ and hence find how many eigenvalues, say q_l, are smaller than λ_l.
2. Apply the Sturm sequence check at $\mathbf{K} - \lambda_u \mathbf{M}$ and hence find how many eigenvalues, say q_u, are smaller than λ_u, There are thus $q_u - q_l$ eigenvalues between λ_u and λ_l.

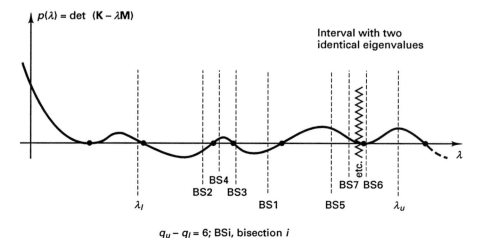

$q_u - q_l = 6$; BSi, bisection i

Figure 11.4   Use of Sturm sequence property to isolate eigenvalues

3. Use a simple scheme of bisection to identify intervals in which the individual eigenvalues lie. In this process, those intervals in which more than one eigenvalue are known to lie are successively bisected and the Sturm sequence check is carried out until all eigenvalues are isolated.

4. Calculate the eigenvalues to the accuracy required and then obtain the corresponding eigenvectors by inverse iteration.

To obtain the eigenvalues accurately in step 4, the method of bisection is abandoned and a more efficient procedure is generally used. For example, the secant iteration presented in Section 11.4.2 can be employed once the eigenvalues have been isolated (see Example 11.20).

The above technique for calculating the required eigenvalues is straightforward. However, the method can be quite inefficient because each iteration in step 3 requires a triangular factorization and because many iterations may be needed. The number of iterations can be particularly high when multiple eigenvalues (see Fig. 11.4) or eigenvalue clusters must be evaluated, in which case additional strategies to accelerate the process must be included. In general, the method is effective if only a few factorizations are needed to identify intervals of individual eigenvalues and the smallest required eigenvalue is much larger than λ_1.

EXAMPLE 11.20:   Use the bisection method followed by secant iteration to calculate λ_2 in the problem $\mathbf{K}\boldsymbol{\phi} = \lambda\mathbf{M}\boldsymbol{\phi}$, where

$$\mathbf{K} = \begin{bmatrix} 2 & -1 & 0 \\ -1 & 4 & -1 \\ 0 & -1 & 2 \end{bmatrix}; \qquad \mathbf{M} = \begin{bmatrix} \frac{1}{2} & & \\ & 1 & \\ & & \frac{1}{2} \end{bmatrix}$$

We considered this problem in Example 10.5, where we isolated the eigenvalues using the bisection technique. Specifically, we found that

$$\lambda_1 < 3 < \lambda_2 < 5 < \lambda_3$$

Hence, we can start the secant iteration with $\mu_1 = 3$, $\mu_2 = 5$, and using the results of Example 10.5,

$$p(\mu_1) = -\tfrac{3}{4}; \qquad p(\mu_2) = \tfrac{3}{4}$$

Using (11.119), we obtain

$$\mu_3 = 5 - \frac{\frac{3}{4}}{(\frac{3}{4}) - (-\frac{3}{4})}(5 - 3)$$

or

$$\mu_3 = 4$$

Next we need to evaluate $p(\mu_3) = \det(\mathbf{K} - \mu_3\mathbf{M})$

and we find that $p(\mu_3) = 0.0$. Hence, $\lambda_2 = \mu_3 = 4$. Therefore, in this case one step of secant iteration was sufficient to calculate λ_2. But it may be noted that to evaluate $p(\mu_3)$ by Gauss factorization of $\mathbf{K} - \mu_3\mathbf{M}$, a row interchange is needed (see Example 10.4).

It is important to note that we assumed in the above presentation that the factorization of $\mathbf{K} - \mu_k\mathbf{M}$ into $\mathbf{LDL}^T$ can be obtained. However, we discussed in Sections 8.2.5 and 11.4.2 that if $\mu_k > \lambda_1$, interchanges may be required. If interchanges are needed, the same considerations as mentioned in these sections are applicable and proper account has to be taken of the effect of each row interchange on the Sturm sequence property.

The bisection method has two major disadvantages: (1) it is necessary to complete the factorization of $\mathbf{K} - \mu_k \mathbf{M}$ with as much accuracy as possible, although the coefficient matrix may be ill-conditioned (indeed, this may still be the case even when row interchanges are included), and (2) convergence can be very slow when a cluster of eigenvalues has to be solved. However, the Sturm sequence property can be employed in conjunction with other solution strategies, and it is in such cases that the property can be extremely useful. In particular, the Sturm sequence property is employed in the determinant search algorithm (see K. J. Bathe and E. L. Wilson [C]), in which the factorization of $\mathbf{K} - \mu_k \mathbf{M}$ is carried out without interchanges but is completed only provided that no instability occurs. If the factorization proves to be unstable, a different μ_k is selected. This is possible because the final accuracy with which the eigenvalues and eigenvectors are calculated does not depend on the specific shift μ_k used in the solution.

11.4.4 Exercises

11.9. Perform an implicit secant polynomial iteration on the eigenproblem in Exercise 11.1 to calculate λ_1. Next use instead of $p(\lambda)$ the characteristic polynomial deflated by λ_1, given by

$$p^{(1)}(\lambda) = \frac{p(\lambda)}{\lambda - \lambda_1}$$

where $p(\lambda) = \det(\mathbf{K} - \lambda\mathbf{M})$, to calculate λ_2.

Plot $p(\lambda)$ and $p^{(1)}(\lambda)$ and show on these plots the iterative steps you have performed.

11.10. Consider the eigenproblem in Exercise 11.1 and develop a quadratic interpolation for an iterative scheme to solve for λ_1.

11.11. Use the Sturm sequence property to evaluate λ_1 and λ_2 in the eigenvalue problem in Exercise 11.8.

11.12. Use the Sturm sequence property to evaluate λ_1 in the eigenvalue problem in Exercise 11.1. (If a zero pivot is encountered, use row and column interchanges.)

11.5 THE LANCZOS ITERATION METHOD

Very effective procedures for the solution of p eigenvalues and eigenvectors of finite element equations have been developed based on iterations with Lanczos transformations.

In his seminal work, C. Lanczos [A] proposed a transformation for the tridiagonalization of matrices. However, as already recognized by Lanczos, the tridiagonalization procedure has a major shortcoming in that the constructed vectors, which in theory should be orthogonal, are, as a result of round-off errors, not orthogonal in practice. A remedy is to use Gram-Schmidt orthogonalization, but such an approach is also sensitive to round-off errors and renders the process inefficient when a *complete* matrix is to be tridiagonalized. Other techniques such as the Householder method (see Section 11.3.3) are significantly more efficient.

If, on the other hand, the objective is to calculate only a few eigenvalues and corresponding eigenvectors of the problem $\mathbf{K}\boldsymbol{\phi} = \lambda\mathbf{M}\boldsymbol{\phi},$ an iteration based on the Lanczos transformation can be very efficient (see C. C. Paige [A, B] and T. Ericsson and A. Ruhe [A]).

In the following sections, we first present the basic Lanczos transformation with its important properties, and then we discuss the use of this transformation in an iterative manner for the solution of p eigenvalues and vectors of the problem $\mathbf{K}\boldsymbol{\phi} = \lambda\mathbf{M}\boldsymbol{\phi}$, where $p \ll n$ and n is the order of the matrices.

11.5.1 The Lanczos Transformation

The basic steps of the Lanczos method transform, in theory, our generalized eigenproblem $\mathbf{K}\boldsymbol{\phi} = \lambda\mathbf{M}\boldsymbol{\phi}$ into a standard form with a tridiagonal coefficient matrix. Let us summarize the steps of transformation.

Pick a starting vector $\mathbf{x}$ and calculate

$$\mathbf{x}_1 = \frac{\mathbf{x}}{\gamma}; \qquad \gamma = (\mathbf{x}^T\mathbf{M}\mathbf{x})^{1/2} \tag{11.122}$$

Let $\beta_0 = 0$; then calculate for $i = 1, \ldots, n$,

$$\mathbf{K}\overline{\mathbf{x}}_i = \mathbf{M}\mathbf{x}_i \tag{11.123}$$

$$\alpha_i = \overline{\mathbf{x}}_i^T\mathbf{M}\mathbf{x}_i \tag{11.124}$$

and if $i \neq n$, $\qquad\qquad \tilde{\mathbf{x}}_i = \overline{\mathbf{x}}_i - \alpha_i\mathbf{x}_i - \beta_{i-1}\mathbf{x}_{i-1} \tag{11.125}$

$$\beta_i = (\tilde{\mathbf{x}}_i^T\mathbf{M}\tilde{\mathbf{x}}_i)^{1/2} \tag{11.126}$$

and $\qquad\qquad\qquad \mathbf{x}_{i+1} = \dfrac{\tilde{\mathbf{x}}_i}{\beta_i} \tag{11.127}$

Theoretically, the vectors $\mathbf{x}_i$, $i = 1, \ldots, n$, generated using (11.122) to (11.127) are $\mathbf{M}$-orthonormal

$$\mathbf{x}_i^T\mathbf{M}\mathbf{x}_j = \delta_{ij} \tag{11.128}$$

and the matrix $\qquad\qquad \mathbf{X}_n = [\mathbf{x}_1, \ldots, \mathbf{x}_n] \tag{11.129}$

satisfies the relationship $\qquad \mathbf{X}_n^T(\mathbf{M}\mathbf{K}^{-1}\mathbf{M})\mathbf{X}_n = \mathbf{T}_n \tag{11.130}$

where
$$\mathbf{T}_n = \begin{bmatrix} \alpha_1 & \beta_1 & & & \\ \beta_1 & \alpha_2 & \beta_2 & & \\ & & \ddots & & \\ & & & \alpha_{n-1} & \beta_{n-1} \\ & & & \beta_{n-1} & \alpha_n \end{bmatrix} \tag{11.131}$$

We can now relate the eigenvalues and vectors of $\mathbf{T}_n$ to those of the problem $\mathbf{K}\boldsymbol{\phi} = \lambda\mathbf{M}\boldsymbol{\phi}$, which can be written in the form

$$\mathbf{M}\mathbf{K}^{-1}\mathbf{M}\boldsymbol{\phi} = \frac{1}{\lambda}\mathbf{M}\boldsymbol{\phi} \tag{11.132}$$

Using the transformation

$$\boldsymbol{\phi} = \mathbf{X}_n\tilde{\boldsymbol{\phi}} \tag{11.133}$$

and (11.128) and (11.130), we obtain from (11.132),

$$\mathbf{T}_n\tilde{\boldsymbol{\phi}} = \frac{1}{\lambda}\tilde{\boldsymbol{\phi}} \tag{11.134}$$

Hence, the eigenvalues of $\mathbf{T}_n$ are the reciprocals of the eigenvalues of $\mathbf{K}\boldsymbol{\phi} = \lambda \mathbf{M}\boldsymbol{\phi}$ and the eigenvectors of the two problems are related as in (11.133).

As further discussed later, we assume in the above transformational steps that these steps can be completed. We defer the proof that the vectors $\mathbf{x}_i$ are $\mathbf{M}$-orthonormal to Exercise 11.13 but show in the following example that (11.130) holds.

EXAMPLE 11.21: Show that $\mathbf{T}_n$ in (11.131) is obtained by the transformation of (11.130). Using (11.123), we obtain

$$\bar{\mathbf{x}}_i = \mathbf{K}^{-1}\mathbf{M}\mathbf{x}_i$$

Substituting from (11.124) and (11.127), we obtain

$$\mathbf{K}^{-1}\mathbf{M}\mathbf{x}_i = \beta_{i-1}\mathbf{x}_{i-1} + \alpha_i\mathbf{x}_i + \beta_i\mathbf{x}_{i+1}$$

Using this relation for $i = 1, \ldots, j$, we obtain

$$\mathbf{K}^{-1}\mathbf{M}[\mathbf{x}_1, \ldots, \mathbf{x}_j] = [\mathbf{x}_1, \ldots, \mathbf{x}_j]\begin{bmatrix} \alpha_1 & \beta_1 & & & & \\ \beta_1 & \alpha_2 & \beta_2 & & & \\ & & \ddots & & & \\ & & & \alpha_{j-1} & \beta_{j-1} \\ & & & \beta_{j-1} & \alpha_j \end{bmatrix} + [\mathbf{0}, \ldots, \mathbf{0}, \beta_j\mathbf{x}_{j+1}]$$

Hence,
$$\mathbf{K}^{-1}\mathbf{M}\mathbf{X}_j = \mathbf{X}_j\mathbf{T}_j + \beta_j\mathbf{x}_{j+1}\mathbf{e}_j^T \qquad\qquad \text{(a)}$$

where $\mathbf{e}_j$ is a vector of length j,

$$\mathbf{e}_j^T = [0 \quad \ldots \quad 0 \quad 1]$$

Premultiplying (a) by $\mathbf{X}_j^T\mathbf{M}$ and using the $\mathbf{M}$-orthonormality of the vectors $\mathbf{x}_i$, we obtain

$$\mathbf{T}_j = \mathbf{X}_j^T\mathbf{M}\mathbf{K}^{-1}\mathbf{M}\mathbf{X}_j \qquad\qquad \text{(b)}$$

which for $j = n$ proves the desired result.

Note that when $j = n$, we also have $\tilde{\mathbf{x}}_n = \mathbf{0}$ in (11.125) because the complete space is spanned by $\mathbf{X}_n$ and no vector $\mathbf{M}$-orthogonal to all vectors in $\mathbf{X}_n$ exists.

We use the relation in (b) in Lanczos iteration when only a few eigenvalues and corresponding vectors are to be calculated. Also, the relation in (a) gives in that case error bounds on the calculated eigenvalue approximations.

As we have already mentioned, the tridiagonalization procedure in (11.122) to (11.127) does not, in practice, produce the desired $\mathbf{M}$-orthonormal vectors because of round-off errors, and if additional Gram-Schmidt orthogonalizations are used, the method of tridiagonalization for a *complete* matrix is inefficient.

However, there are certain important properties of the transformation in (11.122) to (11.127) when $i = 1, \ldots, q$, with $q \ll n$, that can provide the basis of an effective iterative solution scheme. If we perform the Lanczos transformation in truncated form, we calculate, with $i = 1, \ldots, q$,

$$\mathbf{X}_q = [\mathbf{x}_1, \ldots, \mathbf{x}_q] \qquad\qquad (11.135)$$

and the elements of the matrix T_q,

$$
\mathbf{T}_q = \begin{bmatrix}
\alpha_1 & \beta_1 & & & \\
\beta_1 & \alpha_2 & \beta_2 & & \\
& & \ddots & & \\
& & & \alpha_{q-1} & \beta_{q-1} \\
& & & \beta_{q-1} & \alpha_q
\end{bmatrix}
\tag{11.136}
$$

This matrix $\mathbf{T}_q$ is actually the result of a Rayleigh-Ritz transformation on the eigenvalue problem (11.132). Namely, using

$$
\overline{\boldsymbol{\phi}} = \mathbf{X}_q \mathbf{s}
\tag{11.137}
$$

in a Rayleigh-Ritz transformation (see Section 10.3.2) on the problem (11.132), equivalent to $\mathbf{K}\boldsymbol{\phi} = \lambda \mathbf{M}\boldsymbol{\phi}$, we obtain the eigenproblem

$$
\mathbf{T}_q \mathbf{s} = \nu \mathbf{s}
\tag{11.138}
$$

Hence, using the transformation from (11.132) to (11.134), all exact eigenvalues λ_i and eigenvectors $\boldsymbol{\phi}_i$ of the problem $\mathbf{K}\boldsymbol{\phi} = \lambda \mathbf{M}\boldsymbol{\phi}$ are calculated by solving (11.134), while using (11.137) and (11.138) only approximations to eigenvalues and eigenvectors are computed.

However, we also realize that in (11.123) an inverse iteration step is performed, and therefore, the Ritz vectors in $\mathbf{X}_q$ should largely correspond to a space close to the least dominant subspace of $\mathbf{K}\boldsymbol{\phi} = \lambda \mathbf{M}\boldsymbol{\phi}$ (i.e., the subspace corresponding to the smallest eigenvalues). For this reason, the solution of (11.138) may yield good approximations to the smallest eigenvalues and corresponding eigenvectors of $\mathbf{K}\boldsymbol{\phi} = \lambda \mathbf{M}\boldsymbol{\phi}$.

Of course, in the computations we never calculate the matrix $\mathbf{MK}^{-1}\mathbf{M}$ but directly use the values α_i, β_i obtained from (11.124) and (11.126) to form $\mathbf{T}_q$. We also note that since in exact arithmetic, the inverses of the exact eigenvalues are calculated when $q = n$, in general we may expect better approximations to the inverses of the smallest eigenvalues as q increases.

During the calculation of the eigenvalues ν_i in (11.138) we also directly obtain error bounds on the accuracy of these values. These error bounds are derived as follows.

Using the decomposition $\mathbf{M} = \mathbf{SS}^T$ (see Section 10.2.5), we can transform the problem (11.132) to

$$
\mathbf{S}^T \mathbf{K}^{-1} \mathbf{S} \boldsymbol{\psi} = \frac{1}{\lambda} \boldsymbol{\psi}
\tag{11.139}
$$

where

$$
\boldsymbol{\psi} = \mathbf{S}^T \boldsymbol{\phi}
\tag{11.140}
$$

We can now directly use the error bound formula (10.101). Assume $(\nu_i, \mathbf{s}_i)$ is an eigenpair of (11.138) and $\overline{\boldsymbol{\phi}}_i$ is the corresponding vector obtained using (11.137). Then from (11.140),

$$
\overline{\boldsymbol{\psi}}_i = \mathbf{S}^T \overline{\boldsymbol{\phi}}_i
\tag{11.141}
$$

and hence,

$$
\begin{aligned}
\| \mathbf{r}_i \| &= \| \mathbf{S}^T \mathbf{K}^{-1} \mathbf{S} \overline{\boldsymbol{\psi}}_i - \nu_i \overline{\boldsymbol{\psi}}_i \| \\
&= \| \mathbf{S}^T \mathbf{K}^{-1} \mathbf{SS}^T \mathbf{X}_q \mathbf{s}_i - \nu_i \mathbf{S}^T \mathbf{X}_q \mathbf{s}_i \| \\
&= \| \mathbf{S}^T (\mathbf{K}^{-1}\mathbf{MX}_q - \mathbf{X}_q \mathbf{T}_q) \mathbf{s}_i \| \\
&= \| \mathbf{S}^T (\beta_q \mathbf{x}_{q+1} \mathbf{e}_q^T) \mathbf{s}_i \|
\end{aligned}
\tag{11.142}
$$

where we used the result (a) in Example 11.21. Since $\| \mathbf{S}^T \mathbf{x}_{q+1} \| = 1$, we thus have

$$\| \mathbf{r}_i \| \le | \beta_q s_{qi} | \tag{11.143}$$

where s_{qi} is the qth element, i.e. the last element, in the eigenvector $\mathbf{s}_i$ of (11.138).

Using (10.101), we thus have

$$| \lambda_k^{-1} - \nu_i | \le | \beta_q s_{qi} | \tag{11.144}$$

for some value k. This bound hence requires only the calculation of β_q used for all values of ν_i. In an actual solution we need to establish k, by a Sturm sequence check or otherwise, so as to know which eigenvalue has been approximated.

We demonstrate the truncated Lanczos transformation and solution of approximate eigenvalues in the following example.

EXAMPLE 11.22:   Use the Lanczos transformation to calculate approximations to the two smallest eigenvalues of the eigenproblem $\mathbf{K}\boldsymbol{\phi} = \lambda \mathbf{M}\boldsymbol{\phi}$ considered in Example 10.18.

Using the algorithm in (11.122) to (11.127) with $\mathbf{x}$ a full unit vector, we obtain

$$\gamma = 2.121; \qquad \mathbf{x}_1 = 0.4714 \begin{bmatrix} 1 \\ 1 \\ 1 \\ 1 \\ 1 \end{bmatrix}$$

for $i = 1$:
$$\bar{\mathbf{x}}_1 = \begin{bmatrix} 2.121 \\ 3.771 \\ 4.950 \\ 5.657 \\ 5.893 \end{bmatrix}; \qquad \alpha_1 = 9.167; \qquad \tilde{\mathbf{x}}_1 = \begin{bmatrix} -2.200 \\ -0.5500 \\ 0.6285 \\ 1.336 \\ 1.571 \end{bmatrix};$$

$$\beta_1 = 2.925; \qquad \mathbf{x}_2 = \begin{bmatrix} -.7521 \\ -.1880 \\ 0.2149 \\ 0.4566 \\ 0.5372 \end{bmatrix}$$

for $i = 2$:
$$\bar{\mathbf{x}}_2 = \begin{bmatrix} 0.000 \\ 0.7521 \\ 1.692 \\ 2.417 \\ 2.686 \end{bmatrix}; \qquad \alpha_2 = 2.048$$

Hence, we have
$$\mathbf{T}_2 = \begin{bmatrix} 9.167 & 2.925 \\ 2.925 & 2.048 \end{bmatrix}$$

Approximations to the eigenvalues of $\mathbf{K}\boldsymbol{\phi} = \lambda \mathbf{M}\boldsymbol{\phi}$ are obtained by solving

$$\mathbf{T}_2 \mathbf{s} = \frac{1}{\rho}\mathbf{s}; \qquad \nu_1 = \frac{1}{\rho_2}, \qquad \nu_2 = \frac{1}{\rho_1}$$

which gives $\rho_1 = 0.09790; \qquad \rho_2 = 1.000$

Comparing these values with the exact eigenvalues of $\mathbf{K}\boldsymbol{\phi} = \lambda\mathbf{M}\boldsymbol{\phi}$ (see Example 10.18), we find that ρ_1 is a good approximation to λ_1 but ρ_2 is not very close to λ_2. Of course, $\rho_i \geq \lambda_i$, $i = 1, 2$. The smallest eigenvalue is well predicted in this solution because the starting vector $\mathbf{x}$ is relatively close to $\boldsymbol{\phi}_1$. The error bound calculations of (11.144) give here

$$| \lambda_1^{-1} - \nu_2 | = 0.0016 \leq 0.123$$

$$| \lambda_2^{-1} - \nu_1 | = 0.213 \leq 0.343$$

11.5.2 Iteration with Lanczos Transformations

As discussed in the previous section, a truncated Lanczos transformation is a Rayleigh-Ritz analysis and therefore the predicted eigenvalues and eigenvectors may or may not be accurate approximations of the values sought. It is a further step to develop, based on Lanczos transformations, an algorithm that in an iterative manner calculates the required eigenvalues and vectors to the required accuracy.

As an example, consider the following proposal of a simple iterative algorithm. Assume that we require the p smallest eigenvalues and corresponding eigenvectors of $\mathbf{K}\boldsymbol{\phi} = \lambda\mathbf{M}\boldsymbol{\phi}$, where n is the number of equations and $n \gg p$.

Perform the Lanczos transformation with $q = 2p$ and solve for the largest p eigenvalues of $\mathbf{T}_{2p}$. [Note that we seek the smallest values of λ in (11.134).]

Then perform the Lanczos transformation with $q = 3p$ and solve for the largest p eigenvalues of $\mathbf{T}_{3p}$.

Continue this process to $q = rp$, with $r = 4, 5, \ldots$, until the largest p eigenvalues satisfy the accuracy criterion $| \beta_q s_{qi} | < tol$ for $i = 1, \ldots, p$ [see (11.144) where tol is a selected tolerance]. Of course, there is no need to increase the number of vectors in each stage by p, but depending on the problem considered, a smaller increase may be used.

This simple process appears very attractive; unfortunately, however, it is unstable because in finite digit arithmetic, loss of $\mathbf{M}$-orthogonality of the actually calculated vectors $\mathbf{x}_i$ occurs. When this loss of orthogonality occurs, some values obtained from the solution are approximations to spurious copies of the actual eigenvalues; in other words, for example, a single eigenvalue may be approximated a few times. Such a result is of course unacceptable, and we would have to sort out which calculated values are approximations to actual eigenvalues and whether any actual eigenvalue has been missed. For this purpose, Sturm sequence checks could be performed, but too many such checks render the complete solution inefficient.

A remedy to prevent spurious copies of eigenvalues is to use Gram-Schmidt orthogonalization of the Lanczos vectors. In some cases, selective reorthogonalization may be sufficient (see B. N. Parlett and D. S. Scott [A]). However, the Gram-Schmidt process is also sensitive to round-off errors (see Section 11.2.6), and it actually may be necessary to perform the orthogonalization completely on all earlier established vectors not only once but twice, as reported by H. Matthies [B].

Considering the Lanczos iteration method in exact arithmetic, we also notice that the vector $\tilde{\mathbf{x}}_i$ may be a null vector after some vectors have been established with $\mathbf{x}_1$ as the starting vector. This phenomenon occurs when $\mathbf{x}_1$ contains only components of q eigenvectors, that is, $\mathbf{x}_1$ lies in a q-dimensional subspace of the entire n-dimensional space corresponding to the matrices $\mathbf{K}$ and $\mathbf{M}$ (then $\tilde{\mathbf{x}}_q = \mathbf{0}$). Let us demonstrate this observation and what can happen when a multiple eigenvalue is present in the following simple example.

EXAMPLE 11.23: Use the Lanczos method in the solution of the eigenproblem $\mathbf{K}\boldsymbol{\phi} = \lambda\mathbf{M}\boldsymbol{\phi}$, where

$$\mathbf{K} = \begin{bmatrix} \lambda_1 & & & & \\ & \lambda_2 & & & \\ & & \lambda_3 & & \\ & & & \lambda_4 & \\ & & & & \lambda_5 \end{bmatrix}; \quad \mathbf{M} = \begin{bmatrix} 1 & & & & \\ & 1 & & & \\ & & 1 & & \\ & & & 1 & \\ & & & & 1 \end{bmatrix} \quad \text{(a)}$$

and $\lambda_1 = \lambda_2 < \lambda_3 < \lambda_4 < \lambda_5$.

(i) Let $\mathbf{x}_1 = \dfrac{1}{\sqrt{2}} \begin{bmatrix} 1 \\ 1 \\ 0 \\ 0 \\ 0 \end{bmatrix}$ and calculate the Lanczos vectors.

(ii) Let $\mathbf{x}_1 = \dfrac{1}{\sqrt{2}} \begin{bmatrix} 0 \\ 0 \\ 1 \\ 1 \\ 0 \end{bmatrix}$ and calculate the Lanczos vectors.

Although the matrices used here are of special diagonal form, the observations in this example are of a general nature. Namely, we can imagine that the matrices in (a) have been obtained by a transformation of more general matrices to their eigenvector basis, but this transformation is performed here merely to display more readily the ingredients of the solution algorithm (in the same way as we proceeded in the analysis of the vector iteration methods; see Section 11.2.1).
  In case (i) we obtain, using (11.123) to (11.125),

$$\tilde{\mathbf{x}}_1 = \mathbf{0} \quad \text{(b)}$$

In case (ii) we obtain $\qquad \mathbf{x}_2 = \begin{bmatrix} 0 \\ 0 \\ \dfrac{1}{\sqrt{2}} \\ -\dfrac{1}{\sqrt{2}} \\ 0 \end{bmatrix} \quad \text{(c)}$

and $\qquad\qquad\qquad\qquad \tilde{\mathbf{x}}_2 = \mathbf{0}$

Hence (b) shows that because $\mathbf{x}_1$ is an eigenvector, we cannot continue with the process, and (c) shows that because $\mathbf{x}_1$ lies in the subspace corresponding to λ_3 and λ_4, we cannot find more than two Lanczos vectors including $\mathbf{x}_1$.

In practice, the solution process usually does not break down as mentioned above because of round-off errors. However, the preceding discussion shows that two features are important in a Lanczos iteration method, namely, Gram-Schmidt orthogonalization and, when necessary, restarting of the algorithm with a new Lanczos vector **x**.

To present a general solution approach, let us define a Lanczos step, a Lanczos stage, and restarting.

A *Lanczos step* is the use of (11.123) to (11.127), in which we now include reorthogonalization.

A *Lanczos stage* consists of q Lanczos steps and the calculation of the eigenvalues and eigenvectors of $\mathbf{T}_q\mathbf{s} = \nu\mathbf{s}$. If one of the following conditions is satisfied, the eigenvalues and eigenvectors of $\mathbf{T}_q\mathbf{s} = \nu\mathbf{s}$ are calculated and hence the stage is completed.

1. The preassigned maximum number of Lanczos steps, q_{max}, is reached.
2. The loss of orthogonality in the Lanczos vectors or between the Lanczos vectors and the converged eigenvectors is detected.

In case (1), $q = q_{max}$, and in case (2), q is the number of Lanczos steps completed prior to the loss of orthogonality.

At the end of each Lanczos stage, we check whether all required eigenvalues and eigenvectors have been calculated. If the required eigenpairs have not yet been obtained, we *restart* for a new Lanczos stage with a new vector **x** in (11.122). Prior to the restart, it can be effective to introduce a shift μ so that the inverse iteration step in (11.123) is performed with $\mathbf{K} - \mu\mathbf{M}$ (see Section 11.2.3).

Without giving all details, a complete solution algorithm can therefore be summarized as follows.

Start of a new Lanczos stage: Choose a starting vector **x** that is orthogonal to all previously calculated eigenvector approximations and calculate

$$\mathbf{x}_1 = \frac{\mathbf{x}}{\gamma}; \qquad \gamma = (\mathbf{x}^T\mathbf{M}\mathbf{x})^{1/2} \tag{11.122}$$

Choose a shift μ (usually $\mu = 0$ for the first Lanczos stage).
Perform the Lanczos steps, using $i = 1, 2, \ldots$; $\beta_0 = 0$,

$$(\mathbf{K} - \mu\mathbf{M})\bar{\mathbf{x}}_i = \mathbf{M}\mathbf{x}_i$$

$$\alpha_i = \bar{\mathbf{x}}_i^T\mathbf{M}\mathbf{x}_i$$

$$\tilde{\mathbf{x}}_i' = \bar{\mathbf{x}}_i - \alpha_i\mathbf{x}_i - \beta_{i-1}\mathbf{x}_{i-1}$$

$$\tilde{\mathbf{x}}_i = \tilde{\mathbf{x}}_i' - \sum_{k=1}^{i}(\tilde{\mathbf{x}}_i'^T\mathbf{M}\mathbf{x}_k)\mathbf{x}_k - \sum_{j=1}^{n_c}(\tilde{\mathbf{x}}_i'^T\mathbf{M}\boldsymbol{\phi}_j)\boldsymbol{\phi}_j \tag{11.145}$$

$$\beta_i = (\tilde{\mathbf{x}}_i^T\mathbf{M}\tilde{\mathbf{x}}_i)^{1/2}$$

$$\mathbf{x}_{i+1} = \frac{\tilde{\mathbf{x}}_i}{\beta_i}$$

where n_c is the number of converged eigenvalues in the preceding stages. Although a Gram-Schmidt orthogonalization has been performed, the vector $\mathbf{x}_{i+1}$ is checked for loss of orthogonality and if the loss occurs, this Lanczos stage is terminated with $q = i$; otherwise perform a maximum number of steps, q_{max}, and set $q = q_{max}$.

Compute r additional converged eigenvalues $\lambda_{nc+1}, \ldots, \lambda_{nc+r}$ and corresponding eigenvectors $\phi_{nc+1}, \ldots, \phi_{nc+r}$ by solving (using, for example, QR-inverse iteration, see Section 11.3.3)

$$\mathbf{T}_q \mathbf{s} = \nu \mathbf{s} \qquad (11.138)$$

Convergence is defined by satisfying the criterion (11.144). Reset nc to the new value.

If the required eigenvalues and eigenvectors have not yet been obtained, restart for an additional Lanczos stage.

Continue until all required eigenvalues and eigenvectors have been calculated or until the maximum number of assigned Lanczos steps has been reached.

These solution steps give the general steps (including a simple and single full reorthogonalization) of a Lanczos iterative scheme. As mentioned earlier, the details of the actual implementation—which are not given here—are most important to render the method effective and reliable. Some important and subtle aspects of an actual Lanczos iterative scheme are to select the actual reorthogonalization to be performed, to identify efficiently and reliably the loss of orthogonality and then restart with an effective new vector $\mathbf{x}$, to ensure that only converged values to true eigenvalues and not spuriously duplicated values are accepted as eigenvalues, to restart for a new stage when such is more effective than to continue with the present stage, to select an appropriate value for q_{max}, and to use an effective shifting strategy. Also, Sturm sequence checks need to be performed in order to ensure that all required eigenvalues have been calculated (see Section 11.6.4 for more information on such checking strategies). The rate of convergence of the eigenvalues depends of course on the actual algorithm used.

Finally, we should mention that the Lanczos algorithm has been developed also to work with blocks of vectors (instead of individual vectors only) (see, for example, G. H. Golub and R. Underwood [A] and H. Matthies [B]).

11.5.3 Exercises

11.13. Show that the vectors $\mathbf{x}_i$ generated in the Lanczos transformation are (in exact arithmetic) $\mathbf{M}$-orthonormal. (*Hint:* Show that $\mathbf{x}_1$, $\mathbf{x}_2$, and $\mathbf{x}_3$ are $\mathbf{M}$-orthonormal and then use the method of induction.)

11.14. Assume that the loss of vector orthogonality in the Lanczos transformation is only a result of the vector subtraction step (11.125). Then show that the loss of orthogonality can be predicted using the equation

$$\left| \mathbf{x}_i^T \mathbf{M} \mathbf{x}_{j+1} \right| \lesssim \frac{f_{ij}}{\beta_j} \epsilon$$

where the symbol $\lesssim$ stands for "approximately smaller than" and

$$j = \text{Lanczos step number;}$$

$$1 \leq i \leq j$$

$$\left| \mathbf{x}_i^T \mathbf{M} \mathbf{x}_k \right| \leq \epsilon \quad (1 \leq i, k \leq j; \quad k \neq i)$$

$$f_{ij} = \begin{cases} \left| \alpha_i - \alpha_j \right| + \beta_{j-1} + \beta_{i-1} + \beta_i & (i \leq j - 2) \\ \left| \alpha_i - \alpha_j \right| + \beta_{j-2} & (i = j - 1) \\ \beta_{j-1} & (i = j) \end{cases}$$

11.15. Use a Lanczos iteration method that you design to solve for the smallest eigenvalue and corresponding eigenvector of the problem

$$\begin{bmatrix} 4 & -1 & 0 & 0 \\ -1 & 4 & -1 & 0 \\ 0 & -1 & 2 & -1 \\ 0 & 0 & -1 & 1 \end{bmatrix} \phi = \lambda \begin{bmatrix} 2 & & & \\ & 1 & & \\ & & 1 & \\ & & & 1 \end{bmatrix} \phi$$

11.16. Use a Lanczos iteration method that you design to calculate the smallest two eigenvalues and corresponding eigenvectors of the problem

$$\begin{bmatrix} 2 & -1 & & \\ -1 & 1 & -\frac{1}{4} & \\ & -\frac{1}{4} & 1 & -1 \\ & & -1 & 2 \end{bmatrix} \phi = \lambda \begin{bmatrix} 1 & & & \\ & \frac{1}{2} & & \\ & & \frac{1}{2} & \\ & & & 1 \end{bmatrix} \phi$$

11.17. Write a computer program for a Lanczos iteration method. Use this program to solve for the smallest p eigenvalues and corresponding eigenvectors of the problem

$$\begin{bmatrix} 101 & -10 & & & \\ -10 & 102 & -10 & & \\ & -10 & 103 & & \\ & & & \ddots & \\ & & & & -10 \\ & & & -10 & 100+n \end{bmatrix} \phi = \lambda \begin{bmatrix} 1 & & & & \\ & 2 & & & \\ & & 3 & & \\ & & & \ddots & \\ & & & & n \end{bmatrix} \phi$$

Use
$$p = 4; \qquad n = 40$$
$$p = 8; \qquad n = 80$$
$$p = 16; \qquad n = 80$$

Use the error bounds in (10.106) to identify the accuracy of the calculated eigenvalues and ensure that no eigenvalues have been missed or are spuriously given as multiple eigenvalues.

11.6 THE SUBSPACE ITERATION METHOD

An effective method widely used in engineering practice for the solution of eigenvalues and eigenvectors of finite element equations is the subspace iteration procedure. This technique is particularly suited for the calculation of a few eigenvalues and eigenvectors of large finite element systems.

The subspace iteration method developed and so named by K. J. Bathe [A] consists of the following three steps.

1. Establish q starting iteration vectors, $q > p$, where p is the number of eigenvalues and vectors to be calculated.
2. Use simultaneous inverse iteration on the q vectors and Ritz analysis to extract the "best" eigenvalue and eigenvector approximations from the q iteration vectors.
3. After iteration convergence, use the Sturm sequence check to verify that the required eigenvalues and corresponding eigenvectors have been calculated.

The solution procedure was named the subspace iteration method because the iteration is equivalent to iterating with a q-dimensional subspace and should not be regarded as a simultaneous iteration with q individual iteration vectors. Specifically, we should note that the selection of the starting iteration vectors in step 1 and the Sturm sequence check in step 3 are very important parts of the iteration procedure. Altogether, the subspace iteration method is largely based on various techniques that have been used earlier, namely, simultaneous vector iteration (see F. L. Bauer [A] and A. Jennings [A]), Sturm sequence information (see Section 10.2.2), and Rayleigh-Ritz analysis (see Section 10.3.2), but very enlightening has been the work of H. Rutishauser [B].

Some advantages of the subspace iteration method are that the theory is relatively easy to understand and that the method is robust and can be programmed with little effort (see K. J. Bathe [A] and K. J. Bathe and E. L. Wilson [D]).

In the following sections, we describe the basic theory and iterative steps of the subspace iteration method and then present a complete program of the basic algorithm. Our only objective here is to discuss the basic subspace iteration method and reinforce this understanding by presenting a computer program. In actual engineering practice, a well-programmed subroutine of the Lanczos method (see Section 11.5) or of an accelerated subspace iteration method that includes shifting can be substantially more effective.

11.6.1 Preliminary Considerations

The basic objective in the subspace iteration method is to solve for the smallest p eigenvalues and corresponding eigenvectors satisfying

$$\mathbf{K\Phi} = \mathbf{M\Phi\Lambda} \tag{11.146}$$

where $\mathbf{\Lambda} = \text{diag}(\lambda_i)$ and $\mathbf{\Phi} = [\boldsymbol{\phi}_1, \ldots, \boldsymbol{\phi}_p]$.

In addition to the relation in (11.146), the eigenvectors also satisfy the orthogonality conditions

$$\mathbf{\Phi}^T\mathbf{K\Phi} = \mathbf{\Lambda}; \qquad \mathbf{\Phi}^T\mathbf{M\Phi} = \mathbf{I} \tag{11.147}$$

where $\mathbf{I}$ is a unit matrix of order p because $\mathbf{\Phi}$ stores only p eigenvectors. It is important to note that the relation in (11.146) is a necessary and sufficient condition for the vectors in $\mathbf{\Phi}$ to be eigenvectors but that the eigenvector orthogonality conditions in (11.147) are necessary but not sufficient. In other words, if we have p vectors that satisfy (11.147), $p < n$, then these vectors are not necessarily eigenvectors. However, if the p vectors satisfy (11.146), they are definitely eigenvectors, although we still need to make sure that they are indeed the p specific eigenvectors sought (see Section 10.2.1).

The essential idea of the subspace iteration method uses the fact that the eigenvectors in (11.146) form an $\mathbf{M}$-orthonormal basis of the p-dimensional least dominant subspace of the matrices $\mathbf{K}$ and $\mathbf{M}$, which we will now call E_∞ (see Section 2.3). In the solution the iteration with p linearly independent vectors can therefore be regarded as an iteration with a subspace. The starting iteration vectors span E_1, and iteration continues until, to sufficient accuracy, E_∞ is spanned. The fact that iteration is performed with a subspace has some important consequences. The total number of required iterations depends on how "close" E_1 is to E_∞ and not on how close each iteration vector is to an eigenvector. Hence, the effectiveness of the algorithm lies in that it is much easier to establish a p-dimensional starting subspace which is close to E_∞ than to find p vectors that are each close to a required eigenvector. The specific algorithm used to establish the starting iteration vectors is described later. Also, *because iteration is performed with a subspace, convergence of the subspace is all that is required and not convergence of individual iteration vectors to eigenvectors. In other words, if the iteration vectors are linear combinations of the required eigenvectors, the solution algorithm converges in one step.*

To demonstrate the essential idea, we first consider simultaneous vector inverse iteration on p vectors. Let $\mathbf{X}_1$ store the p starting iteration vectors, which span the starting subspace E_1. Simultaneous inverse iteration on the p vectors can be written

$$\mathbf{K}\mathbf{X}_{k+1} = \mathbf{M}\mathbf{X}_k; \qquad k = 1, 2, \ldots \tag{11.148}$$

where we now observe that the p iteration vectors in $\mathbf{X}_{k+1}$ span a p-dimensional subspace E_{k+1}, and the sequence of subspaces generated converges to E_∞, provided the starting vectors are not orthogonal to E_∞. This seems to contradict the fact that in this iteration each column in $\mathbf{X}_{k+1}$ is known to converge to the least dominant eigenvector unless the column is deficient in $\boldsymbol{\phi}_1$ (see Section 11.2.1). Actually, there is no contradiction. Although in exact arithmetic the vectors in $\mathbf{X}_{k+1}$ span E_{k+1}, they do become more and more parallel and therefore a poorer and poorer basis for E_{k+1}. One way to preserve numerical stability is to generate orthogonal bases in the subspaces E_{k+1} using the Gram-Schmidt process (see Section 11.2.5). In this case we iterate for $k = 1, 2, \ldots$, as follows:

$$\mathbf{K}\bar{\mathbf{X}}_{k+1} = \mathbf{M}\mathbf{X}_k \tag{11.149}$$

$$\mathbf{X}_{k+1} = \bar{\mathbf{X}}_{k+1}\mathbf{R}_{k+1} \tag{11.150}$$

where $\mathbf{R}_{k+1}$ is an upper triangular matrix chosen in such way that $\mathbf{X}_{k+1}^T\mathbf{M}\mathbf{X}_{k+1} = \mathbf{I}$. Then provided that the starting vectors in $\mathbf{X}_1$ are not deficient in the eigenvectors $\boldsymbol{\phi}_1, \boldsymbol{\phi}_2, \ldots \boldsymbol{\phi}_p$, we have

$$\mathbf{X}_{k+1} \to \boldsymbol{\Phi}; \qquad \mathbf{R}_{k+1} \to \boldsymbol{\Lambda}$$

It is important to note that the iteration in (11.148) generates the same sequence of subspaces as the iteration in (11.149) and (11.150). However, the ith column in $\mathbf{X}_{k+1}$ of (11.150) converges linearly to $\boldsymbol{\phi}_i$ with the convergence rate equal to max $\{\lambda_{i-1}/\lambda_i, \lambda_i/\lambda_{i+1}\}$. To demonstrate the solution procedure, consider the following example.

EXAMPLE 11.24:   Consider the eigenproblem $\mathbf{K}\boldsymbol{\phi} = \lambda\mathbf{M}\boldsymbol{\phi}$, where

$$\mathbf{K} = \begin{bmatrix} 2 & -1 & 0 \\ -1 & 4 & -1 \\ 0 & -1 & 2 \end{bmatrix}; \qquad \mathbf{M} = \begin{bmatrix} \frac{1}{2} & & \\ & 1 & \\ & & \frac{1}{2} \end{bmatrix}$$

The two smallest eigenvalues and corresponding eigenvectors are (see Example 10.4)

$$\lambda_1 = 2, \quad \boldsymbol{\phi}_1 = \begin{bmatrix} \dfrac{1}{\sqrt{2}} \\ \dfrac{1}{\sqrt{2}} \\ \dfrac{1}{\sqrt{2}} \end{bmatrix}; \qquad \lambda_2 = 4, \quad \boldsymbol{\phi}_2 = \begin{bmatrix} -1 \\ 0 \\ 1 \end{bmatrix}$$

Use the simultaneous vector iteration with Gram-Schmidt orthogonalization given in (11.149) and (11.150) with starting vectors

$$\mathbf{X}_1 = \begin{bmatrix} 0 & 2 \\ 1 & 1 \\ 2 & 0 \end{bmatrix}$$

to calculate approximations to λ_1, $\boldsymbol{\phi}_1$ and λ_2, $\boldsymbol{\phi}_2$.

The relation $\mathbf{K}\overline{\mathbf{X}}_2 = \mathbf{M}\mathbf{X}_1$ gives

$$\overline{\mathbf{X}}_2 = \begin{bmatrix} 0.25 & 0.75 \\ 0.50 & 0.50 \\ 0.75 & 0.25 \end{bmatrix}$$

$\mathbf{M}$-orthonormalizing $\overline{\mathbf{X}}_2$ gives

$$\mathbf{X}_2 = \begin{bmatrix} 0.3333 & 1.179 \\ 0.6667 & 0.2357 \\ 1.000 & -0.7071 \end{bmatrix}; \qquad \mathbf{R}_2 = \begin{bmatrix} 1.333 & -1.650 \\ 0 & 2.121 \end{bmatrix}$$

Proceeding similarly, we obtain the following results:

$$\mathbf{X}_3 = \begin{bmatrix} 0.5222 & 1.108 \\ 0.6963 & 0.1231 \\ 0.8704 & -0.8614 \end{bmatrix}; \qquad \mathbf{R}_3 = \begin{bmatrix} 2.089 & -0.9847 \\ 0 & 3.830 \end{bmatrix}$$

$$\mathbf{X}_4 = \begin{bmatrix} 0.6163 & 1.058 \\ 0.7044 & 0.0622 \\ 0.7924 & -0.9339 \end{bmatrix}; \qquad \mathbf{R}_4 = \begin{bmatrix} 2.023 & -0.5202 \\ 0 & 3.954 \end{bmatrix}$$

$$\mathbf{X}_5 = \begin{bmatrix} 0.6623 & 1.030 \\ 0.7064 & 0.0312 \\ 0.7506 & -0.9678 \end{bmatrix}; \qquad \mathbf{R}_5 = \begin{bmatrix} 2.006 & -0.2639 \\ 0 & 3.988 \end{bmatrix}$$

$$\mathbf{X}_6 = \begin{bmatrix} 0.6848 & 1.015 \\ 0.7069 & 0.0156 \\ 0.7290 & -0.9841 \end{bmatrix}; \qquad \mathbf{R}_6 = \begin{bmatrix} 2.001 & -0.1324 \\ 0 & 3.997 \end{bmatrix}$$

$$\mathbf{X}_7 = \begin{bmatrix} 0.6960 & 1.008 \\ 0.7071 & 0.0078 \\ 0.7181 & -0.9921 \end{bmatrix}; \qquad \mathbf{R}_7 = \begin{bmatrix} 2.000 & -0.0663 \\ 0 & 3.999 \end{bmatrix}$$

$$\mathbf{X}_8 = \begin{bmatrix} 0.7016 & 1.004 \\ 0.7071 & 0.0039 \\ 0.7126 & -0.9961 \end{bmatrix}; \qquad \mathbf{R}_8 = \begin{bmatrix} 2.000 & -0.0331 \\ 0 & 4.000 \end{bmatrix}$$

$$\mathbf{X}_9 = \begin{bmatrix} 0.7043 & 1.002 \\ 0.7071 & 0.0020 \\ 0.7099 & -0.9980 \end{bmatrix}; \qquad \mathbf{R}_9 = \begin{bmatrix} 2.000 & -0.0166 \\ 0 & 4.000 \end{bmatrix}$$

$$\mathbf{X}_{10} = \begin{bmatrix} 0.7057 & 1.001 \\ 0.7071 & 0.0010 \\ 0.7085 & -0.9990 \end{bmatrix}; \qquad \mathbf{R}_{10} = \begin{bmatrix} 2.000 & -0.0083 \\ 0 & 4.000 \end{bmatrix}$$

and after nine iterations we have

$$\boldsymbol{\phi}_1 \doteq \begin{bmatrix} 0.7057 \\ 0.7071 \\ 0.7085 \end{bmatrix}; \qquad \lambda_1 \doteq 2.000$$

$$\boldsymbol{\phi}_2 \doteq \begin{bmatrix} 1.001 \\ 0.0010 \\ -0.9990 \end{bmatrix}; \qquad \lambda_2 \doteq 4.000$$

It should be noted that although the vectors in $\mathbf{X}_1$ already span the space of $\boldsymbol{\phi}_1$ and $\boldsymbol{\phi}_2$, we need a relatively large number of iterations for convergence.

The solution in the preceding example demonstrates the iteration procedure in (11.149) and (11.150) and also shows the main deficiency of the method. Namely, each iteration vector is forced to converge to a different eigenvector by orthogonalizing the ith iteration vector to the $(i - 1)$ iteration vectors that have been orthogonalized already without allowing a more effective linear combination of the vectors to take place. In the example, the iteration was started with two iteration vectors that were linear combinations of the required eigenvectors, and this did not yield any advantage. In general, if the iteration vectors in $\mathbf{X}_{k+1}$ span E_∞ but are not eigenvectors (i.e., the vectors in $\mathbf{X}_{k+1}$ are linear combinations of the eigenvectors $\boldsymbol{\phi}_1, \ldots, \boldsymbol{\phi}_p$), then, although the subspace E_{k+1} has already converged, many more iterations may be needed in order to turn the orthogonal basis of iteration vectors into the basis of eigenvectors.

11.6.2 Subspace Iteration

The following algorithm, which we call *subspace iteration*, finds an orthogonal basis of vectors in E_{k+1}, thus preserving numerical stability in the iteration of (11.148), and also calculates in one step the required eigenvectors when E_{k+1} converges to E_∞. This algorithm is the iteration used in the subspace iteration method, i.e., step 2 of the complete solution phase.

For $k = 1, 2, \ldots$, iterate from E_k to E_{k+1}:

$$\mathbf{K}\overline{\mathbf{X}}_{k+1} = \mathbf{M}\mathbf{X}_k \tag{11.151}$$

Find the projections of the matrices $\mathbf{K}$ and $\mathbf{M}$ onto E_{k+1}:

$$\mathbf{K}_{k+1} = \overline{\mathbf{X}}_{k+1}^T \mathbf{K} \overline{\mathbf{X}}_{k+1} \tag{11.152}$$

$$\mathbf{M}_{k+1} = \overline{\mathbf{X}}_{k+1}^T \mathbf{M} \overline{\mathbf{X}}_{k+1} \tag{11.153}$$

Solve for the eigensystem of the projected matrices:

$$\mathbf{K}_{k+1}\mathbf{Q}_{k+1} = \mathbf{M}_{k+1}\mathbf{Q}_{k+1}\boldsymbol{\Lambda}_{k+1} \tag{11.154}$$

Find an improved approximation to the eigenvectors:

$$\mathbf{X}_{k+1} = \overline{\mathbf{X}}_{k+1}\mathbf{Q}_{k+1} \tag{11.155}$$

Then, provided that the vectors $\mathbf{X}_1$ are not orthogonal to one of the required eigenvectors, we have

$$\mathbf{\Lambda}_{k+1} \to \mathbf{\Lambda} \quad \text{and} \quad \mathbf{X}_{k+1} \to \mathbf{\Phi} \qquad \text{as } k \to \infty$$

In the subspace iteration, it is implied that the iteration vectors are ordered in an appropriate way; i.e., the iteration vectors converging to $\mathbf{\phi}_1, \mathbf{\phi}_2, \ldots$, are stored as the first, second, $\ldots$, columns of $\mathbf{X}_{k+1}$. We demonstrate the iteration procedure by calculating the solution to the problem considered in Example 11.24.

EXAMPLE 11.25: Use the subspace iteration algorithm to solve the problem considered in Example 11.24.

Using the relations in (11.151) to (11.155) with $\mathbf{K}$, $\mathbf{M}$, and $\mathbf{X}_1$ given in Example 11.24, we obtain

$$\overline{\mathbf{X}}_2 = \frac{1}{4} \begin{bmatrix} 1 & 3 \\ 2 & 2 \\ 3 & 1 \end{bmatrix}$$

$$\mathbf{K}_2 = \frac{1}{4} \begin{bmatrix} 5 & 3 \\ 3 & 5 \end{bmatrix}; \qquad \mathbf{M}_2 = \frac{1}{16} \begin{bmatrix} 9 & 7 \\ 7 & 9 \end{bmatrix}$$

Hence,

$$\mathbf{\Lambda}_2 = \begin{bmatrix} 2 & 0 \\ 0 & 4 \end{bmatrix}; \qquad \mathbf{Q}_2 = \begin{bmatrix} \dfrac{1}{\sqrt{2}} & 2 \\ \dfrac{1}{\sqrt{2}} & -2 \end{bmatrix}$$

and

$$\mathbf{X}_2 = \begin{bmatrix} \dfrac{1}{\sqrt{2}} & -1 \\ \dfrac{1}{\sqrt{2}} & 0 \\ \dfrac{1}{\sqrt{2}} & 1 \end{bmatrix}$$

Comparing the results with the solution obtained in Example 11.24, we observe that we have calculated the exact eigenvalues and eigenvectors in the first subspace iteration. This must be the case because the starting iteration vectors $\mathbf{X}_1$ span the subspace defined by $\mathbf{\phi}_1$ and $\mathbf{\phi}_2$.

Considering the subspace iteration, a first observation is that $\mathbf{K}_{k+1}$ and $\mathbf{M}_{k+1}$ in (11.152) and (11.153), respectively, tend toward diagonal form as the number of iterations increases; i.e., $\mathbf{K}_{k+1}$ and $\mathbf{M}_{k+1}$ are diagonal matrices when the columns in $\mathbf{X}_{k+1}$ store multiples of eigenvectors. Hence, it follows from the discussion in Section 11.3.2 that the generalized Jacobi method can be used effectively for the solution of the eigenproblem in (11.154).

An important aspect is the convergence of the method. Assuming that in the iteration the vectors in $\mathbf{X}_{k+1}$ are ordered in such way that the ith diagonal element in $\mathbf{\Lambda}_{k+1}$ is larger than the $(i - 1)$st element, $i = 2, \ldots, p$, then *the ith column in $\mathbf{X}_{k+1}$ converges linearly to $\mathbf{\phi}_i$ and the convergence rate is λ_i/λ_{p+1}* (see K. J. Bathe [B]). Although this is an asymptotic convergence rate, it indicates that the smallest eigenvalues converge fastest. In addition, a higher convergence rate can be obtained by using q iteration vectors, with $q > p$. However, using more iteration vectors will also increase the computer effort for one iteration. In practice, we have found that $q = \min \{2p,\ p + 8\}$ is, in general, the effective, and we use this value. Considering the convergence rate, it should be noted that multiple eigenvalues do not decrease the rate of convergence, provided that $\lambda_{q+1} > \lambda_p$.

As for the iteration schemes presented earlier, the theoretical convergence behavior can be observed in practice only when the iteration vectors are relatively close to eigenvectors. However, in practice, we are very much interested in knowing what happens in the first few iterations when E_{k+1} is not yet "close" to E_∞. Indeed, the effectiveness of the algorithm lies to a large extent in that a few iterations can already give good approximations to the required eigenpairs, the reason being that one subspace iteration given in (11.151) to (11.155) is, in fact, a Ritz analysis, as described in Section 10.3.2. Therefore, *all characteristics of the Ritz analysis pertain also to the subspace iteration; i.e., the smallest eigenvalues are approximated best in the iteration, and all eigenvalue approximations are upper bounds on the actual eigenvalues sought.* It follows that we may think of the subspace iteration as a repeated application of the Ritz analysis method in Section 10.3.2, in which the eigenvector approximations calculated in the previous iteration are used to form the right-hand-side load vectors in the current iteration.

It is important to realize that using either one of the iteration procedures given in (11.148) to (11.150) or (11.151) to (11.155), the same subspace E_{k+1} is spanned by the iteration vectors. Therefore, there is no need to always iterate as in (11.151) to (11.155), but we may first use the simple inverse iteration in (11.148) or inverse iteration with Gram-Schmidt orthogonalization as given in (11.149) and (11.150), and finally use the subspace iteration scheme given in (11.151) to (11.155). The calculated results would be the same in theory as those obtained when only subspace iterations are performed. However, the difficulty then lies in deciding at what stage to orthogonalize the iteration vectors by using (11.152) to (11.155) because the iteration in (11.151) yields vectors that are more and more parallel. Also, the Gram-Schmidt orthogonalization is numerically not very stable. If the iteration vectors have become "too close to each other" because either the initial assumptions gave iteration vectors that were almost parallel or by iterating without orthogonalization, it may be impossible to orthogonalize them because of finite precision arithmetic in the computer. Unfortunately, considering large finite element systems, the starting iteration vectors can in some cases be nearly parallel, although they span a subspace that is close to E_∞, and it is best to immediately orthogonalize the iteration vectors using the projections of $\mathbf{K}$ and $\mathbf{M}$ onto E_2. In addition, using the subspace iteration, we obtain in each iteration the "best" approximations to the required eigenvalues and eigenvectors and can measure convergence in each iteration.

11.6.3 Starting Iteration Vectors

The first step in the subspace iteration method is the selection of the starting iteration vectors in $\mathbf{X}_1$ [see (11.151)]. As pointed out earlier, if starting vectors are used that span the least dominant subspace, the iteration converges in one step. This is the case, for example, when there are only p nonzero masses in a diagonal mass matrix and the starting vectors are unit vectors $\mathbf{e}_i$ with the entries $+1$ corresponding to the mass degrees of freedom. In this case one subspace iteration is in effect a static condensation analysis or a Guyan reduction. This follows from the discussion in Section 10.3.2 and because a subspace iteration embodies a Ritz analysis. Consider the following example.

EXAMPLE 11.26:   Use the subspace iteration to calculate the eigenpairs $(\lambda_1, \boldsymbol{\phi}_1)$ and $(\lambda_2, \boldsymbol{\phi}_2)$ of the problem $\mathbf{K}\boldsymbol{\phi} = \lambda \mathbf{M}\boldsymbol{\phi}$, where

$$\mathbf{K} = \begin{bmatrix} 2 & -1 & 0 & 0 \\ -1 & 2 & -1 & 0 \\ 0 & -1 & 2 & -1 \\ 0 & 0 & -1 & 1 \end{bmatrix}; \qquad \mathbf{M} = \begin{bmatrix} 0 & & & \\ & 2 & & \\ & & 0 & \\ & & & 1 \end{bmatrix}$$

As suggested above, we use as starting vectors the unit vectors $\mathbf{e}_2$ and $\mathbf{e}_4$. Following (11.151) to (11.155), we then obtain

$$\begin{bmatrix} 2 & -1 & 0 & 0 \\ -1 & 2 & -1 & 0 \\ 0 & -1 & 2 & -1 \\ 0 & 0 & -1 & 1 \end{bmatrix} \overline{\mathbf{X}}_2 = \begin{bmatrix} 0 & 0 \\ 2 & 0 \\ 0 & 0 \\ 0 & 1 \end{bmatrix}$$

$$\overline{\mathbf{X}}_2 = \begin{bmatrix} 2 & 1 \\ 4 & 2 \\ 4 & 3 \\ 4 & 4 \end{bmatrix}$$

and

$$\mathbf{K}_2 = 4\begin{bmatrix} 2 & 1 \\ 1 & 1 \end{bmatrix}; \qquad \mathbf{M}_2 = 8\begin{bmatrix} 6 & 4 \\ 4 & 3 \end{bmatrix}$$

Hence,

$$\Lambda_2 = \begin{bmatrix} \left(\dfrac{1}{2} - \dfrac{\sqrt{2}}{4}\right) & 0 \\ 0 & \left(\dfrac{1}{2} + \dfrac{\sqrt{2}}{4}\right) \end{bmatrix}; \qquad \mathbf{Q}_2 = \begin{bmatrix} \dfrac{1}{8 + 4\sqrt{2}} & \dfrac{1}{4\sqrt{2} - 8} \\ \dfrac{1}{4 + 4\sqrt{2}} & \dfrac{1}{4\sqrt{2} - 4} \end{bmatrix}$$

and

$$\mathbf{X}_2 = \begin{bmatrix} \dfrac{1}{4} & -\dfrac{1}{4} \\ \dfrac{1}{2} & -\dfrac{1}{2} \\ \dfrac{1 + \sqrt{2}}{4} & \dfrac{-1 + \sqrt{2}}{4} \\ \dfrac{\sqrt{2}}{2} & \dfrac{\sqrt{2}}{2} \end{bmatrix}$$

Comparing these results with the solution calculated in Example 10.12, we observe that we obtained the exact results with one subspace iteration.

A second case for which the subspace iteration can converge in one step arises when $\mathbf{K}$ and $\mathbf{M}$ are both diagonal. This is a rather trivial case, but it is considered for the development of an effective procedure for the selection of starting iteration vectors when general matrices are involved in the analysis. When $\mathbf{K}$ and $\mathbf{M}$ are diagonal, the iteration vectors should be unit vectors with the entries $+1$ corresponding to those degrees of freedom that have the smallest ratios k_{ii}/m_{ii}. These vectors are the eigenvectors corresponding to the smallest eigenvalues, and this is why convergence is achieved in one step. We demonstrate the procedure in the following example.

EXAMPLE 11.27: Construct starting iteration vectors for the solution of the smallest two eigenvalues by subspace iteration when considering the problem $\mathbf{K}\boldsymbol{\phi} = \lambda\mathbf{M}\boldsymbol{\phi}$, where

$$
\mathbf{K} = \begin{bmatrix} 3 & & & \\ & 2 & & \\ & & 4 & \\ & & & 8 \end{bmatrix}; \qquad \mathbf{M} = \begin{bmatrix} 2 & & & \\ & 0 & & \\ & & 4 & \\ & & & 1 \end{bmatrix}
$$

The ratios k_{ii}/m_{ii} are here $\frac{3}{2}$, ∞, 1, and 8 for $i = 1, \ldots, 4$, and indeed these are the eigenvalues of the problem. The starting vectors to be used are therefore

$$
\mathbf{X}_1 = \begin{bmatrix} 0 & \vdots & 1 \\ 0 & \vdots & 0 \\ 1 & \vdots & 0 \\ 0 & \vdots & 0 \end{bmatrix}
$$

The vectors $\mathbf{X}_1$ are multiples of the required eigenvectors, and hence convergence occurs in the first step of iteration.

The two cases that we dealt with above involved rather special matrices; i.e., in the first case static condensation could be performed, and in the second case the matrices $\mathbf{K}$ and $\mathbf{M}$ were diagonal. In both cases unit vectors $\mathbf{e}_i$ were employed, where $i = r_1, r_2, \ldots, r_p$, and the r_j, $j = 1, 2, \ldots, p$, corresponded to the p smallest values of k_{ii}/m_{ii} over all i. Using this notation, we have $r_1 = 2$ and $r_2 = 4$ for Example 11.26 and $r_1 = 3$, $r_2 = 1$ for Example 11.27.

Although such specific matrices will hardly be encountered in general practical analysis, the results concerning the construction of the starting iteration vectors indicate how in general analysis effective starting iteration vectors may be selected. A general observation is that starting vectors that span the least dominant subspace E_∞ could be selected in the above cases because the mass and stiffness properties have been lumped to a sufficient degree. In a general case, such lumping is not possible or would result in inaccurate stiffness and mass representations of the actual structure. However, although the matrices $\mathbf{K}$ and $\mathbf{M}$ do not have exactly the same form used above, the discussion shows that the starting iteration vectors should be constructed to excite those degrees of freedom with which large mass and small stiffness are associated. Based on this observation, in essence, the following algorithm has been used effectively for the selection of the starting iteration vectors. The first column in $\mathbf{M}\mathbf{X}_1$ is simply the diagonal of $\mathbf{M}$. This ensures that all mass degrees of freedom are excited. The other columns in $\mathbf{M}\mathbf{X}_1$, except for the last column, are unit vectors $\mathbf{e}_i$ with entries $+1$ at the degrees of freedom with the smallest ratios k_{ii}/m_{ii}, and the last column in $\mathbf{M}\mathbf{X}_1$ is a random vector. (In the analysis of large systems, an appropriate spacing between the unit entries in the starting vectors is also important and taken into account; see program SSPACE.)

The starting subspace described above is, in general, only an approximation to the actual subspace required, which we denoted as E_∞; however, the closer $\mathbf{K}$ and $\mathbf{M}$ are to the matrix forms used in Examples 11.26 and 11.27, the "better" the starting subspace, i.e., the fewer iterations to be expected until convergence. In practice, the number of iterations required for convergence depends on the matrices $\mathbf{K}$ and $\mathbf{M}$, the number of eigenvalues sought, the number of iteration vectors used, and on the accuracy required in the eigenvalues and eigenvectors. Experience has shown that when p is small, using the starting sub-space described above and $q = \min(2p, p + 8)$, about 10 to 20 iterations are needed to calculate the largest eigenvalue λ_p to about six-digit precision, with the smaller eigenvalues being predicted more accurately.

As an alternative to using the above starting subspace, it can also be effective to employ the Lanczos procedure to generate the starting iteration vectors. With these starting vectors it may be of advantage to use q considerably larger than p, say $q = 2p$, and then only a few iterations are usually needed for convergence.

The starting subspaces above have proven by experience to be suitable. However, "better" starting vectors may still be available in specific applications. For instance, in dynamic optimization, as the structure is modified in small steps, the eigensystem of the previous structure may be a good approximation to the eigensystem of the new structure. Similarly, if some eigenvectors have already been evaluated and we now want to solve for more eigenvectors, the eigenvectors already calculated would effectively be used in $\mathbf{X}_1$. If the eigenvectors of substructures have already been obtained, these may also be used in establishing the starting iteration vectors in $\mathbf{X}_1$ (see Section 10.3.3).

11.6.4 Convergence

In the subspace iteration it is necessary to measure convergence. Assume that in iteration $(k - 1)$ the eigenvalue approximations $\lambda_i^{(k)}$, $i = 1, \ldots, p$, have been calculated. Then we use (10.107) to measure convergence, in the form

$$\left[1 - \frac{(\lambda_i^{(k)})^2}{(\mathbf{q}_i^{(k)})^T \mathbf{q}_i^{(k)}} \right]^{1/2} \le tol; \qquad i = 1, \ldots, p \qquad (11.156)$$

where $\mathbf{q}_i^{(k)}$ is the vector in the matrix $\mathbf{Q}_k$ corresponding to $\lambda_i^{(k)}$ (see Exercise 11.20) and $tol = 10^{-2s}$ when the eigenvalues shall be accurate to about $2s$ digits. For example, if we iterate until all p bounds in (11.156) are smaller than 10^{-6}, we find that λ_p has been approximated to at least six-digit accuracy, and the smaller eigenvalues have usually been evaluated more accurately. Since the eigenvalue approximations are calculated using a Rayleigh quotient, the eigenvector approximations are accurate to only about s (or more) digits. It should be noted that the iteration is performed with q vectors, $q > p$, but convergence is measured only on the approximations obtained for the p smallest eigenvalues.

Another important point when using the subspace iteration technique is verifying that in fact the required eigenvalues and vectors have been calculated since the relations in (11.146) and (11.147) are satisfied by any eigenpairs. This verification is the third important phase of the subspace iteration method. As pointed out, the iteration in (11.151) to (11.155) converges in the limit to the eigenvectors $\boldsymbol{\phi}_1, \ldots, \boldsymbol{\phi}_p$, provided the starting iteration vectors in $\mathbf{X}_1$ are not orthogonal to any one of the required eigenvectors. The starting subspaces described above have proven, by experience, to be very satisfactory in this regard, although there is no formal mathematical proof available that convergence will indeed always occur. However, once the convergence tolerance in (11.156) is satisfied, with s being at least equal to 3, we can make sure that the smallest eigenvalues and corresponding eigenvectors have indeed been calculated. For the check we use the Sturm sequence prop-

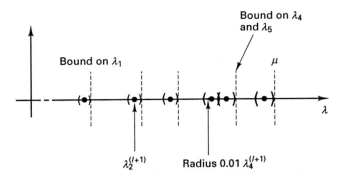

Figure 11.5 Bounds on eigenvalues to apply Sturm sequence check, $p = 6$

erty of the characteristic polynomials of problems $\mathbf{K}\boldsymbol{\phi} = \lambda\mathbf{M}\boldsymbol{\phi}$ and $\mathbf{K}^{(r)}\boldsymbol{\phi}^{(r)} = \lambda^{(r)}\mathbf{M}^{(r)}\boldsymbol{\phi}^{(r)}$ at a shift μ, where μ is just to the right of the calculated value for λ_p (see Fig. 11.5). The Sturm sequence property yields that in the Gauss factorization of $\mathbf{K} - \mu\mathbf{M}$ into $\mathbf{LDL}^T$, the number of negative elements in $\mathbf{D}$ is equal to the number of eigenvalues smaller than μ. Hence, in the case considered, we should have p negative elements in $\mathbf{D}$. However, in order to apply the Sturm sequence check, a meaningful μ must be used that takes account of the fact that we have obtained only approximations to the exact eigenvalues of the problem $\mathbf{K}\boldsymbol{\phi} = \lambda\mathbf{M}\boldsymbol{\phi}$. Let l be the last iteration, so that the calculated eigenvalues are $\lambda_1^{(l+1)}$, $\lambda_2^{(l+1)}, \ldots, \lambda_p^{(l+1)}$. Since (11.156) is satisfied, we can use

$$0.99\lambda_i^{(l+1)} \leq \lambda_i < 1.01\lambda_i^{(l+1)} \tag{11.157}$$

or tighter bounds based on the actual accuracy reached in (11.156). The relation in (11.157) can then be used to establish bounds on all exact eigenvalues, and hence a realistic Sturm sequence check can be applied.

11.6.5 Implementation of the Subspace Iteration Method

The equations of subspace iteration have been presented in (11.151) to (11.155). However, in actual implementation, the solution can be performed more effectively as summarized in Table 11.3, which also gives the corresponding number of operations used.

The solution method is presented in a compact manner in the computer program SSPACE. This program provides only an implementation of the basic steps of the subspace iteration method described above without including acceleration techniques that are important in practice. One important aspect of the method is its relative simplicity when compared with other solution techniques, and this simplicity is also reflected in the program SSPACE.

Subroutine SSPACE.   Program SSPACE is an implementation of the basic subspace iteration method presented above for the solution of the smallest eigenvalues and corresponding eigenvectors of the generalized eigenproblem $\mathbf{K}\boldsymbol{\phi} = \lambda\mathbf{M}\boldsymbol{\phi}$. The argument variables and use of the subroutine are defined using comment lines in the program.

TABLE 11.3 *Summary of subspace iteration solution*

Operation	Calculation	Number of operations		Required storage
		$m = m_K = m_M$	$m = m_K,\ m_M = 0$	
Factorization of $\mathbf{K}$	$\mathbf{K} = \mathbf{L}\mathbf{D}\mathbf{L}^T$	$\frac{1}{2}nm^2 + \frac{3}{2}nm$	$\frac{1}{2}nm^2 + \frac{3}{2}nm$	
Subspace iteration	$\mathbf{K}\overline{\mathbf{X}}_{k+1} = \mathbf{Y}_k$ $\mathbf{K}_{k+1} = \overline{\mathbf{X}}_{k+1}^T \mathbf{Y}_k$ $\overline{\mathbf{Y}}_{k+1} = \mathbf{M}\overline{\mathbf{X}}_{k+1}$ $\mathbf{M}_{k+1} = \overline{\mathbf{X}}_{k+1}^T \overline{\mathbf{Y}}_{k+1}$ $\mathbf{K}_{k+1}\mathbf{Q}_{k+1} = \mathbf{M}_{k+1}\mathbf{Q}_{k+1}\mathbf{\Lambda}_{k+1}$ $\mathbf{Y}_{k+1} = \overline{\mathbf{Y}}_{k+1}\mathbf{Q}_{k+1}$	$nq(2m + 1)$ $\frac{1}{2}nq(q + 1)$ $nq(2m + 1)$ $\frac{1}{2}nq(q + 1)$ $o(q^3)$ neglected nq^2	$nq(2m + 1)$ $\frac{1}{2}nq(q + 1)$ nq $\frac{1}{2}nq(q + 1)$ nq^2	Algorithm is effectively implemented as out-of-core solver
Sturm sequence check	$\overline{\mathbf{K}} = \mathbf{K} - \mu\mathbf{M}$ $\overline{\mathbf{K}} = \mathbf{L}\mathbf{D}\mathbf{L}^T$	$n(m + 1)$ $\frac{1}{2}nm^2 + \frac{3}{2}nm$	n $\frac{1}{2}nm^2 + \frac{3}{2}nm$	
Error* measures	$\dfrac{\left\| \mathbf{K}\boldsymbol{\phi}_i^{(l+1)} - \lambda_i^{(l+1)}\mathbf{M}\boldsymbol{\phi}_i^{(l+1)} \right\|_2}{\left\| \mathbf{K}\boldsymbol{\phi}_i^{(l+1)} \right\|_2}$	$4nm + 5n$	$2nm + 5n$	
Total for solution of p lowest eigenvalues and associated eigenvectors, assuming that ten iterations are required and $q = \min\{2p,\ p + 8\}$		$nm^2 + nm(4 + 4p) + 5np$ $+ 20nq(2m + q + \frac{3}{2})$	$nm^2 + nm(3 + 2p) + 5np$ $+ 20nq(m + q + \frac{3}{2})$	

*The error measures are not needed but may be of interest.

```
      SUBROUTINE SSPACE (A,B,MAXA,R,EIGV,TT,W,AR,BR,VEC,D,RTOLV,BUP,BLO,SSP00001
     1 BUPC,NN,NNM,NWK,NWM,NROOT,RTOL,NC,NNC,NITEM,IFSS,IFPR,NSTIF,IOUT)SSP00002
C . . . . . . . . . . . . . . . . . . . . . . . . . . . . . . . . .  . SSP00003
C .                                                                   . SSP00004
C .    P R O G R A M                                                   . SSP00005
C .        TO SOLVE FOR THE SMALLEST EIGENVALUES-- ASSUMED .GT. 0 --   . SSP00006
C .        AND CORRESPONDING EIGENVECTORS IN THE GENERALIZED           . SSP00007
C .        EIGENPROBLEM USING THE SUBSPACE ITERATION METHOD            . SSP00008
C .                                                                   . SSP00009
C .    - - INPUT VARIABLES - -                                         . SSP00010
C .        A(NWK)     = STIFFNESS MATRIX IN COMPACTED FORM (ASSUMED     . SSP00011
C .                     POSITIVE DEFINITE)                             . SSP00012
C .        B(NWM)     = MASS MATRIX IN COMPACTED FORM                   . SSP00013
C .        MAXA(NNM)  = VECTOR CONTAINING ADDRESSES OF DIAGONAL         . SSP00014
C .                     ELEMENTS OF STIFFNESS MATRIX A                 . SSP00015
C .        R(NN,NC)   = STORAGE FOR EIGENVECTORS                        . SSP00016
C .        EIGV(NC)   = STORAGE FOR EIGENVALUES                         . SSP00017
C .        TT(NN)     = WORKING VECTOR                                  . SSP00018
C .        W(NN)      = WORKING VECTOR                                  . SSP00019
C .        AR(NNC)    = WORKING MATRIX STORING PROJECTION OF K         . SSP00020
C .        BR(NNC)    = WORKING MATRIX STORING PROJECTION OF M         . SSP00021
C .        VEC(NC,NC) = WORKING MATRIX                                  . SSP00022
C .        D(NC)      = WORKING VECTOR                                  . SSP00023
C .        RTOLV(NC)  = WORKING VECTOR                                  . SSP00024
C .        BUP(NC)    = WORKING VECTOR                                  . SSP00025
C .        BLO(NC)    = WORKING VECTOR                                  . SSP00026
C .        BUPC(NC)   = WORKING VECTOR                                  . SSP00027
C .        NN         = ORDER OF STIFFNESS AND MASS MATRICES           . SSP00028
C .        NNM        = NN + 1                                          . SSP00029
C .        NWK        = NUMBER OF ELEMENTS BELOW SKYLINE OF            . SSP00030
C .                     STIFFNESS MATRIX                               . SSP00031
C .        NWM        = NUMBER OF ELEMENTS BELOW SKYLINE OF            . SSP00032
C .                     MASS MATRIX                                    . SSP00033
C .                     I. E. NWM=NWK FOR CONSISTENT MASS MATRIX       . SSP00034
C .                          NWM=NN   FOR LUMPED MASS MATRIX           . SSP00035
C .        NROOT      = NUMBER OF REQUIRED EIGENVALUES AND EIGENVECTORS.SSP00036
C .        RTOL       = CONVERGENCE TOLERANCE ON EIGENVALUES           . SSP00037
C .                     ( 1.E-06 OR SMALLER )                          . SSP00038
C .        NC         = NUMBER OF ITERATION VECTORS USED               . SSP00039
C .                     (USUALLY SET TO MIN(2*NROOT, NROOT+8), BUT NC  . SSP00040
C .                     CANNOT BE LARGER THAN THE NUMBER OF MASS       . SSP00041
C .                     DEGREES OF FREEDOM)                            . SSP00042
C .        NNC        = NC*(NC+1)/2 DIMENSION OF STORAGE VECTORS AR,BR . SSP00043
C .        NITEM      = MAXIMUM NUMBER OF SUBSPACE ITERATIONS PERMITTED.SSP00044
C .                     (USUALLY SET TO 16)                            . SSP00045
C .                     THE PARAMETERS NC AND/OR NITEM MUST BE         . SSP00046
C .                     INCREASED IF A SOLUTION HAS NOT CONVERGED      . SSP00047
C .        IFSS       = FLAG FOR STURM SEQUENCE CHECK                  . SSP00048
C .                       EQ.0  NO CHECK                               . SSP00049
C .                       EQ.1  CHECK                                  . SSP00050
C .        IFPR       = FLAG FOR PRINTING DURING ITERATION             . SSP00051
C .                       EQ.0  NO PRINTING                            . SSP00052
C .                       EQ.1  PRINT                                  . SSP00053
C .        NSTIF      = SCRATCH FILE                                   . SSP00054
C .        IOUT       = UNIT USED FOR OUTPUT                           . SSP00055
C .                                                                   . SSP00056
C .    - - OUTPUT - -                                                  . SSP00057
C .        EIGV(NROOT) = EIGENVALUES                                   . SSP00058
C .        R(NN,NROOT) = EIGENVECTORS                                  . SSP00059
C .                                                                   . SSP00060
C . . . . . . . . . . . . . . . . . . . . . . . . . . . . . . . . .  . SSP00061
      IMPLICIT DOUBLE PRECISION (A-H,O-Z)                               SSP00062
C .                                                                   . SSP00063
C . THIS PROGRAM IS USED IN SINGLE PRECISION ARITHMETIC ON CRAY        . SSP00064
C . EQUIPMENT AND DOUBLE PRECISION ARITHMETIC ON IBM MACHINES,         . SSP00065
C . ENGINEERING WORKSTATIONS AND PCS. DEACTIVATE ABOVE LINE FOR        . SSP00066
C . SINGLE PRECISION ARITHMETIC.                                       . SSP00067
C . . . . . . . . . . . . . . . . . . . . . . . . . . . . . . . . .  . SSP00068
      INTEGER MAXA(NNM)                                                 SSP00069
      DIMENSION A(NWK),B(NWM),R(NN,NC),TT(NN),W(NN),EIGV(NC),           SSP00070
```

```
      1                 D(NC),VEC(NC,NC),AR(NNC),BR(NNC),RTOLV(NC),BUP(NC),        SSP00071
      2                 BLO(NC),BUPC(NC)                                           SSP00072
C                                                                                  SSP00073
C        SET TOLERANCE FOR JACOBI ITERATION                                        SSP00074
         TOLJ=1.0D-12                                                              SSP00075
C                                                                                  SSP00076
C        INITIALIZATION                                                            SSP00077
C                                                                                  SSP00078
         ICONV=0                                                                   SSP00079
         NSCH=0                                                                    SSP00080
         NSMAX=12                                                                  SSP00081
         N1=NC + 1                                                                 SSP00082
         NC1=NC - 1                                                                SSP00083
         REWIND NSTIF                                                              SSP00084
         WRITE (NSTIF) A                                                           SSP00085
         DO 2 I=1,NC                                                               SSP00086
    2    D(I)=0.                                                                   SSP00087
C                                                                                  SSP00088
C        ESTABLISH STARTING ITERATION VECTORS                                      SSP00089
C                                                                                  SSP00090
         ND=NN/NC                                                                  SSP00091
         IF (NWM.GT.NN) GO TO 4                                                    SSP00092
         J=0                                                                       SSP00093
         DO 6 I=1,NN                                                               SSP00094
         II=MAXA(I)                                                                SSP00095
         R(I,1)=B(I)                                                               SSP00096
         IF (B(I).GT.0) J=J + 1                                                    SSP00097
    6    W(I)=B(I)/A(II)                                                           SSP00098
         IF (NC.LE.J) GO TO 16                                                     SSP00099
         WRITE (IOUT,1007)                                                         SSP00100
         GO TO 800                                                                 SSP00101
    4    DO 10 I=1,NN                                                              SSP00102
         II=MAXA(I)                                                                SSP00103
         R(I,1)=B(II)                                                              SSP00104
   10    W(I)=B(II)/A(II)                                                          SSP00105
   16    DO 20 J=2,NC                                                              SSP00106
         DO 20 I=1,NN                                                              SSP00107
   20    R(I,J)=0.                                                                 SSP00108
C                                                                                  SSP00109
         L=NN - ND                                                                 SSP00110
         DO 30 J=2,NC                                                              SSP00111
         RT=0.                                                                     SSP00112
         DO 40 I=1,L                                                               SSP00113
         IF (W(I).LT.RT) GO TO 40                                                  SSP00114
         RT=W(I)                                                                   SSP00115
         IJ=I                                                                      SSP00116
   40    CONTINUE                                                                  SSP00117
         DO 50 I=L,NN                                                              SSP00118
         IF (W(I).LE.RT) GO TO 50                                                  SSP00119
         RT=W(I)                                                                   SSP00120
         IJ=I                                                                      SSP00121
   50    CONTINUE                                                                  SSP00122
         TT(J)=FLOAT(IJ)                                                           SSP00123
         W(IJ)=0.                                                                  SSP00124
         L=L - ND                                                                  SSP00125
   30    R(IJ,J)=1.                                                                SSP00126
C                                                                                  SSP00127
         WRITE (IOUT,1008)                                                         SSP00128
         WRITE (IOUT,1002) (TT(J),J=2,NC)                                          SSP00129
C                                                                                  SSP00130
C        A RANDOM VECTOR IS ADDED TO THE LAST VECTOR                               SSP00131
C                                                                                  SSP00132
         PI=3.141592654D0                                                          SSP00133
         XX=0.5D0                                                                  SSP00134
         DO 60 K=1,NN                                                              SSP00135
         XX=(PI + XX)**5                                                           SSP00136
         IX=INT(XX)                                                                SSP00137
         XX=XX - FLOAT(IX)                                                         SSP00138
   60    R(K,NC)=R(K,NC) + XX                                                      SSP00139
C                                                                                  SSP00140
```

```
C     FACTORIZE MATRIX A INTO (L)*(D)*(L(T))                    SSP00141
C                                                               SSP00142
                                                                SSP00143
      ISH=0                                                     SSP00144
      CALL DECOMP (A,MAXA,NN,ISH,IOUT)                          SSP00145
C                                                               SSP00146
C - - - S T A R T   O F   I T E R A T I O N   L O O P           SSP00147
C                                                               SSP00148
      NITE=0                                                    SSP00149
      TOLJ2=1.0D-24                                             SSP00150
  100 NITE=NITE + 1                                             SSP00151
      IF (IFPR.EQ.0) GO TO 90                                   SSP00152
      WRITE (IOUT,1010) NITE                                    SSP00153
C                                                               SSP00154
C     CALCULATE THE PROJECTIONS OF A AND B                      SSP00155
C                                                               SSP00156
   90 IJ=0                                                      SSP00157
      DO 110 J=1,NC                                             SSP00158
      DO 120 K=1,NN                                             SSP00159
  120 TT(K)=R(K,J)                                              SSP00160
      CALL REDBAK (A,TT,MAXA,NN)                                SSP00161
      DO 130 I=J,NC                                             SSP00162
      ART=0.                                                    SSP00163
      DO 140 K=1,NN                                             SSP00164
  140 ART=ART + R(K,I)*TT(K)                                    SSP00165
      IJ=IJ + 1                                                 SSP00166
  130 AR(IJ)=ART                                                SSP00167
      DO 150 K=1,NN                                             SSP00168
  150 R(K,J)=TT(K)                                              SSP00169
  110 CONTINUE                                                  SSP00170
      IJ=0                                                      SSP00171
      DO 160 J=1,NC                                             SSP00172
      CALL MULT (TT,B,R(1,J),MAXA,NN,NWM)                       SSP00173
      DO 180 I=J,NC                                             SSP00174
      BRT=0.                                                    SSP00175
      DO 190 K=1,NN                                             SSP00176
  190 BRT=BRT + R(K,I)*TT(K)                                    SSP00177
      IJ=IJ + 1                                                 SSP00178
  180 BR(IJ)=BRT                                                SSP00179
      IF (ICONV.GT.0) GO TO 160                                 SSP00180
      DO 200 K=1,NN                                             SSP00181
  200 R(K,J)=TT(K)                                              SSP00182
  160 CONTINUE                                                  SSP00183
C                                                               SSP00184
C     SOLVE FOR EIGENSYSTEM OF SUBSPACE OPERATORS               SSP00185
C                                                               SSP00186
      IF (IFPR.EQ.0) GO TO 320                                  SSP00187
      IND=1                                                     SSP00188
  210 WRITE (IOUT,1020)                                         SSP00189
      II=1                                                      SSP00190
      DO 300 I=1,NC                                             SSP00191
      ITEMP=II + NC - I                                         SSP00192
      WRITE (IOUT,1005) (AR(J),J=II,ITEMP)                      SSP00193
  300 II=II + N1 - I                                            SSP00194
      WRITE (IOUT,1030)                                         SSP00195
      II=1                                                      SSP00196
      DO 310 I=1,NC                                             SSP00197
      ITEMP=II + NC - I                                         SSP00198
      WRITE (IOUT,1005) (BR(J),J=II,ITEMP)                      SSP00199
  310 II=II + N1 - I                                            SSP00200
      IF (IND.EQ.2) GO TO 350                                   SSP00201
C                                                               SSP00202
  320 CALL JACOBI (AR,BR,VEC,EIGV,W,NC,NNC,TOLJ,NSMAX,IFPR,IOUT) SSP00203
C                                                               SSP00204
      IF (IFPR.EQ.0) GO TO 350                                  SSP00205
      WRITE (IOUT,1040)                                         SSP00206
      IND=2                                                     SSP00207
      GO TO 210                                                 SSP00208
C                                                               SSP00209
C     ARRANGE EIGENVALUES IN ASCENDING ORDER                    SSP00210
C
```

```
  350 IS=0                                                          SSP00211
      II=1                                                          SSP00212
      DO 360 I=1,NC1                                                SSP00213
      ITEMP=II + N1 - I                                             SSP00214
      IF (EIGV(I+1).GE.EIGV(I)) GO TO 360                           SSP00215
      IS=IS + 1                                                     SSP00216
      EIGVT=EIGV(I+1)                                               SSP00217
      EIGV(I+1)=EIGV(I)                                             SSP00218
      EIGV(I)=EIGVT                                                 SSP00219
      BT=BR(ITEMP)                                                  SSP00220
      BR(ITEMP)=BR(II)                                              SSP00221
      BR(II)=BT                                                     SSP00222
      DO 370 K=1,NC                                                 SSP00223
      RT=VEC(K,I+1)                                                 SSP00224
      VEC(K,I+1)=VEC(K,I)                                           SSP00225
  370 VEC(K,I)=RT                                                   SSP00226
  360 II=ITEMP                                                      SSP00227
      IF (IS.GT.0) GO TO 350                                        SSP00228
      IF (IFPR.EQ.0) GO TO 375                                      SSP00229
      WRITE (IOUT,1035)                                             SSP00230
      WRITE (IOUT,1006) (EIGV(I),I=1,NC)                            SSP00231
C                                                                   SSP00232
C     CALCULATE B TIMES APPROXIMATE EIGENVECTORS (ICONV.EQ.0)       SSP00233
C        OR        FINAL EIGENVECTOR APPROXIMATIONS (ICONV.GT.0)    SSP00234
C                                                                   SSP00235
  375 DO 420 I=1,NN                                                 SSP00236
      DO 422 J=1,NC                                                 SSP00237
  422 TT(J)=R(I,J)                                                  SSP00238
      DO 424 K=1,NC                                                 SSP00239
      RT=0.                                                         SSP00240
      DO 430 L=1,NC                                                 SSP00241
  430 RT=RT + TT(L)*VEC(L,K)                                        SSP00242
  424 R(I,K)=RT                                                     SSP00243
  420 CONTINUE                                                      SSP00244
C                                                                   SSP00245
C     CALCULATE ERROR BOUNDS AND CHECK FOR CONVERGENCE OF EIGENVALUES  SSP00246
C                                                                   SSP00247
      DO 380 I=1,NC                                                 SSP00248
      VDOT=0.                                                       SSP00249
      DO 382 J=1,NC                                                 SSP00250
  382 VDOT=VDOT + VEC(I,J)*VEC(I,J)                                 SSP00251
      EIGV2=EIGV(I)*EIGV(I)                                         SSP00252
      DIF=VDOT - EIGV2                                              SSP00253
      RDIF=MAX(DIF,TOLJ2*EIGV2)/EIGV2                               SSP00254
      RDIF=SQRT(RDIF)                                               SSP00255
      RTOLV(I)=RDIF                                                 SSP00256
  380 CONTINUE                                                      SSP00257
      IF (IFPR.EQ.0 .AND. ICONV.EQ.0) GO TO 385                     SSP00258
      WRITE (IOUT,1050)                                             SSP00259
      WRITE (IOUT,1005) (RTOLV(I),I=1,NC)                           SSP00260
  385 IF (ICONV.GT.0) GO TO 500                                     SSP00261
C                                                                   SSP00262
      DO 390 I=1,NROOT                                              SSP00263
      IF (RTOLV(I).GT.RTOL) GO TO 400                               SSP00264
  390 CONTINUE                                                      SSP00265
      WRITE (IOUT,1060) RTOL                                        SSP00266
      ICONV=1                                                       SSP00267
      GO TO 100                                                     SSP00268
  400 IF (NITE.LT.NITEM) GO TO 100                                  SSP00269
      WRITE (IOUT,1070)                                             SSP00270
      ICONV=2                                                       SSP00271
      IFSS=0                                                        SSP00272
      GO TO 100                                                     SSP00273
C                                                                   SSP00274
C - - - E N D   O F   I T E R A T I O N   L O O P                   SSP00275
C                                                                   SSP00276
  500 WRITE (IOUT,1100)                                             SSP00277
      WRITE (IOUT,1006) (EIGV(I),I=1,NROOT)                         SSP00278
      WRITE (IOUT,1110)                                             SSP00279
      DO 530 J=1,NROOT                                              SSP00280
  530 WRITE (IOUT,1005) (R(K,J),K=1,NN)                             SSP00281
```

```
C                                                               SSP00282
C     CALCULATE AND PRINT ERROR MEASURES                        SSP00283
C                                                               SSP00284
      REWIND NSTIF                                              SSP00285
      READ (NSTIF) A                                            SSP00286
C                                                               SSP00287
      DO 580 L=1,NROOT                                          SSP00288
      RT=EIGV(L)                                                SSP00289
      CALL MULT(TT,A,R(1,L),MAXA,NN,NWK)                        SSP00290
      VNORM=0.                                                  SSP00291
      DO 590 I=1,NN                                             SSP00292
  590 VNORM=VNORM + TT(I)*TT(I)                                 SSP00293
      CALL MULT(W,B,R(1,L),MAXA,NN,NWM)                         SSP00294
      WNORM=0.                                                  SSP00295
      DO 600 I=1,NN                                             SSP00296
      TT(I)=TT(I) - RT*W(I)                                     SSP00297
  600 WNORM=WNORM + TT(I)*TT(I)                                 SSP00298
      VNORM=SQRT(VNORM)                                         SSP00299
      WNORM=SQRT(WNORM)                                         SSP00300
      D(L)=WNORM/VNORM                                          SSP00301
  580 CONTINUE                                                  SSP00302
      WRITE (IOUT,1115)                                         SSP00303
      WRITE (IOUT,1005) (D(I),I=1,NROOT)                        SSP00304
C                                                               SSP00305
C     APPLY STURM SEQUENCE CHECK                                SSP00306
C                                                               SSP00307
      IF (IFSS.EQ.0) GO TO 900                                  SSP00308
      CALL SCHECK (EIGV,RTOLV,BUP,BLO,BUPC,D,NC,NEI,RTOL,SHIFT,IOUT)  SSP00309
C                                                               SSP00310
      WRITE (IOUT,1120) SHIFT                                   SSP00311
C                                                               SSP00312
C     SHIFT MATRIX A                                            SSP00313
C                                                               SSP00314
      REWIND NSTIF                                              SSP00315
      READ (NSTIF) A                                            SSP00316
      IF (NWM.GT.NN) GO TO 645                                  SSP00317
      DO 640 I=1,NN                                             SSP00318
      II=MAXA(I)                                                SSP00319
  640 A(II)=A(II) - B(I)*SHIFT                                  SSP00320
      GO TO 660                                                 SSP00321
  645 DO 650 I=1,NWK                                            SSP00322
  650 A(I)=A(I) - B(I)*SHIFT                                    SSP00323
C                                                               SSP00324
C     FACTORIZE SHIFTED MATRIX                                  SSP00325
C                                                               SSP00326
  660 ISH=1                                                     SSP00327
      CALL DECOMP (A,MAXA,NN,ISH,IOUT)                          SSP00328
C                                                               SSP00329
C     COUNT NUMBER OF NEGATIVE DIAGONAL ELEMENTS                SSP00330
C                                                               SSP00331
      NSCH=0                                                    SSP00332
      DO 664 I=1,NN                                             SSP00333
      II=MAXA(I)                                                SSP00334
      IF (A(II).LT.0.) NSCH=NSCH + 1                            SSP00335
  664 CONTINUE                                                  SSP00336
      IF (NSCH.EQ.NEI) GO TO 670                                SSP00337
      NMIS=NSCH - NEI                                           SSP00338
      WRITE (IOUT,1130) NMIS                                    SSP00339
      GO TO 900                                                 SSP00340
  670 WRITE (IOUT,1140) NSCH                                    SSP00341
      GO TO 900                                                 SSP00342
C                                                               SSP00343
  800 STOP                                                      SSP00344
  900 RETURN                                                    SSP00345
C                                                               SSP00346
 1002 FORMAT (' ',10F10.0)                                      SSP00347
 1005 FORMAT (' ',12E11.4)                                      SSP00348
 1006 FORMAT (' ',6E22.14)                                      SSP00349
 1007 FORMAT (////,' STOP, NC IS LARGER THAN THE NUMBER OF MASS ',  SSP00350
     1        'DEGREES OF FREEDOM')                             SSP00351
```

```
1008 FORMAT (////,' DEGREES OF FREEDOM EXCITED BY UNIT STARTING ',      SSP00352
    1          'ITERATION VECTORS')                                      SSP00353
1010 FORMAT (//,' I T E R A T I O N   N U M B E R ',I8)                  SSP00354
1020 FORMAT (/,' PROJECTION OF A (MATRIX AR)')                           SSP00355
1030 FORMAT (/,' PROJECTION OF B (MATRIX BR)')                           SSP00356
1035 FORMAT (/,' EIGENVALUES OF AR-LAMBDA*BR')                           SSP00357
1040 FORMAT (//,' AR AND BR AFTER JACOBI DIAGONALIZATION')               SSP00358
1050 FORMAT (/,' ERROR BOUNDS REACHED ON EIGENVALUES')                   SSP00359
1060 FORMAT (///,' CONVERGENCE REACHED FOR RTOL ',E10.4)                 SSP00360
1070 FORMAT (' *** NO CONVERGENCE IN MAXIMUM NUMBER OF ITERATIONS',      SSP00361
    1          ' PERMITTED',//,                                          SSP00362
    2          ' WE ACCEPT CURRENT ITERATION VALUES',/,                  SSP00363
    3          ' THE STURM SEQUENCE CHECK IS NOT PERFORMED')             SSP00364
1100 FORMAT (///,' THE CALCULATED EIGENVALUES ARE')                      SSP00365
1115 FORMAT (//,' ERROR MEASURES ON THE EIGENVALUES')                    SSP00366
1110 FORMAT (//,' THE CALCULATED EIGENVECTORS ARE',/)                    SSP00367
1120 FORMAT (///,' CHECK APPLIED AT SHIFT ',E22.14)                      SSP00368
1130 FORMAT (//,' THERE ARE ',I8,' EIGENVALUES MISSING')                 SSP00369
1140 FORMAT (//,' WE FOUND THE LOWEST ',I8,' EIGENVALUES')               SSP00370
C                                                                        SSP00371
     END                                                                 SSP00372
     SUBROUTINE DECOMP (A,MAXA,NN,ISH,IOUT)                              SSP00373
C . . . . . . . . . . . . . . . . . . . . . . . . . . . . . . . . . .   SSP00374
C .                                                                  .   SSP00375
C .  P R O G R A M                                                   .   SSP00376
C .      TO CALCULATE (L)*(D)*(L)(T) FACTORIZATION OF                .   SSP00377
C .      STIFFNESS MATRIX                                            .   SSP00378
C .                                                                  .   SSP00379
C . . . . . . . . . . . . . . . . . . . . . . . . . . . . . . . . . .   SSP00380
C                                                                        SSP00381
     IMPLICIT DOUBLE PRECISION (A-H,O-Z)                                 SSP00382
     DIMENSION A(1),MAXA(1)                                              SSP00383
     IF (NN.EQ.1) GO TO 900                                              SSP00384
C                                                                        SSP00385
     DO 200 N=1,NN                                                       SSP00386
     KN=MAXA(N)                                                          SSP00387
     KL=KN + 1                                                           SSP00388
     KU=MAXA(N+1) - 1                                                    SSP00389
     KH=KU - KL                                                          SSP00390
     IF (KH) 304,240,210                                                 SSP00391
 210 K=N - KH                                                            SSP00392
     IC=0                                                                SSP00393
     KLT=KU                                                              SSP00394
     DO 260 J=1,KH                                                       SSP00395
     IC=IC + 1                                                           SSP00396
     KLT=KLT - 1                                                         SSP00397
     KI=MAXA(K)                                                          SSP00398
     ND=MAXA(K+1) - KI - 1                                               SSP00399
     IF (ND) 260,260,270                                                 SSP00400
 270 KK=MIN0(IC,ND)                                                      SSP00401
     C=0.                                                                SSP00402
     DO 280 L=1,KK                                                       SSP00403
 280 C=C + A(KI+L)*A(KLT+L)                                              SSP00404
     A(KLT)=A(KLT) - C                                                   SSP00405
 260 K=K + 1                                                             SSP00406
 240 K=N                                                                 SSP00407
     B=0.                                                                SSP00408
     DO 300 KK=KL,KU                                                     SSP00409
     K=K - 1                                                             SSP00410
     KI=MAXA(K)                                                          SSP00411
     C=A(KK)/A(KI)                                                       SSP00412
     IF (ABS(C).LT.1.E07) GO TO 290                                      SSP00413
     WRITE (IOUT,2010) N,C                                               SSP00414
     GO TO 800                                                           SSP00415
 290 B=B + C*A(KK)                                                       SSP00416
 300 A(KK)=C                                                             SSP00417
     A(KN)=A(KN) - B                                                     SSP00418
 304 IF (A(KN)) 310,310,200                                              SSP00419
 310 IF (ISH.EQ.0) GO TO 320                                             SSP00420
     IF (A(KN).EQ.0.) A(KN)=-1.E-16                                      SSP00421
```

```
         GO TO 200                                                    SSP00422
    320 WRITE (IOUT,2000) N,A(KN)                                     SSP00423
         GO TO 800                                                    SSP00424
    200 CONTINUE                                                      SSP00425
         GO TO 900                                                    SSP00426
  C                                                                   SSP00427
    800 STOP                                                          SSP00428
    900 RETURN                                                        SSP00429
  C                                                                   SSP00430
   2000 FORMAT (//' STOP - STIFFNESS MATRIX NOT POSITIVE DEFINITE',//, SSP00431
      1         ' NONPOSITIVE PIVOT FOR EQUATION ',I8,//,             SSP00432
      2         ' PIVOT = ',E20.12)                                   SSP00433
   2010 FORMAT (//' STOP - STURM SEQUENCE CHECK FAILED BECAUSE OF',   SSP00434
      1         ' MULTIPLIER GROWTH FOR COLUMN NUMBER ',I8,//,        SSP00435
      2         ' MULTIPLIER = ',E20.8)                               SSP00436
         END                                                          SSP00437
         SUBROUTINE REDBAK (A,V,MAXA,NN)                              SSP00438
  C . . . . . . . . . . . . . . . . . . . . . . . . . . . . . . . .   SSP00439
  C .                                                               . SSP00440
  C .  P R O G R A M                                                . SSP00441
  C .      TO REDUCE AND BACK-SUBSTITUTE ITERATION VECTORS          . SSP00442
  C .                                                               . SSP00443
  C . . . . . . . . . . . . . . . . . . . . . . . . . . . . . . . .   SSP00444
  C                                                                   SSP00445
         IMPLICIT DOUBLE PRECISION (A-H,O-Z)                          SSP00446
         DIMENSION A(1),V(1),MAXA(1)                                  SSP00447
  C                                                                   SSP00448
         DO 400 N=1,NN                                                SSP00449
         KL=MAXA(N) + 1                                               SSP00450
         KU=MAXA(N+1) - 1                                             SSP00451
         IF (KU-KL) 400,410,410                                       SSP00452
    410 K=N                                                           SSP00453
         C=0.                                                         SSP00454
         DO 420 KK=KL,KU                                              SSP00455
         K=K - 1                                                      SSP00456
    420 C=C + A(KK)*V(K)                                              SSP00457
         V(N)=V(N) - C                                                SSP00458
    400 CONTINUE                                                      SSP00459
  C                                                                   SSP00460
         DO 480 N=1,NN                                                SSP00461
         K=MAXA(N)                                                    SSP00462
    480 V(N)=V(N)/A(K)                                                SSP00463
         IF (NN.EQ.1) GO TO 900                                       SSP00464
         N=NN                                                         SSP00465
         DO 500 L=2,NN                                                SSP00466
         KL=MAXA(N) + 1                                               SSP00467
         KU=MAXA(N+1) - 1                                             SSP00468
         IF (KU-KL) 500,510,510                                       SSP00469
    510 K=N                                                           SSP00470
         DO 520 KK=KL,KU                                              SSP00471
         K=K - 1                                                      SSP00472
    520 V(K)=V(K) - A(KK)*V(N)                                        SSP00473
    500 N=N - 1                                                       SSP00474
  C                                                                   SSP00475
    900 RETURN                                                        SSP00476
         END                                                          SSP00477
         SUBROUTINE MULT (TT,B,RR,MAXA,NN,NWM)                        SSP00478
  C . . . . . . . . . . . . . . . . . . . . . . . . . . . . . . . .   SSP00479
  C .                                                               . SSP00480
  C .  P R O G R A M                                                . SSP00481
  C .      TO EVALUATE PRODUCT OF B TIMES RR AND STORE RESULT IN TT . SSP00482
  C .                                                               . SSP00483
  C . . . . . . . . . . . . . . . . . . . . . . . . . . . . . . . .   SSP00484
  C                                                                   SSP00485
         IMPLICIT DOUBLE PRECISION (A-H,O-Z)                          SSP00486
         DIMENSION TT(1),B(1),RR(1),MAXA(1)                           SSP00487
  C                                                                   SSP00488
         IF (NWM.GT.NN) GO TO 20                                      SSP00489
         DO 10 I=1,NN                                                 SSP00490
     10 TT(I)=B(I)*RR(I)                                              SSP00491
```

```
         GO TO 900                                              SSP00492
C                                                               SSP00493
   20 DO 40 I=1,NN                                              SSP00494
   40 TT(I)=0.                                                  SSP00495
      DO 100 I=1,NN                                             SSP00496
      KL=MAXA(I)                                                SSP00497
      KU=MAXA(I+1) - 1                                          SSP00498
      II=I + 1                                                  SSP00499
      CC=RR(I)                                                  SSP00500
      DO 100 KK=KL,KU                                           SSP00501
      II=II - 1                                                 SSP00502
  100 TT(II)=TT(II) + B(KK)*CC                                  SSP00503
      IF (NN.EQ.1) GO TO 900                                    SSP00504
      DO 200 I=2,NN                                             SSP00505
      KL=MAXA(I) + 1                                            SSP00506
      KU=MAXA(I+1) - 1                                          SSP00507
      IF (KU-KL) 200,210,210                                    SSP00508
  210 II=I                                                      SSP00509
      AA=0.                                                     SSP00510
      DO 220 KK=KL,KU                                           SSP00511
      II=II - 1                                                 SSP00512
  220 AA=AA + B(KK)*RR(II)                                      SSP00513
      TT(I)=TT(I) + AA                                          SSP00514
  200 CONTINUE                                                  SSP00515
C                                                               SSP00516
  900 RETURN                                                    SSP00517
      END                                                       SSP00518
      SUBROUTINE SCHECK (EIGV,RTOLV,BUP,BLO,BUPC,NEIV,NC,NEI,RTOL,  SSP00519
     1                   SHIFT,IOUT)                            SSP00520
C . . . . . . . . . . . . . . . . . . . . . . . . . . . . . .  SSP00521
C .                                                          .  SSP00522
C .    P R O G R A M                                         .  SSP00523
C .        TO EVALUATE SHIFT FOR STURM SEQUENCE CHECK        .  SSP00524
C .                                                          .  SSP00525
C . . . . . . . . . . . . . . . . . . . . . . . . . . . . . .  SSP00526
C                                                               SSP00527
      IMPLICIT DOUBLE PRECISION (A-H,O-Z)                       SSP00528
      DIMENSION EIGV(NC),RTOLV(NC),BUP(NC),BLO(NC),BUPC(NC),NEIV(NC)  SSP00529
C                                                               SSP00530
      FTOL=0.01                                                 SSP00531
C                                                               SSP00532
      DO 100 I=1,NC                                             SSP00533
      BUP(I)=EIGV(I)*(1.+FTOL)                                  SSP00534
  100 BLO(I)=EIGV(I)*(1.-FTOL)                                  SSP00535
      NROOT=0                                                   SSP00536
      DO 120 I=1,NC                                             SSP00537
  120 IF (RTOLV(I).LT.RTOL) NROOT=NROOT + 1                     SSP00538
      IF (NROOT.GE.1) GO TO 200                                 SSP00539
      WRITE (IOUT,1010)                                         SSP00540
      GO TO 800                                                 SSP00541
C                                                               SSP00542
C       FIND UPPER BOUNDS ON EIGENVALUE CLUSTERS                SSP00543
C                                                               SSP00544
  200 DO 240 I=1,NROOT                                          SSP00545
  240 NEIV(I)=1                                                 SSP00546
      IF (NROOT.NE.1) GO TO 260                                 SSP00547
      BUPC(1)=BUP(1)                                            SSP00548
      LM=1                                                      SSP00549
      L=1                                                       SSP00550
      I=2                                                       SSP00551
      GO TO 295                                                 SSP00552
  260 L=1                                                       SSP00553
      I=2                                                       SSP00554
  270 IF (BUP(I-1).LE.BLO(I)) GO TO 280                         SSP00555
      NEIV(L)=NEIV(L) + 1                                       SSP00556
      I=I + 1                                                   SSP00557
      IF (I.LE.NROOT) GO TO 270                                 SSP00558
  280 BUPC(L)=BUP(I-1)                                          SSP00559
      IF (I.GT.NROOT) GO TO 290                                 SSP00560
      L=L + 1                                                   SSP00561
```

```
         I=I + 1                                              SSP00562
         IF (I.LE.NROOT) GO TO 270                            SSP00563
         BUPC(L)=BUP(I-1)                                     SSP00564
     290 LM=L                                                 SSP00565
         IF (NROOT.EQ.NC) GO TO 300                           SSP00566
     295 IF (BUP(I-1).LE.BLO(I)) GO TO 300                    SSP00567
         IF (RTOLV(I).GT.RTOL) GO TO 300                      SSP00568
         BUPC(L)=BUP(I)                                       SSP00569
         NEIV(L)=NEIV(L) + 1                                  SSP00570
         NROOT=NROOT + 1                                      SSP00571
         IF (NROOT.EQ.NC) GO TO 300                           SSP00572
         I=I + 1                                              SSP00573
         GO TO 295                                            SSP00574
C                                                             SSP00575
C        FIND SHIFT                                           SSP00576
C                                                             SSP00577
     300 WRITE (IOUT,1020)                                    SSP00578
         WRITE (IOUT,1005) (BUPC(I),I=1,LM)                   SSP00579
         WRITE (IOUT,1030)                                    SSP00580
         WRITE (IOUT,1006) (NEIV(I),I=1,LM)                   SSP00581
         LL=LM - 1                                            SSP00582
         IF (LM.EQ.1) GO TO 310                               SSP00583
     330 DO 320 I=1,LL                                        SSP00584
     320 NEIV(L)=NEIV(L) + NEIV(I)                            SSP00585
         L=L - 1                                              SSP00586
         LL=LL - 1                                            SSP00587
         IF (L.NE.1) GO TO 330                                SSP00588
     310 WRITE (IOUT,1040)                                    SSP00589
         WRITE (IOUT,1006) (NEIV(I),I=1,LM)                   SSP00590
         L=0                                                  SSP00591
         DO 340 I=1,LM                                        SSP00592
         L=L + 1                                              SSP00593
         IF (NEIV(I).GE.NROOT) GO TO 350                      SSP00594
     340 CONTINUE                                             SSP00595
     350 SHIFT=BUPC(L)                                        SSP00596
         NEI=NEIV(L)                                          SSP00597
         GO TO 900                                            SSP00598
C                                                             SSP00599
     800 STOP                                                 SSP00600
     900 RETURN                                               SSP00601
C                                                             SSP00602
    1005 FORMAT (' ',6E22.14)                                 SSP00603
    1006 FORMAT (' ',6I22)                                    SSP00604
    1010 FORMAT (' *** ERROR ***  SOLUTION STOP IN *SCHECK*',/,SSP00605
        1         ' NO EIGENVALUES FOUND',/)                  SSP00606
    1020 FORMAT (////,' UPPER BOUNDS ON EIGENVALUE CLUSTERS') SSP00607
    1030 FORMAT (//,' NO. OF EIGENVALUES IN EACH CLUSTER')    SSP00608
    1040 FORMAT (' NO. OF EIGENVALUES LESS THAN UPPER BOUNDS')SSP00609
         END                                                  SSP00610
         SUBROUTINE JACOBI (A,B,X,EIGV,D,N,NWA,RTOL,NSMAX,IFPR,IOUT)  SSP00611
C ...............................................................  SSP00612
C .                                                           . SSP00613
C .   P R O G R A M                                           . SSP00614
C .       TO SOLVE THE GENERALIZED EIGENPROBLEM USING THE     . SSP00615
C .       GENERALIZED JACOBI ITERATION                        . SSP00616
C ...............................................................  SSP00617
         IMPLICIT DOUBLE PRECISION (A-H,O-Z)                  SSP00618
         DIMENSION A(NWA),B(NWA),X(N,N),EIGV(N),D(N)          SSP00619
C                                                             SSP00620
C        INITIALIZE EIGENVALUE AND EIGENVECTOR MATRICES       SSP00621
C                                                             SSP00622
         N1=N + 1                                             SSP00623
         II=1                                                 SSP00624
         DO 10 I=1,N                                          SSP00625
         IF (A(II).GT.0. .AND. B(II).GT.0.) GO TO 4           SSP00626
         WRITE (IOUT,2020) II,A(II),B(II)                     SSP00627
         GO TO 800                                            SSP00628
       4 D(I)=A(II)/B(II)                                     SSP00629
         EIGV(I)=D(I)                                         SSP00630
      10 II=II + N1 - I                                       SSP00631
```

```
      DO 30 I=1,N                                                          SSP00632
      DO 20 J=1,N                                                          SSP00633
   20 X(I,J)=0.                                                            SSP00634
   30 X(I,I)=1.                                                            SSP00635
      IF (N.EQ.1) GO TO 900                                                SSP00636
C                                                                          SSP00637
C     INITIALIZE SWEEP COUNTER AND BEGIN ITERATION                         SSP00638
C                                                                          SSP00639
      NSWEEP=0                                                             SSP00640
      NR=N - 1                                                             SSP00641
   40 NSWEEP=NSWEEP + 1                                                    SSP00642
      IF (IFPR.EQ.1) WRITE (IOUT,2000) NSWEEP                              SSP00643
C                                                                          SSP00644
C     CHECK IF PRESENT OFF-DIAGONAL ELEMENT IS LARGE ENOUGH TO REQUIRE     SSP00645
C     ZEROING                                                              SSP00646
C                                                                          SSP00647
      EPS=(.01)**(NSWEEP*2)                                                SSP00648
      DO 210 J=1,NR                                                        SSP00649
      JP1=J + 1                                                            SSP00650
      JM1=J - 1                                                            SSP00651
      LJK=JM1*N - JM1*J/2                                                  SSP00652
      JJ=LJK + J                                                           SSP00653
      DO 210 K=JP1,N                                                       SSP00654
      KP1=K + 1                                                            SSP00655
      KM1=K - 1                                                            SSP00656
      JK=LJK + K                                                           SSP00657
      KK=KM1*N - KM1*K/2 + K                                               SSP00658
      EPTOLA=(A(JK)/A(JJ))*(A(JK)/A(KK))                                   SSP00659
      EPTOLB=(B(JK)/B(JJ))*(B(JK)/B(KK))                                   SSP00660
      IF (EPTOLA.LT.EPS .AND. EPTOLB.LT.EPS) GO TO 210                     SSP00661
C                                                                          SSP00662
C     IF ZEROING IS REQUIRED, CALCULATE THE ROTATION MATRIX ELEMENTS CA    SSP00663
C     AND CG                                                               SSP00664
C                                                                          SSP00665
      AKK=A(KK)*B(JK) - B(KK)*A(JK)                                        SSP00666
      AJJ=A(JJ)*B(JK) - B(JJ)*A(JK)                                        SSP00667
      AB=A(JJ)*B(KK) - A(KK)*B(JJ)                                         SSP00668
      SCALE=A(KK)*B(KK)                                                    SSP00669
      ABCH=AB/SCALE                                                        SSP00670
      AKKCH=AKK/SCALE                                                      SSP00671
      AJJCH=AJJ/SCALE                                                      SSP00672
      CHECK=(ABCH*ABCH+4.0*AKKCH*AJJCH)/4.0                                SSP00673
      IF (CHECK) 50,60,60                                                  SSP00674
   50 WRITE (IOUT,2020) JJ,A(JJ),B(JJ)                                     SSP00675
      GO TO 800                                                            SSP00676
   60 SQCH=SCALE*SQRT(CHECK)                                               SSP00677
      D1=AB/2. + SQCH                                                      SSP00678
      D2=AB/2. - SQCH                                                      SSP00679
      DEN=D1                                                               SSP00680
      IF (ABS(D2).GT.ABS(D1)) DEN=D2                                       SSP00681
      IF (DEN) 80,70,80                                                    SSP00682
   70 CA=0.                                                                SSP00683
      CG=-A(JK)/A(KK)                                                      SSP00684
      GO TO 90                                                             SSP00685
   80 CA=AKK/DEN                                                           SSP00686
      CG=-AJJ/DEN                                                          SSP00687
C                                                                          SSP00688
C     PERFORM THE GENERALIZED ROTATION TO ZERO THE PRESENT OFF-DIAGONAL    SSP00689
C     ELEMENT                                                              SSP00690
C                                                                          SSP00691
   90 IF (N-2) 100,190,100                                                 SSP00692
  100 IF (JM1-1) 130,110,110                                               SSP00693
  110 DO 120 I=1,JM1                                                       SSP00694
      IM1=I - 1                                                            SSP00695
      IJ=IM1*N - IM1*I/2 + J                                               SSP00696
      IK=IM1*N - IM1*I/2 + K                                               SSP00697
      AJ=A(IJ)                                                             SSP00698
      BJ=B(IJ)                                                             SSP00699
      AK=A(IK)                                                             SSP00700
      BK=B(IK)                                                             SSP00701
```

```
          A(IJ)=AJ + CG*AK                                      SSP00702
          B(IJ)=BJ + CG*BK                                      SSP00703
          A(IK)=AK + CA*AJ                                      SSP00704
      120 B(IK)=BK + CA*BJ                                      SSP00705
      130 IF (KP1-N) 140,140,160                                SSP00706
      140 LJI=JM1*N - JM1*J/2                                   SSP00707
          LKI=KM1*N - KM1*K/2                                   SSP00708
          DO 150 I=KP1,N                                        SSP00709
          JI=LJI + I                                            SSP00710
          KI=LKI + I                                            SSP00711
          AJ=A(JI)                                              SSP00712
          BJ=B(JI)                                              SSP00713
          AK=A(KI)                                              SSP00714
          BK=B(KI)                                              SSP00715
          A(JI)=AJ + CG*AK                                      SSP00716
          B(JI)=BJ + CG*BK                                      SSP00717
          A(KI)=AK + CA*AJ                                      SSP00718
      150 B(KI)=BK + CA*BJ                                      SSP00719
      160 IF (JP1-KM1) 170,170,190                              SSP00720
      170 LJI=JM1*N - JM1*J/2                                   SSP00721
          DO 180 I=JP1,KM1                                      SSP00722
          JI=LJI + I                                            SSP00723
          IM1=I - 1                                             SSP00724
          IK=IM1*N - IM1*I/2 + K                                SSP00725
          AJ=A(JI)                                              SSP00726
          BJ=B(JI)                                              SSP00727
          AK=A(IK)                                              SSP00728
          BK=B(IK)                                              SSP00729
          A(JI)=AJ + CG*AK                                      SSP00730
          B(JI)=BJ + CG*BK                                      SSP00731
          A(IK)=AK + CA*AJ                                      SSP00732
      180 B(IK)=BK + CA*BJ                                      SSP00733
      190 AK=A(KK)                                              SSP00734
          BK=B(KK)                                              SSP00735
          A(KK)=AK + 2.*CA*A(JK) + CA*CA*A(JJ)                  SSP00736
          B(KK)=BK + 2.*CA*B(JK) + CA*CA*B(JJ)                  SSP00737
          A(JJ)=A(JJ) + 2.*CG*A(JK) + CG*CG*AK                  SSP00738
          B(JJ)=B(JJ) + 2.*CG*B(JK) + CG*CG*BK                  SSP00739
          A(JK)=0.                                              SSP00740
          B(JK)=0.                                              SSP00741
C                                                               SSP00742
C         UPDATE THE EIGENVECTOR MATRIX AFTER EACH ROTATION     SSP00743
C                                                               SSP00744
          DO 200 I=1,N                                          SSP00745
          XJ=X(I,J)                                             SSP00746
          XK=X(I,K)                                             SSP00747
          X(I,J)=XJ + CG*XK                                     SSP00748
      200 X(I,K)=XK + CA*XJ                                     SSP00749
      210 CONTINUE                                              SSP00750
C                                                               SSP00751
C         UPDATE THE EIGENVALUES AFTER EACH SWEEP               SSP00752
C                                                               SSP00753
          II=1                                                  SSP00754
          DO 220 I=1,N                                          SSP00755
          IF (A(II).GT.0. .AND. B(II).GT.0.) GO TO 215          SSP00756
          WRITE (IOUT,2020) II,A(II),B(II)                      SSP00757
          GO TO 800                                             SSP00758
      215 EIGV(I)=A(II)/B(II)                                   SSP00759
      220 II=II + N1 - I                                        SSP00760
          IF (IFPR.EQ.0) GO TO 230                              SSP00761
          WRITE (IOUT,2030)                                     SSP00762
          WRITE (IOUT,2010) (EIGV(I),I=1,N)                     SSP00763
C                                                               SSP00764
C         CHECK FOR CONVERGENCE                                 SSP00765
C                                                               SSP00766
      230 DO 240 I=1,N                                          SSP00767
          TOL=RTOL*D(I)                                         SSP00768
          DIF=ABS(EIGV(I)-D(I))                                 SSP00769
          IF (DIF.GT.TOL) GO TO 280                             SSP00770
      240 CONTINUE                                              SSP00771
```

```
C                                                                      SSP00772
C       CHECK ALL OFF-DIAGONAL ELEMENTS TO SEE IF ANOTHER SWEEP IS     SSP00773
C       REQUIRED                                                       SSP00774
C                                                                      SSP00775
        EPS=RTOL**2                                                    SSP00776
        DO 250 J=1,NR                                                  SSP00777
        JM1=J - 1                                                      SSP00778
        JP1=J + 1                                                      SSP00779
        LJK=JM1*N - JM1*J/2                                            SSP00780
        JJ=LJK + J                                                     SSP00781
        DO 250 K=JP1,N                                                 SSP00782
        KM1=K - 1                                                      SSP00783
        JK=LJK + K                                                     SSP00784
        KK=KM1*N - KM1*K/2 + K                                         SSP00785
        EPSA=(A(JK)/A(JJ))*(A(JK)/A(KK))                               SSP00786
        EPSB=(B(JK)/B(JJ))*(B(JK)/B(KK))                               SSP00787
        IF (EPSA.LT.EPS .AND. EPSB.LT.EPS) GO TO 250                   SSP00788
        GO TO 280                                                      SSP00789
  250 CONTINUE                                                         SSP00790
C                                                                      SSP00791
C       SCALE EIGENVECTORS                                             SSP00792
C                                                                      SSP00793
  255 II=1                                                             SSP00794
        DO 275 I=1,N                                                   SSP00795
        BB=SQRT(B(II))                                                 SSP00796
        DO 270 K=1,N                                                   SSP00797
  270 X(K,I)=X(K,I)/BB                                                 SSP00798
  275 II=II + N1 - I                                                   SSP00799
        GO TO 900                                                      SSP00800
C                                                                      SSP00801
C       UPDATE  D  MATRIX AND START NEW SWEEP, IF ALLOWED              SSP00802
C                                                                      SSP00803
  280 DO 290 I=1,N                                                     SSP00804
  290 D(I)=EIGV(I)                                                     SSP00805
        IF (NSWEEP.LT.NSMAX) GO TO 40                                  SSP00806
        GO TO 255                                                      SSP00807
C                                                                      SSP00808
  800 STOP                                                             SSP00809
  900 RETURN                                                           SSP00810
C                                                                      SSP00811
 2000 FORMAT (//,' SWEEP NUMBER IN *JACOBI* = ',I8)                    SSP00812
 2010 FORMAT (' ',6E20.12)                                             SSP00813
 2020 FORMAT (' *** ERROR *** SOLUTION STOP',/,                        SSP00814
     1          ' MATRICES NOT POSITIVE DEFINITE',/,                   SSP00815
     2          ' II = ',I8,' A(II) = ',E20.12,' B(II) = ',E20.12)     SSP00816
 2030 FORMAT (/,' CURRENT EIGENVALUES IN *JACOBI* ARE',/)              SSP00817
        END                                                            SSP00818
```

The subspace iteration method presented here is for the solution of the smallest eigenvalues and corresponding eigenvectors, where p is assumed to be small (say $p < 20$). Considering the solution of problems for a larger number of eigenpairs, say $p > 40$, experience shows that the cost of solution using the subspace iteration method rises rapidly as the number of eigenpairs considered is increased. This rapid increase in cost is due to a number of factors that can be neglected when the solution of only a few eigenpairs is required. An important point is that a relatively large number of subspace iterations may be required if $q = p + 8$. Namely, in this case, when p is large, the convergence rate to ϕ_p, equal to λ_p/λ_{q+1}, can be close to 1. On the other hand, if q is increased, the numerical operations per subspace iteration are increased significantly. Another shortcoming of the solution with subroutine SSPACE and q large is that a relatively large number of iteration vectors is used throughout *all* subspace iterations, although convergence to the smallest eigenvalues of those required is generally already achieved in the first few iterations. Finally, we should note that the number of numerical operations required in the solution of the reduced eigenproblem in (11.154) becomes significant when q is large.

The above considerations show that procedures for accelerating the basic subspace iteration solution given in subroutine SSPACE are very desirable, in particular, when a larger number of eigenpairs is to be calculated. Various acceleration procedures for the basic subspace iteration method have indeed been proposed (see, for example, Y. Yamamoto and H. Ohtsubo [A], and F. A. Akl, W. H. Dilger, and B. M. Irons [A]), and a comprehensive solution algorithm that can be significantly more effective than the basic method is presented by K. J. Bathe and S. Ramaswamy [A]. In this program the solution steps of the basic subspace iteration method are accelerated using vector overrelaxation, shifting techniques, and the Lanczos method to generate the starting subspace. Also, with the method it can be particularly effective to employ fewer iteration vectors than the number of eigenpairs to be calculated (i.e., q can be smaller than p) and the solution procedure can also be employed to calculate eigenvalues and corresponding eigenvectors in a specified interval. Further developments to increase the effectiveness of the subspace iteration solution have been published by F. A. Dul and K. Arczewski [A].

11.6.6 Exercises

11.18. Show explicitly that the iteration vectors $\mathbf{X}_{k+1}$ in the subspace iteration are **K**- and **M**-orthogonal.

11.19. Use two iteration vectors in the subspace iteration method to solve for the two smallest eigenvalues and corresponding eigenvectors of the problem considered in Exercise 11.1.

11.20. Show that in the subspace iteration the use of (10.107) results after $(k-1)$ iterations into

$$\left[1 - \frac{(\lambda_i^{(k)})^2}{(\mathbf{q}_i^{(k)})^T(\mathbf{q}_i^{(k)})}\right]^{1/2} \le tol$$

where $\lambda_i^{(k)}$ is the calculated eigenvalue approximation and $\mathbf{q}_i^{(k)}$ is the corresponding eigenvector in $\mathbf{Q}_k$.

11.21. The number of numerical operations used in program SSPACE can be decreased at the expense of using more memory. Then no additional iteration is performed after convergence. Reprogram SSPACE to achieve this decrease in numerical operations used.

11.22. Develop a program such as SSPACE using the programming language C (instead of Fortran), and compare the efficiencies of the two implementations.

CHAPTER TWELVE

Implementation of the Finite Element Method

12.1 INTRODUCTION

In this book we have presented formulations, general theories, and numerical methods of finite element analysis. The objective in this final chapter is to discuss some important computational aspects pertaining to the implementation of finite element procedures. Although the implementation of displacement-based finite element analysis is discussed, it should be noted that most of the concepts presented can also be employed in finite element analysis using mixed formulations. Note, in particular, that the mixed interpolations of the u/p formulation for two- and three-dimensional continuum elements (see Sections 4.4.3, 5.3.5, and 6.4) and the mixed interpolations for beam, plate, and shell elements (see Sections 5.4 and 6.5) have only nodal displacements and rotations as final element degrees of freedom, and hence the process of element assemblage and solution of equations is as in the pure displacement-based formulation.

The main advantage that the finite element method has over other analysis techniques is its large generality. Normally, as was pointed out, it seems possible, by using many elements, to virtually approximate any continuum with complex boundary and loading conditions to such a degree that an accurate analysis can be carried out. In practice, however, obvious engineering limitations arise, a most important one being the cost of the analysis. This cost consists of the purchase and/or leasing of hardware and software, the analyst's effort and time required to prepare the analysis input data, the computer program execution time, and the analyst's time to interpret the results. Of course, as discussed in Section 1.2, a number of program runs may be required. Also, the limitations of the computer and the program employed may prevent the use of a sufficiently fine discretization to obtain accurate results. Hence, it is clearly desirable to use an efficient finite element program.

The effectiveness of a program depends essentially on the following factors. First, the use of efficient finite elements is important.

Second, efficient programming methods and sophisticated use of the available computer hardware and software are important. Although this aspect of program development is computer-dependent, using standard FORTRAN 77 or C and high- and low-speed storage in a system-independent manner, very effective computer programs can be developed. If such a program is to be permanently installed on a specific computer, its efficiency may normally be increased with relatively little effort by making use of the specific hardware and software options available. In the following, we therefore discuss the design of finite element programs in which largely computer-independent procedures are used.

The third very important aspect of the development of a finite element program is the use of appropriate numerical techniques. As an example, if inappropriate techniques for the solution of the frequencies of a system in a dynamic analysis are employed, the cost may be many times greater than with effective techniques, and, even worse, a solution may not be possible at all if an unstable algorithm is employed. In order to implement the finite element method in practice, we need to use the digital computer. However, even with a relatively large-capacity computer available, the feasibility of a problem solution and the effectiveness of an analysis depend directly on the numerical procedures employed.

Assume that an actual structure has been idealized as an assemblage of finite elements. The stress analysis process can be understood to consist of essentially three phases:

1. Calculation of system matrices $\mathbf{K}$, $\mathbf{M}$, $\mathbf{C}$, and $\mathbf{R}$, whichever are applicable.
2. Solution of equilibrium equations.
3. Evaluation of element stresses.

In the analysis of a heat transfer, field, or fluid mechanics problem, the steps are identical, but the pertinent matrices and solution quantities need to be used.

The objective in this chapter is to describe a program implementation of the first and third phases and to present a small computer program that has all the important features of a general code. Although the total solution may be subdivided into the above three phases, it should be realized that the specific implementation of one phase can have a pronounced effect on the efficiency of another phase, and, indeed, in some programs the first two phases are carried out simultaneously (e.g., when using the frontal solution method; see Section 8.2.4).

As might be imagined, there is no unique optimum program organization for the evaluation of the system matrices; however, although program designs may appear to be quite different, in effect, some basic steps are followed. For this reason, it is most instructive to discuss in detail all the important features of one implementation that is based on classical methods. First we discuss the algorithms used, and then we present a small example program. This implementation is for a single processor machine but can be adapted for use of multiple processors and parallel computing.

12.2 COMPUTER PROGRAM ORGANIZATION FOR CALCULATION OF SYSTEM MATRICES

The final results of this phase are the required structure matrices for the solution of the system equilibrium equations. In a static analysis the computer program needs to calculate the structure stiffness matrix and the load vectors. In a dynamic analysis, the program must also establish the system mass and damping matrices. In the implementation to be described here, the calculation of the structure matrices is performed as follows.

1. The nodal point and element information are read and/or generated.
2. The element stiffness matrices, mass and damping matrices, and equivalent nodal loads are calculated.
3. The structure matrices **K**, **M**, **C**, and **R**, whichever are applicable, are assembled.

12.2.1 Nodal Point and Element Information Read-in

Consider first the data that correspond to the nodal points. Assume that the program is set up to allow a maximum of six degrees of freedom at each node, three translational and three rotational degrees of freedom, as shown in Fig. 12.1. Corresponding to each nodal point, it must then be identified which of these degrees of freedom shall actually be used in the analysis, i.e., which of the six possible nodal degrees of freedom correspond to degrees of freedom of the finite element assemblage. This is achieved by defining an identification array, the array ID, of dimension 6 times NUMNP, where NUMNP is equal to the number of nodal points in the system. Element (i, j) in the ID array corresponds to the ith degree of freedom at the nodal point j. If ID(I, J) = 0, the corresponding degree of freedom is defined in the global system, and if ID(I, J) = 1, the degree of freedom is not defined. It should be noted that using the same procedure, an ID array for more (or less) than six degrees of freedom per nodal point could be established, and, indeed, the number of degrees of freedom per nodal point could be a variable. Consider the following simple example.

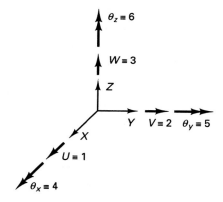

Figure 12.1 Possible degrees of freedom at a nodal point

EXAMPLE 12.1: Establish the ID array for the plane stress element idealization of the cantilever in Fig. E12.1 in order to define the active and nonactive degrees of freedom.

The active degrees of freedom are defined by ID(I, J) = 0, and the nonactive degrees of freedom are defined by ID(I, J) = 1. Since the cantilever is in the X, Y plane and plane stress elements are used in the idealization, only X and Y translational degrees of freedom are active. By inspection, the ID array is given by

$$
ID = \begin{bmatrix}
1 & 1 & 1 & 0 & 0 & 0 & 0 & 0 & 0 \\
1 & 1 & 1 & 0 & 0 & 0 & 0 & 0 & 0 \\
1 & 1 & 1 & 1 & 1 & 1 & 1 & 1 & 1 \\
1 & 1 & 1 & 1 & 1 & 1 & 1 & 1 & 1 \\
1 & 1 & 1 & 1 & 1 & 1 & 1 & 1 & 1 \\
1 & 1 & 1 & 1 & 1 & 1 & 1 & 1 & 1
\end{bmatrix}
$$

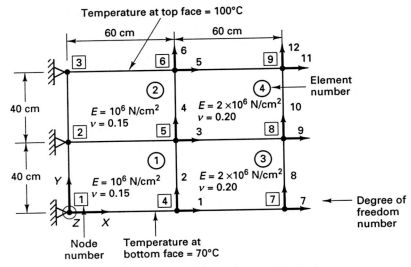

Figure E12.1   Finite element cantilever idealization

Once all active degrees of freedom have been defined by zeros in the ID array, the equation numbers corresponding to these degrees of freedom are assigned. The procedure is to simply scan column after column through the ID array and replace each zero by an equation number, which increases successively from 1 to the total number of equations. At the same time, the entries corresponding to the nonactive degrees of freedom are set to zero.

EXAMPLE 12.2: Modify the ID array obtained in Example 12.1 for the analysis of the cantilever plate in Fig. E12.1 to obtain the ID array that defines the equation numbers corresponding to the active degrees of freedom.

As explained above, we simply replace the zeros, column by column, in succession by equation numbers to obtain

$$
\text{ID} = \begin{bmatrix}
0 & 0 & 0 & 1 & 3 & 5 & 7 & 9 & 11 \\
0 & 0 & 0 & 2 & 4 & 6 & 8 & 10 & 12 \\
0 & 0 & 0 & 0 & 0 & 0 & 0 & 0 & 0 \\
0 & 0 & 0 & 0 & 0 & 0 & 0 & 0 & 0 \\
0 & 0 & 0 & 0 & 0 & 0 & 0 & 0 & 0 \\
0 & 0 & 0 & 0 & 0 & 0 & 0 & 0 & 0
\end{bmatrix}
$$

Apart from the definition of all active degrees of freedom, we also need to read the X, Y, Z global coordinates and, if required, the temperature corresponding to each nodal point. For the cantilever beam in Fig. E12.1, the X, Y, Z coordinate arrays and nodal point temperature array T would be as follows:

$$
\begin{aligned}
X &= [0.0 \quad 0.0 \quad 0.0 \quad 60.0 \quad 60.0 \quad 60.0 \quad 120.0 \quad 120.0 \quad 120.0] \\
Y &= [0.0 \quad 40.0 \quad 80.0 \quad 0.0 \quad 40.0 \quad 80.0 \quad 0.0 \quad 40.0 \quad 80.0] \\
Z &= [0.0 \quad 0.0 \quad 0.0 \quad 0.0 \quad 0.0 \quad 0.0 \quad 0.0 \quad 0.0 \quad 0.0] \\
T &= [70.0 \quad 85.0 \quad 100.0 \quad 70.0 \quad 85.0 \quad 100.0 \quad 70.0 \quad 85.0 \quad 100.0]
\end{aligned}
\tag{12.1}
$$

At this stage, with all the nodal point data known, the program may read and generate the element information. It is expedient to consider each element type in turn. For example, in the analysis of a container structure, all beam elements, all plane stress elements, and all shell elements are read and generated together. This is efficient because specific information must be provided for each element of a certain type, which, because of its repetitive nature, can be generated to some degree if all elements of the same type are specified together. Furthermore, the element routine for an element type that reads the element data and calculates the element matrices needs to be called only once.

The required data corresponding to an element depend on the specific element type. In general, the information required for each element is the element node numbers that correspond to the nodal point numbers of the complete element assemblage, the element material properties, and the surface and body forces applied to the element. Since the element material properties and the element loading are the same for many elements, it is efficient to define material property sets and load sets pertaining to an element type. These sets are specified at the beginning of each group of element data. Therefore, any one of the material property sets and element load sets can be assigned to an element at the same time the element node numbers are read.

EXAMPLE 12.3: Consider the analysis of the cantilever plate shown in Fig. E12.1 and the local element node numbering defined in Fig. 5.4. For each element give the node numbers that correspond to the nodal point numbers of the complete element assemblage. Also indicate the use of material property sets.

In this analysis we define two material property sets: material property set 1 for $E = 10^6$ N/cm^2 and $\nu = 0.15$, and material property set 2 for $E = 2 \times 10^6$ N/cm^2 and $\nu = 0.20$. We then have the following node numbers and material property sets for each element:

Element 1: node numbers: 5, 2, 1, 4; material property set: 1
Element 2: node numbers: 6, 3, 2, 5; material property set: 1
Element 3: node numbers: 8, 5, 4, 7; material property set: 2
Element 4: node numbers: 9, 6, 5, 8; material property set: 2

12.2.2 Calculation of Element Stiffness, Mass, and Equivalent Nodal Loads

The general procedure for calculating element matrices was discussed in Chapters 4 and 5, and a computer implementation was presented in Section 5.6. The program organization during this phase consists of calling the appropriate element subroutines for each element. During the element matrix calculations, the element coordinates, properties, and load sets, which have been read and stored in the preceding phase (Section 12.2.1), are needed. After calculation, either an element matrix may be stored on backup storage, because the assemblage into the structure matrices is carried out later, or the element matrix may be added immediately to the appropriate structure matrix.

12.2.3 Assemblage of Matrices

The assemblage process for obtaining the structure stiffness matrix **K** is symbolically written

$$\mathbf{K} = \sum_i \mathbf{K}^{(i)} \tag{12.2}$$

where the matrix $\mathbf{K}^{(i)}$ is the stiffness matrix of the ith element and the summation goes over all elements in the assemblage. In an analogous manner the structure mass matrix and load vectors are assembled from the element mass matrices and element load vectors, respectively. In addition to the element stiffness, mass, and load matrices, concentrated stiffnesses, masses, and loads corresponding to specific degrees of freedom can also be added.

It should be noted that the element stiffness matrices $\mathbf{K}^{(i)}$ in (12.2) are of the same order as the structure stiffness matrix $\mathbf{K}$. However, considering the internal structure of the matrices $\mathbf{K}^{(i)}$, nonzero elements are in only those rows and columns that correspond to element degrees of freedom (see Section 4.2). Therefore, in practice, we only need to store the compacted element stiffness matrix, which is of order equal to the number of element degrees of freedom, together with an array that relates to each element degree of freedom the corresponding assemblage degree of freedom. This array is conveniently a connectivity array LM in which entry i gives the equation number that corresponds to the element degree of freedom i.

EXAMPLE 12.4:   Using the convention for the element degrees of freedom in Fig. 5.4, establish the connectivity arrays defining the assemblage degrees of freedom of the elements in the assemblage in Fig. E12.1.

Consider element 1 in Fig. E12.1. For this element, nodes 5, 2, 1, and 4 of the element assemblage correspond to the element nodes 1, 2, 3, and 4, respectively (Fig. 5.4). Using the ID array, the equation numbers corresponding to the nodes 5, 2, 1, and 4 of the element assemblage are obtained, and hence the relation between the column (and row) numbers of the compacted, or local, element stiffness matrix and the global stiffness matrix is as follows:

	Corresponding column and row numbers							
For compacted matrix	1	2	3	4	5	6	7	8
For $\mathbf{K}^{(1)}$	3	4	0	0	0	0	1	2

The array LM, storing the assemblage degrees of freedom of this element, is therefore

$$\text{LM} = [3 \quad 4 \quad 0 \quad 0 \quad 0 \quad 0 \quad 1 \quad 2]$$

where a zero means that the corresponding column and row of the compacted element stiffness are ignored and do not enter the global structure stiffness matrix.

Similarly, we can obtain the LM arrays that correspond to the elements 2, 3, and 4. We have

for element 2: $\text{LM} = [5 \quad 6 \quad 0 \quad 0 \quad 0 \quad 0 \quad 3 \quad 4]$

for element 3: $\text{LM} = [9 \quad 10 \quad 3 \quad 4 \quad 1 \quad 2 \quad 7 \quad 8]$

and for element 4: $\text{LM} = [11 \quad 12 \quad 5 \quad 6 \quad 3 \quad 4 \quad 9 \quad 10]$

As shown in the example, the connectivity array of an element is determined from the nodal points to which the element is connected and the equation numbers that have been assigned to those nodal points. Once the array LM has been defined, the corresponding element stiffness matrix can be added in compact form to the structure stiffness matrix $\mathbf{K}$, but the process must take due account of the specific storage scheme used for $\mathbf{K}$. As already pointed out in Section 2.2, an effective storage scheme for the structure stiffness matrix is to store only the elements below the skyline of the matrix $\mathbf{K}$ (i.e., the active columns of $\mathbf{K}$) in a one-dimensional array A. However, together with the active column storage scheme, we also need a specific procedure for addressing the elements of $\mathbf{K}$ in A when they are stored as indicated in Section 2.2. Thus, before we are able to proceed with the assemblage of the element stiffness matrices, it is necessary to establish the addresses of the stiffness matrix elements in the one-dimensional array A.

Figure 12.2 shows the element pattern of a typical stiffness matrix. Let us derive the storage scheme and addressing procedure that we propose to use, and that are employed with the active column solver discussed in Section 8.2.3. Since the matrix is symmetric, we choose to store and work on only the part above and including the diagonal. However, in addition, we observe that the elements (i, j) of $\mathbf{K}$ (i.e., k_{ij}) are zero for $j > i + m_K$. The

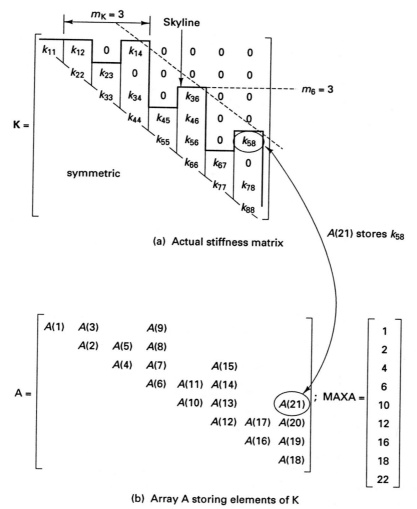

(a) Actual stiffness matrix

A(21) stores k_{58}

(b) Array A storing elements of K

Figure 12.2   Storage scheme used for a typical stiffness matrix

value m_K is known as the *half-bandwidth* of the matrix. Defining by m_i the row number of the first nonzero element in column i (Fig. 12.2), the variables m_i, $i = 1, \ldots, n$, define the *skyline* of the matrix, and the variables $i - m_i$ are the *column heights*. Furthermore, the half-bandwidth of the stiffness matrix, m_K, equals max$\{i - m\}$, $i = 1, \ldots, n$; i.e., m_K *is equal to the maximum difference in global degrees of freedom pertaining to any one of the finite elements in the mesh.* In many finite element analyses, the column heights vary with i, and it is important that all zero elements outside the skyline not be included in the equation solution (see Section 8.2.3).

The columns heights are determined from the connectivity arrays, LM, of the elements; i.e., by evaluating m_i, we also obtain the column height $i - m_i$. Consider, as an example, that m_{10} of the stiffness matrix that corresponds to the element assemblage in Fig. E12.1 is required. The LM arrays of the four elements have been given in Example 12.4. We note that only elements 3 and 4 couple into degree of freedom 10, and that the smallest number of degree of freedom in the LM array of these elements is 1; hence, $m_{10} = 1$ and the column height of column 10 is 9.

With the column heights of a stiffness matrix defined, we can now store all elements below the skyline of K as a one-dimensional array in A; i.e., the active columns of K including the diagonal elements are stored consecutively in A. Figure 12.2 shows which storage locations the elements of the matrix K given in the figure would take in A. In addition to A, we also define an array MAXA, which stores the addresses of the diagonal elements of K in A; i.e., the address of the ith diagonal element of K, k_{ii}, in A is MAXA(I). Referring to Fig. 12.2, it is noted that MAXA(I) is equal to the sum of the column heights up to the $(i - 1)$st column plus I. Hence the number of nonzero elements in the ith column of K is equal to MAXA(I + 1) − MAXA(I), and the element addresses are MAXA(I), MAXA(I) + 1, MAXA(I) + 2, $\ldots$, MAXA(I + 1) − 1. It follows that using this storage scheme of K in A together with the address array MAXA, each element of K in A can be addressed easily.

This storage scheme is used in the computer program STAP presented in Section 12.4 and in the equation and eigenvalue solution subroutines in Sections 8.2.3 and 11.6.5. The scheme is quite effective because no elements outside the skyline are stored and processed in the calculations.

In the discussion of algorithms for the solution of the equations $KU = R$, where K, U, and R are the stiffness matrix, the displacement vector, and the load vector of the element assemblage, respectively, we pointed out that the active column and other solution procedures require about $\frac{1}{2}nm_K^2$ operations, where n is the order of the stiffness matrix, m_K is its half-bandwidth, and we assume constant column heights; i.e., $i - m_i = m_K$ for nearly all i. Therefore, it can be important to minimize m_K from considerations of both storage requirements and number of operations. If the column heights vary, a mean or "effective" value for m_K must be used (see Section 8.2.3). In practice we can frequently determine a reasonable nodal point numbering by inspection. However, this nodal point numbering may not be particularly easy to generate, and various automatic schemes are currently used for bandwidth reduction; see Section 8.2.3. Figure 12.3 shows a typical good and a typical bad nodal point numbering.

It should be pointed out that in the discussion of the above storage scheme, we implicitly assumed that the entire array A (i.e., the sum of all active columns of the matrix K) does fit into the available high-speed storage of the computer. For instructional purposes

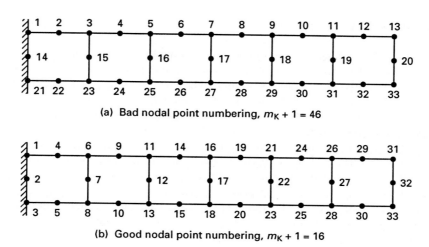

(a) Bad nodal point numbering, $m_K + 1 = 46$

(b) Good nodal point numbering, $m_K + 1 = 16$

Figure 12.3   Bad and good nodal point numbering for finite element assemblage

it is most appropriate to concentrate on in-core solution, although in practice large systems are solved by storing the matrices in blocks. Considering out-of-core solution, in principle, the same storage scheme is effective as for in-core solutions. The main additional problem is one of program logistics; namely, the individual blocks of the matrices must be stored on backup storage and called into high-speed storage in an effective manner. Specific attention must then be given to minimize the amount of disk writing and reading required in the assemblage. However, once an effective in-core finite element solution has been studied, little difficulty should be encountered in understanding an out-of-core implementation.

12.3 CALCULATION OF ELEMENT STRESSES

In the previous section we described the process of assembling individual finite element matrices into total structure matrices. The next step is the calculation of nodal point displacements using the procedures discussed in Chapters 8 and 9. Once the nodal point displacements have been obtained, element stresses are calculated in the final phase of the analysis.

The equations employed in the element stress calculations are (4.11) and (4.12). However, as in the assemblage of the structure matrices, it is again effective to manipulate compacted finite element matrices, i.e., deal only with the nonzero columns of $\mathbf{B}^{(m)}$ in (4.11). Using the implementation described in the previous section, we calculate the element compacted strain-displacement transformation matrix and then extract the element nodal point displacements from the total displacement vector using the LM array of the element. The procedure is implemented in the program STAP described next. Of course, in linear analysis the finite element stresses can be calculated at any desired location by simply establishing the strain-displacement transformation matrix for the point under consideration in the element. In isoparametric finite element analysis we use the procedures given in Chapter 5.

12.4 EXAMPLE PROGRAM STAP

Probably the best way of getting familiar with the implementation of finite element analysis is to study an actual computer program that, although simplified in various areas, shows all the important features of more general codes. The following program, STAP (STatic Analysis Program), is a simple computer program for static linear elastic finite element analysis.

The main objective in the presentation of the program is to show the overall flow of a typical finite element analysis program, and for this reason only a truss element has been made available in STAP. However, the code can generally be used for one-, two-, and three-dimensional analysis, and additional elements can be added with relative ease.[1]

Figure 12.4 shows a flowchart of the program, and Fig. 12.5 gives the storage allocations used during the various program phases. We should note that the elements are processed in element groups. This concept is valuable when implementing the program on parallel processing machines. Next we give the instructions describing the data input to the program.

12.4.1 Data Input to Computer Program STAP

I. HEADING LINE (20A4)

Note	Columns	Variable	Entry
(1)	1–80	HED (20)	Enter the master heading information for use in labeling the output

NOTES/

1. Begin each new data case with a new heading line. Two blank lines must be input after the last data case.

II. CONTROL LINE (4I5)

Note	Columns	Variable	Entry
(1)	1–5	NUMNP	Total number of nodal points; EQ.0, program stop
(2)	6–10	NUMEG	Total number of element groups, GT.0
(3)	11–15	NLCASE	Number of load cases, GT.0
(4)	16–20	MODEX	Flag indicating solution mode; EQ.0, data check only EQ.1, execution

NOTES/

1. The total number of nodes (NUMNP) controls the amount of data to be read in Section III. If NUMNP.EQ.0, the program stops.

[1] The program has been tested on a Cray, various engineering workstations, and PCs.

2. The total number of elements are dealt with in element groups. An element group consists of a convenient collection of elements. Each element group is input as given in Section V. There must be at least one element per element group, and there must be at least one element group.

3. The number of load cases (NLCASE) gives the number of load vectors for which the displacement and stress solution is sought.

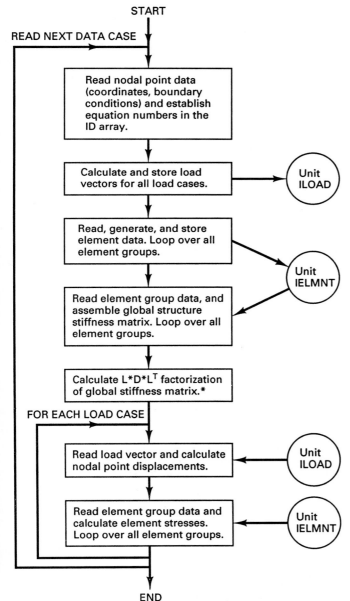

Figure 12.4 Flowchart of program STAP

* The equation solver used is COLSOL described in Section 8.2.3.

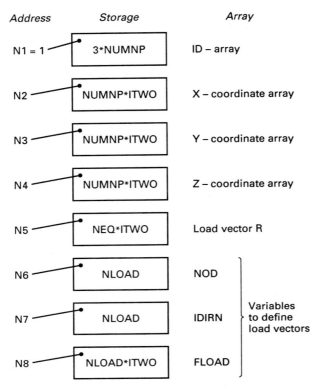

(a) Input of ID array, nodal point coordinates, and load vectors.

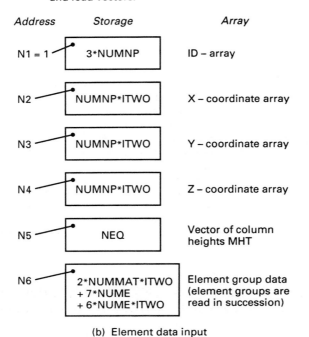

(b) Element data input

Figure 12.5 High-speed storage allocation in program STAP.
ITWO = 1 in single precision arithmetic.
ITWO = 2 in double precision arithmetic.

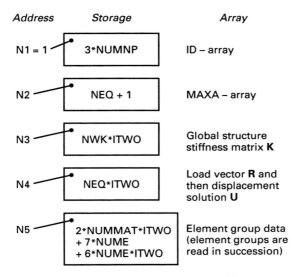

Address	Storage	Array
N1 = 1	3*NUMNP	ID – array
N2	NEQ + 1	MAXA – array
N3	NWK*ITWO	Global structure stiffness matrix **K**
N4	NEQ*ITWO	Load vector **R** and then displacement solution **U**
N5	2*NUMMAT*ITWO + 7*NUME + 6*NUME*ITWO	Element group data (element groups are read in succession)

(c) Assemblage of global structure stiffness; displacement and stress solution phase

Figure 12.5   (*continued*)

4. The MODEX parameter determines whether the program is to check the data without executing the analysis (i.e., MODEX. EQ. 0) or if the program is to solve the problem (i.e., MODEX. EQ. 1). In the data-check-only mode, the program only reads and prints all data.

III. NODAL POINT DATA LINES (4I5, 3F10.0, I5)

Note	Columns	Variable	Entry
(1)	1–5	N	Node (joint) number; GE.1 and LE.NUMNP
(2)	6–10	ID (1, N)	X—translation boundary code
	11–15	ID (2, N)	Y—translation boundary code
	16–20	ID (3, N)	Z—translation boundary code
(3)	21–30	X(N)	X—coordinate
	31–40	Y(N)	Y—coordinate
	41–50	Z(N)	Z—coordinate
(4)	51–55	KN	Node number increment for node data generation; EQ.0, no generation

NOTES/

1. Nodal data must be defined for all (NUMNP) nodes. Node data may be input directly (i.e., each node on its own individual line) or the generation option may be used if applicable (see note 4 below). Admissible node numbers range from 1 to the total number of nodes (NUMNP). The last node that is input must be NUMNP.

2. Boundary condition codes can be assigned only the following values ($M = 1, 2, 3$)

$$ID(M, N) = 0; \quad \text{unspecified (free) displacement}$$

$$ID(M, N) = 1; \quad \text{deleted (fixed) displacement}$$

An unspecified $[ID(M, N) = 0]$ degree of freedom is free to translate as the solution dictates. Concentrated forces may be applied in this degree of freedom.

One system equilibrium equation is established for each unspecified degree of freedom in the model. The total number of equilibrium equations is defined as NEQ and is always less than three times the total number of nodes in the system.

Deleted $[ID(M, N) = 1]$ degrees of freedom are removed from the final set of equilibrium equations. Deleted degrees of freedom are used to define fixities (points of external reaction), and any loads applied in these degrees of freedom are ignored by the program.

3. The geometric location of each node is specified by its X, Y, and Z coordinates.

4. Node lines need not be input in node order sequence; eventually, however, all nodes in the set $[1, \text{NUMNP}]$ must be defined. Nodal data for a series of nodes

$$[N_1, N_1 + 1 * KN_1, N_1 + 2 * KN_1, \ldots, N_2]$$

may be generated from information given on two lines in sequence—

$$\text{LINE } 1 - N_1, ID(1, N_1), \ldots, X(N_1), \ldots, KN_1$$

$$\text{LINE } 2 - N_2, ID(1, N_2), \ldots, X(N_2), \ldots, KN_2$$

KN_1 is the node generation parameter given on the first line in the sequence. The first generated node is $N_1 + 1 * KN_1$; the second generated node is $N_1 + 2 * KN_1$; etc. Generation continues until node number $N_2 - KN_1$ is established. Note that the node difference $N_2 - N_1$ must be evenly divisible by KN_1.

In the generation the boundary condition codes $[ID(L, J)$ values] of the generated nodes are set equal to those of node N_1. The coordinate values of the generated nodes are interpolated linearly.

IV. LOAD DATA LINES

Each load case requires the following set of lines. The total number of load cases was defined on the CONTROL LINE (Section II).

LINE 1 (2I5)

Note	Columns	Variable	Entry
(1)	1–5	LL	Enter the load case number
(2)	6–10	NLOAD	Enter the number of concentrated loads applied in this load case

NOTES/

1. Load cases must be input in ascending sequence beginning with 1.
2. The variable NLOAD defines the number of lines to be read next for this load case.

NEXT LINES (2I5, F10.0)

Note	Columns	Variable	Entry
(1)	1–5	NOD	Node number to which this load is applied; GE.1 and LE.NUMNP
(2)	6–10	IDIRN	Degree of freedom number for this load component; EQ.1, X-direction EQ.2, Y-direction EQ.3, Z-direction
	11–20	FLOAD	Magnitude of load

NOTES/

1. For each concentrated load applied in this load case, one line must be supplied.
2. All loads must be acting into the global X-, Y-, or Z-direction.

V. TRUSS ELEMENTS

TRUSS elements are two-node members allowed arbitrary orientation in the X, Y, Z system. The truss transmits axial force only, and in general is a six degree of freedom element (i.e., three global translation components at each end of the member). The following sequence of lines is input for each element group. The total number of element groups (NUMEG) was defined on the CONTROL LINE (Section II).

V.1 Element Group Control Line (3I5)

Note	Columns	Variable	Entry
	1–5	NPAR(1)	Enter the number 1
(1)	6–10	NPAR(2)	Number of TRUSS elements in this group; NPAR(2) = NUME GE.1
(2)	11–15	NPAR(3)	Number of different sets of material/section properties; NPAR(3) = NUMMAT GE.1 EQ.0, default set to 1

NOTES/

1. TRUSS element numbers begin with 1 and end with the total number of elements in this group, NPAR(2). Element data are input in Section V.3.
2. The variable NPAR(3) defines the number of sets of material/section properties to be read in Section V.2.

V.2 Material/Section Property Lines (I5, 2F10.0)

NUMMAT lines are read in this section.

Note	Columns	Variable	Entry
(1)	1–5	N	Number of property set
	6–15	E(N)	Young's modulus
	16–25	AREA(N)	Section area

NOTES/

1. Property sets are input in ascending sequence beginning with 1 and ending with NUMMAT. The Young's modulus and section area of each TRUSS element input below are defined using one of the property sets input here.

V.3 Element Data Lines (5I5)

NUME elements must be input and/or generated in this section in ascending sequence beginning with 1.

Note	Columns	Variable	Entry
	1–5	M	TRUSS element number; GE.1 and LE.NUME
	6–10	II	Node number at one end
	11–15	JJ	Node number at other end; GE.1 and LE.NUMNP
(1)	16–20	MTYP	Material property set; GE.1 and LE.NUMMAT
(2)	21–25	KG	Node generation increment used to compute node numbers for missing elements; EQ.0, default set to 1

NOTES/

1. The material/section property sets have been defined in Section V.2.

2. Elements must be input in increasing element number order. If lines for elements $[M + 1, M + 2, \ldots, M + J]$ are omitted, these J missing elements are generated using MTYP of element M and by incrementing the node numbers of successive elements with the value KG; KG is taken from the first line of the element generation sequence (i.e., from the Mth element line). The last element (NUME) must always be input.

12.4.2 Listing of Program STAP

```
C . . . . . . . . . . . . . . . . . . . . . . . . . . . . . . . . . . . . .   STA00001
C .                                                                       .   STA00002
C .                              S T A P                                   .   STA00003
C .                                                                       .   STA00004
C .            AN IN-CORE SOLUTION STATIC ANALYSIS PROGRAM                 .   STA00005
C .                                                                       .   STA00006
C . . . . . . . . . . . . . . . . . . . . . . . . . . . . . . . . . . . . .   STA00007
      COMMON /SOL/ NUMNP,NEQ,NWK,NUMEST,MIDEST,MAXEST,MK                       STA00008
      COMMON /DIM/ N1,N2,N3,N4,N5,N6,N7,N8,N9,N10,N11,N12,N13,N14,N15          STA00009
      COMMON /EL/ IND,NPAR(10),NUMEG,MTOT,NFIRST,NLAST,ITWO                     STA00010
      COMMON /VAR/ NG,MODEX                                                    STA00011
      COMMON /TAPES/ IELMNT,ILOAD,IIN,IOUT                                     STA00012
C                                                                             STA00013
      DIMENSION TIM(5), HED(20)                                               STA00014
      DIMENSION IA(1)                                                         STA00015
      EQUIVALENCE (A(1),IA(1))                                                STA00016
C . . . . . . . . . . . . . . . . . . . . . . . . . . . . . . . . . . . . .   STA00017
C . THE FOLLOWING TWO LINES ARE USED TO DETERMINE THE MAXIMUM HIGH .           STA00018
C . SPEED STORAGE THAT CAN BE USED FOR SOLUTION. TO CHANGE THE HIGH .          STA00019
C . SPEED STORAGE AVAILABLE FOR EXECUTION, CHANGE THE VALUE OF MTOT .          STA00020
C . AND CORRESPONDINGLY COMMON A(MTOT).                                .       STA00021
C . . . . . . . . . . . . . . . . . . . . . . . . . . . . . . . . . . . . .   STA00022
      COMMON A(10000)                                                         STA00023
      MTOT=10000                                                              STA00024
C . . . . . . . . . . . . . . . . . . . . . . . . . . . . . . . . . . . . .   STA00025
C . DOUBLE PRECISION LINE                                              .       STA00026
C .    ITWO = 1 SINGLE PRECISION ARITHMETIC                            .       STA00027
C .    ITWO = 2 DOUBLE PRECISION ARITHMETIC                            .       STA00028
C . . . . . . . . . . . . . . . . . . . . . . . . . . . . . . . . . . . . .   STA00029
      ITWO=2                                                                  STA00030
C                                                                             STA00031
C     THE FOLLOWING SCRATCH FILES ARE USED                                    STA00032
C         IELMNT = UNIT STORING ELEMENT DATA                                  STA00033
C         ILOAD  = UNIT STORING LOAD VECTORS                                  STA00034
C         IIN    = UNIT USED FOR INPUT                                        STA00035
C         IOUT   = UNIT USED FOR OUTPUT                                       STA00036
C                                                                             STA00037
C     ON SOME MACHINES THESE FILES MUST BE EXPLICITLY OPENED                  STA00038
C                                                                             STA00039
      IELMNT = 1                                                              STA00040
      ILOAD = 2                                                               STA00041
      IIN = 5                                                                 STA00042
      IOUT = 6                                                                STA00043
C                                                                             STA00044
  200 NUMEST=0                                                                STA00045
      MAXEST=0                                                                STA00046
C     * * * * * * * * * * * * * * * * * * * * * *                             STA00047
C                                                                             STA00048
C     * * *   I N P U T   P H A S E   * * *                                   STA00049
C                                                                             STA00050
C     * * * * * * * * * * * * * * * * * * * * * *                             STA00051
      CALL SECOND (TIM(1))                                                    STA00052
C                                                                             STA00053
C                                                                             STA00054
C     R E A D   C O N T R O L   I N F O R M A T I O N                         STA00055
C                                                                             STA00056
C                                                                             STA00057
      READ (IIN,1000) HED,NUMNP,NUMEG,NLCASE,MODEX                            STA00058
      IF (NUMNP.EQ.0) GO TO 800                                               STA00059
      WRITE (IOUT,2000) HED,NUMNP,NUMEG,NLCASE,MODEX                          STA00060
C                                                                             STA00061
C                                                                             STA00062
C     R E A D   N O D A L   P O I N T   D A T A                               STA00063
C                                                                             STA00064
C                                                                             STA00065
      N1= 1                                                                   STA00066
```

```
          N2=N1 + 3*NUMNP                                        STA00067
          N2=(N2/2)*2 + 1                                        STA00068
          N3=N2 + NUMNP*ITWO                                     STA00069
          N4=N3 + NUMNP*ITWO                                     STA00070
          N5=N4 + NUMNP*ITWO                                     STA00071
          IF (N5.GT.MTOT) CALL ERROR (N5-MTOT,1)                 STA00072
C                                                                STA00073
          CALL INPUT (A(N1),A(N2),A(N3),A(N4),NUMNP,NEQ)         STA00074
C                                                                STA00075
          NEQ1=NEQ + 1                                           STA00076
C                                                                STA00077
C                                                                STA00078
C         C A L C U L A T E   A N D   S T O R E   L O A D   V E C T O R S   STA00079
C                                                                STA00080
C                                                                STA00081
          N6=N5 + NEQ*ITWO                                       STA00082
          WRITE (IOUT,2005)                                      STA00083
C                                                                STA00084
          REWIND ILOAD                                           STA00085
C                                                                STA00086
          DO 300 L=1,NLCASE                                      STA00087
C                                                                STA00088
          READ (IIN,1010) LL,NLOAD                               STA00089
C                                                                STA00090
          WRITE (IOUT,2010) LL,NLOAD                             STA00091
          IF (LL.EQ.L) GO TO 310                                 STA00092
          WRITE (IOUT,2020)                                      STA00093
          GO TO 800                                              STA00094
      310 CONTINUE                                               STA00095
C                                                                STA00096
          N7=N6 + NLOAD                                          STA00097
          N8=N7 + NLOAD                                          STA00098
          N9=N8 + NLOAD*ITWO                                     STA00099
C                                                                STA00100
          IF (N9.GT.MTOT) CALL ERROR (N9-MTOT,2)                 STA00101
C                                                                STA00102
          CALL LOADS (A(N5),A(N6),A(N7),A(N8),A(N1),NLOAD,NEQ)   STA00103
C                                                                STA00104
      300 CONTINUE                                               STA00105
C                                                                STA00106
C                                                                STA00107
C         R E A D , G E N E R A T E   A N D   S T O R E          STA00108
C         E L E M E N T   D A T A                                STA00109
C                                                                STA00110
C         CLEAR STORAGE                                          STA00111
C                                                                STA00112
          N6=N5 + NEQ                                            STA00113
          N6=(N6/2)*2 + 1                                        STA00114
          DO 10 I=N5,N6                                          STA00115
       10 IA(I)=0                                                STA00116
          IND=1                                                  STA00117
C                                                                STA00118
          CALL ELCAL                                             STA00119
C                                                                STA00120
          CALL SECOND (TIM(2))                                   STA00121
C         * * * * * * * * * * * * * * * * * * * * * * *          STA00122
C                                                                STA00123
C         * * *   S O L U T I O N   P H A S E   * * *            STA00124
C                                                                STA00125
C         * * * * * * * * * * * * * * * * * * * * * * *          STA00126
C                                                                STA00127
C         A S S E M B L E   S T I F F N E S S   M A T R I X      STA00128
C                                                                STA00129
C                                                                STA00130
          CALL ADDRES (A(N2),A(N5))                              STA00131
C                                                                STA00132
          MM=NWK/NEQ                                             STA00133
          N3=N2 + NEQ + 1                                        STA00134
          N3=(N3/2)*2 + 1                                        STA00135
          N4=N3 + NWK*ITWO                                       STA00136
```

```
      N5=N4 + NEQ*ITWO                                            STA00137
      N6=N5 + MAXEST                                              STA00138
      IF (N6.GT.MTOT) CALL ERROR (N6-MTOT,4)                      STA00139
C                                                                 STA00140
C     WRITE TOTAL SYSTEM DATA                                     STA00141
C                                                                 STA00142
      WRITE (IOUT,2025) NEQ,NWK,MK,MM                             STA00143
C                                                                 STA00144
C     IN DATA CHECK ONLY MODE WE SKIP ALL FURTHER CALCULATIONS    STA00145
C                                                                 STA00146
      IF (MODEX.GT.0) GO TO 100                                   STA00147
      CALL SECOND (TIM(3))                                        STA00148
      CALL SECOND (TIM(4))                                        STA00149
      CALL SECOND (TIM(5))                                        STA00150
      GO TO 120                                                   STA00151
C                                                                 STA00152
C     CLEAR STORAGE                                               STA00153
C                                                                 STA00154
  100 NNL=NWK + NEQ                                               STA00155
      CALL CLEAR (A(N3),NNL)                                      STA00156
C                                                                 STA00157
      IND=2                                                       STA00158
C                                                                 STA00159
      CALL ASSEM (A(N5))                                          STA00160
C                                                                 STA00161
      CALL SECOND (TIM(3))                                        STA00162
C                                                                 STA00163
C                                                                 STA00164
C     T R I A N G U L A R I Z E   S T I F F N E S S   M A T R I X STA00165
C                                                                 STA00166
C                                                                 STA00167
      KTR=1                                                       STA00168
      CALL COLSOL (A(N3),A(N4),A(N2),NEQ,NWK,NEQ1,KTR)           STA00169
C                                                                 STA00170
   35 CALL SECOND (TIM(4))                                        STA00171
C                                                                 STA00172
      KTR=2                                                       STA00173
      IND=3                                                       STA00174
C                                                                 STA00175
      REWIND ILOAD                                                STA00176
      DO 400 L=1,NLCASE                                           STA00177
C                                                                 STA00178
      CALL LOADV (A(N4),NEQ)                                      STA00179
C                                                                 STA00180
C                                                                 STA00181
C     C A L C U L A T I O N   O F   D I S P L A C E M E N T S     STA00182
C                                                                 STA00183
C                                                                 STA00184
      CALL COLSOL (A(N3),A(N4),A(N2),NEQ,NWK,NEQ1,KTR)           STA00185
C                                                                 STA00186
      WRITE (IOUT,2015) L                                         STA00187
      CALL WRITED (A(N4),A(N1),NEQ,NUMNP)                        STA00188
C                                                                 STA00189
C                                                                 STA00190
C     C A L C U L A T I O N   O F   S T R E S S E S               STA00191
C                                                                 STA00192
C                                                                 STA00193
      CALL STRESS (A(N5))                                         STA00194
C                                                                 STA00195
  400 CONTINUE                                                    STA00196
C                                                                 STA00197
      CALL SECOND (TIM(5))                                        STA00198
C                                                                 STA00199
C     PRINT SOLUTION TIMES                                        STA00200
C                                                                 STA00201
  120 TT=0.                                                       STA00202
      DO 500 I=1,4                                                STA00203
      TIM(I)=TIM(I+1) - TIM(I)                                    STA00204
  500 TT=TT + TIM(I)                                              STA00205
      WRITE (IOUT,2030) HED,(TIM(I),I=1,4),TT                    STA00206
```

```
C                                                             STA00207
C                                                             STA00208
C     READ NEXT ANALYSIS CASE                                 STA00209
C                                                             STA00210
      GO TO 200                                               STA00211
C                                                             STA00212
  800 STOP                                                    STA00213
C                                                             STA00214
 1000 FORMAT (20A4,/,4I5)                                     STA00215
 1010 FORMAT (2I5)                                            STA00216
C                                                             STA00217
 2000 FORMAT (///,' ',20A4,///,                               STA00218
     1     ' C O N T R O L    I N F O R M A T I O N',//,      STA00219
     2     '          NUMBER OF NODAL POINTS',10(' .'),' (NUMNP)  = ',I5,//, STA00220
     3     '          NUMBER OF ELEMENT GROUPS',9(' .'),' (NUMEG)  = ',I5,//, STA00221
     4     '          NUMBER OF LOAD CASES',11(' .'),' (NLCASE) = ',I5,//,   STA00222
     5     '          SOLUTION MODE ',14(' .'),' (MODEX)  = ',I5,/,          STA00223
     6     '            EQ.0, DATA CHECK',/,                  STA00224
     7     '            EQ.1, EXECUTION')                     STA00225
 2005 FORMAT (///,' L O A D    C A S E    D A T A')           STA00226
 2010 FORMAT (/////,'      LOAD CASE NUMBER',7(' .'),' = ',I5,//, STA00227
     1     '        NUMBER OF CONCENTRATED LOADS . = ',I5)    STA00228
 2015 FORMAT (///,' LOAD CASE ',I3)                           STA00229
 2020 FORMAT (' *** ERROR *** LOAD CASES ARE NOT IN ORDER')   STA00230
 2025 FORMAT (///,' TOTAL SYSTEM DATA',///,                   STA00231
     1     '          NUMBER OF EQUATIONS',14(' .'),'(NEQ) = ',I5,//,  STA00232
     2     '          NUMBER OF MATRIX ELEMENTS',11(' .'),'(NWK) = ',I5,//, STA00233
     3     '          MAXIMUM HALF BANDWIDTH ',12(' .'),'(MK) = ',I5,//, STA00234
     4     '          MEAN HALF BANDWIDTH',14(' .'),'(MM) = ',I5)      STA00235
 2030 FORMAT (///,' S O L U T I O N    T I M E    L O G    I N    S E C',//, STA00236
     1     '       FOR PROBLEM',//,' ',20A4,///,              STA00237
     2     '    TIME FOR INPUT PHASE ',14(' .'),' =',F12.2,//,  STA00238
     3     '    TIME FOR CALCULATION OF STIFFNESS MATRIX  . . . . =',F12.2, STA00239
     4 //,                                                    STA00240
     5     '    TIME FOR FACTORIZATION OF STIFFNESS MATRIX  . . . =',F12.2, STA00241
     6 //,                                                    STA00242
     7     '    TIME FOR LOAD CASE SOLUTIONS ',10(' .'),' =',F12.2,///, STA00243
     8     '    T O T A L    S O L U T I O N    T I M E . . . . =',F12.2)STA00244
C                                                             STA00245
      END                                                     STA00246
      SUBROUTINE ERROR (N,I)                                  STA00247
C . . . . . . . . . . . . . . . . . . . . . . . . . . . . .  STA00248
C .                                                        .  STA00249
C .  P R O G R A M                                         .  STA00250
C .    TO PRINT MESSAGES WHEN HIGH-SPEED STORAGE IS EXCEEDED .  STA00251
C .                                                        .  STA00252
C . . . . . . . . . . . . . . . . . . . . . . . . . . . . .  STA00253
      COMMON /TAPES/ IELMNT,ILOAD,IIN,IOUT                    STA00254
C                                                             STA00255
      GO TO (1,2,3,4),I                                       STA00256
C                                                             STA00257
    1 WRITE (IOUT,2000)                                       STA00258
      GO TO 6                                                 STA00259
    2 WRITE (IOUT,2010)                                       STA00260
      GO TO 6                                                 STA00261
    3 WRITE (IOUT,2020)                                       STA00262
      GO TO 6                                                 STA00263
    4 WRITE (IOUT,2030)                                       STA00264
C                                                             STA00265
    6 WRITE (IOUT,2050) N                                     STA00266
      STOP                                                    STA00267
C                                                             STA00268
 2000 FORMAT (//,' NOT ENOUGH STORAGE FOR ID ARRAY AND NODAL POINT ', STA00269
     1     'COORDINATES')                                     STA00270
 2010 FORMAT (//,' NOT ENOUGH STORAGE FOR DEFINITION OF LOAD VECTORS') STA00271
 2020 FORMAT (//,' NOT ENOUGH STORAGE FOR ELEMENT DATA INPUT')  STA00272
 2030 FORMAT (//,' NOT ENOUGH STORAGE FOR ASSEMBLAGE OF GLOBAL ', STA00273
     1'STRUCTURE STIFFNESS, AND DISPLACEMENT AND STRESS SOLUTION PHASE')STA00274
 2050 FORMAT (//,' *** ERROR ***  STORAGE EXCEEDED BY ', I9)  STA00275
C                                                             STA00276
      END
```

```
      SUBROUTINE INPUT (ID,X,Y,Z,NUMNP,NEQ)                          STA00277
C . . . . . . . . . . . . . . . . . . . . . . . . . . . . . . . . . STA00278
C .                                                               .  STA00279
C .    P R O G R A M                                              .  STA00280
C .       .TO READ, GENERATE, AND PRINT NODAL POINT INPUT DATA    .  STA00281
C .       .TO CALCULATE EQUATION NUMBERS AND STORE THEM IN ID ARRRAY. STA00282
C .                                                               .  STA00283
C .           N=ELEMENT NUMBER                                    .  STA00284
C .           ID=BOUNDARY CONDITION CODES (0=FREE,1=DELETED)      .  STA00285
C .           X,Y,Z= COORDINATES                                  .  STA00286
C .           KN= GENERATION CODE                                 .  STA00287
C .                   I.E. INCREMENT ON NODAL POINT NUMBER        .  STA00288
C .                                                               .  STA00289
C . . . . . . . . . . . . . . . . . . . . . . . . . . . . . . . . . STA00290
      IMPLICIT DOUBLE PRECISION (A-H,O-Z)                            STA00291
C . . . . . . . . . . . . . . . . . . . . . . . . . . . . . . . . . STA00292
C .  THE PROGRAM STAP IS USED IN SINGLE PRECISION ARITHMETIC ON CRAY. STA00293
C .  EQUIPMENT AND DOUBLE PRECISION ARITHMETIC ON IBM MACHINES,    .  STA00294
C .  ENGINEERING WORKSTATIONS AND PCS. DEACTIVATE ABOVE LINE (ALSO .  STA00295
C .  OCCURRING IN OTHER SUBROUTINES) FOR SINGLE PRECISION ARITHMETIC.. STA00296
C . . . . . . . . . . . . . . . . . . . . . . . . . . . . . . . . . STA00297
      COMMON /TAPES/ IELMNT,ILOAD,IIN,IOUT                           STA00298
      DIMENSION X(1),Y(1),Z(1),ID(3,NUMNP)                           STA00299
C                                                                    STA00300
C     READ AND GENERATE NODAL POINT DATA                             STA00301
C                                                                    STA00302
      WRITE (IOUT,2000)                                              STA00303
      WRITE (IOUT,2010)                                              STA00304
      WRITE (IOUT,2020)                                              STA00305
      KNOLD=0                                                        STA00306
      NOLD=0                                                         STA00307
C                                                                    STA00308
   10 READ (IIN,1000) N,(ID(I,N),I=1,3),X(N),Y(N),Z(N),KN            STA00309
      WRITE (IOUT,2030) N,(ID(I,N),I=1,3),X(N),Y(N),Z(N),KN          STA00310
      IF (KNOLD.EQ.0) GO TO 50                                       STA00311
      NUM=(N-NOLD)/KNOLD                                             STA00312
      NUMN=NUM - 1                                                   STA00313
      IF (NUMN.LT.1) GO TO 50                                        STA00314
      XNUM=NUM                                                       STA00315
      DX=(X(N)-X(NOLD))/XNUM                                         STA00316
      DY=(Y(N)-Y(NOLD))/XNUM                                         STA00317
      DZ=(Z(N)-Z(NOLD))/XNUM                                         STA00318
      K=NOLD                                                         STA00319
      DO 30 J=1,NUMN                                                 STA00320
      KK=K                                                           STA00321
      K=K + KNOLD                                                    STA00322
      X(K)=X(KK) + DX                                                STA00323
      Y(K)=Y(KK) + DY                                                STA00324
      Z(K)=Z(KK) + DZ                                                STA00325
      DO 30 I=1,3                                                    STA00326
      ID(I,K)=ID(I,KK)                                               STA00327
   30 CONTINUE                                                       STA00328
C                                                                    STA00329
   50 NOLD=N                                                         STA00330
      KNOLD=KN                                                       STA00331
      IF (N.NE.NUMNP) GO TO 10                                       STA00332
C                                                                    STA00333
C     WRITE COMPLETE NODAL DATA                                      STA00334
C                                                                    STA00335
      WRITE (IOUT,2015)                                              STA00336
      WRITE (IOUT,2020)                                              STA00337
      DO 200 N=1,NUMNP                                               STA00338
  200 WRITE (IOUT,2030) N,(ID(I,N),I=1,3),X(N),Y(N),Z(N),KN          STA00339
C                                                                    STA00340
C     NUMBER UNKNOWNS                                                STA00341
C                                                                    STA00342
      NEQ=0                                                          STA00343
      DO 100 N=1,NUMNP                                               STA00344
      DO 100 I=1,3                                                   STA00345
      IF (ID(I,N)) 110,120,110                                       STA00346
```

```
  120 NEQ=NEQ + 1                                              STA00347
      ID(I,N)=NEQ                                              STA00348
      GO TO 100                                                STA00349
  110 ID(I,N)=0                                                STA00350
  100 CONTINUE                                                 STA00351
C                                                              STA00352
C     WRITE EQUATION NUMBERS                                   STA00353
C                                                              STA00354
      WRITE (IOUT,2040) (N,(ID(I,N),I=1,3),N=1,NUMNP)          STA00355
C                                                              STA00356
      RETURN                                                   STA00357
C                                                              STA00358
 1000 FORMAT (4I5,3F10.0,I5)                                   STA00359
 2000 FORMAT(//,' N O D A L   P O I N T   D A T A',/)          STA00360
 2010 FORMAT(' INPUT NODAL DATA',//)                           STA00361
 2015 FORMAT(//,' GENERATED NODAL DATA',//)                    STA00362
 2020 FORMAT('  NODE',10X,'BOUNDARY',25X,'NODAL POINT',17X,'MESH',/,  STA00363
     1' NUMBER      CONDITION  CODES',21X,'COORDINATES',14X,'GENERATING',STA00364
     2/,77X,'CODE',/,                                          STA00365
     315X,'X      Y      Z',15X,'X',12X,'Y',12X,'Z',10X,'KN')  STA00366
 2030 FORMAT (I5,6X,3I5,6X,3F13.3,3X,I6)                       STA00367
 2040 FORMAT(//,' EQUATION NUMBERS',//,'   NODE',9X,           STA00368
     1 'DEGREES OF FREEDOM',/,' NUMBER',//,                    STA00369
     2 '       N',13X,'X      Y      Z',/,(1X,I5,9X,3I5))      STA00370
C                                                              STA00371
      END                                                      STA00372
      SUBROUTINE LOADS (R,NOD,IDIRN,FLOAD,ID,NLOAD,NEQ)        STA00373
C . . . . . . . . . . . . . . . . . . . . . . . . . . . . . . STA00374
C .                                                          . STA00375
C .  P R O G R A M                                           . STA00376
C .     . TO READ NODAL LOAD DATA                            . STA00377
C .     . TO CALCULATE THE LOAD VECTOR R FOR EACH LOAD CASE AND . STA00378
C .         WRITE ONTO UNIT ILOAD                            . STA00379
C .                                                          . STA00380
C . . . . . . . . . . . . . . . . . . . . . . . . . . . . . . STA00381
      IMPLICIT DOUBLE PRECISION (A-H,O-Z)                      STA00382
      COMMON /VAR/ NG,MODEX                                    STA00383
      COMMON /TAPES/ IELMNT,ILOAD,IIN,IOUT                     STA00384
      DIMENSION R(NEQ),NOD(1),IDIRN(1),FLOAD(1)                STA00385
      DIMENSION ID(3,1)                                        STA00386
C                                                              STA00387
      WRITE (IOUT,2000)                                        STA00388
      READ (IIN,1000) (NOD(I),IDIRN(I),FLOAD(I),I=1,NLOAD)     STA00389
      WRITE (IOUT,2010) (NOD(I),IDIRN(I),FLOAD(I),I=1,NLOAD)   STA00390
      IF (MODEX.EQ.0) GO TO 900                                STA00391
C                                                              STA00392
      DO 210 I=1,NEQ                                           STA00393
  210 R(I)=0.                                                  STA00394
C                                                              STA00395
      DO 220 L=1,NLOAD                                         STA00396
      LN=NOD(L)                                                STA00397
      LI=IDIRN(L)                                              STA00398
      II=ID(LI,LN)                                             STA00399
      IF (II) 220,220,240                                      STA00400
  240 R(II)=R(II) + FLOAD(L)                                   STA00401
C                                                              STA00402
  220 CONTINUE                                                 STA00403
C                                                              STA00404
      WRITE (ILOAD) R                                          STA00405
C                                                              STA00406
  200 CONTINUE                                                 STA00407
C                                                              STA00408
  900 RETURN                                                   STA00409
C                                                              STA00410
 1000 FORMAT (2I5,F10.0)                                       STA00411
 2000 FORMAT (//,'   NODE      DIRECTION        LOAD',/,       STA00412
     1       '   NUMBER',19X,'MAGNITUDE')                      STA00413
 2010 FORMAT (' ',I6,9X,I4,7X,E12.5)                           STA00414
C                                                              STA00415
      END                                                      STA00416
```

```
      SUBROUTINE ELCAL                                              STA00417
C . . . . . . . . . . . . . . . . . . . . . . . . . . . . . . . .  STA00418
C .                                                              .  STA00419
C .    P R O G R A M                                             .  STA00420
C .         TO LOOP OVER ALL ELEMENT GROUPS FOR READING,         .  STA00421
C .         GENERATING AND STORING THE ELEMENT DATA              .  STA00422
C .                                                              .  STA00423
C . . . . . . . . . . . . . . . . . . . . . . . . . . . . . . . .  STA00424
      COMMON /SOL/ NUMNP,NEQ,NWK,NUMEST,MIDEST,MAXEST,MK           STA00425
      COMMON /EL/ IND,NPAR(10),NUMEG,MTOT,NFIRST,NLAST,ITWO         STA00426
      COMMON /TAPES/ IELMNT,ILOAD,IIN,IOUT                          STA00427
      COMMON A(1)                                                   STA00428
C                                                                   STA00429
      REWIND IELMNT                                                 STA00430
      WRITE (IOUT,2000)                                             STA00431
C                                                                   STA00432
C     LOOP OVER ALL ELEMENT GROUPS                                  STA00433
C                                                                   STA00434
      DO 100 N=1,NUMEG                                              STA00435
      IF (N.NE.1) WRITE (IOUT,2010)                                 STA00436
C                                                                   STA00437
      READ (IIN,1000) NPAR                                          STA00438
C                                                                   STA00439
      CALL ELEMNT                                                   STA00440
C                                                                   STA00441
      IF (MIDEST.GT.MAXEST) MAXEST=MIDEST                           STA00442
C                                                                   STA00443
      WRITE (IELMNT) MIDEST,NPAR,(A(I),I=NFIRST,NLAST)              STA00444
C                                                                   STA00445
  100 CONTINUE                                                      STA00446
C                                                                   STA00447
      RETURN                                                        STA00448
C                                                                   STA00449
 1000 FORMAT (10I5)                                                 STA00450
 2000 FORMAT (//,' E L E M E N T   G R O U P   D A T A',//)         STA00451
 2010 FORMAT (' ')                                                  STA00452
C                                                                   STA00453
      END                                                           STA00454
      SUBROUTINE ELEMNT                                             STA00455
C . . . . . . . . . . . . . . . . . . . . . . . . . . . . . . . .  STA00456
C .                                                              .  STA00457
C .    P R O G R A M                                             .  STA00458
C .         TO CALL THE APPROPRIATE ELEMENT SUBROUTINE           .  STA00459
C .                                                              .  STA00460
C . . . . . . . . . . . . . . . . . . . . . . . . . . . . . . . .  STA00461
      COMMON /EL/ IND,NPAR(10),NUMEG,MTOT,NFIRST,NLAST,ITWO         STA00462
C                                                                   STA00463
      NPAR1=NPAR(1)                                                 STA00464
C                                                                   STA00465
      GO TO (1,2,3),NPAR1                                           STA00466
C                                                                   STA00467
    1 CALL TRUSS                                                    STA00468
      GO TO 900                                                     STA00469
C                                                                   STA00470
C     OTHER ELEMENT TYPES WOULD BE CALLED HERE, IDENTIFYING EACH    STA00471
C     ELEMENT TYPE BY A DIFFERENT NPAR(1) PARAMETER                 STA00472
C                                                                   STA00473
    2 GO TO 900                                                     STA00474
C                                                                   STA00475
    3 GO TO 900                                                     STA00476
C                                                                   STA00477
  900 RETURN                                                        STA00478
      END                                                           STA00479
      SUBROUTINE COLHT (MHT,ND,LM)                                  STA00480
C . . . . . . . . . . . . . . . . . . . . . . . . . . . . . . . .  STA00481
C .                                                              .  STA00482
C .    P R O G R A M                                             .  STA00483
C .         TO CALCULATE COLUMN HEIGHTS                          .  STA00484
C .                                                              .  STA00485
C . . . . . . . . . . . . . . . . . . . . . . . . . . . . . . . .  STA00486
```

```
      COMMON /SOL/ NUMNP,NEQ,NWK,NUMEST,MIDEST,MAXEST,MK      STA00487
      DIMENSION LM(1),MHT(1)                                  STA00488
C                                                             STA00489
      LS=100000                                               STA00490
      DO 100 I=1,ND                                           STA00491
      IF (LM(I)) 110,100,110                                  STA00492
  110 IF (LM(I)-LS) 120,100,100                               STA00493
  120 LS=LM(I)                                                STA00494
  100 CONTINUE                                                STA00495
C                                                             STA00496
      DO 200 I=1,ND                                           STA00497
      II=LM(I)                                                STA00498
      IF (II.EQ.0) GO TO 200                                  STA00499
      ME=II - LS                                              STA00500
      IF (ME.GT.MHT(II)) MHT(II)=ME                           STA00501
  200 CONTINUE                                                STA00502
C                                                             STA00503
      RETURN                                                  STA00504
      END                                                     STA00505
      SUBROUTINE ADDRES (MAXA,MHT)                            STA00506
C . . . . . . . . . . . . . . . . . . . . . . . . . . . . .  STA00507
C .                                                        .  STA00508
C .   P R O G R A M                                        .  STA00509
C .       TO CALCULATE ADDRESSES OF DIAGONAL ELEMENTS IN BANDED . STA00510
C .       MATRIX WHOSE COLUMN HEIGHTS ARE KNOWN            .  STA00511
C .                                                        .  STA00512
C .       MHT  = ACTIVE COLUMN HEIGHTS                     .  STA00513
C.        MAXA = ADDRESSES OF DIAGONAL ELEMENTS            .  STA00514
C .                                                        .  STA00515
C . . . . . . . . . . . . . . . . . . . . . . . . . . . . .  STA00516
      COMMON /SOL/ NUMNP,NEQ,NWK,NUMEST,MIDEST,MAXEST,MK      STA00517
      DIMENSION MAXA(*),MHT(*)                                STA00518
C                                                             STA00519
C     CLEAR ARRAY MAXA                                        STA00520
C                                                             STA00521
      NN=NEQ + 1                                              STA00522
      DO 20 I=1,NN                                            STA00523
   20 MAXA(I)=0.0                                             STA00524
C                                                             STA00525
      MAXA(1)=1                                               STA00526
      MAXA(2)=2                                               STA00527
      MK=0                                                    STA00528
      IF (NEQ.EQ.1) GO TO 100                                 STA00529
      DO 10 I=2,NEQ                                           STA00530
      IF (MHT(I).GT.MK) MK=MHT(I)                             STA00531
   10 MAXA(I+1)=MAXA(I) + MHT(I) + 1                          STA00532
  100 MK=MK + 1                                               STA00533
      NWK=MAXA(NEQ+1) - MAXA(1)                               STA00534
C                                                             STA00535
      RETURN                                                  STA00536
      END                                                     STA00537
      SUBROUTINE CLEAR (A,N)                                  STA00538
C . . . . . . . . . . . . . . . . . . . . . . . . . . . . .  STA00539
C .                                                        .  STA00540
C .   P R O G R A M                                        .  STA00541
C .       TO CLEAR ARRAY A                                 .  STA00542
C .                                                        .  STA00543
C . . . . . . . . . . . . . . . . . . . . . . . . . . . . .  STA00544
      IMPLICIT DOUBLE PRECISION (A-H,O-Z)                     STA00545
      DIMENSION A(1)                                          STA00546
      DO 10 I=1,N                                             STA00547
   10 A(I)=0.                                                 STA00548
      RETURN                                                  STA00549
      END                                                     STA00550
      SUBROUTINE ASSEM (AA)                                   STA00551
C . . . . . . . . . . . . . . . . . . . . . . . . . . . . .  STA00552
C .                                                        .  STA00553
C .   P R O G R A M                                        .  STA00554
C .       TO CALL ELEMENT SUBROUTINES FOR ASSEMBLAGE OF THE . STA00555
C .       STRUCTURE STIFFNESS MATRIX                       .  STA00556
```

```
C .                                                                  . STA00557
C . . . . . . . . . . . . . . . . . . . . . . . . . . . . . . . . . . . STA00558
      COMMON /EL/ IND,NPAR(10),NUMEG,MTOT,NFIRST,NLAST,ITWO           STA00559
      COMMON /TAPES/ IELMNT,ILOAD,IIN,IOUT                            STA00560
      DIMENSION AA(1)                                                 STA00561
C                                                                     STA00562
      REWIND IELMNT                                                   STA00563
C                                                                     STA00564
      DO 200 N=1,NUMEG                                                STA00565
      READ (IELMNT) NUMEST,NPAR,(AA(I),I=1,NUMEST)                    STA00566
C                                                                     STA00567
      CALL ELEMNT                                                     STA00568
C                                                                     STA00569
  200 CONTINUE                                                        STA00570
C                                                                     STA00571
      RETURN                                                          STA00572
      END                                                             STA00573
      SUBROUTINE ADDBAN (A,MAXA,S,LM,ND)                              STA00574
C . . . . . . . . . . . . . . . . . . . . . . . . . . . . . . . . . . . STA00575
C .                                                                  . STA00576
C .   P R O G R A M                                                  . STA00577
C .        TO ASSEMBLE UPPER TRIANGULAR ELEMENT STIFFNESS INTO       . STA00578
C .        COMPACTED GLOBAL STIFFNESS                                . STA00579
C .                                                                  . STA00580
C .        A = GLOBAL STIFFNESS                                      . STA00581
C .        S = ELEMENT STIFFNESS                                     . STA00582
C .        ND = DEGREES OF FREEDOM IN ELEMENT STIFFNESS              . STA00583
C .                                                                  . STA00584
C .                  S(1)        S(2)       S(3)       . . .         . STA00585
C .        S   =                 S(ND+1)    S(ND+2)    . . .         . STA00586
C .                                         S(2*ND)    . . .         . STA00587
C .                                                    . . .         . STA00588
C .                                                    . . .         . STA00589
C .                                                                  . STA00590
C .                  A(1)        A(3)       A(6)       . . .         . STA00591
C .        A   =                 A(2)       A(5)       . . .         . STA00592
C .                                         A(4)       . . .         . STA00593
C .                                                    . . .         . STA00594
C .                                                                  . STA00595
C .                                                                  . STA00596
C . . . . . . . . . . . . . . . . . . . . . . . . . . . . . . . . . . . STA00597
      IMPLICIT DOUBLE PRECISION (A-H,O-Z)                             STA00598
      DIMENSION A(1),MAXA(1),S(1),LM(1)                               STA00599
C                                                                     STA00600
      NDI=0                                                           STA00601
      DO 200 I=1,ND                                                   STA00602
      II=LM(I)                                                        STA00603
      IF (II) 200,200,100                                             STA00604
  100 MI=MAXA(II)                                                     STA00605
      KS=I                                                            STA00606
      DO 220 J=1,ND                                                   STA00607
      JJ=LM(J)                                                        STA00608
      IF (JJ) 220,220,110                                             STA00609
  110 IJ=II - JJ                                                      STA00610
      IF (IJ) 220,210,210                                             STA00611
  210 KK=MI + IJ                                                      STA00612
      KSS=KS                                                          STA00613
      IF (J.GE.I) KSS=J + NDI                                         STA00614
      A(KK)=A(KK) + S(KSS)                                            STA00615
  220 KS=KS + ND - J                                                  STA00616
  200 NDI=NDI + ND - I                                                STA00617
C                                                                     STA00618
      RETURN                                                          STA00619
      END                                                             STA00620
      SUBROUTINE COLSOL (A,V,MAXA,NN,NWK,NNM,KKK)                     STA00621
C . . . . . . . . . . . . . . . . . . . . . . . . . . . . . . . . . . . STA00622
C .                                                                  . STA00623
C .   P R O G R A M                                                  . STA00624
C .        TO SOLVE FINITE ELEMENT STATIC EQUILIBRIUM EQUATIONS IN   . STA00625
C .        CORE, USING COMPACTED STORAGE AND COLUMN REDUCTION SCHEME . STA00626
```

```
C .                                                                    . STA00627
C .   - - INPUT VARIABLES - -                                          . STA00628
C .        A(NWK)    = STIFFNESS MATRIX STORED IN COMPACTED FORM        . STA00629
C .        V(NN)     = RIGHT-HAND-SIDE LOAD VECTOR                      . STA00630
C .        MAXA(NNM) = VECTOR CONTAINING ADDRESSES OF DIAGONAL          . STA00631
C .                    ELEMENTS OF STIFFNESS MATRIX IN A                . STA00632
C .        NN        = NUMBER OF EQUATIONS                              . STA00633
C .        NWK       = NUMBER OF ELEMENTS BELOW SKYLINE OF MATRIX       . STA00634
C .        NNM       = NN + 1                                           . STA00635
C .        KKK       = INPUT FLAG                                       . STA00636
C .            EQ. 1    TRIANGULARIZATION OF STIFFNESS MATRIX           . STA00637
C .            EQ. 2    REDUCTION AND BACK-SUBSTITUTION OF LOAD VECTOR  . STA00638
C .        IOUT      = UNIT USED FOR OUTPUT                             . STA00639
C .                                                                     . STA00640
C .   - - OUTPUT - -                                                    . STA00641
C .        A(NWK)    = D AND L - FACTORS OF STIFFNESS MATRIX            . STA00642
C .        V(NN)     = DISPLACEMENT VECTOR                              . STA00643
C .                                                                     . STA00644
C . . . . . . . . . . . . . . . . . . . . . . . . . . . . . . . . . . . . STA00645
      IMPLICIT DOUBLE PRECISION (A-H,O-Z)                                STA00646
      COMMON /TAPES/ IELMNT,ILOAD,IIN,IOUT                               STA00647
      DIMENSION A(NWK),V(1),MAXA(1)                                      STA00648
C                                                                        STA00649
C     PERFORM L*D*L(T) FACTORIZATION OF STIFFNESS MATRIX                 STA00650
C                                                                        STA00651
      IF (KKK-2) 40,150,150                                              STA00652
   40 DO 140 N=1,NN                                                      STA00653
      KN=MAXA(N)                                                         STA00654
      KL=KN + 1                                                          STA00655
      KU=MAXA(N+1) - 1                                                   STA00656
      KH=KU - KL                                                         STA00657
      IF (KH) 110,90,50                                                  STA00658
   50 K=N - KH                                                           STA00659
      IC=0                                                               STA00660
      KLT=KU                                                             STA00661
      DO 80 J=1,KH                                                       STA00662
      IC=IC + 1                                                          STA00663
      KLT=KLT - 1                                                        STA00664
      KI=MAXA(K)                                                         STA00665
      ND=MAXA(K+1) - KI - 1                                              STA00666
      IF (ND) 80,80,60                                                   STA00667
   60 KK=MIN0(IC,ND)                                                     STA00668
      C=0.                                                               STA00669
      DO 70 L=1,KK                                                       STA00670
   70 C=C + A(KI+L)*A(KLT+L)                                             STA00671
      A(KLT)=A(KLT) - C                                                  STA00672
   80 K=K + 1                                                            STA00673
   90 K=N                                                                STA00674
      B=0.                                                               STA00675
      DO 100 KK=KL,KU                                                    STA00676
      K=K - 1                                                            STA00677
      KI=MAXA(K)                                                         STA00678
      C=A(KK)/A(KI)                                                      STA00679
      B=B + C*A(KK)                                                      STA00680
  100 A(KK)=C                                                            STA00681
      A(KN)=A(KN) - B                                                    STA00682
  110 IF (A(KN)) 120,120,140                                             STA00683
  120 WRITE (IOUT,2000) N,A(KN)                                          STA00684
      GO TO 800                                                          STA00685
  140 CONTINUE                                                           STA00686
      GO TO 900                                                          STA00687
C                                                                        STA00688
C     REDUCE RIGHT-HAND-SIDE LOAD VECTOR                                 STA00689
C                                                                        STA00690
  150 DO 180 N=1,NN                                                      STA00691
      KL=MAXA(N) + 1                                                     STA00692
      KU=MAXA(N+1) - 1                                                   STA00693
      IF (KU-KL) 180,160,160                                             STA00694
  160 K=N                                                                STA00695
      C=0.                                                               STA00696
```

```
        DO 170 KK=KL,KU                                    STA00697
        K=K - 1                                            STA00698
  170 C=C + A(KK)*V(K)                                     STA00699
        V(N)=V(N) - C                                      STA00700
  180 CONTINUE                                             STA00701
C                                                          STA00702
C       BACK-SUBSTITUTE                                    STA00703
C                                                          STA00704
        DO 200 N=1,NN                                      STA00705
        K=MAXA(N)                                          STA00706
  200 V(N)=V(N)/A(K)                                       STA00707
        IF (NN.EQ.1) GO TO 900                             STA00708
        N=NN                                               STA00709
        DO 230 L=2,NN                                      STA00710
        KL=MAXA(N) + 1                                     STA00711
        KU=MAXA(N+1) - 1                                   STA00712
        IF (KU-KL) 230,210,210                             STA00713
  210 K=N                                                  STA00714
        DO 220 KK=KL,KU                                    STA00715
        K=K - 1                                            STA00716
  220 V(K)=V(K) - A(KK)*V(N)                               STA00717
  230 N=N - 1                                              STA00718
        GO TO 900                                          STA00719
C                                                          STA00720
  800 STOP                                                 STA00721
  900 RETURN                                               STA00722
C                                                          STA00723
 2000 FORMAT (//' STOP - STIFFNESS MATRIX NOT POSITIVE DEFINITE',//,  STA00724
     1             ' NONPOSITIVE PIVOT FOR EQUATION ',I8,//,           STA00725
     2             ' PIVOT = ',E20.12 )                                STA00726
C                                                          STA00727
        END                                                STA00728
        SUBROUTINE LOADV (R,NEQ)                           STA00729
C . . . . . . . . . . . . . . . . . . . . . . . . . . . .  STA00730
C .                                                     .  STA00731
C .    P R O G R A M                                    .  STA00732
C .        TO OBTAIN THE LOAD VECTOR                    .  STA00733
C . . . . . . . . . . . . . . . . . . . . . . . . . . . .  STA00734
        IMPLICIT DOUBLE PRECISION (A-H,O-Z)                STA00735
        COMMON /TAPES/ IELMNT,ILOAD,IIN,IOUT               STA00736
        DIMENSION R(NEQ)                                   STA00737
C                                                          STA00738
        READ (ILOAD) R                                     STA00739
C                                                          STA00740
        RETURN                                             STA00741
        END                                                STA00742
        SUBROUTINE WRITED (DISP,ID,NEQ,NUMNP)              STA00743
C . . . . . . . . . . . . . . . . . . . . . . . . . . . .  STA00744
C .                                                     .  STA00745
C .    P R O G R A M                                    .  STA00746
C .        TO PRINT DISPLACEMENTS                       .  STA00747
C . . . . . . . . . . . . . . . . . . . . . . . . . . . .  STA00748
        IMPLICIT DOUBLE PRECISION (A-H,O-Z)                STA00749
        COMMON /TAPES/ IELMNT,ILOAD,IIN,IOUT               STA00750
        DIMENSION DISP(NEQ),ID(3,NUMNP)                    STA00751
        DIMENSION D(3)                                     STA00752
C                                                          STA00753
C       PRINT DISPLACEMENTS                                STA00754
C                                                          STA00755
        WRITE (IOUT,2000)                                  STA00756
        IC=4                                               STA00757
C                                                          STA00758
        DO 100 II=1,NUMNP                                  STA00759
        IC=IC + 1                                          STA00760
        IF (IC.LT.56) GO TO 105                            STA00761
        WRITE (IOUT,2000)                                  STA00762
        IC=4                                               STA00763
  105 DO 110 I=1,3                                         STA00764
  110 D(I)=0.                                              STA00765
C                                                          STA00766
```

```
          DO 120 I=1,3                                        STA00767
          KK=ID(I,II)                                         STA00768
          IL=I                                                STA00769
   120 IF (KK.NE.0) D(IL)=DISP(KK)                            STA00770
C                                                             STA00771
   100 WRITE (IOUT,2010) II,D                                 STA00772
C                                                             STA00773
       RETURN                                                 STA00774
C                                                             STA00775
 2000 FORMAT (///,' D I S P L A C E M E N T S',//,' NODE ',10X,  STA00776
      1           'X-DISPLACEMENT    Y-DISPLACEMENT    Z-DISPLACEMENT')  STA00777
 2010 FORMAT (1X,I3,8X,3E18.6)                                STA00778
C                                                             STA00779
       END                                                    STA00780
       SUBROUTINE STRESS (AA)                                 STA00781
C . . . . . . . . . . . . . . . . . . . . . . . . . . . .     STA00782
C .                                                      .    STA00783
C .   P R O G R A M                                      .    STA00784
C .         TO CALL THE ELEMENT SUBROUTINE FOR THE CALCULATION OF  .  STA00785
C .         STRESSES                                     .    STA00786
C .                                                      .    STA00787
C . . . . . . . . . . . . . . . . . . . . . . . . . . . .     STA00788
       COMMON /VAR/ NG,MODEX                                  STA00789
       COMMON /EL/ IND,NPAR(10),NUMEG,MTOT,NFIRST,NLAST,ITWO  STA00790
       COMMON /TAPES/ IELMNT,ILOAD,IIN,IOUT                   STA00791
       DIMENSION AA(1)                                        STA00792
C                                                             STA00793
C     LOOP OVER ALL ELEMENT GROUPS                            STA00794
C                                                             STA00795
       REWIND IELMNT                                          STA00796
C                                                             STA00797
       DO 100 N=1,NUMEG                                       STA00798
       NG=N                                                   STA00799
C                                                             STA00800
       READ (IELMNT) NUMEST,NPAR,(AA(I),I=1,NUMEST)           STA00801
C                                                             STA00802
       CALL ELEMNT                                            STA00803
C                                                             STA00804
   100 CONTINUE                                               STA00805
C                                                             STA00806
       RETURN                                                 STA00807
       END                                                    STA00808
       SUBROUTINE TRUSS                                       STA00809
C . . . . . . . . . . . . . . . . . . . . . . . . . . . .     STA00810
C .                                                      .    STA00811
C .   P R O G R A M                                      .    STA00812
C .         TO SET UP STORAGE AND CALL THE TRUSS ELEMENT SUBROUTINE  .  STA00813
C .                                                      .    STA00814
C . . . . . . . . . . . . . . . . . . . . . . . . . . . .     STA00815
       COMMON /SOL/ NUMNP,NEQ,NWK,NUMEST,MIDEST,MAXEST,MK     STA00816
       COMMON /DIM/ N1,N2,N3,N4,N5,N6,N7,N8,N9,N10,N11,N12,N13,N14,N15  STA00817
       COMMON /EL/ IND,NPAR(10),NUMEG,MTOT,NFIRST,NLAST,ITWO  STA00818
       COMMON /TAPES/ IELMNT,ILOAD,IIN,IOUT                   STA00819
       COMMON A(1)                                            STA00820
C                                                             STA00821
       EQUIVALENCE (NPAR(2),NUME),(NPAR(3),NUMMAT)            STA00822
C                                                             STA00823
       NFIRST=N6                                              STA00824
       IF (IND.GT.1) NFIRST=N5                                STA00825
       N101=NFIRST                                            STA00826
       N102=N101 + NUMMAT*ITWO                                STA00827
       N103=N102 + NUMMAT*ITWO                                STA00828
       N104=N103 + 6*NUME                                     STA00829
       N105=N104 + 6*NUME*ITWO                                STA00830
       N106=N105 + NUME                                       STA00831
       NLAST=N106                                             STA00832
C                                                             STA00833
       IF (IND.GT.1) GO TO 100                                STA00834
       IF (NLAST.GT.MTOT) CALL ERROR (NLAST-MTOT,3)           STA00835
       GO TO 200                                              STA00836
```

```
    100 IF (NLAST.GT.MTOT) CALL ERROR (NLAST-MTOT,4)                  STA00837
C                                                                     STA00838
    200 MIDEST=NLAST - NFIRST                                         STA00839
C                                                                     STA00840
        CALL RUSS (A(N1),A(N2),A(N3),A(N4),A(N4),A(N5),A(N101),A(N102),  STA00841
       1 A(N103),A(N104),A(N105))                                     STA00842
C                                                                     STA00843
        RETURN                                                        STA00844
C                                                                     STA00845
        END                                                           STA00846
        SUBROUTINE RUSS (ID,X,Y,Z,U,MHT,E,AREA,LM,XYZ,MATP)           STA00847
C . . . . . . . . . . . . . . . . . . . . . . . . . . . . . . . . .   STA00848
C .                                                               .   STA00849
C .          TRUSS ELEMENT SUBROUTINE                             .   STA00850
C .                                                               .   STA00851
C . . . . . . . . . . . . . . . . . . . . . . . . . . . . . . . . .   STA00852
        IMPLICIT DOUBLE PRECISION (A-H,O-Z)                           STA00853
        REAL A                                                        STA00854
        COMMON /SOL/ NUMNP,NEQ,NWK,NUMEST,MIDEST,MAXEST,MK            STA00855
        COMMON /DIM/ N1,N2,N3,N4,N5,N6,N7,N8,N9,N10,N11,N12,N13,N14,N15  STA00856
        COMMON /EL/ IND,NPAR(10),NUMEG,MTOT,NFIRST,NLAST,ITWO         STA00857
        COMMON /VAR/ NG,MODEX                                         STA00858
        COMMON /TAPES/ IELMNT,ILOAD,IIN,IOUT                          STA00859
        COMMON A(1)                                                   STA00860
C                                                                     STA00861
        DIMENSION X(1),Y(1),Z(1),ID(3,1),E(1),AREA(1),LM(6,1),        STA00862
       1          XYZ(6,1),MATP(1),U(1),MHT(1)                        STA00863
        DIMENSION S(21),ST(6),D(3)                                    STA00864
C                                                                     STA00865
        EQUIVALENCE (NPAR(1),NPAR1),(NPAR(2),NUME),(NPAR(3),NUMMAT)   STA00866
        ND=6                                                          STA00867
C                                                                     STA00868
        GO TO (300,610,800),IND                                       STA00869
C                                                                     STA00870
C                                                                     STA00871
C       R E A D   A N D   G E N E R A T E   E L E M E N T            STA00872
C       I N F O R M A T I O N                                         STA00873
C                                                                     STA00874
C       READ MATERIAL INFORMATION                                     STA00875
C                                                                     STA00876
    300 WRITE (IOUT,2000) NPAR1,NUME                                  STA00877
        IF (NUMMAT.EQ.0) NUMMAT=1                                     STA00878
        WRITE (IOUT,2010) NUMMAT                                      STA00879
C                                                                     STA00880
        WRITE (IOUT,2020)                                             STA00881
        DO 10 I=1,NUMMAT                                              STA00882
        READ (IIN,1000) N,E(N),AREA(N)                                STA00883
     10 WRITE (IOUT,2030) N,E(N),AREA(N)                              STA00884
C                                                                     STA00885
C       READ ELEMENT INFORMATION                                      STA00886
C                                                                     STA00887
        WRITE (IOUT,2040)                                             STA00888
        N=1                                                           STA00889
    100 READ (IIN,1020) M,II,JJ,MTYP,KG                               STA00890
        IF (KG.EQ.0) KG=1                                             STA00891
    120 IF (M.NE.N) GO TO 200                                         STA00892
        I=II                                                          STA00893
        J=JJ                                                          STA00894
        MTYPE=MTYP                                                     STA00895
        KKK=KG                                                        STA00896
C                                                                     STA00897
C       SAVE ELEMENT INFORMATION                                      STA00898
C                                                                     STA00899
    200 XYZ(1,N)=X(I)                                                 STA00900
        XYZ(2,N)=Y(I)                                                 STA00901
        XYZ(3,N)=Z(I)                                                 STA00902
C                                                                     STA00903
        XYZ(4,N)=X(J)                                                 STA00904
        XYZ(5,N)=Y(J)                                                 STA00905
        XYZ(6,N)=Z(J)                                                 STA00906
```

```
C                                                                STA00907
      MATP(N)=MTYPE                                              STA00908
C                                                                STA00909
      DO 390 L=1,6                                               STA00910
  390 LM(L,N)=0                                                  STA00911
      DO 400 L=1,3                                               STA00912
      LM(L,N)=ID(L,I)                                            STA00913
  400 LM(L+3,N)=ID(L,J)                                          STA00914
C                                                                STA00915
C     UPDATE COLUMN HEIGHTS AND BANDWIDTH                        STA00916
C                                                                STA00917
      CALL COLHT (MHT,ND,LM(1,N))                                STA00918
C                                                                STA00919
      WRITE (IOUT,2050) N,I,J,MTYPE                              STA00920
      IF (N.EQ.NUME) GO TO 900                                   STA00921
      N=N + 1                                                    STA00922
      I=I + KKK                                                  STA00923
      J=J + KKK                                                  STA00924
      IF (N.GT.M) GO TO 100                                      STA00925
      GO TO 120                                                  STA00926
C                                                                STA00927
C                                                                STA00928
C     A S S E M B L E   S T U C T U R E   S T I F F N E S S   M A T R I X    STA00929
C                                                                STA00930
C                                                                STA00931
  610 DO 500 N=1,NUME                                            STA00932
      MTYPE=MATP(N)                                              STA00933
      XL2=0.                                                     STA00934
      DO 505 L=1,3                                               STA00935
      D(L)=XYZ(L,N) - XYZ(L+3,N)                                 STA00936
  505 XL2=XL2 + D(L)*D(L)                                        STA00937
      XL=SQRT(XL2)                                               STA00938
      XX=E(MTYPE)*AREA(MTYPE)*XL                                 STA00939
      DO 510 L=1,3                                               STA00940
      ST(L)=D(L)/XL2                                             STA00941
  510 ST(L+3)=-ST(L)                                             STA00942
C                                                                STA00943
      KL=0                                                       STA00944
      DO 600 L=1,6                                               STA00945
      YY=ST(L)*XX                                                STA00946
      DO 600 K=L,6                                               STA00947
      KL=KL + 1                                                  STA00948
  600 S(KL)=ST(K)*YY                                             STA00949
      CALL ADDBAN (A(N3),A(N2),S,LM(1,N),ND)                     STA00950
  500 CONTINUE                                                   STA00951
      GO TO 900                                                  STA00952
C                                                                STA00953
C                                                                STA00954
C     S T R E S S   C A L C U L A T I O N S                      STA00955
C                                                                STA00956
C                                                                STA00957
  800 IPRINT=0                                                   STA00958
      DO 830 N=1,NUME                                            STA00959
      IPRINT=IPRINT + 1                                          STA00960
      IF (IPRINT.GT.50) IPRINT=1                                 STA00961
      IF (IPRINT.EQ.1) WRITE (IOUT,2060) NG                      STA00962
      MTYPE=MATP(N)                                              STA00963
      XL2=0.                                                     STA00964
      DO 820 L=1,3                                               STA00965
      D(L) = XYZ(L,N) - XYZ(L+3,N)                               STA00966
  820 XL2=XL2 + D(L)*D(L)                                        STA00967
      DO 814 L=1,3                                               STA00968
      ST(L)=(D(L)/XL2)*E(MTYPE)                                  STA00969
  814 ST(L+3)=-ST(L)                                             STA00970
      STR=0.0                                                    STA00971
      DO 806 L=1,3                                               STA00972
      I=LM(L,N)                                                  STA00973
      IF (I.LE.0) GO TO 807                                      STA00974
      STR=STR + ST(L)*U(I)                                       STA00975
  807 J=LM(L+3,N)                                                STA00976
      IF (J.LE.0) GO TO 806                                      STA00977
      STR=STR + ST(L+3)*U(J)                                     STA00978
```

```
  806 CONTINUE                                                          STA00979
      P=STR*AREA(MTYPE)                                                 STA00980
      WRITE (IOUT,2070) N,P,STR                                         STA00981
  830 CONTINUE                                                          STA00982
C                                                                       STA00983
  900 RETURN                                                            STA00984
C                                                                       STA00985
 1000 FORMAT (I5,2F10.0)                                                STA00986
 1010 FORMAT (2F10.0)                                                   STA00987
 1020 FORMAT (5I5)                                                      STA00988
 2000 FORMAT (' E L E M E N T   D E F I N I T I O N',///,               STA00989
    1         ' ELEMENT TYPE ',13(' .'),'( NPAR(1) ) . . =',I5,/,       STA00990
    2         '       EQ.1, TRUSS ELEMENTS',/,                          STA00991
    3         '       EQ.2, ELEMENTS CURRENTLY',/,                      STA00992
    4         '       EQ.3, NOT AVAILABLE',//,                          STA00993
    5         ' NUMBER OF ELEMENTS.',10(' .'),'( NPAR(2) ) . . =',I5,//)STA00994
 2010 FORMAT (' M A T E R I A L   D E F I N I T I O N',///,             STA00995
    1         ' NUMBER OF DIFFERENT SETS OF MATERIAL',/,                STA00996
    2         ' AND CROSS-SECTIONAL  CONSTANTS ',                       STA00997
    3                       4(' .'),'( NPAR(3) ) . . =',I5,//)          STA00998
 2020 FORMAT (' SET         YOUNG''S      CROSS-SECTIONAL',/,           STA00999
    1         ' NUMBER      MODULUS',10X,'AREA',/,                      STA01000
    2         15X,'E',14X,'A')                                          STA01001
 2030 FORMAT (/,I5,4X,E12.5,2X,E14.6)                                   STA01002
 2040 FORMAT (///,' E L E M E N T   I N F O R M A T I O N',///,         STA01003
    1         ' ELEMENT      NODE      NODE       MATERIAL',/,          STA01004
    2         ' NUMBER-N      I         J       SET NUMBER',/)          STA01005
 2050 FORMAT (I5,6X,I5,4X,I5,7X,I5)                                     STA01006
 2060 FORMAT (///,' S T R E S S   C A L C U L A T I O N S   F O R ',    STA01007
    1         'E L E M E N T   G R O U P',I4,//,                        STA01008
    2         ' ELEMENT',13X,'FORCE',12X,'STRESS',/,                    STA01009
    3         ' NUMBER',/)                                              STA01010
 2070 FORMAT (1X,I5,11X,E13.6,4X,E13.6)                                 STA01011
C                                                                       STA01012
      END                                                               STA01013
      SUBROUTINE SECOND (TIM)                                           STA01014
C                                                                       STA01015
C     SUBROUTINE TO OBTAIN TIME                                         STA01016
C     THIS SUBROUTINE HAS BEEN USED ON AN IBM RS/6000 WORKSTATION       STA01017
C                                                                       STA01018
      TIM=0.01*MCLOCK()                                                 STA01019
C                                                                       STA01020
      RETURN                                                            STA01021
      END                                                               STA01022
```

12.5 EXERCISES AND PROJECTS

Exercises

12.1. Consider the truss structure shown. Use the program STAP to solve for the response of the structure. Check your answer.

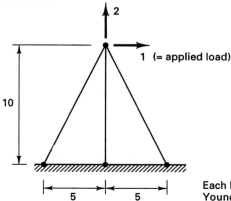

Each bar has cross-sectional area $A = 1$, Young's modulus $E = 200,000$

12.2. Consider the truss structure shown. Use the program STAP to solve for the response of the structure. Check your answer.

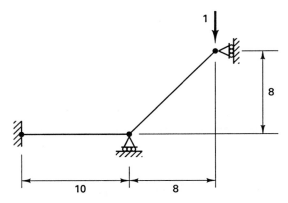

Each bar has cross-sectional area $A = 1$,
Young's modulus $E = 200,000$

12.3. Consider the truss structure shown. Use the program STAP to solve for the response of the structure. Check your answer.

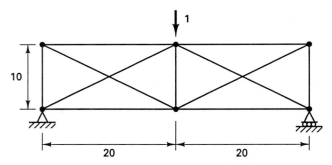

Each bar has cross-sectional area $A = 1$,
Young's modulus $E = 200,000$

12.4. Consider the truss structure shown. Use the program STAP to solve for the response of the structure. Check your answer.

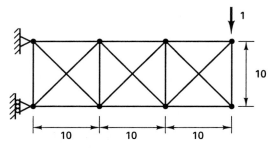

Each bar has cross-sectional area $A = 1$,
Young's modulus $E = 200,000$

Projects

Below we give descriptions of some projects using STAP. Of course, once the program implementations have been performed, various analysis problems could be solved, and we point out only some possibilities. The student is encouraged to solve additional analysis problems.

Project 12.1.   Extend the program STAP to be also applicable to static two-dimensional plane stress, plane strain, and axisymmetric analyses. For this purpose incorporate the subroutine QUADS in Section 5.6 into STAP. Verify the program implementation by solving the patch test problems in Fig. 4.17 and the cantilever plate problem discussed in Example 4.6.

Project 12.2.   Proceed as in project 12.1 but incorporate a modified program QUADS, modified for the u/p formulation and the 4/1 element (see Section 4.4.3).

Project 12.3.   Extend the program STAP to be also applicable to dynamic analysis by direct step-by-step integration. Allow for the selection of a lumped or consistent mass matrix and allow for the use of the central difference method or the Newmark method.
    Use the extended program STAP to solve the problem considered in Example 9.14.

Project 12.4.   Extend the program STAP to be also applicable to dynamic analysis by mode superposition. Allow for the selection of a lumped or consistent mass matrix.
    Incorporate the subroutine JACOBI in Section 11.3.2 to calculate the frequencies and mode shapes and allow for the selection of the number of modes to be included in the mode superposition from 1 to p, where $p \leq n$ and n = number of degrees of freedom.
    Use the extended program STAP to solve the problem considered in Example 9.14.

Project 12.5.   Extend the program STAP as in project 12.4 but allow for the selection and use of all modes with frequencies between ω_l and ω_u. Then solve the following problem. Let $R(t) = \sin \omega_R t$, $\omega_R = 2000$. The bar is initially at rest (i.e., at zero displacement and at zero velocity). Perform the analysis using 4, 8, 40, 60, . . . , equal two-node truss elements in the finite element discretization of the bar. Compare your response predictions.

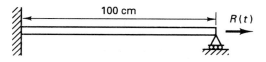

Bar of cross-sectional area A = 4 cm^2
Young's modulus E = 4.4 MPa
ρ = mass density = 1560 kg/m^3

Project 12.6.   Extend the program STAP to allow for large displacements (but small strains) in the analysis of truss structures. Use the information given in Example 6.16. Then solve the analysis problem in Example 6.3.

Project 12.7.   Extend the program STAP to allow for large displacement two-dimensional plane stress, plane strain, and axisymmetric analysis. Use the program QUADS in Section 5.6 as the basis of the element subroutine and extend this program for the total Lagrangian formulation described in Section 6.3.4. Assume an elastic material with Young's modulus E and Poisson's ratio ν. Test the program on the simple analysis problems shown and compare your results with analytical calculations.

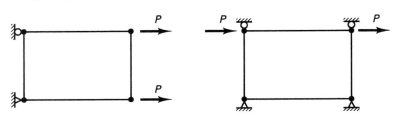

Project 12.8.   Proceed as in project 12.7 but use the u/p formulation and implement the 4/1 element.

Project 12.9.   Extend the program STAP for one-dimensional transient conduction heat transfer analysis, including linear convection boundary conditions. Then solve the problem in Fig. E7.2 with $h = 2$, $L = 20$, $q^S = 2$, $k = 1.0$, $\rho c = 1.0$, and neglecting the radiation heat transfer. Assume various temperature initial conditions and also change the values of k and ρc.

Project 12.10.   Extend the program STAP for the analysis of steady-state two-dimensional planar and axisymmetric linear heat transfer by conduction. Use the subroutine QUADS in Section 5.6 as the basis to develop the element routine. Then solve the analysis problem in Exercise 7.7.

Project 12.11.   Extend the program STAP to the analysis of one of the field problems: seepage (see Section 7.3.1), incompressible inviscid fluid flow (see Section 7.3.2), solution of torsional stiffness (see Section 7.3.3), or analysis of acoustic fluids (see Section 7.3.4). In each case consider only planar conditions and solve an analysis problem of your choice.

Project 12.12.   Extend the program STAP for the analysis of viscous incompressible fluid flow at a very low Reynolds number (Stokes flow). Use the u/p formulation and the 4/1 element. Solve a problem of your choice (for example, the problem in Exercise 7.28).

References

AHMAD, S., IRONS, B. M., and ZIENKIEWICZ, O. C.
[A] "Analysis of Thick and Thin Shell Structures by Curved Elements," *International Journal for Numerical Methods in Engineering,* Vol. 2, pp. 419–451, 1970.

AKL, F. A., DILGER, W. H., and IRONS, B. M.
[A] "Acceleration of Subspace Iteration," *International Journal for Numerical Methods in Engineering,* Vol. 18, pp. 583–589, 1982.

ANAND, L.
[A] "On H. Hencky's Approximate Strain Energy Function for Moderate Deformations," *Journal of Applied Mechanics,* Vol. 46, pp. 78–82, 1979.

ARGYRIS, J. H.
[A] "Continua and Discontinua," *Proceedings, Conference on Matrix Methods in Structural Mechanics,* Wright-Patterson A.F.B., Ohio, pp. 11–189, Oct. 1965.
[B] "An Excursion into Large Rotations," *Computer Methods in Applied Mechanics and Engineering,* Vol. 32, pp. 85–155, 1982.

ARGYRIS, J. H., and KELSEY, S.
[A] "Energy Theorems and Structural Analysis," *Aircraft Engineering,* Vols. 26 and 27, Oct. 1954 to May 1955. Part I is by J. H. Argyris, and Part II is by J. H. Argyris and S. Kelsey.

ARNOLD, D. N., and BREZZI, F.
[A] "Some New Elements for the Reissner-Mindlin Plate Model" and "Locking Free Finite Elements for Shells," Publicazioni N. 898, Istituto di Analisi Numerica del Consiglio Nazionale delle Ricerche, Pavia, Nov. 1993.

ARNOLD, D. N., BREZZI, F., and FORTIN, M.
[A] "A Stable Finite Element for the Stokes Equations," *Calcolo,* Vol. 21, pp. 337–344, 1984.

ARNOLD, D. N., and FALK, R. S.
[A] "The Boundary Layer for the Reissner-Mindlin Plate Model," *SIAM Journal on Mathematical Analysis,* Vol. 21, pp. 281–312, 1990.

ASARO, R. J.
[A] "Micromechanics of Crystals and Polycrystals," *Advances in Applied Mechanics,* Vol. 23, pp. 1–115, 1983.

ATLURI, S. N.
  [A]   "Alternate Stress and Conjugate Strain Measures, and Mixed Variational Formulations Involving Rigid Rotations, for Computational Analysis of Finitely Deformed Solids, with Application to Plates and Shells: I. Theory," *Computers & Structures,* Vol. 18, pp. 93–116, 1984.

BABUŠKA, I.
  [A]   "The Finite Element Method with Lagrangian Multipliers," *Numerische Mathematik,* Vol. 20, pp. 179–192, 1973.

BARSOUM, R. S.
  [A]   "On the Use of Isoparametric Finite Elements in Linear Fracture Mechanics," *International Journal for Numerical Methods in Engineering,* Vol. 10, pp. 25–37, 1976.
  [B]   "Triangular Quarter-Point Elements as Elastic and Perfectly-Plastic Crack Tip Elements," *International Journal for Numerical Methods in Engineering,* Vol. 11, pp. 85–98, 1977.

BATHE, K. J.
  [A]   "Solution Methods of Large Generalized Eigenvalue Problems in Structural Engineering," Report UC SESM 71–20, Civil Engineering Department, University of California, Berkeley, 1971.
  [B]   "Convergence of Subspace Iteration," in *Formulations and Numerical Algorithms in Finite Element Analysis* (K. J. Bathe, J. T. Oden, and W. Wunderlich, eds.), M.I.T. Press, Cambridge, MA, pp. 575–598, 1977.

BATHE, K. J., and ALMEIDA, C. A.
  [A]   "A Simple and Effective Pipe Elbow Element—Linear Analysis," and "A Simple and Effective Pipe Elbow Element—Interaction Effects," *Journal of Applied Mechanics,* Vol. 47, pp. 93–100, 1980, and *Journal of Applied Mechanics,* Vol. 49, pp. 165–171, 1982.

BATHE, K. J., and BOLOURCHI, S.
  [A]   "Large Displacement Analysis of Three-Dimensional Beam Structures," *International Journal for Numerical Methods in Engineering,* Vol. 14, pp. 961–986, 1979.
  [B]   "A Geometric and Material Nonlinear Plate and Shell Element," *Computers & Structures,* Vol. 11, pp. 23–48, 1980.

BATHE, K. J., and BREZZI, F.
  [A]   "On the Convergence of a Four-Node Plate Bending Element Based on Mindlin/Reissner Plate Theory and a Mixed Interpolation," in *The Mathematics of Finite Elements and Applications* V (J. R. Whiteman, ed.), Academic Press, New York, pp. 491–503, 1985.
  [B]   "A Simplified Analysis of Two Plate Bending Elements—The MITC4 and MITC9 Elements," *Proceedings, Numerical Methods in Engineering: Theory and Applications,* University College, Swansea, U.K., 1987.

BATHE, K. J., BUCALEM, M. L., and BREZZI, F.
  [A]   "Displacement and Stress Convergence of Our MITC Plate Bending Elements," *Engineering Computations,* Vol. 7, pp. 291–302, 1990.

BATHE, K. J., and CHAUDHARY, A. B.
  [A]   "On the Displacement Formulation of Torsion of Shafts with Rectangular Cross-sections," *International Journal for Numerical Methods in Engineering,* Vol. 18, pp. 1565–1580, 1982.
  [B]   "A Solution Method for Planar and Axisymmetric Contact Problems," *International Journal for Numerical Methods in Engineering,* Vol. 21, pp. 65–88, 1985.

BATHE, K. J., CHAUDHARY, A. B., DVORKIN, E. N., and KOJIĆ, M.
  [A]   "On the Solution of Nonlinear Finite Element Equations," in *Proceedings, International Conference on Computer-Aided Analysis and Design of Concrete Structures* I (F. Damjanić et al., eds.), pp. 289–299, Pineridge Press, Swansea, U.K., 1984.

BATHE, K. J., and CIMENTO, A. P.
  [A]   "Some Practical Procedures for the Solution of Nonlinear Finite Element Equations," *Computer Methods in Applied Mechanics and Engineering,* Vol. 22, pp. 59–85, 1980.

BATHE, K. J., and DVORKIN, E. N.
  [A] "A Four-Node Plate Bending Element Based on Mindlin/Reissner Plate Theory and a Mixed Interpolation," *International Journal for Numerical Methods in Engineering*, Vol. 21, pp. 367–383, 1985.
  [B] "A Formulation of General Shell Elements—The Use of Mixed Interpolation of Tensorial Components," *International Journal for Numerical Methods in Engineering*, Vol. 22, pp. 697–722, 1986.
  [C] "On the Automatic Solution of Nonlinear Finite Element Equations," *Computers & Structures*, Vol. 17, pp. 871–879, 1983.

BATHE, K. J., and GRACEWSKI, S.
  [A] "On Nonlinear Dynamic Analysis Using Substructuring and Mode Superposition," *Computers & Structures*, Vol. 13, pp. 699–707, 1981.

BATHE, K. J., and KHOSHGOFTAAR, M. R.
  [A] "Finite Element Formulation and Solution of Nonlinear Heat Transfer," *Nuclear Engineering and Design*, Vol. 51, pp. 389–401, 1979.
  [B] "Finite Element Free Surface Seepage Analysis Without Mesh Iteration," *International Journal for Numerical and Analytical Methods in Geomechanics*, Vol. 3, pp. 13–22, 1979.

BATHE, K. J., LEE, N. S., and BUCALEM, M. L.
  [A] "On the Use of Hierarchical Models in Engineering Analysis," *Computer Methods in Applied Mechanics and Engineering*, Vol. 82, pp. 5–26, 1990.

BATHE, K. J., and RAMASWAMY, S.
  [A] "An Accelerated Subspace Iteration Method," *Computer Methods in Applied Mechanics and Engineering*, Vol. 23, pp. 313–331, 1980.

BATHE, K. J., RAMM, E., and WILSON, E. L.
  [A] "Finite Element Formulations for Large Deformation Dynamic Analysis," *International Journal for Numerical Methods in Engineering*, Vol. 9, pp. 353–386, 1975.

BATHE, K. J., and SONNAD, V.
  [A] "On Effective Implicit Time Integration of Fluid-Structure Problems," *International Journal for Numerical Methods in Engineering*, Vol. 15, pp. 943–948, 1980.

BATHE, K. J., WALCZAK, J., WELCH, A., and MISTRY, N.
  [A] "Nonlinear Analysis of Concrete Structures," *Computers & Structures*, Vol. 32, pp. 563–590, 1989.

BATHE, K. J., WALCZAK, J., and ZHANG, H.
  [A] "Some Recent Advances for Practical Finite Element Analysis," *Computers & Structures*, Vol. 47, pp. 511–521, 1993.

BATHE, K. J., and WILSON, E. L.
  [A] "Stability and Accuracy Analysis of Direct Integration Methods," *International Journal of Earthquake Engineering and Structural Dynamics*, Vol. 1, pp. 283–291, 1973.
  [B] "NONSAP—A General Finite Element Program for Nonlinear Dynamic Analysis of Complex Structures," Paper No. M3–1, *Proceedings, Second Conference on Structural Mechanics in Reactor Technology*, Berlin, Sept. 1973.
  [C] "Eigensolution of Large Structural Systems with Small Bandwidth," *ASCE Journal of Engineering Mechanics Division*, Vol. 99, pp. 467–479, 1973.
  [D] "Large Eigenvalue Problems in Dynamic Analysis," *ASCE Journal of Engineering Mechanics Division*, Vol. 98, pp. 1471–1485, 1972.

BATHE, K. J., ZHANG, H., and WANG, M. H.
  [A] "Finite Element Analysis of Incompressible and Compressible Fluid Flows with Free Surfaces and Structural Interactions," *Computers & Structures*, Vol. 56, pp. 193–214, 1995.

BATOZ, J.-L., BATHE, K. J., and HO, L. W.
[A]   "A Study of Three-Node Triangular Plate Bending Elements," *International Journal for Numerical Methods in Engineering,* Vol. 15, pp. 1771–1812, 1980.

BAUER, F. L.
[A]   "Das Verfahren der Treppen-Iteration und Verwandte Verfahren zur Lösung Algebraischer Eigenwertprobleme," *Zeitschrift für Angewandte Mathematik und Physik,* Vol. 8, pp. 214–235, 1957.

BELYTSCHKO, T., and HUGHES, T. J. R. (eds.)
[A]   *Computational Methods for Transient Analysis,* North-Holland, New York, 1983.

BELYTSCHKO, T., LIU, W. K., ONG, J. S-J., and LAM, D.
[A]   "Implementation and Application of a 9-Node Lagrange Shell Element with Spurious Mode Control," *Computers & Structures,* Vol. 20, pp. 121–128, 1985.

BELYTSCHKO, T., YEN, H. J., and MULLEN, R.
[A]   "Mixed Methods for Time Integration," *Computer Methods in Applied Mechanics and Engineering,* Vol. 17/18, pp. 259–275, 1979.

BERTSEKAS, D. P.
[A]   *Constrained Optimization and Lagrange Multiplier Methods,* Academic Press, New York, 1982.

BIĆANIĆ, N., and JOHNSON, K. H.
[A]   "Who Was '-Raphson'?" *International Journal for Numerical Methods in Engineering,* Vol. 14, pp. 148–152, 1978.

BREZZI, F.
[A]   "On the Existence, Uniqueness and Approximation of Saddle-Point Problems Arising from Lagrangian Multipliers," *Revue Française d'Automatique Informatique Recherche Operationnelle, Analyse Numérique,* Vol. 8, pp. 129–151, 1974.

BREZZI, F., and BATHE, K. J.
[A]   "Studies of Finite Element Procedures—The Inf-Sup Condition, Equivalent Forms and Applications," in *Reliability of Methods for Engineering Analysis* (K. J. Bathe and D. R. J. Owen, eds.), pp. 197–219, Pineridge Press, Swansea, U.K., 1986.
[B]   "A Discourse on the Stability Conditions for Mixed Finite Element Formulations," *Computer Methods in Applied Mechanics and Engineering,* Vol. 82, pp. 27–57, 1990.

BREZZI, F., BATHE, K. J., and FORTIN, M.
[A]   "Mixed-Interpolated Elements for Reissner/Mindlin Plates," *International Journal for Numerical Methods in Engineering,* Vol. 28, pp. 1787-1801, 1989.

BREZZI, F., and FORTIN, M.
[A]   *Mixed and Hybrid Finite Element Methods,* Springer-Verlag, New York, 1991.

BREZZI, F., FORTIN, M., and STENBERG, R.
[A]   "Error Analysis of Mixed-Interpolated Elements for Reissner-Mindlin Plates," *Mathematical Models and Methods in Applied Sciences,* Vol. 1, pp. 125–151, 1991.

BREZZI, F., and RUSSO, A.
[A]   "Choosing Bubbles for Advection-Diffusion Problems," *Mathematical Models and Methods in Applied Sciences* (in press).

BROOKS, A. N., and HUGHES, T. J. R.
[A]   "Streamline Upwind/Petrov-Galerkin Formulations for Convection Dominated Flows with Particular Emphasis on the Incompressible Navier-Stokes Equations," *Computer Methods in Applied Mechanics and Engineering,* Vol. 32, pp. 199–259, 1982.

BUCALEM, M. L., and BATHE, K. J.
[A]   "Higher-Order MITC General Shell Elements," *International Journal for Numerical Methods in Engineering,* Vol. 36, pp. 3729–3754, 1993.

BUSHNELL, D., ALMROTH, B. O., and BROGAN, F.
[A] "Finite-Difference Energy Method for Nonlinear Shell Analysis," *Computers & Structures,* Vol. 1, pp. 361–387, 1971.

CHAPELLE, D., and BATHE, K. J.
[A] "The Inf-Sup Test," *Computers & Structures,* Vol. 47, pp. 537–545, 1993.

CHEUNG, Y. K.
[A] "Finite Strip Method of Analysis of Elastic Slabs," *Proceedings of the American Society of Civil Engineers,* Vol. 94, EM6, pp. 1365–1378, 1968.

CHRISTIE, I., GRIFFITHS, D. F., MITCHELL, A. R., and ZIENKIEWICZ, O. C.
[A] "Finite Element Methods for Second Order Differential Equations with Significant First Derivatives," *International Journal for Numerical Methods in Engineering,* Vol. 10, pp. 1389–1396, 1976.

CIARLET, P. G.
[A] *The Finite Element Method for Elliptic Problems,* North Holland, New York, 1978.

CIARLET, P. G., and RAVIART, P.-A.
[A] "Interpolation Theory over Curved Elements with Applications to Finite Element Methods," *Computer Methods in Applied Mechanics and Engineering,* Vol. 1, pp. 217–249, 1972.

CLOUGH, R. W.
[A] "The Finite Element Method in Plane Stress Analysis," *Proceedings, Second ASCE Conference on Electronic Computation,* Pittsburgh, PA, pp. 345–378, Sept. 1960.

CLOUGH, R. W., and PENZIEN, J.
[A] *Dynamics of Structures,* McGraw-Hill, New York, 1975.

CLOUGH, R. W., and WILSON, E. L.
[A] "Stress Analysis of a Gravity Dam by the Finite Element Method," *Proceedings, Symposium on the Use of Computers in Civil Engineering,* pp. 29.1–29.22, Laboratorio Nacional de Engenharia Civil, Lisbon, Portugal, Oct. 1962.

COLLATZ, L.
[A] *The Numerical Treatment of Differential Equations,* 3rd ed., Springer-Verlag, New York, 1966. York, 1966.

COURANT, R.
[A] "Variational Methods for the Solution of Problems of Equilibrium and Vibrations," *Bulletin of the American Mathematical Society,* Vol. 49, pp. 1–23, 1943.

COURANT, R., FRIEDRICHS, K., AND LEWY, H.
[A] "Über die partiellen Differenzengleichungen der mathematischen Physik," *Mathematische Annalen,* Vol. 100, pp. 32–74, 1928.

COURANT, R., and HILBERT, D.
[A] *Methods of Mathematical Physics,* John Wiley, New York, 1953.

COURANT, R., ISAACSON, E., and REES, M.
[A] "On the Solution of Non-Linear Hyperbolic Differential Equations by Finite Differences," *Communications on Pure and Applied Mathematics,* Vol. 5, pp. 243–255, 1952.

COWPER, G. R.
[A] "Gaussian Quadrature Formulas for Triangles," *International Journal for Numerical Methods in Engineering,* Vol. 7, pp. 405–408, 1973.

CRAIG, R. R., JR.
[A] *Structural Dynamics,* John Wiley, New York, 1981.

CRANDALL, S. H.
[A] *Engineering Analysis,* McGraw-Hill, New York, 1956.

CRANDALL, S. H., DAHL, N. C., and LARDNER, T. J.
[A] *An Introduction to the Mechanics of Solids,* 2nd ed., McGraw-Hill, New York, 1978.

CRISFIELD, M. A.
[A]   "A Fast Incremental/Iterative Solution Procedure That Handles Snap-Through," *Computers & Structures,* Vol. 13, pp. 55–62, 1981.

CROUZEIX, M., and RAVIART, P.-A.
[A]   "Conforming and Non-conforming Finite Element Methods for Solving the Stationary Stokes Equations," *Revue Française d'Automatique Informatique Recherche Operationnelle, Analyse Numérique,* Vol. 7, pp. 33–76, 1973.

CUTHILL, E., and McKEE, J.
[A]   "Reducing the Bandwidth of Sparse Symmetric Matrices," *Proceedings of 24th National Conference, Association for Computing Machinery,* pp. 157–172, 1969.

DENNIS, J. E., JR.
[A]   "A Brief Survey of Convergence Results for Quasi-Newton Methods," *SIAM-AMS Proceedings,* Vol. 9, pp. 185–200, 1976.

DESAI, C. S.
[A]   "Finite Element Residual Schemes for Unconfined Flow," *International Journal for Numerical Methods in Engineering,* Vol. 10, pp. 1415–1418, 1976.

DESAI, C. S., and SIRIWARDANE, H. J.
[A]   *Constitutive Laws for Engineering Materials*, Prentice Hall, Englewood Cliffs, NJ, 1984.

DRUCKER, D. C., and PRAGER, W.
[A]   "Soil Mechanics and Plastic Analysis or Limit Design," *Quarterly of Applied Mathematics,* Vol. 10, N. 2, pp. 157–165, 1952.

DUL, F. A., and ARCZEWSKI, K.
[A]   "The Two-Phase Method for Finding a Great Number of Eigenpairs of the Symmetric or Weakly Non-symmetric Large Eigenvalue Problems," *Journal of Computational Physics,* Vol. 111, pp. 89–109, 1994.

DVORKIN, E. N., and BATHE, K. J.
[A]   "A Continuum Mechanics Based Four-Node Shell Element for General Nonlinear Analysis," *Engineering Computations,* Vol. 1, pp. 77–88, 1984.

ERICSSON, T., and RUHE, A.
[A]   "The Spectral Transformation Lanczos Method for the Numerical Solution of Large Sparse Generalized Symmetric Eigenvalue Problems," *Mathematics of Computation,* Vol. 35, pp. 1251–1268, 1980.

ETEROVIC, A. L., and BATHE, K. J.
[A]   "A Hyperelastic-Based Large Strain Elasto-Plastic Constitutive Formulation with Combined Isotropic-Kinematic Hardening Using the Logarithmic Stress and Strain Measures," *International Journal for Numerical Methods in Engineering,* Vol. 30, pp. 1099–1114, 1990.
[B]   "On Large Strain Elasto-Plastic Analysis with Frictional Contact Conditions," *Proceedings, Conference on Numerical Methods in Applied Science and Industry*, Politecnica di Torino, Torino, pp. 81–93, 1990.
[C]   "On the Treatment of Inequality Constraints Arising from Contact Conditions in Finite Element Analysis," *Computers & Structures*, Vol. 40, pp. 203–209, 1991.

EVERSTINE, G. C.
[A]   "A Symmetric Potential Formulation for Fluid-Structure Interaction," *Journal of Sound and Vibration*, Vol. 79, pp. 157–160, 1981.

FALK, S., and LANGEMEYER, P.
[A]   "Das Jacobische Rotationsverfahren für reellsymmetrische Matrizenpaare," *Elektronische Datenverarbeitung,* pp. 30–34, 1960.

FLETCHER, R.
[A]   "Conjugate Gradient Methods for Indefinite Systems," *Lecture Notes in Mathematics,* Vol. 506, pp. 73–89, Springer-Verlag, New York, 1976.

FORTIN, M., and GLOWINSKI, R.
[A] *Augmented Lagrangian Methods: Applications to the Numerical Solution of Boundary-Value Problems*, Elsevier Science Publishers, Amsterdam, 1983.

FRANCA, L. P., FREY, S. L., and HUGHES, T. J. R.
[A] "Stabilized Finite Element Methods: I. Application to the Advective-Diffusive Model," *Computer Methods in Applied Mechanics and Engineering*, Vol. 95, pp. 221–242, 1992.

FRANCIS, J. G. F.
[A] "The QR Transformation, Parts 1 and 2," *The Computer Journal,* Vol. 4, pp. 265–271, 332–345, 1961.

FRIEDRICHS, K. O., and DRESSLER, R. F.
[A] "A Boundary-Layer Theory for Elastic Plates," *Communications on Pure and Applied Mathematics,* Vol. 14, pp. 1–33, 1961.

FRÖBERG, C. E.
[A] *Introduction to Numerical Analysis*, Addison-Wesley, Reading, MA, 1969.

FUNG, Y. C.
[A] *Foundations of Solid Mechanics*, Prentice-Hall, Englewood Cliffs, NJ, 1965.

GALLAGHER, R. H.
[A] "Analysis of Plate and Shell Structures," *Proceedings, Symposium on the Application of Finite Element Methods in Civil Engineering*, Vanderbilt University, Nashville, TN, pp. 155–205, 1969.

GAUSS, C. F.,
[A] *Carl Friedrich Gauss Werke,* von der Königlichen Gesellschaft der Wissenschaften zu Göttingen, Vol. 4, 1873.

GEORGE, A., GILBERT, J. R., and LIU, J. W. H. (eds.)
[A] *"Graph Theory and Sparse Matrix Computation,"* Institute for Mathematics and Its Applications, Vol. 56, Springer-Verlag, 1993.

GHALI, A., and BATHE, K. J.
[A] "Analysis of Plates Subjected to In-Plane Forces Using Large Finite Elements," and "Analysis of Plates in Bending Using Large Finite Elements," *International Association for Bridge and Structural Engineering Bulletin*, Vol. 30-I, pp. 69–72, Vol. 30-II, pp. 29–40, 1970.

GIBBS, N. E., POOLE, W. G., JR., and STOCKMEYER, P. K.
[A] "An Algorithm for Reducing the Bandwidth and Profile of a Sparse Matrix," *SIAM Journal on Numerical Analysis,* Vol. 13, pp. 236–250, 1976.

GOLUB, G. H., and UNDERWOOD, R.
[A] "The Block Lanczos Method for Computing Eigenvalues," in *Mathematical Software* III (J. R. Rice, ed.), pp. 361–377, Academic Press, New York, 1977.

GOLUB, G. H., and VAN LOAN, C. F.
[A] *Matrix Computations,* Johns Hopkins University Press, Baltimore, 1984.

GREEN, A. E., and NAGHDI, P. M.
[A] "A General Theory of an Elastic-Plastic Continuum," *Archive for Rational Mechanics and Analysis,* Vol. 18, pp. 251–281, 1965.

GREEN, A. E., and ZERNA, W.
[A] *Theoretical Elasticity*, Clarendon Press, Oxford, 1954.

GRESHO, P. M., LEE, R. L., CHAN, S. T., and LEONE, J. M., JR.
[A] "A New Finite Element for Incompressible or Boussinesq Fluids," in *Third International Conference on Finite Elements in Flow Problems* (D. H. Norrie, ed.), Banff, Alberta, Canada, pp. 204–215, 1980.

GUYAN, R. J.
[A] "Reduction of Stiffness and Mass Matrices," *AIAA Journal*, Vol. 3, No. 2, p. 380, 1965.

HÄGGBLAD, B., and BATHE, K. J.
[A] "Specifications of Boundary Conditions for Reissner/Mindlin Plate Bending Finite Elements," *International Journal for Numerical Methods in Engineering*, Vol. 30, pp. 981–1011, 1990.

HAMMER, P. C., MARLOWE, O. J., and STROUD, A. H.
[A] "Numerical Integration over Simplexes and Cones," *Mathematical Tables and other Aids to Computation*, Vol. 10, pp. 130–137, The National Research Council, Washington, DC, 1956.

HELLINGER, E.
[A] "Die allgemeinen Ansätze der Mechanik der Kontinua," in *Encyklopädie der Mathematischen Wissenschaften*, (F. Klein and C. Müller, eds.), Vol. 4, Pt. 4, pp. 601–694, Teubner Verlag, Leipzig, 1914.

HENSHELL, R. D., and SHAW, K. G.
[A] "Crack Tip Finite Elements Are Unnecessary," *International Journal for Numerical Methods in Engineering*, Vol. 9, pp. 495–507, 1975.

HERRMANN, L. R.
[A] "Elasticity Equations for Incompressible and Nearly Incompressible Materials by a Variational Theorem," *AIAA Journal*, Vol. 3, pp. 1896–1900, 1965.

HESTENES, M. R., and STIEFEL, E.
[A] "Methods of Conjugate Gradients for Solving Linear Systems," *Journal of Research of the National Bureau of Standards*, Vol. 49, pp. 409–436, 1952.

HILBER, H. M., HUGHES, T. J. R., and TAYLOR, R. L.
[A] "Improved Numerical Dissipation for Time Integration Algorithms in Structural Mechanics," *International Journal of Earthquake Engineering and Structural Dynamics*, Vol. 5, pp. 283–292, 1977.

HILL, R.
[A] "Aspects of Invariance in Solid Mechanics," in *Advances in Applied Mechanics* (C.-S. Yih, ed.), Vol. 18, pp. 1–75, Academic Press, New York, 1978.
[B] *The Mathematical Theory of Plasticity*, Oxford University Press, Oxford, 1983.

HINTON, E., and CAMPBELL, J. S.
[A] "Local and Global Smoothing of Discontinuous Finite Element Functions Using Least Squares Method," *International Journal for Numerical Methods in Engineering*, Vol. 8, pp. 461–480, 1979.

HODGE, P. G., BATHE, K. J., and DVORKIN, E. N.
[A] "Causes and Consequences of Nonuniqueness in an Elastic-Perfectly-Plastic Truss," *Journal of Applied Mechanics*, Vol. 53, pp. 235–241, 1986.

HOLDEN, J. T.
[A] "On the Finite Deflections of Thin Beams," *International Journal of Solids and Structures*, Vol. 8, pp. 1051–1055, 1972.

HOOD, P., and TAYLOR, C.
[A] "Navier-Stokes Equations Using Mixed Interpolation," in *Finite Element Methods in Flow Problems* (J. T. Oden, O. C. Zienkiewicz, R. H. Gallagher, and C. Taylor, eds.), UAH Press, The University of Alabama in Huntsville, Huntsville, AL, pp. 121–132, 1974.

HOUBOLT, J. C.
[A] "A Recurrence Matrix Solution for the Dynamic Response of Elastic Aircraft," *Journal of the Aeronautical Sciences*, Vol. 17, pp. 540–550, 1950.

HU, H. C.
[A] "On Some Variational Principles in the Theory of Elasticity and the Theory of Plasticity," *Scientia Sinica*, Vol. 4, pp. 33–54, 1955.

HUANG, H. C., and HINTON, E.
[A] "A New Nine Node Degenerated Shell Element with Enhanced Membrane and Shear Interpolation," *International Journal for Numerical Methods in Engineering*, Vol. 22, pp. 73–92, 1986.

HUERTA, A., and LIU, W. K.

[A] "Viscous Flow with Large Free Surface Motion," *Computer Methods in Applied Mechanics and Engineering,* Vol. 69, pp. 277–324, 1988.

HUGHES, T. J. R.

[A] *The Finite Element Method,* Prentice Hall, Englewood Cliffs, NJ, 1987.

HUGHES, T. J. R., FRANCA, L. P., and HULBERT, G. M.

[A] "A New Finite Element Formulation for Computational Fluid Dynamics: VIII. The Galerkin/Least Squares Method for Advective-Diffusive Equations," *Computer Methods in Applied Mechanics and Engineering.,* Vol. 73, pp. 173–189, 1989.

HUGHES, T. J. R., TAYLOR, R. L., SACKMAN, J. L., CURNIER, A., and KANOKNUKULCHAI, W.

[A] "A Finite Element Method for a Class of Contact-Impact Problems," *Computer Methods in Applied Mechanics and Engineering,* Vol. 8, pp. 249–276, 1976.

HUGHES, T. J. R., and TEZDUYAR, T. E.

[A] "Finite Elements Based upon Mindlin Plate Theory with Particular Reference to the Four-Node Bilinear Isoparametric Element," *Journal of Applied Mechanics,* Vol. 48, pp. 587–596, 1981.

IRONS, B. M.

[A] "Engineering Application of Numerical Integration in Stiffness Method," *AIAA Journal,* Vol. 4, pp. 2035–2037, 1966.

[B] "Numerical Integration Applied to Finite Element Methods," *Conference on the Use of Digital Computers in Structural Engineering,* University of Newcastle, England, 1966.

[C] "Quadrature Rules for Brick-Based Finite Elements," *International Journal for Numerical Methods in Engineering,* Vol. 3, pp. 293–294, 1971.

[D] "A Frontal Solution Program for Finite Element Analysis," *International Journal for Numerical Methods in Engineering,* Vol. 2, pp. 5–32, 1970.

IRONS, B. M., and RAZZAQUE, A.

[A] "Experience with the Patch Test for Convergence of Finite Elements," in *The Mathematical Foundations of the Finite Element Method with Applications to Partial Differential Equations* (A. K. Aziz, ed.), Academic Press, New York, pp. 557–587, 1972.

JACOBI, C. G. J.

[A] "Über ein leichtes Verfahren die in der Theorie der Säcularstörungen vorkommenden Gleichungen numerisch aufzulösen," *Crelle's Journal,* Vol. 30, pp. 51–94, 1846.

JANG, J., and PINSKY, P. M.

[A] "An Assumed Covariant Strain Based 9-Node Shell Element," *International Journal for Numerical Methods in Engineering,* Vol. 24, pp. 2389–2411, 1987.

JENNINGS, A.

[A] "A Direct Iteration Method of Obtaining Latent Roots and Vectors of a Symmetric Matrix," *Proceedings of the Cambridge Philosophical Society,* Vol. 63, pp. 755–765, 1967.

JOHNSON, C., NÄVERT, U., and PITKÄRANTA, J.

[A] "Finite Element Methods for the Linear Hyperbolic Problem," *Computer Methods in Applied Mechanics and Engineering,* Vol. 45, pp. 285–312, 1984.

KARDESTUNCER, H., and NORRIE, D. H. (eds.)

[A] *Finite Element Handbook,* McGraw-Hill, New York, 1987.

KATO, K., LEE, N. S., and BATHE, K. J.

[A] "Adaptive Finite Element Analysis of Large Strain Elastic Response," *Computers & Structures,* Vol. 47, pp. 829–855, 1993.

KEY, S. W.

[A] "A Variational Principle for Incompressible and Nearly Incompressible Anisotropic Elasticity," *International Journal of Solids and Structures,* Vol. 5, pp. 951–964, 1969.

KOJIĆ, M., and BATHE, K. J.

[A] "Studies of Finite Element Procedures—Stress Solution of a Closed Elastic Strain Path with Stretching and Shearing Using the Updated Lagrangian Jaumann Formulation," *Computers & Structures,* Vol. 26, pp. 175–179, 1987.

[B] "The 'Effective-Stress-Function' Algorithm for Thermo-Elasto-Plasticity and Creep," *International Journal for Numerical Methods in Engineering*, Vol. 24, pp. 1509–1532, 1987.

KONDO, N., TOSAKA, N., and NISHIMURA, T.
[A] "Computation of Incompressible Viscous Flows by the Third-Order Upwind Finite Element Method," *International Journal for Numerical Methods in Fluids*, Vol. 15, pp. 1013–1024, 1992.

KRAUS, H.
[A] *Creep Analysis,* John Wiley, New York, 1980.

KREYSZIG, E.
[A] *Advanced Engineering Mathematics,* 5th ed., John Wiley, New York, 1983.

KRIEG, R. D., and KRIEG, D. B.
[A] "Accuracies of Numerical Solution Methods for the Elastic-Perfectly Plastic Model," *Journal of Pressure Vessel Technology,* Vol. 99, No. 4, pp. 510–515, Nov. 1977.

LANCZOS, C.
[A] "An Iteration Method for the Solution of the Eigenvalue Problem of Linear Differential and Integral Operators," *Journal of Research of the National Bureau of Standards,* Vol. 45, pp. 255–282, 1950.

LEE, E. H.
[A] "Elastic-Plastic Deformation at Finite Strains," *Journal of Applied Mechanics,* Vol. 36, pp. 1–6, 1969.

LEE, N. S., and BATHE, K. J.
[A] "Effects of Element Distortions on the Performance of Isoparametric Elements," *International Journal for Numerical Methods in Engineering,* Vol. 36, pp. 3553–3576, 1993.
[B] "Error Indicators and Adaptive Remeshing in Large Deformation Finite Element Analysis," *Finite Elements in Analysis and Design,* Vol. 16, pp. 99–139, 1994.

LE TALLEC, P., and RUAS, V.
[A] "On the Convergence of the Bilinear Velocity-Constant Pressure Finite Element Method in Viscous Flow," *Computer Methods in Applied Mechanics and Engineering,* Vol. 54, pp. 235–243, 1986.

LIENHARD, J. H.
[A] *A Heat Transfer Textbook,* Prentice-Hall, Englewood Cliffs, NJ, 1987.

LIGHTFOOT, E.
[A] *Moment Distribution,* E. & F. N. Spon, London, 1961.

LOWAN, A. N., DAVIDS, N., and LEVENSON, A.
[A] "Table of the Zeros of the Legendre Polynomials of Order 1–16 and the Weight Coefficients for Gauss' Mechanical Quadrature Formula," *Bulletin of the American Mathematical Society,* Vol. 48, pp. 739–743, 1942.

LUBLINER, J.
[A] "Normality Rules in Large-Deformation Plasticity," *Mechanics of Materials,* Vol. 5, pp. 29–34, 1986.

MA, S. N., and BATHE, K. J.
[A] "On Finite Element Analysis of Pipe Whip Problems," *Nuclear Engineering and Design,* Vol. 37, pp. 413–430, 1976.

MACNEAL, R. H.
[A] "Derivation of Element Stiffness Matrices by Assumed Strain Distributions," *Nuclear Engineering and Design,* Vol. 70, pp. 3–12, 1982.

MALKUS, D. S., and HUGHES, T. J. R.
[A] "Mixed Finite Element Methods—Reduced and Selective Integration Techniques: A Unification of Concepts," *Computer Methods in Applied Mechanics and Engineering,* Vol. 15, pp. 63–81, 1978.

MALVERN, L. E.
[A] *Introduction to the Mechanics of a Continuous Medium,* Prentice-Hall, Englewood Cliffs, NJ, 1969.

MANTEUFFEL, T. A.
[A] "An Incomplete Factorization Technique for Positive Definite Linear Systems," *Mathematics of Computation,* Vol. 34, pp. 473–497, 1980.

MARTIN, R. S., PETERS, G., and WILKINSON, J. H.
[A] "Symmetric Decomposition of a Positive Definite Matrix," *Numerische Mathematik,* Vol. 7, pp. 362–383, 1965.

MARTIN, R. S., REINSCH, C., and WILKINSON, J. H.
[A] Householder's Tridiagonalization of a Symmetric Matrix," *Numerische Mathematik,* Vol. 11, pp. 181–195, 1968.

MATTHIES, H.
[A] "Computable Error Bounds for the Generalized Symmetric Eigenproblem," *Communications in Applied Numerical Methods,* Vol. 1, pp. 33–38, 1985.
[B] "A Subspace Lanczos Method for the Generalized Symmetric Eigenproblem," *Computers & Structures,* Vol. 21, pp. 319–325, 1985.

MATTHIES, H., and STRANG, G.
[A] "The Solution of Nonlinear Finite Element Equations," *International Journal for Numerical Methods in Engineering,* Vol. 14, pp. 1613–1626, 1979.

MEIJERINK, J. A., and VAN DER VORST, H. A.
[A] "Guidelines for the Usage of Incomplete Decompositions in Solving Sets of Linear Equations as They Occur in Practical Problems," *Journal of Computational Physics,* Vol. 44, pp. 134–155, 1981.

MENDELSON, A.
[A] *Plasticity: Theory and Application,* Robert E. Krieger, Malabar, FL, 1983.

MIKHLIN, S. G.
[A] *Variational Methods in Mathematical Physics,* Pergamon Press, Elmsford, NY, 1964.

MINDLIN, R. D.
[A] "Influence of Rotary Inertia and Shear on Flexural Motion of Isotropic Elastic Plates," *Journal of Applied Mechanics,* Vol. 18, pp. 31–38, 1951.

MINKOWYCZ, W. J., SPARROW, E. M., SCHNEIDER, G. E., AND PLETCHER, R. H.
[A] *Handbook of Numerical Heat Transfer,* John Wiley & Sons, Inc., 1988.

NEWMARK, N. M.
[A] "A Method of Computation for Structural Dynamics," *ASCE Journal of Engineering Mechanics Division,* Vol. 85, pp. 67–94, 1959.

NITIKITPAIBOON, C., and BATHE, K. J.
[A] "Fluid-Structure Interaction Analysis with a Mixed Displacement-Pressure Formulation," Finite Element Research Group, Mechanical Engineering Department, Report 92-1, Massachusetts Institute of Technology, Cambridge, MA, June 1992.
[B] "An Arbitrary Lagrangian-Eulerian Velocity Potential Formulation for Fluid-Structure Interaction," *Computers & Structures,* Vol. 47, pp. 871–891, 1993.

NOBLE, B.
[A] *Applied Linear Algebra,* Prentice-Hall, Englewood Cliffs, NJ, 1969.

NOOR, A. K.
[A] "Bibliography of Books and Monographs on Finite Element Technology," *Applied Mechanics Reviews,* Vol. 44, No. 6, pp. 307–317, June 1991.

ODEN, J. T., and BATHE, K. J.
[A] "A Commentary on Computational Mechanics," *Applied Mechanics Reviews,* Vol. 31, No. 8, pp. 1053–1058, August 1978.

ODEN, J. T., and MARTINS, J. A. C.
[A] "Models and Computational Methods for Dynamic Friction Phenomena," *Computer Methods in Applied Mechanics and Engineering,* Vol. 52, pp. 527–634, 1985.

ODEN, J. T., and PIRES, E. B.
[A] "Nonlocal and Nonlinear Friction Laws and Variational Principles for Contact Problems in Elasticity," *Journal of Applied Mechanics,* Vol. 50, pp. 67–76, 1983.

ODEN, J. T., and REDDY, J. N.
[A] *Variational Methods in Theoretical Mechanics,* 2nd ed., Springer-Verlag, New York, 1983.

OGDEN, R. W.
[A] *Nonlinear Elastic Deformations,* Ellis Horwood, Chichester, U.K., 1984.

OLSON, L. G., and BATHE, K. J.
[A] "Analysis of Fluid-Structure Interactions. A Direct Symmetric Coupled Formulation Based on the Fluid Velocity Potential," *Computers & Structures,* Vol. 21, pp. 21–32, 1985.

ORTIZ, M., and POPOV, E. P.
[A] "Accuracy and Stability of Integration Algorithms for Elastoplastic Constitutive Relations," *International Journal for Numerical Methods in Engineering,* Vol. 21, 1561–1576, 1985.

OSTROWSKI, A. M.
[A] "On the Convergence of the Rayleigh Quotient Iteration for the Computation of the Characteristic Roots and Vectors, Parts I–VI," *Archive for Rational Mechanics and Analysis,* Vols. 1–3, 1958–1959.

PAIGE, C. C.
[A] "Computational Variants of the Lanczos Method for the Eigenproblem," *Journal of the Institute of Mathematics and Its Applications,* Vol. 10, pp. 373–381, 1972.
[B] "Accuracy and Effectiveness of the Lanczos Algorithm for the Symmetric Eigenproblem," *Linear Algebra and Its Applications,* Vol. 34, pp. 235–258, 1980.

PARK, K. C., and STANLEY, G. M.
[A] "A Curved C^0 Shell Element Based on Assumed Natural-Coordinate Strains," *Journal of Applied Mechanics,* Vol. 53, pp. 278–290, 1986.

PARLETT, B. N.
[A] "Global Convergence of the Basic QR Algorithm on Hessenberg Matrices," *Mathematics of Computation,* Vol. 22, pp. 803–817, 1968.
[B] "Convergence of the QR Algorithm," *Numerische Mathematik,* Vol. 7, pp. 187–193, 1965; Vol. 10, pp. 163–164, 1967.

PARLETT, B. N., and SCOTT, D. S.
[A] "The Lanczos Algorithm with Selective Orthogonalization," *Mathematics of Computation,* Vol. 33, No. 145, pp. 217–238, 1979.

PATANKAR, S. V.
[A] *Numerical Heat Transfer and Fluid Flow,* Hemisphere Publishing, 1980.

PATERA, A. T.
[A] "A Spectral Element Method for Fluid Dynamics: Laminar Flow in a Channel Expansion," *Journal of Computational Physics,* Vol. 54, pp. 468–488, 1984.

PERZYNA, P.
[A] "Fundamental Problems in Viscoplasticity," *Advances in Applied Mechanics,* Vol. 9, pp. 243–377, 1966.

PIAN, T. H. H., and TONG, P.
  [A] "Basis of Finite Element Methods for Solid Continua," *International Journal for Numerical Methods in Engineering,* Vol. 1, pp. 3–28, 1969.

PITKÄRANTA, J.
  [A] "The Problem of Membrane Locking in Finite Element Analysis of Cylindrical Shells," Report, Helsinki University of Technology, Otakaari 1 SF-02159 Espoo, Finland, 1991.

PRZEMIENIECKI, J. S.
  [A] "Matrix Structural Analysis of Substructures," *AIAA Journal,* Vol. 1, pp. 138–147, 1963.

RABINOWICZ, E.
  [A] *Friction and Wear of Materials,* John Wiley, 1965.

RAMM, E.
  [A] "Strategies for Tracing Nonlinear Responses Near Limit Points," *Nonlinear Finite Element Analysis in Structural Mechanics* (W. Wunderlich, E. Stein, and K. J. Bathe, eds.), pp. 63–89, Springer-Verlag, New York, 1981.

REID, J. K.
  [A] "On the Method of Conjugate Gradients for the Solution of Large Sparse Systems of Linear Equations," *Conference on Large Sparse Sets of Linear Equations,* St. Catherine's College, Oxford, pp. 231–254, April 1970.

REISSNER, E.
  [A] "On a Variational Theorem in Elasticity," *Journal of Mathematics and Physics,* Vol. 29, pp. 90–95, 1950.
  [B] "The Effect of Transverse Shear Deformation on the Bending of Elastic Plates," *Journal of Applied Mechanics,* Vol. 67, pp. A69–A77, 1945.
  [C] "On the Theory of Transverse Bending of Elastic Plates," *International Journal of Solids and Structures,* Vol. 12, pp. 545–554, 1976.

RICE, J. R.
  [A] "Continuum Mechanics and Thermodynamics of Plasticity in Relation to Microscale Deformation Mechanisms," in *Constitutive Equations in Plasticity* (A. S. Argon, ed.), pp. 23–79, M.I.T. Press, Cambridge, MA, 1975.

RICHTMYER, R. D., and MORTON, K. W.
  [A] *Difference Methods for Initial Value Problems,* 2nd ed., John Wiley, 1967.

RIKS, E.
  [A] "An Incremental Approach to the Solution of Snapping and Buckling Problems," *International Journal of Solids and Structures,* Vol. 15, pp. 529–551, 1979.

RITCHIE, R. O., and BATHE, K. J.
  [A] "On the Calibration of the Electrical Potential Technique for Monitoring Crack Growth Using Finite Element Methods," *International Journal of Fracture,* Vol. 15, No. 1, pp. 47–55, 1979.

RITZ, W.
  [A] "Über eine neue Methode zur Lösung gewisser Variationsprobleme der mathematischen Physik," *Zeitschrift für Angewandte Mathematik und Mechanik,* Vol. 135, Heft 1, pp. 1–61, 1908.

RIVLIN, R. S.
  [A] "Large Elastic Deformations of Isotropic Materials IV. Further Developments of the General Theory," *Philosophical Transactions of the Royal Society of London,* Vol. A 241, pp. 379–397, 1948.

RODI, W.
  [A] "Turbulence Models and their Application in Hydraulics—A State of the Art Review," *International Association for Hydraulic Research,* Delft, 1984.

ROLPH, W. D., III, and BATHE, K. J.
[A] "An Efficient Algorithm for Analysis of Nonlinear Heat Transfer with Phase Changes," *International Journal for Numerical Methods in Engineering,* Vol. 18, pp. 119–134, 1982.

RUBINSTEIN, M. F.
[A] "Combined Analysis by Substructures and Recursion," *ASCE Journal of the Structural Division,* Vol. 93, No. ST2, pp. 231–235, 1967.

RUTISHAUSER, H.
[A] "Deflation bei Bandmatrizen," *Zeitschrift für Angewandte Mathematik und Physik*, Vol. 10, pp. 314–319, 1959.
[B] "Computational Aspects of F. L. Bauer's Simultaneous Iteration Method," *Numerische Mathematik*, Vol. 13, pp. 4–13, 1969.

SAAD, Y., and SCHULTZ, M. H.
[A] "GMRES: A Generalized Minimal Residual Algorithm for Solving Nonsymmetric Linear Systems," *SIAM Journal on Scientific and Statistical Computing,* Vol. 7, pp. 856–869, 1986.

SCHLICHTING, H.
[A] *Boundary-Layer Theory,* 7th ed., McGraw-Hill, New York, 1979.

SCHREYER, H. L., KULAK, R. F., and KRAMER, J. M.
[A] "Accurate Numerical Solutions for Elastic-Plastic Models," *Journal of Pressure Vessel Technology,* Vol. 101, pp. 226–234, 1979.

SCHWEIZERHOF, K., and RAMM, E.
[A] "Displacement Dependent Pressure Loads in Nonlinear Finite Element Analysis," *Computers & Structures,* Vol. 18, pp. 1099–1114, 1984.

SEIDEL, L.
[A] "Über ein Verfahren die Gleichungen auf welche die Methode der Kleinsten Quadrate führt, sowie lineare Gleichungen überhaupt durch successive Annäherung aufzulösen," *Abhandlungen Bayerische Akademie der Wissenschaften,* Vol. 11, pp. 81–108, 1874.

SILVESTER, P.
[A] "Newton-Cotes Quadrature Formulae for N-dimensional Simplexes," *Proceedings, 2nd Canadian Congress on Applied Mechanics,* Waterloo, Canada, pp. 361–362, 1969.

SIMO, J. C.
[A] "A Framework for Finite Strain Elastoplasticity Based on Maximum Plastic Dissipation and the Multiplicative Decomposition: Part I: Continuum Formulation," *Computer Methods in Applied Mechanics and Engineering,* Vol. 66, pp. 199–219, 1988; "Part II: Computational Aspects," *Computer Methods in Applied Mechanics and Engineering,* Vol. 68, pp. 1–31, 1988.

SIMO, J. C., WRIGGERS, P., and TAYLOR, R. L.
[A] "A Perturbed Lagrangian Formulation for the Finite Element Solution of Contact Problems," *Computer Methods in Applied Mechanics and Engineering*, Vol. 50, pp. 163–180, 1985.

SNYDER, M. D., and BATHE, K. J.
[A] "A Solution Procedure for Thermo-Elastic-Plastic and Creep Problems," *Nuclear Engineering and Design,* Vol. 64, pp. 49–80, 1981.

SPALDING, D. B.
[A] "A Novel Finite-Difference Formulation for Differential Expressions Involving Both First and Second Derivatives," *International Journal for Numerical Methods in Engineering*, Vol. 4, pp. 551–559, 1972.

SPARROW, E. M., and CESS, R. D.
[A] *Radiation Heat Transfer* (augmented edition), Hemisphere Publishing, 1978.

STOER, J., and BULIRSCH, R.

[A] *Introduction to Numerical Analysis,* Springer-Verlag, 1993.

STOLARSKI, H., and BELYTSCHKO, T.

[A] "Shear and Membrane Locking in Curved C^0 Elements," *Computer Methods in Applied Mechanics and Engineering,* Vol. 41, pp. 279–296, 1983.

STRANG, G., and FIX, G. F.

[A] *An Analysis of the Finite Element Method,* Prentice-Hall, Englewood Cliffs, NJ, 1973.

STROUD, A. H., and SECREST, D.

[A] *Gaussian Quadrature Formulas,* Prentice-Hall, Englewood Cliffs, NJ, 1966.

SUSSMAN, T., and BATHE, K. J.

[A] "Studies of Finite Element Procedures—Stress Band Plots and the Evaluation of Finite Element Meshes," *Engineering Computations,* Vol. 3, pp. 178–191, 1986.

[B] "A Finite Element Formulation for Nonlinear Incompressible Elastic and Inelastic Analysis," *Computers & Structures,* Vol. 26, pp. 357–409, 1987.

SYNGE, J. L.

[A] *The Hypercircle in Mathematical Physics,* Cambridge University Press, London, 1957.

SZABÓ, B., and BABUŠKA, I.

[A] *Introduction to Finite Element Analysis,* John Wiley, New York, 1991.

TAIG, I. C.

[A] *Structural Analysis by the Matrix Displacement Method,* English Electric Aviation Report S017, 1961.

TAN, L. H., and BATHE, K. J.

[A] "Studies of Finite Element Procedures—The Conjugate Gradient and GMRes Methods in ADINA and ADINA-F," *Computers & Structures,* Vol. 40, pp. 441–449, 1991.

THOMAS, G. B., and FINNEY, R. L.

[A] *Calculus and Analytical Geometry,* 8th ed., Addison-Wesley, Reading, MA, 1992.

TIMOSHENKO, S., and GOODIER, J. N.

[A] *Theory of Elasticity,* 3rd ed., McGraw-Hill, New York, 1970.

TIMOSHENKO, S., and WOINOWSKY-KRIEGER, S.

[A] *Theory of Plates and Shells,* 2nd ed., McGraw-Hill, New York, 1959.

TURNER, M. J., CLOUGH, R. W., MARTIN, H. C., and TOPP, L. J.

[A] "Stiffness and Deflection Analysis of Complex Structures," *Journal of the Aeronautical Sciences,* Vol. 23, pp. 805–823, 1956.

VARGA, R. S.

[A] *Matrix Iterative Analysis,* Prentice-Hall, Englewood Cliffs, NJ, 1962.

VERRUIJT, A.

[A] *Theory of Groundwater Flow,* Gordon and Breach, New York, 1970.

WASHIZU, K.

[A] "On the Variational Principles of Elasticity and Plasticity," Aeroelastic and Structures Research Laboratory Technical Report No. 25-18, Massachusetts Institute of Technology, Cambridge, MA, March 1955.

[B] *Variational Methods in Elasticity and Plasticity,* Pergamon Press, Elmsford, NY, 1975.

WHITE, F. M.

[A] *Fluid Mechanics,* McGraw-Hill, 1986.

WILKINS, M. L.
   [A]   "Calculation of Elastic-Plastic Flow," in B. Alder, S. Fernbach, and M. Rotenberg (eds.), *Methods in Computational Physics,* Vol. 3, pp. 211–263, Academic Press, New York, 1964.

WILKINSON, J. H.
   [A]   *The Algebraic Eigenvalue Problem,* Oxford University Press, New York, 1965.
   [B]   "The QR Algorithm for Real Symmetric Matrices with Multiple Eigenvalues," *The Computer Journal,* Vol. 8, pp. 85–87, 1965.

WILSON, E. L.
   [A]   "Structural Analysis of Axisymmetric Solids," *AIAA Journal,* Vol. 3, pp. 2269–2274, 1965.
   [B]   "The Static Condensation Algorithm," *International Journal for Numerical Methods in Engineering,* Vol. 8, pp. 199–203, 1974.

WILSON, E. L., FARHOOMAND, I., and BATHE, K. J.
   [A]   "Nonlinear Dynamic Analysis of Complex Structures," *International Journal of Earthquake Engineering and Structural Dynamics,* Vol. 1, pp. 241–252, 1973.

WILSON, E. L., and IBRAHIMBEGOVIC, A.
   [A]   "Use of Incompatible Displacement Modes for the Calculation of Element Stiffness and Stresses," *Finite Elements in Analysis and Design,* Vol. 7, pp. 229–241, 1990.

WILSON, E. L., TAYLOR, R. L., DOHERTY, W. P., and GHABOUSSI, J.
   [A]   "Incompatible Displacement Models," in *Numerical and Computer Methods in Structural Mechanics* (S. J. Fenves, N. Perrone, A. R. Robinson, and W. C. Schnobrich, eds.), Academic Press, New York, pp. 43–57, 1973.

WUNDERLICH, W.
   [A]   "Ein verallgemeinertes Variationsverfahren zur vollen oder teilweisen Diskretisierung mehrdimensionaler Elastizitätsprobleme," *Ingenieur-Archiv,* Vol. 39, pp. 230–247, 1970.

YAMAMOTO, Y., and OHTSUBO, H.
   [A]   "Subspace Iteration Accelerated by Using Chebyshev Polynomials for Eigenvalue Problems with Symmetric Matrices," *International Journal for Numerical Methods in Engineering,* Vol. 10, pp. 935–944, 1976.

ZHONG, W., and QIU, C.
   [A]   "Analysis of Symmetric or Partially Symmetric Structures," *Computer Methods in Applied Mechanics and Engineering,* Vol. 38, pp. 1–18, 1983.

ZIENKIEWICZ, O. C., and CHEUNG, Y. K.
   [A]   *The Finite Element Method in Structural and Continuum Mechanics,* McGraw-Hill, 1967; 4th ed. by O. C. Zienkiewicz and R. L. Taylor, Vols. 1 and 2, 1989/1990.

ŻYCZKOWSKI, M.
   [A]   *Combined Loadings in the Theory of Plasticity,* Polish Scientific, 1981.

Index